Welcome to

# SRA Real Math

## Discover the Difference of Real Math

SRA Making the Difference

# Discover Real Math to help meet today's standards

**Let quality mathematics research support the daily challenges you face.**

Great teachers need great tools to meet the demands of education today. Just as each teacher takes a different approach to teaching, each student has individual ways of understanding. ***Real Math*** offers you meaningful instruction specifically designed to reach each student.

***Real Math's*** true-to-life applications, standards-based curriculum, and extensive teacher resources will help you open your students' eyes to all math has to offer. They learn essential math skills while understanding the important role of math in daily life.

### The nuts and bolts.

Understanding is at the heart of every ***Real Math*** lesson. Success in basic computational skills is only the beginning. The difference with ***Real Math*** is that it elevates basic learning to a new level of engagement and application by connecting thinking and reasoning to learning.

### Why settle for merely "Adequate" Yearly Progress?

More than ever before, teachers are accountable for the performance of their students. Your focus as a teacher is being directed toward meeting mandated goals like Adequate Yearly Progress (AYP) or student performance on mandated tests.

***Real Math*** offers you **differentiated instruction** designed to help you make AYP and meet standards by offering **research-based, standards-based**, quality education for all students, including English language learners, high-achieving students, and those in need of intervention.

### The test of time.

Incorporating over 30 years of research with the latest mathematical findings, ***Real Math*** helps you build and reinforce learning with proven lessons. ***Real Math*** is an all-inclusive tool for engaging your students while building their math competency.

### Take five.

Just as Reading First has identified key elements for teaching children to read, the mathematics research community* has identified five key proficiencies that students need to achieve in math. Those strands are: understanding, computing, applying, reasoning, and engaging.

> ***Real Math*** **is the first program to fully integrate all five strands of mathematical proficiency throughout every lesson.**

**CONSIDER THIS:** Teaching strategies in ***Real Math*** incorporate **games** not just for skill practice, but also to stimulate critical thinking as students formulate strategies and solve true-to-life problems.

*"The program has been very beneficial for teachers and students. Teachers have a variety of tools to help struggling students as well as those children doing an outstanding job who need enrichment. The teacher manual is so user-friendly that our teachers can pick it up on a daily basis and implement a successful lesson with ease."*

–Kim Leitzke
Math Teacher Leader
Barton Elementary School
NCLB Blue Ribbon Award 2003
Milwaukee, WI

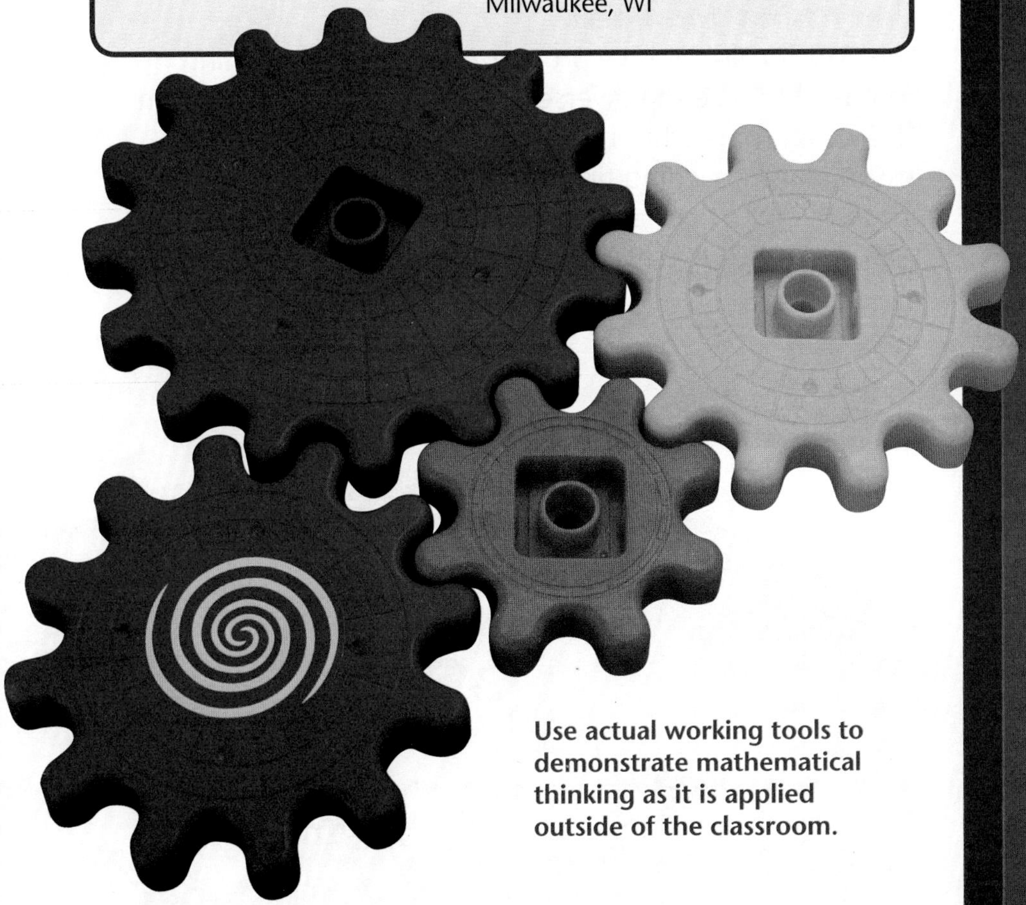

**Use actual working tools to demonstrate mathematical thinking as it is applied outside of the classroom.**

## Real Math is the first program to fully integrate all five strands of mathematical proficiency as defined by today's research *

The five key proficiencies that students need to achieve in math are:

**1 Understanding**
Comprehending mathematical concepts, operations, and relations — knowing what mathematical symbols, diagrams, and procedures mean

**2 Computing**
Carrying out mathematical procedures, such as adding, subtracting, multiplying, and dividing numbers flexibly, accurately, efficiently, and appropriately

**3 Applying**
Being able to formulate problems mathematically and devise strategies for solving them using concepts and procedures appropriately

**4 Reasoning**
Using logic to explain and justify a solution to a problem or to extend from something known to something not yet known

**5 Engaging**
Seeing mathematics as sensible, useful, and doable

By incorporating all five strands, ***Real Math*** frees you from the daily challenge of gathering materials to meet state standards, allowing you to pursue your passion for doing what you love most – teaching.

* Kilpatrick, J., Swafford, J. and Findell, B. eds. *Adding It Up: Helping Children Learn Mathematics*. Washington, D.C.: National Research Council/National Academy Press, 2001.

Kilpatrick, Jeremy, Martin, W. Gary, and Schifter, Deborah, eds. *A Research Companion to Principles and Standards for School Mathematics*. Reston, VA: National Council of Teachers of Mathematics, Inc. 2003.

SRA Real Math
Discover the Difference

# Discover meaningful, true-to-life instruction

**Reach each student with explicit instruction and conceptual development.**

Engaging lessons that appeal to your students' personal interests go a long way toward maintaining their attention. Revisiting concepts in different contexts over time ensures understanding by making math personal. This personal understanding and appreciation of mathematical concepts helps you develop greater thinking and mastery in each student.

**A dual approach.**
***Real Math's*** explicit lessons combine **skill-building** and **problem-solving instruction** that includes unique lesson ideas, the latest technology, and engaging games.

*Thinking Stories*, which are narratives interspersed with questions for students to answer, require students to consider problems in novel ways. As an integral part of ***Real Math*** lessons, games provide skill practice and stimulate critical thinking as students formulate strategies and solve true-to-life problems.

**Everything you need.**
***Real Math's*** all-inclusive program gives you everything you need to face the diverse challenges of your classroom. The wealth of teacher resources includes easy-to-use lesson plans, teaching tips, activity ideas, reteaching strategies, practice sessions, professional development, technology, and assessment opportunities at every level.

Show students how math adds adventure in and out of the classroom.

**CONSIDER THIS:** Students develop concepts and practice skills through **technology tools** and **resources** integrated throughout the curriculum.

**Five-a-day.**
All five math proficiencies are integrated and interwoven into every lesson so your students develop a full understanding of mathematics with every turn of the page. ***Real Math*** concepts are carefully developed using research-supported strategies, including features like *Teaching for Understanding* that emphasize concept development to build comprehension of mathematical concepts, operations, and relations.

**Boost thinking power.**
Some other math programs show a quick increase in test scores as students develop computational skills, then see scores drop off as students fail to develop critical thinking skills. However, every lesson in ***Real Math*** features questions and problems that require thinking, not just calculating. As you help students build math comprehension, they will excel on standardized tests, which require constructed responses and problem-solving skills.

**_Real Math_ doesn't just help you teach why math is important, but shows students how it can be applied in their after-school activities.**

SRA
# Real Math
Discover the Difference

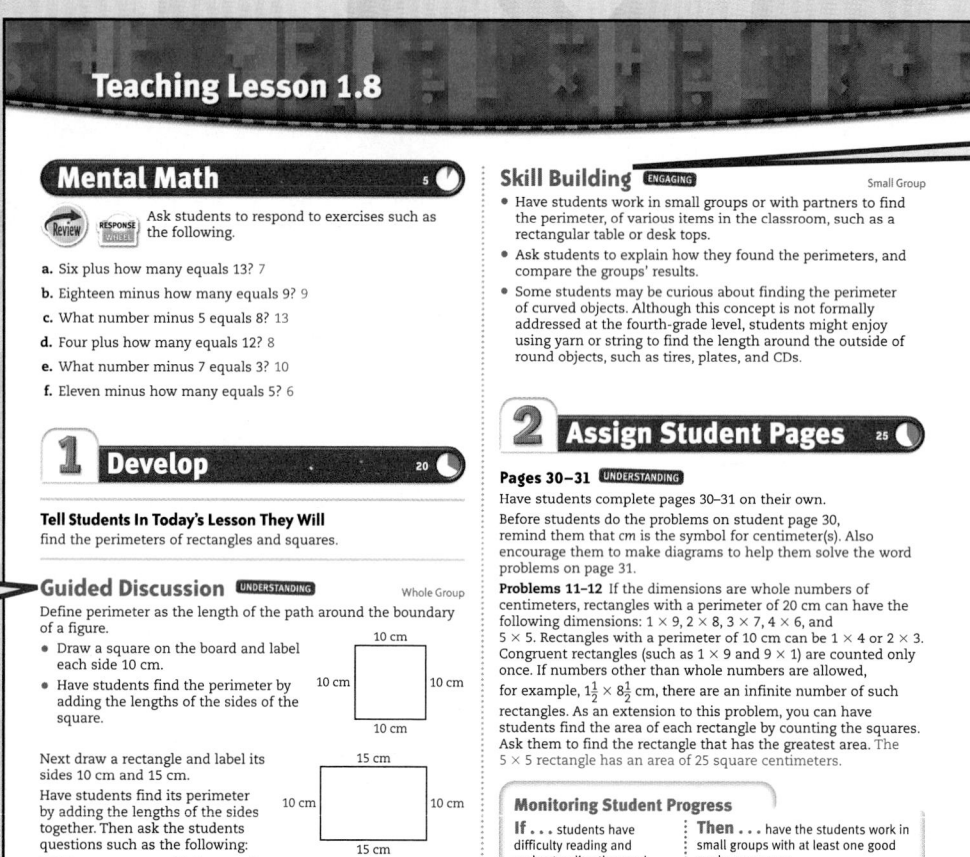

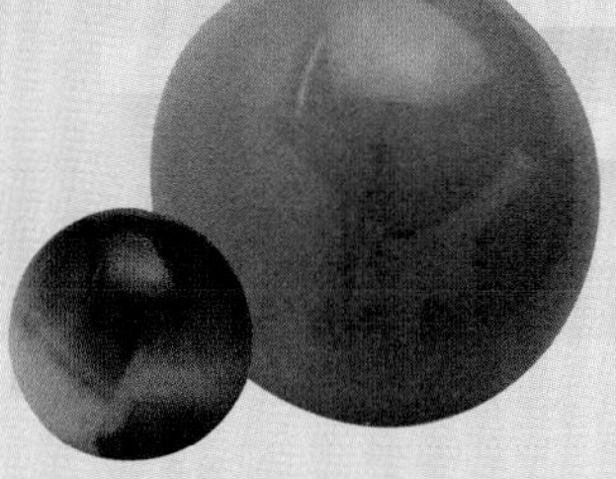

# Discover a versatile way to teach

**All-inclusive, flexible lessons offer guided instruction, practice, and assessment for every task.**

**Step-by-step guide.**
Explicit instruction walks you through the details of each *Real Math* lesson, offering everything you need to perform each task. Because *Real Math* is flexible to fit your teaching style, it frees you from time spent planning so you can focus on what's most important: teaching.

## Teaching Lesson 1.8

### Mental Math 5

Review RESPONSE WHEEL Ask students to respond to exercises such as the following.

a. Six plus how many equals 13? 7
b. Eighteen minus how many equals 9? 9
c. What number minus 5 equals 8? 13
d. Four plus how many equals 12? 8
e. What number minus 7 equals 3? 10
f. Eleven minus how many equals 5? 6

### 1 Develop 20

**Tell Students In Today's Lesson They Will**
find the perimeters of rectangles and squares.

**Guided Discussion** UNDERSTANDING Whole Group
Define perimeter as the length of the path around the boundary of a figure.

- Draw a square on the board and label each side 10 cm.
- Have students find the perimeter by adding the lengths of the sides of the square.

10 cm 10 cm 10 cm 10 cm

Next draw a rectangle and label its sides 10 cm and 15 cm.
Have students find its perimeter by adding the lengths of the sides together. Then ask the students questions such as the following:

15 cm 10 cm 10 cm 15 cm

■ **What are some realistic examples of situations that might require finding the perimeter?** Possible answers: determining the jogging distance around a field; building a fence around a garden; making a frame for a picture

**Skill Building** ENGAGING Small Group
- Have students work in small groups or with partners to find the perimeter, of various items in the classroom, such as a rectangular table or desk tops.
- Ask students to explain how they found the perimeters, and compare the groups' results.
- Some students may be curious about finding the perimeter of curved objects. Although this concept is not formally addressed at the fourth-grade level, students might enjoy using yarn or string to find the length around the outside of round objects, such as tires, plates, and CDs.

### 2 Assign Student Pages 25

**Pages 30–31** UNDERSTANDING
Have students complete pages 30–31 on their own.
Before students do the problems on student page 30, remind them that *cm* is the symbol for centimeter(s). Also encourage them to make diagrams to help them solve the word problems on page 31.
**Problems 11–12** If the dimensions are whole numbers of centimeters, rectangles with a perimeter of 20 cm can have the following dimensions: $1 \times 9$, $2 \times 8$, $3 \times 7$, $4 \times 6$, and $5 \times 5$. Rectangles with a perimeter of 10 cm can be $1 \times 4$ or $2 \times 3$. Congruent rectangles (such as $1 \times 9$ and $9 \times 1$) are counted only once. If numbers other than whole numbers are allowed, for example, $1\frac{1}{2} \times 8\frac{1}{2}$ cm, there are an infinite number of such rectangles. As an extension to this problem, you can have students find the area of each rectangle by counting the squares. Ask them to find the rectangle that has the greatest area. The $5 \times 5$ rectangle has an area of 25 square centimeters.

**Monitoring Student Progress**

| | |
|---|---|
| **If . . .** students have difficulty reading and understanding the word problems, | **Then . . .** have the students work in small groups with at least one good reader per group. |

**As Students Finish**
Game **Roll a 15 Game** or **Roll 20 to 5 Game** (introduced in Lesson 1.7)
e Games **Roll a 15 Game** or **Roll 20 to 5 Game**

**30B** Chapter 1 • Lesson 8

**Easy teaching. Easy learning.**
Multiple opportunities for students to understand each exercise make preparing to meet state standards part of every lesson.

**Game on.**
*Real Math* activities, such as games and technology projects, ensure that students use key skills to absorb essential ideas and information.



SRA *Making the Difference*

**Leave a lasting impression.**
Practice through games, realistic problem solving, interactive projects, and writing activities assures student engagement and piques interest.

Student Page

LESSON 1.8 Perimeter

**Key Ideas**

**The perimeter of a figure is the length of the path around it.**

3 cm / 3 cm / 3 cm / 3 cm

To find the perimeter of this square, add 3 + 3 + 3 + 3.

The perimeter is 12 centimeters.

**Find** the perimeter.

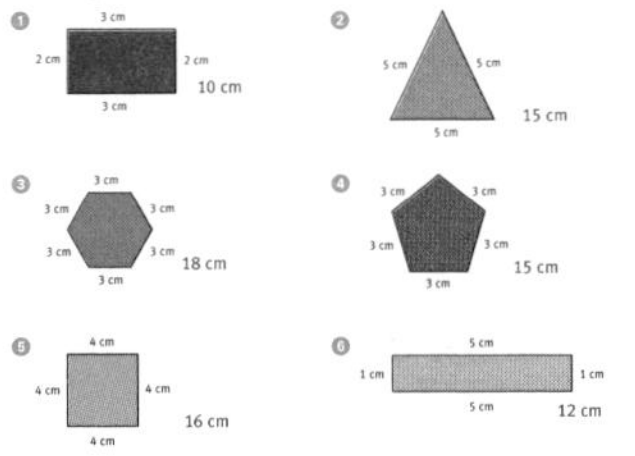


30 — Textbook This lesson is available in the *eTextbook*.

Student Page

**Solve** these problems. Drawing diagrams might help.

7. Extended Response Central Park is shaped like a rectangle. The length of one side of the park is 300 yards. A second side is 200 yards.
   a. If Troy runs around the perimeter of the park, how far will he run? 1,000 yards
   b. How did you find the perimeter? See the *Teacher's Edition*, page 30-31.
8. Seward Park is square-shaped. One side measures 200 yards. How much fencing is needed to completely fence in the park? 800 yards
9. In an equilateral triangle, all three sides are equal. The perimeter of a garden shaped like an equilateral triangle is 24 feet. What is the length of each of the sides? 8 feet
10. In an isosceles triangle, two sides are equal. The perimeter of an isosceles triangle is 30 inches. One of its sides is 12 inches. What are the lengths of the other sides? 9 inches; or 12 inches, 6 inches (Multistep)
11. How many rectangles can you draw that have a perimeter of 20 centimeters? Draw the rectangles on graph paper using whole numbers for the lengths of the sides. 5 (1 × 9, 2 × 8, 3 × 7, 4 × 6, 5 × 5)
12. How many rectangles can you draw that have a perimeter of 10 centimeters? Draw the rectangles on graph paper using whole numbers for the lengths of the sides. 2 (1 × 4, 2 × 3)

Writing + Math **Journal**

Write directions for how to find the perimeter of a room in your home.

Answers should mention measuring the length of each side of the room then adding all the measurements together.

Chapter 1 • Lesson 8 — 31

Perimeter LESSON 1.8

## 3 Reflect (10)

**Guided Discussion** UNDERSTANDING — Whole Group

Ask students questions such as the following:

- **What is perimeter?** The length of the path around a figure.
- **How do you find the perimeter of a figure that has straight line segments for all its sides?** Add the lengths of all the sides together to get a total.
- **Why is finding perimeter useful?** Knowing how to find perimeter can help us solve problems such as determining how much fence to buy for a garden or yard, determining how much framing to buy for a picture, or keeping track of the jogging distance around a park.

**Extended Response**

**Problem 7** Ask students to explain how they found the perimeter of the park. Since the park is a rectangle, the opposite sides are equal in length. Therefore, students should determine that since one side is 300 yards long, the side opposite it is also 300 yards. To find the perimeter, students should add all the sides together (300 + 300 + 200 + 200).

Writing + Math **Journal**

The directions students wrote for finding the perimeter of a room should mention measuring the length of each side of the room and adding all the measurements together.

**Applications** APPLYING — Small Group

Have students estimate the perimeter of the classroom, and then work together to find the actual perimeter. After measuring the first wall, ask students if they would like to change their estimates.

**Cumulative Review:** For review of fractional amounts, assign Problems 12–17 on page 37.

**Family Involvement:** Assign the ***Practice, Reteach,*** or ***Enrichment*** activities depending on the needs of your students. Have students determine the perimeter of their bed, a window, and a table at home. Have them sketch each object and label its dimensions.

**Concept/Question Board:** Have students attempt to answer any unanswered questions on the Concept/Question Board.

**Math Puzzler:** Alex, Brett, and Chen have a total of $18. Together Chen and Alex have as much money as Brett has by herself. Together Brett and Alex have $6 more than Chen has. How much money does each person have? Alex has $3, Brett has $9, and Chen has $6.

Chapter 1 • Lesson 8 **30–31**

**Make it personal.**
Encouraging students to explain their thinking personalizes math and helps them internalize and apply concepts.

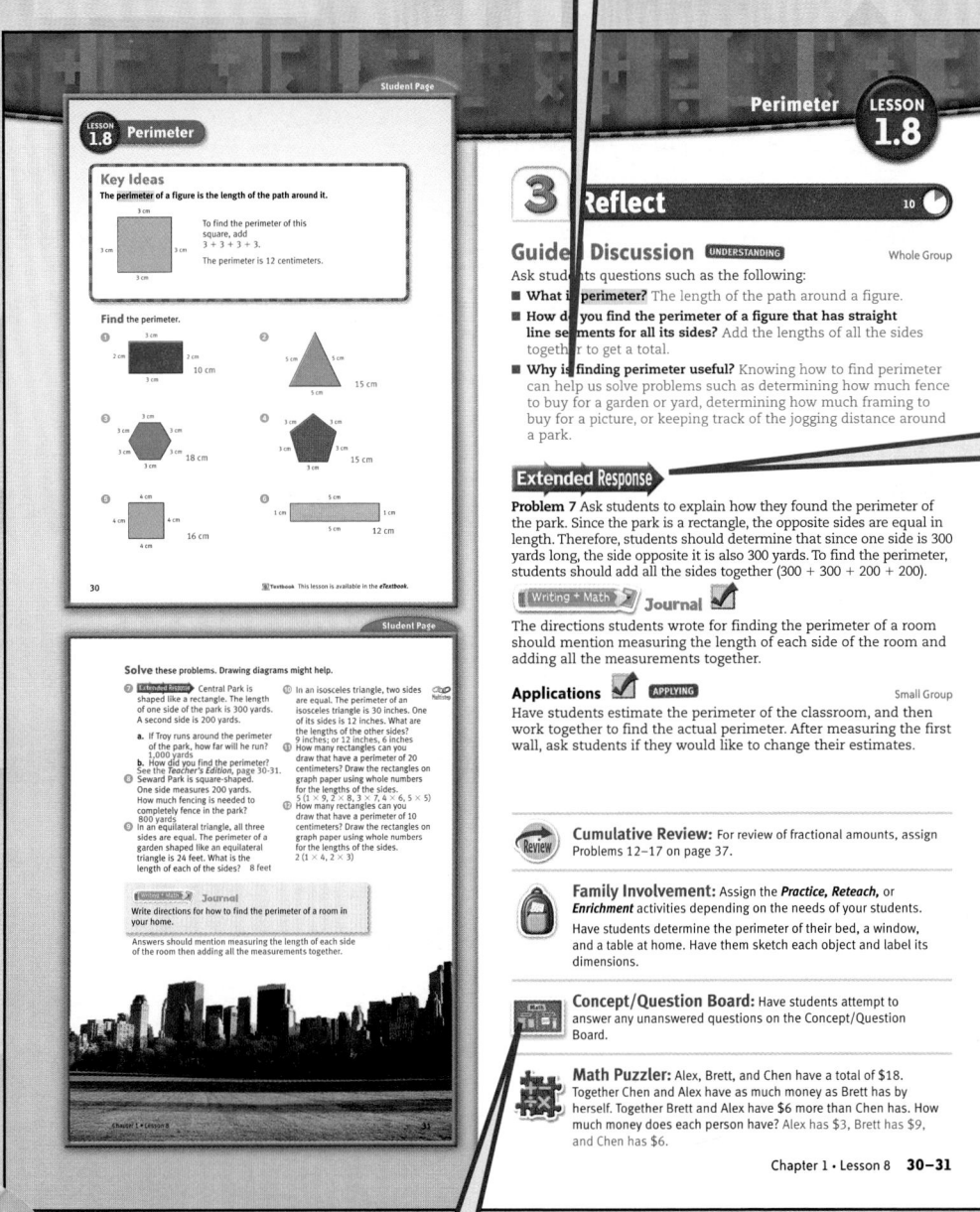

Fun materials maintain student interest and help reinforce computational thinking skills.

**Teach them to think for themselves.**
*Real Math* helps you promote realistic thinking and problem solving skills. Your students learn to ask relevant questions while you help them learn to find answers by conducting their own research.

SRA Real Math
Discover the Difference

# Discover the value of ongoing assessment

**Use resources and strategies to differentiate instruction for each student.**

**Making progress.**
Look for specific ongoing assessment and progress monitoring strategies in each lesson for a complete evaluation of student understanding. This ongoing assessment offers you strategic solutions for every learning situation and helps you make certain that your students fully grasp content. With enrich, practice, and reteach materials, you'll ensure no student is left behind.

**Vital extras.**
Valuable tools, such as the English Learner Support Guide, extended response, guided discussion, Writing + Math Journal prompts, projects, and WebQuests, provide opportunities for students to demonstrate understanding in real contexts, not just on tests.

Perimeter LESSON 1.8

## 4 Assess and Differentiate

e Assess Use *eAssess* to record and analyze evidence of student understanding.

### A Gather Evidence

Use the Daily Class Assessment Records in ***Assessment*** or ***eAssess*** to record daily observations.

**Portfolio Assessment**
☑ Journal
Did the student APPLYING
- ❑ provide a clear explanation?
- ❑ communicate reasons and strategies?
- ❑ choose appropriate strategies?
- ❑ argue logically?

**Performance Assessment**
☑ Applications
Did the student APPLYING
- ❑ apply learning in new situations?
- ❑ contribute concepts?
- ❑ contribute answers?
- ❑ connect mathematics to real-world situations?

### B Summarize Findings

Analyze and summarize assessment data for each student. Determine which Assessment Follow-Up is appropriate for each student. Use the Student Assessment Record in ***Assessment*** or ***eAssess*** to update assessment records.

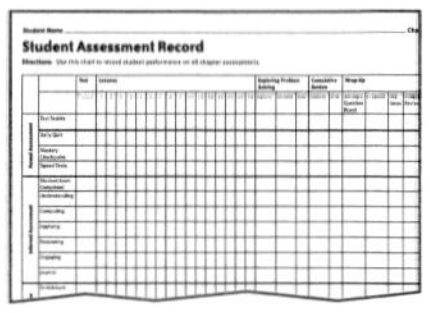

Assessment Page T41

### C Assessment Follow-Up • DIFFERENTIATE INSTRUCTION

Based on your observations, use these teaching strategies for assessment follow-up.

**INTERVENTION**
Review student performance on ***Intervention*** Lesson 1.B.

**ENGLISH LEARNER**
Review
Use Lesson 1.8 in ***English Learner Support Guide*** to review concepts and vocabulary involving perimeter.

**ENRICH**
**If . . .** students are proficient in solving problems involving perimeter,
**Then . . .** encourage them to work on ***Enrichment*** Lesson 1.8 to explore a pattern involving perimeter.

Enrichment Lesson 1.8

**PRACTICE**
**If . . .** students would benefit from additional practice in calculating perimeter,
**Then . . .** assign ***Practice*** Lesson 1.8 to provide more opportunities to find perimeters.

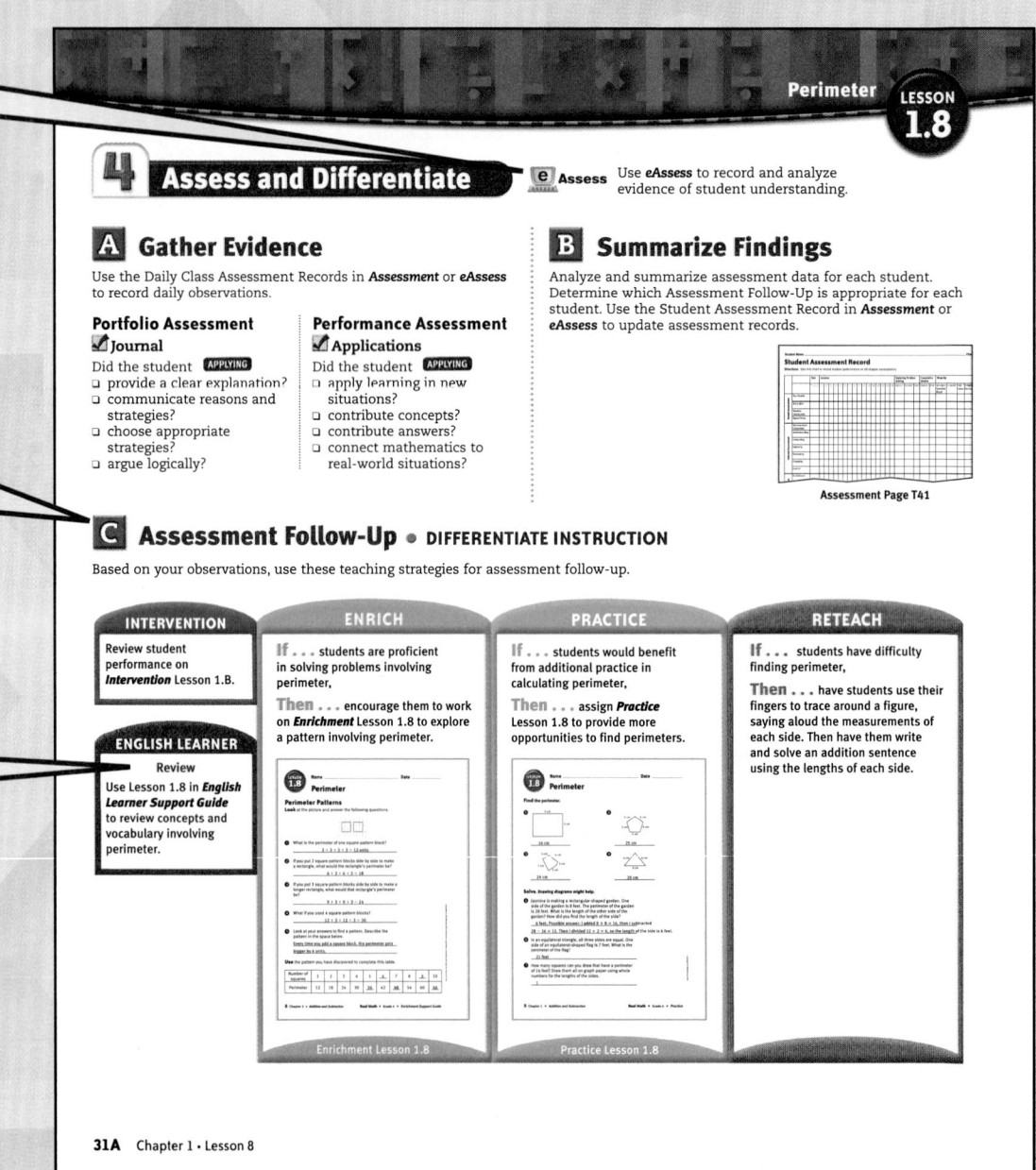

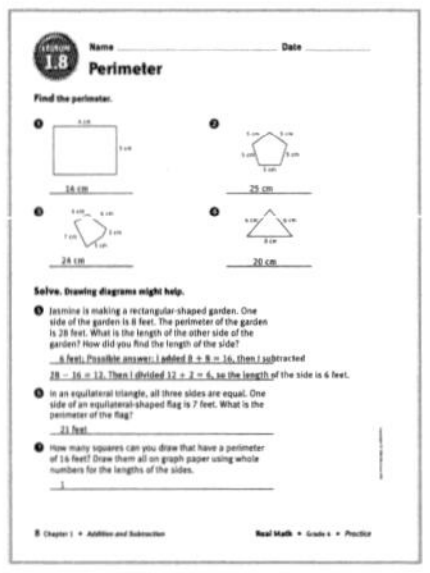

Practice Lesson 1.8

**RETEACH**
**If . . .** students have difficulty finding perimeter,
**Then . . .** have students use their fingers to trace around a figure, saying aloud the measurements of each side. Then have them write and solve an addition sentence using the lengths of each side.

31A Chapter 1 • Lesson 8



SRA *Making the Difference*

**⊕ CONSIDER THIS: Technology** in your classroom opens the door to mathematical understanding and application that will prepare students for the real world.

# Discover how technology can take your lessons beyond the everyday

**Prepare students for a lifetime of learning with interactive instruction.**

### Keeping up with technology.

Technology resources for teachers and students enrich instruction and expand learning. ***Real Math*** helps you build skills by offering the latest in technology to help take your classroom to the next level. ***Real Math*** features useful materials such as:

- **ePlanner** online lesson planning helps make your work easier by offering daily, weekly, and monthly lesson plans and homework detail.
- **ePresentation** enables you to present each lesson electronically through an interactive presentation. It also provides lesson summaries and electronic lessons that can be accessed from home.
- **eAssess** online assessment tools allow you to give, track, and report electronic versions of all assessments including all lesson assessments, state guideline database correlated to specific test items, and reports.
- **eMath Tools** are math technology resources including number lines and multiplication tables, geometric exploration tools, and probability simulations.
- **eGames** offer electronic versions of games from each grade level. *Building Blocks Activities* are engaging, research-based computer activities that develop math understanding.
- **eTextbook** gives students access from home with an electronic version of the Student Edition.

For additional resources, visit **SRAonline.com.**

### Online Professional Development

Build confidence and expertise in delivering ***Real Math*** lessons using Online Professional Development. This series of six online courses includes video excerpts and demonstrates how ***Real Math*** lessons implement each of the following:

- Teaching Computational Fluency
- Teaching for Understanding
- Teaching Applications of Mathematics
- Teaching Mathematical Reasoning and Problem Solving
- Engaging Children in Mathematics
- Mathematics Classroom Management

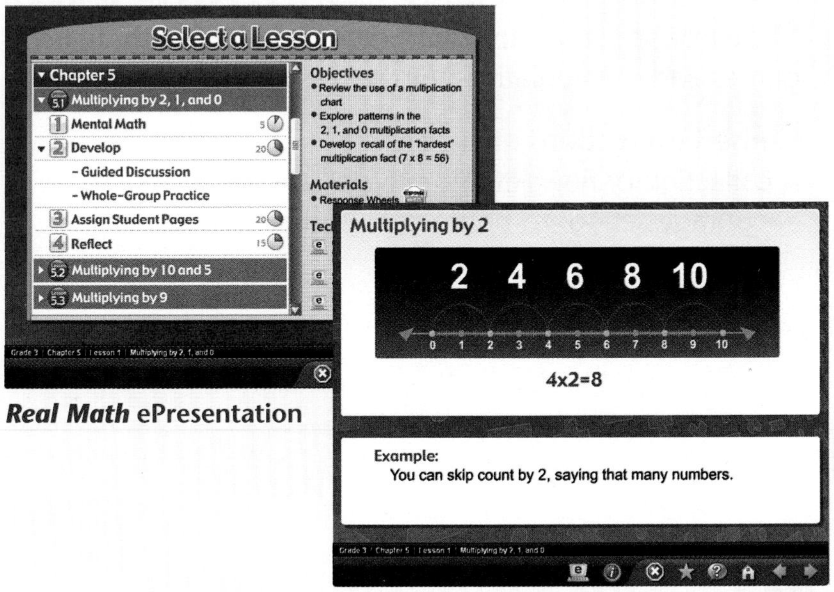


***Real Math*** **ePresentation**

SRA Real Math
Discover the Difference

# Discover the confidence of comprehensive teacher support

**Extensive resources include empowering materials for you and your students.**

## TEACHER MATERIALS prepare you with great tools and resources.

- **Teacher's Edition,** Grades Pre-K–6
  A wealth of background information and strategies helps you provide quality instruction.
- **Manipulative Kits,** Grades Pre-K–6
  These complete Manipulative Kits support concept development and are available in individual, module, and teacher manipulative packages.
- **Assessment,** Grades K–6
  A variety of assessment options helps you evaluate student proficiency and inform instruction.
- **Game Mat Package,** Grades Pre-K–6
  Make learning enjoyable with these exciting math board games and manipulatives for the classroom.
- **Home Connection,** Grades Pre-K–6
  A collection of newsletters, surveys, and activities encourage school-to-home communications.
- **Home Connection Game Package,** Grades K–6
  Support learning at home with this math games kit.

## STUDENT MATERIALS are unique and engaging, giving you a fresh approach to teaching mathematics.

- **Big Books,** Grade Pre-K
  These counting books include math concepts specifically chosen for preschoolers.
- **Student Edition,** Grades K–6
  Research-based lessons offer development and practice for all concepts.
- **Across the Curriculum Math Connections,** Grades K–6
  Engaging cross-curricular projects and WebQuests help develop mathematical proficiency.
- **Student Assessment Booklet,** Grades K–6
  This convenient assessment tool helps keep students on track.
- **Exercise Book,** Grades 3–6
  Build math skills using these exercises from the hardbound student books to help students record their answers and show their work.

Materials that offer hands-on learning go a long way in engaging conceptual thinking skills and problem solving.

**With materials to DIFFERENTIATE INSTRUCTION, you meet the needs of all your students.**

- **Intervention Support Guide,** Grades K–6
  Bring all students up-to-speed with alternative approaches, more intense instruction, and additional practice of prerequisite skills for every chapter.
- **English Learner Support Guide,** Grades K–6
  Take advantage of strategies for previewing and reviewing lesson concepts and vocabulary.
- **Enrichment Support Guide,** Grades K–6
  This guide includes activities for every lesson designed to expand lesson concepts.
- **Practice Workbook,** Grades Pre-K–6
  This workbook version offers extra practice for your convenience.
- **Practice Blackline Masters,** Grades Pre-K–6
  Reproducible pages offer extra practice for every lesson.
- **Reteach Support Guide,** Grades K–6
  Use this tool to offer alternative strategies for presenting lesson concepts.

**Professional development from SRA/McGraw-Hill provides you with an unparalleled level of support, resources, and partnership.**

*Real Math* is based on a strong, standards-based philosophy of instruction. A key to successful implementation of the program within your school or district is to have an understanding of its background and how to apply its research-based principles in your classroom. You'll find that professional development opportunities for *Real Math* are hands-on, giving you the chance to gain valuable experience with each component of the program.

Because each school is different, your SRA/McGraw-Hill sales representative will customize a professional development plan to fit your needs. Here are some resources your school or district may utilize:

- On-site training upon implementation
- Weekend seminars and regional training
- Summer institutes
- Online professional development
- Workbooks and guides
- Classroom demonstrations
- After-school workshops with teachers and administrators
- Orientation sessions for the community, parents, and parent groups
- Mentor teachers and coaches
- Resources online at **SRAonline.com**

# Discover the experience Real Math authors bring to every lesson

**Steve Willoughby** is Professor Emeritus at both New York University and the University of Arizona. He has taught all grades from first through twelfth. He has been a professor of both education and of mathematics at the University of Wisconsin and at New York University (where he also was the Head of the Division of Mathematics, Science, and Statistics Education), and a Professor of Mathematics at the University of Arizona. Dr. Willoughby has published more than 200 books and articles on mathematics and mathematics education and is the principal author of ***Real Math***. In 1995, he received the Lifetime Achievement Medal for Leadership in Mathematics Education from the Mathematics Education Trust.

**Carl Bereiter** is a Professor Emeritus of Educational Psychology and Special Advisor on Learning Technology at the Ontario Institute for Studies of the University of Toronto. He has published widely on a variety of topics in instruction, cognitive psychology, and educational policy. Honors include a Guggenheim Fellowship, fellowships at the Center for Advanced Study in the Behavioral Sciences, and election to the U.S. National Academy of Education.

**Peter Hilton** is Distinguished Professor of Mathematics Emeritus of the State University of New York, Binghamton, and Distinguished Professor of Mathematics at the University of Central Florida, Orlando. He is the author of 18 books and over 500 research articles. His areas of special interest are algebraic topology, homological algebra, and group theory. Professor Hilton has served as Chairman of the United States Commission on Mathematical Instruction and Secretary/Treasurer of the International Commission on Mathematical Instruction.

**Joseph H. Rubinstein** is a professor of education at Coker College in Hartsville, South Carolina, where he teaches prospective teachers how to teach mathematics and science. He was chairperson of the education department at Coker for 15 years. He served as Director of the Open Court Publishing Company's Mathematics and Science Curriculum Development Center for its first seven years, where he co-authored and directed a nationwide field-testing program for ***Real Math***.

**Douglas H. Clements**, professor of early childhood, mathematics, and computer education at the University at Buffalo, State University of New York, has conducted research and published widely on the learning and teaching of geometry, computer applications in mathematics education, the early development of mathematical ideas, and the effects of social interactions on learning. Along with Julie Sarama, Dr. Clements has directed several research projects funded by the National Science Foundation and the U.S. Department of Education's Institute of Educational Sciences, one of which resulted in the mathematics software and activities included in ***Real Math***.

**Joan Moss** is a professor of mathematics education at University of Toronto. She has more than 20 years experience as a classroom teacher, scholar, and researcher. Her extensive research has included studies of the development of children's understanding of rational numbers and the development of early algebraic reasoning. Dr. Moss has been widely published with research articles and chapters for the National Council of Teachers of Mathematics as well as the National Academy of Science. She is a member of the National Council of Teachers of Mathematics, American Educational Research Association, the North American Chapter of the Psychology of Mathematics Education, and the Canadian Mathematics Education Study Group.

**Jean Pedersen** is Professor of Mathematics and Computer Science at Santa Clara University, California. Along with Peter Hilton, she has published six books and over 90 research articles in mathematics. Her research interests include polyhedral geometry, combinatorics, and the teaching of mathematics, especially geometry, to pre-college students.

**Julie Sarama** is an associate professor of mathematics education at the University at Buffalo, State University of New York. She conducts research on the implementation and effects of software and curricula in mathematics classrooms, young children's development of mathematical concepts and competencies, implementation and scale-up of educational reform, and professional development. Dr. Sarama has taught secondary mathematics and computer science, gifted math at the middle school level, preschool and kindergarten mathematics enrichment classes, and mathematics methods and content courses for elementary to secondary teachers.

## Contributing Authors

**Hortensia Soto-Johnson** is Assistant Professor of Mathematics, University of Northern Colorado. B.S. Chadron State College (Mathematics); MS in Mathematics, University of Arizona; Ph.D. in Educational Mathematics, University of Northern Colorado.

**Erica Walker** is Assistant Professor of Mathematics and Education, Teachers College, Columbia University. B.S. cum laude, Birmingham-Southern College (Mathematics, Spanish minor); M.Ed., Wake Forest University (Mathematics Education); Ed.M., Ed.D., Harvard University (Administration, Planning, and Social Policy).

# SRA Real Math

## Teacher's Edition

### Grade 4 • Volume 2


Stephen S. Willoughby
•
Carl Bereiter
•
Peter Hilton
•
Joseph H. Rubinstein
•
Joan Moss
•
Jean Pedersen



SRA
Columbus, OH

The McGraw·Hill Companies

# Authors


**Stephen S. Willoughby**
Professor Emeritus of Mathematics
University of Arizona
Tucson, AZ

**Carl Bereiter**
Professor Emeritus
Centre for Applied Cognitive Science
Ontario Institute for Studies in Education
University of Toronto, Canada

**Peter Hilton**
Distinguished Professor of
Mathematics Emeritus
State University of New York
Binghamton, NY

**Joseph H. Rubinstein**
Professor of Education
Coker College,
Hartsville, SC

**Joan Moss**
Associate Professor, Department of Human
Development and Applied Psychology
Ontario Institute for Studies in Education
University of Toronto, Canada

**Jean Pedersen**
Professor, Department of
Mathematics and Computer Science
Santa Clara University, Santa Clara, CA


## PreKindergarten and Building Blocks Authors


**Douglas H. Clements**
Professor of Early Childhood and Mathematics Education
University at Buffalo
State University of New York, NY

**Julie Sarama**
Associate Professor of Mathematics Education
University at Buffalo
State University of New York, NY


## Contributing Authors


**Hortensia Soto-Johnson**
Assistant Professor of Mathematics
University of Northern Colorado, CO

**Erika Walker**
Assistant Professor of Mathematics and Education
Teachers College, Columbia University, NY


### Research Consultants


**Jeremy Kilpatrick**
Regents Professor of Mathematics Education
University of Georgia, GA

**Alfinio Flores**
Professor of Mathematics Education
Arizona State University, AZ

**Gilbert J. Cuevas**
Professor of Mathematics Education
University of Miami, Coral Gables, FL


### Contributing Writers


**Holly MacLean,** Ed.D., Supervisor Principal, Treasure Valley Mathematics and Science Center, Boise, ID
**Edward Manfre,** Mathematics Education Consultant, Albuquerque, NM
**Elizabeth Jimenez,** English Language Learner Consultant, Pomona, CA
**Kim L. Pettig,** Ed.D., Instructional Challenge Coordinator Pittsford Central School District, Pittsford, NY
**Rosemary Tolliver,** M.Ed., Gifted Coordinator/Curriculum Director, Columbus, OH


### National Advisory Board


**Justin Anderson,** Teacher, Robey Elementary School, Indianapolis, IN
**David S. Bradley,** Administrator, Granite, UT
**Donna M. Bradley,** Head of the Lower School, St. Marks Episcopal Palm Beach Gardens, FL
**Grace Dublin,** Teacher, Laurelhurst Elementary, Seattle, WA
**Leisha W. Fordham,** Teacher, Bolton Academy, Atlanta, GA
**Ebony Frierson,** Teacher, Eastminister Day School, Columbia, SC
**Flavia Gunter,** Teacher, Morningside Elementary School, Atlanta, GA
**Audrey Marie Jacobs,** Teacher, Lewis & Clark Elementary, St. Louis, MO
**Florencetine Jasmin,** Elementary Math Curriculum Specialist, Baltimore, MD
**Kim Leitzke,** Teacher, Clara Barton Elementary School, Milwaukee, WI
**Nick Restivo,** Principal, Long Beach High School, Long Island, NY



**SRAonline.com**

SRA





Printed in the United States of America.

Send all inquiries to:
SRA/McGraw-Hill
4400 Easton Commons
Columbus, OH 43219

ISBN 0-07-603717-7

3 4 5 6 7 8 9 WEB 12 11 10 09 08 07

*The McGraw·Hill Companies*

# Addition and Subtraction

CHAPTER 1

## Exploring Problem Solving Theme: Space

# CHAPTER 2 Multidigit Addition and Subtraction

## Exploring Problem Solving Theme: Playground Safety

# Multiplication and Division

## Exploring Problem Solving Theme: Product Testing

# CHAPTER 4 Graphing Functions

**Exploring Problem Solving** Theme: Photography Business

# Multiplying with Multidigit Numbers

CHAPTER 5

## Exploring Problem Solving Theme: Fitness

# CHAPTER 6 Multidigit Multiplication

## Exploring Problem Solving Theme: Nutrition

# Introduction to Fractions, Decimals, and Percentages

CHAPTER 7

## Exploring Problem Solving Theme: Arctic Exploration

# CHAPTER 8 Fractions, Probability, and Measurement

## Exploring Problem Solving Theme: Finding Survivors

# Decimals and Measurement

CHAPTER 9

## Exploring Problem Solving Theme: Television Ratings

# CHAPTER 10 Geometry

Exploring Problem Solving Theme: Braille Symbols

# Dividing Greater Numbers

CHAPTER 11

## Exploring Problem Solving Theme: Voyage to New Worlds

# CHAPTER 12 Organizing and Interpreting Data

**Exploring Problem Solving** Theme: Sampling in Exploration of Gold, Oil, Etcetera



## Back Matter

# Getting Started

*This section provides an overview of classroom management issues and explanations of the* **Real Math** *program elements and how to use them.*

## *Real Math* is a comprehensive program designed to achieve these goals:

*Teach basic skills with understanding so students can use them fluently to solve real problems and help understand the real world*

•

*Teach students to think mathematically so they can reason, understand, and apply mathematics meaningfully in order to identify, solve, and communicate about real problems*

•

*Engage students in mathematics so they enjoy math, see it as understandable and useful, and willingly use it to help them understand their environment*

**Real Math** is a program that acknowledges the critical role teachers play in math education. The program is designed to provide thorough background, teaching strategies, and resources to support teacher delivery of a coherent mathematics curriculum that will develop student understanding and enjoyment of mathematics.

The following pages are designed to help you get started with **Real Math.**

*A variety of program materials are designed to help teachers provide a quality mathematics curriculum. The first step in getting started is to familiarize yourself with the program resources.*

# Core Materials

## Teacher's Edition

The ***Teacher's Edition*** is the heart of the ***Real Math*** curriculum. It provides background for teachers and complete lesson plans with explicit suggestions on how to develop math concepts. It explains when and how to use the program resources.

## Student Edition

The ***Student Edition*** includes developmental activities, practice exercises, games to help develop higher order thinking skills and practice traditional basic skills, as well as problem-solving explorations, and cumulative reviews.

## Essential Materials

The key materials beyond the textbook that students must have to complete the program activities are ***Number Cubes*** and ***Number Strips*** at Grades K–2, and ***Response Wheels, Equivalence Cards,*** and ***Number Cubes*** at Grades 3–6. The materials are in the ***Individual Manipulative Kits*** or the ***Essential Materials Module.***

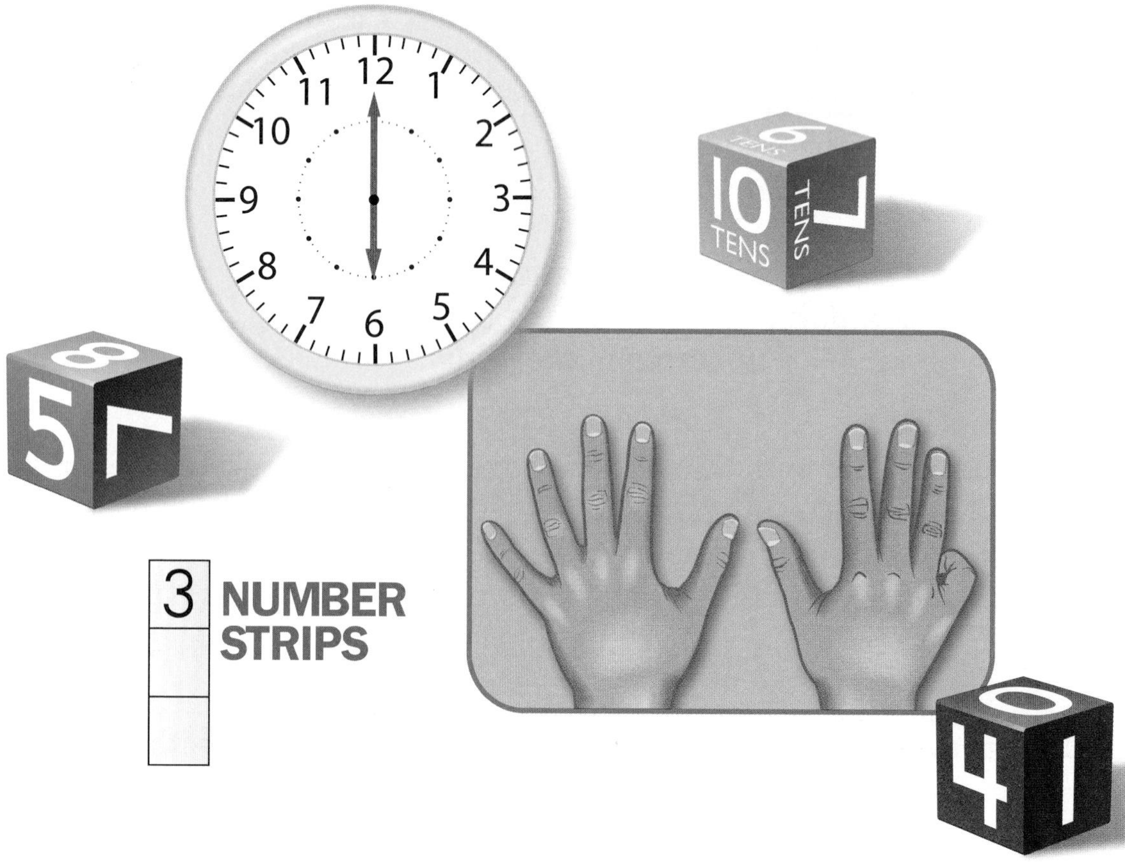

In addition to these Core Components of the program, the following materials provide specific resources to facilitate instruction.

| Component | Grades | Purpose |
|---|---|---|
| Practice Blackline Masters | K–6 | Extra practice for every lesson |
| Practice Workbook | K–6 | Workbook version of extra practice for teacher convenience |
| Enrichment Support Guide | K–6 | Activities for every lesson designed to expand lesson concepts |
| Reteach Support Guide | K–6 | Alternative strategies for presenting lesson concepts |
| Intervention Support Guide | K–6 | Instruction and practice of prerequisite skills for every chapter to bring all students up to speed |
| English Learner Support Guide | K–6 | Strategies for previewing and reviewing lesson concepts and vocabulary for students learning English |
| Assessment | K–6 | Variety of assessment options to evaluate student proficiency and inform instruction |
| Student Assessment Booklet | K–6 | Assessment booklets for teacher convenience |
| Home Connection | PreK–6 | Newsletters, surveys, and activities to encourage home and school communications |
| Across the Curriculum Math Connections | K–6 | Cross-Curricular projects and WebQuests that develop math proficiency and provide interesting math applications |
| Exercise Book | 3–6 | A duplication of the ***Student Edition*** exercises in a workbook format |
| Big Book | PreK | Counting book specifically chosen for preschoolers |
| Game Mat Kit | K–6 | Contains 15 copies of each of the Game Mats at each grade level and enough playing pieces, ***Number Cubes,*** and play money for an entire class; includes a ***Guide for Using the Game Mats*** and a set of color transparencies of the basic version of each game |
| Home Connection Game Kit | K–6 | Math games kit for home use that includes the game mats and cube games |
| Manipulative Kits | PreK–6 | Available in Topic Modules or Individual Kits to support concept development; available in convenient packaging options |
| Professional Development<br>• Online/CD<br>• Books | | Six professional development courses that offer school districts complete staff development in math education |
| ***Calculator Package*** | | Calculators available for classroom convenience |

## *Real Math* Technology Resources

Math resources designed to facilitate instruction and record keeping and to expand student learning

| For Teachers | | For Students | |
|---|---|---|---|
| e Planner | A tool to help teachers plan daily lessons and plot out year-long goals | Building Blocks | **Activities** (PreK–6) Engaging research-based activities designed to reinforce levels of mathematical development in different strands of mathematics |
| e Presentation | An online presentation tool to enable teachers to present each lesson electronically that includes ***eGames*** and ***eMathTools*** for demonstration purposes | e Textbook | An electronic version of the ***Student Edition*** that students can access from home |
| e Assess | An assessment tool to grade, track, and report electronic versions of all assessments<br>• Electronic version of all assessments in print product<br>• State guideline database correlated to specific test items<br>• Reports | e Games | (K–6) Electronic versions of twelve games from each grade level of ***Real Math;*** competitive games that involve luck, skill, and strategy to help practice skills and develop mathematical thinking |
| | **Professional Development**<br>A series of six online courses that teach different aspects of mathematics | e MathTools | Electronic math tools to help students solve problems and explore concepts |

# Chapter Organization

*The first few pages of each chapter help you understand the chapter focus and to see how concepts are developed.*

## Chapter Overview

- **Teaching for Understanding** provides the big ideas of the chapter.
- **Skills Trace** shows where concepts were previously introduced and how they will be followed up.
- **Prerequisite Skills** help determine if students are ready for the chapter.
- **Games** and **Problem Solving** provide an overview of key chapter experiences.
- **Math Background** provides mathematical and pedagogical information relevant to the chapter.
- **What Research Says** offers insights into how children learn and research-based teaching strategies.
- **Planning Guide** includes objectives that explain how the key concepts are developed lesson by lesson and which resources can be used in each lesson.
- **Technology Resources** list resources that are available to help with planning or to support instruction.

## Chapter Introduction

Each Chapter Introduction introduces concepts and provides ways to assess prior knowledge.

- **Pretest** helps evaluate what students know and do not know about the chapter concepts in order to determine what to reteach, emphasize, or skip.
- **Access Prior Knowledge** offers preliminary discussion about chapter concepts to determine what students know.
- **Exploring Problem Solving** introduces the chapter theme and concepts by exploring the ways in which students solve real-world problems.
- **Concept/Question Board** establishes connections and applications of the chapter concepts to students' thinking and lives outside the classroom.
- **Assess and Differentiate** uses assessments to summarize and analyze evidence of student understanding and to plan for differentiating instruction.
- **Project Overview** outlines two projects that students can work on during the course of the chapter that apply chapter concepts across the curriculum.

## Lessons

Lessons provide overview, ideas for differentiating instruction, complete lesson plans, teaching strategies, and assessments that inform instruction.

## Exploring Problem Solving

These lessons introduce, compare, and use problem-solving strategies and appear in the beginning, middle, and end of each chapter.

## Cumulative Review

Cumulative Review exercises provide practice for standardized-test formats in the middle and end of the chapter and allow you to evaluate if students are retaining previously developed concepts and skills.

## Individual Oral Assessment

These individual assessment interviews in the middle of each chapter provide an opportunity to individually evaluate student understanding.

## Thinking Stories (K–3) and Exploring Problem Solving

These activities at the end of each chapter offer applications of lesson concepts and development of students' mathematical thinking and problem-solving abilities.

## Chapter Wrap-Up

The Chapter Wrap-up provides ways to review chapter concepts and assess student understanding.

- **Key Ideas Review** refreshes student knowledge of the key concepts.
- **Chapter Review** provides a review of chapter concepts.
- **Practice Test** is in the same format as the Chapter Test and gives students a chance for self-assessment before taking the Chapter Test.

*Once you understand how a chapter is organized, survey the resources in each lesson.*

## Lesson Planning

The first page of each lesson helps teachers prepare to teach each lesson.

- **Context of the Lesson** explains how the lesson is developed in the context of the chapter and includes information about how concepts were previously developed, as well as specific information about expectations of student performance.
- **Planning for Learning: Differentiate Instruction** provides ideas for planning how to adapt the lesson depending on assessments of student understanding.
- **Lesson Planner** includes Objectives, Materials lists, and Looking Ahead tips to prepare for upcoming lessons.

## Lesson Plans

Every lesson throughout ***Real Math*** is structured in the same way.

### Mental Math

- **Mental Math** is a five-minute warm-up at the beginning of each lesson that provides cumulative review.

### Develop

- **Develop** is the heart of the lesson instruction. Here are suggestions for how to introduce lesson concepts, ideas for Guided Discussion, Skill Building, and Strategy Building activities to develop student understanding.

### Assign Student Pages

- **Assign Student Pages** explains when to have students complete the lesson pages and ideas for what they can do when they finish.

### Reflect

- **Reflect** is a vital part of the lesson that offers ways to help students summarize, reflect, and expand on their understanding of the lesson concepts.

### Assess and Differentiate

- **Assess and Differentiate** uses informal and formal assessments to summarize and analyze evidence of student understanding and plan for differentiating instruction.

*In* **Real Math** *there are activities that will occur again and again. Establishing rules or routines for these activities with students will facilitate instruction.*

# Mental Math

Mental Math exercises provide cumulative review and computation practice for students and provide opportunities to assess students' skills quickly. Mental Math is an essential component of ***Real Math*** since it helps students review skills they have already learned that are prerequisite skills for upcoming lessons.

Most Mental Math exercises are done in the following four steps, which include the **Find, Hide,** and **Show** routine. The pace should be lively enough to keep things moving, yet not so fast that students do not have time to think.

## Step 1

Present a problem orally, by writing it on the board, or by using ***ePresentation.***

## Step 2

Students **find** the answer and arrange their ***Response Wheels, Number Cubes,*** or other response device to display it.

## Step 3

Students **hide** the answer while you provide enough time for most students to find the answer.

## Step 4

Students **show** the answer to you, while you show and explain the answer to the class.

This four-step process allows students to participate in a nonthreatening way. You can tell instantly whether all students are participating and whether they have the right answer. If a student gets a wrong answer, only that student and you know it. You can make note of students who are struggling and give them extra help later on.

## Tips

- Occasionally add a "peek-to-be-sure" step to the Find, Hide, and Show procedure. Some students will have found an answer and hide it while waiting for others in the class to do the same. This is the time to give the "Peek" command, which asks the students who have found answers to check them. This keeps them involved during the few seconds of waiting for the "Show" command.
- Use judgment to decide when to give the "Show" command. You do not have to wait for every student to find and hide an answer. But you should wait long enough so that students who are making progress toward a solution have time to finish. Remember, too, that students who cannot answer in time will know they are having difficulty, and you will also know they are having difficulty. The rest of the class need not know. Prolonged waiting only calls attention to the slower students. Furthermore, after you say "Show," a few more seconds will pass while you are checking answers, and during this time students still have time to find and show their responses.
- Encourage students. Because response exercises are active exchanges between you and the students, use these opportunities to let them know you are pleased with their efforts and that you have confidence in them.
- If it is difficult for you to see all the response card answers when the students are at their seats, have them sit on the floor closer to you. Or you might walk around the room, but do this quickly so you do not slow the lively pace of the exercise.

# Guided Discussion

*"Teachers must make judgments about when to tell, when to question, and when to correct. They must decide when to guide with prompting and when to let students grapple with a mathematical issue.... The point of classroom discourse is to develop students' understanding of key ideas. But it also provides opportunities to emphasize and model mathematical reasoning and problem solving and to enhance students' disposition toward mathematics."*

—Kilpatrick, J., Swafford, J. and Findell, B. eds. *Adding It Up: Helping Children Learn Mathematics*. Washington, D.C.: National Research Council/National Academy Press, 2001, pp. 346.

Guided Discussion is expected in almost all ***Real Math*** lessons. In Guided Discussion students speak the language of mathematics, communicate mathematically, explain their thinking, and demonstrate understanding.

Routines or rules for Guided Discussion established at the beginning of the year can make discussions more productive and promote listening and speaking skills.

1. Pay attention to others. Give full attention to the person who is speaking. This includes looking at the speaker and nodding to show that you understand.
2. Wait for speakers to answer and complete their thoughts. Sometimes teachers and other students get impatient and move on, ask someone else, or give the answer before someone has a chance to think and speak. Giving students time to answer is a vital part of teaching for understanding.
3. Listen. Let yourself finish listening before you begin to speak. You cannot listen if you are busy thinking about what you want to say next.
4. Respect speakers by taking turns and making sure that everyone gets a chance to speak and that no one dominates the conversation.
5. Build on others' ideas by making connections, drawing analogies, or expanding on the idea.
6. Ask questions. Asking questions of another speaker shows that you were listening. Ask if you are not sure you understand what the speaker has said, or ask for clarification or explanation. It is a good idea to repeat in your own words what the speaker said so you can be sure your understanding is correct.

**RESEARCH IN ACTION**

"One of the most striking aspects of Japanese classrooms, especially at the first-grade level, was the amount of verbal explanation that occurred during mathematics class. We were able to identify segments that contained explanations by either the teacher, a student, or both the teacher and a student.... Nearly 50 percent of all Japanese first-grade segments contained verbal explanations, compared with only about 20 percent of the American segments....Whereas the American teachers were more likely to stress participation in nonverbal activities or the asking of short-answer questions to lead students into a new topic, Japanese teachers would give, and ask students to give, lengthy verbal explanations of mathematical concepts and algorithms."

—Stigler, James W. *"The Use of Verbal Explanation in Japanese and American Classrooms,"* Arithmetic Teacher, October 1988.

## Questions to Ask

Questions help teachers learn about student thinking and consider instructional implications of that knowledge. Teachers should be prepared for unexpected answers and probe further with questions to understand student thought processes. Sometimes the unexpected answer demonstrates true insight.

Not all questions are the same. Questions have different purposes.

- **Engaging Questions** invite students into a discussion, keep them engaged in conversation, and invite them to share their work. Engaging questions are typically open-ended and encourage different ways of responding.
- **Exploring Questions** ask students to provide explanations, make analogies, or identify problems and solutions.
- **Synthesizing Questions** ask students to identify patterns, make generalizations or rules, or argue, prove, or demonstrate their assumptions.
- **Clarifying Questions** help students explain their thinking or help you understand their thinking.
- **Refocusing Questions** help students get back on track or move away from a dead-end strategy.

See Appendix A for more information about Guided Discussion.

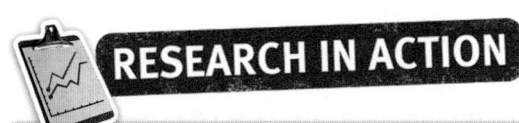

# Games

Games

Games are a vital part of ***Real Math.*** They have been written specifically for the program to support the concepts and skills being taught. Students enjoying the friendly competition may not even realize how much math they are learning and practicing.

## Purposes of Games

- Games provide practice to reinforce new skills and review previously covered topics.
- Most ***Real Math*** games place students in an environment in which they are expected to recognize situations that can be analyzed by mathematical thought, to formulate their own problems, to solve those problems, to use their solutions to improve their game-playing strategies, and to communicate with other players about their strategies.
- Games give students a chance to work out important mathematical ideas and problem-solving strategies.
- Games give you an opportunity to informally monitor student progress by watching students as they play.
- Games allow students of all ability levels to compete fairly. Winning games requires a mix of chance, skills, and thinking strategies.

## Types of Games

**Game Mats** are found in the ***Game Mat Kit*** and are reproduced in Appendix D. The ***Game Mat Kit*** contains fifteen copies of each of the different **Game Mats** in a grade level, which should accommodate a class of thirty since most games are played by two or more players. The package also contains enough playing pieces, ***Number Cubes,*** and play money for an entire class, along with a ***Guide for Using the Game Mats*** and a set of color transparencies of the basic version of each game. Reduced-size copies of the **Game Mats** can also be found in the back of this ***Teacher's Edition.***

Many of the **Game Mats** have both a basic and a harder version for differentiating instruction.

## Cube and Other Games

Directions for **Cube Games** that require only ***Number Cubes*** are in the ***Teacher's Edition*** or ***Student Edition*** of appropriate lessons. Directions for all **Cube Games** are reproduced in the ***Home Connection Support Guide*** and in the ***Home Connection Game Kit.***

Many of the **Cube Games** have variations that extend the mathematics or provide applications for new thinking strategies. Variations can be learned quickly, making the **Cube Games** even more practical and useful in the classroom.

***eGames*** are electronic versions of some of the **Game Mats** and **Cube Games.**

***Building Blocks*** electronic activities and games are referenced in appropriate lessons. These activities provide additional opportunities for practice and exploration.

## Routines for Introducing Games

1. Familiarize yourself with the rules of each game by playing it before showing students how to play it.
2. Demonstrate, do not just tell, how a game is played. Overhead projector versions of the **Game Mats** are provided for demonstrating games in front of the class. The ***ePresentation*** or ***eGames*** can be displayed for the class to see how to play those games.
3. Let students who already know the game rules (perhaps from a previous grade) help students who are new to the games.
4. Do not teach students. Rather, encourage students to develop their own game-playing strategies and discuss their strategies in small groups or as a class.

## Tips for Using Games

- Stress enjoyment and learning rather than competition. Emphasize sportsmanship, fair play, and taking turns.
- Change the composition of the game-playing groups from day to day. Students can learn different things by playing with different partners. From time to time, use groups of both similar and mixed ability levels.
- Assign a referee to each group. The referee makes sure that rules are followed, reminds players when it is their turn, keeps track of the score, and in some games acts as banker. Referees are especially helpful in the lower grades.
- Encourage students to play games during their free time in school and at home. Make the games easily accessible, perhaps in a math center.

See Appendix A for more information about ***Real Math*** Games.

# Thinking Stories and Exploring Problem Solving

*"Problem solving is a complex endeavor that requires critical thinking and therefore, on a logical basis, more development than most other types of lessons."*

—Grouws, Douglas A. and Thomas L. Good. "Issues in Problem-Solving Instruction," *Arithmetic Teacher,* April 1989.

***Real Math*** Exploring Problem Solving lessons and Thinking Stories are designed to provide further opportunities to explore and discuss problem-solving strategies and alternative approaches to solving problems.

## What are Thinking Stories?

Thinking Stories are an essential component of ***Real Math*** Grades K–3 that help develop students' problem-solving skills. The stories describe people using mathematics and logic in correct and incorrect ways. The stories are designed to be read to students. Interspersed throughout the stories are questions that ask students to solve problems, make predictions, and analyze the characters' thinking. The same Thinking Story characters appear in all grade levels, so they "grow" with the students. Each character has peculiar thinking patterns that students come to know. For example, Mr. Muddle takes things too literally, Ferdie jumps to conclusions, Mrs. Eng does not provide enough information, and Mr. Breezy provides too much information.

## Routines for Thinking Stories

1. Read each story aloud.
2. Stop for each question and discuss possible answers after you ask it. Some questions have brief answers and should be handled quickly. Others call for deeper thinking or have a range of possible answers and will require several minutes of discussion. Encourage and discuss answers. Wait for students to respond. A minute or two of silence while students think is a good idea.

Problem Solving

3. If your students enjoy a particular story, consider reading it again another day.

## What are Exploring Problem Solving Lessons?

The Exploring Problem Solving lessons at the beginning, middle, and end of each chapter in Grades K–6 also promote development of reasoning and problem-solving abilities. These lessons provide real problems that can be solved in a variety of ways. The lessons model different problem-solving strategies and provide opportunities for students to solve rich problems and discuss their problem-solving strategies. In Grades 4–6, Exploring Problem Solving includes nonfiction articles from which interesting problems are derived and explored.

## Routines for Exploring Problem Solving

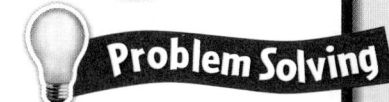

1. Read the lessons with students.
2. Discuss the problems and any sample solutions so that everyone understands what the problem is asking.
3. Allow students to solve problems on their own or in small groups. Showing students how to do a problem robs them of valuable thinking and their investment and confidence in their own solutions.
4. Facilitate a discussion of alternative problem solutions and have students discuss advantages, limitations, unique features, and generalizable features of different solutions.

See Appendix A for more information about Thinking Stories and Exploring Problem Solving.

# Assign Student Pages, As Students Finish, and Reflect

In almost every lesson, teachers will assign student pages to complete during class. Students will finish at different times and should know what they can do to use their extra time productively until the Reflect part of the lesson. Students should not feel penalized for finishing early and should do something that is mathematically rewarding.

## Assign Student Pages

### Assign Student Pages Routines

Student book exercises in ***Real Math*** are primarily nonmechanical. Student book pages help students learn to think about the problems. For example, addition and subtraction problems are mixed earlier than in traditional programs so students learn to pay attention to what a problem says, rather than to add unthinkingly whenever they see two numbers. This early mixing of problems also helps establish the relationship between addition and subtraction.

Because student book exercises are nonmechanical, they sometimes require your active participation.

1. Make sure students know what pages to work on and any special requirements of those pages.
2. Tell students whether they should work independently or in small groups as they complete the pages.
3. Tell students how long they have to work on the student pages before you plan to begin the Reflect part of the lesson.
4. Tell students what their options are if they finish early. Suggested options are listed under the Assign Student Pages heading in each lesson. These include
   a. suggested ***eMathTools*** to use.
   b. ***Game Mats,* Cube Games, *eGames,*** and ***Building Blocks*** activities to play.
   c. Writing+Math Journal suggestions.
5. As students work on the student pages, circulate the room to monitor their progress. Use the Monitoring Student Progress suggestions for ideas on what to look for. Comment positively on student work and stop to ask exploring, synthesizing, clarifying, or refocusing questions.
6. You may also use this time to work with English Learners or students who need intervention.
7. Complete the Informal Assessment Checklists on the last page of each lesson.
8. Since games are an important and integral part of the program that provide necessary practice in traditional basic skills as well as higher-order thinking skills, when games are included in a lesson, be sure to stop work on student pages early enough to leave enough time to play the game.

## Reflect

### Reflect Routines

1. At the designated time, have students stop their activity and direct their attention to reflecting on the lesson.
2. Use the suggested questions in Reflect or ask students to consider these ideas:
   a. Think about related matters that go beyond the scope of the lesson
   b. Summarize ideas about the lesson concepts
   c. Compare how the lesson concept or skill is similar to or different from other skills
   d. Ask how students have seen or can apply the lesson in other curricular areas, other strands of mathematics, or in the world outside of school
   e. Discuss student solutions to Extended Response questions

## Assess and Differentiate

### Assessment Follow-up: Differentiate Instruction

Based on your informal assessments and observations, choose from the following to differentiate for homework:

a. Complete the student pages
b. Family Involvement suggestions
c. Enrichment ideas
d. Practice
e. Reteach

# Differentiate Instruction

*"Classrooms grounded in best-practice education, and modified to be responsive to student differences, benefit virtually all students. Differentiation addresses the needs of struggling and advanced learners. It addresses the needs of students for whom English is a second language and students who have strong learning style preferences. It addresses gender differences and cultural differences."*

—Tomlinson, Carol Ann, *The Differentiated Classroom: Responding to the Needs of All Learners.* 1999, p.24

## Instruction can be differentiated in three key ways:

- **Content** is what the teacher wants students to learn and the materials or mechanisms through which that is accomplished. Differentiating the content may be teaching prerequisite concepts to students who need intervention, or by asking questions that cause students to think beyond concepts covered in the lesson.
- **Process** is how or which activities the students do to ensure they use key skills to make sense of the content. Differentiating the process may include alternating the pace of the lesson.
- **Product** is how the student demonstrates what he or she has come to know. Differentiating the product may include assigning Enrichment, Practice, or Reteach activities to complete.

***Real Math*** provides a wealth of support for differentiating instruction, but teachers must make decisions based on their assessments of student understanding and performance.

## Routines for Differentiating Instruction

**1. Plan for differentiation**

a. To prepare for a lesson, scan the suggestions in Planning for All Learners for differentiating instruction on the first page of each lesson. Be prepared to differentiate the content or process depending on your estimation of student understanding.

b. English Learner strategies **differentiate the process** for introducing the lesson by previewing key concepts and vocabulary.

c. Intervention lessons **differentiate content** for those students who have not yet mastered prerequisite skills.

d. Enrich strategies **differentiate the process** if students already understand the content.

e. Practice strategies **differentiate the process** if students need practice.

f. Reteach strategies **differentiate the process** if students are not understanding lesson material.

**2. Monitor student progress** As students participate in Mental Math, Guided Discussion, Skill Building, Strategy Building, Games, and other lesson activities, be alert to signs of understanding and misunderstanding. The Informal Assessment Checklists include rubrics to help gather evidence about students' math proficiency.

**3. Follow-Up** Summarize your formal assessments and informal observations, and consider how to differentiate student products in the lesson follow-up assignments. Program resources include

a. **Enrichment** activities for students who have a secure understanding.

b. **Practice** activities for students who have adequate understanding.

c. **Reteach** activities for student who have an emerging understanding.

**4. Adjust tomorrow's lesson** Based on student understanding and performance, consider how the next lesson should be adjusted for different learners.

*"Differentiating instruction does not mean just having students do different things. When a teacher lacks clarity about what a student should know, understand, and be able to do as a result of a lesson, the learning tasks she creates may or may not be engaging and we can almost be certain the tasks won't help students understand essential ideas or principles. A fuzzy sense of the essentials results in fuzzy activities, which in tern results in fuzzy student understanding. That's a barrier to high-quality teaching and learning."*

—Tomlinson, Carol Ann, *The Differentiated Classroom: Responding to the Needs of All Learners.* 1999, p. 4

See Appendix A for more information about Differentiating Instruction.

# Using Technology

## Technology Resources for Teachers

***Real Math*** includes several pieces of integrated technology for teachers designed to increase efficiency and effectiveness of instruction and assessment.

## Suggested Procedures for Using Technology

### e Planner

- **Yearly Planning** Use the ***ePlanner*** before school begins to plan out the mathematics course for the year. Plot out school events, holidays, and testing periods and then lessons to ensure that key topics are addressed.
- **Weekly Planning** Use the ***ePlanner*** to adjust daily lesson plans based on your assessment of student understanding.

### e Assess

- **Daily Records** Use ***eAssess*** to record daily formal and informal assessments.
- **Report Cards** Use ***eAssess*** to print student and class reports to determine grades.
- **Parent-Teacher Conferences** Use ***eAssess*** to print student reports to discuss with parents.

### e Presentation

- **Planning** Use ***ePresentation*** to preview lesson concepts and activities before class.
- **Presentation** Use ***ePresentation*** to present multimedia lessons to students. ***ePresentation*** includes the complete lesson, including Guided Discussion questions, ***eGame*** demonstrations, and ***eMathTools.***

## Technology Resources for Students

***Real Math*** provides engaging technology resources to enrich, apply, and extend learning.

**e Games** are electronic versions of appropriate Cube and Mat Games to extend practice and skill- and strategy-building activities in engaging contexts.

**e MathTools** are electronic tools that students can use to solve problems, test solutions, explore concepts, or demonstrate understanding.

**Building Blocks** activities are designed to reinforce key concepts and develop mathematics understanding.

**e Textbook** is the complete ***Student Edition*** in electronic format.

## Routines for Using Technology

1. Determine rules for computer use and communicate them to students. Rules should include
   a. sharing available computers. Some teachers have a computer sign-up chart for each computer. Some teachers have the students track this themselves.
   b. computer time. You might limit the amount of time students can be at the computer or allow students to work in pairs. Some teachers have students work until they complete an activity. Others allow students to continue on with additional activities.
2. Familiarize students with your rules for proper use of computers, including how to turn computers on, load programs, and shut down the computer. Some teachers manage computers themselves; others have an aide or student in charge of computer management.
3. Using the suggestions for As Students Finish under **Assign Student Pages** in each lesson, make sure the computers are on, the programs are loaded, and that students know how to access the software.
4. Make sure students know what to do once they complete the computer activity.

See Appendix A for more information about using ***Real Math*** Technology.

# Managing Materials

## Managing Materials

***Real Math*** provides a wealth of resources. Establishing procedures for use of materials will simplify management issues and allow students to spend more time developing mathematical understanding.

## Books

***Teacher's Edition*** and ***Support Guides*** should be at your fingertips.

***Student Editions*** may be kept at student desks or on a shelf in the classroom.

## Response Wheel*

Each student in Grades 3–6 gets one ***Response Wheel.*** Because they are used daily, ***Response Wheels*** should be kept in students' desks, notebooks, or mathematics books. They should be stored in such a way that they are not likely to become bent or lost. You may wish to number or otherwise identify each card so that each student can be responsible for his or her card.

## Number Cubes*

Each student in Grades 1 and 2 gets four ***Number Cubes.*** Because they are used frequently, it may be best to have the students keep the cubes in their desks, perhaps with their play money. In Grades 3–6, students have two cubes that are used to generate random numbers.

* ***Response Wheels*** and ***Number Cubes*** are packaged in the ***Essential Materials Module*** and as part of the ***Individual Student Manipulative Kit,*** for your convenience.

## Game Mat Kits

The ***Game Mat Kit*** includes fifteen copies of each **Game Mat** and game kit playing pieces packaged in individual bags. There is storage space for the **Game Mat** and the playing pieces in the ***Game Mat Kit*** box. Students will benefit from a demonstration of how you want to have students put pieces back in bags and return them and the **Game Mats** to the kit.

## Manipulatives

***Real Math*** manipulatives come in three configurations.

- ***Individual Manipulative Kits*** These kits include ***Number Cubes,*** money, clock faces, rulers, interlocking cubes, counters, pattern blocks, tape measures, and spinners. A kit appropriate for Grades K–2 and another kit for 3–6 are available. These kits can be stored at student desks or in a designated tub or shelf in the classroom.
- **Manipulative Modules** Manipulatives are also available in modules for specific topics: Counting, Base-Ten, Fractions, Geometry, Measurement, Money, and Time. These kits contain enough materials for class use.
- **Teacher Manipulative Kit** This kit provides presentation-style manipulatives and overhead projector manipulatives for demonstration purposes.

See Appendix A for more information about Materials.

*It is important to keep parents informed about what their children are doing in mathematics so they can support students' mathematical understanding and development at home.*

# Family Involvement

Family members can play a critical role in students' success in mathematics if they understand how to help. For example, the games, Thinking Stories, and other activities in ***Real Math*** may be unfamiliar to parents. Parents need to be assured that these are important activities designed to develop a solid understanding of mathematical concepts and provide essential practice with arithmetic skills.

***Real Math*** has several elements built into the program that can enable family-school communications.

## Home Connection Support Guide

This book includes ready-made Parent and Student Surveys, Newsletters, and Games that teachers can use to communicate with student families. Newsletters are available for every chapter.

## Home Connection Game Kit

This kit includes all the **Game Mats** and **Cube Games** for a grade level, packaged in a game box along with the pieces needed to play the games. Families can purchase the kit or you can establish a "lending game library."

## Assessment Resources

***Assessment*** includes several resources to communicate with families.

- **Student Assessment Record** is a convenient form to record all student assessments on a daily or weekly basis. These forms are handy to use at parent-teacher conferences.
- **Parent-Teacher Conference Checklist** provides a helpful way to organize thoughts about students in preparation for parent-teacher conferences.

## Parent Aides

Often parents are willing to volunteer to help out in the classroom. There are many ways they can help.

- Computer Management—Make sure computers are on and loaded with appropriate software. Be available to trouble shoot and answer questions while students use the computers.
- Intervention Aide—Use the ***Intervention Support Guide*** to work with students to build prerequisite skills.
- English Learner Aide—Use the ***English Learner Support Guide*** to work with English Learners to preview and review lesson concepts.
- Manipulatives Manager—Make sure manipulatives are available for student use, when appropriate.

## Family Participation

There are many ways that families can assist students in learning math.

### Playing Games

Playing games with students is an enjoyable way to help them practice their math skills. The ***Home Connection Support Guide*** contains reproducible directions for each of the **Cube Games.** Reproductions of the **Game Mats** are in the back of this ***Teacher's Edition.*** The ***Home Connection Game Kit*** is also available.

### Practicing Basic Facts

***Home Connection*** contains reproducible flash cards for basic facts and directions for games using the cards. Make sure parents and helpers understand how best to use flash cards.

- Never ridicule students for incorrect answers.
- Stop practice when the student becomes disinterested.

### Using Math in Everyday Life

Encourage parents to show students how they use mathematics throughout the day and to ask for students' help. For example, families can estimate the total cost of a shopping trip, measure ingredients and adjust recipes for new quantities when cooking, and estimate when to leave on a trip to arrive by a certain time.

*The lessons are designed to be taught at a lively pace. Students should move quickly from activity to activity. In this way, they will remain alert and interested in what they are learning.*

# Pacing

## Here are some tips for proper pacing:

- Be prepared. Materials must be ready, and you must be ready. Sections in the lesson plans titled Looking Ahead and Materials will help you prepare the items you will need in time for when they are needed. Also, read the lesson plan in advance or preview the ***ePresentation*** so you will not lose time figuring out what to do while the lesson is in progress.
- Use the time estimates. To help you manage time, lesson plans suggest a number of minutes for each activity. These times cannot be precise for every teacher and for every lesson. Some activities will take you more time and some will take less. Even so, the suggested times will help you to plan in advance how you will carry out each activity.
- Watch the clock. Use it as an ally. The clock can tell you when you have concentrated on an activity too long, even before students show signs of restlessness. It can tell you when you have lapsed into too much talking or when you are shifting too slowly from one activity to another.

## Using Lessons over Two Days

Most lessons can be completed in one day (about 45–60 minutes of class time). However, you may find that you occasionally need to spend an extra day on some lessons. Refer to the Lesson Plans chart at the beginning of each unit for pacing suggestions. When you decide to take two days for a lesson, try dividing it as follows:

### Day 1

- Review skills that students will need for the lesson.
- Do all suggested Teach activities, but not the ***Student Edition*** pages.

### Day 2

- Review and/or adapt the Mental Math exercises from the previous day.
- Provide additional teaching and practice on related skills.
- Allow plenty of time for students to work on the ***Student Edition*** pages.
- Devote time to a related **Cube Game** or **Game Mat.**
- Extend the Reflect discussion.

## Adjusting Instruction for Longer or Shorter Math Sessions

Most teachers have about 45–60 minutes each day to devote to mathematics. If your schedule varies greatly from that consider the following tips for adjusting instruction.

### If you have more than 60 minutes for math...

- Lengthen Guided Discussion and game times by five minutes each (more when new games are introduced).
- Repeat whole-group activities when you feel that students will remain interested.
- Use the ***Reteach, Practice,*** and ***Enrichment Masters*** and the ***Cross-Curricular Connections*** provided throughout the ***Teacher's Edition.***

### If you have fewer than 45 minutes for math...

- Do not eliminate the Games or Thinking Stories. These help develop mathematical intelligence and are essential portions of the curriculum.
- Do the Thinking Story and Exploring Problem Solving activities outside the regular mathematics period (e.g., first thing in the morning, right after lunch, or at read-aloud time).
- Play games that reinforce previous lessons outside the regular class period, such as every Friday, perhaps.
- Conduct Mental Math on basic facts outside the regular mathematics period.
- Reduce time spent on a few lesson components by a minute or two.
- Have students spend more time working on student pages outside of class.

*Real Math is rich in opportunities and resources to conduct comprehensive assessments that inform instruction. The **Real Math** Assessments are designed to evaluate all math proficiencies.*

# Assessment

## Goals of Assessment

1. To improve instruction by informing teachers about the effectiveness of their lessons
2. To promote growth of students by identifying where they need additional instruction and support
3. To recognize accomplishments

## Phases of Assessment

**Planning** As you develop lesson plans, you can consider how you might assess the instruction, determining how you will tell if students have grasped the material.

**Gather Evidence** Throughout the instructional phase, you can informally and formally gather evidence of student understanding. The Informal Assessment Checklists and Student Assessment Records are provided to help you record data.

**Summarize Findings** Taking time to reflect on the assessments to summarize findings and make plans for follow-up is a critical part of any lesson.

**Use Results** Use the results of your findings to differentiate instruction or to adjust or confirm future lessons.

***Real Math*** is rich in opportunities to monitor student progress to accomplish these goals.

## Informal Daily Assessment

Informal Daily Assessments evaluate students' math proficiencies in computational fluency, reasoning, understanding, applying, and engaging. Mental Math exercises, Games, Thinking Stories, and ***Student Edition*** pages can be used for day-to-day observation and assessment of how well each student is learning skills and grasping concepts. Because of their special nature, these activities are an effective and convenient means of monitoring students. Games, for example, allow you to watch students practice particular skills under conditions more natural to them than most classroom activities. Mental Math exercises allow you to provide adequate work and time to see individual responses, give immediate feedback, and involve the entire class.

Simple rubrics enable teachers to record and track their observations. These can later be recorded by hand in the Student Assessment Record or in ***eAssess*** to help provide a more complete view of student proficiency.

## Formal Assessments

The ***Student Edition*** and ***Assessment*** provide formal assessments for each chapter. Included are Pretests, Speed Tests, Daily Quizzes, Practice Tests, and Chapter Tests to evaluate students' understanding of chapter concepts. Cumulative Review, Key Ideas Review, and Chapter Review are available to prepare students for formal assessments.

Mastery Checkpoints provide periodic progress checks.

## Individual Oral Assessment

Oral Assessment, which is in the middle of the chapter, provides an opportunity for teachers to interview students and get a first-hand assessment of student reasoning and understanding.

## Individual Portfolio Assessment

Journals and Chapter Projects can be used for Portfolio Assessment.

See Appendix A for more information about Assessment.

# Assessment

The Mastery Checkpoints are key Grade 4 skills for which students are expected to demonstrate mastery. ***Assessment*** contains a blackline master for each Mastery Checkpoint.

Grade 4 includes key skills that are important for students' future progress. To help monitor progress for each student, corresponding Mastery Checkpoints appear throughout the Grade 4 ***Teacher's Edition.*** Each Mastery Checkpoint appears in the lesson where most students are expected to have achieved proficiency. The table to the right provides a list of the Grade 4 skills and corresponding lessons that include the Mastery Checkpoints.

Do not delay the progress of the entire class while waiting for all students to demonstrate success with a particular skill. More teaching and practice on that skill is always given in a later lesson, usually the following lesson. At that time, you can focus on students who need extra help.

## Mastery Checkpoints

The Mastery Checkpoint Chart in ***Assessment*** provides a convenient way to keep track of your students' progress.

- Fill in the names of all the students in the class.
- When a Mastery Checkpoint is encountered in the ***Teacher's Edition,*** follow the suggestions for observing each student. Then record students' progress, as follows:

Place a check mark in the appropriate column beside the name of each student who demonstrates success on the skill in question.

Pencil in a *P* in the appropriate column for each student who grasps the concept but still needs further practice to sharpen his or her skill. Assign extra practice to these students.

Pencil in a *T* for each student who has not yet grasped the idea and needs further teaching. Give extra teaching to these students.

Change Ts (needs teaching) to Ps (needs practice) and Ps to Rs (just needs refreshing), as students demonstrate success on the skill.

### Grade 4 Checkpoints

| Number | Lesson | Topic |
|---|---|---|
| 1 | 1.3 | Numerical Sequence |
| 2 | 1.5 | Basic Addition and Subtraction Facts |
| 3 | 2.3 | Multidigit Addition and Subtraction |
| 4 | 2.6 | Detecting Obviously Wrong Answers |
| 5 | 3.6 | Basic Multiplication Facts |
| 6 | 3.11 | Basic Division Facts, Including Remainders |
| 7 | 3.14 | Arithmetic Applications |
| 8 | 4.7 | Functions and Inverses |
| 9 | 4.12 | Graphing Functions |
| 10 | 5.4 | Multiplying by Powers of 10 and Multiplying Multiples of 10 |
| 11 | 5.7 | Approximating Answers to Multidigit Multiplication Problems |
| 12 | 5.10 | Multiplying Two- and Three-Digit Numbers by One-Digit Numbers |
| 13 | 6.3 | Multiplying Two Two-Digit Numbers |
| 14 | 6.8 | Multiplying Multidigit Numbers |
| 15 | 8.1 | Understanding Fractions |
| 16 | 8.2 | Fractions of Fractions |
| 17 | 8.14 | Adding and Subtracting Simple Fractions |
| 18 | 9.4 | Understanding Decimals |
| 19 | 9.7 | Multiplying and Dividing Decimals by Powers of 10 |
| 20 | 9.9 | Addition and Subtraction of Decimal Numbers |
| 21 | 9.14 | Measuring Length, Weight, and Volume |
| 22 | 11.5 | Dividing by a One-Digit Divisor |

See Appendix A for more about Assessment.

# Fractions, Decimals, and Percentages

## Lessons



## Teaching for Understanding

***This chapter focuses on understanding ways of describing fractional amounts.*** Students will explore similarities and the relationships between decimals, percentages, and fractions, and will add and subtract decimals and calculate percentges and fractions of whole numbers through measurement. These lessons introduce students to basic information about fractions, decimals, and percentages to ensure students' success in Chapters 8 and 9.

## Prerequisite Skills and Concepts

- Meaning of Fractions and Decimals
- Comparing Numbers through 100
- Measuring to the Nearest Centimeter

## Fractions, Decimals, and Percents Skills Trace

| Before Grade 4 | Grade 4 | After Grade 4 |
|---|---|---|
| **Grades K–3**<br>Formally introduced to fraction benchmarks ($\frac{1}{2}$, $\frac{1}{4}$, and $\frac{1}{8}$) and decimals as fractions | **Chapter 3** reviewed multiplication and division.<br>**This chapter** formally introduces percentages as fractions and decimals.<br>**Chapter 8** expands knowledge of fractions.<br>**Chapter 9** extends students' knowledge of decimals. | Review and mastery of fractions, decimals, and percentages<br>Use decimals, fractions, and percentages as representations in various ways, such as probability experiments, numeral representations, and numerals for computing |

### Problem Solving

Problem solving is in every lesson. This chapter includes the following:

**CHAPTER INTRODUCTION** Students solve a problem that uses number sense and spatial sense to compare different sizes of wholes (pp. 293I–293C).

**EXPLORING PROBLEM SOLVING** The first lesson provides practice using fractions and percentages to relate parts and wholes (pp. 304–305A). The second lesson compares the use of fractions and percentages when analyzing data while putting students in a position to use proportional reasoning (pp. 316–318A).

### Games

Develop reasoning skills, and provide extensive practice.

**Order Game** (Lesson 5.1), **Greater Number Card Game** (Lesson 7.6)

# Math Background

## Fractions, Decimals, and Percentages

### What Are Fractions, Decimals, and Percentages?

Fractions, decimals, and percentages can all represent a part of a whole. They are called *rational numbers* because they can be written as ratios, one number divided by another.

- A fraction is based on the number of equal parts into which the whole is divided (the denominator). The numerator describes the number of parts, and the denominator describes the number of parts in the whole.
- Fractions are used to describe parts of wholes. They also name rational numbers. (This use of fractions is introduced in Chapter 8.)
- Decimals are written as numbers using place values of tenths, hundredths, thousandths, and so on. They are sometimes used to describe parts of measurement units (for example, 0.3 meters or 12.27 seconds).
- Percent means "out of 100." Percentages almost always refer to part of something.

### Common Uses

Fractions, decimals, and percentages are commonly used in different ways. Listed below are some of the ways in which they are often used.

**FRACTIONS** Fractions are typically used to report customary measurements. They may also be used to describe statistical results (for example, "one-fourth of the students bring their lunch from home every day").

**DECIMALS** Decimals are usually used to describe amounts of money. They are also frequently used to report metric measurements.

**PERCENTAGES** Percentages are often used in contexts involving money. Interest is frequently expressed as a percentage, as are taxes and discounts. Percentages are also commonly used in statistics. For example, survey results are often reported as percentages (for example, "seventy percent of the people surveyed voted in the last election"). Another common use of percentages is for rates of change (for example, "the state's population increased by twelve percent over the last ten years").

### Common Errors

A firm understanding of rational numbers (fractions, decimals, and percentages) is difficult for many students. Common errors with rational numbers include the following:

- Confusing decimals and whole numbers
  Students may say, for example, that 0.08 is greater than 0.2. Combating this error requires a focus on the place value of each digit.
- Failing to recognize that fractions, decimals, and percentages are different ways to describe the same quantities or proportions
  When fractions, decimals, and percentages are taught separately, it is more difficult for students to make connections between these representations. The activities in this chapter are carefully designed to help students see the equivalences among fractions, decimals, and percentages.
- Failing to see decimals as representing a proportion of a whole
  Students are used to using decimals with money, but may not understand that a decimal number represents a number part of the way between two whole numbers. The stopwatch activities in this chapter illustrate clearly that decimals can represent parts of a whole unit.

# What Research Says

## About Fractions, Decimals, and Percentages

### How Children Develop Awareness of Equivalence in Numbers

*We know from extensive research that many people—adults, students, even teachers—find the rational-number system to be very difficult. Introduced in early elementary school, this number system requires that students reformulate their concept of number in a major way. They must go beyond whole-number ideas to understand numbers that are expressed in relationship to other numbers. These proportional relationships are grounded in multiplicative reasoning that is quite different from the additive reasoning that characterizes whole numbers.*

(Moss, Joan. *Pipes, Tubes, and Beakers: New Approaches to Teaching the Rational-Number System* in Donovan, M. Suzanne and Bransford, John D. eds. *How Students Learn: Mathematics in the Classroom*. Washington, D.C. National Research Council/National Academies Press. 2005. p. 310.)

*Research reveals that the kinds of errors students make when beginning to operate with rational numbers often come because they have not yet developed meaning for these numbers and are applying poorly understood rules for whole numbers. Operations with rational numbers challenge students' naïve understanding of multiplication and division that multiplication "makes bigger" and division "makes smaller.*

(Kilpatrick, J.; Swafford, J.; and Findell, B. eds. *Adding It Up: Helping Children Learn Mathematics*. Washington, D.C.: National Research Council/National Academy Press, 2001, p. 416.)

### Research-Based Teaching Strategies

Fourth-grade students' development of number sense should continue, with a focus on the structure of numbers and the relationships among numbers. Students need opportunities to recognize and generate equivalent representations for the same rational number. By studying fractions, decimals, and percentages simultaneously, students can learn to move among equivalent forms, flexibly choosing and using appropriate and convenient forms of a number to solve problems and express quantities.

*Children need to learn that rational numbers are numbers in the same way that whole numbers are numbers. For children to use rational numbers to solve problems, they need to learn that the same rational number may be represented in different ways, as a fraction, a decimal, or a percent. Fraction concepts and representations need to be related to those of division, measurement, and ratio. Decimal and fractional representations need to be connected and understood. Building these connections take extensive experience with rational numbers over a substantial period of time. Researchers have documented that difficulties in working with rational numbers can often be traced to weak conceptual understanding. Instructional sequences in which more time is spent at the outset on developing meaning for the various representations of rational numbers and the concept of unit have been shown to promote mathematical proficiency.*

(Kilpatrick, J.; Swafford, J.; and Findell, B. eds. *Adding It Up: Helping Children Learn Mathematics*. Washington, D.C.: National Research Council/National Academy Press, 2001, pp. 415–416.)

### RESEARCH IN ACTION

**Rational Numbers** Chapter 7 carefully develops concepts of rational numbers starting with percentages and building to decimals to clearly establish the relationships of part to whole.

**Base-Ten Number System** Throughout Chapter 7 the child will develop greater understanding of the multiplicative nature of the base-ten number system through continued work with comparing fractions, decimals, and percentages.

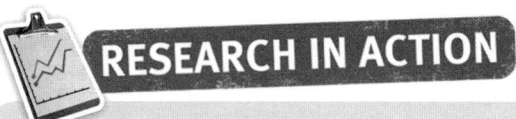

## Vocabulary

**benchmark** (Lesson 7.2) something that serves as a standard or reference by which something else can be measured or compared

**centi-** (Lesson 5.2) one hundred

**centisecond** (Lesson 7.5) a hundredth ($\frac{1}{100}$) of a second

**equivalent** (Lesson 7.3) having the same value

**mixed number** (Lesson 7.5) a number consisting of a whole number and a fraction

**number line** (Lesson 7.7) a line of infinite extent whose points correspond to the real numbers according to their distance in a positive or negative direction from a point arbitrarily taken as zero

**percent** (Lesson 7.1) the number of parts in every hundred

**tenth** (Lesson 7.8) one of ten equal parts

## English Learner

### Cognates

For English learners, a quick way to acquire new English vocabulary words is to build on what is known in the primary language.

| English | Spanish |
|---|---|
| equivalent fractions | fracción equivalente |
| decimal | decimal |
| percent | porcentaje |
| situations | situaciones |

### Access Vocabulary

English learners may understand words in different contexts or not understand idioms. Review chapter vocabulary for this concern. For example:

| | |
|---|---|
| standard percents | beakers |
| cm | ten percent of something is the same as $\frac{1}{10}$ of it |
| stopwatch | |
| quarter | |

# Chapter Planner

| Lessons | Objectives | NCTM Standards | State Standards |
|---|---|---|---|
| 7.1 **Learning about Percentages** pages 294A–295A | **Begin to develop the concept of percentages** by understanding their relationship to fractions | Number and Operations<br>Representation | |
| 7.2 **Percent Benchmarks** pages 296A–297A | **Explore strategies for calculating percentages** by mentally halving numbers | Number and Operations<br>Representation<br>Communication | |
| 7.3 **Understanding $12\frac{1}{2}$% and $\frac{1}{8}$** pages 298A–301B | **Learn about $12\frac{1}{2}$% and $\frac{1}{8}$** by finding percentages and fractions of whole numbers | Number and Operations<br>Reasoning and Proof<br>Problem Solving | |
| 7.4 **Applying Percent Benchmarks** pages 302A–303A | **Explore percentages** by examining them in the context of measurement | Measurement<br>Data Analysis | |
| 7.5 **Decimals and Stopwatches** pages 308A–309A | **Explore the relationships between decimals, percentages, and fractions** while using stopwatches | Number and Operations<br>Problem Solving<br>Communication | |
| 7.6 **Adding and Subtracting Decimal Numbers** pages 310A–311A | **Begin to add and subtract decimals** by using stopwatches to work with two-place decimals | Number and Operations<br>Measurement<br>Problem Solving | |
| 7.7 **Number Lines** pages 312A–313A | **Explore the placement of fractions, decimals, and percentages on a number line** to further explore decimal arithmetic | Representation<br>Measurement<br>Problem Solving | |
| 7.8 **Understanding 10% and $\frac{1}{10}$** pages 314A–315A | **Explore the relationships between 10% and $\frac{1}{10}$** by visualizing segments of wholes as quantities | Number and Operations<br>Measurement<br>Reasoning and Proof | |

| Vocabulary | Manipulatives and Materials | Games to reinforce skills and concepts |
|---|---|---|
| percent | • Response Wheels<br>• Rulers<br>• 2 Percent-Slider Posters<br>• Plastic beaker<br>• Masking tape<br>• String | |
| benchmark | • Response Wheels<br>• Meter stick<br>• Centimeter rulers<br>• Colored pencils | |
| equivalent | • Response Wheels<br>• Copies of ***Practice*** p. 145 (24 cm strips)<br>• Scissors<br>• Pencils<br>• Rulers | Order Game (Lesson 5.1) |
| benchmark | • Response Wheels<br>• Rulers or measuring tape<br>• String<br>• Construction paper<br>• Markers<br>• Glue sticks<br>• Strings relating to three "mystery objects" | |
| centi-<br>centisecond<br>mixed number | • Response Wheels<br>• Stopwatches showing hundredths of a second | |
| centisecond | • Response Wheels<br>• Stopwatches<br>• Equivalency Card Deck | Greater Number Card Game (New) |
| number line | • Response Wheels<br>• Stopwatches | |
| tenth | • Response Wheels<br>• Centimeter ruler<br>• Scissors<br>• Strings from "mystery objects" | |

# Additional Resources

## Differentiated Instruction

*Intervention Support Guide* provides instruction for the following prerequisite skills:

- Lesson 7.A Meaning of Fractions and Decimals
- Lesson 7.B Comparing Numbers through 100
- Lesson 7.C Measuring to the Nearest Centimeter

*Enrichment Support Guide*

*Practice*

*Reteach Support Guide*

*English Learner Support Guide*

## Technology

The following electronic resources are available:

e **Planner** Lessons 7.1–7.8

e **Presentation** Lessons 7.1–7.8

e **Textbook** Lessons 7.1–7.8

e **Assess** Lessons 7.1–7.8

e **MathTools Stopwatch** Lessons 7.5–7.7

e **Games Order Game** Lesson 7.3

# Chapter Planner, continued

| Problem Solving | When to Use | Objectives | NCTM Standards | Skills Covered |
|---|---|---|---|---|
| **Chapter Introduction** pages 292I–293C 15–30 minutes | Use after the Chapter 7 Pretest | Introduce chapter concepts in a problem-solving setting | Problem Solving<br>Data Analysis and Probability | Estimation<br>Data Analysis |
| **Exploring Problem Solving** pages 304–305A 30–45 minutes | Use any time during the chapter | Explore methods of solving nonroutine problems | Communication<br>Representation<br>Data Analysis and Probability | Data Analysis<br>Computing |
| **Exploring Problem Solving** pages 316–318A 45–60 minutes | Use any time after the first Exploring Problem Solving | Develop logical reasoning while integrating reading skills with mathematics | Data Analysis and Probability<br>Reasoning and Proof | Fractions<br>Decimals<br>Percentages |

| Review | When to Use | Objectives | NCTM Standards | Skills Covered |
|---|---|---|---|---|
| **Cumulative Review** pages 306–307 15–30 minutes | Use any time after Lesson 7.4 | Review concepts and skills taught earlier in the year | Geometry<br>Number and Operations<br>Problem Solving | Addition, Subtraction, Multiplication, Division, Graphing |
| **Cumulative Review** pages 319–320 15–30 minutes | Use any time after Lesson 7.8 | Review concepts and skills taught earlier in the year | Geometry<br>Algebra | Multiplication, Division, Computing Integers |
| **Chapter 7 Review** pages 322A–323 30–45 minutes | Use after Lesson 7.8 | Review concepts and skills taught in the chapter | Measurement<br>Number and Operations<br>Problem Solving | Computing Percentages and Decimals<br>Measuring Percentages |

| Assessment | When to Use | Objectives | NCTM Standards | Skills Covered |
|---|---|---|---|---|
| **Informal Assessment Rubrics** (p. 294A–315A) 5 minutes per student | Use at the end of the lesson | Provide daily evaluation of math proficiency | Problem Solving<br>Reasoning and Proof<br>Communication | Computing, Understanding, Reasoning, Applying, Engaging |
| **Pretest** (*Assessment* p. 100) 15–30 minutes | Use after or in place of the Chapter 6 Review | Provide assessment or additional practice of the chapter concepts | Number and Operations<br>Algebra<br>Problem Solving | Multiplying by Powers and Multiples of 10<br>Finding a Missing Factor<br>Comparing Numbers |
| **Individual Oral Assessment** (p. 307A) 5 minutes per student | Begin after Lesson 7.4 | Provide alternate means of assessing students' progress | Number and Operations | Fractions<br>Percentages |
| **Chapter 7 Practice Test** (pp. 324–327A) 30–45 minutes | Use after or in place of the Chapter 7 Review | Provide assessment or additional practice of the chapter concepts | Problem Solving<br>Number and Operations | Percentages, Fractions, Decimals |
| **Chapter 7 Test** (*Assessment* pp. 106–109) 30–45 minutes | Use after or in place of the Chapter 7 Review | Provide assessment or additional practice of the chapter concepts | Number and Operations<br>Reasoning and Proof<br>Problem Solving | Comparing Percentages and Decimals of Whole Numbers<br>Computing Decimals<br>Multiplication, Division |

# Technology Resources and Support

Visit SRAonline.com for online versions of the ***Real Math eSuite.***

## Technology for Teachers

| | |
|---|---|
| **Presentation** | Lessons 7.1–7.8 Use the ***ePresentation*** to interactively present chapter content. |
| **Planner** | Use the Chapter and Lesson Planners to outline activities and time frames for Chapter 7. |
| **Assess** | Students can take the following assessment in ***eAssess:***<br>• Chapter Pretest<br>• Chapter Test<br>Teachers can record results and print reports for all assessments in this chapter. |
| **MathTools** | **Stopwatch** Lessons 7.5–7.7 |

## Technology for Students

| | |
|---|---|
| **Textbook** | An electronic, interactive version of the ***Student Edition*** is available for all lessons in Chapter 7. |
| **MathTools** | **Stopwatch** Lessons 7.5–7.7 |
| **Games** | **The Ordering Game** Lesson 7.3 |
| SRA TECH KNOWLEDGE | ***TechKnowledge*** Level 4 provides lessons that specifically teach the Unit 10 Internet, Unit 2 Keyboarding, and Unit 3 Word Processing applications that students can use while working on this chapter's projects. |

# Introduction to Fractions, Decimals, and Percentages

## 1 Introduce Chapter 7 5

### Chapter Objectives

Explain to students that in this chapter they will build on what they already know about fractions, decimals, and percentages. They will

- learn about the relationship between percentages and fractions.
- calculate percentages.
- use stopwatches to explore decimals, percentages, and fractions.

### Pretest COMPUTING

Administer the Pretest in ***Assessment.***

The Pretest for Chapter 7 covers the following prerequisite skills:

- Relation signs (Problems 1–2)
- Missing factors (Problems 3–8)
- Multiplying by multiples and powers of 10 (Problems 9–13)

The Pretest also covers the following topics from this chapter:

- Percentages (Problems 14–21)
- Decimals and stopwatches (Problem 22)

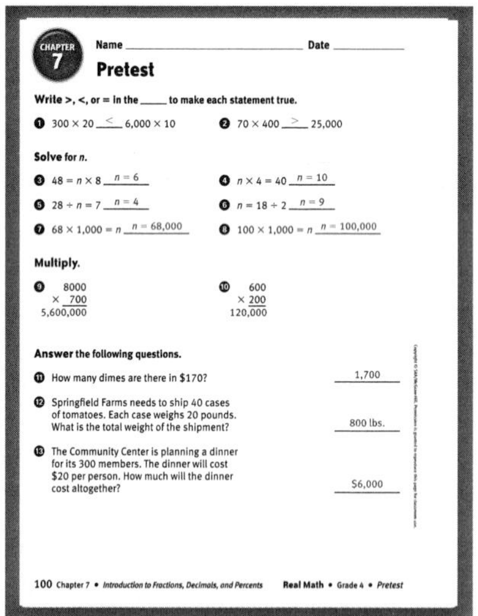
CHAPTER 7 Name ______ Date ______

**Pretest**

**Write >, <, or = in the ____ to make each statement true.**

1. 300 × 20 __<__ 6,000 × 10
2. 70 × 400 __>__ 25,000

**Solve for *n*.**

3. 48 = *n* × 8 __*n* = 6__
4. *n* × 4 = 40 __*n* = 10__
5. 28 ÷ *n* = 7 __*n* = 4__
6. *n* = 18 ÷ 2 __*n* = 9__
7. 68 × 1,000 = *n* __*n* = 68,000__
8. 100 × 1,000 = *n* __*n* = 100,000__

**Multiply.**

9. 8000 × 700 = 5,600,000
10. 600 × 200 = 120,000

**Answer the following questions.**

11. How many dimes are there in $170? __1,700__
12. Springfield Farms needs to ship 40 cases of tomatoes. Each case weighs 20 pounds. What is the total weight of the shipment? __800 lbs.__
13. The Community Center is planning a dinner for its 300 members. The dinner will cost $20 per person. How much will the dinner cost altogether? __$6,000__

100 Chapter 7 • *Introduction to Fractions, Decimals, and Percents* **Real Math** • Grade 4 • *Pretest*

Chapter 7 Pretest

### Access Prior Knowledge UNDERSTANDING

Have students share what they know about the North Pole and the Arctic region. If you have a globe, use it to show students the region near and within the Arctic Circle. Ask questions such as the following:

- **Who lives in the Arctic?** Possible answer: mostly Inuit people
- **What kind of animals are associated with the North Pole?** Possible answers: polar bears
- **What kind of transportation would you use to travel to the North Pole?** Possible answers: airplane or dogsled

## 2 Exploring Problem Solving 20

### Tell Students In Today's Lesson They Will

- find out about people who live in the Arctic.
- compare the Arctic populations in the United States and Canada.

### Using Student Pages

Read page 293 with the class. Make sure students understand the graphs. Ask questions such as the following:

- **Why are the circle graphs different sizes?** to show that different countries have different numbers of people living in the Arctic
- **About how many people in Russia live in the Arctic?** about 2 million
- **Are there more than one million native Arctic inhabitants in Russia?** No, less than half of the Arctic inhabitants in Russia are native.
- **About how many people in the Arctic live in Canada?** Estimates will vary. The size of Canada on the circle graph is about halfway between the sizes of the two circles representing 50,000 and 150,000. A reasonable estimate is about 100,000.
- **About how many Canadians who live in the Arctic are native?** About half of the Arctic Canadians are native. If you estimate the total Arctic population in Canada to be 100,000, then about 50,000 are native.

Have students work in small groups to discuss and solve Problems 1–3. Provide help as needed.

### CyberSolver

To extend problem solving have students use the Internet to find the answers to the following questions:

- **Which two people were the first to reach the North Pole?**
- **When did they get there?**
- **How did they do it?**

Students can find information about the first expedition to reach the North Pole by conducting a search with appropriate key words, such as *North Pole, expedition,* and *first*. They can also visit http://www.pearyhenson.org/ and http://www.matthewhenson.org.

Student Page

# CHAPTER 7 Introduction to Fractions, Decimals, and Percentages

**In This Chapter You Will Learn**

- about the relationship between percents and fractions.
- how to calculate percents.
- how to use stopwatches to explore decimals, percents, and fractions.

## Concept/Question Board APPLYING

### Questions

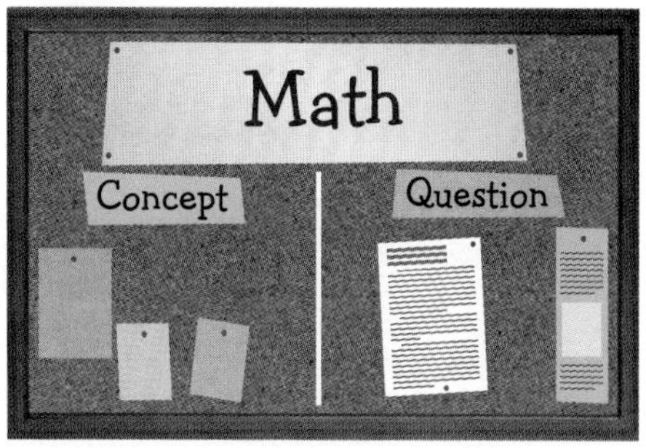


Have students write three questions they have about fractions, decimals, and percentages and how they can be used. Then have them select one question to post on the Question side of the Board.

### Concepts

As students work through the chapter, have them collect examples of how fractions, decimals, and percentages are used in everyday situations. For each example, have students write problems that relate to the item(s). Have them display their examples on the Concept side of the Board.

Suggest the following:

- sales signs
- recipes
- instruction manuals

### Answers

Throughout the chapter, have students post answers to the questions and solutions to the problems on the Board.

Student Page

## Problem Solving

The Arctic is a region that is rich in beauty and natural resources. It includes parts of the United States and many other countries. The graphs on the map show how many people from different countries live in the Arctic. The graphs also show that many of these inhabitants, especially from the United States and Canada, have immigrated to the Arctic.

SOCIAL STUDIES

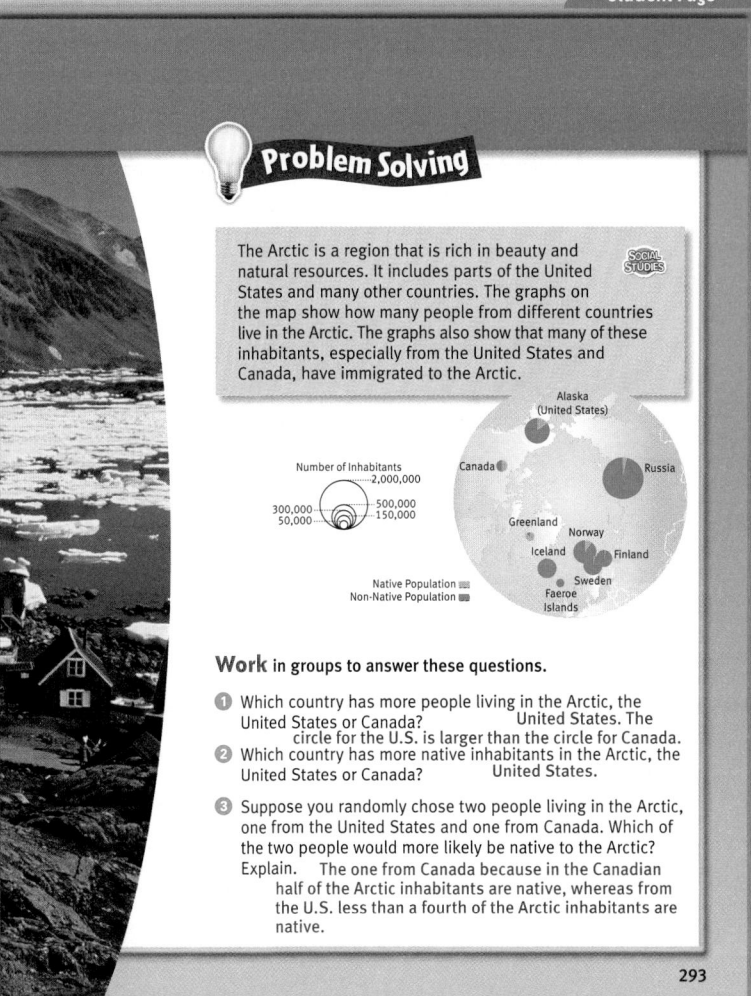

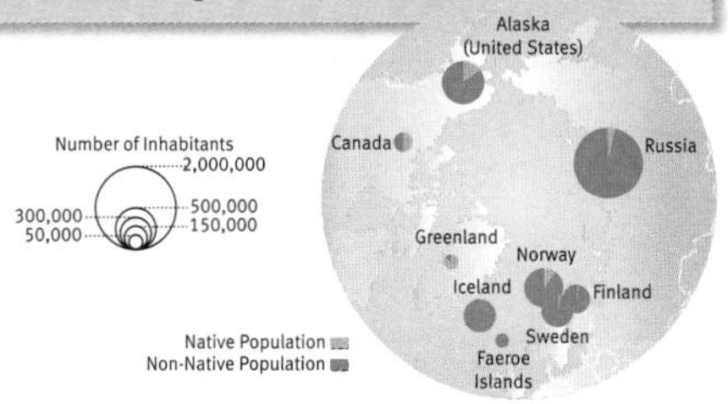


**Work** in groups to answer these questions.

1. Which country has more people living in the Arctic, the United States or Canada? United States. The circle for the U.S. is larger than the circle for Canada.
2. Which country has more native inhabitants in the Arctic, the United States or Canada? United States.
3. Suppose you randomly chose two people living in the Arctic, one from the United States and one from Canada. Which of the two people would more likely be native to the Arctic? Explain. The one from Canada because in the Canadian half of the Arctic inhabitants are native, whereas from the U.S. less than a fourth of the Arctic inhabitants are native.

293

## 3 Reflect

5

### Knowledge Age Skills

**Effective Communication** Have each group present its answers and reasoning to the class. After each presentation, ask students whether they agree or disagree with the reasoning and why.

Discuss the following points:

- A small part of a large thing can be greater than a large part of a small thing.
- When you compare parts, it's important to communicate clearly what you are comparing.

## Sample Solutions Strategies

Here are some strategies students could use to solve Problem 2:

### Use Estimation and Number Sense

Students might estimate the total Arctic population in the United States to be about 500,000. About one-fifth of those people are native. So the United States has about 100,000 native inhabitants in the Arctic. As noted above, a reasonable estimate for the number of native Arctic inhabitants in Canada is about 50,000.

### Make a Diagram to Estimate

Students could compare the sizes of the regions in the graphs for the United States and Canada by tracing one of those regions and laying it over the other.

## Home Connection

At this time, you may want to send home the letter on pages 26–29 of ***Home Connection.*** This letter describes what students will be learning and what activities they can do at home to support their work in school.

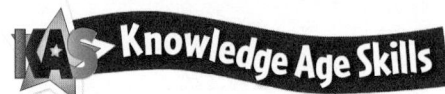

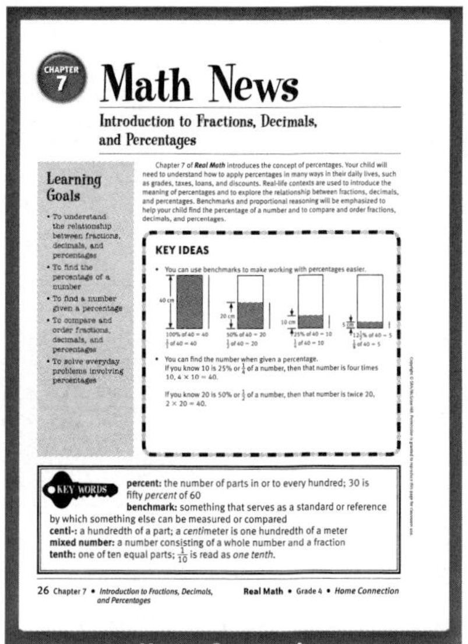

CHAPTER 7 **Math News**

**Introduction to Fractions, Decimals, and Percentages**

**Learning Goals**

- To understand the relationship between fractions, decimals, and percentages
- To find the percentage of a number
- To find a number given a percentage
- To compare and order fractions, decimals, and percentages
- To solve everyday problems involving percentages

Chapter 7 of ***Real Math*** introduces the concept of percentages. Your child will need to understand how to apply percentages in many ways in their daily lives, such as grades, taxes, loans, and discounts. Real-life contexts are used to introduce the meaning of percentages and to explore the relationship between fractions, decimals, and percentages. Benchmarks and proportional reasoning will be emphasized to help your child find the percentage of a number and to compare and order fractions, decimals, and percentages.

**KEY IDEAS**

- You can use benchmarks to make working with percentages easier.



- You can find the number when given a percentage. If you know 10 is 25% or $\frac{1}{4}$ of a number, then that number is four times 10, $4 \times 10 = 40$.

  If you know 20 is 50% or $\frac{1}{2}$ of a number, then that number is twice 20, $2 \times 20 = 40$.

KEY WORDS

**percent:** the number of parts in or to every hundred; 30 is fifty *percent* of 60

**benchmark:** something that serves as a standard or reference by which something else can be measured or compared

**centi-:** a hundredth of a part; a *centi*meter is one hundredth of a meter

**mixed number:** a number consisting of a whole number and a fraction

**tenth:** one of ten equal parts; $\frac{1}{10}$ is read as *one tenth.*

26 Chapter 7 • *Introduction to Fractions, Decimals, and Percentages* **Real Math** • Grade 4 • *Home Connection*

Home Connection page 26

**Assess and Differentiate**

 **Assess** Use *eAssess* to record and analyze evidence of student understanding.

## A Gather Evidence

Use the Daily Class Assessment Records in **Assessment** or *eAssess* to record daily observations.

### Informal Assessment
☑ **Access Prior Knowledge**
Did the student **UNDERSTANDING**
- ❑ make important observations?
- ❑ extend or generalize learning?
- ❑ provide insightful answers?
- ❑ pose insightful questions?

### Informal Assessment
☑ **Concept/Question Board**
Did the student **APPLYING**
- ❑ apply learning in new situations?
- ❑ contribute concepts?
- ❑ contribute answers?
- ❑ connect mathematics to real-world situations?

### Formal Assessment
☑ **Pretest**  **COMPUTING**
Review student answers in each problem set.
- ❑ Relation signs (Problems 1–2)
- ❑ Missing factors (Problems 3–8)
- ❑ Multiplying by multiples and powers of 10 (Problems 9–13)
- ❑ Percentages (Problems 14–21)
- ❑ Decimals and stopwatches (Problem 22)

## B Summarize Findings

Analyze and summarize assessment data for each student. Determine which Assessment Follow-Up is appropriate for each student. Use the Student Assessment Record on **Assessment** or *eAssess* to update assessment records.

## C Assessment Follow-Up ● DIFFERENTIATE INSTRUCTION

| ENRICH | PRACTICE | RETEACH | INTERVENTION | ENGLISH LEARNER |
|---|---|---|---|---|
| **If . . .** students demonstrate a secure understanding of chapter concepts, <br><br>**Then . . .** move quickly through the chapter or use *Enrichment* Lessons 7.1–7.8 as assessment follow-up to extend and apply understanding. | **If . . .** students grasp chapter concepts with competent understanding, <br><br>**Then . . .** use *Practice* Lessons 7.1–7.8 as lesson follow-up to develop fluency. | **If . . .** students have prerequisite understanding but demonstrate emerging understanding of chapter concepts, <br><br>**Then . . .** use *Reteach* Lessons 7.5 and 7.6 to reteach lesson concepts. | **If . . .** students are not competent with prerequisite skills, <br><br>**Then . . .** use *Intervention* Lessons 7.A–7.C before each lesson to develop fluency with prerequisite skills. | Use *English Learner Support Guide* Lessons 7.1–7.8 for strategies to preteach lesson vocabulary and concepts. |

# Chapter Projects

## Math Across the Curriculum

Preview the chapter projects with students. Assign or have students choose from the projects to extend and enrich concepts in this chapter.

### Describe Matthew Henson's Expeditions

2–3 weeks

**Math Objective**
To reinforce studies of percentages by implementing them into a written description

**Language Arts Objective**
To reinforce studies of biography by studying and describing Matthew Henson's expeditions

**Technology Objective**
To use a word processing program to write a description

Have students use mathematics to describe Matthew Henson's expeditions. To broaden the language arts concept, have students use biographical sources you are currently studying.

As part of the project, students should consider the following issues:

- what biographical resources to use
- the events of Matthew Henson's expeditions
- what to include in a short description of his expeditions
- how percentages can be used to describe his expeditions

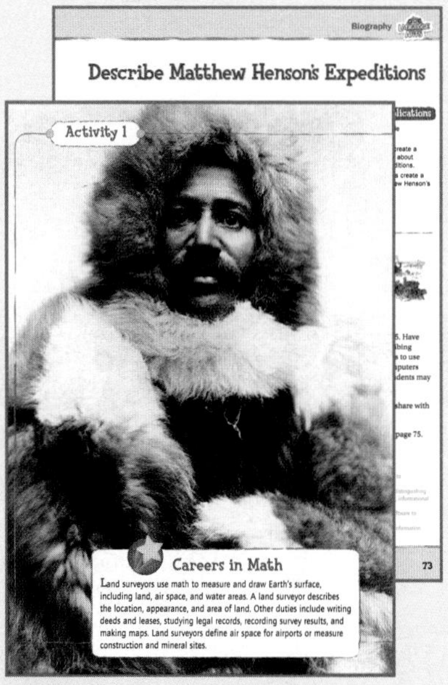


For specific step-by-step instructions for this project, see ***Across the Curriculum Math Connections*** pages 72–75.

#### Knowledge Age Skills

**High-Level Responsibility** Students should become "experts" on Matthew Henson's expeditions.

**Effective Communication** Students get ideas across clearly and convincingly in writing biographical descriptions.

### Budget an Arctic Expedition

1–2 weeks

**Math Objective**
To reinforce studies of decimals by adding the cost of items to plan a budget

**Science Objective**
To reinforce studies of human survival needs by planning an expedition to the Arctic

**Technology Objective**
To use keyboarding skills by producing a document

Have students use the Internet to research and then make a list of items they would need for an Arctic expedition and create a budget for the expedition, each in separate word processing documents.

For this project, students use the Internet to research the following:

- the Arctic environment
- the distance and length of time needed to reach the North Pole
- conversion of the cost of the expedition from British pounds to American dollars

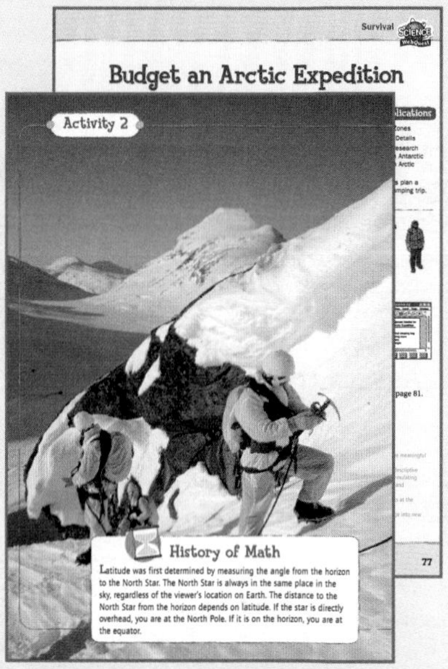


For specific step-by-step instructions for this project, see ***Across the Curriculum Math Connections*** pages 76–81.

#### Knowledge Age Skills

**Problem Formulation, Planning, and Strategizing** Students strategize, plan, and create a budget for an Arctic expedition.

**High-Level Responsibility** Students prepare and analyze a budget for an Arctic expedition.

*TechKnowledge* Level 4 provides lessons that specifically teach the Unit 10 Internet, Unit 2 Keyboarding, and Unit 3 Word Processing applications that students can use in this project.

## Lesson Planner

**OBJECTIVES**
- To introduce percentages in the context of daily life
- To establish benchmark percentages: 100%, 50%, 25%, and 75%
- To explore the relation between percentages and fractions

**NCTM STANDARDS**

**Number and Operations**
- Understand percentages as parts of 100
- Use % notation
- Express a part of a whole as a percentage

**Representation**
Represent fractions as percentages using concrete and pictorial models

**MATERIALS**
- *Response Wheels
- *Rulers
- *Percent Slider Poster
- Plastic beaker
- Masking tape
- String

**TECHNOLOGY**
**Presentation** Lesson 7.1
**Games** More or Less Game

**TEST PREP**

**Cumulative Review**
Mental Math reviews halving (Lesson 3.10).

**Extended Response**
Problems 3, 4, 6, and 7

**Writing + Math**
Journal

*Manipulative Kit Item

# Learning about Percentages

**Context of the Lesson** This is the first of eight lessons in which students learn how to use percentages in daily life. In this lesson, students visually estimate percentages and learn to apply halving to move between benchmark percentages (100%, 50%, and 25%). This lesson also contains light fraction use in the context of percentages. Students have worked with fractions in Grades 1–3 of ***Real Math;*** fractions will be covered in great detail in Chapter 8 of Grade 4.
See page 292B for Math Background for teachers for this lesson.

## Planning for Learning • DIFFERENTIATE INSTRUCTION

### INTERVENTION

**If . . .** students lack the prerequisite skill of comparing numbers through 100,

**Then . . .** teach ***Intervention*** Lesson 7.B.

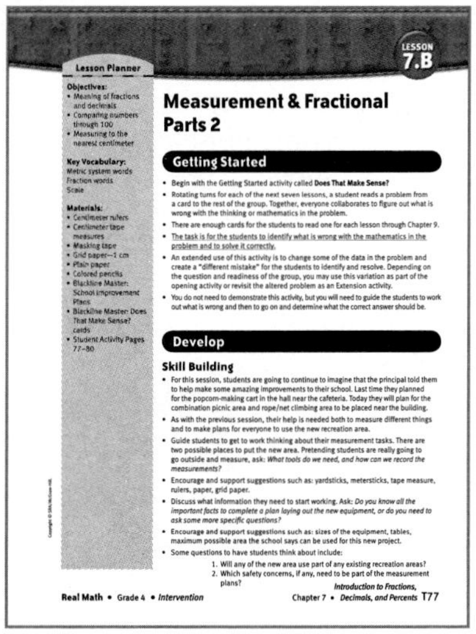


Intervention Lesson 7.B

### ENGLISH LEARNER

**Preview**

**If . . .** students need language support,

**Then . . .** use Lesson 7.1 in ***English Learner Support Guide*** to preview lesson concepts and vocabulary.

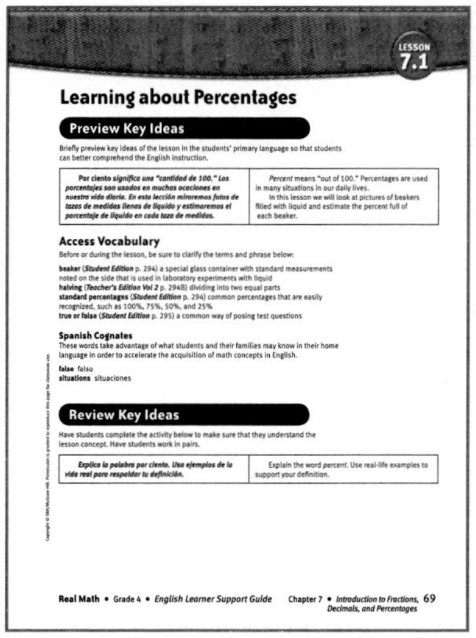


English Learner Lesson 7.1

### ENRICH

**If . . .** students are proficient in the lesson concepts,

**Then . . .** encourage them to find percentages other than the benchmarks.

### PRACTICE

**If . . .** students would benefit from additional practice,

**Then . . .** extend Guided Discussion by working through more examples together.

### RETEACH

**If . . .** students are having difficulty understanding the meaning of *percent,*

**Then . . .** have them use each of the described methods for each of the first three facts.

**Vocabulary**
**percent \pər sent´\ *n.*** the number of parts in every hundred

**Access Vocabulary**
**standard percent** common percentages that are easily recognized—100%, 75%, 50%, and 25%

**Spanish Cognates**
**false** falso
**situations** situaciones

# Teaching Lesson 7.1

## Mental Math 5

Provide exercises, such as the following, that give students practice with halving. What is half of

**a.** 10? 5 **b.** 100? 50
**c.** 1,000? 500 **d.** 40? 20
**e.** 60? 30 **f.** 30? 15
**g.** 300? 150 **h.** 50? 25

## 1 Develop 30

**Tell Students In Today's Lesson They Will**
look at pictures of beakers filled with liquid and estimate the percent full of each beaker.

## Guided Discussion

### Percentages in Everyday Life UNDERSTANDING Whole Group

1. Begin the lesson by asking students to think about what they know about percentages and where they have seen percentages in their daily lives. If students have trouble coming up with examples, you might suggest things such as school grades, store sales, taxes, tips at restaurants, election results, and probability.

   As students mention their ideas, list them on the board. Encourage them to explain what *percent* means in each of the situations that they suggest. If no one volunteers the definition, explain that *percent* means "out of 100."
2. Now present students with the Percent Slider Poster. Ask students to consider how they might show percentages using this prop. Suggest that they might think about how they would explain percentages to a younger student.

   Ask students to show 50% on the Percent Slider Poster. Check to see if others in the class agree. Ask them to explain what 50% means, and introduce the fraction $\frac{1}{2}$ and the process of *halving.*
3. While introducing $\frac{1}{2}$, take the opportunity to briefly review fractions. Remind students that the number on the bottom of the fraction is called the *denominator*. The denominator tells how many equal parts a whole has been divided into. Go on to remind students that the number on the top is called the *numerator*. The numerator describes how many of the equal sized parts we are dealing with. Review these terms with the example of $\frac{1}{2}$, in which a whole is divided into two equal parts, and we are dealing with one of those parts. This can be shown visually on the slider poster with the slide set at the halfway mark.
4. Returning to the slider, ask students to show 25%, then 75%. Ask them to explain how they think these are related. 75% of something is 3 times as much as 25% of it, or the whole thing with 25% removed.
5. Next, have students look at the percent sliders on their **Response Wheels.** Ask them to show 50%. Ask them to think about how students might be confused if both sliders are at their respective 50% heights. Ask them how they would explain this to younger children. A possible answer is that 50% of a longer distance is longer than 50% of a shorter distance.

## Skill Building

### Filling a Beaker UNDERSTANDING Whole Group

The second representation for percentage uses the plastic demonstration beaker filled to percentages of its height.

1. Attach a vertical strip of masking tape, running the beaker's full height, to the side of the beaker. Tell the students, *I would like to fill this beaker so that the water comes up to 50% of the height.* Invite a student to the front of the class. Have that student use a marker to put a line on the masking tape showing where the 50% mark would be.

   Accept any measure that looks like 50%. Tell the students that you have cut a piece of string that has the same length as the height of the beaker so that you can check the 50% estimate.
2. Invite a student to come up to the front of the class and use the string to find a more exact 50% spot by folding the string in half. Once the adjustment has been made, and the 50% mark is more accurate, demonstrate how we write 50%. Ask a student to come to the board and write the fraction $\frac{1}{2}$. Fill the beaker to the adjusted 50% mark.
3. Repeat the demonstration in the same way for 25%. This time the string will be folded in half and then in half again (quarters) in order to check the visual estimates.
4. Now that the students have seen how to estimate and then check 50% and 25%, challenge them to find one other percentage of the height—for example, 75% (50% + 25% or 100% − 75%) or 12.5% (half of 25%).

## 2 Assign Student Pages 15

**Pages 294–295** APPLYING
Have students complete pages 294 and 295 independently.

**As Students Finish**

Game **Cube 100 Game**

eGames ***More or Less Game***

Student Page

LESSON 7.1 **Learning about Percents**

## Key Ideas

***Percent*** **means "out of 100."**

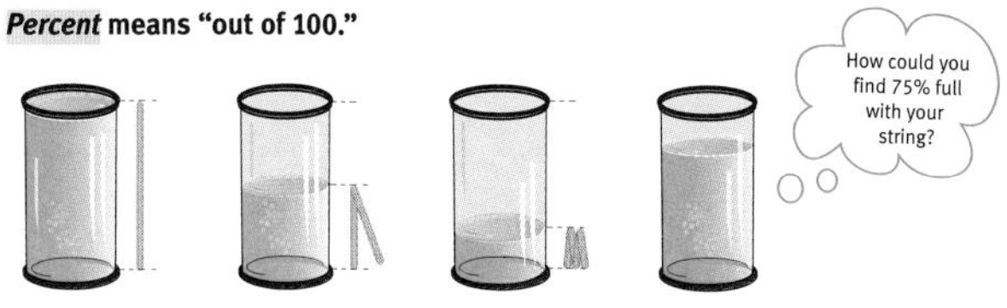

How could you find 75% full with your string?


100% of 1 = 1 — 50% of 1 = $\frac{1}{2}$ of 1 — 25% of 1 = $\frac{1}{4}$ of 1 — 75% of 1 = $\frac{3}{4}$ of 1

A beaker can be filled with liquid to different levels. The height of the liquid relates to how full the beaker is. This percent full can be thought of in standard percentages that are easy to recognize: 100% full (completely full), 50% full (half full), 25% full (one-quarter full) and 75% full (three-quarters full).

Imagine a string stretched to the full height of a beaker. If we folded this string in half, it would stretch to the 50% full level. If we folded it in half again, or quartered it, it would stretch to the 25% full level. One way to find 75% full with your string is to imagine shortening the string by 25%. Try to think of other ways.

Percentages are used in many situations in our daily lives. Several examples are shown here.

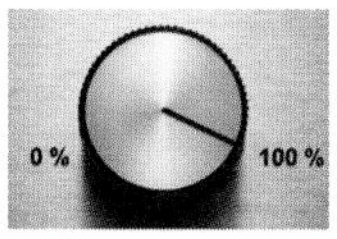

eTextbook This lesson is available in the *eTextbook*.

Student Page

**For** each excercise write *true* if the percentage written below the beaker correctly shows how full it is. If you think a label is *false,* explain what you believe the correct percentage to be.

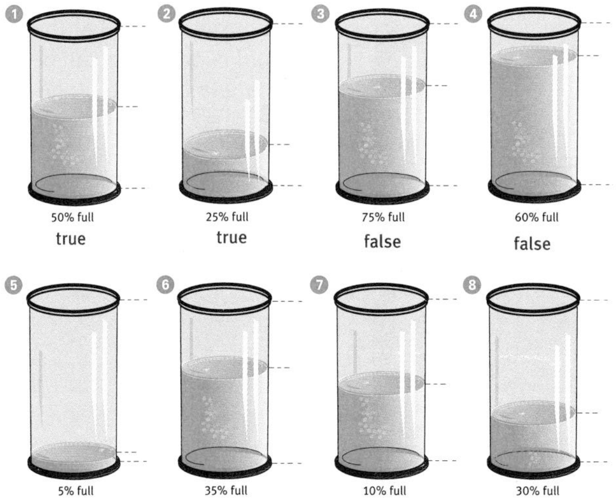

1. 50% full — true
2. 25% full — true
3. 75% full — false
4. 60% full — false
5. 5% full — true
6. 35% full — false
7. 10% full — false
8. 30% full — true

Writing + Math **Journal**

Explain in your own words the meaning of the word *percent.*



★ Students should realize some of the labels are false by comparing them with others that are true.



# 3 Reflect

10

## Guided Discussion REASONING

Whole Group

Ask the students to write about how percentages and fractions are related. Have them draw a diagram and present an example of the relationship between percentages and fractions. Discuss their diagrams and ask students how they could be used to teach younger students about percentages.

## Extended Response

**Problem 3** is false because the shaded part is only slightly greater than the beaker in Problem 1, which is about 50% full. The correct percentage might be 55%.

**Problem 4** is false because the beaker is almost completely full. This means the answer is close to 100%. The correct percentage might be 90%.

**Problem 6** is false because the beaker is half full, which is the same as 50% full.

**Problem 7** is false because too much is shaded for it to be 10% full. If Problem 5 is 5% full, then 10% full would be double that amount of shading. The correct percentage might be 40% full.

Writing + Math **Journal**

Answers will vary but should mention that *percentage* means "out of 100."

## Applications APPLYING

Ask students to think about percentages in sales. Would they rather shop in a sports store that has a 25% sale or a 50% sale? Ask them if it is possible for the same item to be cheaper in the store that is having the 25% sale than the store that is having the 50% sale. Yes, if the original price at the store with the 25% sale is much less than the original price at the store with the 50% sale, the 25% sale would be a better deal.

**Cumulative Review:** For review of addition and subtraction, assign Problems 1–6 on student page 306.

**Family Involvement:** Assign the ***Practice, Reteach,*** or ***Enrichment*** activities depending on the needs of your students.

**Concept/Question Board:** Have students look for additional examples using percents, fractions, and decimals and post them on the Concept/Question Board.

**Math Puzzler:** Rafael has 80¢. He has twice as many nickels as dimes but no other kinds of coins. What coins does Rafael have? 8 nickels, 4 dimes

# 4 Assess and Differentiate

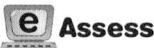

**e Assess** Use ***eAssess*** to record and analyze evidence of student understanding.

## A Gather Evidence

Use the Daily Class Assessment Records in ***Assessment*** or ***eAssess*** to record daily observations.

### Informal Assessment

**✓ Mental Math**

Did the student COMPUTING

- ❑ respond accurately?
- ❑ respond quickly?
- ❑ respond with confidence?
- ❑ self-correct?

### Portfolio Assessment

**✓ Extended Response**

Did the student REASONING

- ❑ provide a clear explanation?
- ❑ communicate reasons and strategies?
- ❑ choose appropriate strategies?
- ❑ argue logically?

## B Summarize Findings

Analyze and summarize assessment data for each student. Determine which Assessment Follow-Up is appropriate for each student. Use the Student Assessment Record in ***Assessment*** or ***eAssess*** to update assessment records.

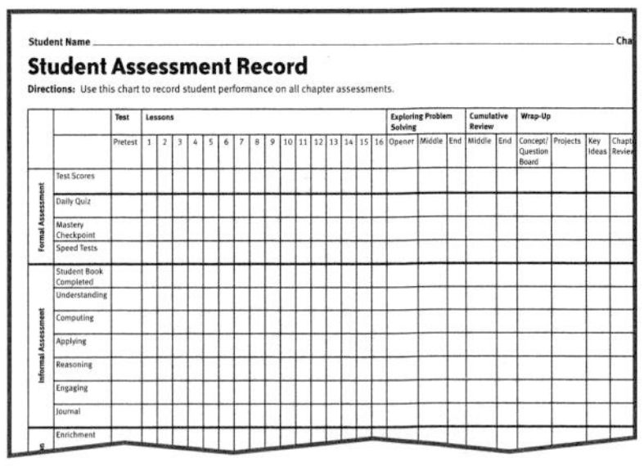
Student Assessment Record

Assessment Page T41

## C Assessment Follow-Up • DIFFERENTIATE INSTRUCTION

Based on your observations, use these teaching strategies for asssessment follow-up.

### INTERVENTION

Review student performance on ***Intervention*** Lesson 7.B to see if students have mastered prerequisite skills for this lesson.

### ENGLISH LEARNER

**Review**

Use Lesson 7.1 in ***English Learner Support Guide*** to review lesson concepts and vocabulary.

### ENRICH

**If . . .** students are proficient in the lesson concepts,

**Then . . .** encourage them to work on the chapter projects or ***Enrichment*** Lesson 7.1.

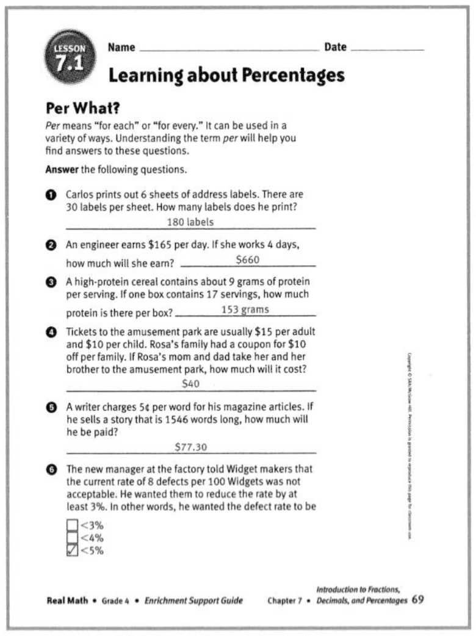
LESSON 7.1 Name ______ Date ______

Learning about Percentages

**Per What?**

*Per* means "for each" or "for every." It can be used in a variety of ways. Understanding the term *per* will help you find answers to these questions.

**Answer** the following questions.

1. Carlos prints out 6 sheets of address labels. There are 30 labels per sheet. How many labels does he print? 180 labels
2. An engineer earns $165 per day. If she works 4 days, how much will she earn? $660
3. A high-protein cereal contains about 9 grams of protein per serving. If one box contains 17 servings, how much protein is there per box? 153 grams
4. Tickets to the amusement park are usually $15 per adult and $10 per child. Rosa's family had a coupon for $10 off per family. If Rosa's mom and dad take her and her brother to the amusement park, how much will it cost? $40
5. A writer charges 5¢ per word for his magazine articles. If he sells a story that is 1546 words long, how much will he be paid? $77.30
6. The new manager at the factory told Widget makers that the current rate of 8 defects per 100 Widgets was not acceptable. He wanted them to reduce the rate by at least 3%. In other words, he wanted the defect rate to be
   - ☐ <3%
   - ☐ <4%
   - ☑ <5%

Real Math • Grade 4 • *Enrichment Support Guide* Chapter 7 • *Introduction to Fractions, Decimals, and Percentages* 69

Enrichment Lesson 7.1

### PRACTICE

**If . . .** students would benefit from additional practice,

**Then . . .** assign ***Practice*** Lesson 7.1.

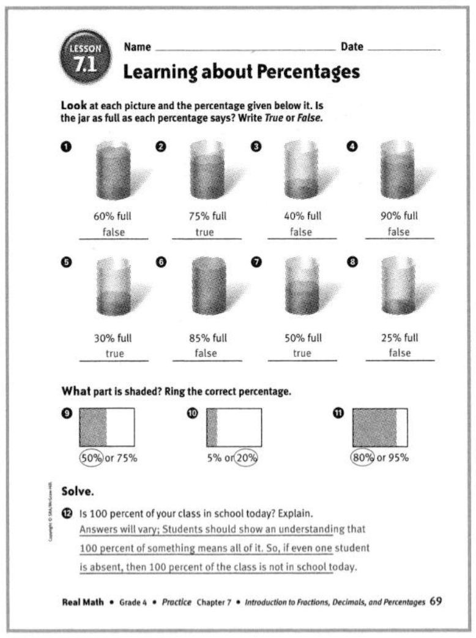
LESSON 7.1 Name ______ Date ______

Learning about Percentages

**Look** at each picture and the percentage given below it. Is the jar as full as each percentage says? Write *True* or *False*.

1. 60% full false
2. 75% full true
3. 40% full false
4. 90% full false
5. 30% full true
6. 85% full false
7. 50% full true
8. 25% full false

**What part is shaded? Ring the correct percentage.**

9. (50%) or 75%
10. 5% or (20%)
11. (80%) or 95%

**Solve.**

12. Is 100 percent of your class in school today? Explain. Answers will vary; Students should show an understanding that 100 percent of something means all of it. So, if even one student is absent, then 100 percent of the class is not in school today.

Real Math • Grade 4 • *Practice* Chapter 7 • *Introduction to Fractions, Decimals, and Percentages* 69

Practice Lesson 7.1

### RETEACH

**If . . .** students struggle with some of the nonbenchmark percentages,

**Then . . .** have them visualize the beaker as a number line with 0 at the bottom and 100 at the top. If the liquid is at 60% in the beaker, then it would be up to 60 on the number line.

## Lesson Planner

### Objectives
- To continue performing visual estimation of percentages of lengths and heights
- To present strategies for calculating percentages by mental halving
- To apply proportional understanding of percentage to numeric measurements

### NCTM Standards
**Number and Operations**
- Understand percentages as parts out of 100, use percent notation, and express a part of a whole as a percentage
- Identify equivalent relationships among fractions and percentages

**Representation**
Represent fractions as percentages using concrete and pictorial models

**Communication**
Develop terminology relating to percentage and compute percentages of a number

### Materials
- *Response Wheels
- *Meterstick
- *Centimeter rulers
- Colored pencils

### Technology
**e Presentation** Lesson 7.2

### Test Prep
**Cumulative Review**
- Mental Math reviews halving of numbers (Lesson 3.10).
- The activity on page 296 reviews estimation and measurement (Lesson 3.8).

**Multistep Problems**
Problem 25

### Looking Ahead
For Lesson 7.3, make a copy of ***Practice*** page 145 for each student in the class. Students will cut out a set of five paper strips from this blackline master.

*Manipulative Kit Item

# Percent Benchmarks

**Context of the Lesson** This is the second of eight lessons which focuses on percentages. In Lesson 7.1, students visually estimated percentages. This lesson expands on those estimation skills by showing students how to calculate percentages of heights from given measurements. The results of these calculations can then be checked against the previous estimates.

See page 292B for Math Background for teachers for this lesson.

## Planning for Learning • DIFFERENTIATE INSTRUCTION

### INTERVENTION
**If . . .** students lack the prerequisite skill of understanding fractions and decimals,

**Then . . .** teach ***Intervention*** Lesson 7.A.

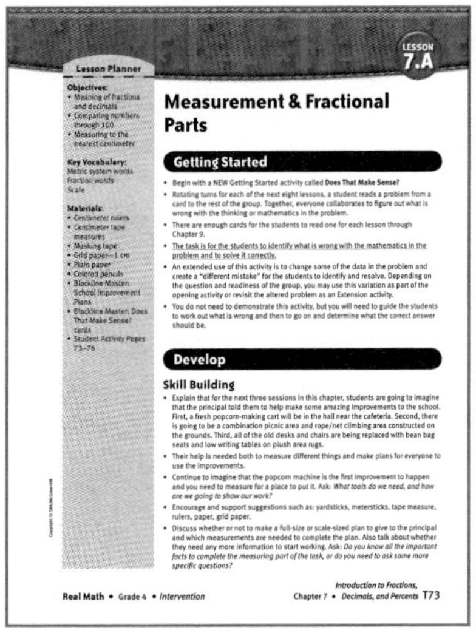
LESSON 7.A
Measurement & Fractional Parts
Getting Started
Develop
Skill Building

Intervention Lesson 7.A

### ENGLISH LEARNER
Preview

**If . . .** students need language support,

**Then . . .** use Lesson 7.2 in ***English Learner Support Guide*** to preview lesson concepts and vocabulary.

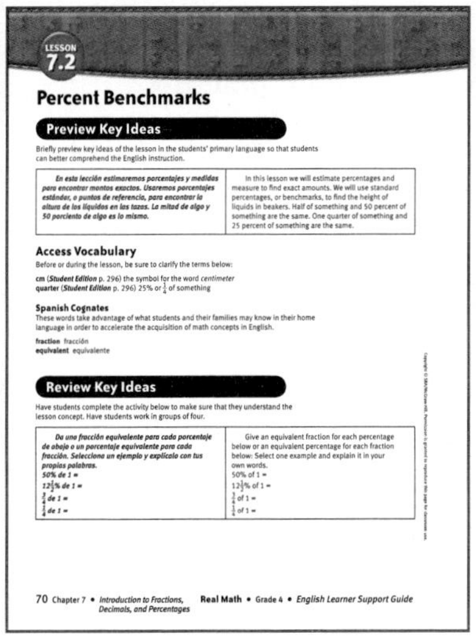
LESSON 7.2
Percent Benchmarks
Preview Key Ideas
Access Vocabulary
Spanish Cognates
Review Key Ideas

English Learner Lesson 7.2

### ENRICH
**If . . .** students are proficient in the lesson concepts,

**Then . . .** encourage them to work with percentages other than the benchmarks.

### PRACTICE
**If . . .** students would benefit from additional practice,

**Then . . .** extend the amount of time provided for Guided Discussion.

### RETEACH
**If . . .** students have difficulty understanding percentages of heights,

**Then . . .** extend Guided Discussion before assigning the student pages.

### Vocabulary
**benchmark \bench märk\ *n.*** a standard or reference by which something else can be measured or compared

### Access Vocabulary
**cm** the abbreviation for the word *centimeter*
**quarter** a United States coin that is worth 25%, or $\frac{1}{4}$, of 1 dollar

### Spanish Cognates
**equivalent fraction** fracción equivalente

## Mental Math

5

Review · RESPONSE WHEEL

Provide exercises, such as the following, that involve the halving procedure for 50%:

**a.** $\frac{1}{2}$ of 20 10 **b.** $\frac{1}{2}$ of 30 15 **c.** $\frac{1}{2}$ of 40 20 **d.** $\frac{1}{2}$ of 12 6

**e.** $\frac{1}{2}$ of 18 9 **f.** $\frac{1}{2}$ of 24 12 **g.** $\frac{1}{2}$ of 32 16 **h.** $\frac{1}{2}$ of 66 33

## 1 Develop

25

### Tell Students In Today's Lesson They Will

estimate percentages and measure to find exact amounts.

### Guided Discussion

UNDERSTANDING

Whole Group

1. Draw two rectangles on the board. The first rectangle should be 24 inches tall and 4 inches wide. Make the second rectangle 16 inches tall and 4 inches wide. The heights need to be exact. Tell students they should think of these rectangles as beakers that will be filled to different percentages of the rectangles' heights.
2. Starting with the 24-inch beaker, ask a volunteer to come to the board and draw a line showing where the liquid level will be when the beaker is 50% full. Write 50% beside this line on the beaker.

   Ask the students questions such as the following:
   - **How you would express that using a fraction?** $\frac{1}{2}$ full

     Write $\frac{1}{2}$ on the board.
   - **What about a fraction with a denominator of 100?** $\frac{50}{100}$ full

     Write $\frac{50}{100}$ on the board as well.
3. Leaving the 50% line on the board, repeat the same procedure for students to estimate the 25% line. Again, ask students to volunteer two fractional equivalents, one with a numerator of 1 and the other with a denominator of 100. $\frac{1}{4}$ full and $\frac{25}{100}$ full

   Write those beside the 25% line on the beaker.
4. Repeat the entire procedure one more time, inviting a new volunteer to draw a line representing the liquid level if the beaker was 75% full. Have students volunteer, like before, to create the fraction $\frac{75}{100}$ and its equivalent fraction in lowest terms, $\frac{3}{4}$. Write those next to the 75% line on the beaker.
5. Tell students that their estimates were good but you would like them to find the exact places where the lines should go. Explain that when you drew the beaker and measured it, you found it to be 24 inches tall.

   Ask students questions such as the following:
   - **What is 50% of 24?** 12. Write the answer on the board.
   - **How did you know?** Halving 24 will give you 12.

   Using a yardstick, check the accuracy of the 50% estimate previously drawn on the board. Alter it as necessary.

   Then ask students questions such as the following:
   - **What is 25% of 24?** 6. Write the answer on the board.

   As before, use a yard stick to check the accuracy of the 25% estimate previously drawn on the board. Alter it as necessary.
6. Now ask students if there is a way to calculate the exact height of the 75% line.
   - **What percentages do we already know that could be combined to get 75%?** 25% of 24 + 50% of 24 = 75% of 24, or 24 − 25% of 24 = 18, or 24 − 6 = 18
   - **What is 75% of 24?** 12 + 6 = 18

   Measure 18 inches up from the bottom of the beaker and adjust the previously drawn 75% line as appropriate.
7. Repeat this process with the 16-inch beaker, finishing up by writing the equations that match the set of calculations the students have done mentally:

| | | |
|---|---|---|
| 50% of 16 = 8 | $\frac{3}{4}$ of 16 = 12 | 25% of 16 = 4 |
| $\frac{50}{100}$ of 16 = 8 | 75% of 16 = 12 | $\frac{25}{100}$ of 16 = 4 |
| $\frac{1}{2}$ of 16 = 8 | $\frac{75}{100}$ of 16 = 12 | $\frac{1}{4}$ of 16 = 4 |

## 2 Assign Student Pages

25

### Pages 296–297

APPLYING

Have students complete pages 296 and 297 independently. On page 297, remind the students to first estimate where the line of the given percentage should be drawn and then draw this line on their beaker. Before the students work on page 297, it may be helpful to complete the first two problems as a class.

#### Monitoring Student Progress

| If . . . | Then . . . |
|---|---|
| **If . . .** students put the 25% mark where the 75% mark should go, | **Then . . .** ask them to imagine that the beakers are being filled with water. For example, draw a line to show how much water there would be in a beaker that was 25% full. |
| **If . . .** students have trouble computing 75% of quantities, | **Then . . .** have them draw a beaker and cut it in half to make 50%, and then cut each half in half again to make quarters or 25% sections. Then look at how these quantities go together to make 75%. Or, have students subtract 25% of the whole from the whole. |

### As Students Finish

Game **Roll a Problem Game (Multiplication)**

Student Page

LESSON 7.2 **Percent Benchmarks**

## Key Ideas

**Half of something and 50% of something are the same. Similarly, one quarter of something and 25% of something are the same.**

Some percentages, such as 100%, 50%, 25%, and 75%, are easier to work with than others. Percentages like these make good reference points. We call them benchmarks. The beakers below illustrate these benchmark percentages.

Because we know the actual height of the liquid in the first beaker, we can use our knowledge about percentages and their equivalent fractions to find the actual heights of the liquid in the other beakers.

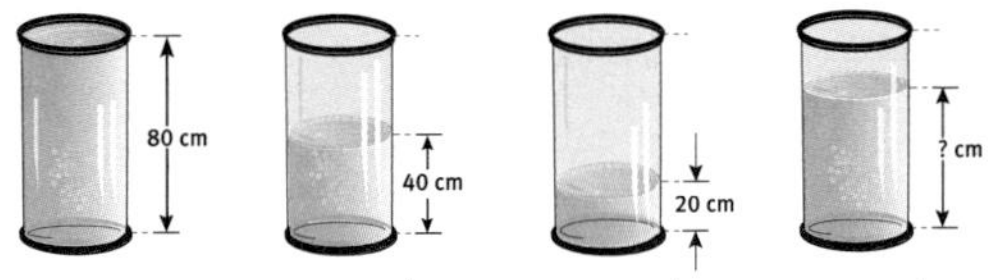


Suppose an 80-centimeter tall beaker was half full. That would mean the height of the liquid was 50% of 80, or half of 80, which is 40 centimeters.

If it was 25% full, the height would be half of the 50% height, or half of 40 centimeters, which is 20 centimeters.

296 Textbook This lesson is available in the ***eTextbook.***

Student Page

**Draw** four rectangles (12 cm × 2 cm) on a separate sheet of paper. These four rectangles will be your set of beakers. Label the beakers with the following percentages: 100%, 50%, 25%, and 75%. Estimate the location of the percent line on each beaker, and use a pencil to mark the spot. Use your ruler to measure the height of the beaker in centimeters, and then use this measurement to find the exact percent line. Show that line with a marker.

**Complete.**

1. 100% of 12 = ■ 12
2. 50% of 12 = ■ 6
3. 25% of 12 = ■ 3
4. 75% of 12 = ■ 9

**Solve** the following exercises.

5. 50% of 80 = ■ 40
6. 25% of 80 = ■ 20
7. 75% of 80 = ■ 60
8. $\frac{1}{2}$ of 200 = ■ 100
9. $\frac{1}{4}$ of 200 = ■ 50
10. $\frac{3}{4}$ of 200 = ■ 150
11. 50% of 16 = ■ 8
12. 25% of 16 = ■ 4
13. 75% of 16 = ■ 12
14. $\frac{1}{2}$ of 44 = ■ 22
15. $\frac{1}{4}$ of 44 = ■ 11
16. $\frac{3}{4}$ of 44 = ■ 33

**Solve** the following exercises.

17. 25% of 12 = ■ 3
18. $\frac{1}{4}$ of 16 = ■ 4
19. 75% of 8 = ■ 6
20. $\frac{1}{2}$ of 24 = ■ 12
21. $\frac{3}{4}$ of 20 = ■ 15
22. $\frac{1}{4}$ of 60 = ■ 15
23. $\frac{1}{2}$ of 54 = ■ 27
24. 75% of 120 = ■ 90

Multistep

25. Clownfish are orange with black and white stripes and live near coral reefs in the wild. Jehan wanted a clownfish that was $24. Jehan had saved a total of $18 when the pet store announced a sale. The sale was 25% off the regular price of all fish in the store. Do you think that Jehan can afford the clownfish at the sale price? Will it cost her all of her savings, or will she get change? yes; the sale price will be $18, so she will have no money left over

Chapter 7 • Lesson 2 297

# 3 Reflect

5

## Guided Discussion REASONING

Whole Group

Discuss the difficulties some students may have when thinking about percentages. One problem students encounter is that they cannot understand that 50% could be 20 inches when you are thinking about the percentage of one object or quantity, but it could also be 30 inches when you are referring to another object or quantity. Ask the students to share ideas about how they might explain this kind of problem to another student.

**Curriculum Connection:** Students may be interested in researching clownfish on the internet.

**Cumulative Review:** For review of multiplication and division, assign Problems 7–14 on student page 306.

**Family Involvement:** Assign the ***Practice, Reteach,*** or ***Enrichment*** activities depending on the needs of your students.

**Concept/Question Board:** Have students look for additional examples using percentages, fractions, and decimals and post them on the Concept/Question Board.

**Math Puzzler:** Thea has five coins—a penny, a nickel, a dime, a quarter, and a half-dollar. Find all the amounts of money she can make using just two of her coins. 6¢, 11¢, 15¢, 26¢, 30¢, 35¢, 51¢, 55¢, 60¢, 75¢

# 4 Assess and Differentiate

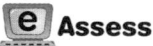

**e Assess** Use ***eAssess*** to record and analyze evidence of student understanding.

## A Gather Evidence

Use the Daily Class Assessment Records in ***Assessment*** or ***eAssess*** to record daily observations.

### Informal Assessment

**✓ Student Pages**

Did the student UNDERSTANDING

- ❑ make important observations?
- ❑ extend or generalize learning?
- ❑ provide insightful answers?
- ❑ pose insightful questions?

### Informal Assessment

**✓ Guide Discussion**

Did the student REASONING

- ❑ provide a clear explanation?
- ❑ communicate reasons and strategies?
- ❑ choose appropriate strategies?
- ❑ argue logically?

## B Summarize Findings

Analyze and summarize assessment data for each student. Determine which Assessment Follow-Up is appropriate for each student. Use the Student Assessment Record in ***Assessment*** or ***eAssess*** to update assessment records.

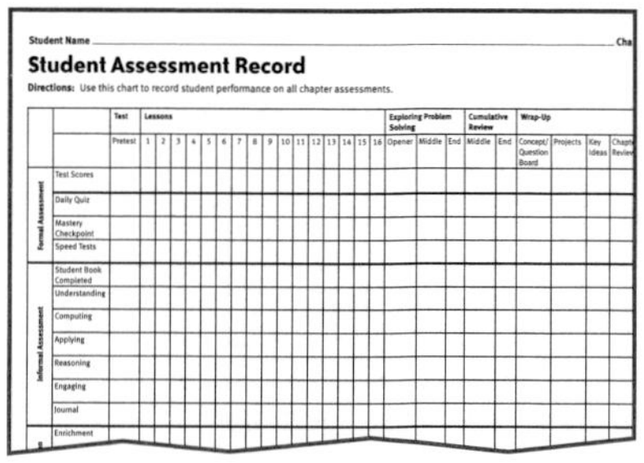


**Assessment Page T41**

## C Assessment Follow-Up • DIFFERENTIATE INSTRUCTION

Based on your observations, use these teaching strategies for assessment follow-up.

### INTERVENTION

Review student performance on ***Intervention*** Lesson 7.A to see if students have mastered prerequisite skills for this lesson.

### ENGLISH LEARNER

**Review**

Use Lesson 7.2 in ***English Learner Support Guide*** to review lesson concepts and vocabulary.

### ENRICH

**If . . .** students are proficient in the lesson concepts,

**Then . . .** encourage them to work on the chapter projects or ***Enrichment*** Lesson 7.2.

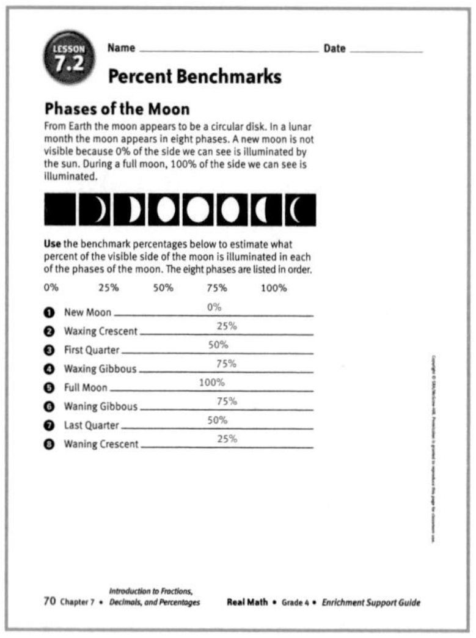

LESSON 7.2 Name ______ Date ______

**Percent Benchmarks**

**Phases of the Moon**

From Earth the moon appears to be a circular disk. In a lunar month the moon appears in eight phases. A new moon is not visible because 0% of the side we can see is illuminated by the sun. During a full moon, 100% of the side we can see is illuminated.

**Use** the benchmark percentages below to estimate what percent of the visible side of the moon is illuminated in each of the phases of the moon. The eight phases are listed in order.

0% 25% 50% 75% 100%

1. New Moon 0%
2. Waxing Crescent 25%
3. First Quarter 50%
4. Waxing Gibbous 75%
5. Full Moon 100%
6. Waning Gibbous 75%
7. Last Quarter 50%
8. Waning Crescent 25%

70 Chapter 7 • *Introduction to Fractions, Decimals, and Percentages* **Real Math** • Grade 4 • *Enrichment Support Guide*

Enrichment Lesson 7.2

### PRACTICE

**If . . .** students would benefit from additional practice,

**Then . . .** assign ***Practice*** Lesson 7.2.

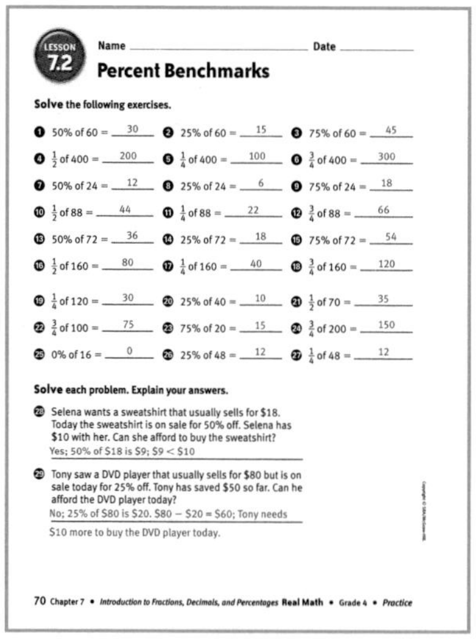

LESSON 7.2 Name ______ Date ______

**Percent Benchmarks**

**Solve** the following exercises.

1. 50% of 60 = 30
2. 25% of 60 = 15
3. 75% of 60 = 45
4. $\frac{1}{2}$ of 400 = 200
5. $\frac{1}{4}$ of 400 = 100
6. $\frac{3}{4}$ of 400 = 300
7. 50% of 24 = 12
8. 25% of 24 = 6
9. 75% of 24 = 18
10. $\frac{1}{2}$ of 88 = 44
11. $\frac{1}{4}$ of 88 = 22
12. $\frac{3}{4}$ of 88 = 66
13. 50% of 72 = 36
14. 25% of 72 = 18
15. 75% of 72 = 54
16. $\frac{1}{2}$ of 160 = 80
17. $\frac{1}{4}$ of 160 = 40
18. $\frac{3}{4}$ of 160 = 120
19. $\frac{1}{4}$ of 120 = 30
20. 25% of 40 = 10
21. $\frac{1}{2}$ of 70 = 35
22. $\frac{3}{4}$ of 100 = 75
23. 75% of 20 = 15
24. $\frac{3}{4}$ of 200 = 150
25. 0% of 16 = 0
26. 25% of 48 = 12
27. $\frac{1}{4}$ of 48 = 12

**Solve** each problem. Explain your answers.

28. Selena wants a sweatshirt that usually sells for $18. Today the sweatshirt is on sale for 50% off. Selena has $10 with her. Can she afford to buy the sweatshirt?
Yes; 50% of $18 is $9; $9 < $10
29. Tony saw a DVD player that usually sells for $80 but is on sale today for 25% off. Tony has saved $50 so far. Can he afford the DVD player today?
No; 25% of $80 is $20. $80 − $20 = $60; Tony needs $10 more to buy the DVD player today.

70 Chapter 7 • *Introduction to Fractions, Decimals, and Percentages* **Real Math** • Grade 4 • *Practice*

Practice Lesson 7.2

### RETEACH

**If . . .** students are having difficulty understanding percentages of heights,

**Then . . .** have them model the exercises with pieces of string cut to the correct length. Have them fold the string to the correct percentage and measure their result.

## Lesson Planner

**Objectives**
- To introduce $12\frac{1}{2}\%$ and $\frac{1}{8}$
- To practice finding percentages and fractions of whole numbers
- To translate among percentages and fractions of the same quantity

**NCTM Standards**

**Number and Operations**
Use multiplication or division to find parts of whole numbers

**Reasoning and Proof**
Explain fractional relationships

**Problem Solving**
Use mathematical logic and reasoning to guide decision making

**Materials**
- *Response Wheels (RESPONSE WHEEL)
- Copy of *Practice* page 145 (containing the 5 24-cm strips) for each student
- *Equivalencies Card Deck
- Scissors
- Pencils
- *Rulers

**Technology**
- e Presentation Lesson 7.3
- e Games Order Card Game

**Test Prep**

**Cumulative Review** (Review)
Mental Math reviews solutions for 25% of whole numbers (Lesson 3.10).

**Multistep Problems**
Problems 12–38

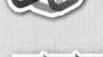

**Extended Response**
Problem 37

**Writing + Math**
Journal

### Looking Ahead

In preparation for Lesson 7.4, you will need to pick three "mystery items" in the classroom. Make sure these items are visible to all students. For further details see page 302B in the *Teacher's Edition.*

*Manipulative Kit Item

# Understanding $12\frac{1}{2}\%$ and $\frac{1}{8}$

**Context of the Lesson** This is the third of eight lessons in this chapter that introduce percentages, fractions, and decimals. In the previous two lessons the students used a halving procedure to name benchmark percentages and fractions of the whole. They performed mental computations to find percentages of whole numbers. In this lesson, the students continue to work with linear measurement and are introduced to $12\frac{1}{2}\%$, or $\frac{1}{8}$.

See page 292B for Math Background for teachers for this lesson.

## Planning for Learning • DIFFERENTIATE INSTRUCTION

### INTERVENTION

**If . . .** students lack the prerequisite skill of meaning of fractions and decimals,

**Then . . .** teach ***Intervention*** Lesson 7.A.

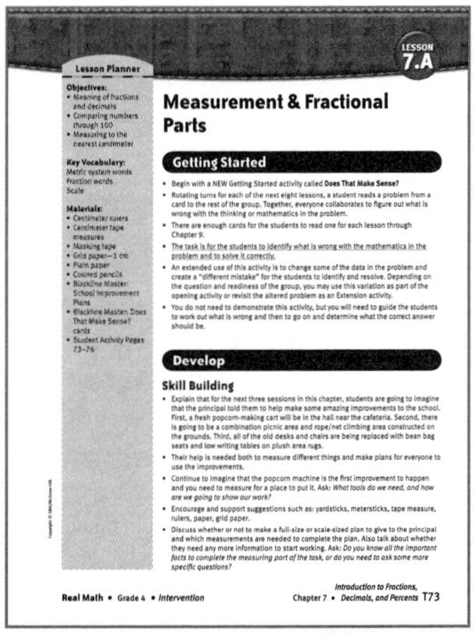


Intervention Lesson 7.A

### ENGLISH LEARNER

Preview

**If . . .** students need language support,

**Then . . .** use Lesson 7.3 in ***English Learner Support Guide*** to preview lesson concepts and vocabulary.

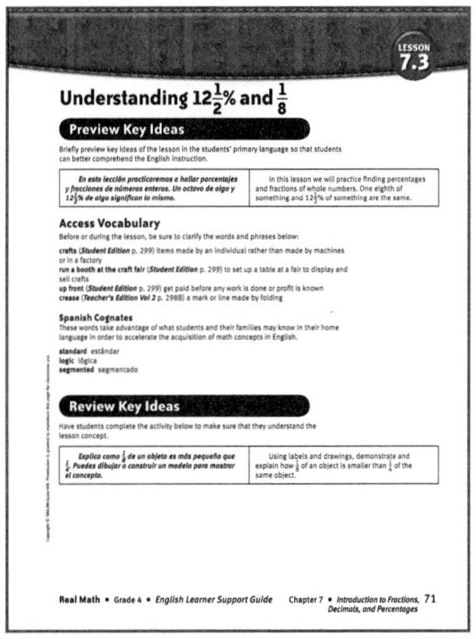


English Learner Lesson 7.3

### ENRICH

**If . . .** students are proficient in the lesson concepts,

**Then . . .** encourage them to create new **Order Card Game** strategies.

### PRACTICE

**If . . .** students would benefit from additional practice,

**Then . . .** extend the time allotted for the **Order Card Game** before assigning the student pages.

### RETEACH

**If . . .** students have difficulty with percentages and height,

**Then . . .** extend Guided Discussion before assigning the student pages.

**Vocabulary**
**equivalent \i kwiv′ ə lənt\ *adj.*** having the same value

**Access Vocabulary**
**beaker** a special glass container with measurements noted on the side used in laboratory experiments with liquids

**Spanish Cognates**
**standard** estándar

## Mental Math

5'

Review RESPONSE WHEEL Provide exercises, such as the following, that practice quartering:

**a.** 25% of 20 = 5
**b.** 25% of 16 = 4
**c.** 25% of 8 = 2
**d.** 25% of 40 = 10
**e.** 25% of 32 = 8
**f.** 25% of 4 = 1
**g.** 25% of 24 = 6
**h.** 25% of 44 = 11

## 1 Develop

35

### Tell Students In Today's Lesson They Will

practice finding percentages and fractions of whole numbers.

### Guided Discussion

UNDERSTANDING

Whole Group

**1.** Hand out a copy of ***Practice*** page 145 to each student. Have them use scissors to cut each of the five strips.

When students are finished cutting their strips, demonstrate how to fold the paper so it is 50% of its original length. Write 50% on the crease of the fold. Also write the fraction $\frac{1}{2}$ on the fold and ask students to do the same.

**2.** Next pick up the second strip and ask the students to fold the paper to get the 25% mark (fold it in half twice). Have the students write 25% and $\frac{1}{4}$ on the appropriate crease.

Repeat this process using a third strip for 75%. Ask the students to show and label 75% and $\frac{3}{4}$.

Take the fourth strip and tell the students they will learn a new percentage ($12\frac{1}{2}$%). Ask the students to fold this fourth strip to show 25%; with normal notebook paper this third fold should not be difficult. If thicker paper is used, students may fold just the bottom portion of their strip.

Discuss what percentage this new fold has created ($12\frac{1}{2}$%, half of 25%) and discuss what fraction of the whole strip this is ($\frac{1}{8}$). Ask the students questions such as the following:

- **How many eighths are there in a whole strip?** 8
- **How many $12\frac{1}{2}$% are there in a whole strip?** 8

**3.** Next ask the students to use scissors to cut strips on the creases so they will have separate segments that are 50%, 75%, 25%, and $12\frac{1}{2}$% of the total length. When they are finished, pick up the last, full-length strip. Ask students what they estimate the length of this strip to be in centimeters. Record the students' suggestions and ask them to use their rulers to measure (it is 24 cm long).

**4.** Now ask students to tell you, without measuring, how long each of the segment strips—50%, 75%, 25%, $12\frac{1}{2}$%—is. Write these equations on the board as a record:

| | |
|---|---|
| 100% of 24 = 24 | $\frac{1}{1}$ of 24 = 24 |
| 50% of 24 = 12 | $\frac{1}{2}$ of 24 = 12 |
| 25% of 24 = 6 | $\frac{1}{4}$ of 24 = 6 |
| $12\frac{1}{2}$% of 24 = 3 | $\frac{1}{8}$ of 24 = 3 |
| 75% of 24 = 18 | $\frac{3}{4}$ of 24 = 18 |

Have students measure their segmented strips and check their mental calculations against the actual lengths.

### Skill and Strategy Building

APPLYING

Whole Group

The **Order Card Game** is the first in a series of playing card activities that will give students practice in moving among the representations of percentages, fractions, and later, decimals. The card activities are also intended to help the students think about equivalencies and to compare and order rational numbers. As in all games, students decide whether there is a strategy and if so, what it is.

**1.** At this point in the chapter, the decimal cards should be removed, as well as any fractions not pertaining to percentages covered to this point—100%, 75%, 50%, 25%, and $12\frac{1}{2}$%.

Stress to students that percentages and fractions are parts of the same whole. So when comparing 75% and $\frac{1}{2}$, they are comparing 75% of a whole and $\frac{1}{2}$ of the same whole (75% of 1 and $\frac{1}{2}$ of 1).

**2.** Discuss the steps for playing the **Order Card Game** on page 302.

Remind students that once a number card has been entered into a square on the response sheet, it may not be moved to a different position.

# 2 Assign Student Pages

15

## Pages 298–299 COMPUTING

Have students complete pages 298–299 independently. On page 298, read through the Key Idea with the whole class and then help students complete the first three problems. On page 299, students should answer with a T (true) or an F (false). The first half of the problems concern comparisons of quantities and the students may need to review the symbols for greater than (>) and less than (<) before getting started. Remind them that the smaller end of the symbol points toward the smaller number, and the greater end points toward the greater number. These are challenging problems, so it is important to go over several examples with the class as a whole.

### Monitoring Student Progress

**If . . .** students are having difficulty finding $12\frac{1}{2}\%$ of a number,

**Then . . .** review the steps or draw a picture of a beaker and have the students work with you to find 50%, 25%, and $12\frac{1}{2}\%$ of the number.

Student Page

LESSON 7.3

## Understanding $12\frac{1}{2}\%$ and $\frac{1}{8}$

### Key Ideas

**One-eighth of something and $12\frac{1}{2}\%$ of something are the same.**

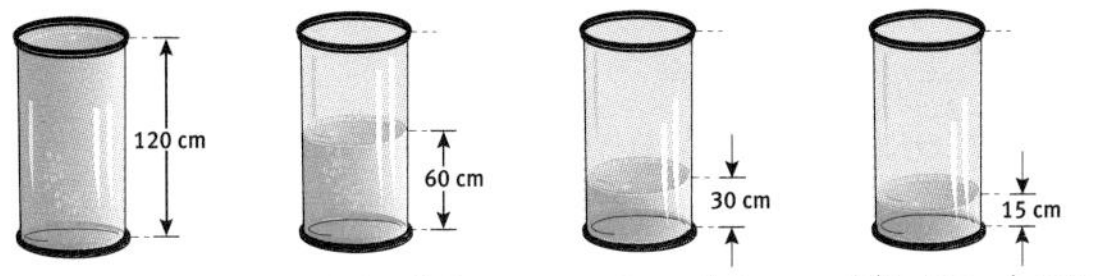


100% of 120 = 120 | 50% of 120 = $\frac{1}{2}$ of 120 | 25% of 120 = $\frac{1}{4}$ of 120 | $12\frac{1}{2}\%$ of 120 = $\frac{1}{8}$ of 120

**Finding $12\frac{1}{2}\%$**

Example: Let's find $12\frac{1}{2}\%$ of 120.

Step 1: Find 100% of the number. 100% of 120 = 120

Step 2: Half of 100% is 50%. Find half of the number. 50% of 120 (half of 120) = 60

Step 3: Half of 50% is 25%. Find half of your previous answer. 25% of 120 (half of 60) = 30

Step 4: Half of 25% is $12\frac{1}{2}\%$. Find half of your previous answer. $12\frac{1}{2}\%$ of 120 (half of 30) = 15

**Find** $12\frac{1}{2}\%$ of the following quantities.

1. $12\frac{1}{2}\%$ of 16 = ▢ 2
2. $12\frac{1}{2}\%$ of 80 = ▢ 10
3. $12\frac{1}{2}\%$ of 40 = ▢ 5
4. $12\frac{1}{2}\%$ of 24 = ▢ 3
5. $12\frac{1}{2}\%$ of 32 = ▢ 4
6. $12\frac{1}{2}\%$ of 200 = ▢ 25

**Create** your own problem.

7. $12\frac{1}{2}\%$ of ▢ = ▢ Answers will vary. Possible answer: $12\frac{1}{2}\%$ of 64 = 8



eTextbook This lesson is available in the *eTextbook*.

Student Page

**Give** an equivalent fraction for each percentage or an equivalent percentage for each fraction.

8. 50% of 1 = ▢ $\frac{1}{2}$ of 1
9. $\frac{3}{4}$ of 1 = ▢ 75% of 1
10. $12\frac{1}{2}\%$ of 1 = ▢ $\frac{1}{8}$ of 1
11. $\frac{1}{4}$ of 1 = ▢ 25% of 1

Multistep **Compare** the statements below, and answer true or false. If the answer is false, explain what would make the statement true. The first one is done for you.

12. 50% of 4 < $\frac{3}{4}$ of 4 **true**
13. $12\frac{1}{2}\%$ of 24 < $\frac{1}{4}$ of 24 true
14. 75% of 1 > $\frac{3}{4}$ of 1 false; they are equal
15. $\frac{1}{8}$ of 8 < 25% of 8 true
16. $\frac{3}{4}$ of 20 < 80% of 20 true
17. 10% of 100 > $\frac{1}{8}$ of 100 false; $\frac{1}{8}$ of 100 is greater

Multistep **Look** at the following exercises. Answer if the statement is true or false. If it is false, write the correct percentage or fraction for the right side of the equation.

18. 25% of 1 + 25% of 1 = $\frac{1}{2}$ of 1 true
19. $12\frac{1}{2}\%$ of 1 + 25% of 1 = $\frac{1}{4}$ of 1 false; $\frac{3}{8}$ or $37\frac{1}{2}\%$ of 1
20. $\frac{3}{4}$ of 1 + $\frac{1}{8}$ of 1 = 100% of 1 false; $\frac{7}{8}$ or $87\frac{1}{2}\%$ of 1
21. $\frac{1}{4}$ of 1 + $\frac{1}{2}$ of 1 = 75% of 1 true
22. 25% of 1 + 75% of 1 = 1 true
23. 100% of 1 − 25% of 1 = $\frac{1}{2}$ of 1 false; 75% or $\frac{3}{4}$ of 1

# Assign Student Pages, continued

### Pages 300–301 COMPUTING

Have students complete page 300 independently.

### As Students Finish

**Game** Order Card Game

**e Games** *Order Card Game*

### RESEARCH IN ACTION

"Children need to learn that rational numbers are numbers in the same way that whole numbers are numbers. For children to use rational numbers to solve problems, they need to learn that the same rational number may be represented in different ways, as a fraction, a decimal, or a percent. Fraction concepts and representations need to be related to those of division, measurement, and ratio. Decimal and fractional representations need to be connected and understood. Building these connections takes extensive experience with rational numbers over a substantial period of time. Researchers have documented that difficulties in working with rational numbers can often be traced to weak conceptual understanding . . . Instructional sequences in which more time is spent at the outset on developing meaning for the various representations of rational numbers and the concept of unit have been shown to promote mathematical proficiency."

Kilpatrick, J., Swafford, J. and Findell, B. eds. *Adding It Up: Helping Children Learn Mathematics*. Washington, D.C.: National Research Council/National Academy Press, 2001, p. 415–416.

Student Page

LESSON 7.3 • Understanding $12\frac{1}{2}$% and $\frac{1}{8}$

**Complete** the following exercises.

24. 50% of 40 = ■ 20
25. 25% of 40 = ■ 10
26. $12\frac{1}{2}$% of 40 = ■ 5
27. 75% of 40 = ■ 30
28. $\frac{1}{8}$ of 80 = ■ 10
29. $\frac{1}{4}$ of 80 = ■ 20
30. $\frac{1}{2}$ of 80 = ■ 40
31. $\frac{3}{4}$ of 80 = ■ 60
32. 50% of 64 = ■ 32
33. 25% of 64 = ■ 16
34. $12\frac{1}{2}$% of 64 = ■ 8
35. $37\frac{1}{2}$% of 64 = ■ 16 + 8 = 24
36. $\frac{3}{8}$ of 64 = ■ 24

**Solve** the following problems.

37. Extended Response Lauren was helping her Aunt Margo run a booth at the craft fair. Aunt Margo offered Lauren a choice as to how she would like to get paid—she could either have $50 up front or keep $12\frac{1}{2}$% of Aunt Margo's total sales from the craft fair. At last year's craft fair, Aunt Margo made $480. Which payment method do you think Lauren should choose? Explain your answer.

37. If sales equal or exceed those of last year, $12\frac{1}{2}$% of the total sales would be more than $50 since $12\frac{1}{2}$% of 480 is 60.

38. Naudia's mother asked her for a list of her spelling test scores. Naudia tried to disguise some of the scores by writing them as percents and fractions of the total possible answers: 90%, $\frac{65}{100}$, $37\frac{1}{2}$%, $\frac{3}{4}$, and $\frac{2}{8}$. Help Naudia's mother arrange the test scores from least to greatest as a fraction or percentage. Draw pictures to help explain how you know your order is correct.

38. One way is $\frac{2}{8}$, $\frac{37.5}{100}$, $\frac{65}{100}$, $\frac{3}{4}$, $\frac{90}{100}$. Another possibility is 25%, $37\frac{1}{2}$%, 65%, 75%, 90%.

Writing + Math **Journal**

Using words and pictures, explain how $\frac{1}{8}$ of an object is smaller than $\frac{1}{4}$ of the same object.

Answers will vary, but may involve drawings that show a glass of water that is $\frac{1}{4}$ full and a similar glass that is $\frac{1}{8}$ full.

300 eTextbook This lesson is available in the *eTextbook*.

Student Page

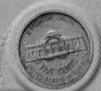

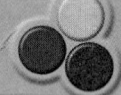

**Game**

Ordering and Strategies Practice

## The Order Card Game

**Players:** Two or more

**Materials:** ***Equivalence Card Deck***, response sheet

**Object:** Order quantities from least to greatest

**Math Focus:** Comparing and ordering percentages and fractions of 1

**HOW TO PLAY**

1. Have each player make a response sheet with blank squares like the one below. The game starts with a four-card sequence, but with each round of play the number of squares in a sequence can be increased (by drawing more squares on your grid).
2. The first player pulls a random card facedown from the deck. This player then flips the card over, and all players record the number in one of the squares in sequence on their response sheet. Note that once a number is entered in a square on the response sheet, a player is not allowed to change its position.
3. Play continues with each player alternately pulling another card until all the squares in the response sheet have been filled. The winner will be the player(s) who has managed to correctly place his or her cards in sequence from least to greatest. If no player has a correct sequence, the game is a tie.
4. Multiple rounds can include longer sequences and reversing the order (putting cards in sequence from greatest to least).
5. Cards that have the same value but different representations (for example, 75% of 1 and $\frac{3}{4}$ of 1) will also be put in sequence, but they may be considered interchangeable when determining the winning order.

| | | | |
|---|---|---|---|
| $12\frac{1}{2}$% of 1 | $\frac{1}{8}$ of 1 | 50% of 1 | $\frac{3}{4}$ of 1 |

or

| | | | |
|---|---|---|---|
| $\frac{1}{8}$ of 1 | $12\frac{1}{2}$% of 1 | 50% of 1 | $\frac{3}{4}$ of 1 |

Chapter 7 • Lesson 3 301

## 3 Reflect

5

### Guided Discussion

UNDERSTANDING

Whole Group

Discuss why some students may think $\frac{1}{8}$ of a strip of paper must be larger than $\frac{1}{4}$ of a strip of the same paper. Ask students to explain why they think this happens. Possible answer: Some students reason that since 8 is greater than 4, $\frac{1}{8}$ must be greater than $\frac{1}{4}$. Encourage students to come up with a way to explain to other students how $\frac{1}{8}$ is **less** than $\frac{1}{4}$.

### Extended Response

**Problem 37** Look for explanations about sales being equal or greater than $400, in which case Lauren would want to get paid by percentage. Or, students may say the reverse, if sales are less than $400 then Lauren would want to take the $50.

Writing + Math **Journal**

Students will want to describe objects being cut into four pieces and into eight pieces. From their diagrams, $\frac{1}{8}$ should be less than $\frac{1}{4}$. Rationales will vary; however, $\frac{1}{8}$ needs to be portrayed as less than $\frac{1}{4}$.

**Cumulative Review:** For review of multidigit multiplication, assign Problems 15–19 on student page 307.

**Family Involvement:** Assign the ***Practice, Reteach,*** or ***Enrichment*** activities depending on the needs of your students.

**Concept/Question Board:** Encourage students to continue to post questions, answers, and examples on the Concept/Question Board.

**Math Puzzler:** Jacob wants to make exactly $1 using at least one of each of the five kinds of coins. Which ten coins could he use? 1 half-dollar, 1 quarter, 1 dime, 2 nickels, 5 pennies

# 4 Assess and Differentiate

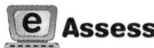

**e Assess** Use ***eAssess*** to record and analyze evidence of student understanding.

## A Gather Evidence

Use the Daily Class Assessment Records in ***Assessment*** or ***eAssess*** to record daily observations.

### Informal Assessment

**Guided Discussion**

Did the student UNDERSTANDING

- ❑ make important observations?
- ❑ extend or generalize learning?
- ❑ provide insightful answers?
- ❑ pose insightful questions?

### Performance Assessment

**Game**

Did the student APPLYING

- ❑ apply learning in new situations?
- ❑ contribute concepts?
- ❑ contribute answers?
- ❑ connect mathematics to real-world situations?

## B Summarize Findings

Analyze and summarize assessment data for each student. Determine which Assessment Follow-Up is appropriate for each student. Use the Student Assessment Record in ***Assessment*** or ***eAssess*** to update assessment records.

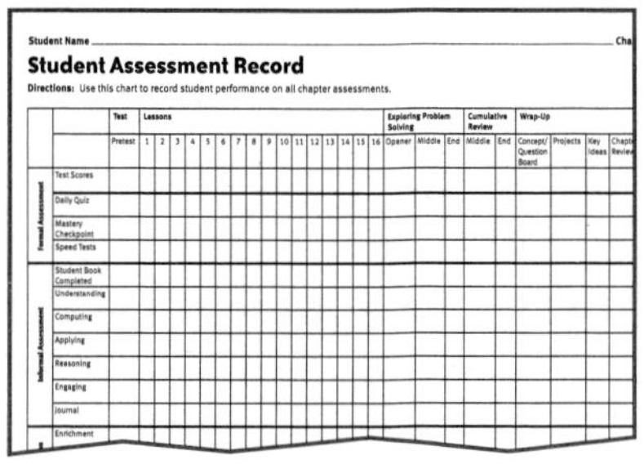
Student Name
Student Assessment Record
Directions: Use this chart to record student performance on all chapter assessments.

**Assessment Page T41**

## C Assessment Follow-Up • DIFFERENTIATE INSTRUCTION

Based on your observations, use these teaching strategies for assessment follow-up.

### INTERVENTION

Review student performance on ***Intervention*** Lesson 7.A to see if students have mastered prerequisite skills for this lesson.

### ENGLISH LEARNER

**Review**

Use Lesson 7.3 in ***English Learner Support Guide*** to review lesson concepts and vocabulary.

### ENRICH

**If . . .** students are proficient in the lesson concepts,

**Then . . .** encourage them to work on the chapter projects or ***Enrichment*** Lesson 7.3.

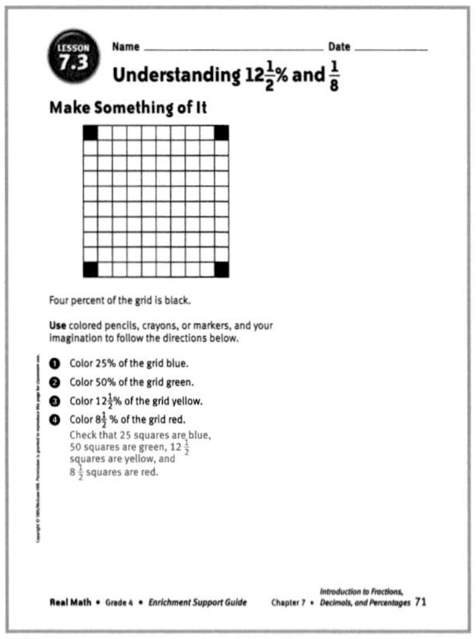
LESSON 7.3 Name ________ Date ________

Understanding $12\frac{1}{2}\%$ and $\frac{1}{8}$

Make Something of It

Four percent of the grid is black.

**Use** colored pencils, crayons, or markers, and your imagination to follow the directions below.

1. Color 25% of the grid blue.
2. Color 50% of the grid green.
3. Color $12\frac{1}{2}\%$ of the grid yellow.
4. Color $8\frac{1}{2}\%$ of the grid red.

Check that 25 squares are blue, 50 squares are green, $12\frac{1}{2}$ squares are yellow, and $8\frac{1}{2}$ squares are red.

Real Math • Grade 4 • *Enrichment Support Guide* Chapter 7 • *Introduction to Fractions, Decimals, and Percentages* 71

Enrichment Lesson 7.3

### PRACTICE

**If . . .** students would benefit from additional practice,

**Then . . .** assign ***Practice*** Lesson 7.3.

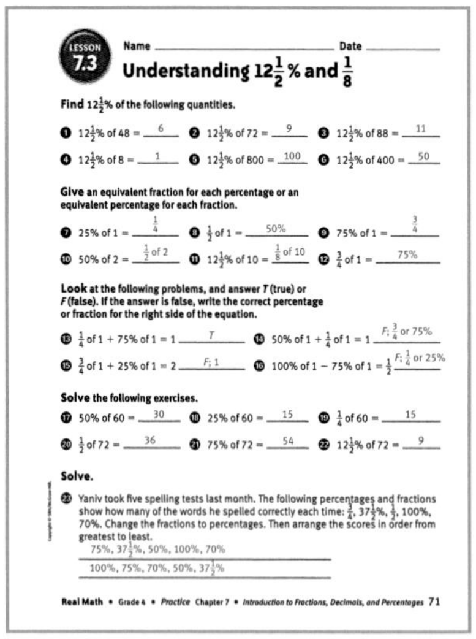
LESSON 7.3 Name ________ Date ________

Understanding $12\frac{1}{2}\%$ and $\frac{1}{8}$

**Find** $12\frac{1}{2}\%$ of the following quantities.

1. $12\frac{1}{2}\%$ of 48 = 6
2. $12\frac{1}{2}\%$ of 72 = 9
3. $12\frac{1}{2}\%$ of 88 = 11
4. $12\frac{1}{2}\%$ of 8 = 1
5. $12\frac{1}{2}\%$ of 800 = 100
6. $12\frac{1}{2}\%$ of 400 = 50

**Give** an equivalent fraction for each percentage or an equivalent percentage for each fraction.

7. 25% of 1 = $\frac{1}{4}$
8. $\frac{1}{2}$ of 1 = 50%
9. 75% of 1 = $\frac{3}{4}$
10. 50% of 2 = $\frac{1}{2}$ of 2
11. $12\frac{1}{2}\%$ of 10 = $\frac{1}{8}$ of 10
12. $\frac{3}{4}$ of 1 = 75%

**Look** at the following problems, and answer *T* (true) or *F* (false). If the answer is false, write the correct percentage or fraction for the right side of the equation.

13. $\frac{1}{4}$ of 1 + 75% of 1 = 1 *T*
14. 50% of 1 + $\frac{1}{4}$ of 1 = 1 *F*; $\frac{3}{4}$ or 75%
15. $\frac{3}{4}$ of 1 + 25% of 1 = 2 *F*; 1
16. 100% of 1 − 75% of 1 = $\frac{1}{2}$ *F*; $\frac{1}{4}$ or 25%

**Solve** the following exercises.

17. 50% of 60 = 30
18. 25% of 60 = 15
19. $\frac{1}{4}$ of 60 = 15
20. $\frac{1}{2}$ of 72 = 36
21. 75% of 72 = 54
22. $12\frac{1}{2}\%$ of 72 = 9

**Solve.**

23. Yaniv took five spelling tests last month. The following percentages and fractions show how many of the words he spelled correctly each time: $\frac{3}{4}$, $37\frac{1}{2}\%$, $\frac{1}{2}$, 100%, 70%. Change the fractions to percentages. Then arrange the scores in order from greatest to least.
75%, $37\frac{1}{2}\%$, 50%, 100%, 70%
100%, 75%, 70%, 50%, $37\frac{1}{2}\%$

Real Math • Grade 4 • *Practice* Chapter 7 • *Introduction to Fractions, Decimals, and Percentages* 71

Practice Lesson 7.3

### RETEACH

**If . . .** students struggle with finding $12\frac{1}{2}\%$,

**Then . . .** have them find 25% of the number and divide their answer by 2, or divide the original number by 8.

# Overview

**LESSON 7.4**

## Lesson Planner

### OBJECTIVES
- To continue finding percentages of whole numbers
- To continue relating percent benchmarks to their fractional counterparts
- To provide opportunities for informal proportional reasoning

### NCTM STANDARDS
**Measurement**
Use rulers to create percentages of measurements

**Data Analysis**
Reference data to hypothesize what objects are being designated "mystery objects"

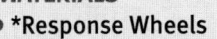

### MATERIALS
- ***Response Wheels**
- *Rulers or measuring tape for each group of students
- String (2 meters) for each group of students
- Construction paper (either $8\frac{1}{2}'' \times 11''$ or $11'' \times 17''$)
- Markers
- Glue sticks
- Strings relating to three "mystery objects" (as explained in the Looking Ahead section of Lesson 7.3)

### TECHNOLOGY
**e Presentation** Lesson 7.4
**e Games** Order Card Game

### TEST PREP
**Cumulative Review**
Mental Math reviews fractional parts of whole numbers (Lesson 7.2).

**Multistep Problems**
Problems 1–2

*Manipulative Kit Item

# Applying Percent Benchmarks

**Context of the Lesson** This is the fourth of eight lessons involving percentages and measurement. The activities in this lesson are designed to help students consolidate and extend their ability to compute percentages.

See page 292B for Math Background for teachers for this lesson.

## Planning for Learning • DIFFERENTIATE INSTRUCTION

### INTERVENTION

**If . . .** students lack the prerequisite skill of measuring to the nearest centimeter,

**Then . . .** teach ***Intervention*** Lesson 7.C.

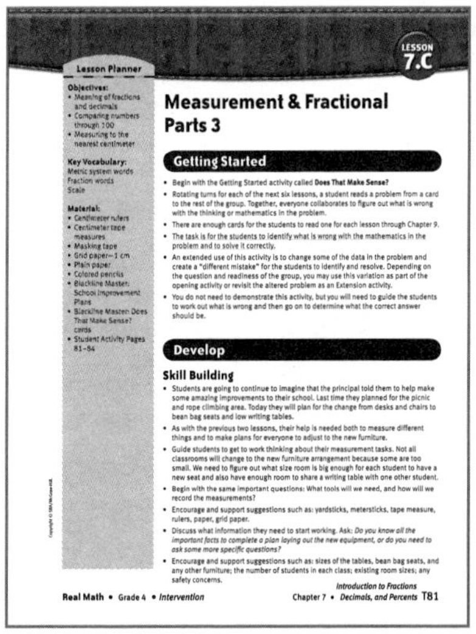
LESSON 7.C
Lesson Planner
Measurement & Fractional Parts 3
Getting Started
Develop
Skill Building

Intervention Lesson 7.C

### ENGLISH LEARNER

Preview

**If . . .** students need language support,

**Then . . .** use Lesson 7.4 in ***English Learner Support Guide*** to preview lesson concepts and vocabulary.

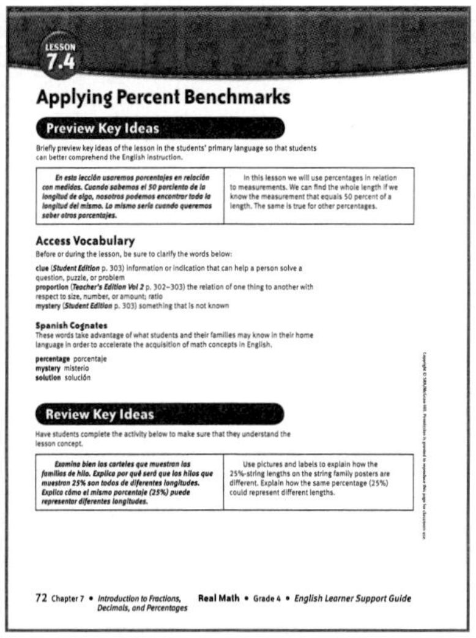
LESSON 7.4
Applying Percent Benchmarks
Preview Key Ideas
Access Vocabulary
Spanish Cognates
Review Key Ideas

English Learner Lesson 7.4

### ENRICH

**If . . .** students are proficient in the lesson concepts,

**Then . . .** encourage them to create new strategies for the **Order Card Game.**

### PRACTICE

**If . . .** students would benefit from additional practice,

**Then . . .** extend Skill Practice before assigning the student pages.

### RETEACH

**If . . .** students have difficulty remembering how to find the perimeter of a rectangle,

**Then . . .** extend Guided Discussion before assigning the student pages.

**Access Vocabulary**
**a clue to the mystery** information that can help us solve a question, puzzle, or problem

**Spanish Cognates**
**percent** porcentaje
**mystery** misterio

## Mental Math

5

Provide students with exercises, such as the following, that review repeated halving to find quarters and eighths:

**a.** $\frac{1}{4}$ of 20 = 5 **b.** $\frac{1}{4}$ of 16 = 4 **c.** $\frac{1}{4}$ of 100 = 25 **d.** $\frac{1}{4}$ of 40 = 10

**e.** $\frac{1}{8}$ of 8 = 1 **f.** $\frac{1}{8}$ of 24 = 3 **g.** $\frac{1}{8}$ of 40 = 5 **h.** $\frac{1}{8}$ of 32 = 4

## 1 Develop

30

**Tell Students In Today's Lesson They Will**
learn to use percentages in relation to measurements.

### Guided Discussion ENGAGING

Whole Group

**1.** Write 25% on the board. Hold up the piece of precut string measured to 25% of the height of a certain object in the room (for example, 25% of the height of the chalkboard). Tell students that the length of string is 25% of the height of a mystery object in the classroom. Ask students to guess what the mystery object might be. Have students use the string to illustrate for the class the methods they would use to solve the problem.

Ask students to explain their reasoning. Students may respond that they imagined placing the string along the length of the object four times. Others may say they could picture it in their mind or they used a halving benchmark.

Have a volunteer write a fractional equivalent of 25% on the board. Accept all correct responses: $\frac{1}{4}$, $\frac{25}{100}$, and so on.

**2.** Now hold up the piece of string that has been cut to 75% of the height of a second mystery object. Repeat the procedure above to have students guess the object. Again, solicit students' explanations and have a student write 75% and a fractional equivalent on the board. $\frac{3}{4}$, $\frac{75}{100}$, and so on

Using the 75% string to determine the mystery object might be more difficult for students to explain. A possible solution is to fold the 75% string into three equal sections (each would be equal to a third of the string length or a fourth of the object length) and then look for an object that the folded string could be placed along four times.

**3.** Repeat the steps above using the final string that is 50% of the **perimeter** of a mystery object (a good perimeter challenge is to cut a string that is half the perimeter of a computer screen). Ask students to explain what they know about perimeter.

### Skill Building APPLYING

Small Group

**1.** Place students in small groups to challenge their classmates with mystery objects.

Give each group a piece of string (2 meters long), a ruler or measuring tape, and a sheet of paper (construction paper, if available). The larger the paper used, the more flexibility the group will have in picking their mystery object. Students should write 100%, 75%, 50%, 25%, and 12.5% across the bottom of the page, leaving space below these headings to record measurements of string lengths.

**2.** Have each group measure a mystery object they choose. Then have them cut a piece of string with a length equal to 100% of the measurement. Demonstrate by showing the string you cut to 100% of the length of your own mystery object.

Once students have glued or taped their 100% string onto the page, they can cut another piece of string equal in length to the 100% string. If the students fold this new piece of string in half and cut it, they will have two strings with lengths 50% of the length of their mystery object. One of these strings should be attached to their poster above the 50% heading.

**3.** Students can now take the other half of the string from the previous step and fold it in half again. One of these strings should be attached above the 25% heading. Repeat this procedure with the remaining half to get the $12\frac{1}{2}$% string.

**4.** Now ask students how they might come up with the 75% measurement. The students could use their 50% and 25% strings to measure out the length of the string that is 75% of the length of the original measurement, or they could subtract the 25% length from the 100% length.

Once students have all their strings attached to their posters, they write the measurements below the appropriate heading on their posters. Posters will be presented during the Reflect portion of the lesson, so students should write on the back of their posters what the mystery object is.

## 2 Assign Student Pages

10

**Pages 302–303** ENGAGING
Have students complete pages 302 and 303 independently.

### Monitoring Student Progress

**If . . .** the strings are not decreasing in length as they move toward the $12\frac{1}{2}$% mark,

**Then . . .** check that students understand that when the percentage of the original measurement decreases, the length of the string representing it will decrease as well.

### As Students Finish

Game **Order Card Game**

e **Games** *Order Card Game*

## LESSON 7.4 Applying Percent Benchmarks

### Key Ideas

**If you know 50% of a length, you can find the whole length.**
The same is true for other percentages.

| 100% of 64 = 64 | 75% of 64 $= \frac{3}{4}$ of 64 | 50% of 64 $= \frac{1}{2}$ of 64 | 25% of 64 $= \frac{1}{4}$ of 64 | $12\frac{1}{2}$% of 64 $= \frac{1}{8}$ of 64 |

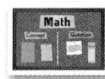

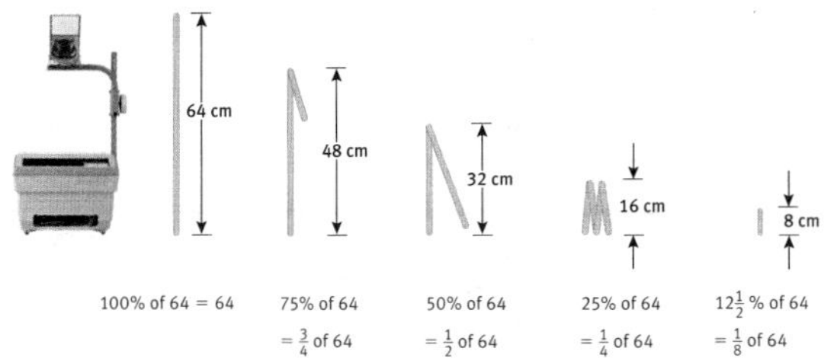

After measuring a real-life object, you can easily cut a piece of string that has the same length as your measurement (in the case above, the height of the overhead projector).

Using what we've learned in previous lessons, we don't have to limit ourselves to the total length of our measurement. We can cut strings of different lengths that represent percentages of the object's total height.

For example, we know that 25% of the height of the overhead projector above would be 16 centimeters. Do you remember how to calculate this? If we placed four strings that were 16 centimeters long end-to-end, the result would equal the height of the overhead projector.

You can make a puzzle out of these relationships by picking a mystery object and cutting strings to different percentages of your measurement. Show these strings to other people, and have them guess what your mystery object might be.

302    🔲 **Textbook** This lesson is available in the *eTextbook*.

---

A mystery object has a rectangular surface that is 40 centimeters long.

 ① For this mystery object, complete the following table.

| Length of Mystery Object | | |
|---|---|---|
| Benchmark Percentage of Measurement | Fraction | Length (cm) |
| 100% | $\frac{1}{1}$ (or 1) | 40 |
| 75% | $\frac{3}{4}$ | 30 |
| 50% | $\frac{1}{2}$ | 20 |
| 25% | $\frac{1}{4}$ | 10 |
| $12\frac{1}{2}$% | $\frac{1}{8}$ | 5 |

Information about the mystery object can be given in ways other than just the measurement of a side. A further clue is that its rectangular surface is 32 centimeters wide.

② Complete the chart of benchmark percentages for the perimeter of the mystery object.

| Perimeter of Mystery Object | | |
|---|---|---|
| Benchmark Percentage of Perimeter | Fraction | Length (cm) |
| 100% | $\frac{1}{1}$ | 144 |
| 75% | $\frac{3}{4}$ | 108 |
| 50% | $\frac{1}{2}$ | 72 |
| 25% | $\frac{1}{4}$ | 36 cm |
| 12.5% | $\frac{1}{8}$ | 18 |

③ Based on the information, is this mystery object likely to be a

**a.** chalkboard?    **b.** computer monitor?    **c.** stopwatch?

Think about other objects that might match this description.

Chapter 7 • Lesson 4    303

---

## 3 Reflect    15 ⏱

### Guided Discussion    **UNDERSTANDING**    Whole Group

At the end of the lesson, have students present their string family posters. Have the class guess from its poster what each mystery object might be. Have students talk about how the Mystery Object Activity might help younger students learn about proportions. For example, students might notice that all of the 25% strings are different lengths. This can be confusing to some students—percentages need to be thought of in relation to a specific whole. For example, the term 25% may look the same in two different circumstances, but 25% of 200 is a much different quantity from 25% of 4 (50 versus 1).

---

 **Cumulative Review:** For review of perimeter and area and multiplication and estimating, assign Problems 20–23 on student page 307.

 **Family Involvement:** Assign the *Practice, Reteach,* or *Enrichment* activities depending on the needs of your students.

**Concept/Question Board:** Encourage students to continue to post questions, answers, and examples on the Concept/Question Board.

 **Math Puzzler:** Find the pattern in the following numbers and then provide the next four numbers: 590; 1,085; 1,580; 2,075; and 2,570. The numbers in the series are found by adding 495, and the next four are 3,065; 3,560; 4,055; and 4,550.

# 4 Assess and Differentiate

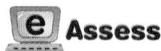

**e Assess** Use ***eAssess*** to record and analyze evidence of student understanding.

## A Gather Evidence

Use the Daily Class Assessment Records in ***Assessment*** or ***eAssess*** to record daily observations.

### Performance Assessment

**Skill Building**

Did the student APPLYING
- ❑ apply learning in new situations?
- ❑ contribute concepts?
- ❑ contribute answers?
- ❑ connect mathematics to real world situations?

### Informal Assessment

**Mental Math**

Did the student COMPUTING
- ❑ respond accurately?
- ❑ respond quickly?
- ❑ respond with confidence?
- ❑ self-correct?

## B Summarize Findings

Analyze and summarize assessment data for each student. Determine which Assessment Follow-Up is appropriate for each student. Use the Student Assessment Record in ***Assessment*** or ***eAssess*** to update assessment records.

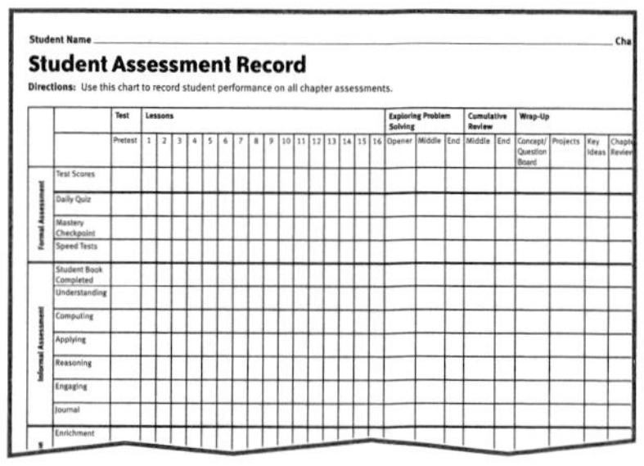
Student Assessment Record

**Assessment Page T41**

## C Assessment Follow-Up • DIFFERENTIATE INSTRUCTION

Based on your observations, use these teaching strategies for assessment follow-up.

### INTERVENTION

Review student performance on ***Intervention*** Lesson 7.C to see if students have mastered prerequisite skills for this lesson.

### ENGLISH LEARNER

**Review**

Use Lesson 7.4 in ***English Learner Support Guide*** to review lesson concepts and vocabulary.

### ENRICH

**If . . .** students are proficient in the lesson concepts,

**Then . . .** encourage them to work on the chapter projects or ***Enrichment*** Lesson 7.4.

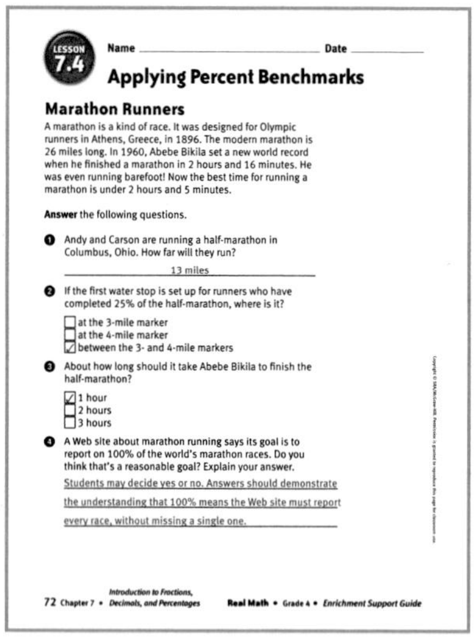
LESSON 7.4 Name ______ Date ______

**Applying Percent Benchmarks**

**Marathon Runners**

A marathon is a kind of race. It was designed for Olympic runners in Athens, Greece, in 1896. The modern marathon is 26 miles long. In 1960, Abebe Bikila set a new world record when he finished a marathon in 2 hours and 16 minutes. He was even running barefoot! Now the best time for running a marathon is under 2 hours and 5 minutes.

**Answer** the following questions.

1. Andy and Carson are running a half-marathon in Columbus, Ohio. How far will they run?
   13 miles
2. If the first water stop is set up for runners who have completed 25% of the half-marathon, where is it?
   - ☐ at the 3-mile marker
   - ☐ at the 4-mile marker
   - ☑ between the 3- and 4-mile markers
3. About how long should it take Abebe Bikila to finish the half-marathon?
   - ☑ 1 hour
   - ☐ 2 hours
   - ☐ 3 hours
4. A Web site about marathon running says its goal is to report on 100% of the world's marathon races. Do you think that's a reasonable goal? Explain your answer.
   Students may decide yes or no. Answers should demonstrate the understanding that 100% means the Web site must report every race, without missing a single one.

72 Chapter 7 • *Introduction to Fractions, Decimals, and Percentages* **Real Math** • Grade 4 • *Enrichment Support Guide*

Enrichment Lesson 7.4

### PRACTICE

**If . . .** students would benefit from additional practice,

**Then . . .** assign ***Practice*** Lesson 7.4.

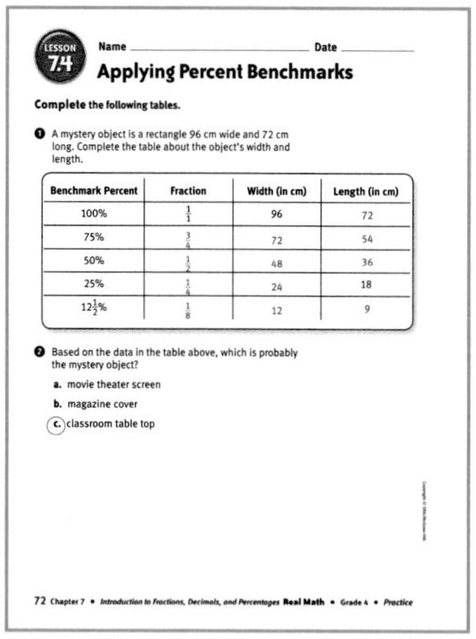
LESSON 7.4 Name ______ Date ______

**Applying Percent Benchmarks**

**Complete** the following tables.

1. A mystery object is a rectangle 96 cm wide and 72 cm long. Complete the table about the object's width and length.

| Benchmark Percent | Fraction | Width (in cm) | Length (in cm) |
|---|---|---|---|
| 100% | $\frac{1}{1}$ | 96 | 72 |
| 75% | $\frac{3}{4}$ | 72 | 54 |
| 50% | $\frac{1}{2}$ | 48 | 36 |
| 25% | $\frac{1}{4}$ | 24 | 18 |
| $12\frac{1}{2}$% | $\frac{1}{8}$ | 12 | 9 |

2. Based on the data in the table above, which is probably the mystery object?
   a. movie theater screen
   b. magazine cover
   (c.) classroom table top

72 Chapter 7 • *Introduction to Fractions, Decimals, and Percentages* **Real Math** • Grade 4 • *Practice*

Practice Lesson 7.4

### RETEACH

**If . . .** students struggle with filling in the second table,

**Then . . .** have them determine the perimeter using the given measurements for the answer to the 100% row.

# Exploring Problem Solving

**Objectives**

- To provide practice understanding and analyzing other people's solutions
- To provide practice using fractions and percents to relate parts and wholes
- To explore methods of solving and presenting solutions to nonroutine problems

**Context of the Lesson** The strategies that students analyze in this lesson make use of what they learned about percents in the first part of this chapter and prepare them to use linear models of percent in the remaining lessons of the chapter.

## 1 Develop 5

### Tell Students In Today's Lesson They Will

- read a challenging problem about downloading music.
- look at how two students try two different ways to solve the same problem.
- solve the problem with their group and share their strategy.

## Guided Discussion

Have students talk about using computers to download music. Ask them to describe how computers and other electronic devices use colored bars to show how far along they are when downloading a file, installing a program, or doing some other task.

## 2 Exploring Problem Solving 25

## Using Student Pages

Have students look at page 304. Read through the problem together. Ask questions such as the following:

- **What happens to the blue bar as the music is downloaded?** It gets longer.
- **How much of the bar was blue at 12:00?** none
- **What time is it in the picture?** 1:00
- **How much of the bar will be blue when the downloading is done?** all of it

Student Page

## Exploring Problem Solving

You begin downloading songs from a music service at noon. You need to be finished by 1:30, but your connection is slow. It is already 1:00, and the task is only 75 percent complete. If the downloading continues at the same speed, will you finish in time?

**Brian solved the problem this way:**

*I Made a Diagram and Made a Plan to solve the problem.*

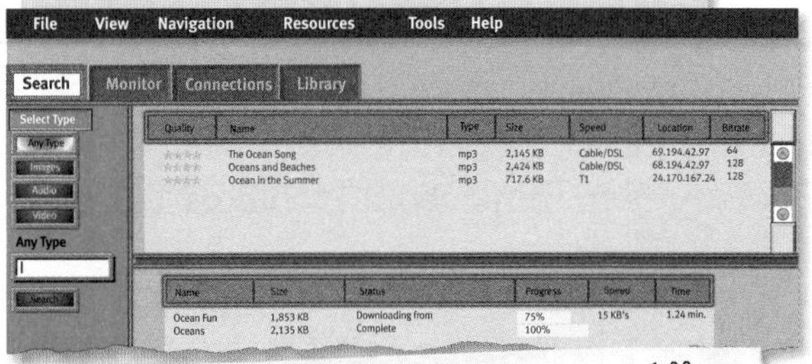


*First I'll sketch the bar. I know that 75% is $\frac{3}{4}$. I will divide the whole bar into fourths to show that the blue part is $\frac{3}{4}$ of the whole. Then I'll figure out how many minutes each fourth is. Then I'll use that number to figure out when the downloading will finish.*

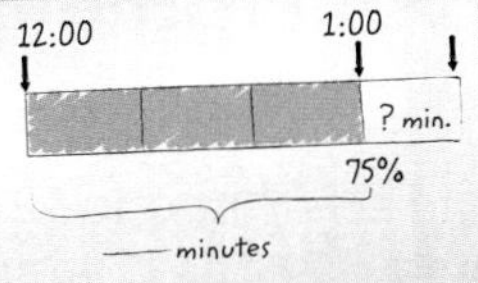


**Think** about Brian's strategy. Answer these questions.

1. How many minutes has the computer been downloading? 60
2. How will Brian decide if the computer will finish on time? See the *Teacher's Edition.*
3. Do you think Brian's strategy will work? Why or why not? See the *Teacher's Edition.*



eTextbook This lesson is available in the *eTextbook*.

Student Page

**Susanna used a different plan.**

*My plan involved using the Guess, Check, and Adjust and Make a Table strategies.*

The downloadng must be done by 1:30. So, the total time must be 90 minutes or less.

Here's how I'll find the total time:
After 60 minutes, the computer is 75%, or $\frac{3}{4}$, finished.
So, $\frac{3}{4}$ of the total time is 60 minutes.
So, $\frac{3}{4}$ of what number is 60?
I'll guess, check, and adjust to find that out.
I'll keep track of my guesses in a table.

| Total Time | $\frac{3}{4}$ of Total Time | Check |
|---|---|---|
| 120 min. | 90 | 90>60, too high |
| 100 min. | 75 | 75 > 60, still too high |
| 80 min. | 60 | 60 = 60 ✓ |

**Think** about Susanna's strategy. Answer these questions.

4. How will knowing the total time help Susanna solve the problem? She can compare it to 90 minutes to see if the download will be done in time.
5. How will Susanna use Guess, Check, and Adjust to find the total time? She can try different numbers until she finds one that works (so that $\frac{3}{4}$ of the number is 60).
6. Should Susanna's next try be greater than or less than 120? Why? It should be less, because 120 was too high.
7. Do you think Susanna's plan will work? Why or why not? Yes.
8. In this problem, do you need to find the exact time the computer finishes? No, you just need to know if it will finish by 1:30.
9. Solve the problem. Use Brian's or Susanna's strategy, or use a strategy of your own. What strategy did you use? Why? No matter which strategy students use, they should discover that the download will be done before 1:30.

Guide students through Brian's plan. Ask questions such as the following:

- **Brian divided the whole bar into 4 equal parts. How does that show that 75 percent of the downloading is done?** 75 percent is $\frac{3}{4}$, and 3 of the 4 sections, or $\frac{3}{4}$, of the whole bar is blue.
- **How can Brian find how many minutes each part is equal to?** Because 3 of the parts make 60 minutes, he can find $\frac{1}{3}$ of 60, or he can find what number times 3 is 60.

Give students time to think about Problems 1–3, then discuss them.

## Answers to Problems 2–3

### Problem 2

Help students see that once Brian knows how many more minutes it will take the computer to finish, the problem is almost solved. He simply needs to add those minutes to 1:00 P.M. to determine if the computer will finish by 1:30 P.M.

### Problem 3

Students may simply say that it will work because Brian will find the number of minutes remaining. Then he will know whether the computer will finish by 1:30. If students disagree with one another, encourage them to express their reasons as clearly as they can. Use this opportunity to give students practice in communicating mathematical ideas.

Guide students through Susanna's plan. Ask questions such as the following:

- **Why does Susanna say that 60 minutes is $\frac{3}{4}$ of the total time?** The computer has been downloading for 60 minutes (from 12:00 to 1:00) and is 75 percent, or $\frac{3}{4}$, finished.

You may want to draw a diagram, such as the one below, to help students see this.

From 12:00 to 1:00 is 60 minutes.

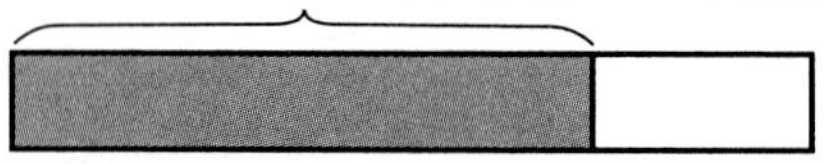

Give students time to think about Problems 4–8, then discuss them. When discussing Problem 7, bring up the following point:

Students should see that Susanna will eventually find a number that 60 is $\frac{3}{4}$ of the total. Help them see that this number is the total number of minutes it will take the computer to finish the task.

Once she finds the number, she can add those minutes to 12:00 to see when the computer will finish.

Note that Problem 8 may help students to find a strategy that does not focus on finding the exact finish time.

**Assign Problem 9.** Have students work in small groups to solve the problem, either by carrying out one of the plans presented or by using some other strategy.

## 3 Reflect 10

**Knowledge Age Skills**

**Effective Communication** Have groups present their solutions. See below for additional strategies that students may have used. After each method is presented, ask questions such as the following:

- **Did the group carry out Brian's plan, Susanna's plan, or did they use some other strategy?** Students should explain which strategy or combination of strategies they used.
- **What did you like about the method or the way it was presented?**

Discuss the fact that Brian's plan involves finding the number of minutes remaining, whereas Susanna's plan involves finding the total number of minutes.

## 4 Assess 10

When evaluating student work, focus on whether students thought rationally about the problem and the solutions. Some questions to consider include the following:

- Did the student understand the problem?
- Did the student understand the steps in the sample solutions?
- Could the student understand and articulate what was useful and not useful about a strategy?

Keep in mind, that as with communicating in general, the ability to express mathematical ideas continues to develop and improve over time.

## Sample Solutions Strategies

### Work Backward

Start from the end. Pretend the computer finishes at exactly 1:30. The download would have taken a total of 90 minutes. Then see if all the numbers work out. That is, see if 60 minutes is greater than, less than, or equal to 75 percent of 90 minutes.

### Ask the Question a Different Way

Students do not need to know exactly when the computer will finish; they just need to know if it will finish by 1:30. So, they can ask themselves if the computer is ahead of schedule. To answer that, they can consider the following:

- The computer has been downloading for 60 minutes.
- It needs a total of 90 minutes to finish.
- What does the 75 percent represent?

# Cumulative Review

## Assign Pages 306–307

Use this Cumulative Review as a review of concepts and skills that students have previously learned.

Here are different ways you can assign these problems to your students as they work through the chapter:

- For each lesson in the chapter, assign a set of Cumulative Review problems to be completed as practice or for homework.
  - Lesson 7.1—Problems 1–6
  - Lesson 7.2—Problems 7–14
  - Lesson 7.3—Problems 15–19
  - Lesson 7.4—Problems 20–23
- At any point during the chapter, assign part or all of the Cumulative Review problems to be completed as practice or for homework.

### Cumulative Review

**Problems 1–6** review addition and subtraction, Lessons 2.3 and 2.5.

**Problems 7–14** review multiplication and division, Lessons 3.10–3.11.

**Problems 15–19** review multidigit multiplication, Lessons 5.8–5.9.

**Problems 20–23** review perimeter and area, Lesson 6.1; and multiplication and estimating, Lessons 5.6 and 6.2.

### Monitoring Student Progress

**If . . .** students miss more than one problem in a section, **Then . . .** refer to the indicated lesson for remediation suggestions.

Student Page

## Cumulative Review

**Addition and Subtraction** Lessons 2.3 and 2.5

**Add** or subtract to find $n$.

1. $12 + 16 = n$
   a. $n = 28$
   b. $n = 27$
   c. $n = 24$
2. $40 - 18 = n$
   a. $n = 38$
   b. $n = 58$
   c. $n = 22$
3. $354 + 452 = n$
   a. $n = 806$
   b. $n = 7{,}106$
   c. $n = 860$
4. $7{,}000 - 654 = n$
   a. $n = 7{,}654$
   b. $n = 6{,}346$
   c. $n = 6{,}246$
5. $n + 483 = 768$
   a. $n = 285$
   b. $n = 1{,}251$
   c. $n = 325$
6. $6{,}000 - n = 5{,}676$
   a. $n = 1{,}676$
   b. $n = 324$
   c. $n = 224$

**Multiplication and Division** Lessons 3.10–3.11

**Multiply** or divide.

7. $8 \times 7 =$ ■
   a. 49
   b. 65
   c. 56
8. $36 \div 6 =$ ■
   a. 8
   b. 6
   c. 9
9. $3 \times 7 =$ ■
   a. 2 R1
   b. 21
   c. 12
10. $81 \div 9 =$ ■
    a. 9
    b. 8
    c. 8R7
11. $9 \times 4 =$ ■
    a. 36
    b. 32
    c. 63
12. $24 \div 6 =$ ■
    a. 3
    b. 5
    c. 4
13. $56 \div 8 =$ ■
    a. 8
    b. 7
    c. 7 R1
14. $8 \times 0 =$ ■
    a. 0
    b. 1
    c. 8



eTextbook This lesson is available in the *eTextbook*.

Student Page

**Multidigit Multiplication** Lesson 5.8–5.9

**Multiply.**

15. $75 \times 6 =$ ■ 450
16. $200 \times 9 =$ ■ 1,800
17. $6 \times 264 =$ ■ 1,584
18. $349 \times 5 =$ ■ 1,745
19. Aaron went fishing with his father. They fished for 4 hours. Each hour they fished, Aaron caught 5 fish. His father caught 18 fish in all. Who caught more fish? Explain your answer. Aaron caught more; he caught 20 fish.

**Perimeter and Area** Lesson 6.1

**Decide** if the following calculations are correct.

20. 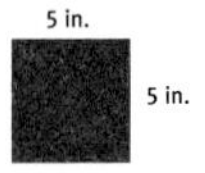

Area = 25 square inches
Perimeter = 20 inches
a. yes b. no

21. 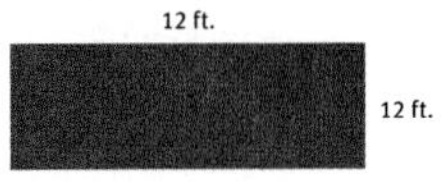

Area = 30 square feet
Perimeter = 36 feet
a. yes b. no

**Multiplication and Estimating** Lessons 5.6 and 6.2

**Solve** the following multiplication problems. Give both an approximation and an exact answer.

22. $36 \times 12 =$ ■ 360; 432
23. $82 \times 70 =$ ■ 5,600; 5,740

Approximations may vary, but should be reasonable.

## Mid-Test

# Individual Oral Assessment

## Purpose of the Test

The Individual Oral Assessment is designed to measure students' growing knowledge of chapter concepts. It is administered to each student individually, and it requires oral responses from each student. The test takes about five minutes to complete.

See ***Assessment*** for detailed instructions for administering and interpreting the test, and record students' answers on the Student Assessment Recording Sheet.

Name Date
Individual Oral Assessment

Assessment Page T33

### Directions

Read each question to the student, and record his or her oral response. If the student answers correctly, go to the next question. Stop when the student misses two questions at the same level. Students may use paper and pencil to solve the starred questions.

## Questions

### Level 1: Prerequisite

**1.** What is 50 ÷ 10? 5

**2.** What is 30 ÷ 10? 3

**3.** What is $\frac{1}{2}$ of 40? 20

**4.** What is $\frac{1}{2}$ of 16? 8

### Level 2: Basic

**5.** Which is longer—$\frac{1}{2}$ of a string or $\frac{3}{4}$ of the same string? $\frac{3}{4}$ of the string

**6.** What fraction is the same as 50%? $\frac{1}{2}$ or $\frac{50}{100}$

**7.** What is 25% of 28? 7

**8.** What is $\frac{1}{2}$ of 24? 12

### Level 3: At Level

**9.** What fraction is the same as 25%? $\frac{1}{4}$ or $\frac{25}{100}$

**10.** What percent is the same as $\frac{1}{8}$? $12\frac{1}{2}\%$

**11.** What is 75% of 32? 24

**12.** What is $12\frac{1}{2}\%$ of 16? 2

### Level 4: Challenge Application

**13.** Suppose a string is 48 centimeters long. How many centimeters long is one-fourth of the string? 12

***14.** Which is greater—50% of 14 or 25% of 32? 25% of 32

***15.** Which is greater—$\frac{1}{4}$ of 20 or 50% of 12? 50% of 12

***16.** Which is greater—25% of 40 or $12\frac{1}{2}\%$ of 64? 25% of 40

### Level 5: Content Beyond Mid-Chapter

**17.** Is 0.35 closer to 0 or closer to 1? closer to 0

**18.** What is the difference between 2.54 and 2.32? 0.22

**19.** What is $\frac{1}{10}$ of 20? 2

**20.** What is 40% of 80? 32

## Objectives
- To introduce two-place decimals in the context of time and stopwatches
- To help show how decimals, percentages, and fractions are related
- To review writing two-place decimals
- To review writing mixed numbers

## NCTM Standards
**Number and Operations**
Discover equivalence between decimals, fractions, and percentages

**Problem Solving**
Find solutions to problems

**Communication**
Communicate mathematical situations

## Materials
- ***Response Wheels**
- *Stopwatches showing hundredths of a second
- **Time Game Mat**

## Technology
**e Presentation** Lesson 7.5
**e Games** Order Card Game
**e MathTools** Stopwatch

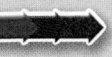

## Test Prep
**Cumulative Review**
- Mental Math reviews finding solutions for 50% of whole numbers (Lesson 7.2).
- Problems 6 and 8 review elapsed time.

**Extended Response**
Problem 8

*Manipulative Kit Item

# Decimals and Stopwatches

**Context of the Lesson** In this lesson students are introduced to two-place decimals in the context of percentages and fractions. Students have worked with decimals previously in Grades 1–3 of ***Real Math,*** and decimals will be covered in greater detail in Chapter 9 of Grade 4. This is the first of two lessons in which students use stopwatches, and the emphasis of this lesson is on understanding the numbers displayed on the stopwatch and recording them properly.

See page 292B for Math Background for teachers for this lesson.

## Planning for Learning • DIFFERENTIATE INSTRUCTION

### INTERVENTION
**If . . .** students lack the prerequisite skill of meaning of fractions and decimals,

**Then . . .** teach ***Intervention*** Lesson 7.A.

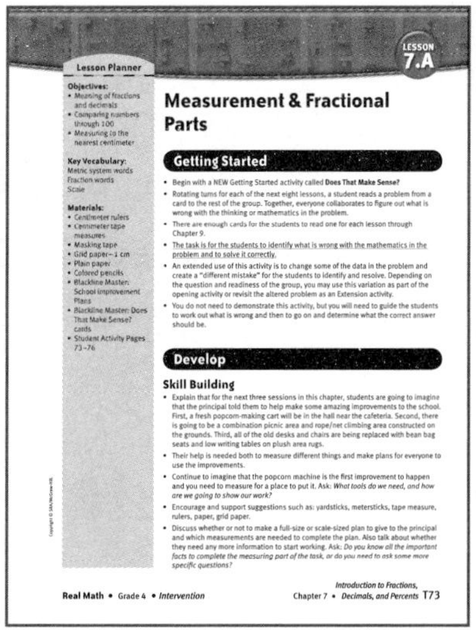


Intervention Lesson 7.A

### ENGLISH LEARNER
**Preview**

**If . . .** students need language support,

**Then . . .** use Lesson 7.5 in ***English Learner Support Guide*** to preview lesson concepts and vocabulary.

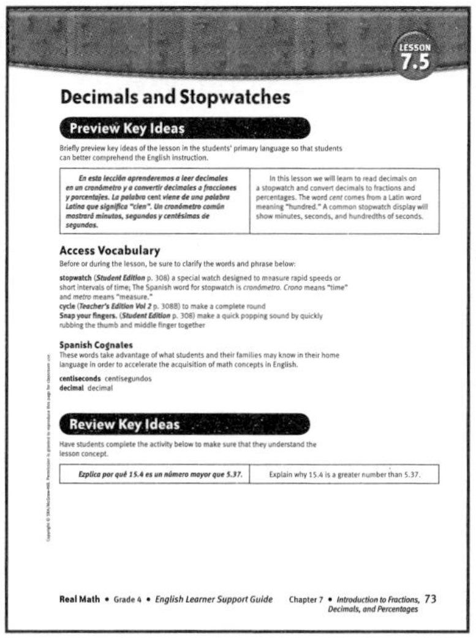


English Learner Lesson 7.5

### ENRICH
**If . . .** students are proficient in the lesson concepts,

**Then . . .** encourage them to create their own timing challenges.

### PRACTICE
**If . . .** students would benefit from additional practice,

**Then . . .** extend Skill Building by working through additional exercises together.

### RETEACH
**If . . .** students have difficulty understanding how to read a stopwatch,

**Then . . .** extend Guided Discussion before assigning the student pages.

**Vocabulary**
**centi- \sen´ ti\ *prefix.*** a hundredth of a part
**centisecond \sen´ ti sek´ ənd\ *n.*** a hundredth of a second

**Access Vocabulary**
**stopwatch** a special watch designed to measure rapid speeds or short intervals of time

**Spanish Cognates**
**centiseconds** centisegundos

## Mental Math

5

Review RESPONSE WHEEL Provide students with exercises, such as the following, that involve the halving procedure:

**a.** 50% of 20 10
**b.** 50% of 10 5
**c.** 50% of 60 30
**d.** 50% of 160 80
**e.** 50% of 88 44
**f.** 50% of 180 90
**g.** 50% of 60 30
**h.** 50% of 32 16

## 1 Develop

35

**Tell Students In Today's Lesson They Will**
learn to read decimals on a stopwatch and convert decimals to fractions and percentages.

Whole Group

### Guided Discussion e MathTools UNDERSTANDING

1. Prior to starting the discussion, distribute the stopwatches to the class, one stopwatch per pair of students. They might also use ***eMathTools: Stopwatch.*** Begin the lesson by directing the students to examine their stopwatches. The zeros in the two last columns are hundredths of seconds. Ask students to take note of these numbers in the last two columns, and ask them what they think these small numerals might mean.

   Although these "smaller numerals" are hundredths of a second (or *centiseconds*), typically students will assert that they are "milliseconds," or thousandths of a second. Write the word *millisecond* on the board for later reference.

   Have students experiment with their watches by starting and stopping them. Ask them to consider how they could explain these units in terms of percentages. Students might suggest they are like percentages of seconds.

2. Remind students that our number system is based on tens and tenths and that it follows similar patterns on both sides of the ones place. The pattern to the left of the ones place for numbers *larger* than 1—tens, hundreds, thousands—is repeated on the right of the decimal point for numbers *smaller* than 1—tenths, hundredths, thousandths.

   If the students suggest that centiseconds are milliseconds, question them about the meaning of the prefix *milli-*. *Milli-* also comes from Latin and means "thousand" (a *mile* originally meant "1,000 double paces by Roman soldiers").

   Ask students questions such as the following:

   - **What do we call units that are one-hundredth of a meter?** centimeters
   - **If thousandths of a second are called milliseconds, what would hundredths be called?** Centisecond is a term that is rarely used, but accurately describes a hundredth of a second.

### Skill Building ENGAGING

Small Group

1. Have students work on timing challenges such as counting by 10, writing the alphabet as fast as possible, drawing 15 rectangles, or standing up and sitting down 25 times.
   - Students should work in pairs, with one partner called Student A and the other called Student B. Student A will do the activity first with Student B working the stopwatch. Student A will have two tries for the timed challenge, and should record both times on a score sheet (have students make their own score sheets).
   - As Student A records his or her first time, Student B needs to reset the stopwatch. Once Student A has completed his or her two attempts, the students will switch roles and repeat the challenge. This procedure is followed for the remaining challenges.
   - Do not give students specific instruction on how to write their times. Rather, encourage students to find a method to record their times so others can understand. The conventional way to write these quantities will be shown at the end of the exercise.
2. Once students have done a few activities and have a sense of the time involved, have them make an estimate first and record it before trying the activity. Then students should record their actual time next to their estimate for comparison.

   After the activity, ask for volunteers to write their times on the board. Notice how students represent these times. Some will mimic what is shown on the LCD screen, while others may record their times as seconds and a fraction over 100. They should also understand that a decimal number such as 5.35 should be read as "five and thirty-five hundredths."

## 2 Assign Student Pages

10

**Pages 308–309** UNDERSTANDING
Have students work on pages 308 and 309 independently. If students finish early you may wish to have them play the **Time Game Mat.**

#### Monitoring Student Progress

| If . . . | Then . . . |
|---|---|
| **If . . .** students are confused about how to record their activity times, | **Then . . .** review with them that the times are in seconds and hundredths of seconds, and show them how to write these numbers in standard decimal form. |

### As Students Finish

e **Games** **Order Game**

e **MathTools** ***Stopwatch***

Student Page

## LESSON 7.5 Decimals and Stopwatches

### Key Ideas

**A centisecond, which is equal to $\frac{1}{100}$ of a second, is a fractional part of a whole second.**

The word *cent* comes from the Latin word meaning "hundred." It is used in situations involving 100 of something.

- 1 cent = 1 penny = $\frac{1}{100}$ of a dollar
- 1 century = 100 years
- percent = "out of one hundred" or *x* percent of = $\frac{x}{100}$
- centimeter = $\frac{1}{100}$ of a meter or $\frac{1}{100}$ m

A common stopwatch display will show minutes, seconds, and hundredths of seconds. Some people mistakenly believe these parts of a second shown on a stopwatch are called *milliseconds* (which are thousandths, or $\frac{1}{1{,}000}$, of a second). However, as you might guess from what we learned about the word *cent* above, $\frac{1}{100}$ of a second is called a centisecond.

In a fourth-grade class, students timed one another doing several different challenges. The table below shows the fastest times for Jeanie.

**Write** the missing information.

| | Activity | Fastest Time | Seconds | Centiseconds |
|---|---|---|---|---|
| | Write the numbers from 1–100 by 10s. | 6.89 | 6 | 89 |
| 1 | Snap your fingers or tap your foot 25 times. | 5.76 | 5 | 76 |
| 2 | Draw 15 rectangles. | 12.73 | 12 | 73 |
| 3 | Write the alphabet. | 11.34 | 11 | 34 |



e Textbook This lesson is available in the *eTextbook*.

Student Page

### Key Ideas

Stopwatch times are generally written as decimals or as fractions over 100. Some of the fractions contain whole numbers, such as $3\frac{1}{2}$. Jeanie's fastest time on the first activity can be shown as a decimal—6.89 seconds—or a whole number and a fraction —$6\frac{89}{100}$ seconds.

**Complete** the following.

4 Using the decimal form, write Jeanie's fastest time for snapping her fingers and for drawing rectangles. 5.76 and 12.73

5 Using a mixed number (with 100 as the denominator of the fraction), show Jeanie's fastest time for drawing rectangles and writing the alphabet. $12\frac{73}{100}$ and $11\frac{34}{100}$

6 Manolita and Ferdie timed how fast they could say the alphabet. Manolita's time was 4 and 35 hundreths seconds on the stopwatch. It took Ferdie $4\frac{1}{2}$ seconds.

a. Write both times in seconds. 4.35 and 4.50

b. Who was faster? Manolita

c. Write both of the girls' times as a whole number and a fraction. $4\frac{35}{100}$ and $4\frac{50}{100}$ (or $4\frac{1}{2}$)

7 List three times between 0.65 seconds and 0.75 seconds. Show each of your choices as a decimal and as a fraction with a denominator of 100.

8 **Extended Response** It took Jalen 0.25 seconds to snap his fingers twice. Julie said she was faster because it took her only $\frac{1}{4}$ of a second to snap her fingers twice. Who was faster? Explain using decimals, fractions, and percents.

7 Anything within the range of 0.65–0.75 seconds is acceptable. Possible answers include 0.66, $\frac{66}{100}$, 0.72, or $\frac{72}{100}$.

8 They had the same time; 0.25 seconds = $\frac{1}{4}$ of a second = 25% of a second.

**Write** which is the shorter time. Show your answers using the $<$, $>$, or $=$ symbol.

9 $\frac{70}{100}$ seconds or 0.75 seconds $\frac{70}{100}$ seconds; $0.70 < 0.75$

10 1.25 seconds or $1\frac{1}{8}$ seconds $1\frac{1}{8}$ seconds; $1.125 < 1.25$

11 0.82 seconds or $\frac{82}{100}$ seconds times are equal; $0.82 = \frac{82}{100}$



## 3 Reflect

10

## Guided Discussion REASONING

Whole Group

Pick one of the activities and have students volunteer their slowest time. Write several of these on the board. Do the same with students' best times and either write a sample of these on the board or invite the students to write them by themselves. With the different times as comparisons, write two decimals on the board—15.4 and 15.37—and ask students which time is faster. If some students say 15.4, ask them why (students may say 4 is smaller than 37) and review what the decimal notation means. Encourage students to write the decimals they will compare to the same number of places if that is how much precision there was. If the stopwatch says 15.40, record the 0.

### Extended Response

**Problem 8** Students should discover the times are equal and should then list the equivalent fractions, decimals, and percentages for $\frac{1}{4}$.

### Applications APPLYING

Ask students to think about measurement of time.

- **A runner runs 49.25 seconds in the 400-yard dash. A second runner runs a time of 49.56. How do we know the first runner was faster?** His time is faster because the number is less than the other runner.
- **What if a runner ran a time of $49\frac{1}{2}$ seconds and her opponent ran a time of $49\frac{1}{4}$ seconds?** The runner who ran $49\frac{1}{4}$ seconds was faster because $\frac{1}{4}$ of a second is less than $\frac{1}{2}$.

**Cumulative Review:** For review of multiplication and division, assign Problems 1–15 on student page 319.

**Family Involvement:** Assign the ***Practice, Reteach,*** or ***Enrichment*** activities depending on the needs of your students.

**Concept/Question Board:** Encourage students to continue to post questions, answers, and examples on the Concept/Question Board.

**Math Puzzler:** Tino has a digital clock in his room. One night he could not sleep. As he tossed and turned, he would see the image of his clock in a mirror. Twice between 9:00 P.M. and midnight, the numbers in the mirror looked just the same as the digits on the clock. At what times did this happen? 10:01 P.M., 11:11 P.M.

# 4 Assess and Differentiate

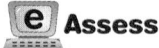

e Assess Use ***eAssess*** to record and analyze evidence of student understanding.

## A Gather Evidence

Use the Daily Class Assessment Records in ***Assessment*** or ***eAssess*** to record daily observations.

### Informal Assessment

**✓Skill Building**

Did the student ENGAGING

- ❑ pay attention to others' contributions?
- ❑ contribute information and ideas?
- ❑ improve on a strategy?
- ❑ reflect on and check the accuracy of his or her work?

### Portfolio Assessment

**✓Extended Response**

Did the student REASONING

- ❑ provide a clear explanation?
- ❑ communicate reasons and strategies?
- ❑ choose appropriate strategies?
- ❑ argue logically?

## B Summarize Findings

Analyze and summarize assessment data for each student. Determine which Assessment Follow-Up is appropriate for each student. Use the Student Assessment Record in ***Assessment*** or ***eAssess*** to update assessment records.

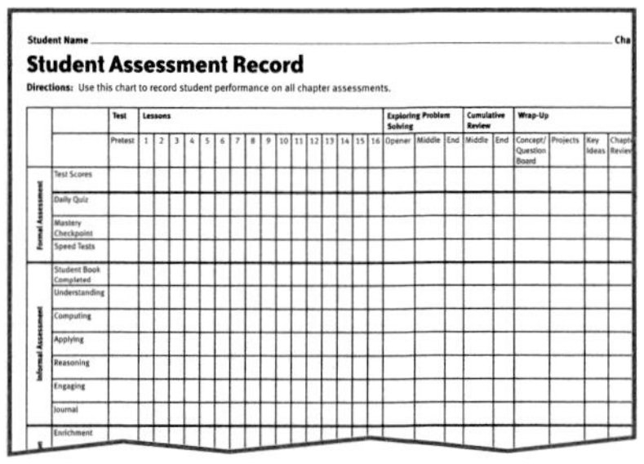
Student Assessment Record

Assessment Page T41

## C Assessment Follow-Up • DIFFERENTIATE INSTRUCTION

Based on your observations, use these teaching strategies for assessment follow-up.

### INTERVENTION

Review student performance on ***Intervention*** Lesson 7.A to see if students have mastered prerequisite skills for this lesson.

### ENGLISH LEARNERS

**Review**

Use Lesson 7.5 in ***English Learner Support Guide*** to review lesson concepts and vocabulary.

### ENRICH

**If . . .** students are proficient in the lesson concepts,

**Then . . .** encourage them to work on the chapter projects or ***Enrichment*** Lesson 7.5.

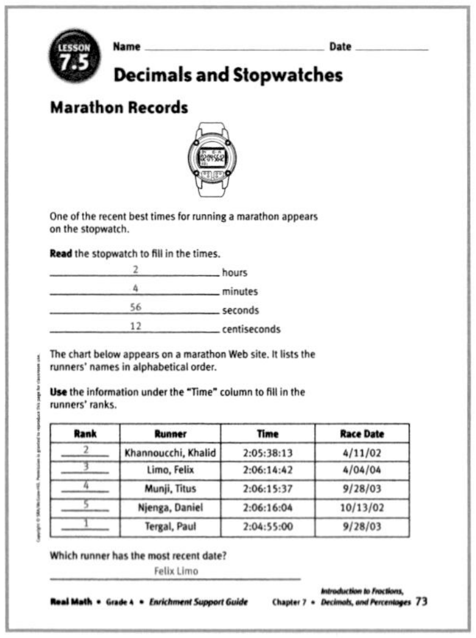
LESSON 7.5 Name ________ Date ________

Decimals and Stopwatches

Marathon Records

One of the recent best times for running a marathon appears on the stopwatch.

**Read** the stopwatch to fill in the times.

2 hours
4 minutes
56 seconds
12 centiseconds

The chart below appears on a marathon Web site. It lists the runners' names in alphabetical order.

**Use** the information under the "Time" column to fill in the runners' ranks.

| Rank | Runner | Time | Race Date |
|---|---|---|---|
| 2 | Khannoucchi, Khalid | 2:05:38:13 | 4/11/02 |
| 3 | Limo, Felix | 2:06:14:42 | 4/04/04 |
| 4 | Munji, Titus | 2:06:15:37 | 9/28/03 |
| 5 | Njenga, Daniel | 2:06:16:04 | 10/13/02 |
| 1 | Tergal, Paul | 2:04:55:00 | 9/28/03 |

Which runner has the most recent date? Felix Limo

Real Math • Grade 4 • *Enrichment Support Guide* Chapter 7 • *Introduction to Fractions, Decimals, and Percentages* 73

Enrichment Lesson 7.5

### PRACTICE

**If . . .** students would benefit from additional practice,

**Then . . .** assign ***Practice*** Lesson 7.5.

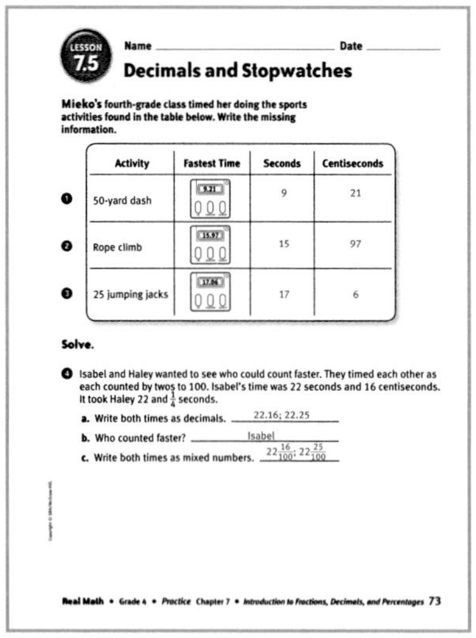
LESSON 7.5 Name ________ Date ________

Decimals and Stopwatches

**Mieko's fourth-grade class timed her doing the sports activities found in the table below. Write the missing information.**

| | Activity | Fastest Time | Seconds | Centiseconds |
|---|---|---|---|---|
| 1 | 50-yard dash | 9.21 | 9 | 21 |
| 2 | Rope climb | 15.97 | 15 | 97 |
| 3 | 25 jumping jacks | 17.06 | 17 | 6 |

**Solve.**

4. Isabel and Haley wanted to see who could count faster. They timed each other as each counted by twos to 100. Isabel's time was 22 seconds and 16 centiseconds. It took Haley 22 and $\frac{1}{4}$ seconds.
   a. Write both times as decimals. 22.16; 22.25
   b. Who counted faster? Isabel
   c. Write both times as mixed numbers. $22\frac{16}{100}$; $22\frac{25}{100}$

Real Math • Grade 4 • *Practice* Chapter 7 • *Introduction to Fractions, Decimals, and Percentages* 73

Practice Lesson 7.5

### RETEACH

**If . . .** students are having difficulty with decimals,

**Then . . .** have them practice place value with money using ***Reteach*** Lesson 7.5.

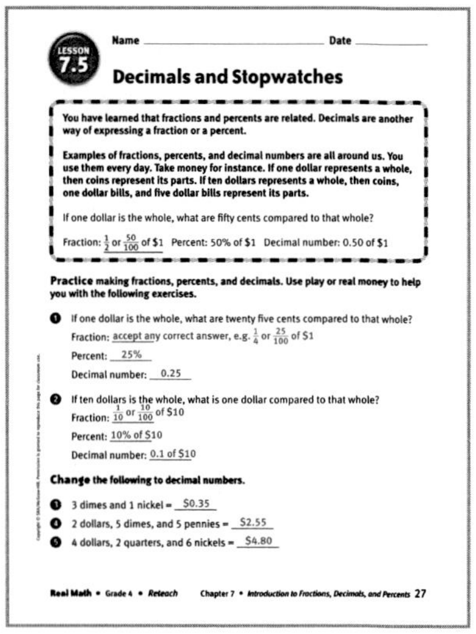
LESSON 7.5 Name ________ Date ________

Decimals and Stopwatches

**You have learned that fractions and percents are related. Decimals are another way of expressing a fraction or a percent.**

**Examples of fractions, percents, and decimal numbers are all around us. You use them every day. Take money for instance. If one dollar represents a whole, then coins represent its parts. If ten dollars represents a whole, then coins, one dollar bills, and five dollar bills represent its parts.**

If one dollar is the whole, what are fifty cents compared to that whole?

Fraction: $\frac{1}{2}$ or $\frac{50}{100}$ of $1 Percent: 50% of $1 Decimal number: 0.50 of $1

**Practice making fractions, percents, and decimals. Use play or real money to help you with the following exercises.**

1. If one dollar is the whole, what are twenty five cents compared to that whole?
   Fraction: accept any correct answer, e.g. $\frac{1}{4}$ or $\frac{25}{100}$ of $1
   Percent: 25%
   Decimal number: 0.25
2. If ten dollars is the whole, what is one dollar compared to that whole?
   Fraction: $\frac{1}{10}$ or $\frac{10}{100}$ of $10
   Percent: 10% of $10
   Decimal number: 0.1 of $10

**Change the following to decimal numbers.**

3. 3 dimes and 1 nickel = $0.35
4. 2 dollars, 5 dimes, and 5 pennies = $2.55
5. 4 dollars, 2 quarters, and 6 nickels = $4.80

Real Math • Grade 4 • *Reteach* Chapter 7 • *Introduction to Fractions, Decimals, and Percents* 27

Reteach Lesson 7.5

## Lesson Planner

**OBJECTIVES**
- To provide an opportunity to work with informal addition and subtraction of decimals
- To extend learning of decimals to include comparing and ordering

**NCTM STANDARDS**

**Number and Operations**
Add and subtract decimals

**Measurement**
Measure different events and equivalents in seconds and hundredths of seconds

**Problem Solving**
Create solutions for problems involving time

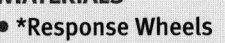

**MATERIALS**
- *Response Wheels
- *Stopwatches (1 per pair of students)
- *Equivalencies Card Deck
- Overhead projector

**TECHNOLOGY**
**Presentation** Lesson 7.6
**MathTools** Stopwatch

**TEST PREP**

**Cumulative Review**
- Mental Math reviews computing fractions and percentages of whole numbers (Lesson 7.2).
- Problems 3–10 review addition and subtraction (Lesson 2.3).

**Multistep Problems**
Problems 1–2

### Looking Ahead
Lesson 7.7 uses an overhead projector copy of *Practice* page 144, which has a number line segment from 0–1 calibrated in hundredths.

*Manipulative Kit Item

# Adding and Subtracting Decimal Numbers

**Context of the Lesson** This is the sixth in a series of percent measurement lessons and the second lesson in which students use stopwatches to work with two-place decimals. In this second stopwatch lesson, the students work on exercises where they are required to perform simple addition and subtraction with two-place decimals.
See page 292B for Math Background for teachers for this lesson.

## Planning for Learning • DIFFERENTIATE INSTRUCTION

### INTERVENTION
**If . . .** students lack the prerequisite skill of understanding fractions and decimal,
**Then . . .** teach ***Intervention*** Lesson 7.A.

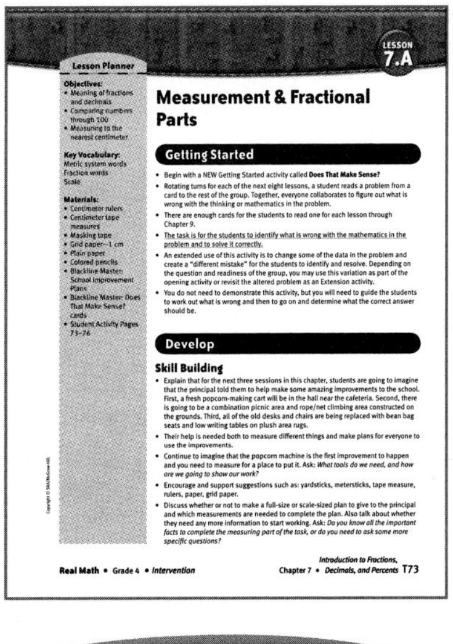
LESSON 7.A
Measurement & Fractional Parts
Getting Started
Develop
Skill Building

Intervention Lesson 7.A

### ENGLISH LEARNER
Preview
**If . . .** students need language support,
**Then . . .** use Lesson 7.6 in ***English Learner Support Guide*** to preview lesson concepts and vocabulary.

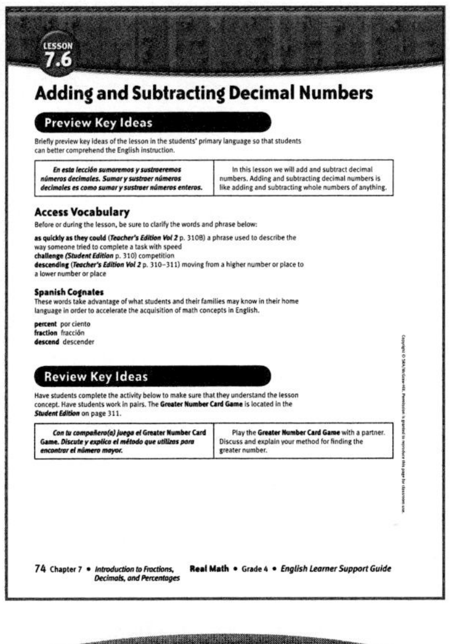
LESSON 7.6
Adding and Subtracting Decimal Numbers
Preview Key Ideas
Access Vocabulary
Spanish Cognates
Review Key Ideas

English Language Lesson 7.6

### ENRICH
**If . . .** students are proficient in the lesson concepts,
**Then . . .** encourage them to create new game strategies.

### PRACTICE
**If . . .** students would benefit from additional practice,
**Then . . .** extend the time allotted for playing the **Greater Number Card Game.**

### RETEACH
**If . . .** students have difficulty lining up the addition or subtraction problems,
**Then . . .** have them review the place value chart for decimals.

**Access Vocabulary**
**as fast as he could** phrase used to describe the way someone tried to complete a task with speed

**Spanish Cognates**
**percent** porciento

# Teaching Lesson 7.6

## Mental Math 5

Review RESPONSE WHEEL Provide students with exercises, such as the following, that involve percentages, fractions, and decimal equivalencies:

**a.** 50% of 80 40
**b.** 25% of 80 20
**c.** 75% of 80 60
**d.** $\frac{1}{2}$ of 22 11
**e.** $\frac{1}{4}$ of 44 11
**f.** $\frac{1}{8}$ of 88 11
**g.** 50% of 1 as a decimal 0.50
**h.** 75% of 1 as a decimal 0.75
**i.** $\frac{1}{2}$ of 1 as a decimal 0.50
**j.** $\frac{3}{4}$ of 1 as a decimal 0.75

## 1 Develop 30

**Tell Students In Today's Lesson They Will**
add and subtract decimal numbers.

### Skill Building ENGAGING Whole Group

To review some of the ideas from Lesson 7.5, students will be attempting the Stop-Start Challenge, which requires them to start and stop a stopwatch as quickly as possible. Students will probably get times that are less than 1 second.

Let students know they each have three tries and should record each of their three times. Students with quick reflexes will be able to accomplish this challenge with times such as 0.09 seconds, while students with slower reflexes might take between 0.18 and 0.25 seconds.

Before students start, model how to start and stop the stopwatch and read the time. Ask a volunteer to write your time on the board. If the volunteer does not place a 0 in front of the decimal point, write the time with the zero included on the board next to it. Let the students discuss why we put a zero in front of the decimal point. After they have had a chance to discuss, tell students that the zero in front of the decimal point is there simply to call attention to the decimal point. So, although it is useful, it is not incorrect if it is omitted.

When it is clear that all of the students can record their times, let them try the Stop-Start Challenge. Ask the students to write their times on scrap paper and collect the papers for use in the Reflect section of the discussion.

### Guided Discussion UNDERSTANDING Whole Group

1. Present the class with a problem to give students a chance to think about the equivalency of centiseconds and hundredths of a second. Make sure to write the different forms (for example, 0.11, $\frac{11}{100}$, and so on) on the board, because they will sound identical if only read orally.

   An example problem might be: *Joan and her friends Luke, Antonio, and Rochelle tried to stop the stopwatch as quickly as they could. When they had finished, Joan and all of her friends claimed they had the fastest time. Joan reported her time as 11 centiseconds, Luke said his time was 0.11 of a second, Antonio finished the challenge in 11 hundredths of a second, while Rochelle said that it only took her 11 percent of a second to stop the watch. Can you help Joan and her friends? How would you explain who won?* They all had the same time; they used different ways to describe the same time.

2. Tell the students that they will now continue to think about math with stopwatches. On an overhead projector, show a stopwatch display such as 25.65 seconds. Tell students that this was how long it took Jason to sign his name 10 times. Ask for a volunteer to come to the board and write Jason's time as both a decimal and a number that includes a fraction with a denominator of 100 (25.65 and $25\frac{65}{100}$). Check to see if there is agreement.
   - Now present another stopwatch display with the time 28.85 seconds (you can say this is the time of another fictional child). Ask the students who was faster. Jason
   - Ask students if they could figure out the difference between the two times. Tell the students to confer with each other and to write down the answer. 3.20 seconds or $3\frac{20}{100}$ seconds
   - Invite another student to the board to write the answer and explain how he or she figured it out. Accept all methods that lead to the correct answer. For example, subtracting the whole number of seconds first and then the number of centiseconds, then converting the answer to the correct form.
3. Now repeat this process with an addition story. Use a story of students getting timed as they complete several different tasks. While you tell the story, write the times (in decimal form) across the board with no addition sign. Have students give their answers in whole centiseconds and in seconds using decimals.

### Skill and Strategy Building ENGAGING Whole Group

Demonstrate the **Greater Number Card Game** on student page 311 by playing with a student in the front of the class. Students will use the Equivalencies Card Deck.

A second version of the game emphasizes subtracting the smaller amount from the larger amount.

## 2 Assign Student Pages 20

**Pages 310–311** APPLYING
Have students complete page 310 independently.

**As Students Finish**

Game **Greater Number Card Game**

Student Page

LESSON 7.6 **Adding and Subtracting Decimal Numbers**

## Key Ideas

**Adding and subtracting centiseconds or hundredths of a second is like adding and subtracting whole numbers of anything.**

Santiago timed how fast he could count to 100 by 5s. Two of his times, shown to the right, fall between 4 and 5 seconds. We know from working with stopwatches that the first time is faster. But how much faster is the first time than the second?

0:00' 4" 34

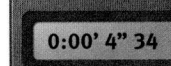

0:00' 4" 64

The difference is in the number of centiseconds. If we subtract 34 centiseconds from 64 centiseconds, we get 30 centiseconds. $64 - 34 = 30$

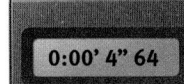

We know from Lesson 7.5 that 30 centiseconds can be shown as $\frac{30}{100}$ of a second, or 0.30 seconds. So, two ways to write the difference between the times would be

- $4\frac{64}{100} - 4\frac{34}{100} = \frac{30}{100}$
- $4.64 - 4.34 = 0.30$

**Solve** the following problems.

1. Multistep When Samantha tried the Write the Alphabet Challenge, she did it in 11.35 seconds. Her partner, Jodie, did it in 11.87 seconds. What is the difference between their times? Write your answer as both a fraction with a denominator of 100 and as a decimal. $\frac{52}{100}$ and 0.52
2. Multistep Najeem tried starting and stopping the stopwatch as fast as he could. His three times were 0.15 seconds, 0.17 seconds, and 0.09 seconds.
   a. Which was his fastest time? 0.09 seconds
   b. Which was his slowest time? 0.17 seconds
   c. What was the difference between his slowest and fastest times? 0.08 seconds

How large is the difference between

3. 0.33 and 0.27? 0.06
4. 6.77 and 6.57? 0.20
5. 4.84 and 4.20? 0.64
6. 0.30 and 0.09? 0.21
7. 3.88 and 3.07? 0.81
8. 5.96 and 5.48? 0.48
9. 5.95 and 5.32? 0.63
10. 7.76 and 7.50? 0.26

310

eTextbook This lesson is available in the ***eTextbook***.

Student Page

## Game

**Comparing and Ordering and Strategies Practice**

### The Greater Number Card Game

**Players:** Two

**Materials:** ***Equivalencies Card Deck***

**Object:** To win all of the cards

**Math Focus:** Comparing and ordering fractions, percentages, and decimals of the same whole

**HOW TO PLAY**

1. Two players sit opposite each other. One player shuffles the cards and deals them one at a time, facedown, until each player has half of the deck. Players keep their pile of cards facedown during play.
2. On the count of three, the players turn over their top cards. Players look at the cards. If a fraction or percent appears, they find that fraction or percent of 1. Then they decide which player has the greater number. The player with the greater number keeps both cards; these two cards are placed facedown at the bottom of that player's pile of cards.
3. In the event that the two cards result in equal numbers (for example, 25% of 1 and $\frac{1}{4}$ of 1), each player pulls three more cards off the top of his or her deck and lays them facedown below the equivalent cards. Then each player's fourth card is turned over. The player whose fourth card results in a greater number wins all of the cards in that round of play. Once a player has won the round, all cards that had not been turned faceup are revealed. (In the unlikely event that the fourth cards result in equal numbers, the above process is repeated until there is a winner).
4. The game continues in the above manner until a single player has won all the cards.

Chapter 7 • Lesson 6 311

## 3 Reflect

5

## Guided Discussion UNDERSTANDING

Whole Group

- Discuss student times from the Stop-Start Challenge. Ask students to give their slowest times. Write several of these on the board. Do the same with students' fastest times and either write a sample of these on the board or invite the students to write them. If one student writes 0.09 as his or her time, write that on the board and ask students how they would write this time as a fraction. $\frac{9}{100}$
- Have students find the difference between the slowest time and the fastest time. Ask them to give you the time in decimal seconds and in whole centiseconds.

Review **Cumulative Review:** For review of common multiples and common factors, assign Problems 16–21 on student page 319.

**Family Involvement:** Assign the ***Practice, Reteach,*** or ***Enrichment*** activities depending on the needs of your students.

**Concept/Question Board:** Encourage students to continue to post questions, answers, and examples on the Concept/Question Board.

**Math Puzzler:** Describe the following pattern in two ways. Then find the next three numbers. 90, 81, 72, 63, 54 . . . The pattern is in descending multiples of 9; or, as the tens digit decreases by 1, the ones digit increases by 1. The next three numbers are 45, 36, and 27.

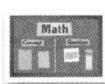

# 4 Assess and Differentiate

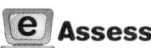

**e Assess** Use ***eAssess*** to record and analyze evidence of student understanding.

## A Gather Evidence

Use the Daily Class Assessment Records in ***Assessment*** or ***eAssess*** to record daily observations.

### Informal Assessment

**✓ Guided Discussion**

Did the student **UNDERSTANDING**

- ❑ make important observation?
- ❑ extend or generalize learning?
- ❑ provide insightful answers?
- ❑ pose insightful questions?

### Performance Assessment

**✓ Game**

Did the student **ENGAGING**

- ❑ pay attention to others' contributions?
- ❑ contribute information and ideas?
- ❑ improve on a strategy?
- ❑ reflect on and check the accuracy of his or her work?

## B Summarize Findings

Analyze and summarize assessment data for each student. Determine which Assessment Follow-Up is appropriate for each student. Use the Student Assessment Record in ***Assessment*** or ***eAssess*** to update assessment records.

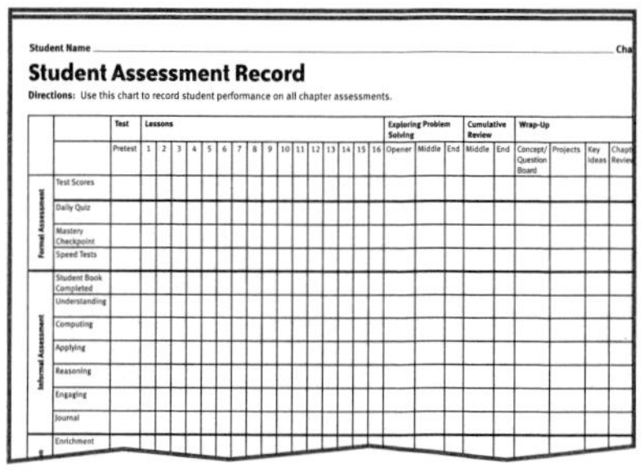
Student Name
Student Assessment Record
Directions: Use this chart to record student performance on all chapter assessments.

**Assessment Page T41**

## C Assessment Follow-Up • DIFFERENTIATE INSTRUCTION

Based on your observations, use these teaching strategies for assessment follow-up.

### INTERVENTION

Review student performance on ***Intervention*** Lesson 7.A to see if students have mastered prerequisite skills for this lesson.

### ENGLISH LEARNER

**Review**

Use Lesson 7.6 in ***English Learner Support Guide*** to review lesson concepts and vocabulary.

### ENRICH

**If . . .** students are proficient in the lesson concepts,

**Then . . .** encourage them to work on the chapter projects or ***Enrichment*** Lesson 7.6.

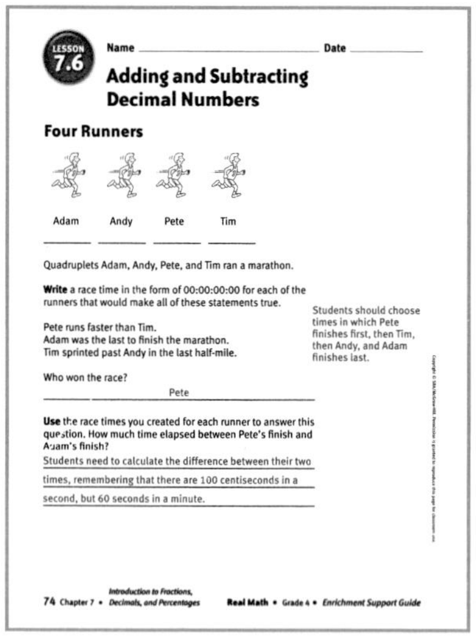
LESSON 7.6 Name ______ Date ______

Adding and Subtracting Decimal Numbers

Four Runners

Adam Andy Pete Tim

Quadruplets Adam, Andy, Pete, and Tim ran a marathon.

**Write** a race time in the form of 00:00:00:00 for each of the runners that would make all of these statements true.

Pete runs faster than Tim.
Adam was the last to finish the marathon.
Tim sprinted past Andy in the last half-mile.

Students should choose times in which Pete finishes first, then Tim, then Andy, and Adam finishes last.

Who won the race? Pete

**Use** the race times you created for each runner to answer this question. How much time elapsed between Pete's finish and Adam's finish?
Students need to calculate the difference between their two times, remembering that there are 100 centiseconds in a second, but 60 seconds in a minute.

74 Chapter 7 • *Introduction to Fractions, Decimals, and Percentages* **Real Math** • Grade 4 • *Enrichment Support Guide*

Enrichment Lesson 7.6

### PRACTICE

**If . . .** students would benefit from additional practice,

**Then . . .** assign ***Practice*** Lesson 7.6.

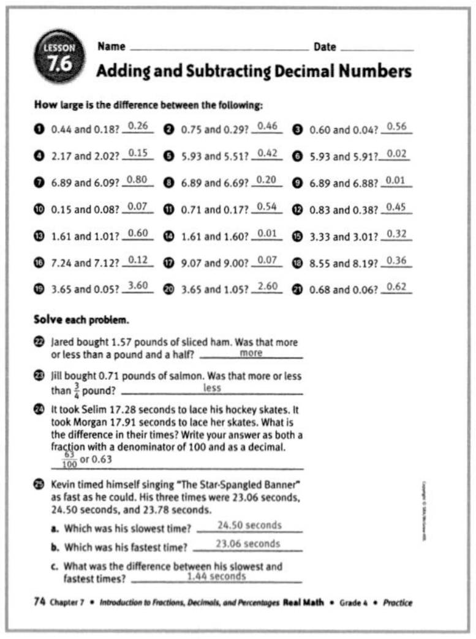
LESSON 7.6 Name ______ Date ______

Adding and Subtracting Decimal Numbers

**How large is the difference between the following:**

1. 0.44 and 0.18? 0.26
2. 0.75 and 0.29? 0.46
3. 0.60 and 0.04? 0.56
4. 2.17 and 2.02? 0.15
5. 5.93 and 5.51? 0.42
6. 5.93 and 5.91? 0.02
7. 6.89 and 6.09? 0.80
8. 6.89 and 6.69? 0.20
9. 6.89 and 6.88? 0.01
10. 0.15 and 0.08? 0.07
11. 0.71 and 0.17? 0.54
12. 0.83 and 0.38? 0.45
13. 1.61 and 1.01? 0.60
14. 1.61 and 1.60? 0.01
15. 3.33 and 3.01? 0.32
16. 7.24 and 7.12? 0.12
17. 9.07 and 9.00? 0.07
18. 8.55 and 8.19? 0.36
19. 3.65 and 0.05? 3.60
20. 3.65 and 1.05? 2.60
21. 0.68 and 0.06? 0.62

**Solve each problem.**

22. Jared bought 1.57 pounds of sliced ham. Was that more or less than a pound and a half? more
23. Jill bought 0.71 pounds of salmon. Was that more or less than $\frac{3}{4}$ pound? less
24. It took Selim 17.28 seconds to lace his hockey skates. It took Morgan 17.91 seconds to lace her skates. What is the difference in their times? Write your answer as both a fraction with a denominator of 100 and as a decimal. $\frac{63}{100}$ or 0.63
25. Kevin timed himself singing "The Star-Spangled Banner" as fast as he could. His three times were 23.06 seconds, 24.50 seconds, and 23.78 seconds.
    a. Which was his slowest time? 24.50 seconds
    b. Which was his fastest time? 23.06 seconds
    c. What was the difference between his slowest and fastest times? 1.44 seconds

74 Chapter 7 • *Introduction to Fractions, Decimals, and Percentages* **Real Math** • Grade 4 • *Practice*

Practice Lesson 7.6

### RETEACH

**If . . .** students struggle with comparing decimals,

**Then . . .** reteach the concept using ***Reteach*** Lesson 7.6.

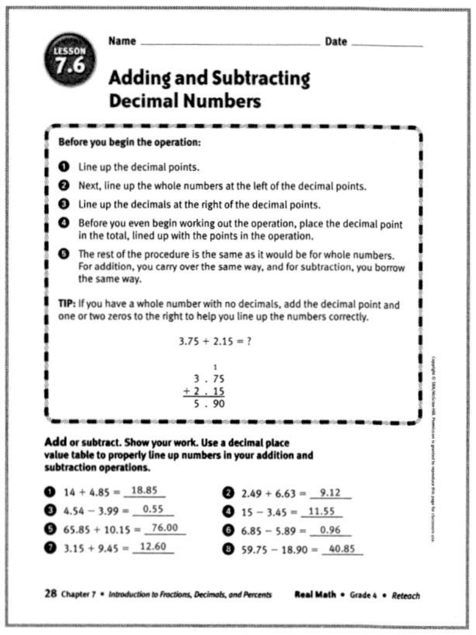
LESSON 7.6 Name ______ Date ______

Adding and Subtracting Decimal Numbers

**Before you begin the operation:**

1. Line up the decimal points.
2. Next, line up the whole numbers at the left of the decimal points.
3. Line up the decimals at the right of the decimal points.
4. Before you even begin working out the operation, place the decimal point in the total, lined up with the points in the operation.
5. The rest of the procedure is the same as it would be for whole numbers. For addition, you carry over the same way, and for subtraction, you borrow the same way.

**TIP:** If you have a whole number with no decimals, add the decimal point and one or two zeros to the right to help you line up the numbers correctly.

3.75 + 2.15 = ?

$$\begin{array}{r} 3.75 \\ +\,2.15 \\ \hline 5.90 \end{array}$$

**Add or subtract. Show your work. Use a decimal place value table to properly line up numbers in your addition and subtraction operations.**

1. 14 + 4.85 = 18.85
2. 2.49 + 6.63 = 9.12
3. 4.54 − 3.99 = 0.55
4. 15 − 3.45 = 11.55
5. 65.85 + 10.15 = 76.00
6. 6.85 − 5.89 = 0.96
7. 3.15 + 9.45 = 12.60
8. 59.75 − 18.90 = 40.85

28 Chapter 7 • *Introduction to Fractions, Decimals, and Percents* **Real Math** • Grade 4 • *Reteach*

Reteach Lesson 7.6

## Lesson Planner

**OBJECTIVES**
- To interpret decimals on a number line
- To further explore decimal arithmetic
- To read and represent number quantities on number lines

**NCTM STANDARDS**

**Representation**
Understand that the number line can be used to present fractions, decimals, and percentages

**Measurement**
Use a stopwatch to make time measurements

**Problem Solving**
Use multiple reasoning steps to find solutions to problems

**MATERIALS**
- *Response Wheels
- *Stopwatches (1 per pair of students)
- Overhead projector
- *0–1 Number Line Transparency

**TECHNOLOGY**
e **Presentation** Lesson 7.7
e **MathTools** Stopwatch
Building Blocks Rocket Blast 4

**TEST PREP**

**Cumulative Review**
- Mental Math reviews converting between fractions, decimals, and percentages (Lessons 7.1–7.3).
- Problems 1–6 review subtracting decimal numbers (Lesson 7.6).

**Extended Response**
Problem 6

### Looking Ahead
Lesson 7.8 uses paper strips that need to be cut for students ahead of time. A copy of Practice page 144 will be needed for each student.

*Manipulative Kit Item

# Number Lines

**Context of the Lesson** This is the seventh of eight lessons that introduce percentages, fractions, and decimals. It is the third lesson in which students use stopwatches to explore two-place decimal arithmetic. This lesson expands on Lessons 7.5 and 7.6 by linking two conceptually challenging mathematical ideas: identifying numbers on a number line and performing two-place decimal arithmetic.

See page 292B for Math Background for teachers for this lesson.

## Planning for Learning • DIFFERENTIATE INSTRUCTION

### INTERVENTION
**If . . .** students lack the prerequisite skill of comparing numbers through 100,

**Then . . .** teach ***Intervention*** Lesson 7.B.

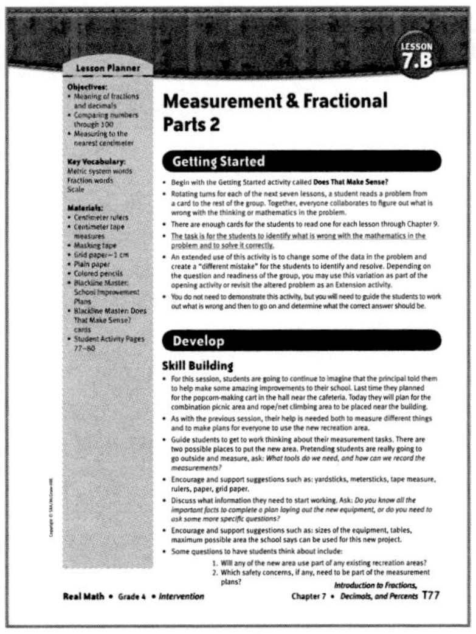


Intervention Lesson 7.B

### ENGLISH LEARNER
Preview

**If . . .** students need language support,

**Then . . .** use Lesson 7.7 in ***English Learner Support Guide*** to preview lesson concepts and vocabulary.

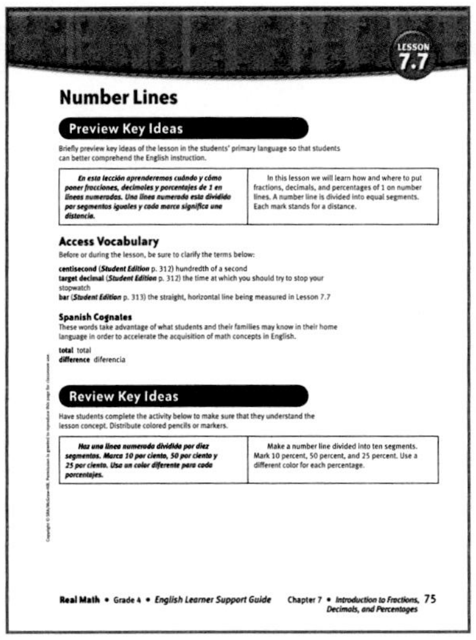


English Learner Lesson 7.7

### ENRICH
**If . . .** students are proficient in the lesson concepts,

**Then . . .** encourage them to add and subtract greater decimal numbers.

### PRACTICE
**If . . .** students would benefit from additional practice,

**Then . . .** extend Skill Practice before assigning the student pages.

### RETEACH
**If . . .** students have difficulty comparing the number line to a ruler,

**Then . . .** have them look at a metric ruler and a nonmetric ruler. The number line is similar to a metric ruler.

**Vocabulary**
**number line** \ˈnəm-ber ˈlīn\ *n.* a line of infinite extent whose points correspond to the real numbers.

**Access Vocabulary**
**goal time** here, *goal* means the number of seconds you are trying to achieve in competition

**Spanish Cognates**
**difference** differencia

# Teaching Lesson 7.7

## Mental Math

5

Review RESPONSE WHEEL Provide students with exercises, such as the following, that practice conversion between fractions, decimals, and percentages. Students can use their finger as the fraction bar for answers that require a fractional answer.

**a.** What decimal is $\frac{1}{8}$ of 1? 0.125

**b.** What decimal is $\frac{3}{4}$ of 1? 0.75

**c.** What percentage is $\frac{1}{8}$ of 1? $12\frac{1}{2}\%$

**d.** What decimal is $\frac{2}{8}$ of 1? 0.25

**e.** What percentage is $\frac{3}{8}$ of 1? 37.5%

**f.** What decimal is $\frac{6}{10}$ of 1? 0.6

**g.** What decimal is $\frac{1}{10}$ of 1? 0.1

## 1 Develop

30

### Tell Students In Today's Lesson They Will

learn how and where to put fractions, decimals, and percentages on number lines.

Whole Group

### Guided Discussion

eMathTools UNDERSTANDING

1. Begin the lesson using a transparency copy of *Practice* page 144 on an overhead projector.
   - Place an arrow over the mark that indicates 0.25 on the line and ask students to tell you what this quantity is.
   - Have volunteers come and write the number on the board. Possible answers are 0.25, $\frac{25}{100}$, $\frac{1}{4}$, or even 25% of 1. Accept all correct answers.
2. Erase the first arrow and draw an arrow over the line showing 0.75. Repeat the same process as above.
3. Give the students a final challenge by drawing an arrow over 0.09. This quantity might be more challenging for the students to record properly, as the zero in the tenths place is a more difficult concept for students when working with two-place decimals.

### Skill Building

COMPUTING

Whole Group

Using either the ***eMathTools: Stopwatch*** or a traditional stopwatch, invite a student to come to the front. Ask the student to try to stop it at 0.38 seconds (give the student only one chance). When the student finishes the attempt, ask him or her to read the stopwatch time aloud. Record the following on the board:

- Target time: 0.38 seconds
- Your time: enter student's time; for this example: 0.21

Ask a volunteer what the difference is between his or her time and the target time. Even though this subtraction could be solved in a procedural way, let the students find their own strategies.

Students may suggest that they thought in terms of centiseconds, so that 38 centiseconds less 21 centiseconds would be 17 centiseconds. Seventeen centiseconds equals $\frac{17}{100}$ of a second, which is 0.17 seconds. Write the difference 0.17 on the board with the other information:

- Target time: 0.38 seconds
- Your time: 0.21 seconds
- Difference: 0.17 seconds

Allow students to discuss any problems they have with understanding the subtraction above. If a number of students do not seem to understand how to do this exercise, ask all of the students to try the first problem on student page 313 together. (The first problem has the arrow over 0.50.)

When students have finished making their attempts, ask for volunteers to tell their times and the difference between their scores and the target decimal.

## 2 Assign Student Pages

20

### Pages 312–313

ENGAGING

Have students complete pages 312 and 313 independently. Remind students that the problems on these pages involve the two steps they practiced during the class discussion (record your time and write the difference).

#### Monitoring Student Progress

| If . . . | Then . . . |
| --- | --- |
| students have trouble subtracting their times as decimals, | have students convert their decimal times into whole centiseconds, subtract in a normal fashion, then convert their answer to decimal seconds. |

### As Students Finish

Game **Greater Number Card Game**

eMathTools ***Stopwatch***

Building Blocks ***Rocket Blast 4***

Student Page

LESSON 7.7 Number Lines

## Key Ideas

**Percents, fractions, and decimals can all be presented on a number line.**

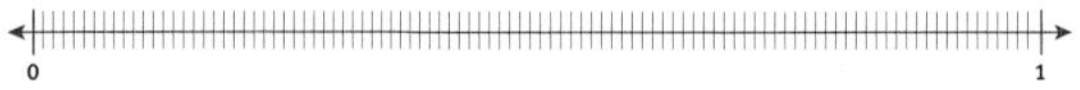


The number line above is divided into one hundred segments. Each mark stands for a distance that is one hundredth of the total length of the number line. If we count fifty segment marks starting at 0, we will be $\frac{50}{100}$, or 50 percent of the way along the number line. As a decimal, this can be written as 0.5.

The hundredth marks on the number line have a similar relationship to percents as do the centiseconds we learned about in Lessons 7.5 and 7.6. We saw how fifty centiseconds was $\frac{50}{100}$ (or $\frac{1}{2}$) of a second, or 50 percent of the time between whole seconds.

Both centiseconds and number lines help us better understand how percents work.

**For** each exercise on the following page, record the following three numbers:

**a.** Write the decimal that describes the location of the arrow on the number line.

**b.** Try to stop your stopwatch as close as possible to this target decimal. For example, if the arrow is at the 25% mark, you will try to stop the stopwatch at 0.25 seconds. Record your actual time from the stopwatch.

**c.** Find the difference between your actual time and the target decimal. Write that amount.



Textbook This lesson is available in the *eTextbook*.

Student Page

1
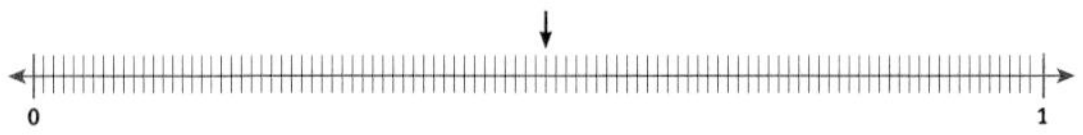


**a.** Target Decimal: 0.50
**b.** Your Time:
**c.** Difference:

2

**a.** Target Decimal: 0.25
**b.** Your Time:
**c.** Difference:

3

**a.** Target Decimal: 0.40
**b.** Your Time:
**c.** Difference:

4

**a.** Target Decimal: 0.68
**b.** Your Time:
**c.** Difference:

5

**a.** Target Decimal: 0.92
**b.** Your Time:
**c.** Difference:

6 **Extended Response** Jack and Maria each tried to get a stopwatch time between $\frac{1}{4}$ of a second and $\frac{1}{2}$ of a second; they also decided that a time equal to one of the two targets would count as well. Jack's time was 0.23 seconds while Maria had a time of 0.41 seconds. Did both Jack and Maria succeed? If not, how much did he or she miss the goal by? Explain how you found your answer.

6 Jack missed 0.25 seconds by 0.02 seconds.



# 3 Reflect

5

## Guided Discussion REASONING

Whole Group

Show the transparency from ***Practice*** page 144 once more. Have students tell you again how many marks there are between 0 and 1. 99 (101 if you include 0 and 1) Ask questions such as the following:

- **How many fractions with a denominator of 100 are between 0 and 1?** 99 if we don't include 0 and 1
- **How many fractions do you think can fit between 0 and 1?**

Allow students to discuss their ideas and explain their reasoning. If they are having trouble, ask them if it is possible to fit 1,000 marks between 0 and 1. Then, if each of those marks represented a fraction with a denominator of 1,000, how many fractions would there be between 0 and 1? a minimum of 1,000 Ask further questions such as the following:

- **Would it be possible to fit 10,000 marks on the line?** yes, if they were close together
- **Would it be possible to fit one million marks on the line?** yes, if they were closer still
- **Is there a limit to the number of fractions between 0 and 1?** no; there are an infinite number of fractions between 0 and 1

## Extended Response

**Problem 6** Students should recognize that Maria's time was inside the parameters of $\frac{1}{4}$ and $\frac{1}{2}$ while Jack's time was not. Students should also know that they need to convert $\frac{1}{4}$ to 0.25 and then subtract 0.23.

**Cumulative Review:** For review of problem solving, assign Problems 22–30 on student page 320.

**Family Involvement:** Assign the ***Practice, Reteach,*** or ***Enrichment*** activities depending on the needs of your students.

**Concept/Question Board:** Have students attempt to answer any unanswered questions on the Concept/Question Board.

**Math Puzzler:** What is $10 \times 8 \times 2 \times 0 \times 7 \times 3$? 0, because anything multiplied by 0 is 0

# 4 Assess and Differentiate

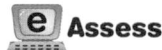

**eAssess** Use ***eAssess*** to record and analyze evidence of student understanding.

## A Gather Evidence

Use the Daily Class Assessment Records in ***Assessment*** or ***eAssess*** to record daily observations.

### Informal Assessment
**Student Pages**

Did the student ENGAGING
- ❑ pay attention to others' contributions?
- ❑ contribute information and ideas?
- ❑ improve on a strategy?
- ❑ reflect on and check the accuracy of his or her work?

### Informal Assessment
**Concept/Question Board**

Did the student APPLYING
- ❑ apply learning in new situations?
- ❑ contribute concepts?
- ❑ contribute answers?
- ❑ connect mathematics to real-world situations?

## B Summarize Findings

Analyze and summarize assessment data for each student. Determine which Assessment Follow-Up is appropriate for each student. Use the Student Assessment record in ***Assessment*** or ***eAssess*** to update assessment records.

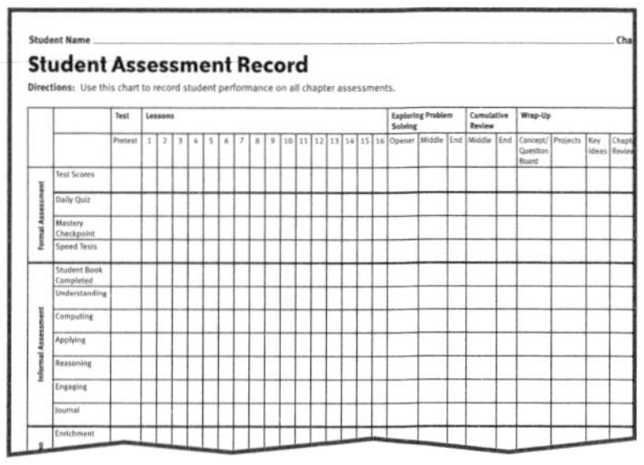
Student Assessment Record

Assessment Page T41

## C Assessment Follow-Up • DIFFERENTIATE INSTRUCTION

Based on your observations, use these teaching strategies for assessment follow-up.

### INTERVENTION

Review student performance on ***Intervention*** Lesson 7.B to see if students have mastered prerequisite skills for this lesson.

### ENGLISH LEARNER

**Review**

Use Lesson 7.7 in ***English Learner Support Guide*** to review lesson concepts and vocabulary.

### ENRICH

**If . . .** students are proficient in the lesson concepts,

**Then . . .** encourage them to work on the chapter projects or ***Enrichment*** Lesson 7.7.

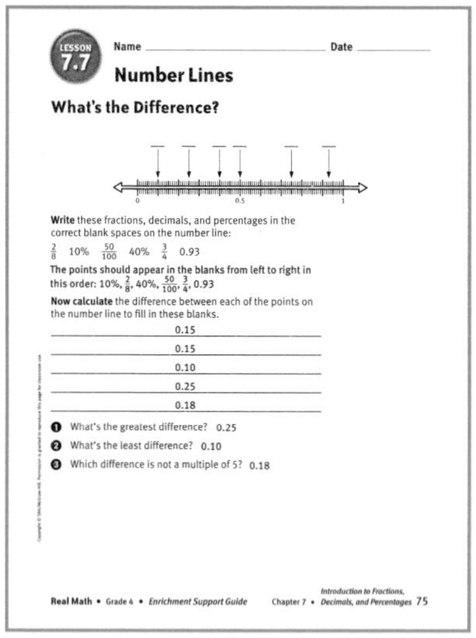
LESSON 7.7 Name ________ Date ________

**Number Lines**

**What's the Difference?**

**Write** these fractions, decimals, and percentages in the correct blank spaces on the number line:

$\frac{2}{8}$ 10% $\frac{50}{100}$ 40% $\frac{3}{4}$ 0.93

The points should appear in the blanks from left to right in this order: 10%, $\frac{2}{8}$, 40%, $\frac{50}{100}$, $\frac{3}{4}$, 0.93

**Now calculate** the difference between each of the points on the number line to fill in these blanks.

0.15
0.15
0.10
0.25
0.18

1. What's the greatest difference? 0.25
2. What's the least difference? 0.10
3. Which difference is not a multiple of 5? 0.18

Real Math • Grade 4 • *Enrichment Support Guide* Chapter 7 • *Introduction to Fractions, Decimals, and Percentages* 75

Enrichment Lesson 7.7

### PRACTICE

**If . . .** students would benefit from additional practice,

**Then . . .** assign ***Practice*** Lesson 7.7.

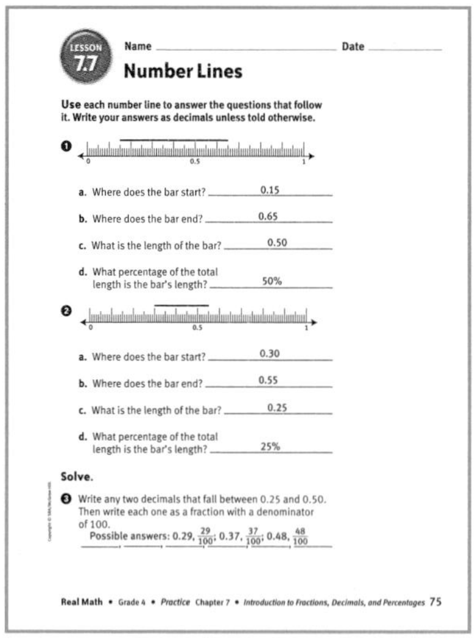
LESSON 7.7 Name ________ Date ________

**Number Lines**

**Use each number line to answer the questions that follow it. Write your answers as decimals unless told otherwise.**

1.
   a. Where does the bar start? 0.15
   b. Where does the bar end? 0.65
   c. What is the length of the bar? 0.50
   d. What percentage of the total length is the bar's length? 50%
2.
   a. Where does the bar start? 0.30
   b. Where does the bar end? 0.55
   c. What is the length of the bar? 0.25
   d. What percentage of the total length is the bar's length? 25%

**Solve.**

3. Write any two decimals that fall between 0.25 and 0.50. Then write each one as a fraction with a denominator of 100.
   Possible answers: 0.29, $\frac{29}{100}$; 0.37, $\frac{37}{100}$; 0.48, $\frac{48}{100}$

Real Math • Grade 4 • *Practice* Chapter 7 • *Introduction to Fractions, Decimals, and Percentages* 75

Practice Lesson 7.7

### RETEACH

**If . . .** students struggle with the meanings of specific fractions or decimals,

**Then . . .** have them review the benchmark percentages and compare the numbers in the problem to the benchmarks.

## Lesson Planner

**OBJECTIVES**
- To help students understand that 10 percent of something is $\frac{1}{10}$ of that thing
- To continue comparing and ordering decimals, fractions, and percents

**NCTM STANDARDS**

**Number and Operations**
Find solutions to problems about 10% and $\frac{1}{10}$

**Measurement**
Use percentages of objects to approximate height or length

**Reasoning and Proof**
Explain the meaning of $\frac{1}{10}$ or 10%

**MATERIALS**
- *Response Wheels
- *Centimeter ruler
- Scissors
- Strings from three mystery items (as outlined in Looking Ahead section of Lesson 7.7)

**TECHNOLOGY**
ePresentation Lesson 7.8
eMathTools Number Line

**TEST PREP**

**Cumulative Review**
- Mental Math reviews fractions, decimals, and percentages of whole numbers (Lesson 7.2).
- Problems 12–20 use multiplication to find percentages of whole numbers (Lessons 3.10 and 7.2).

**Multistep Problems**
Problems 12–20

**Writing + Math**
Journal

*Manipulative Kit Item

# Understanding 10% and $\frac{1}{10}$

**Context of the Lesson** This is the final lesson in the introduction to percentages, fractions, and decimals. In this lesson, students work with 10% and $\frac{1}{10}$. Although students have had experience with tenths as well as dividing by 10, in this lesson they will work with visualizing segments with proportional reasoning. This gives students a new way to conceptualize $\frac{1}{10}$ as an operator as well as a quantity.

See page 292B for Math Background for teachers for this lesson.

## Planning for Learning • DIFFERENTIATE INSTRUCTION

### INTERVENTION

**If . . .** students lack the prerequisite skill of understanding fractions and decimals,

**Then . . .** teach ***Intervention*** Lesson 7.A.

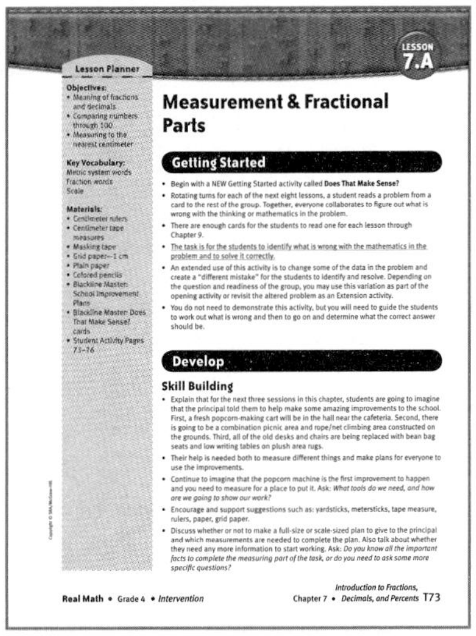
Lesson Planner

LESSON 7.A

Measurement & Fractional Parts

Getting Started

Develop

Skill Building

Real Math • Grade 4 • Intervention

Introduction to Fractions, Decimals, and Percents T73

Intervention Lesson 7.A

### ENGLISH LEARNER

Preview

**If . . .** students need language support,

**Then . . .** use Lesson 7.8 in ***English Learner Support Guide*** to preview lesson concepts and vocabulary.

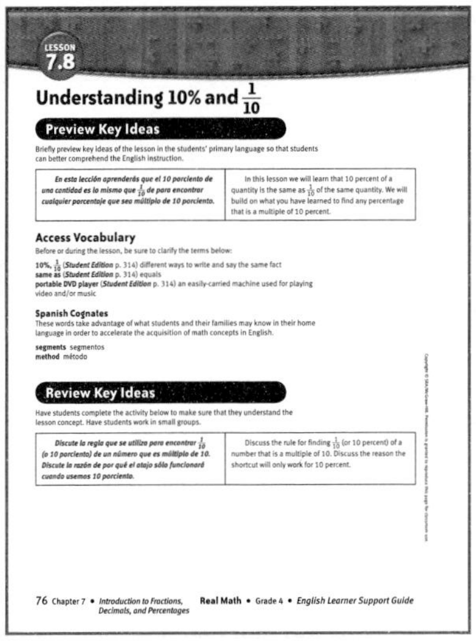
LESSON 7.8

Understanding 10% and $\frac{1}{10}$

Preview Key Ideas

Access Vocabulary

Spanish Cognates

Review Key Ideas

76 Chapter 7 • Introduction to Fractions, Decimals, and Percentages

Real Math • Grade 4 • English Learner Support Guide

English Learner Lesson 7.8

### ENRICH

**If . . .** students are proficient in the lesson concepts,

**Then . . .** encourage them to explore the ***eMathTools: Number Line.***

### PRACTICE

**If . . .** students would benefit from additional practice,

**Then . . .** extend the time allotted for Skill Practice before assigning the student pages.

### RETEACH

**If . . .** students have difficulty remembering what *tenth* means,

**Then . . .** have them review the place value chart and find the location of the tenth place.

**Vocabulary**
**tenth** \ˈten(t)th\ *n.* one of ten equal parts

**Access Vocabulary**
**10% of something is the same as $\frac{1}{10}$ of it** 10% and $\frac{1}{10}$ are different representations of the same fact

**Spanish Cognates**
**segments** segmentos
**fraction** fracción

## Mental Math 5

RESPONSE WHEEL

Provide students with exercises, such as the following, that practice finding fractions and percentages of whole numbers:

**a.** $\frac{1}{2}$ of 60 is 30
**b.** $\frac{1}{4}$ of 120 is 30
**c.** $\frac{1}{8}$ of 240 is 30
**d.** 50% of 160 is 80
**e.** 25% of 160 is 40
**f.** $12\frac{1}{12}$% of 160 is 20
**g.** 75% of 160 is 120
**h.** $\frac{1}{4}$ of 200 is 50
**i.** 50% of 200 is 100
**j.** $\frac{3}{4}$ of 200 is 150

## 1 Develop 30

### Tell Students In Today's Lesson They Will

learn that 10% of something is the same as $\frac{1}{10}$ of it.

### Guided Discussion UNDERSTANDING

Whole Group

1. This lesson begins with a new series of string challenges which are carried out in the same manner as in Lesson 7.4. Hold up a piece of precut string that has been measured to 25% of the height of a certain object in the room. Tell the students that the length of string is 25% of the height of a mystery object within their view in the classroom. Ask students what 25% of a whole is as a fraction of the whole. $\frac{1}{4}$

   Ask them how many times this piece of string would fit along the height of the mystery object. 4 times

   Write 25% on the board. Then ask students if they have any ideas as to what the mystery object might be. When a student offers a suggestion, ask him or her to use the string to illustrate their method of solving the problem. Then have the students write the quantity as a percentage and as a fraction.

   The string is ___% of the height of the ___.

   The string is ___ (fraction) of the height of the ___.

2. Next, repeat the entire procedure with the line segment that is $12\frac{1}{2}$% of the height of the second object. Ask students what $12\frac{1}{2}$% of a whole is as a fraction of the whole. $\frac{1}{8}$ Ask them how many times the string will go into the length of the whole object. 8 Now tell students that you have a new percentage for them to learn today—10%. Ask for new volunteers from the class who would like to discuss what 10% might mean. Show them a piece of string that has been cut to be 10% of the length of an object in the room.

   Ask questions such as the following:

   - **Is 10% longer or shorter than a string representing $12\frac{1}{2}$% of the same object?** a little shorter

   Allow the students to guess what the third secret object might be. Ask students who make good guesses to come to the front and show the class how they figured it out. If the student does not show that the piece of string can be moved along the object in question 10 times, ask the students to think about how many 10% are in 100%. Have students verify this by moving the string along the object 10 times.

3. Next, tell them the full length of a mystery object, for example, 80 cm. Tell the students that after you measured the object you cut the string so it was 10% of the original length. Let them know you did this without folding the string but by calculating the length in your head. Ask students to try to estimate how many centimeters the 10% piece might be. 8 cm

### Strategy Building ENGAGING

Small Group

**Calculating 10%**

Present the following set of questions. Do the first two exercises together. Then have students work in pairs to complete the exercises.

*If the string is ___ cm long, how long is 10% of the string?*

- 20 2 cm
- 30 3 cm
- 40 4 cm
- 50 5 cm
- 60 6 cm
- 70 7 cm
- 80 8 cm
- 90 9 cm

Write the answers on the board discuss them together. Ask questions such as the following:

- **Do you notice a pattern?** Students may say you get the answer by dropping the zero from the original number.
- **Is there an operation that can be used to find the answers?** yes, dividing by ten

Explain that finding 10% of a number only requires dividing it by 10.

### Skill Practice UNDERSTANDING

Whole Group

Let students know they can use their knowledge about finding 10% of a number to help them find *any* percentage that is a multiple of 10. For example, to find 40% of a number, first find 10% of the number, and then multiply that number by 4.

Work through an example such as the following with the class:

40% of 60 cm = ?

10% of 60 cm = 6 cm

$4 \times 6 = 24$ cm

40% of 60 cm = 24 cm

## 2 Assign Student Pages 20

**Pages 314–315** APPLYING

Have students complete pages 314–315 independently.

### As Students Finish

Game **Greater Number Card Game**

eMathTools ***Number Line***

Student Page

LESSON 7.8 **Understanding 10% and $\frac{1}{10}$**

## Key Ideas

**Ten percent of something is the same as $\frac{1}{10}$ of that thing.**

What is 10 percent of 60?

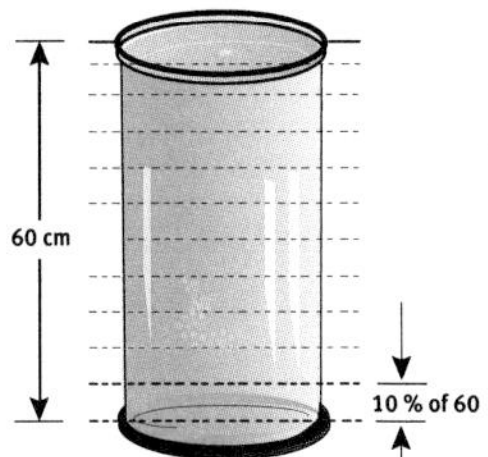


Imagine we have a beaker divided into ten equal parts. Each of these segments would be $\frac{1}{10}$ of the total height, or 10% percent, since $100 \div 10 = 10$.

If the beaker has a height of 60 centimeters, how tall is each segment?

$60 \div 10 = 6$

Therefore, 10% of 60, or $\frac{1}{10}$ of 60, is 6.

**Apply** what you have learned about 10% and $\frac{1}{10}$ to complete the following exercises.

1. 10% of 10 = ▒ 1
2. 10% of 20 = ▒ 2
3. $\frac{1}{10}$ of 30 = ▒ 3
4. $\frac{1}{10}$ of 40 = ▒ 4
5. 10% of 50 = ▒ 5
6. 10% of 90 = ▒ 9
7. $\frac{1}{10}$ of 100 = ▒ 10
8. $\frac{1}{10}$ of 200 = ▒ 20
9. 10% of 300 = ▒ 30
10. 10% of 600 = ▒ 60
11. Presley started looking through the newspaper for deals on a portable DVD player. She found a store that was selling portable DVD players for 10% off. If the original price of the player she wanted was \$210, how much is the sale price? \$189

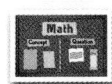

314 Textbook This lesson is available in the *eTextbook*.

Student Page

We can build on what we have learned to find any percentage that is a multiple of 10%.

For example, how would we find 40% of 60 centimeters?

Because 40% is four times greater than 10% ($40 = 10 \times 4$), 40% of 60 = $4 \times$ 10% of 60. We already calculated that 10% of 60 is 6, so 40% of 60 would be equal to $6 \times 4$, or 24. 40% of 60 centimeters is 24 centimeters.

If 10% of 60 centimeters is 6 centimeters, what is 20% of 60 centimeters?

20% of 60 ⟶ 10% of 60 + 10% of 60 ⟶ 6 + 6 = 12

So, 20% of 60 centimeters is 12 centimeters.

How could we find 90% of 40?

There are many ways to do this. One possibility would be to first find 50% of 40, then find 10% of 40. That information could be used to find 90% like this:

50% of 40 = 20

10% of 40 = 4

40% of 40 ⟶ 10% of 40 multiplied by 4 ⟶ $4 \times 4 = 16$

90% of 40 ⟶ 50% of 40 + 40% of 40 ⟶ 20 + 16 = 36

So, 90% of 40 is 36. Can you think of other ways to find 90%?

Multistep **Complete** the following exercises, and explain your strategy.

12. 40% of 40 = 16
13. 60% of 80 = 48
14. 30% of 90 = 27
15. 50% of 30 = 15
16. 20% of 30 = 6
17. 70% of 30 = 21
18. 90% of 30 = 27
19. 30% of 30 = 9
20. 60% of 90 = 54

Writing + Math **Journal**

Look at Exercises 1 to 10 on page 314. Write any patterns you see, and explain a way to find 10% of any multiple of 10 or whole number that ends with 0.

Possible answers include: the zero on the end of each number is dropped; this could be found by dividing by 10; to find 10% of a number, multiply by 0.10

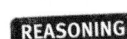

Chapter 7 • Lesson 8 315

## 3 Reflect

5

### Guided Discussion REASONING

Whole Group

Ask a volunteer to remind the rest of the class of the rule for finding $\frac{1}{10}$ (or 10%) of a number that is a multiple of 10. divide the number by ten Ask students questions such as the following:

- **Does this shortcut work for any percentage?** no, only 10%
- **Can we find, for example, 5% of a number by dividing that number by 5?** no

Why does this rule only work for 10% and $\frac{1}{10}$? This answer can be understood by thinking about the nature of percentages. Percentages are fractions out of 100. To find 5%, for example, we would have to divide 100% by 20: $5 \times 20 = 100$. Ten is the only number that when multiplied by *itself* will give you 100: $10 \times 10 = 100$. That is why the rule for 10% works.

Writing + Math **Journal**

Students should explain a way to use 10% to find measurements of height, as well as what operations they should use to find 10% of a whole number.

**Curriculum Connection:** Students may be interested in browsing newspaper ads and calculating sale prices of items they would like to buy.

**Cumulative Review:** For review of addition and subtraction of integers, assign Problems 31–36 on student page 320.

**Family Involvement:** Assign the ***Practice, Reteach,*** or ***Enrichment*** activities depending on the needs of your students.

**Concept/Question Board:** Have students attempt to answer any unanswered questions on the Concept/Question Board.

**Math Puzzler:** There are 6 people in the Ying family. By tradition, on Chinese New Year each member of the family gives a good-luck orange to every other member of the family. How many oranges does the family need to honor this tradition? Each person needs 5 oranges to be able to give one to every other person in the family. So $6 \times 5 = 30$.

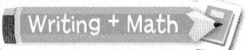

# 4 Assess and Differentiate

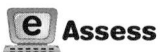

**e Assess** Use ***eAssess*** to record and analyze evidence of student understanding.

## A Gather Evidence

Use the Daily Class Assessment Records in ***Assessment*** or ***eAssess*** to record daily observations.

### Informal Assessment
**Mental Math**

Did the student COMPUTING
- ❑ respond accurately?
- ❑ respond quickly?
- ❑ respond with confidence?
- ❑ self-correct?

### Informal Assessment
**Guided Discussion**

Did the student REASONING
- ❑ provide a clear explanation?
- ❑ communicate reasons and strategies?
- ❑ choose appropriate strategies?
- ❑ argue logically?

## B Summarize Findings

Analyze and summarize assessment data for each student. Determine which Assessment Follow-Up is appropriate for each student. Use the Student Assessment Record in ***Assessment*** or ***eAssess*** to update assessment records.

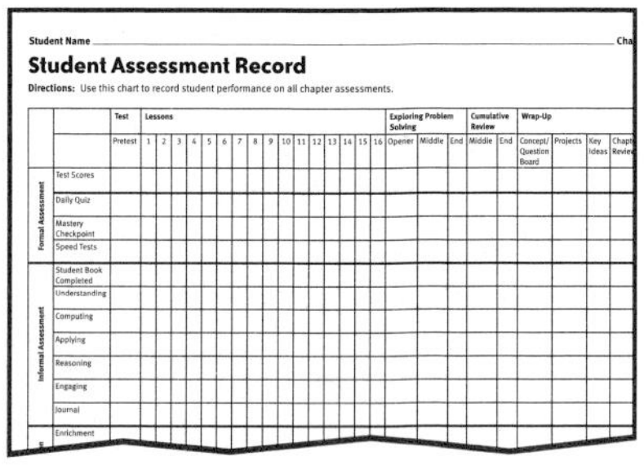


Assessment Page T41

## C Assessment Follow-Up • DIFFERENTIATE INSTRUCTION

Based on your observations, use these teaching strategies for assessment follow-up.

### INTERVENTION

Review student performance on ***Intervention*** Lesson 7.A to see if students have mastered prerequisite skills for this lesson.

### ENGLISH LEARNER

**Review**

Use Lesson 7.8 in ***English Learner Support Guide*** to review lesson concepts and vocabulary.

### ENRICH

**If . . .** students are proficient in the lesson concepts,

**Then . . .** encourage them to work on the chapter projects or ***Enrichment*** Lesson 7.8.

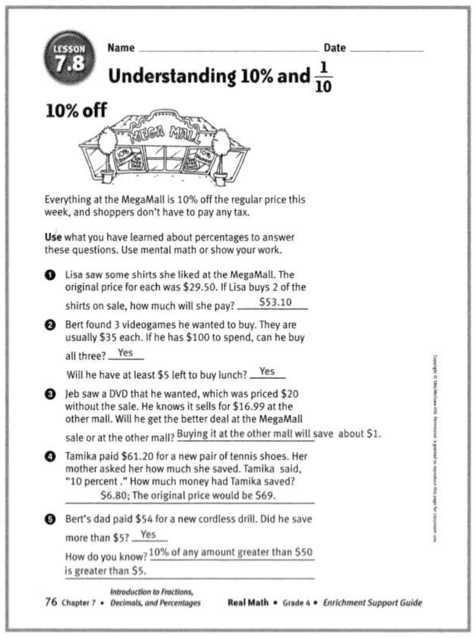
LESSON 7.8 Name ______ Date ______

**Understanding 10% and $\frac{1}{10}$**

**10% off**

Everything at the MegaMall is 10% off the regular price this week, and shoppers don't have to pay any tax.

**Use** what you have learned about percentages to answer these questions. Use mental math or show your work.

1. Lisa saw some shirts she liked at the MegaMall. The original price for each was $29.50. If Lisa buys 2 of the shirts on sale, how much will she pay? $53.10
2. Bert found 3 videogames he wanted to buy. They are usually $35 each. If he has $100 to spend, can he buy all three? Yes
   Will he have at least $5 left to buy lunch? Yes
3. Jeb saw a DVD that he wanted, which was priced $20 without the sale. He knows it sells for $16.99 at the other mall. Will he get the better deal at the MegaMall sale or at the other mall? Buying it at the other mall will save about $1.
4. Tamika paid $61.20 for a new pair of tennis shoes. Her mother asked her how much she saved. Tamika said, "10 percent ." How much money had Tamika saved? $6.80; The original price would be $69.
5. Bert's dad paid $54 for a new cordless drill. Did he save more than $5? Yes
   How do you know? 10% of any amount greater than $50 is greater than $5.

76 Chapter 7 • *Introduction to Fractions, Decimals, and Percentages* **Real Math** • Grade 4 • *Enrichment Support Guide*

Enrichment Lesson 7.8

### PRACTICE

**If . . .** students would benefit from additional practice,

**Then . . .** assign ***Practice*** Lesson 7.8.

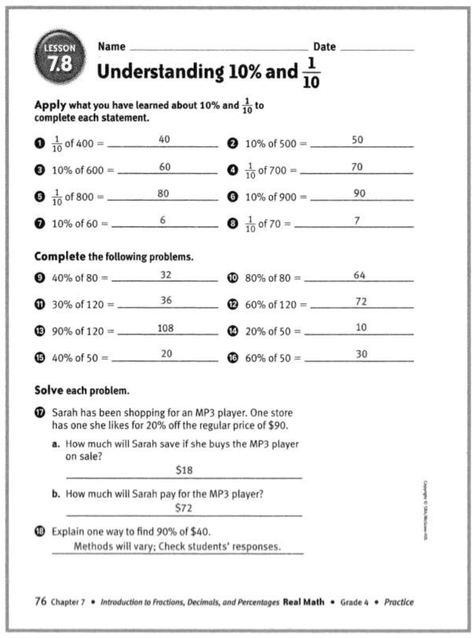
LESSON 7.8 Name ______ Date ______

**Understanding 10% and $\frac{1}{10}$**

**Apply** what you have learned about 10% and $\frac{1}{10}$ to complete each statement.

1. $\frac{1}{10}$ of 400 = 40
2. 10% of 500 = 50
3. 10% of 600 = 60
4. $\frac{1}{10}$ of 700 = 70
5. $\frac{1}{10}$ of 800 = 80
6. 10% of 900 = 90
7. 10% of 60 = 6
8. $\frac{1}{10}$ of 70 = 7

**Complete** the following problems.

9. 40% of 80 = 32
10. 80% of 80 = 64
11. 30% of 120 = 36
12. 60% of 120 = 72
13. 90% of 120 = 108
14. 20% of 50 = 10
15. 40% of 50 = 20
16. 60% of 50 = 30

**Solve** each problem.

17. Sarah has been shopping for an MP3 player. One store has one she likes for 20% off the regular price of $90.
    a. How much will Sarah save if she buys the MP3 player on sale? $18
    b. How much will Sarah pay for the MP3 player? $72
18. Explain one way to find 90% of $40. Methods will vary; Check students' responses.

76 Chapter 7 • *Introduction to Fractions, Decimals, and Percentages* **Real Math** • Grade 4 • *Practice*

Practice Lesson 7.8

### RETEACH

**If . . .** students struggle with comparing decimals and percentages,

**Then . . .** have them make their own number line and fill in some of the percentages that have been introduced in this chapter.

# Exploring Problem Solving

**Objectives**

- To compare the use of fractions and percents for analyzing data
- To explore the usefulness of percents when comparing parts of different-sized wholes
- To use proportional reasoning to determine whether data is appropriate
- To explore solving and presenting solutions to nonroutine problems

**Context of the Lesson** This lesson builds on what students have been learning about percents. In particular, it uses actual data to show that sometimes percents can be more useful than fractions when making comparisons. This lesson also continues to provide exposure of simple decimals.

## 1 Develop

5

### Tell Students In Today's Lesson They Will

- read about the first explorers to reach the North Pole.
- learn how the explorers used a special plan to get there.
- see whether it's easier to use fractions or percents to compare parts of the explorers' journeys.
- examine whether the explorers' claims are reasonable.

## Guided Discussion

Read student page 316 with the class. Explain that the information is true. This information is based in part on an article by Jennifer Mapes, which is available at **http://news.nationalgeographic.com/news/2001/01/1129explorer_2001-01-30.html.**

Help the class to understand the overall plan of the expedition.

- The expedition party traveled by boat to the Coast of Ellesmere Island.
- There is no land near the North Pole; it is a layer of ice on the ocean.
- From their base on land, the expedition team needed a plan to traverse 417 nautical miles of ice.

If students ask, nautical miles are used because they make navigating easier. One nautical mile corresponds to $\frac{1}{60}$ of a degree of latitude, or about 1.15 miles.

Student Page

**Exploring Problem Solving**

~ *November 28* ~

### Henson Received Hubbard Medal

WASHINGTON, D.C. It took a long time for Mathew Henson and Robert Peary to become the first explorers to reach the North Pole, but it took even longer for Henson to get the honor he deserved. Ninety-one years after his historic trek and long after his death in 1955, Mathew Henson received the Hubbard Medal, the highest honor awarded by the National Geographic Society.

American Arctic Explorer, Mathew Henson

In 1937 Henson's contribution was acknowledged when, at age 70, he was made an honorary member of the renowned Explorers Club. In 1944, Congress awarded Henson a joint North Pole Discovery Medal. In 1948, the Geographic Society of Chicago awarded Henson a gold medal. His achievements were further acknowledged by President Truman in 1950 and by President Eisenhower in 1954.

Besides his awards, Henson has been remembered in other ways. There is a Henson school in Charles County, Maryland, where he was born. The United States Navy named an oceanographic ship in his honor, the USNS Henson. Several books have been written about Henson, as well as a movie. Henson has also been commemorated in United States postal stamps, plaques, and medals.

316 Textbook This lesson is available in the *eTextbook*.

# 2 Exploring Problem Solving 30

## Use Student Pages

Read the top of student page 317 with the class. To help students understand the expedition's plan and the map, ask questions such as the following:

- **What do the letters on the map show?** where igloo bases were set up
- **Why did the explorers need bases along the way?** The trip was too long; they needed to stop for food, warmth, and rest.

Read, discuss, and solve Problems 1–3 with the class. These problems provide an example of how percents can often be simpler to use than fractions when making comparisons.

## Answers to Problem 3

### Problem 3a

Students should see that in order to answer the question using fractions, they need to compare $\frac{140}{215}$ and $\frac{281}{417}$. Approximating these fractions is difficult because the numerators and denominators are large and not compatible. Moreover, these fractions are close in value (each is about $\frac{2}{3}$), so rough approximations will not suffice.

### Problem 3c

Comparing percentages is as simple as comparing whole numbers. It is easy to see that 68 percent is greater than 65 percent because 68 is greater than 65. Help students see that comparing percents is like comparing fractions that have denominators of 100. So you need only compare the numerators.





Between Ellesmere Island and the North Pole, there is a barren stretch of ice 417 nautical miles long. (A nautical mile is about 15 percent longer than a regular mile.)

On the Arctic ice, two people could travel faster than a group of twenty-four. The plan was for Peary and Henson to go the last 133 miles to the Pole alone. To set the stage for that last leg, different teams from the group went ahead from the land camp to make the trail and set up igloo camps along the icy route to the Pole. The igloos were stocked with stoves, fuel, and food for Peary and Henson. Each team returned to land after its trailblazing work was done.

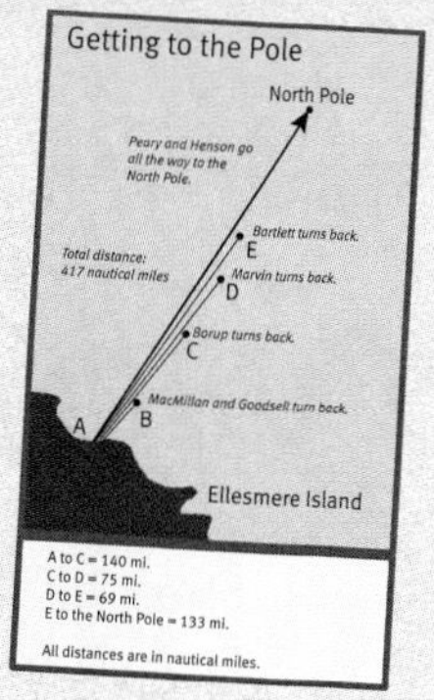


**Solve** the following problems. Use the mile markings on the map.

1. After Camps B and C were set up, the Marvin team set up Camp D. They started from Camp A. When they reached Camp C, what fraction of the way were they to Camp D? $\frac{140}{215}$
2. Peary and Henson also started from Camp A. When they reached Camp E, what fraction of the way were they to the Pole? $\frac{284}{417}$

**Read** this question, but do not answer it yet.

3. Which team had completed a greater part of its trip, the Marvin team when they reached Camp C or Peary and Henson when they reached Camp E?
   a. Why is this question difficult to answer using fractions? **See the *Teacher's Edition*.**
   b. Answer the question using percents instead of fractions. **See the *Teacher's Edition*.**
   c. How did percents make it easier to answer the question? **When Peary and Henson reached Camp E, they were 68 percent of the way to the Pole. When the Marvin team reached Camp C, they were 65 percent of the way to Camp D.**

Student Page

## Exploring Problem Solving

Some people doubted whether Peary and Henson actually made it to the North Pole. One of the reasons for doubt was the extraordinary distance the two explorers traveled in such a short time. Later, some groups made similar journeys to see if Peary's claims were reasonable.

**Read this summary. All distances are listed in nautical miles.**

- Peary and Henson left the main camp at 5 A.M. on April 2 and returned at 12:30 A.M. on April 10. They spent 30 hours in the vicinity of the Pole.
- Peary and Henson covered the distance to the Pole in 5 marches averaging about 27 miles per march, at an average speed of about 2.5 miles an hour. They spent about 50 hours stopping for food and rest. In 1986 Will Steger covered virtually the same distance at the same speed and said that Peary's claims were not unreasonable.
- The return trip, from 4 P.M. on April 7 to 12:30 A.M. on April 10, is more frequently doubted. This trek back was made in 3 marches of about 45 miles each. The trek back totaled about 48 hours of sledding at an average speed of about 2.8 miles an hour, with 9 hours of stops for food and rest.

**Work in groups to discuss and solve these problems.**

4. How many hours did it take Peary and Henson to reach the North Pole? 101 hours
5. How many hours did it take Peary and Henson to return from the North Pole? (Don't forget the time they spent at the Pole.) $57\frac{1}{2}$ hours
6. What was their sledding speed on the way to the Pole and on the way back? 2.5 miles per hour there and 2.8 miles per hour back
7. Do you think the difference in speed explains why it took so much less time to get back? See the *Teacher's Edition.*
8. How much time did Peary and Henson spend stopping for food and rest on the way to the Pole and on the way back? about 50 hours on the way there and 9 hours on the way back

318 eTextbook This lesson is available in the ***eTextbook.***

Read and discuss the information on student page 318 with the class. Have students work in groups on Problems 4–8.

# Answer

## Problem 5

Students can compare the speeds of 2.5 mph and 2.8 mph to get a sense that the speed coming back from the Pole was only about 10 percent faster than the speed going there. Yet the amount of time it took was nearly cut in half. In order for the speed to fully account for the time difference, the speed coming back would need to be nearly double the speed going to the Pole.

## 3 Reflect

15

**Knowledge Age Skills**

**Effective Communication** Have groups present and explain their answers to selected problems from page 318. Ask questions such as the following:

- **Do you understand the reasoning?**
- **Do you agree with the reasoning? Why or why not?**

### Extension Problem

Review the travel information below for Peary's and Henson's final 133-mile dash to the Pole. Then ask students to show how they could use the facts to figure out that Peary and Henson stopped for about 50 hours for food and rest.

- Started trip to the Pole at 5 A.M. on April 2
- Made 5 marches of about 27 miles each
- Sledded at about 2.5 miles per hour while traveling
- Spent 30 hours at or near the Pole
- Started the trip back at 4 P.M. on April 5

### Answer to Extension Problem

Here is one way students might work this through: Traveling for 10 hours at $2\frac{1}{2}$ mph would cover 25 miles. So, a march of 27 miles at that speed took almost 11 hours. That means 5 marches took a total of nearly 55 hours. Subtract that from the total trip time of about 100 hours, and you get a total stopping time of 45 to 50 hours.

## 4 Assess

10

When evaluating student work, focus not only on the correctness of the answer, but also on students' thinking and communication. Some questions to consider include the following:

- Did the student understand the data and use it in reasonable ways?
- Did the student understand percentages in context and use them to make comparisons?
- Did the student use proportional reasoning to support a conclusion?

# Cumulative Review

## Assign Pages 319–320

Use this Cumulative Review as a review of concepts and skills that students have previously learned.

Here are different ways you can assign these problems to your students as they work through the chapter:

- For each lesson in the chapter, assign a set of Cumulative Review problems to be completed as practice or for homework.
  - Lesson 7.5—Problems 1–15
  - Lesson 7.6—Problems 16–21
  - Lesson 7.7—Problems 22–30
  - Lesson 7.8—Problems 31–36
- At any point during the chapter, assign part or all of the Cumulative Review problems to be completed as practice or for homework.

### Cumulative Review

**Problems 1–15** review multiplication and division, Lessons 3.1–3.11.

**Problems 16–21** review common multiples and common factors, Lesson 3.12.

**Problems 22–30** review problem solving, Lessons 5.3, 6.1, and 6.4.

**Problems 31–36** review addition and subtraction of integers, Lesson 2.9.

### Monitoring Student Progress

**If . . .** students miss more than one problem in a section, **Then . . .** refer to the indicated lesson for remediation suggestions.

Student Page

## Cumulative Review

**Multiplication and Division** Lessons 3.1–3.11

**Multiply** or divide.

1. 9 ÷ 3 3
2. 6 × 4 24
3. 24 ÷ 8 3
4. 7 × 5 35
5. 12 ÷ 12 1
6. 12 ÷ 1 12
7. 7 × 7 49
8. 36 ÷ 6 6
9. 6 × 7 42
10. 14 ÷ 3 4 R2
11. 10 × 8 80
12. 2 × 9 18
13. 3 × 11 33
14. 24 ÷ 5 4 R4
15. 49 ÷ 6 8 R1

**Common Multiples and Common Factors** Lesson 3.12

**List** all the factors of each number, and find the greatest common factor.

16. 15 and 18 15: 1, 3, 5, and 15; 18: 1, 2, 3, 6, 9, and 18; GCF is 3
17. 36 and 32 36: 1, 2, 3, 4, 6, 9, 12, 18, and 36; 32: 1, 2, 4, 8, 16, and 32; GCF is 4
18. 20 and 16 20: 1, 2, 4, 5, 10, and 20; 16: 1, 2, 4, 8, and 16; GCF is 4

**List** the first three common multiples for each pair of numbers.

19. 3 and 4 12, 24, and 36
20. 6 and 5 30, 60, and 90
21. 7 and 2 14, 28, and 42



Student Page

## Cumulative Review

**Lessons 5.3, 6.1, and 6.4**

**Solve** the following problems.

22. Jacob's car is 7 feet wide and 12 feet long. How many square feet will be left if he parks in a parking space that is 9 feet wide and 18 feet long? 78 sq. ft
23. Stephanie is putting a lattice fence around the bottom portion of her deck. Her deck is shaped like an octagon, and each side is 6 feet long. How many feet of lattice will she need to surround her deck? 48 ft

25. Yes, the stand has a bigger area than the phone.

24. Melinda placed $1.50 in her piggy bank and was curious to see how much she could save in a month. At the end of the month, to her surprise, she had 10 times more than what she started with. How much money did Melinda have? $15
25. While at the mall, Miguel found a square stand for his new phone. The phone is 12 centimeters by 9 centimeters and the stand is 11 centimeters on all sides. Should Miguel buy this stand? Explain why or why not.

26. 78 × 100 = ■ 7,800
27. 35 × 10 = ■ 350
28. 100 × 3 = ■ 300
29. 325 × 200 = ■ 65,000
30. 43 × 500 = ■ 21,500

**Adding and Subtracting Integers** Lesson 2.9

**Decide** whether the answer is correct or not. If it is wrong, correct it.

31. −6 + −3 = −9 correct
32. 6 + (−5) = 1 correct
33. 12 + (−7) = −5 incorrect; 5
34. −14 + −6 = 20 incorrect; −20
35. 9 + (−9) = 0 correct
36. 18 + (−5) = −13 incorrect; 13

# Wrap-Up

## 1 Discuss 5

### Concept/Question Board

Review the Concept/Question Board with students.

- Discuss students' contributions to the Concept side of the Board.
- Have students repose their questions, and lead a discussion to find satisfactory answers.

## Chapter Projects

Provide an opportunity for students who have worked on one or more of the chapter projects outlined on page 293C to share their work with the class. Allow each student or student group five minutes to present or discuss their projects. For formal assessment, use the rubrics found in ***Across the Curriculum Math Connections;*** the rubric for **Describe Matthew Henson's Expeditions** is on page 75, and the rubric for **Budget an Arctic Expedition** is on page 81. For informal assessment, use the following rubric and questions.

| | Exceeds Expectations | Meets Expectations | Minimally Meets Expectations |
|---|---|---|---|
| Applies mathematics in real-world situations: | ❑ | ❑ | ❑ |
| Demonstrates strong engagement in the activity: | ❑ | ❑ | ❑ |

### Describe Matthew Henson's Expeditions

LANGUAGE ARTS

- What information did you include in your notes about Matthew Henson's expeditions? Was this information useful?
- What information in your document did you express as percentages?
- How did you calculate the percentage for each part of the expedition?
- Are biographies good sources for information? Why or why not?
- If you had to write your own biography, would you? Why or why not?
- What would you include in your autobiography?

### Budget an Arctic Expedition

SCIENCE WebQuest

- What route did you take for your expedition? How many days of travel time was it?
- How did you calculate how many of each item you would need?
- How did you calculate the total cost of the items for your category?
- How did you calculate how much money your group would need for the entire expedition?
- What problems did you find when calculating the total cost of an Arctic expedition for your group?
- If you could go on the expedition you planned, would you? Why or why not?
- Do you think it's possible to completely plan for an Arctic expedition? Explain.

# 2 Assign Student Pages 25

## Key Ideas Review

UNDERSTANDING

Have students complete the Review questions independently or in small groups. Then discuss each question as a class.

### Possible Answers

**Problem 1** The answer is 10. Problems 1–4 deal with percentages of whole numbers. To find the answers to these problems, students should know to divide by a specific number, which is dependent of the percentage.

**Problem 2** The answer is 25.

**Problem 3** The answer is 6.

**Problem 4** The answer is 27.

**Problem 5** Problems 5–7 involve ordering decimals from least to greatest. Students must know the place value of the decimals' positioning. The answer is 0.74, 0.76, 1.04, 1.26, and 1.65.

**Problem 6** The answer is 0.12, 1.26, 12.56, and 125.6.

**Problem 7** The answer is 0.55, 0.58, 0.6, 0.62, and 0.7.

**Problem 8** Problems 8 and 9 ask students to subtract decimals to find the difference. However, to subtract, students must be able to align the decimals and distinguish the larger decimal from the smaller decimal. The answer is 0.53.

**Problem 9** The answer is 10.38.

Extended Response

**Problem 10** One way to find 25% of 40 is by dividing 40 by 4. Since 25% = $\frac{1}{4}$, 40 can be divided by 4 to get 10.

Student Page

## Chapter 7 Key Ideas Review

**In this chapter you determined how decimals and percentages are similar.**

You learned how to find a percentage of a whole number.

You learned how decimals can be placed on a number line and how to determine if one decimal is greater than another.

**Solve the following problems.**

1. 25% of 40 = ☐ 10
2. 100% of 25 = ☐ 25
3. 10% of 60 = ☐ 6
4. 75% of 36 = ☐ 27

**Place the following decimals in order from least to greatest.**

5. 0.74, 1.04, 1.65, 0.76, and 1.26 0.74, 0.76, 1.04, 1.26, and 1.65
6. 12.65, 12.56, 1.26, 0.12, and 125.6 0.12, 1.26, 12.56, 12.65, and 125.6
7. 0.62, 0.6, 0.58, 0.55, and 0.7 0.55, 0.58, 0.6, 0.62, and 0.7

**How large is the difference between the two decimals?**

8. 0.78 and 0.25 0.53
9. 12.36 and 1.98 10.38

**Solve the exercise below.**

10. Extended Response How would you find 25% of 40?
    Possible answer: Since 25% is equal to 1/4, you can divide 40 by 4. The answer is 10.

# CHAPTER 7 Review

## Chapter Review

Use this Chapter 7 Review as a preliminary chapter test to identify areas in which each student is having difficulty or in which the class may need help. If students do well on the Chapter 7 Review, you may wish to skip directly to the next chapter. If not, you may want to spend time helping students overcome their individual difficulties before they take the Chapter Test.

Each set of problems reviews concepts from one or more lessons in the chapter. Students can refer to a specific lesson for additional instruction if they need help. You can also use this information to assign additional practice based on the previous lesson concepts.

Have students complete pages 322–323 on their own. For review purposes, you may want to do some of the word problems on page 323 as a class.

### Monitoring Student Progress

**Problems 1–4 Lesson 7.1–7.2**

**If . . .** students do not understand the concept of percentages,

**Then . . .** try comparing common percentages to quarters in money. Four quarters equal one dollar. One quarter is 25 percent of a dollar, two quarters are 50 percent of a dollar, three quarters are 75 percent of a dollar, and 4 quarters are 100 percent of a dollar.

**Problems 5–16 Lessons 7.2, 7.3, and 7.8**

**If . . .** students miss more than two of these problems,

**Then . . .** review the common percentages and their equivalents. Allow for more practice.

**Problems 17–22 Lesson 7.6**

**If . . .** miss more than one of these subtraction decimal problems,

**Then . . .** assess to see if the problem is in the arithmetic. Provide extra practice, and encourage students to be careful.

**Problems 23–28 Lessons 7.1–7.6**

**If . . .** students have difficulty with these word problems,

**Then . . .** assess whether students are having trouble understanding the problem or solving it. Students may be encouraged to draw a picture or to make a chart or table to help them.

Student Page

# CHAPTER 7 Chapter Review

Lessons 7.1 and 7.2

**Answer** the following in percents.

1. This beaker is:
   a. 25% full
   (b.) 100% full
   c. 75% full
   d. 50% full

2. This beaker is:
   a. 100% full
   b. 25% full
   (c.) 50% full
   d. 75% full

3. This beaker is:
   a. 25% full
   b. 10 % full
   c. 100% full
   (d.) 75% full

4. This beaker is:
   a. 50% full
   (b.) 25% full
   c. 100% full
   d. 75% full

Lessons 7.2, 7.3, and 7.8

**Solve** for *n*.

5. 50% of 30 = $n$   $n = 15$
6. $\frac{1}{8}$ of 320 = $n$   $n = 40$
7. 0.25 of 400 = $n$   $n = 100$
8. $12\frac{1}{2}$% of 24 = $n$   $n = 3$
9. 0.75 of 160 = $n$   $n = 120$
10. 10% of 160 = $n$   $n = 16$
11. $\frac{1}{10}$ of 270 = $n$   $n = 27$
12. 20% of 150 = $n$   $n = 30$
13. 0.50 of 1,000 = $n$   $n = 500$
14. 25% of 24 = $n$   $n = 6$
15. $\frac{1}{2}$ of 420 = $n$   $n = 210$
16. 75% of 80 = $n$   $n = 60$

Lesson 7.6

**Find** the difference.

17. 0.35 − 0.28 = 0.07
18. 0.46 − 0.12 = 0.34
19. 3.66 − 1.77 = 1.89
20. 0.49 − 0.03 = 0.46
21. 2.11 − 1.09 = 1.02
22. 7.02 − 3.49 = 3.53



eTextbook This lesson is available in the *eTextbook*.

Student Page

Lessons 7.1–7.5

**Solve** each problem.

23. Julio bought a skateboard for $25. He got the skateboard at 50% off the original price. What was the original price? $50
24. One eighth of Mrs. Smith's class was absent on Monday. If she has 24 students in her class, how many were absent? 3 students
25. Tonya ran a race against Patrick. Tonya's time was 6.54 seconds, while Patrick's time was 7.02 seconds. How much time passed between Tonya's and Patrick's finishes? 0.48 seconds
26. Extended Response Raven went to the store to buy a purse. She had $20. The purse she liked was originally $28 but is now 25% off.
    a. Does she have enough money for the purse? no
    b. How do you know? The discounted price is $21, so she needs one more dollar.

Lesson 7.6

27. James's shooting statistics for the last four basketball games were: 33%, 0.42, $\frac{18}{36}$, and $\frac{5}{20}$. Arrange his statistics in order from least to greatest. $\frac{5}{20}$, 33%, 0.42, and $\frac{18}{36}$
28. Extended Response Micah bought a pair of shoes at 50% off. A week later at another store, he saw the same shoes for only 25% off, but the shoes cost less than his. How is this possible? The original price of the second pair of shoes was lower than that of the first pair.

## 3 Chapter Tests 40

## Practice Test

### Student Pages 324–327

- The Chapter 7 Practice Test on ***Student Edition*** pages 324–327 provides an opportunity to formally evaluate students' proficiency with concepts developed in this chapter.
- The content is similar to the Chapter 7 Review in standardized format.

**Problem 29** Extended Response

Students will solve Problem 29 by making use of the graphics they sketch. To solve 29b, students can try a visual approach in which they write the numbers next to the graphic benchmarks they sketched and use them for help in calculating 50%, 25%, and 75%

**Problem 30** Extended Response

Students can solve Problem 30 by using either the fraction or decimal values. It may be useful to remind students that either value can be used. Some students may find the decimal values easier to use in solving the problem.

Student Page

CHAPTER 7 **Practice Test**

**Use** the number line to answer questions 1 through 4.

1. Where does the bar start? 0.08
2. Where does the bar end? 0.40
3. What is the length of the bar? 0.32
4. What percentage of the total length is the bar's length? 32%

**Solve** the problems below. Be sure to show your work.

Four pencils that are each 7 centimeters long can be placed end to end. Their overall length equals the length of a book.

5. What percentage of the length of the book is each stick? 25%
6. What is the length of the book? 28 cm

Janet wants to buy a video game for $50. She found a coupon in the newspaper for 30% off the current price.

7. How much money will Janet save if she uses the coupon? $15
8. How much will the video game cost Janet with the coupon? $35

324 Textbook This lesson is available in the *eTextbook*.

Student Page

**Select** the correct answer.

9. How full is the beaker?
   Ⓐ 15% ● 25%
   Ⓒ 55% Ⓓ 90%

10. What is 10% of 30?
   ● 3 Ⓑ 10
   Ⓒ 15 Ⓓ 30
11. What is 75% of 64?
   Ⓐ 8 Ⓑ 16
   ● 48 Ⓓ 60
12. What is $\frac{3}{4}$ of 12?
   Ⓐ 2 Ⓑ 6
   ● 9 Ⓓ 10
13. What is $12\frac{1}{2}$% of 200?
   Ⓐ 10 Ⓑ 12
   Ⓒ 20 ● 25

**Which** symbol makes the statement true?

14. 20% of 17 ☐ 40% of 9
   Ⓐ = Ⓑ >
   ● <
15. 75% of 12 ☐ $\frac{1}{2}$ of 48
   Ⓐ = Ⓑ >
   ● <
16. LaDawn ran 10 meters in 47 centiseconds. Mary ran 10 meters in 50 centiseconds. How much faster was LaDawn ?
   Ⓐ 0.33 seconds Ⓑ 0.30 second
   ● 0.03 seconds Ⓓ 0.003 seconds
17. What is the difference between 3.89 and 3.01?
   Ⓐ 0.60 Ⓑ 0.64
   ● 0.88 Ⓓ 0.91
18. What is 10% of 90?
   Ⓐ 0.9 ● 9
   Ⓒ 90 Ⓓ 900

Real Math • Chapter 7 325

Student Page

# CHAPTER 7 Practice Test

19. What is 10% of 500?
Ⓐ 0.05 Ⓑ 0.5
Ⓒ 5 ● 50

20. Which could be a rule for this function?
64 → ? → 16
Ⓐ −30 ● ÷ 4
Ⓒ ÷ 8 Ⓓ × 4

21. Which could be a rule for this function?
50 → ? → 60
Ⓐ − 10 ● + 10
Ⓒ ÷ 2 Ⓓ × 3

22. How many ounces are in 80 pounds?
Ⓐ 160 Ⓑ 320
Ⓒ 640 ● 1,280

23. How many inches are in 3 yards?
Ⓐ 36 Ⓑ 78
● 108 Ⓓ 216

24. How many pints are in 4 gallons?
Ⓐ 16 Ⓑ 24
● 32 Ⓓ 44

**Multiply.**

25. 812 × 715
Ⓐ 463,170 Ⓑ 475,195
Ⓒ 550,280 ● 580,580

26. 3,210 × 473
Ⓐ 515,280 Ⓑ 518,330
● 1,518,330 Ⓓ 1,528,330

**Divide.**

27. $72 \div 5 = ?$
Ⓐ 14 ● 14R2
Ⓒ 15 Ⓓ 15R3

28. $57 \div 8 = ?$
Ⓐ 7 ● 7R1
Ⓒ 7R3 Ⓓ 8R1

 eTextbook This lesson is available in the *eTextbook.*

Student Page

Extended Response **Solve** the problems below.

29. A full beaker is shown below.
a. Draw pictures to show beakers that are 25%, 50%, and 75% full. Label each beaker.
b. If the height of the liquid in the full beaker is 60 centimeters, what is the height of the liquid in the other three beakers? Explain how you found each answer.

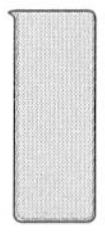

30. Blake made coffee mugs and sold them at the flea market. He spent $12 on the supplies, and sold the mugs for a total of $90. Because Jillian helped Blake for a little while, Blake told Jillian that she could have either 11% of the total sales, or $13\frac{1}{4}$% of the profits. Which payment method should Jillian choose? Explain your answer.

㉙ Students should draw beakers 25%, 50%, and 75% full. Liquid is 15 cm, 30 cm, and 45 cm. Explanations will vary. Possible answers: 50% equals $\frac{1}{2}$; $\frac{1}{2}$ of 60 is 30; 25% is $\frac{1}{2}$ of 50%, so 25% equals $\frac{1}{2}$ of 30, which equals 15; 75% equals 50% + 25% = 30 + 15 = 45

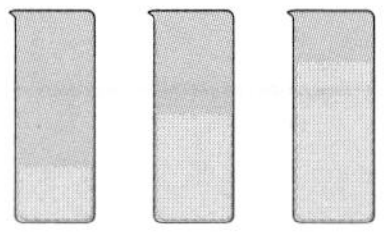

㉚ Jillian should choose $13\frac{1}{4}$% of the profits. 11% of $90 is $9.90. The profits are $90 − $12 = $78. $13\frac{1}{4}$% of $78 is $10.34.



## Chapter Test ✔ COMPUTING

- For further evaluation instead of or in addition to this test, you may wish to have students take the Chapter 1 Test provided in ***Assessment.***

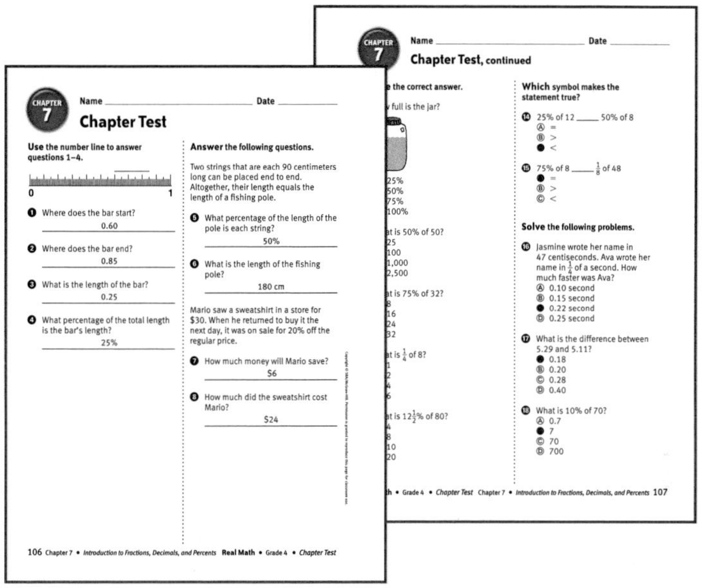

**Assessment, pages 106–107**

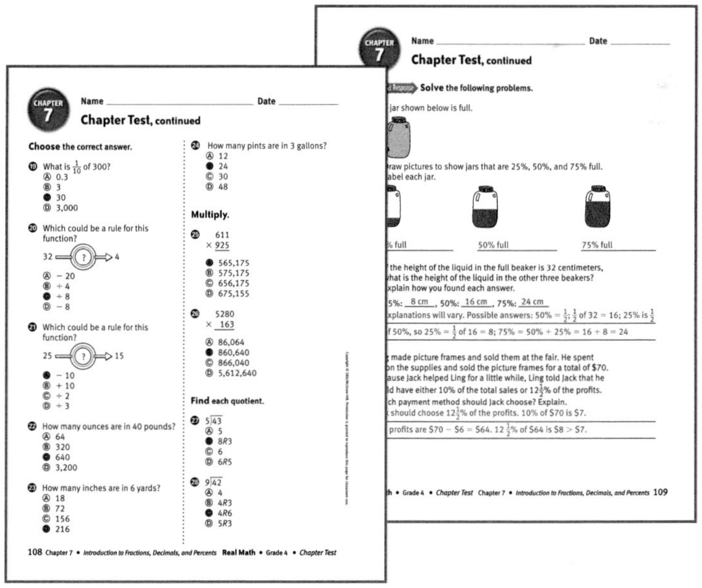

**Assessment, pages 108–109**

# CHAPTER 7 Assessment

## 4 Assess and Differentiate

e Assess Use ***eAssess*** to record and analyze evidence of student understanding.

## A Gather Evidence

Use the Daily Class Assessment Records in ***Assessment*** or ***eAssess*** to record Informal and Formal Assessments.

### Informal Assessment

**Key Ideas Review** UNDERSTANDING

Did the student
- ❑ answer questions?
- ❑ pose new questions?
- ❑ extend the discussion?
- ❑ provide insight?

### Informal Assessment

**Project** APPLYING

Did the student
- ❑ meet the project objectives?
- ❑ communicate clearly?
- ❑ complete the project accurately?
- ❑ connect mathematics to real-world situations?

### Formal Assessment

**Chapter Test** COMPUTING

Score the test, and record the results.

## B Summarize Findings

Analyze and summarize assessment data for each student. Determine which Chapter Follow-Up is appropriate for each student. Use the Student Assessment Record in ***Assessment*** or ***eAssess*** to update assessment records.

## C Chapter Follow-Up • DIFFERENTIATE INSTRUCTION

Based on your observations, use these teaching strategies for chapter follow-up.

| ENRICH | PRACTICE | RETEACH | INTERVENTION |
|---|---|---|---|
| **If . . .** students demonstrate **secure understanding** of chapter concepts,<br>**Then . . .** have them move on to the next chapter. | **If . . .** students exhibit **competent understanding** of chapter concepts,<br>**Then . . .** have them move on to the next chapter. | **If . . .** students demonstrate **emerging understanding** of chapter concepts,<br>**Then . . .** move on to the next chapter, but continue to provide cumulative review. | **If . . .** students demonstrate **minimal understanding** of chapter concepts,<br>**Then . . .** intensive intervention is needed before they start the next chapter. |

CHAPTER 7

# Teacher Reflection

## Lesson Study

Reflect on each of the lessons you taught in this chapter. Rate each one on the following scale, then consider ways to maintain or improve positive teaching experiences in the future.

| Lessons | Very Effective | Effective | Less Effective | What Worked | Ways to Improve |
|---|---|---|---|---|---|
| 7.1 Learning about Percentages | | | | | |
| 7.2 Percent Benchmarks | | | | | |
| 7.3 Understanding $12\frac{1}{2}\%$ and $\frac{1}{8}$ | | | | | |
| 7.4 Applying Percent Benchmarks | | | | | |
| 7.5 Decimals and Stopwatches | | | | | |
| 7.6 Adding and Subtracting Decimal Numbers | | | | | |
| 7.7 Number Lines | | | | | |
| 7.8 Understanding 10% and $\frac{1}{10}$ | | | | | |

CHAPTER 8 Overview

# Fractions, Probability, and Measurement

## Lessons



## Teaching for Understanding

***This chapter focuses on representing and computing with fractions through real-world applications.*** Students will build on their knowledge of fractions by comparing, calculating, and representing equivalent fractions. This chapter makes the connection between fractions as parts of wholes, as they have been used since Grade K, and fractions as rational numbers that can be placed on a number line, as they will be used in later mathematics. Also, students will spend a few lessons learning probability and will practice predicting events based on data.

## Prerequisite Skills and Concepts

- Estimating Using Percent Benchmarks
- Finding a Fraction of a Number
- Measuring Using Inches

## Fractions, Probability, and Measurement Skills Trace

| Before Grade 4 | Grade 4 | After Grade 4 |
|---|---|---|
| **Grades K–3**<br>Formally introduced to whole numbers, fraction benchmarks ($\frac{1}{2}$, $\frac{1}{4}$, and $\frac{1}{8}$), and computing with fractions | **Chapter 7** informally introduced fractions as decimals or percentages.<br>**This chapter** richly immerses students in various ways of comprehending fractions. | Calculate and represent rational numbers |

## Problem Solving

Problem solving is in every lesson. This chapter includes the following:

**CHAPTER INTRODUCTION** Students solve a problem that uses fractions and customary measurements to find a location (pp. 328I–329C).

**EXPLORING PROBLEM SOLVING** The first lesson focuses on the Use Simple Numbers and Make a Diagram strategies (pp. 348–349A). The second lesson provides an example of estimating fractions to analyze actual data (pp. 370–372A).

## Games

**Fraction Game Mat** (Lesson 8.1), **Fracto II Game Mat** (Lesson 8.5), **Fracto I Game Mat** (Lesson 8.5), **Anything but 10 Game** (Lesson 8.6)

# Math Background

Fractions

## About Fractions

- Fractions develop naturally in real life when we divide something into several equal parts and then use some number of these parts. We take $\frac{2}{3}$ of a pie by dividing the pie into three equal parts and taking two of these parts.
- In this setting the numerator of a fraction could not be greater than the denominator, and the fraction is something that operates on other things, including numbers. For example, we may need to know what $\frac{2}{3}$ of 24 is or about what $\frac{1}{4}$ of a cake is.
- A useful extension of the concept of a fraction suggests that if we have several identical things (such as dollars) we may consider a fraction with a numerator greater than its denominator. We also gradually begin to think of fractions as not only *operators* but numbers.
- The "of" operation (taking $\frac{2}{3}$ *of* 24, for example) is naturally associated with multiplication ($\frac{2}{3} \times 24$).
- This natural expansion of how we think of fractions—from "operators" only to numbers as well—makes fractions more useful and easier to use. It also allows us to think of decimals as equivalent to fractions.

## Key Concepts

**DECIMAL EQUIVALENTS AND APPROXIMATIONS**

- The decimal equivalent of a fraction is found by dividing the numerator by the denominator. This procedure is introduced in Grade 5.
- Some fractions have exact decimal equivalents, but most fractions do not. For example, $\frac{1}{2}$ is equal to 0.5 and 3/20 is equal to 0.15, but there is no decimal that names exactly the same number as $\frac{1}{3}$. However, all fractions without exact decimal equivalents can be approximated with decimals to get as close to their value as possible. The fraction $\frac{1}{3}$ can be approximated as 0.33, 0.333, 0.3333, and so on.
- The only fractions with exact decimal equivalents are those whose denominator has prime factors of 2 and 5. For example, $\frac{3}{4}$, $\frac{7}{10}$, $\frac{13}{20}$, and $\frac{18}{25}$ all have exact decimal equivalents, but $\frac{5}{12}$, $\frac{20}{21}$, $\frac{4}{9}$ and $\frac{13}{30}$ do not.

## Types of Word Problems

**BASICS OF PROBABILITY**

**DEFINITION** Probability is the measure of how likely it is for an event to occur. The probability of an event is always a number from 0 to 1.

**THEORETICAL PROBABILITY** Theoretical probability is the chance of events happening as determined by calculating results that would occur under ideal circumstances.

**EXPERIMENTAL PROBABILITY** Experimental probability is the chance of something happening, based on repeated testing and observing results. It is the ratio of the number of times an event occurred to the number of times tested.

## Using Probability

- As they work through the probability lessons in this chapter, students should begin to see that whereas predicting the outcome of only one chance event is not generally possible, we can usually predict the approximate outcomes of a large number of repeated events. Informal intuitive work with this concept has been included since the Kindergarten program.
- If an event cannot happen, its probability is 0. If an event is certain to happen, its probability is 1. However, the converse is not true. If the probability of an event is 0, the event could still occur. For instance, the probability of throwing a dart on any specific point of a dartboard is 0, since there are infinitely many points on the board. However, a dart must hit some point. Similarly, the probability of hitting some point other than the exact center of the dartboard is 1, but it is still possible to hit the center.

# What Research Says

About Fractions

## How Children Develop Part-Whole Concepts for Numbers

*Over time, the child gains a variety of counting strategies and greater understanding of part–whole relationships as part of his or her expanding number sense. The child recognizes that the whole is bigger than parts, but has an inexact grasp of the relative size of parts and wholes. The child develops recognition that larger numbers can be decomposed or broken into smaller parts, while also developing the understanding that when an amount of something is shared with more people, each person will receive a smaller amount of what is being shared. This understanding assists the child in making sense of fractional parts of the whole.*

(Clements, Douglas and Sarama, J. eds. *Engaging Young Children in Mathematics: Standards for Early Childhood Mathematics Education.* Mahwah, New Jersey: Lawrence Erlbaum Associates, Publishers, 2004)

## Research-Based Teaching Strategies

As children work with numbers, they gradually develop flexibility in thinking about numbers, which is a hallmark of number sense. Number sense develops as students understand the size of numbers, develop multiple ways of thinking about and representing numbers, use numbers as referents, and develop accurate perceptions about the effects of operations on numbers.

Fourth-grade students should construct their understanding of fractions as parts of a whole, as well as division. They will need to see and explore a variety of models of fractions, focusing primarily on familiar fractions such as halves, thirds, fourths, fifths, sixths, eighths, and tenths. By using an area model in which part of a region is shaded, students can see how fractions are related to a unit whole, compare fractional parts of a whole, and find equivalent fractions. They should develop strategies for ordering and comparing fractions, often using benchmarks such as $\frac{1}{2}$ and 1.

The use of parallel number lines is beneficial for several purposes. This approach can assist the students in seeing fractions as numbers on a number line relative to the whole numbers of 0 and 1. The number lines can be used to represent various relationships among fractions, including

## Research-Based, continued

equivalence. Students can also begin to understand that between any two fractions, there is always another fraction. Parallel number lines also assist the students in seeing equivalence when it exists between fractions, decimals, and percentages ($\frac{1}{2}$, 0.5, 50%).

Students need to be exposed to a variety of activities to help them develop a rich understanding of equivalence among fractional parts of a whole. For example, calculator activities can help expose students to common fraction–decimal equivalents. By studying fractions, decimals, and percentages simultaneously, students can learn to move among the equivalent forms, choosing and using the form of the number that is best suited for the context of the problem they are solving.

Students will develop an understanding of equivalence among fractions, decimals, and percentages, when they exist, and the information each type of representation conveys, and with these understandings and skills, they should be able to develop strategies for computing with familiar fractions and decimals.

(Adapted from the National Council of Teachers of Mathematics. *Principles and Standards for School Mathematics.* Reston, VA: NCTM, pp. 80, 148–150)

## RESEARCH IN ACTION

**Fractions** Chapter 8 continues to reinforce the development of part–whole number concepts and an understanding of what fractional parts of a whole represent.

**Combining and Separating Collections** Throughout Chapter 8 students will develop strategies, concepts, contexts, and procedures for understanding part–whole number concepts.

**Equivalence** Chapter 8 will provide students with a variety of activities and contexts for thinking about part–whole relationships with numbers.

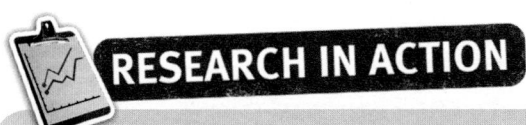

## Vocabulary

**decimal equivalent** (Lesson 8.3) decimals that name the same amount (such as the same amount as a fraction or as another decimal)

**denominator** (Lesson 8.1) the part of the fraction below the bar

**equivalent** (Lesson 7.3) having the same value

**equivalent fractions** (Lesson 8.11) fractions having the same value

**improper fraction** (Lesson 8.10) a fraction whose numerator is greater than, or equal to, its denominator

**mixed number** (Lesson 8.10) a number consisting of a whole number and a fraction

**numerator** (Lesson 8.1) the part of the fraction above the bar

**probability** (Lesson 8.4) the ratio of the number of chances favoring the occurrence of a particular event to the total number of possible occurrences

**rational number** (Lesson 8.3) a number that can be expressed as a quotient of two integers or as an integer (i.e., $\frac{3}{4}$, 5)

## English Learner

### Cognates

For English learners, a quick way to acquire new English vocabulary words is to build on what is known in the primary language.

| English | Spanish |
|---|---|
| denominator | denominador |
| divide | dividase |
| fractions | fracción |
| numerator | numerador |

### Access Vocabulary

English learners may understand words in different contexts or not understand idioms. Review chapter vocabulary for this concern. For example:

- spinner
- parts of a whole
- places
- the "of" operation
- halfway
- figure out the answer
- measuring instruments

# Chapter Planner

| Lessons | Objectives | NCTM Standards | State Standards |
|---|---|---|---|
| 8.1 **Writing Appropriate Fractions** pages 330A–331A | **Review fractional notation** by describing parts of a whole and parts of a set | Number and Operations<br>Problem Solving | |
| 8.2 **Fractions of Fractions** pages 332A–333A | **Explore strategies to find fractions of another fraction** while informally multiplying fractions | Number and Operations<br>Connections | |
| 8.3 **Fractions and Rational Numbers** pages 334A–335A | **Explore how to represent fractions on a number line** while developing understanding that fractions are names for rational numbers and for operators | Algebra<br>Connections | |
| 8.4 **Probability** pages 336A–337A | **Begin to develop the concept of calculating simple probabilities** by applying knowledge of fractions | Data Analysis and Probabilty<br>Connections | |
| 8.5 **Probability Experiments** pages 340A–339A | **Investigate probability** by using fractions for common applications | Number and Operations<br>Data Analysis and Probability | |
| 8.6 **Applying Fractions** pages 338A–341A | **Develop an awareness of equivalent fractions** by applying probability concepts to real situations | Number and Operations<br>Connections | |
| 8.7 **Probability and Fractions** pages 342A–343A | **Explore equivalent fractions** by solving simple probability exercises | Number and Operations<br>Geometry<br>Data Analysis and Probability | |
| 8.8 **Equivalent Fractions** pages 344A–345A | **Practice finding equivalent fractions** by using knowledge of fractions | Number and Operations | |
| 8.9 **Comparing Fractions** pages 346A–347A | **Explore equivalent fractions** by comparing fractions with unlike denominators | Connections | |
| 8.10 **Fractions Greater Than 1** pages 352A–355B | **Explore mixed numbers** by converting them to improper fractions | Number and Operations<br>Connections | |
| 8.11 **Representing Fractions Greater Than 1** pages 356A–359B | **Practice naming rational numbers** by finding equivalent fractions for rational numbers greater than 1 | Number and Operations | |
| 8.12 **Reading a Ruler** pages 360A–361A | **Review customary units** by computing fractional parts of customary units | Measurement<br>Connections | |
| 8.13 **Adding and Subtracting Measurements** pages 362A–363A | **Begin to develop the concept for adding and subtracting fractions** by building familiarity and confidence with simple fractions | Number and Operations<br>Problem Solving | |
| 8.14 **Adding and Subtracting Fractions** pages 364A–365A | **Practice adding and subtracting fractions with unlike denominators** by using fractions with like denominators | Number and Operations | |
| 8.15 **Adding Fractions Greater Than 1** pages. 366A–367A | **Explore addition for fractions greater than 1** by finding common denominators | Number and Operations | |
| 8.16 **Subtracting Fractions Greater Than 1** pages 368A–369A | **Explore subtraction for fractions greater than 1** by building on the algorithm for subtraction of fractions learned in Lesson 8.14 | Number and Operations | |

| Vocabulary | Manipulatives and Materials | Games to reinforce skills and concepts |
|---|---|---|
| denominator<br>numerator | • Response Wheels<br>• Fraction circles<br>• Sets of classroom supplies | Fraction Game (New) |
| denominator<br>numerator | • Response Wheels | Fraction Game (Lesson 8.1) |
| rational number<br>equivalent | • Response Wheels<br>• Meterstick and string<br>• Overhead calculator (optional)<br>• Calculators (optional) | |
| probability | • Response Wheels<br>• Overhead projector spinner | |
| probability | • Response Wheels<br>• Number Cubes<br>• Fracto I or Fracto II Game Mats | Fracto I or Fracto II Game Mats (New) |
| probability | • Number Cubes | Anything but 10 Game (New) |
| fraction | • Number Cubes<br>• Graph paper (optional)<br>• Fracto I or Fracto II Game Mats | Fracto I or Fracto II Game Mats (Lesson 8.5) |
| equivalent | • Response Wheels<br>• Colored pencils or crayons<br>• $8\frac{1}{2}'' \times 11''$ unlined white paper | |
| equivalent | • Response Wheels | |
| mixed number | • Equivalency Card Deck | Fracto I or Fracto II Game Mats (Lesson 8.5) |
| improper fraction | • Response Wheels | |
| | • Response Wheels<br>• Rulers and/or tape measures | |
| | • Inch rulers<br>• Paper strips (optional)<br>• Overhead projector fraction tiles | Fracto I or Fracto II Game Mats (Lesson 8.5) |
| equivalent fractions | • Response Wheels<br>• Fraction tiles and circles<br>• Overhead projector fraction tiles | Fracto I or Fracto II Game Mats (Lesson 8.5) |
| mixed number<br>improper fraction<br>equivalent fraction | • Response Wheels | |
| mixed number<br>improper fraction<br>equivalent fraction | • Response Wheels | |

# Additional Resources

## Differentiated Instruction

*Intervention Support Guide* provides instruction for the following prerequisite skills:

- Lesson 8.A Estimating Using Percent Benchmarks
- Lesson 8.B Finding a Fraction of a Number
- Lesson 8.C Measuring Using Inches

*Enrichment Support Guide*

*Practice*

*Reteach Support Guide*

*English Learner Support Guide*

## Technology

The following electronic resources are available:

**Planner** Lessons 8.1–8.16

**Presentation** Lessons 8.1–8.16

**Textbook** Lessons 8.1–8.16

**Assess** Lessons 8.1–8.16

**MathTools** **Fractions** Lessons 8.1–8.3, 8.5–8.11, 8.13; **Probability** Lesson 8.4; **Electronic Ruler** Lesson 8.12

**Games** **Fraction Game** Lessons 8.1–8.2; **Fracto I** or **Fracto II Game Mats** Lessons 8.5–8.10, 8.13–8.14

# Chapter Planner, continued

| Problem Solving | When to Use | Objectives | NCTM Standards | Skills Covered |
|---|---|---|---|---|
| **Chapter Introduction** pages 328I–329C 15–30 minutes | Use after the Chapter 8 Pretest | Introduce chapter concepts in a problem-solving setting | Communication<br>Reasoning and Proof | Fractions<br>Measurements |
| **Exploring Problem Solving** pages 348–349A 30–45 minutes | Use any time during the chapter | Explore methods of solving nonroutine problems | Reasoning and Proof<br>Connections | Diagram Building<br>Fractions<br>Proportional Reasoning |
| **Exploring Problem Solving** pages 370–372A 45–60 minutes | Use any time after the first Exploring Problem Solving | Develop logical reasoning while integrating reading skills with mathematics | Data Analysis and Probability<br>Communication | Fractions<br>Customary Measurement<br>Circle Graphs |

| Review | When to Use | Objectives | NCTM Standards | Skills Covered |
|---|---|---|---|---|
| **Cumulative Review** pages 350–351 15–30 minutes | Use any time after Lesson 8.9 | Review concepts and skills taught earlier in the year | Problem Solving<br>Algebra<br>Number and Operations | Multidigit Addition and Subtraction<br>Fractions and Percents of Whole Numbers |
| **Cumulative Review** pages 373–374 15–30 minutes | Use any time after Lesson 8.16 | Review concepts and skills taught earlier in the year | Number and Operations<br>Problem Solving<br>Connections | Computing Percents, Exponents, Multidigit Multiplication, Map Reading |
| **Chapter 8 Review** pages 376A–377 30–45 minutes | Use after Lesson 8.16 | Review concepts and skills taught in the chapter | Measurement<br>Data Analysis and Probability<br>Number and Operations | Fractions<br>Probability<br>Measurement |

| Assessment | When to Use | Objectives | NCTM Standards | Skills Covered |
|---|---|---|---|---|
| **Informal Assessment Rubrics** (pp. 328A–378A) 5 minutes per student | Use at the end of the lesson | Provide daily evaluation of math proficiency | Problem Solving<br>Reasoning and Proof<br>Communication | Computing, Understanding, Reasoning, Applying, Engaging |
| **Pretest** (*Assessment* p. 111) 15–30 minutes | Use after or in place of the Chapter 7 Review | Provide assessment or additional practice of the chapter concepts | Number and Operations<br>Measurement<br>Representations | Fractions<br>Customary Measurements |
| **Individual Oral Assessment** (p. 351A) 5 minutes per student | Begin after Lesson 8.9 | Provide alternate means of assessing students' progress | Number and Operations<br>Probability | Fractions<br>Probability |
| **Mastery Checkpoint** (*Assessment* pp. T67–T69) 5 minutes per student | Use after or in place of the Chapter 8 Review | Provide assessment or additional practice of the chapter concepts | Number and Operations<br>Problem Solving<br>Representations | Fractions |
| **Chapter 8 Practice Test** (pp. 378–381A) 30–45 minutes | Use after or in place of the Chapter 8 Review | Provide assessment or additional practice of the chapter concepts | Number and Operations<br>Problem Solving<br>Representations | Fractions<br>Graphing<br>Probability |
| **Chapter 8 Test** (*Assessment* pp. 121–124) 30–45 minutes | Use after or in place of the Chapter 8 Review | Provide assessment or additional practice of the chapter concepts | Number and Operations<br>Problem Solving<br>Representations | Fractions<br>Graphing<br>Probability |

# Technology Resources and Support

Visit SRAonline.com for online versions of the ***Real Math eSuite.***

## Technology for Teachers

| | |
|---|---|
| **Presentation** | Lessons 8.1–8.16 Use the ***ePresentation*** to interactively present chapter content. |
| **Planner** | Use the Chapter and Lesson Planners to outline activities and time frames for Chapter 8. |
| **Assess** | Students can take the following assessment in ***eAssess:***<br>• Chapter Pretest<br>• Mastery Checkpoint Lessons 8.1, 8.2, and 8.14<br>• Chapter Test<br>Teachers can record results and print reports for all assessments in this chapter. |
| **MathTools** | **Fractions** Lessons 8.1–8.3, 8.5–8.11, 8.13; **Probability** Lesson 8.4; **Electronic Ruler** Lesson 8.12 |

## Technology for Students

| | |
|---|---|
| **Textbook** | An electronic, interactive version of the ***Student Edition*** is available for all lessons in Chapter 8. |
| **MathTools** | **Fractions** Lessons 8.1–8.3, 8.5–8.11, 8.13; **Probability** Lesson 8.4; **Electronic Ruler** Lesson 8.12 |
| **Games** | **Fractions** Lessons 8.1–8.2; **Fracto I or II Game Mats** Lessons 8.5–8.10, 8.13–8.14 |
| | ***TechKnowledge*** Level 4 provides lessons that specifically teach the Unit 10 Internet and Unit 4 Drawing and Graphics applications that students can use while working on this chapter's projects. |

# Fractions, Probability, and Measurement

## 1 Introduce Chapter 8 (5)

**Chapter Objectives**

Explain to students that in this chapter they will build on what they already know about fractions and customary measurement. They will

- investigate probability using fractions.
- learn about equivalent fractions and mixed numbers.
- add and subtract fractions.

### Pretest COMPUTING

Administer the Pretest in ***Assessment.***

The Pretest for Chapter 8 covers the following prerequisite skills:

- Simple fractions (Problems 1–2)
- Customary units (Problems 3–4)
- Least common multiples (Problems 5–6)
- Fraction, decimal, and percentages equivalents (Problems 7–9)

The Pretest also covers the following topics from this chapter:

- Fractions of a whole number (Problems 10–11)
- Finding and comparing probabilities (Problem 12)
- Equivalent fractions (Problems 13–14)
- Fractions greater than 1 (Problems 15–16)
- Adding and subtracting fractions (Problems 17–18)

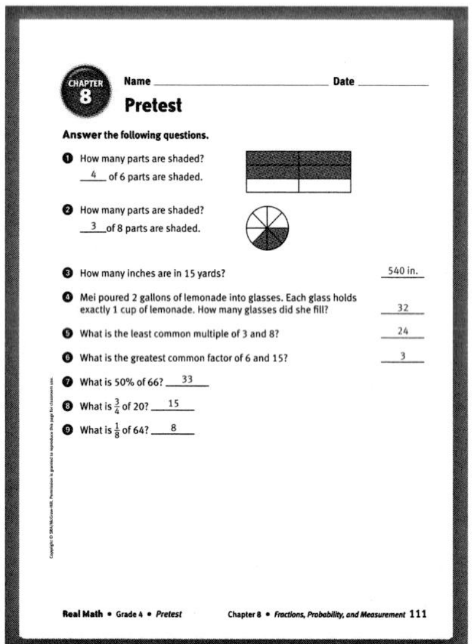

CHAPTER 8 Name ____________ Date ________

**Pretest**

**Answer the following questions.**

1. How many parts are shaded?
   4 of 6 parts are shaded.
2. How many parts are shaded?
   3 of 8 parts are shaded.
3. How many inches are in 15 yards? 540 in.
4. Mei poured 2 gallons of lemonade into glasses. Each glass holds exactly 1 cup of lemonade. How many glasses did she fill? 32
5. What is the least common multiple of 3 and 8? 24
6. What is the greatest common factor of 6 and 15? 3
7. What is 50% of 66? 33
8. What is $\frac{3}{4}$ of 20? 15
9. What is $\frac{1}{8}$ of 64? 8

**Real Math** • Grade 4 • *Pretest* Chapter 8 • *Fractions, Probability, and Measurement* 111

Chapter 8 Pretest

### Access Prior Knowledge UNDERSTANDING

Have students share rescue stories they have read or heard about. Ask questions such as the following:

- **Have you heard of someone being rescued by an animal? What kind of animal was it?**
- **What methods do rescuers use to find people who are lost?** Possible answers: They use search dogs if people are lost in the woods. If people are lost at sea, they use helicopters and divers.

## 2 Exploring Problem Solving (20)

**Tell Students In Today's Lesson They Will**

solve a problem to locate a stranded person.

### Using Student Pages

Briefly discuss the photo on page 328. Ask questions such as the following:

- **Have you ever seen a helicopter like this? Where?** Possible answer: at the beach
- **What did the helicopter do?**

Read page 329 with the class. To help students understand the message, follow a procedure such as the following:

- Tell the students that the sun is at the front of the room.
- To make sure they understand the words *clockwise* and *counterclockwise,* have students make a complete turn clockwise and then a complete turn counterclockwise.
- Have students act out the first part of the message by turning clockwise $\frac{3}{4}$ of a circle.
- Have students act out the second part by facing the front again and then turning clockwise $\frac{1}{3}$ of a circle.

Alternatively, you can have a volunteer demonstrate for the class.

Discuss Problems 1–3 and their answers with the class to make sure students catch on. Discuss the following:

- Fractions can be used to describe a direction or angle by referring to them as part of a turn.
- In the problem, the searcher and the lost friend see the sun in the same direction because the sun is so far from Earth.

Have students work in small groups to discuss and solve Problem 4. Provide help as needed.

Student Page

CHAPTER 8

# Fractions, Probability, and Measurement

**In This Chapter You Will Learn**

- how to investigate probability by using fractions.
- about equivalent fractions and mixed numbers.
- how to add and subtract fractions.

Student Page

## Problem Solving

Old methods and modern technology can work together to save lives. Imagine you and a friend are on a hiking trip. Your friend is lost and uses a walkie-talkie to contact you.

REAL WORLD

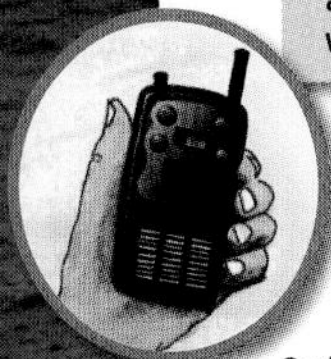

*I don't know where I am, but this may help. If I face the sun and then turn clockwise three-quarters of a complete turn, I'm facing the top of the mountain. If I face the sun and then turn clockwise one-third of a complete turn, then I'm facing the top of the tow . . .*

Suddenly the signal gives out. There is silence. You take out your map and look toward the sun, which is directly north.

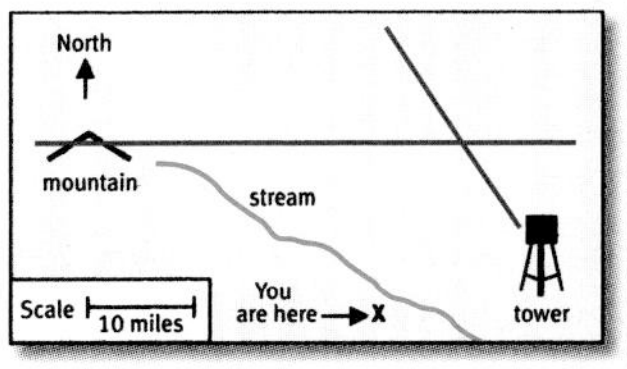


**Copy the map. Then answer these questions.**

1. What fraction of a complete counterclockwise turn would be the same as turning clockwise $\frac{3}{4}$ of a complete turn? $\frac{1}{4}$
2. What compass direction is your friend facing when he or she faces the mountaintop? west
3. Is your friend north or south of the stream? Explain. North of the stream because otherwise he or she would not be facing the mountaintop when he or she faced west.
4. Draw a horizontal line on your map to show how far north or south your friend is. Use the rest of the information to determine your friend's location. See map.

329

## CyberSolver

To extend problem solving, have students use the Internet to find the answers to the following questions:

- **What space-age technology do we use today to locate people who are stranded?**
- **How does this technology work?**

Students can find information about rescue missions by using a key phrase such as *search and rescue*. At the following Web sites, students can find information about a satellite system (SARTSAT) that is used for emergency location: http://www.cospas-sarsat.org/MainPages/indexEnglish.htm **or** http://www.sarsat.noaa.gov/

## Concept/Question Board

APPLYING

### Questions

Have students write three questions they have about fractions, probability, and measurement and how they can be used. Then have them select one question to post on the Question side of the Board.

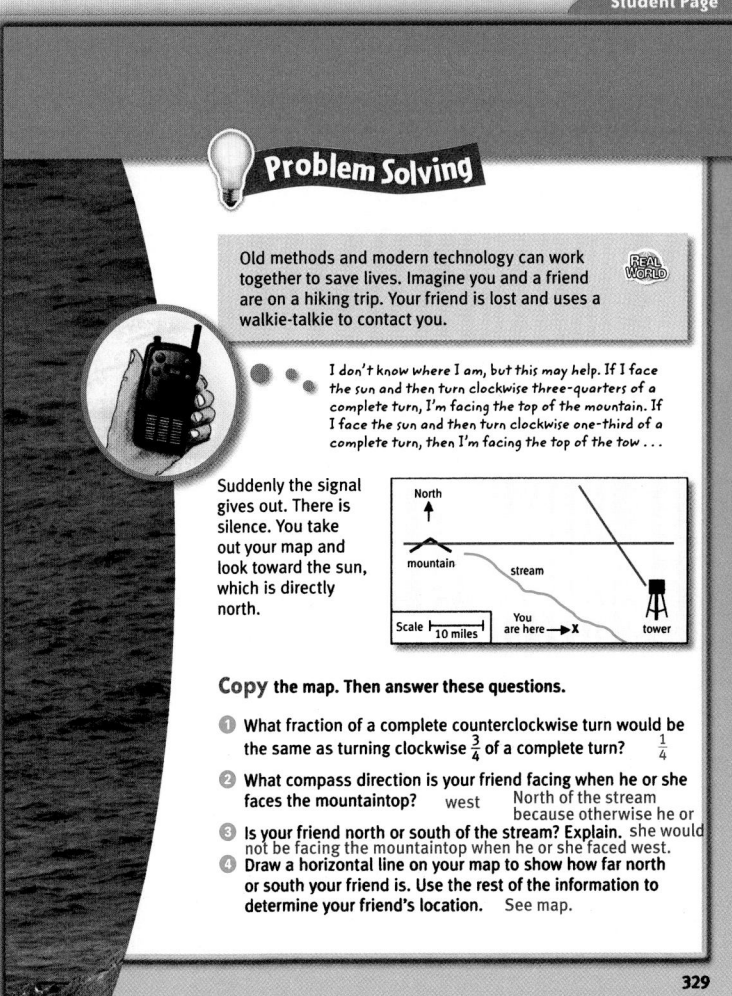

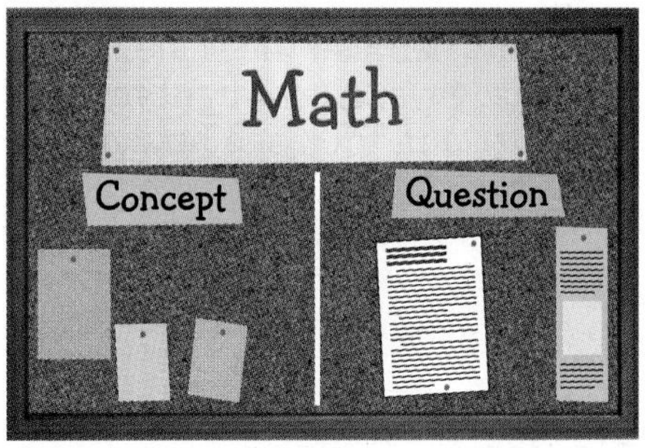


### Concepts

As students work through the chapter, have them collect examples of how fractions, probability, and measurement are used in everyday situations. For each example, have students write problems that relate to the item(s). Have them display their examples on the Concept side of the Board.

Suggest the following:

- photograph of a road sign
- attendance record
- road atlas

### Answers

Throughout the chapter, have students post answers to the questions and solutions to the problems on the Board.

## 3 Reflect

5

**Knowledge Age Skills**

**Effective Communication** Have each group present its answers and reasoning for Problem 4 to the class. After each presentation ask students whether they agree or disagree with the reasoning and why. Ask questions such as the following:

- **How can you express the direction northeast?** Possible answers: Face sun and turn clockwise $\frac{1}{8}$ of a turn. Go halfway between north and east.
- **In what direction and how far will you need to hike to reach your friend?** northeast; about 25 miles

Students can use the scale to find the distance to the friend in various ways. They might mark off the 10-mile length on a scrap of paper and then see how many of those lengths it takes to cover the distance from the X to the friend. They might also use a ruler to measure the 10-mile length, figure out what each inch or centimeter represents, then measure the distance to the lost friend in inches or centimeters.

## Sample Solutions Strategies

Here are some strategies students could use to solve Problem 4.

### Use a Model

Students can imagine the lost friend is at the center of a clock face. The sun is at 12:00. The tower is $\frac{1}{3}$ of the way around the clock face, which would be at 4:00. Then students can draw a line along the direction of the hour hand at 4:00.

### Guess, Check, and Adjust

Students can choose a location on the map, check to see if it fits the information in the message, and adjust accordingly. They can continue until they find a point that works..

## Home Connection

At this time, you may want to send home the letter on pages 30–33 of ***Home Connection.*** This letter describes what students will be learning and what activities they can do at home to support their work in school.

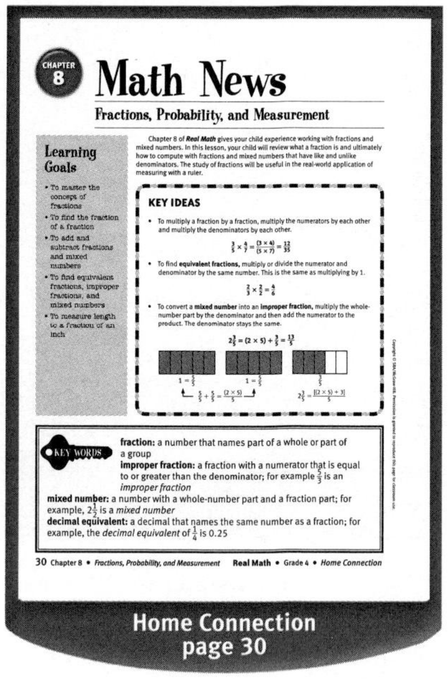

CHAPTER 8 **Math News**

**Fractions, Probability, and Measurement**

Chapter 8 of ***Real Math*** gives your child experience working with fractions and mixed numbers. In this lesson, your child will review what a fraction is and ultimately how to compute with fractions and mixed numbers that have like and unlike denominators. The study of fractions will be useful in the real-world application of measuring with a ruler.

**Learning Goals**

- To master the concept of fractions
- To find the fraction of a fraction
- To add and subtract fractions and mixed numbers
- To find equivalent fractions, improper fractions, and mixed numbers
- To measure length to a fraction of an inch

**KEY IDEAS**

- To multiply a fraction by a fraction, multiply the numerators by each other and multiply the denominators by each other.

$$\frac{3}{5} \times \frac{4}{7} = \frac{(3 \times 4)}{(5 \times 7)} = \frac{12}{35}$$

- To find **equivalent fractions,** multiply or divide the numerator and denominator by the same number. This is the same as multiplying by 1.

$$\frac{2}{3} \times \frac{2}{2} = \frac{4}{6}$$

- To convert a **mixed number** into an **improper fraction,** multiply the whole-number part by the denominator and then add the numerator to the product. The denominator stays the same.

$$2\frac{3}{5} = (2 \times 5) + \frac{3}{5} = \frac{13}{5}$$

$1 = \frac{5}{5}$ $1 = \frac{5}{5}$ $\frac{3}{5}$

$\frac{5}{5} + \frac{5}{5} = \frac{(2 \times 5)}{5}$ $2\frac{3}{5} = \frac{[(2 \times 5) + 3]}{5}$

**KEY WORDS**

**fraction:** a number that names part of a whole or part of a group

**improper fraction:** a fraction with a numerator that is equal to or greater than the denominator; for example $\frac{5}{3}$ is an *improper fraction*

**mixed number:** a number with a whole-number part and a fraction part; for example, $2\frac{1}{2}$ is a *mixed number*

**decimal equivalent:** a decimal that names the same number as a fraction; for example, the *decimal equivalent* of $\frac{1}{4}$ is 0.25

30 Chapter 8 • *Fractions, Probability, and Measurement* **Real Math** • Grade 4 • *Home Connection*

Home Connection page 30

# 4 Assess and Differentiate

e Assess Use ***eAssess*** to record and analyze evidence of student understanding.

## A Gather Evidence

Use the Daily Class Assessment Records in ***Assessment*** or ***eAssess*** to record daily observations.

### Informal Assessment

**Access Prior Knowledge**

Did the student UNDERSTANDING

- ❑ make important observations?
- ❑ extend or generalize learning?
- ❑ provide insightful answers?
- ❑ pose insightful questions?

### Informal Assessment

**Concept/Question Board**

Did the student APPLYING

- ❑ apply learning in new situations?
- ❑ contribute concepts?
- ❑ contribute answers?
- ❑ connect mathematics to real-world situations?

### Formal Assessment

**Pretest** COMPUTING

Review student answers in each problem set.

- ❑ Simple fractions (Problems 1–2)
- ❑ Customary units (Problems 3–4)
- ❑ Least common multiples (Problems 5–6)
- ❑ Fraction, decimal, and percentage equivalents (Problems 7–9)
- ❑ Fractions of a whole number (Problems 10–11)
- ❑ Finding and comparing probabilities (Problem 12)
- ❑ Equivalent fractions (Problems 13–14)
- ❑ Fractions greater than 1 (Problems 15–16)
- ❑ Adding and subtracting fractions (Problems 17–18)

## B Summarize Findings

Analyze and summarize assessment data for each student. Determine which Assessment Follow-Up is appropriate for each student. Use the Student Assessment Record in ***Assessment*** or ***eAssess*** to update assessment records.

## C Assessment Follow-Up • DIFFERENTIATE INSTRUCTION

| ENRICH | PRACTICE | RETEACH | INTERVENTION | ENGLISH LEARNER |
|---|---|---|---|---|
| **If . . .** students demonstrate a secure understanding of chapter concepts,<br>**Then . . .** move quickly through the chapter or use ***Enrichment*** Lessons 8.1–8.16 as assessment follow-up to extend and apply understanding. | **If . . .** students grasp chapter concepts with competent understanding,<br>**Then . . .** use ***Practice*** Lessons 8.1–8.16 as lesson follow-up to develop fluency. | **If . . .** students have prerequisite understanding but demonstrate emerging understanding of chapter concepts,<br>**Then . . .** use ***Reteach*** Lessons 8.1, 8.11, 8.14, 8.15, and 8.16 to reteach lesson concepts. | **If . . .** students are not competent with prerequisite skills,<br>**Then . . .** use ***Intervention*** Lessons 8.A–8.C before each lesson to develop fluency with prerequisite skills. | Use ***English Learner Support Guide*** Lessons 8.1–8.16 for strategies to preteach lesson vocabulary and concepts. |

# Math Across the Curriculum

Preview the chapter projects with students. Assign or have students choose from the projects to extend and enrich concepts in this chapter.

## Create a Sculpture as a Memorial 3–4 weeks

**Math Objective**
To reinforce studies of measurement by creating a sculpture to scale

**Fine Arts Objective**
To reinforce studies of form by creating a sculpture as a memorial

**Technology Objective**
To use a drawing and graphics program to create a sketch for a sculpture

While considering how to create a memorial sculpture for the Great Chicago Fire of 1871, have students use technology to

- gather images and information about the fire.
- create sketches by using a drawing and graphics program.

For this project, students use the Internet to investigate the Great Chicago Fire.

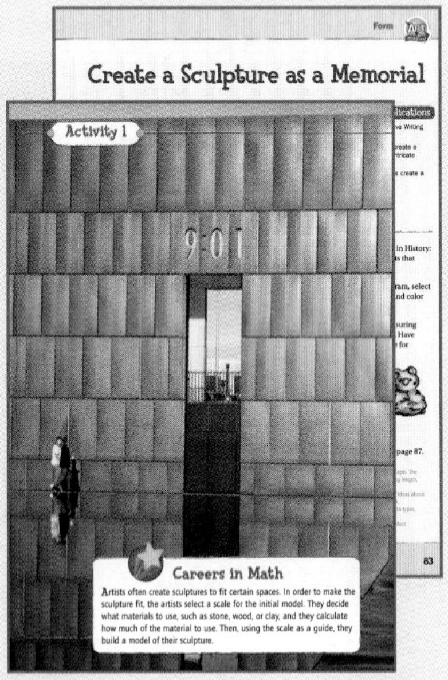


For specific step-by-step instructions for this project, see ***Across the Curriculum Math Connections*** pages 82–87.

### Knowledge Age Skills

**Teamwork** Students create memorial sculptures.

**Problem Strategizing** Students create a plan to solve the central question of the **WebQuest.**

***TechKnowledge*** Level 4 provides lessons that teach the Unit 10 Internet and Unit 4 Drawing and Graphics applications that students can use in this project.

## Make a Slide Show about Surviving a Natural Disaster 3–4 weeks

**Math Objective**
To reinforce studies of fractions by using fractions to present statistics

**Social Studies Objective**
To relate ideas about cooperation survival of a natural disaster

**Technology Objective**
To use presentation software to create a slide show

Have students use mathematics to relate important information about surviving a natural disaster. To broaden the social studies concepts, have students research and communicate how cooperation plays a large part in survival.

As part of the project, students should consider the following issues:

- measures people can take to protect themselves during a natural disaster
- strategies for survival in the aftermath of the disaster
- ways people can cooperate to help one another when disaster strikes

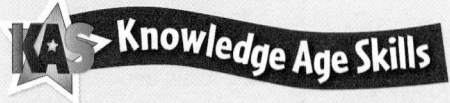

For specific step-by-step instructions for this project, see ***Across the Curriculum Math Connections*** pages 88–91.

### Knowledge Age Skills

**Effective Communication** Students create a communication piece with important yet succinct textual information and associated images.

**Problem Formulation, Planning, and Strategizing** Students plan and strategize to design a slide show that will be appealing and contain useful information.

## Lesson Planner

**OBJECTIVES**
- To review fractional notation and the use of fractions
- To review fractions of areas and of sets
- To provide practice in determining whether a given use of fractions makes sense

**NCTM STANDARDS**

**Number and Operations**
Understand numbers, ways of representing numbers, relationships among numbers, and number systems

**Problem Solving**
Apply and adapt a variety of appropriate strategies to solve problems

**MATERIALS**
- *Response Wheels
- *Fraction circles (optional)
- Sets of classroom supplies (such as pencils, crayons, erasers, and markers)

**TECHNOLOGY**
- **Presentation** Lesson 8.1
- **MathTools** Fractions
- **Games** Fractions

**TEST PREP**

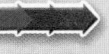

**Cumulative Review**
Mental Math reviews the relationship between fractions and percents (Lessons 7.1–7.3 and 7.8).

**Extended Response**
Problems 9–12

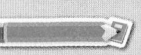

**Writing + Math**
Journal

*Manipulative Kit Item

# Writing Appropriate Fractions

**Context of the Lesson** Students have worked with fractions since Grade 1 of ***Real Math.*** The relationship between fractions and percentages that was introduced in Chapter 7 is also reviewed. This lesson contains a Mastery Checkpoint.

See page 328B for Math Background for teachers for this lesson.

## Planning for Learning • DIFFERENTIATE INSTRUCTION

### INTERVENTION

**If . . .** students lack the prerequisite skill of estimating using percent benchmarks,

**Then . . .** teach ***Intervention*** Lesson 8.A.

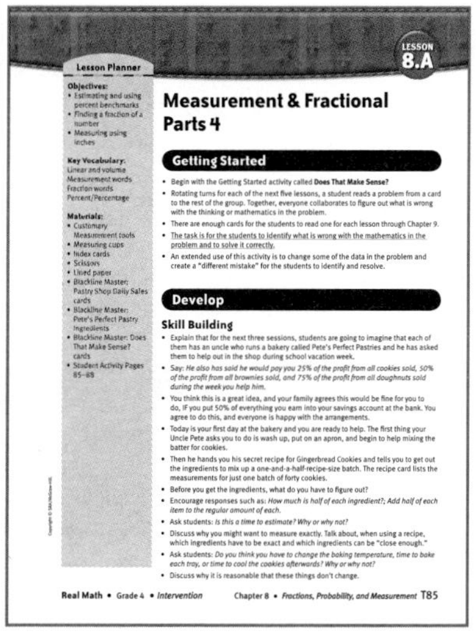

Intervention Lesson 8.A

### ENGLISH LEARNER

**Preview**

**If . . .** students need language support,

**Then . . .** use Lesson 8.1 in ***English Learner Support Guide*** to preview lesson concepts and vocabulary.

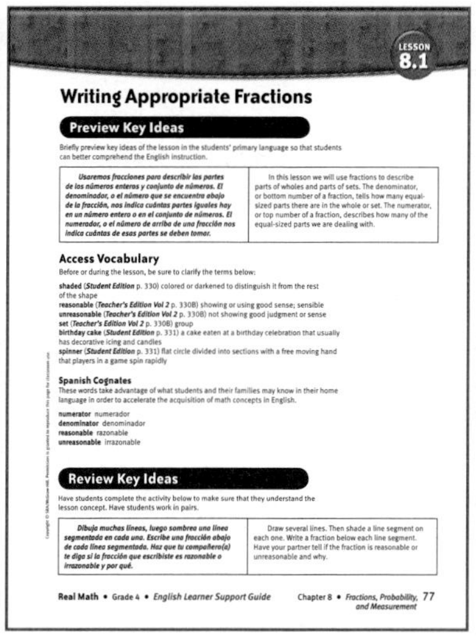

English Learner Lesson 8.1

### ENRICH

**If . . .** students are proficient in the lesson concepts,

**Then . . .** encourage them to create extra fraction statements for the Journal activity.

### PRACTICE

**If . . .** students would benefit from additional practice,

**Then . . .** extend the Skill Building before assigning the student pages.

### RETEACH

**If . . .** students need to review fractions,

**Then . . .** extend the response activity in the Guided Discussion before assigning the student pages.

**Vocabulary**

**denominator** \di nom′ ə nā tər\
*n.* part of the fraction below the line

**numerator** \nü′ mə rā tər\
*n.* part of the fraction above the line

**Access Vocabulary**

**spinner** flat circle divided into sections with a free moving hand that players may spin rapidly

**Spanish Cognates**

**numerator** numerador
**denominator** denominador

## Mental Math

5

Review RESPONSE WHEEL Provide proportional reasoning exercises, such as the following, based on money (answers need not be exact).

**a.** What percent of 1 dollar is 50 cents? 50%
**b.** What percent of 1 dollar is 1 quarter? 25%
**c.** What percent of 1 dime is 5 cents? 50%
**d.** What percent of 1 nickel is 5 cents? 100%
**e.** What percent of 1 dollar is 3 quarters? 75%
**f.** What percent of 1 quarter is 2 nickels? 40%

## 1 Develop

20

**Tell Students In Today's Lesson They Will**
use fractions to describe parts of wholes and parts of sets.

### Guided Discussion UNDERSTANDING

Whole Group

1. Review students' knowledge of fractions. Discuss the denominator, which is the bottom number, that tells the amount of equal-sized parts there are in the whole or set. Discuss the numerator, which is the top number, that describes how many of the equal-sized parts we are dealing with.
2. Ask students to suggest an example of a fraction, and describe how to show it. Write the fraction on the board. Have students illustrate the fraction. Repeat this process with numerous examples, such as $\frac{1}{2}$, $\frac{1}{4}$, $\frac{2}{3}$, $\frac{4}{6}$, and $\frac{5}{8}$.
3. THUMBS UP Draw a line segment on the board and shade a portion of it. Tell the students that you will say and write which fraction of the line is shaded; they need to let you know whether your fraction is reasonable (thumbs-up) or unreasonable (thumbs-down). Use common fractions, and make your unreasonable answers obviously so. Vary the lengths of the line segments.

**Examples:**

| | | |
|---|---|---|
| $\frac{1}{2}$ | //////////////////////------------------ | up |
| $\frac{3}{4}$ | /////////////////////------ | up |
| $\frac{1}{3}$ | ///////////////////////////////------ | down |
| $\frac{1}{10}$ | //////////////---------------------------- | down |
| $\frac{1}{3}$ | -------------//////////////-------------- | up |
| $\frac{4}{5}$ | -----------------------////------- | down |

4. Remind students that fractions can also describe parts of a set of things. When thinking about fractions this way, we commonly call the entire set of objects "the whole," and a subset of the entire group can be called "part of the whole." Use sets of classroom supplies to demonstrate this concept. For example
   - Show 4 pencils (some sharpened and some not) and have students identify the fraction of pencils that are sharpened.
   - Show a set of 5 markers: red, orange, yellow, green, and blue. Ask students to identify the fraction of markers that are warm colors (red, orange, and yellow), and the fraction that are cool colors (green and blue), $\frac{3}{5}$; $\frac{2}{5}$
   - Leave the caps on some markers in the set and remove the caps from the other markers in the set. Ask students to identify the fraction of markers with caps and the fraction without caps.

### Skill Building ENGAGING

Small Group

1. Have students work in pairs or small groups to answer questions such as those below. Encourage them to use fraction manipulatives or to draw pictures to help them decide if the descriptions are correct.
   - Ali's family ordered a pizza. It had mushrooms on one half and peppers on the other half. possible; 2 halves make a whole
   - Israel is beginning a collection of animal pictures. He organizes the pictures by vertebrates and invertebrates. So far Israel has 3 invertebrate pictures and 7 vertebrate pictures. $\frac{3}{7}$ of the pictures are invertebrates. Not correct; there are 10 pictures in all. Three out of 10, or $\frac{3}{10}$, are invertebrate pictures.
2. Regroup as a class to discuss the answers and how students determined the answers.

## 2 Assign Student Pages

20

**Page 330–331** APPLYING
Have students complete pages 330 and 331 independently.

#### Monitoring Student Progress

| If . . . | Then . . . |
|---|---|
| students can correctly answer oral questions about fractions but cannot answer similar written questions | review the meaning of fractional notation and provide extra practice with concrete materials when appropriate. |

**As Students Finish**

eMathTools Have students explore fractional amounts using ***eMathTools: Fractions***

Student Page

LESSON 8.1 **Writing Appropriate Fractions**

### Key Ideas

**Fractions can be used to describe a part of a whole.**

The bottom number of a fraction, the denominator, tells how many equal-sized parts there are in the whole or set. The top number of a fraction, the numerator, describes how many of those equal-sized parts to consider.

numerator → 2
denominator → 5

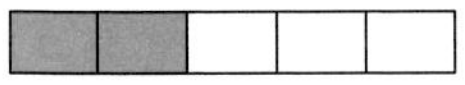

**What** fraction of each of the following figures has been shaded?

1. $\frac{3}{4}$
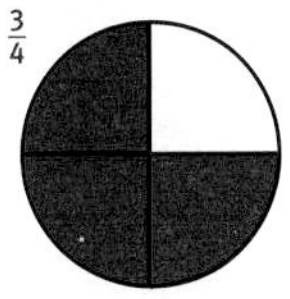
2. $\frac{2}{3}$
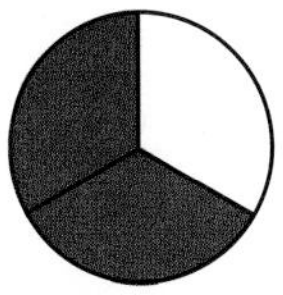
3. $\frac{3}{4}$
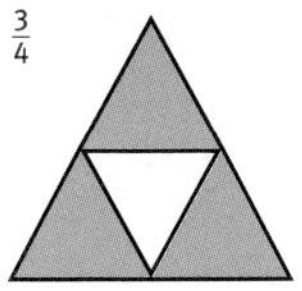
4. $\frac{4}{8}$ or $\frac{1}{2}$
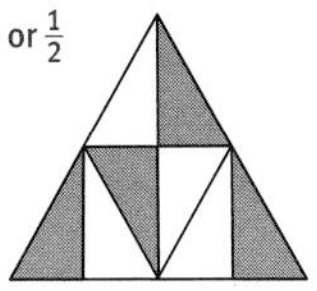
5. $\frac{1}{1}$ or 1

6. $\frac{0}{1}$ or 0
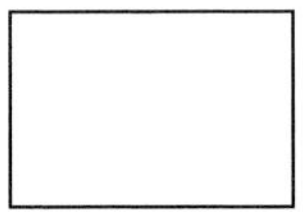

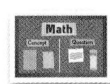

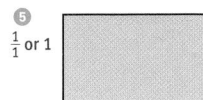

eTextbook This lesson is available in the ***eTextbook.***

Student Page

**Write** a fraction that tells what part of the set is inside the ring.

7. 
$\frac{2}{7}$
8. 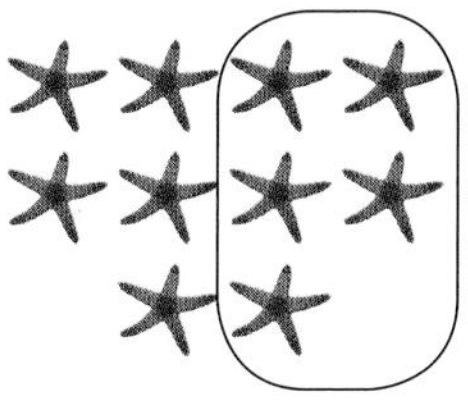
$\frac{5}{10}$ or $\frac{1}{2}$

Extended Response **Explain** which of these sentences are possible, and which are not possible.

9. In Diana's class, $\frac{1}{2}$ of the students are girls, and $\frac{2}{3}$ of the students are boys. Not possible; if $\frac{1}{2}$ of the students are girls, then $\frac{1}{2}$ must be boys.
10. In $\frac{1}{2}$ of an hour, Dan, Rachel, and Leon planted a small flower garden. If they started at 9:00 A.M., they must have worked until 10:30 A.M. Not possible; they should be finished at 9:30 AM
11. A spinner has 6 parts that are the same size.

   a. $\frac{1}{2}$ of the area of the spinner is red. Possible
   b. If you spin the spinner many times, you would land on red about $\frac{1}{2}$ of the times. Possible; red is $\frac{1}{2}$ of the area
12. Mai ate $\frac{1}{2}$ of her birthday cake on Monday, $\frac{1}{2}$ on Tuesday, and $\frac{1}{2}$ on Wednesday. See Reflect in the *Teacher's Edition.*

Writing + Math **Journal**

Make up two of your own fraction statements: one that is possible and one that is not possible. Ask another student or a family member if they can figure out which one is possible and which one isn't. Ask them to explain their answers with pictures, and see if their reasoning is the same as or different from yours. See Reflect in the *Teacher's Edition.*



# 3 Reflect

5

## Guided Discussion APPLYING

Whole Group

Invite 4 girls and 4 boys to come to the front of the classroom. Ask the class questions such as the following:

- **What fraction of the group is girls?** $\frac{1}{2}$
- **What percentage of the group is that?** 50%

This type of questioning provides an opportunity to informally discuss equivalent fractions.

Ask two of the students to put a hand on his/her head. Ask questions such as the following:

- **What fraction of the group has a hand on his/her head?** $\frac{1}{4}$
- **What percentage of the group is that?** 25%
- **What percentage do not have a hand on his/her head?** 75%

## Extended Response

**Problem 12** This problem stresses the importance of a fraction's referent. Taking half of the original cake is impossible after two days, while taking half of what's left could, theoretically, continue forever.

Writing + Math **Journal**

Students should write statements involving fractions that are similar to Problems 9–12. One statement should be a scenario that is possible; the other should be a scenario that is not possible.

Use Mastery Checkpoint 15 found in ***Assessment*** to evaluate student mastery of understanding fractions. By this time students should be able to correctly answer eighty percent of the Mastery Checkpoint items.

**Curriculum Connection:** Page 331 in the ***Student Edition*** discusses a garden, a common strategy in children's literature. Read *The Secret Garden* or *Peter Pan in Kensington Gardens*.

**Cumulative Review:** For review of math vocabulary, assign Problems 1–2 on student page 350.

**Family Involvement:** Assign the ***Practice, Reteach,*** or ***Enrichment*** activities depending on the needs of your students. Have students play a game of their choice with a friend or relative.

**Concept/Question Board:** Have students look for real-world examples of fractions and post them on the Concept/Question Board.

**Math Puzzler:** How many squares can you find in this drawing? 30

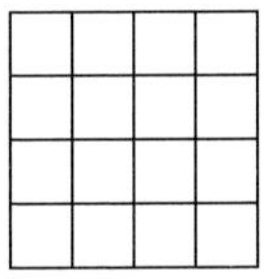

# 4 Assess and Differentiate

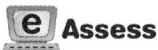

**eAssess** Use ***eAssess*** to record and analyze evidence of student understanding.

## A Gather Evidence

Use the Daily Class Assessment Records in ***Assessment*** or ***eAssess*** to record daily observations.

### Formal Assessment

**Mastery Checkpoint**

Did the student
- ❑ use correct procedures?
- ❑ respond with at least eighty percent accuracy?

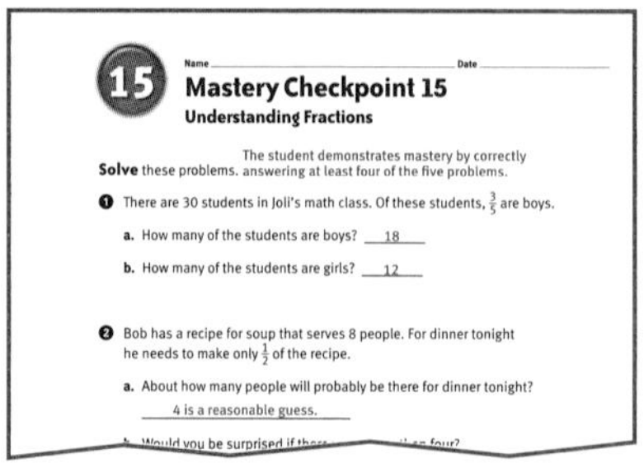

15 Mastery Checkpoint 15
Understanding Fractions

Name ______ Date ______

The student demonstrates mastery by correctly answering at least four of the five problems.

**Solve** these problems.

1. There are 30 students in Joli's math class. Of these students, $\frac{3}{5}$ are boys.
   a. How many of the students are boys? 18
   b. How many of the students are girls? 12
2. Bob has a recipe for soup that serves 8 people. For dinner tonight he needs to make only $\frac{1}{2}$ of the recipe.
   a. About how many people will probably be there for dinner tonight? 4 is a reasonable guess.

Mastery Checkpoint Page T67

## B Summarize Findings

Analyze and summarize assessment data for each student. Determine which Assessment Follow-Up is appropriate for each student. Use the Student Assessment Record in ***Assessment*** or ***eAssess*** to update assessment records.

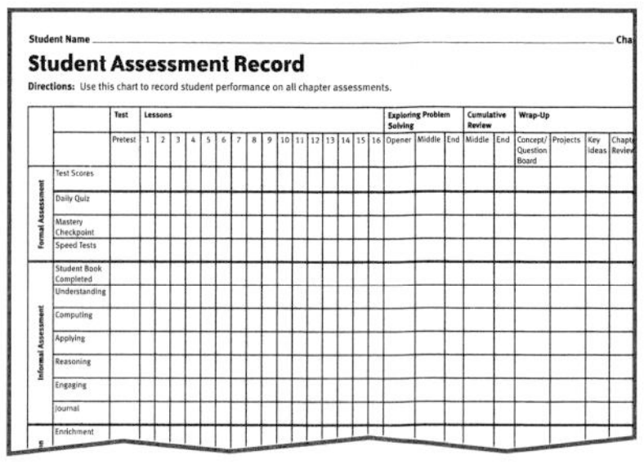

Student Assessment Record

Directions: Use this chart to record student performance on all chapter assessments.

Assessment Page T41

## C Assessment Follow-Up • DIFFERENTIATE INSTRUCTION

Based on your observations, use these teaching strategies for assessment follow-up.

### INTERVENTION

Review student performance on ***Intervention*** Lesson 8.A to see if students have mastered prerequisite skills for this lesson.

### ENGLISH LEARNER

**Review**

Use Lesson 8.1 in ***English Learner Support Guide*** to review lesson concepts and vocabulary.

### ENRICH

**If . . .** students are proficient in the lesson concepts,

**Then . . .** encourage them to work on the chapter projects or ***Enrichment*** Lesson 8.1.

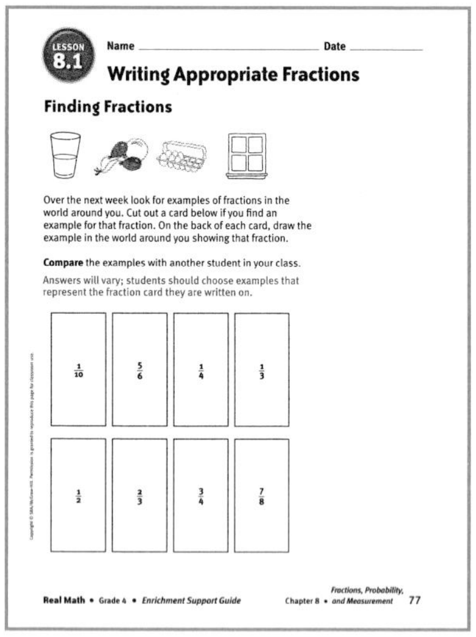

LESSON 8.1 Writing Appropriate Fractions

Finding Fractions

Over the next week look for examples of fractions in the world around you. Cut out a card below if you find an example for that fraction. On the back of each card, draw the example in the world around you showing that fraction.

**Compare** the examples with another student in your class.

Answers will vary; students should choose examples that represent the fraction card they are written on.

Real Math • Grade 4 • Enrichment Support Guide — Chapter 8 • Fractions, Probability, and Measurement 77

Enrichment Lesson 8.1

### PRACTICE

**If . . .** students would benefit from additional practice,

**Then . . .** assign ***Practice*** Lesson 8.1.

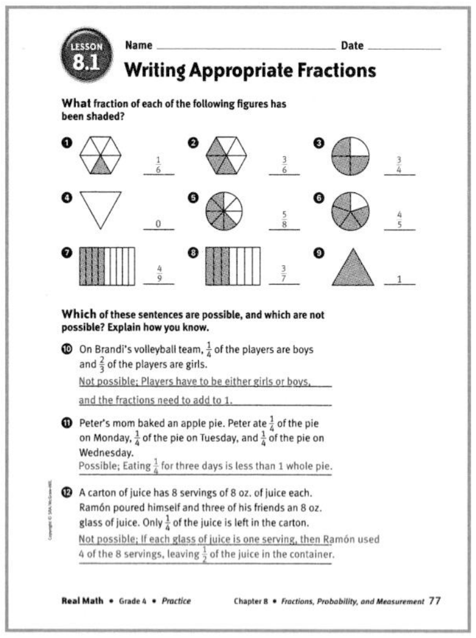

LESSON 8.1 Writing Appropriate Fractions

What fraction of each of the following figures has been shaded?

Which of these sentences are possible, and which are not possible? Explain how you know.

10. On Brandi's volleyball team, $\frac{1}{4}$ of the players are boys and $\frac{2}{3}$ of the players are girls. Not possible; Players have to be either girls or boys, and the fractions need to add to 1.
11. Peter's mom baked an apple pie. Peter ate $\frac{1}{4}$ of the pie on Monday, $\frac{1}{4}$ of the pie on Tuesday, and $\frac{1}{4}$ of the pie on Wednesday. Possible; Eating $\frac{1}{4}$ for three days is less than 1 whole pie.
12. A carton of juice has 8 servings of 8 oz. of juice each. Ramón poured himself and three of his friends an 8 oz. glass of juice. Only $\frac{1}{8}$ of the juice is left in the carton. Not possible; If each glass of juice is one serving, then Ramón used 4 of the 8 servings, leaving $\frac{1}{2}$ of the juice in the container.

Real Math • Grade 4 • Practice — Chapter 8 • Fractions, Probability, and Measurement 77

Practice Lesson 8.1

### RETEACH

**If . . .** students are having difficulty writing appropriate fractions,

**Then . . .** reteach the concept using ***Reteach*** Lesson 8.1.

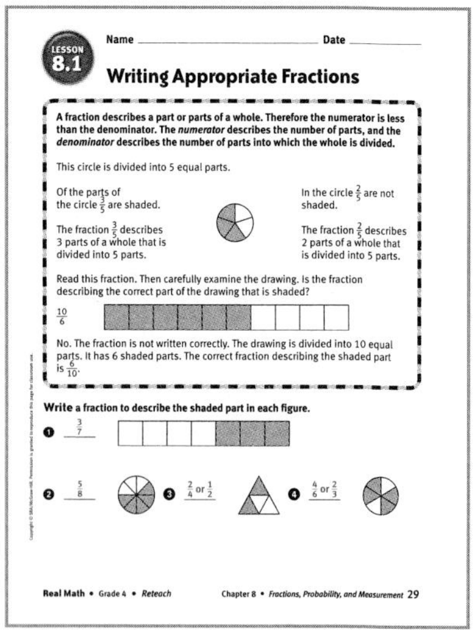

LESSON 8.1 Writing Appropriate Fractions

A fraction describes a part or parts of a whole. Therefore the numerator is less than the denominator. The *numerator* describes the number of parts, and the *denominator* describes the number of parts into which the whole is divided.

This circle is divided into 5 equal parts.

Read this fraction. Then carefully examine the drawing. Is the fraction describing the correct part of the drawing that is shaded?

No. The fraction is not written correctly. The drawing is divided into 10 equal parts. It has 6 shaded parts. The correct fraction describing the shaded part is $\frac{6}{10}$.

Write a fraction to describe the shaded part in each figure.

Real Math • Grade 4 • Reteach — Chapter 8 • Fractions, Probability, and Measurement 29

Reteach Lesson 8.1

## Lesson Planner

### Objectives
- To consider how to find a fraction of a fraction
- To show why it is natural to call taking a fraction of a fraction *multiplication of fractions*

### NCTM Standards
**Number and Operations**
Compute fluently and make reasonable estimates

**Connections**
Recognize and use connections among mathematical ideas

### Materials
- ***Response Wheels**

### Technology
**e Presentation** Lesson 8.2
**e MathTools** Fractions
**e Games** Fractions

### Test Prep
**Cumulative Review**
Mental Math reviews approximate fractions (Lessons 7.2 and 7.4).

*Manipulative Kit Item

# Fractions of Fractions

**Context of the Lesson** At an early age, students think of fractions as operators (for example, $\frac{1}{2}$ of the pie, $\frac{2}{3}$ of the apples, and so on). At this stage of conceptual development, the most natural operation with fractions is the "of" operation. In this lesson, we show that a fraction of a fraction of something can be found by using the product of the numerators as the new numerator and the product of the denominators as the new denominator. In future lessons we show students how to think of fractions as names for rational numbers and will consider addition and subtraction of fractions. This lesson contains a Mastery Checkpoint.

See page 328B for Math Background for teachers for this lesson.

## Planning for Learning • DIFFERENTIATE INSTRUCTION

### INTERVENTION

**If . . .** students lack the prerequisite skill of finding a fraction of a number,

**Then . . .** teach ***Intervention*** Lesson 8.B.

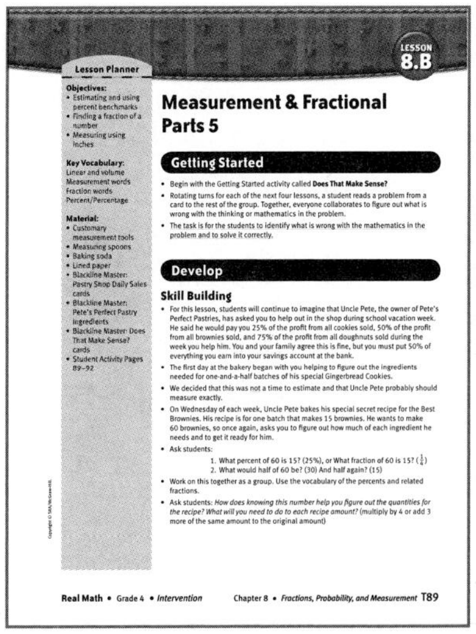
Lesson 8.B
Lesson Planner
Measurement & Fractional Parts 5
Getting Started
Develop
Skill Building
Real Math • Grade 4 • Intervention
Chapter 8 • Fractions, Probability, and Measurement T89

Intervention Lesson 8.B

### ENGLISH LEARNER

**Preview**

**If . . .** students need language support,

**Then . . .** use Lesson 8.2 in ***English Learner Support Guide*** to preview lesson concepts and vocabulary.

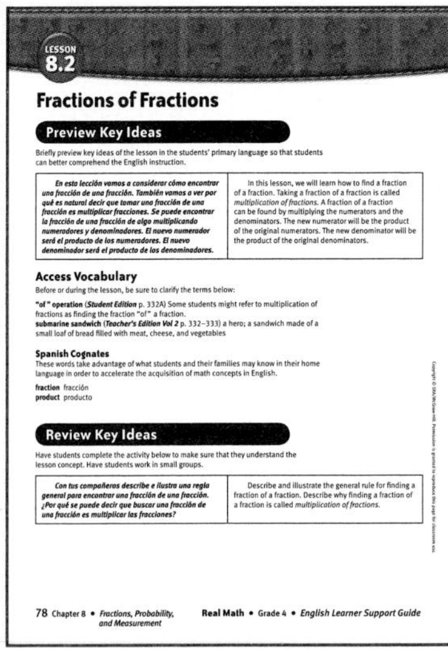
Lesson 8.2
Fractions of Fractions
Preview Key Ideas
Access Vocabulary
Spanish Cognates
Review Key Ideas
78 Chapter 8 • Fractions, Probability, and Measurement
Real Math • Grade 4 • English Learner Support Guide

English Learner Lesson 8.2

### ENRICH

**If . . .** students are proficient in the lesson concepts,

**Then . . .** encourage them to work on the chapter projects.

### PRACTICE

**If . . .** students would benefit from additional practice,

**Then . . .** consider working through additional student page problems as a class.

### RETEACH

**If . . .** students are having difficulty understanding fractions of fractions,

**Then . . .** have them model the intro activity by coloring rectangles on graph paper.

### Access Vocabulary
**"of" operation** this is the way some students might refer to multiplication of fractions, as finding the fraction "of" a fraction

**Spanish Cognates**
**fraction** fracción
**product** producto

# Teaching Lesson 8.2

## Mental Math 5

Review RESPONSE WHEEL Have students show approximate fractions, such as the following, using the percent slider on their **Response Wheels:**

**a.** $\frac{1}{2}$ **b.** $\frac{3}{4}$

**c.** $\frac{1}{3}$ **d.** $\frac{2}{3}$

**e.** $\frac{9}{10}$ **f.** $\frac{90}{100}$

**g.** $\frac{1}{4}$ **h.** $\frac{25}{100}$

## 1 Develop 30

### Tell Students In Today's Lesson They Will

learn how to find a fraction of another fraction.

### Strategy Building UNDERSTANDING Whole Group

**1.** Draw a rectangle on the board. Divide it into 5 equal horizontal strips. Shade 1 strip.

- **What fraction of the rectangle is 1 of the strips?** $\frac{1}{5}$

Shade 2 more of the strips.

- **What fraction of the rectangle are 3 of the strips?** $\frac{3}{5}$

**2.** Divide the shaded area only into 4 vertical strips.

- **What fraction of the shaded area is contained in each of the new vertical strips?** $\frac{1}{4}$

Shade 3 of the new strips in a way that is different from the way you shaded the horizontal strips (a different color, cross hatch, etc.). Point out the part of the rectangle that is shaded both ways. Discuss how this area shows $\frac{3}{4}$.

**3.** In order to tell what fractional part of the whole each small rectangle is, extend the vertical dividing lines down through the whole rectangle. Ask questions such as the following:

- **How many small rectangles are there altogether?** 20
- **Did you have to count all the rectangles or did you have a quick way of deciding that there were 20?** Students probably multiplied $4 \times 5$. If they didn't, mention that they could have.
- **How many of the small rectangles have been shaded both ways?** 9
- **What is the quickest way to count those rectangles?** $3 \times 3 = 9$
- **What fraction of the entire rectangle has been shaded both ways?** $\frac{9}{20}$

**4.** Encourage students to think of a quick way to find $\frac{3}{4}$ of $\frac{3}{5}$ of the rectangle without shading and counting. If necessary, remind them of the quick method they used for counting the number of small rectangles and shaded rectangles. Use $3 \times 3$ for the numerator and $4 \times 5$ as the denominator.

**5.** Explain that when we find a fraction of a fraction, such as $\frac{3}{4}$ of $\frac{3}{5}$, the resulting fraction has a numerator that is equal to the product of the original numerators and the new denominator is equal to the product of the original denominators. For example, $\frac{3}{4}$ of $\frac{3}{5} = \frac{9}{20}$.

**6.** Ask students why finding a fraction of a fraction can be called multiplying fractions. To find a fraction of another fraction, we multiply the numerator and denominator of the fractions together. To find $\frac{3}{4}$ of $\frac{3}{5}$ we multiply $\frac{3 \times 3}{4 \times 5}$. We write this $\frac{3}{4} \times \frac{3}{5} = \frac{9}{20}$.

### Using Student Pages APPLYING Whole Group

Work through Problems 1–5 on student page 332 together.

## 2 Assign Student Pages 20

### Page 332–333 APPLYING

Have students complete page 333 independently. There is no need to "reduce" fractions like $\frac{6}{12}$ unless having equivalent fractions is useful for some purpose, such as comparing two fractions, adding, or subtracting.

#### Monitoring Student Progress

**If . . .** students have difficulty recalling multiplication facts

**Then . . .** encourage them to refer to Fact Helpers in the Student Handbook found in the back of the ***Student Edition*** and practice playing the **Cube 100 Game,** or practice with flashcards.

### As Students Finish

eMathTools Have students explore fractional amounts using ***eMathTools: Fractions***.

Student Page

## LESSON 8.2 Fractions of Fractions

**Key Ideas**

**We can find a fractional part of a fraction by thinking about parts of the whole.**
We can also find a fraction of a fraction by multiplying.

To show $\frac{4}{5}$, we can divide a rectangle horizontally into 5 smaller, equal-sized rectangles and color 4 of them blue.

1. What fraction of the rectangle is colored blue? $\frac{4}{5}$

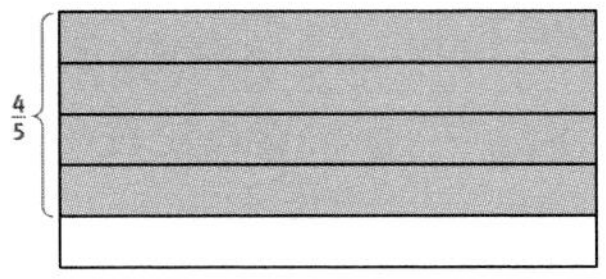

Now we can find a fractional part of the fraction $\frac{4}{5}$. To find $\frac{2}{3}$ of $\frac{4}{5}$, we divide the shaded part into thirds and then shade 2 of the thirds red.

If we shade a section blue and then shade it red, it will look purple.

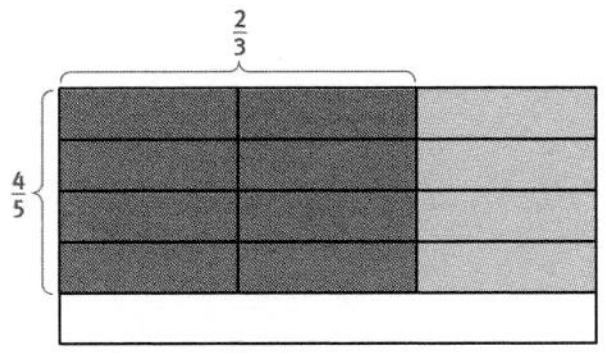

2. What fraction of the blue rectangles is also shaded red? $\frac{2}{3}$

By extending the dividing lines down through the whole rectangle, we can tell what fractional part of the whole each small rectangle is.

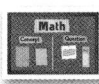

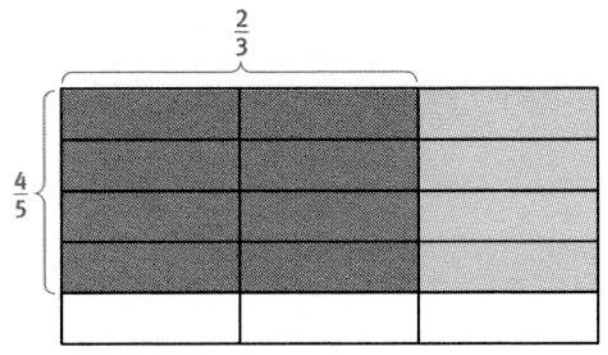

3. Into how many small rectangles was the big rectangle divided? 15
4. How many of those little rectangles are colored purple (both blue and red)? 8
5. Is $\frac{2}{3}$ of $\frac{4}{5}$ of the entire rectangle (the parts that are shaded purple) the same as $\frac{8}{15}$ of the entire rectangle? yes



eTextbook This lesson is available in the ***eTextbook***.

Student Page

Now imagine dividing a big rectangle horizontally into 5 equal-sized rectangles and coloring 2 of them blue. Then divide the big rectangle vertically into 4 equal strips and shade 3 of them red. (You may want to draw a picture to help you.)

6. What fraction of the big rectangle is colored blue? $\frac{2}{5}$
7. What fraction of the blue rectangles is also shaded red? $\frac{3}{4}$
8. How many little rectangles are there altogether? 20

Can you find the total number of little rectangles by multiplying the denominators (bottom parts) of the fractions? yes, $5 \times 4 = 20$

9. How many of the 20 small rectangles, in this case, would be shaded purple (colored both blue and red)? 6

Can you find that number of purple rectangles by multiplying the numerators (top parts) of the two fractions? yes, $2 \times 3 = 6$

10. What fraction of the big rectangle is shaded purple (colored both blue and red)? $\frac{6}{20}$

Can we say that $\frac{3}{4}$ of $\frac{2}{5}$ of the big rectangle is equal to $\frac{6}{20}$ of the big rectangle? yes

When finding a fractional part of a fraction, the new numerator will be the product of the original numerators; the new denominator will be the product of the original denominators. So, we can use multiplication to find a fraction of a fraction.

To find $\frac{3}{4}$ of $\frac{2}{5}$ of something, we can multiply $\frac{3}{4}$ by $\frac{2}{5}$.

$\frac{3}{4}$ of $\frac{2}{5} = \frac{3}{4} \times \frac{2}{5} = \frac{3 \times 2}{4 \times 5} = \frac{6}{20}$

**Complete** the following to make correct statements.

11. $\frac{2}{5}$ of $\frac{3}{4}$ is ■ $\frac{6}{20}$
12. $\frac{3}{4} \times \frac{2}{5} =$ ■ $\frac{6}{20}$
13. $\frac{7}{8} \times \frac{5}{9} =$ ■ $\frac{35}{72}$
14. $\frac{5}{9}$ of $\frac{7}{8}$ is ■ $\frac{35}{72}$
15. $\frac{2}{3}$ of 1 is ■ $\frac{2}{3}$
16. $\frac{1}{2} \times \frac{1}{3} =$ ■ $\frac{1}{6}$

**Replace** the ■ to make each of the following statements true.

17. $\frac{1}{2} \times$ ■ $= \frac{1}{6}$ $\frac{1}{3}$
18. $\frac{1}{3} \times$ ■ $= \frac{1}{6}$ $\frac{1}{2}$
19. $\frac{3}{4}$ of ■ $= \frac{6}{20}$ $\frac{2}{5}$



# 3 Reflect

5

## Guided Discussion ENGAGING

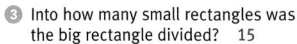

RESPONSE WHEEL Ask students to show 50% using the sliders on their ***Response Wheels***. Ask how 50% is written as a fraction. $\frac{1}{2}$ Then ask them to add 25% to the amount shown on their ***Response Wheels*** and show the new percent. Ask how to write this percent as a fraction. As a fraction, 75 % is $\frac{3}{4}$.

Write the original fraction ($\frac{1}{2}$) and the fraction added to ($\frac{1}{4}$) it on the board.

Ask students if the sum of two fractions can be found by adding numerators and denominators. No. If a student says yes, ask if $\frac{1}{2} + \frac{1}{4} = \frac{2}{6}$. Clearly it does not, since $\frac{2}{6}$ is less than $\frac{1}{2}$.

Use Mastery Checkpoint 16 found in ***Assessment*** to evaluate mastery of finding fractions of numbers. By this time students should be able to correctly answer eighty percent of the Mastery Checkpoint items.

**Cumulative Review:** For review of multidigit addition and subtraction, assign Problems 3–4 on student page 350.

**Family Involvement:** Assign the ***Practice, Reteach,*** or ***Enrichment*** activities depending on the needs of your students. Have students play a game of their choice with a friend or relative.

**Concept/Question Board:** Have students look for real world examples of fractions and post them on the Concept/Question Board.

**Math Puzzler:** Tonya and Emmitt buy a submarine sandwich to share. The clerk cuts it in halves for them before she wraps it.
"I want the bigger half," says Emmitt.
"Impossible!" answers Tonya.
What does Tonya mean? If an object is cut in halves, that means it is in two equal parts; neither half is bigger than the other.

# 4 Assess and Differentiate

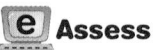

**eAssess** Use ***eAssess*** to record and analyze evidence of student understanding.

## A Gather Evidence

Use the Daily Class Assessment Records in ***Assessment*** or ***eAssess*** to record daily observations.

### Formal Assessment

**Mastery Checkpoint**

Did the student

- ❑ use correct procedures?
- ❑ respond with at least eighty percent accuracy?

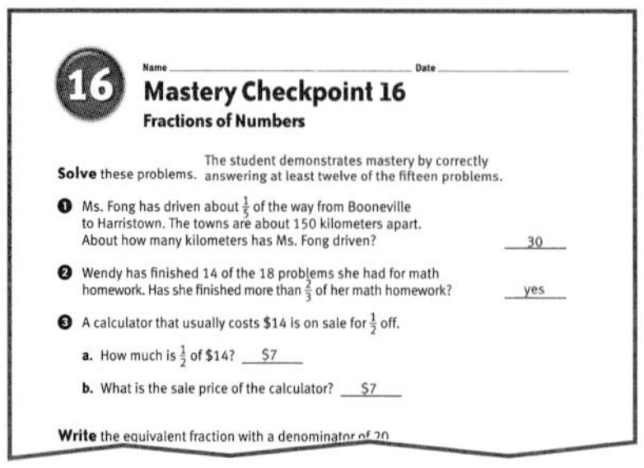

16 Name ____ Date ____

Mastery Checkpoint 16

Fractions of Numbers

The student demonstrates mastery by correctly answering at least twelve of the fifteen problems.

**Solve** these problems.

1. Ms. Fong has driven about $\frac{1}{5}$ of the way from Booneville to Harristown. The towns are about 150 kilometers apart. About how many kilometers has Ms. Fong driven? 30
2. Wendy has finished 14 of the 18 problems she had for math homework. Has she finished more than $\frac{2}{3}$ of her math homework? yes
3. A calculator that usually costs \$14 is on sale for $\frac{1}{2}$ off.
   a. How much is $\frac{1}{2}$ of \$14? \$7
   b. What is the sale price of the calculator? \$7

**Write** the equivalent fraction with a denominator of 20.

**Mastery Checkpoint Page T68**

## B Summarize Findings

Analyze and summarize assessment data for each student. Determine which Assessment Follow-Up is appropriate for each student. Use the Student Assessment Record in ***Assessment*** or ***eAssess*** to update assessment records.

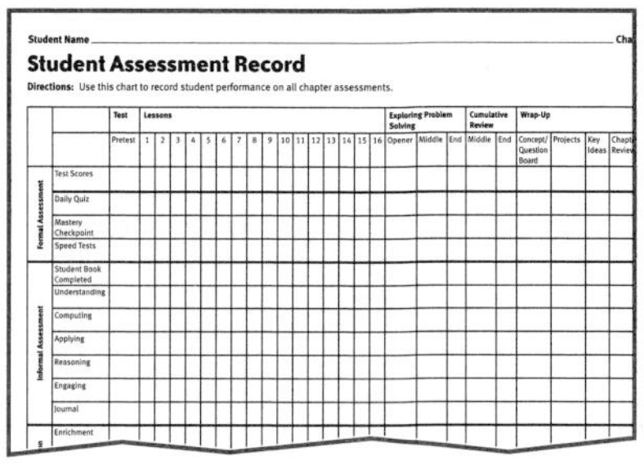

Student Name

Student Assessment Record

**Directions:** Use this chart to record student performance on all chapter assessments.

**Assessment Page T41**

## C Assessment Follow-Up • DIFFERENTIATE INSTRUCTION

Based on your observations, use these teaching strategies for lesson follow-up.

### INTERVENTION

Review student performance on ***Intervention*** Lesson 8.B to see if students have mastered prerequisite skills for this lesson.

### ENGLISH LEARNER

**Review**

Use Lesson 8.2 in ***English Learner Support Guide*** to review lesson concepts and vocabulary.

### ENRICH

**If . . .** students are proficient in the lesson concepts,

**Then . . .** encourage them to work on the chapter projects or ***Enrichment*** Lesson 8.2.

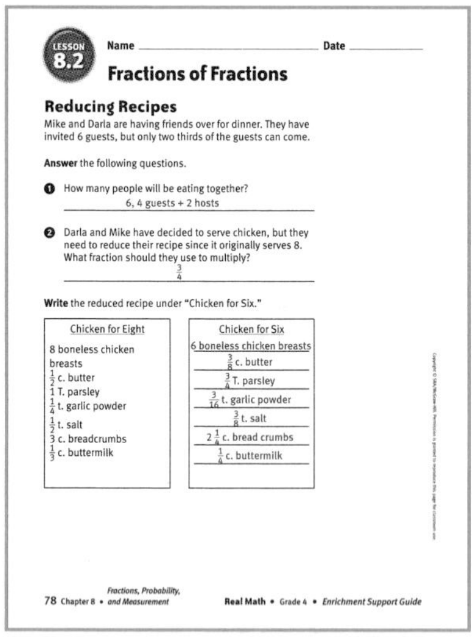

LESSON 8.2 Name ____ Date ____

Fractions of Fractions

**Reducing Recipes**

Mike and Darla are having friends over for dinner. They have invited 6 guests, but only two thirds of the guests can come.

**Answer** the following questions.

1. How many people will be eating together? 6, 4 guests + 2 hosts
2. Darla and Mike have decided to serve chicken, but they need to reduce their recipe since it originally serves 8. What fraction should they use to multiply? $\frac{3}{4}$

**Write** the reduced recipe under "Chicken for Six."

| Chicken for Eight | Chicken for Six |
| --- | --- |
| 8 boneless chicken breasts | 6 boneless chicken breasts |
| $\frac{1}{2}$ c. butter | $\frac{3}{8}$ c. butter |
| 1 T. parsley | $\frac{3}{4}$ T. parsley |
| $\frac{1}{4}$ t. garlic powder | $\frac{3}{16}$ t. garlic powder |
| $\frac{1}{2}$ t. salt | $\frac{3}{8}$ t. salt |
| 3 c. breadcrumbs | $2\frac{1}{4}$ c. bread crumbs |
| $\frac{2}{3}$ c. buttermilk | $\frac{1}{2}$ c. buttermilk |

78 Chapter 8 • Fractions, Probability, and Measurement Real Math • Grade 4 • Enrichment Support Guide

Enrichment Lesson 8.2

### PRACTICE

**If . . .** students would benefit from additional practice,

**Then . . .** assign ***Practice*** lesson 8.2.

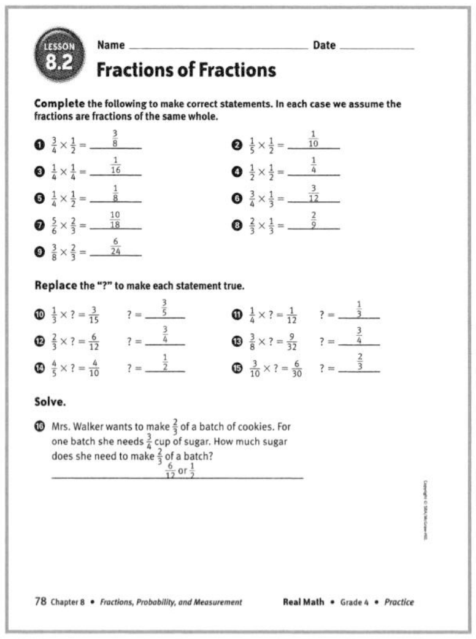

LESSON 8.2 Name ____ Date ____

Fractions of Fractions

**Complete the following to make correct statements. In each case we assume the fractions are fractions of the same whole.**

**Replace the "?" to make each statement true.**

**Solve.**

Mrs. Walker wants to make $\frac{2}{3}$ of a batch of cookies. For one batch she needs $\frac{3}{4}$ cup of sugar. How much sugar does she need to make $\frac{2}{3}$ of a batch?

78 Chapter 8 • Fractions, Probability, and Measurement Real Math • Grade 4 • Practice

Practice Lesson 8.2

### RETEACH

**If . . .** students are having difficulty understanding multiplication of fractions,

**Then . . .** have students work with concrete objects or drawings. Students usually have no difficulty with the algorithm since it seems natural to multiply numerators and denominators, but remind students that this procedure does not work for adding or subtracting fractions.

## Lesson Planner

### Objectives
- To introduce the concept of a rational number as a number that can be represented as $\frac{a}{b}$ where $a$ and $b$ are integers and $b$ is positive
- To introduce the idea that a fraction, as well as being an operator, is a name for a rational number

### NCTM Standards
**Algebra**
Represent and analyze mathematical situations and structures using algebraic symbols

**Connections**
Understand how mathematical ideas interconnect and build on one another to produce a coherent whole

### Materials
- *Response Wheels
- *Meterstick
- String (1m in length)
- *Overhead calculator (optional)
- *Calculators (optional)

### Technology
**Presentation** Lesson 8.3
**MathTools** Fractions

### Test Prep
**Cumulative Review**
Mental Math reviews multiplying multiples of 10 (Lesson 5.3).

*Manipulative Kit Item

# Fractions and Rational Numbers

**Context of the Lesson** Until this point in the program, we have treated fractions as operators, a way that is natural for young children. From this point on, fractions will be thought of both as operators and as names for rational numbers. This dual role for fractions is often confusing for students.

See page 328B for Math Background for teachers for this lesson.

## Planning for Learning • DIFFERENTIATE INSTRUCTION

### INTERVENTION

**If . . .** students lack the prerequisite skill of finding a fraction of a number,

**Then . . .** teach ***Intervention*** Lesson 8.B.

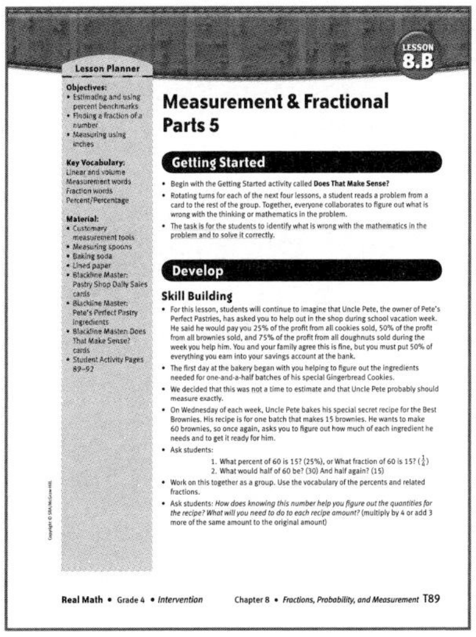
Lesson Planner

LESSON 8.B

Measurement & Fractional Parts 5

Getting Started

Develop

Skill Building

Intervention Lesson 8.B

### ENGLISH LEARNER

**Preview**

**If . . .** students need language support,

**Then . . .** use Lesson 8.3 in ***English Learner Support Guide*** to preview lesson concepts and vocabulary.

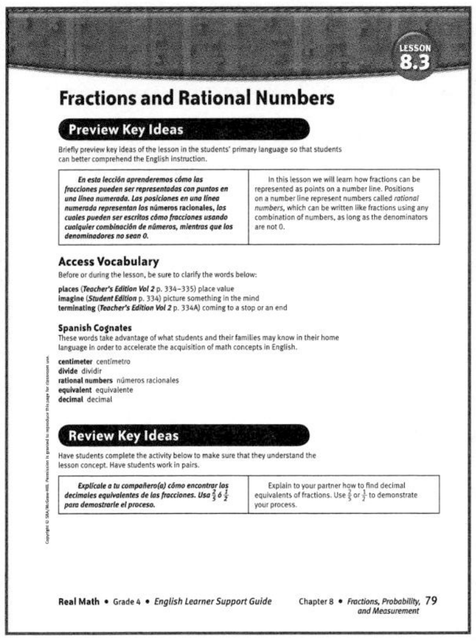
LESSON 8.3

Fractions and Rational Numbers

Preview Key Ideas

Access Vocabulary

Spanish Cognates

Review Key Ideas

English Learner Lesson 8.3

### ENRICH

**If . . .** students are proficient in the lesson concepts,

**Then . . .** encourage them to explore which fractions do not have decimal equivalents and why this might be.

### PRACTICE

**If . . .** students would benefit from additional practice,

**Then . . .** Then...find additional decimal equivalents as a class before assigning the student pages.

### RETEACH

**If . . .** students are having difficulty visualizing the string in the introduction,

**Then . . .** have students model the introduction themselves with their own string.

### Vocabulary
**rational number** ***n.*** a number that can be expressed as a quotient of two integers with a divisor greater than 0

### Access Vocabulary
**places** place value

### Spanish Cognates
**rational numbers** números racionales
**decimal** decimal

# Teaching Lesson 8.3

## Mental Math 5

Review | RESPONSE WHEEL Provide exercises such as the following that review multiplying by multiples of 10:

**a.** 50 × 30 = 1,500 **b.** 200 × 80 = 16,000
**c.** 70 × 400 = 28,000 **d.** 9 × 60 = 540
**e.** 10 × 80 = 800 **f.** 300 × 60 = 18,000
**g.** 4,000 × 10 = 40,000 **h.** 90 × 80 = 7,200

## 1 Develop 25

### Tell Students In Today's Lesson They Will

learn how fractions can be represented as points on the number line.

### Guided Discussion UNDERSTANDING Whole Group

1. Explain to students that most people think of fractions as a way to indicate a part of something, such as $\frac{1}{2}$ of the pie or $\frac{1}{3}$ of the chairs in the room. We also use fractions to name numbers. Numbers that can be represented by fractions are called *rational numbers*. When fractions are used to name rational numbers, they can be greater than 1 and less than 0, even though it doesn't make much sense to talk about negative $\frac{2}{3}$ of the people in the room or $\frac{7}{5}$ of the game, there are real situations in which such fractions do make sense.
2. Show students a piece of string that is 1 meter long. Ask students where they think $\frac{1}{2}$ would be on the string. Students should point to or describe the middle of the string. Fold the string in half and have students use a meterstick to find the length of the half. Students should measure the halved string to be 50 centimeters, or 0.5 meters. Draw a model of the line on the board and mark a point at $\frac{1}{2}$. Label the point with $\frac{1}{2}$, 50 cm, and 0.5 m. Explain to the students that all three of these labels can be used to describe the same point on the number line.
3. Repeat the procedure with $\frac{1}{4}$ of the string and $\frac{1}{5}$ of the string. Even though folding the string into equal fifths will be difficult, students should conclude that $\frac{1}{5}$ of the string should measure 20 centimeters or 0.2 meters. They can check to see that this is correct by adding 20 or 0.2 five times to get 100 or 1.0, respectively.
4. Tell students that we can use division to help us find decimal equivalents or approximations. Demonstrate how to divide a numerator by its denominator on a calculator. Follow the steps below.
   - Use a calculator to find the decimal equivalent for $\frac{1}{4}$. Divide 1 by 4 to get 0.25.
   - Provide students with several fractions to find decimal equivalents, such as $\frac{1}{2}$, $\frac{1}{5}$, and $\frac{1}{10}$.
   - Tell students they must use their knowledge of approximation to adjust answers they get on the calculator for fractions.

## 2 Assign Student Pages 25

### Page 334–335 APPLYING

Have students review page 334 before completing the chart on page 335 independently. You may want to allow students to use calculators. You may also want students to record their answers in their Journals for future reference.

#### Monitoring Student Progress

| If . . . | Then . . . |
| --- | --- |
| students have difficulty finding decimal equivalents of fractions, | remind them to think of the fraction bar as a division symbol. |

### As Students Finish

e MathTools Have students explore fractional amounts using ***eMathTools: Fractions***.

#### RESEARCH IN ACTION

"Research reveals that the kinds of errors students make when beginning to operate with rational numbers often come because they have not yet developed meaning for these numbers and are applying poorly understood rules for whole numbers. Operations with rational numbers challenge students' naive understanding of multiplication and division that multiplication 'makes bigger' and division 'makes smaller.'"

Kilpatrick, J., Swafford, J. and Findell B. eds. *Adding It Up: Helping Children Learn Mathematics.* Washington, D.C.: National Research Council/National Academy Press, 2001, p. 416.

Student Page

LESSON 8.3 **Fractions and Rational Numbers**

## Key Ideas

**Fractions can be used to locate positions on a number line. These positions represent numbers called rational numbers.**

A rational number can be written as a fraction with any combination of numbers, as long as the denominator (bottom number) is not 0.

Imagine a string that is 1 meter long, measured from left to right. Think about where we would be if we started at the left end of the string and moved along the string $\frac{1}{2}$ of the total distance, or 50% of it.

Remembering that a percent is another name for a fraction with a denominator of 100, we could describe this location in centimeters (1 cm = $\frac{1}{100}$ m) as 50 cm. In meters, as a decimal, we would say 0.50 m.

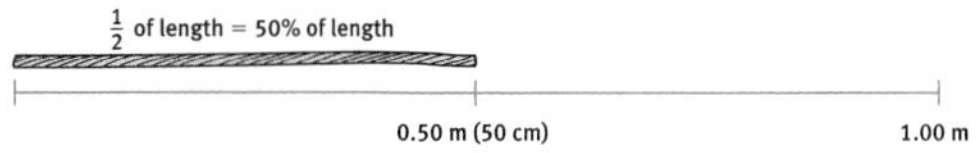


We can represent the string with a number line.

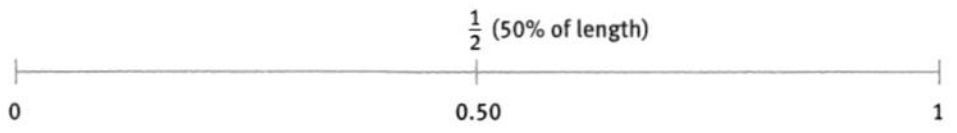




eTextbook This lesson is available in the ***eTextbook***.

Student Page

To find information about *any* rational number's place on the number line, you can divide its numerator by its denominator. For many fractions, like $\frac{1}{2}$, you can find an exact decimal equivalent.

$1 \div 2 = 0.5$, so $\frac{1}{2} = 0.5$

Usually you will not get an exact decimal equivalent when you divide, and you will have to approximate.

**Solve. For each fraction of a meter, find both the equivalent length in centimeters and the decimal equivalent in meters.**

1. $\frac{1}{2}$ 50; 0.50
2. $\frac{1}{4}$ 25; 0.25
3. $\frac{1}{5}$ 20; 0.20
4. $\frac{1}{10}$ 10; 0.10

On the number line, $\frac{1}{4}$, $\frac{1}{5}$, and $\frac{1}{10}$ would all name rational numbers.

**Find the decimal equivalent for each fraction, or percent of 1, shown below.** To help you check your answers, each fraction or percent is placed below its corresponding point on the number line. Use a calculator, if needed.

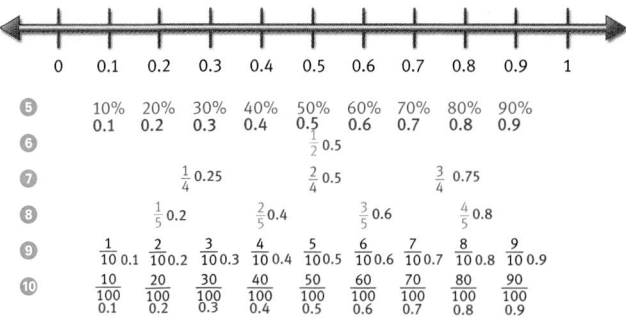

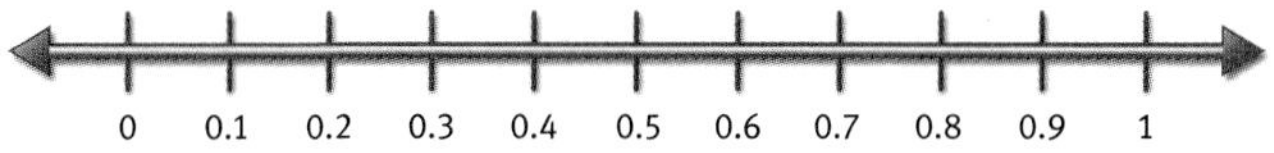


5. 10% 0.1; 20% 0.2; 30% 0.3; 40% 0.4; 50% 0.5; 60% 0.6; 70% 0.7; 80% 0.8; 90% 0.9
6. $\frac{1}{2}$ 0.5
7. $\frac{1}{4}$ 0.25; $\frac{2}{4}$ 0.5; $\frac{3}{4}$ 0.75
8. $\frac{1}{5}$ 0.2; $\frac{2}{5}$ 0.4; $\frac{3}{5}$ 0.6; $\frac{4}{5}$ 0.8
9. $\frac{1}{10}$ 0.1; $\frac{2}{10}$ 0.2; $\frac{3}{10}$ 0.3; $\frac{4}{10}$ 0.4; $\frac{5}{10}$ 0.5; $\frac{6}{10}$ 0.6; $\frac{7}{10}$ 0.7; $\frac{8}{10}$ 0.8; $\frac{9}{10}$ 0.9
10. $\frac{10}{100}$ 0.1; $\frac{20}{100}$ 0.2; $\frac{30}{100}$ 0.3; $\frac{40}{100}$ 0.4; $\frac{50}{100}$ 0.5; $\frac{60}{100}$ 0.6; $\frac{70}{100}$ 0.7; $\frac{80}{100}$ 0.8; $\frac{90}{100}$ 0.9



# 3 Reflect

5

## Guided Discussion UNDERSTANDING

Whole Group

- Review the process for finding decimal equivalents of fractions. Divide the numerator by the denominator.
- Discuss how the decimal equivalents for $\frac{1}{2}$ and $\frac{1}{3}$ are different. Explain that many fractions, like $\frac{1}{2}$, have an exact decimal equivalent, like 0.5. A decimal like 0.5 is called a *terminating decimal* because its digits terminate, or stop, when we divide 1 by 2. That is, after some place the digits are only 0s. So we can write $\frac{1}{2} = 1 \div 2 = 0.5$.

$$3\overline{)1.0000000\ldots} = 0.3333333\ldots$$

Dividing 1 by 3 results in a decimal that does not terminate. So we approximate $\frac{1}{3}$ with a decimal to as many places as we wish. For example, if we approximate to the nearest thousandth, we would say $\frac{1}{3}$ is about 0.333. But we can't write a decimal that is exactly equal to $\frac{1}{3}$.

**Cumulative Review:** For review of addition and subtraction with hidden digits, assign Problems 5–7 on student page 350.

**Family Involvement:** Assign the ***Practice, Reteach,*** or ***Enrichment*** activities depending on the needs of your students. Have students play a game of their choice with a friend or relative.

**Concept/Question Board:** Have students look for real-world examples of fractions and post them on the Concept/Question Board.

**Math Puzzler:** Six boys are playing a guessing game. One boy must find a bead hidden in one of the other boys' closed fists. Five boys each hold out two closed fists so the boy can guess. Which is easier—to pick the correct boy or the correct fist? It is easier to pick the correct boy, because the boy who is choosing has 1 chance in 5 to be right; to pick the correct fist, the probability is $\frac{1}{10}$.

# 4 Assess and Differentiate

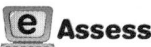

**eAssess** Use ***eAssess*** to record and analyze evidence of student understanding.

## A Gather Evidence

Use the Daily Class Assessment Records in ***Assessment*** or ***eAssess*** to record daily observations.

### Informal Assessment

**✓ Guided Discussion**

Did the student UNDERSTANDING

- ❑ make important observations?
- ❑ extend or generalize learning?
- ❑ provide insightful answers?
- ❑ pose insightful questions?

### Informal Assessment

**✓ Concept Question Board**

Did the student APPLYING

- ❑ apply learning in new situations?
- ❑ contribute concepts?
- ❑ contribute answers?
- ❑ connect mathematics to real-world situations?

## B Summarize Findings

Analyze and summarize assessment data for each student. Determine which Assessment Follow-Up is appropriate for each student. Use the Student Assessment Record in ***Assessment*** or ***eAssess*** to update assessment records.

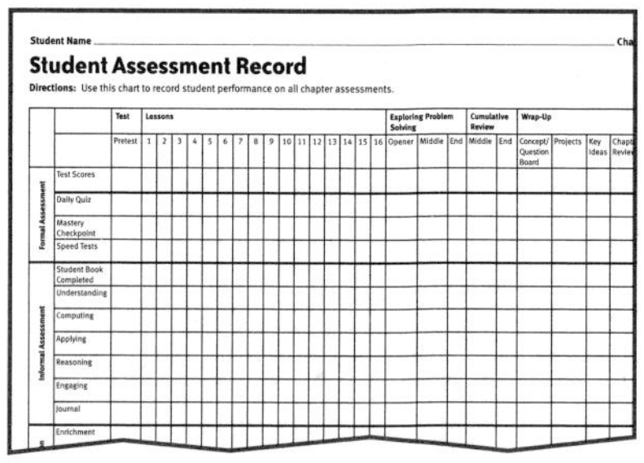


**Assessment Page T41**

## C Assessment Follow-Up • DIFFERENTIATE INSTRUCTION

Based on your observations, use these teaching strategies for assessment follow-up.

### INTERVENTION

Review student performance on ***Intervention*** Lesson 8.B to see if students have mastered prerequisite skills for this lesson.

### ENGLISH LEARNER

**Review**

Use Lesson 8.3 in ***English Learner Support Guide*** to review lesson concepts and vocabulary.

### ENRICH

**If . . .** students are proficient in the lesson concepts,

**Then . . .** encourage them to work on the chapter projects or ***Enrichment*** Lesson 8.3.

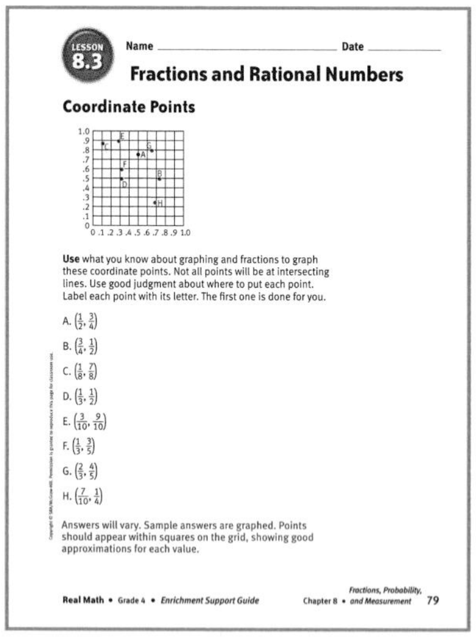
LESSON 8.3 Name ______ Date ______

**Fractions and Rational Numbers**

**Coordinate Points**

**Use** what you know about graphing and fractions to graph these coordinate points. Not all points will be at intersecting lines. Use good judgment about where to put each point. Label each point with its letter. The first one is done for you.

A. $\left(\frac{1}{2}, \frac{3}{4}\right)$
B. $\left(\frac{3}{4}, \frac{1}{2}\right)$
C. $\left(\frac{1}{8}, \frac{7}{8}\right)$
D. $\left(\frac{1}{3}, \frac{1}{2}\right)$
E. $\left(\frac{3}{10}, \frac{9}{10}\right)$
F. $\left(\frac{1}{3}, \frac{3}{5}\right)$
G. $\left(\frac{2}{3}, \frac{4}{5}\right)$
H. $\left(\frac{7}{10}, \frac{1}{4}\right)$

Answers will vary. Sample answers are graphed. Points should appear within squares on the grid, showing good approximations for each value.

Real Math • Grade 4 • *Enrichment Support Guide* Chapter 8 • *Fractions, Probability, and Measurement* 79

Enrichment Lesson 8.3

### PRACTICE

**If . . .** students would benefit from additional practice,

**Then . . .** assign ***Practice*** Lesson 8.3.

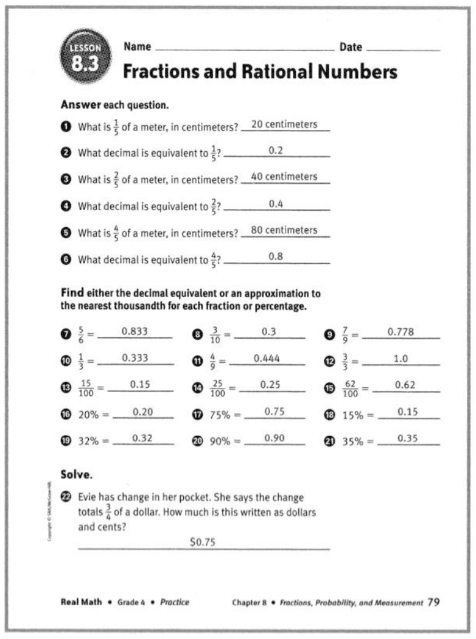
LESSON 8.3 Name ______ Date ______

**Fractions and Rational Numbers**

**Answer each question.**

1. What is $\frac{1}{5}$ of a meter, in centimeters? 20 centimeters
2. What decimal is equivalent to $\frac{1}{5}$? 0.2
3. What is $\frac{2}{5}$ of a meter, in centimeters? 40 centimeters
4. What decimal is equivalent to $\frac{2}{5}$? 0.4
5. What is $\frac{4}{5}$ of a meter, in centimeters? 80 centimeters
6. What decimal is equivalent to $\frac{4}{5}$? 0.8

**Find either the decimal equivalent or an approximation to the nearest thousandth for each fraction or percentage.**

7. $\frac{5}{6}$ = 0.833
8. $\frac{3}{10}$ = 0.3
9. $\frac{7}{9}$ = 0.778
10. $\frac{1}{3}$ = 0.333
11. $\frac{4}{9}$ = 0.444
12. $\frac{3}{3}$ = 1.0
13. $\frac{15}{100}$ = 0.15
14. $\frac{25}{100}$ = 0.25
15. $\frac{62}{100}$ = 0.62
16. 20% = 0.20
17. 75% = 0.75
18. 15% = 0.15
19. 32% = 0.32
20. 90% = 0.90
21. 35% = 0.35

**Solve.**

22. Evie has change in her pocket. She says the change totals $\frac{3}{4}$ of a dollar. How much is this written as dollars and cents? $0.75

Real Math • Grade 4 • *Practice* Chapter 8 • *Fractions, Probability, and Measurement* 79

Practice Lesson 8.3

### RETEACH

**If . . .** students are having difficulty understanding decimal equivalents,

**Then . . .** have students use play money to represent fractions and decimals. For example:

$\frac{1}{4}$ = 1 quarter = 0.25, $\frac{1}{2}$ = 1 half dollar = 0.50, $\frac{3}{4}$ = 3 quarters = 0.75, $\frac{3}{10}$ = 3 dimes = 0.30, and $\frac{1}{20}$ = 1 nickel = 0.05. This can be used for equivalent fractions also. If the money amount is equal, then the fraction would be equivalent. Two quarters equal one-half dollar.

## Lesson Planner

**OBJECTIVES**
- To review the concept of probability as a practical application of fractions
- To provide an explanation of how to calculate simple probabilities

**NCTM STANDARDS**

**Data Analysis and Probability**
- Select and use appropriate statistical methods to analyze data
- Understand and apply basic concepts of probability

**Connections**

Recognize and use connections among mathematical ideas

**MATERIALS**
- *Response Wheels
- *Overhead projector spinner

**TECHNOLOGY**

**Presentation** Lesson 8.4

**MathTools** Probability Tool

**TEST PREP**

**Cumulative Review**
- Mental Math reviews fractional parts of wholes (Lesson 8.1).
- Problems 5–12 review fractional parts of wholes (Lesson 8.1)

*Manipulative Kit Item

# Probability

**Context of the Lesson** This lesson deepens students' understanding of fractions by using them in the context of probability. Students have worked informally with probability since kindergarten. This lesson introduces fraction notation for probability.

See page 328B for Math Background for teachers for this lesson.

## Planning for Learning • DIFFERENTIATE INSTRUCTION

### INTERVENTION

**If . . .** students lack the prerequisite skill of estimating using percent benchmarks,

**Then . . .** teach ***Intervention*** Lesson 8.A.

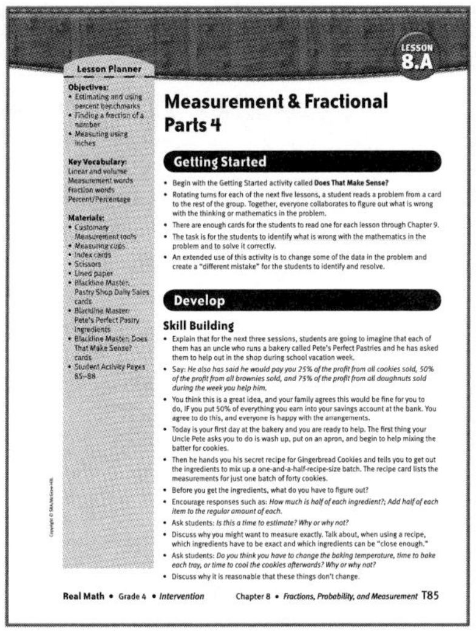
LESSON 8.A
Lesson Planner
Measurement & Fractional Parts 4
Getting Started
Develop

Intervention Lesson 8.A

### ENGLISH LEARNER

Preview

**If . . .** students need language support,

**Then . . .** use Lesson 8.4 in ***English Learner Support Guide*** to preview lesson concepts and vocabulary.

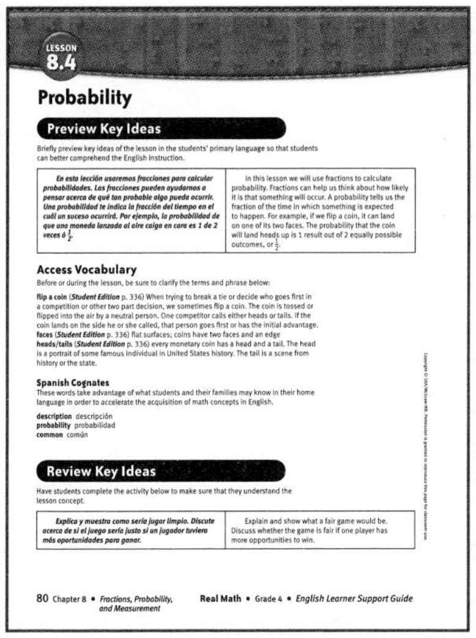
LESSON 8.4
Probability
Preview Key Ideas
Access Vocabulary
Spanish Cognates
Review Key Ideas

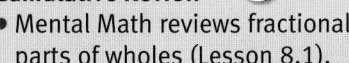

English Learner Lesson 8.4

### ENRICH

**If . . .** students are proficient in the lesson concepts,

**Then . . .** encourage them to design their own spinners for given probabilities.

### PRACTICE

**If . . .** students would benefit from additional practice,

**Then . . .** extend the Mental Math before assigning the student pages.

### RETEACH

**If . . .** students are having difficulty understanding with the concept of probability,

**Then . . .** further discuss real-life applications of probability, such as weather prediction.

### Vocabulary

**probability /prob´ ə bil´ i t ē/** ***n.*** the ratio of the number of chances favoring the occurrence of a particular event to the total number of possible occurrences

### Access Vocabulary

**heads or tails** every monetary coin has a head and a tail. The head is a portrait of some famous individual in US history. The tail is a scene from history or the state.

**land on one of its two faces** the faces of a coin are the flat surfaces. Coins have two faces and an edge.

**Spanish Cognates**

**probability** probabilidad

**common** común

# Teaching Lesson 8.4

## Mental Math 5

RESPONSE WHEEL Provide students with fractions-of-whole practice. Draw five different sets of shapes of various sizes on the board or overhead projector in varying fractional groupings. Ask students questions such as the following:

- **What fraction of the counters are triangles?**
- **What fraction of the counters are shaded red?**
- **What fraction of the counters are green squares?**

Students can display fractional answers on their ***Response Wheels*** by placing a finger between the numerator and denominator.

## 1 Develop 25

**Tell Students In Today's Lesson They Will**
learn how to calculate probabilities.

### Guided Discussion UNDERSTANDING

Whole Group

1. Start with the idea that fractions can be used as a description of probability. We can use fractions to help us think about how likely it is that something will occur. To demonstrate this, use the overhead projector spinner with one half shaded red and one half shaded blue.

- **If you spin the spinner 10 times, how many times would you expect it to land on red?** A reasonable estimate is 5.
- **If you spin the spinner 10 times, how many times would you expect it to land on blue?** A reasonable estimate is 5.

2. Ask a volunteer to explain why 5 would be a reasonable estimate. $\frac{1}{2}$ of the spinner is red and $\frac{1}{2}$ of 10 is 5

Discuss how they could use a fraction to describe getting 5 red spins out of 10 attempts. $\frac{5}{10}$ or any fraction equivalent to $\frac{1}{2}$

Ask questions such as the following:

- **How many times would you expect it to get red if you spin the spinner 4 times?** 2
- **How many times would you expect it to get red if you spin the spinner 6 times?** 3

3. Ask what $\frac{5}{10}$, $\frac{2}{4}$, and $\frac{3}{6}$ have in common. Each is $\frac{1}{2}$ of the total number of tries in each case.

4. Ask questions such as the following:

- **If you spin a spinner 10 times, do you think the spinner will always land on red 5 times?** Not always.
- **Could it land on red 10 times out of 10?** Yes, but that is not likely (1 chance in 1,024).

Explain that people make assumptions when talking about probability. They believe these assumptions are *probably* true, but not *certainly* true. People would describe the probability of spinning red as one half, even if the spinner actually comes up red more or less than half the time. Demonstrate this by spinning the overhead spinner 10 times and recording the color for each spin. Check to see how close the prediction of 5 is to the actual result.

5. Remind students that percents are equivalent to fractions with denominators of 100.

- **If something is expected to happen 50 times out of 100 attempts, what percent do you think this would be?** 50%
- **What fraction is this?** $\frac{50}{100}$ or $\frac{1}{2}$
- **If something is expected to occur 0 times out of 100 attempts, what percent would describe this probability?** 0%
- **If something is expected to occur 100 times out of 100 attempts, what percent would describe that probability?** 100%
- **What kind of spinner would make it impossible to land on blue (0% chance)?** a spinner with no blue
- **What kind of spinner would you need to be certain that it will land on red (a 100% chance)?** a completely red spinner

Ask students if there are ways to make different spinners that all have a probability of $\frac{1}{2}$ for landing on red (a 50% chance). Divide the spinners into different numbers of equal parts but still shade an equal number of parts red and not red.

Write fractions describing the red area of each version suggested by students (e.g., $\frac{2}{4}$, $\frac{3}{6}$, $\frac{5}{10}$, etc.).

## 2 Assign Student Pages 20

**Pages 336–337** APPLYING
Have students complete pages 336 and 337 independently.

### Monitoring Student Progress

| If . . . | Then . . . |
|---|---|
| students have difficulty writing the correct fraction for a probability | remind them that the denominator is the number of all possible outcomes while the numerator is the number of those ways to achieve the desired outcome. |

### As Students Finish

eMathTools Have students probability using ***eMath Tools: Probability Tool***

Student Page

LESSON 8.4 **Probability**

## Key Ideas

**A probability tells us the fraction of the time something is likely to happen.**

We use fractions when we work with probability.For example, if you flip a coin, it has an equal chance to land on either of its two faces. The probability that the coin will land heads up is 1 result out of 2 equally possible outcomes, or $\frac{1}{2}$. Since it is equally likely that the coin will land tails up, that probability is also $\frac{1}{2}$.

Even though we might imagine the coin landing on its edge, this event is so unlikely that we don't usually consider it. We expect a coin to land heads up half of the time and tails up the other half. Nothing else is likely to happen.

If something cannot possibly happen, the probability is 0. If something is certain to happen, the probability is 1.

**Answer** the following questions.

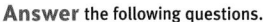

1. If you roll a 0–5 ***Number Cube,*** what is the probability that you will roll 7? 0
2. If you roll a 0–5 ***Number Cube,*** what is the probability that you will roll a number less than 7? 1
3. If you roll a 0–5 ***Number Cube,*** what is the probability that you will roll an even number? $\frac{3}{6}$ or $\frac{1}{2}$, since 0 is even
4. If you roll a 0–5 ***Number Cube,*** what is the probability that you will roll an odd number? $\frac{3}{6}$ or $\frac{1}{2}$



eTextbook This lesson is available in the *eTextbook.*

Student Page

**For** each of the following spinners, give the probability that the pointer will stop on red.

5. $\frac{3}{4}$
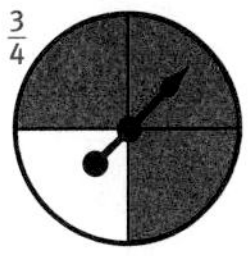
6. $\frac{2}{3}$
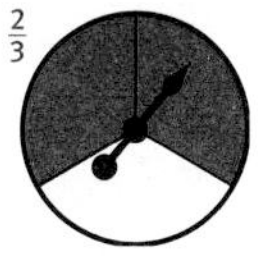
7. $\frac{1}{2}$
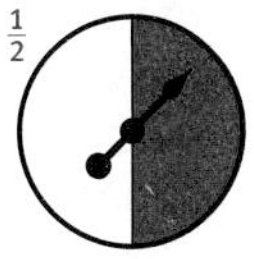
8. $\frac{4}{5}$
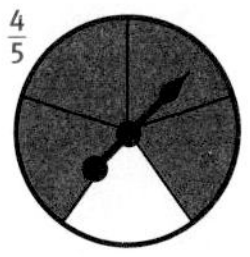
9. 0
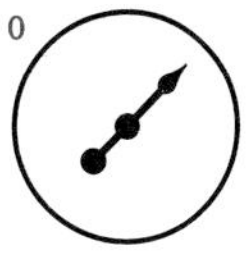
10. 1
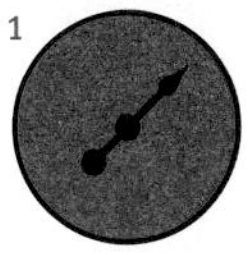
11. $\frac{1}{6}$
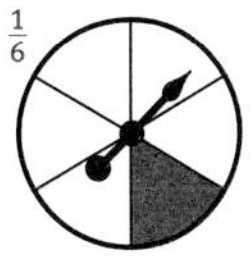
12. $\frac{1}{3}$
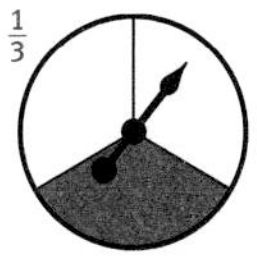

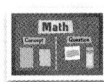

Writing + Math **Journal**

Describe three instances where the probability of those events happening are 0. Describe three instances where the probability of those events happening is 1.

See Reflect in the *Teacher's Edition.*

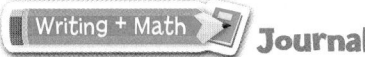

# 3 Reflect

10

## Guided Discussion REASONING

Whole Group

- Discuss how we use fractions. Remind students that they have learned that the denominator tells them how many equal-sized parts to divide something into, such as how to cut a pizza. We also know that the denominator can tell us how many things are in a set, for example, how many red marbles are in a bag of colored marbles. Ask students to explain how this is different from, or the same as, other uses of fractions (e.g., understanding the size of a slice of pizza). One possible answer is that fractions can be used to describe parts of a whole or parts of sets of objects.

Writing + Math **Journal**

Students should consider examples where the outcome is certain (selecting 1 red apple from a bag of red apples has a probability of 1) or not possible (experiencing the 32nd day of April has a probability of 0).

**Curriculum Connection:** This lesson is about the possibility of actions taking place. Have students test their center of gravity by standing against a wall with their feet together and heels touching the wall while trying to pick up a piece of paper laid six inches in front of them without bending at the knees. Discuss what happens.

**Cumulative Review:** For review of perimeter, assign Problems 8–9 on student page 350.

**Family Involvement:** Assign the ***Practice, Reteach,*** or ***Enrichment*** activities depending on the needs of your students. Have students play a game of their choice with a friend or relative.

**Concept/Question Board:** Have students look for real-world examples of fractions and post them on the Concept/Question Board.

**Math Puzzler:** I am a number between 40 and 60. You say my name when you count by 3s, 4s, 6s, and 8s. Who am I? 48

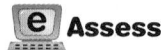

# 4 Assess and Differentiate

**e Assess** Use ***eAssess*** to record and analyze evidence of student understanding.

## A Gather Evidence

Use the Daily Class Assessment Records in ***Assessment*** or ***eAssess*** to record daily observations.

### Informal Assessment

**Mental Math**

Did the student **COMPUTING**
- ❑ respond accurately?
- ❑ respond quickly?
- ❑ respond with confidence?
- ❑ self-correct?

### Portfolio Assessment

**Journal**

Did the student **REASONING**
- ❑ provide a clear explanation?
- ❑ communicate reasons and strategies?
- ❑ choose appropriate strategies?
- ❑ argue logically?

## B Summarize Findings

Analyze and summarize assessment data for each student. Determine which Assessment Follow-Up is appropriate for each student. Use the Student Assessment Record in ***Assessment*** or ***eAssess*** to update assessment records.

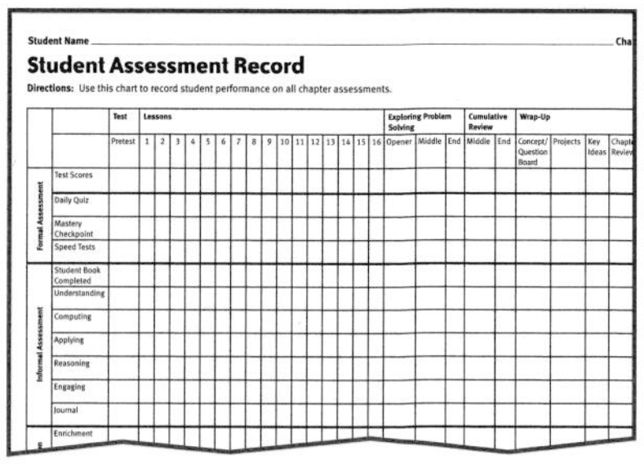
Student Assessment Record

**Assessment Page T41**

## C Assessment Follow-Up • DIFFERENTIATE INSTRUCTION

Based on your observations, use these teaching strategies for assessment follow-up.

### INTERVENTION

Review student performance on ***Intervention*** Lesson 8.A to see if students have mastered prerequisite skills for this lesson.

### ENGLISH LEARNER

**Review**

Use Lesson 8.4 in ***English Learner Support Guide*** to review lesson concepts and vocabulary.

### ENRICH

**If . . .** students are proficient in the lesson concepts,

**Then . . .** encourage them to work on the chapter projects or ***Enrichment*** Lesson 8.4.

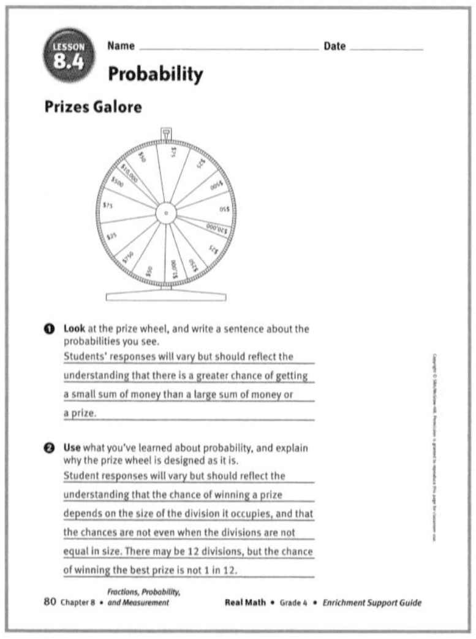
LESSON 8.4 Name ______ Date ______

Probability

Prizes Galore

1. Look at the prize wheel, and write a sentence about the probabilities you see.
Students' responses will vary but should reflect the understanding that there is a greater chance of getting a small sum of money than a large sum of money or a prize.

2. Use what you've learned about probability, and explain why the prize wheel is designed as it is.
Student responses will vary but should reflect the understanding that the chance of winning a prize depends on the size of the division it occupies, and that the chances are not even when the divisions are not equal in size. There may be 12 divisions, but the chance of winning the best prize is not 1 in 12.

80 Chapter 8 • Fractions, Probability, and Measurement     Real Math • Grade 4 • Enrichment Support Guide

Enrichment Lesson 8.4

### PRACTICE

**If . . .** students would benefit from additional practice,

**Then . . .** assign ***Practice*** Lesson 8.4.

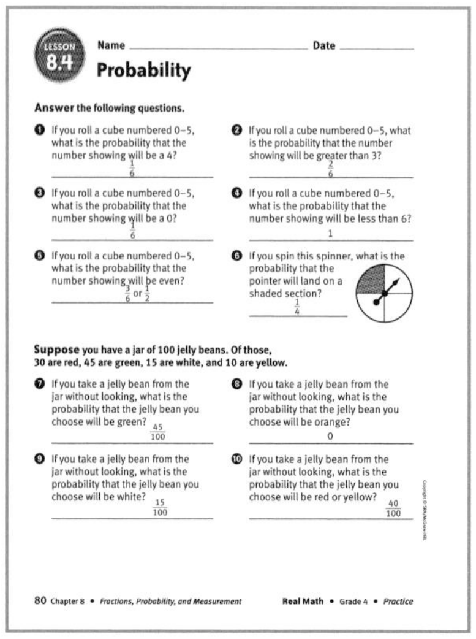
LESSON 8.4 Name ______ Date ______

Probability

Answer the following questions.

1. If you roll a cube numbered 0–5, what is the probability that the number showing will be a 4? $\frac{1}{6}$
2. If you roll a cube numbered 0–5, what is the probability that the number showing will be greater than 3? $\frac{2}{6}$
3. If you roll a cube numbered 0–5, what is the probability that the number showing will be a 0? $\frac{1}{6}$
4. If you roll a cube numbered 0–5, what is the probability that the number showing will be less than 6? 1
5. If you roll a cube numbered 0–5, what is the probability that the number showing will be even? $\frac{3}{6}$ or $\frac{1}{2}$
6. If you spin this spinner, what is the probability that the pointer will land on a shaded section? $\frac{1}{4}$

Suppose you have a jar of 100 jelly beans. Of those, 30 are red, 45 are green, 15 are white, and 10 are yellow.

7. If you take a jelly bean from the jar without looking, what is the probability that the jelly bean you choose will be green? $\frac{45}{100}$
8. If you take a jelly bean from the jar without looking, what is the probability that the jelly bean you choose will be orange? 0
9. If you take a jelly bean from the jar without looking, what is the probability that the jelly bean you choose will be white? $\frac{15}{100}$
10. If you take a jelly bean from the jar without looking, what is the probability that the jelly bean you choose will be red or yellow? $\frac{40}{100}$

80 Chapter 8 • Fractions, Probability, and Measurement     Real Math • Grade 4 • Practice

Practice Lesson 8.4

### RETEACH

**If . . .** students are having difficulty understanding which numbers to use to represent a probability,

**Then . . .** have students conduct hands-on experiments so they can better understand the meaning of probability. Students can predict the probability of a certain outcome and then test their predictions. Make sure students understand that their results may not equal the probability. However, the more trials they run, the closer their results will match the probabilities.

## Lesson Planner

**OBJECTIVES**
- To introduce the idea of associating numbers with probability
- To provide practice using fractions in common applications
- To informally begin simple addition of fractions with like denominators

**NCTM STANDARDS**

**Number and Operations**
Compute fluently and make reasonable estimates

**Data Analysis and Probability**
Understand and apply basic concepts of probability

**MATERIALS**
- ***Response Wheels**
- ***Number Cubes** (one 0–5, one 5–10)
- ***Fracto I or II Game Mat**

**TECHNOLOGY**
**e Presentation** Lesson 8.5
**e Games** Fracto

**TEST PREP**
**Cumulative Review**
- Mental Math reviews simple multiplication of fractions (Lesson 8.2).
- Problem 6 reviews basic addition facts (Lesson 1.5).

*Manipulative Kit Item

# Probability Experiments

**Context of the Lesson** In this lesson, the use of fractions in the common context of probability is continued from Lesson 8.4. This lesson also introduces and expands upon the short introduction of probability concepts from the previous lesson. Probability concepts will be developed further in Grades 5 and 6.

See page 328B for Math Background for teachers for this lesson.

## Planning for Learning • DIFFERENTIATE INSTRUCTION

### INTERVENTION

**If . . .** students lack the prerequisite skill of finding a fraction of a number,

**Then . . .** teach ***Intervention*** Lesson 8.B.

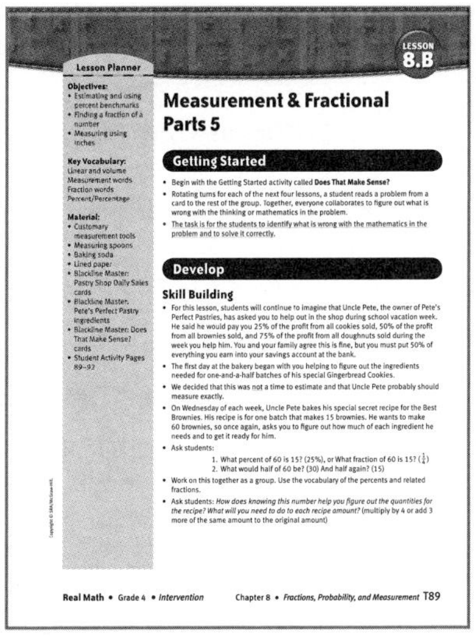
LESSON 8.B
Measurement & Fractional Parts 5
Getting Started
Develop
Skill Building

Intervention Lesson 8.B

### ENGLISH LEARNER

Preview

**If . . .** students need language support,

**Then . . .** use Lesson 8.5 in ***English Learner Support Guide*** to preview lesson concepts and vocabulary.

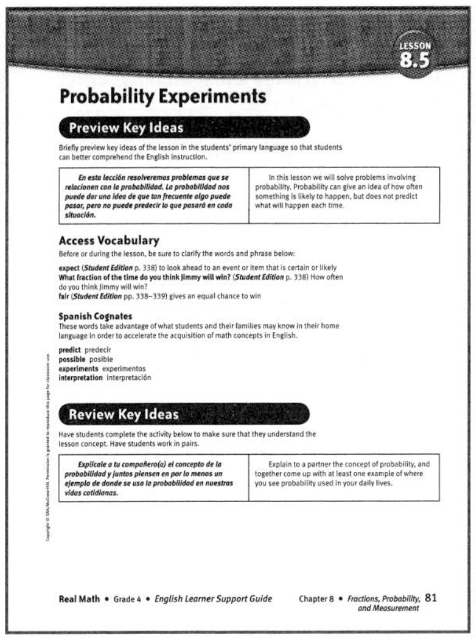
LESSON 8.5
Probability Experiments
Preview Key Ideas
Access Vocabulary
Spanish Cognates
Review Key Ideas

English Learner Lesson 8.5

### ENRICH

**If . . .** students are proficient in the lesson concepts,

**Then . . .** encourage them to design their own probability games.

### PRACTICE

**If . . .** students would benefit from additional practice,

**Then . . .** consider filling out the Table of Sums on the student page as a class.

### RETEACH

**If . . .** students are having difficulty understanding probability experiments,

**Then . . .** extend the Guided Discussion before assigning the student pages.

**Vocabulary**
Review from Lesson 8.4
**probability**

**Access Vocabulary**
**fair** gives an equal chance to win

**Spanish Cognates**
**predict** predecir
**possible** possible
**experiments** experimentos
**interpretation** interpretación

## Mental Math

5

Review · RESPONSE WHEEL

Provide exercises, such as the following, that review simple multiplication of fractions. Students can show answers on their ***Response Wheels*** by using their fingers to be the fraction bar.

**a.** $\frac{1}{2}$ of $\frac{1}{4}$? $\frac{1}{8}$ **b.** $\frac{1}{2}$ of $\frac{1}{3}$? $\frac{1}{6}$ **c.** $\frac{1}{4}$ of $\frac{1}{3}$? $\frac{1}{12}$

**d.** $\frac{1}{2} \times \frac{1}{5} = \frac{1}{10}$ **e.** $\frac{1}{3} \times \frac{1}{3} = \frac{1}{9}$ **f.** $\frac{1}{2} \times \frac{1}{7} = \frac{1}{14}$

## 1 Develop

25

**Tell Students In Today's Lesson They Will**
solve problems involving probability.

### Guided Discussion

UNDERSTANDING · Whole Group

**Probability Races—Single Number**

1. Write the numbers 0–5 across the board. Place eight rows beneath the numbers and add the label "FINISH" to the last row.
2. Tell students that they are going to participate in a Roll-a-Number Race. One red 0–5 ***Number Cube*** will be rolled repeatedly, and the number that comes up for each roll will be marked on the board with an "X." The first number to get 8 marks will cross the finish line and be the winner.
3. Discuss with students which number they think will win. Do they believe one has a better chance than the other? Have volunteers explain their reasoning to the class.
4. Ask students how many ways they could roll a 0. 1

   Repeat this line of questioning for the other numbers and record the number of ways it can be rolled in parentheses above each number on the grid.
5. Ask students questions such as the following:
   - **How many possible outcomes are there?** 6
   - **What is the probability that any one of the numbers will be rolled?** $\frac{1}{6}$
   - **Do all the numbers have the same probability?** yes
6. When you have finished the discussion, perform the race to test the class's predictions. The ***Number Cube*** may be rolled by successive students one at a time. Have students announce their roll to the rest of the class. A completed race grid will look something like the following example.

| (1) 0 | (1) 1 | (1) 2 | (1) 3 | (1) 4 | (1) 5 | |
|---|---|---|---|---|---|---|
| × | × | × | × | × | × | |
| × | × | × | × | × | × | |
| × | × | × | × | × | × | |
| × | × | × | | × | × | |
| × | × | × | | × | × | |
| | × | × | | | × | |
| | × | | | | × | |
| | × | | | | | FINISH |

7. Regardless of which number wins, ask the students, if the number race was performed again, would the same number win again? probably not

As time permits, you could repeat the race to test their predictions.

### Strategy Building

ENGAGING · Whole Group and Small Group

**Probability Races—Sums**

1. Now tell students that they are going to participate in a more complex race—a Roll-a-Sum Race. For this race, two number ***Number Cubes*** will be rolled—one red 0–5 number ***Number Cube*** and one blue 5–10 ***Number Cube***. The number showing on both number ***Number Cubes*** will be added together to make a sum. Each sum that is rolled will be recorded on a new race grid.
2. Ask students what the least possible sum would be. $0 + 5 = 5$ What about the greatest possible sum? $5 + 10 = 15$. All the sums from 5 to 15 are possible.
3. Ask the students if any of the sums are more likely to be rolled than others. Which sum do they think will be rolled the most?
4. Perform the Roll-a-Sum Race to test the predictions of the class. Have all the students roll a blue and a red ***Number Cube*** at the same time. Then have them announce their results one at a time to the rest of the class. Record sums on a new race grid.
5. Discuss how the Roll-a-Sum Race results compare to the students' predictions. Have students suggest why the sums in the middle of the grid seem more likely than the sums at the end of the grid. There are more combinations that produce the sums in the middle of the grid.

### Skill and Strategy Building

ENGAGING · Whole Group

**Fracto I and II**

Game

Before beginning the student pages, introduce the **Fracto I** and/or **Fracto II Game Mat(s).** The games focus on fractional areas of circles and rectangles. Complete directions are found on the game mats, which are reproduced in the back of this ***Teacher's Edition.***

## 2 Assign Student Pages

25

**Pages 338–339** APPLYING

Have students complete pages 338 and 339 independently. Make sure students understand how to correctly fill in the table on page 339. Once the sums table has been filled in correctly, the rest of the problems on page 339 can be solved by counting results from the table.

**As Students Finish**

Game **Fracto Game Mat**

e Games **Fracto**

Student Page

LESSON 8.5 **Probability Experiments**

## Key Ideas

**Probability can give an idea of how often something is likely to happen in the long run, but it cannot predict what will actually happen each time.**

A six-sided number cube has the numbers 0, 1, 2, and 3 on it. The 0 is on three of the faces, while the other numbers appear only once on the number cube. Therefore:

- The probability of rolling 0 is 3 out of 6, or $\frac{3}{6}$.
- The probability of rolling 1 is 1 out of 6, or $\frac{1}{6}$.
- The probability of rolling 2 is 1 out of 6, or $\frac{1}{6}$.
- The probability of rolling 3 is 1 out of 6, or $\frac{1}{6}$.

On each roll of the number cube, we would not be surprised to see any of the numbers come up, because it is *possible* to get 0, 1, 2, or 3 each time we roll. But after many rolls, we would *expect* to see 0 close to $\frac{3}{6}$ of the time, or on approximately $\frac{1}{2}$ of all the rolls.

**Answer** the following questions.

Jimmy and Naomi are rolling a regular 0–5 ***Number Cube.*** Jimmy wins if 0 is rolled. Naomi wins if 1, 2, 3, 4, or 5 is rolled.

1. Who do you think will win more often? Naomi
2. What fraction of the time do you think Jimmy will win? $\frac{1}{6}$
3. What is Naomi's probability of winning? $\frac{5}{6}$
4. If they roll the cube 6 times, how many times would you expect Jimmy to win? What is $\frac{1}{6}$ of 6? probably once; 1
5. Should you be surprised if Jimmy did not win exactly 1 time out of 6 tries? no

 eTextbook This lesson is available in the ***eTextbook.***

Student Page

Think about rolling a red 0–5 ***Number Cube*** and a blue 5–10 ***Number Cube.*** In the table to the right, the column on the left shows the numbers that could be rolled on the red 0–5 cube, while the row at the top shows the possibilities for the blue 5–10 cube. The numbers on the two cubes can be added to get a sum as small as 5 (0 red, 5 blue) or as great as 15 (5 red, 10 blue). The spaces in the table represent the sums for every combination of the two cubes.

**Table of Sums**

| | 5 | 6 | 7 | 8 | 9 | 10 |
|---|---|---|---|---|---|---|
| 0 | 5 | 6 | 7 | 8 | 9 | 10 |
| 1 | 6 | 7 | 8 | 9 | 10 | 11 |
| 2 | 7 | 8 | 9 | 10 | 11 | 12 |
| 3 | 8 | 9 | 10 | 11 | 12 | 13 |
| 4 | 9 | 10 | 11 | 12 | 13 | 14 |
| 5 | 10 | 11 | 12 | 13 | 14 | 15 |

6. Copy the table and fill in the missing sums (a few have been done for you already).

**Use** your completed Table of Sums to answer these questions.

7. When rolling the blue and red cube, how many different sums are made from each roll? sums of 5–15, or 11 total
8. How many different cube combinations are possible? 36
9. How many different ways can you roll a sum of

**a.** 5? 1 **d.** 8? 4 **g.** 11? 5 **j.** 14? 2
**b.** 6? 2 **e.** 9? 5 **h.** 12? 4 **k.** 15? 1
**c.** 7? 3 **f.** 10? 6 **i.** 13? 3 **l.** 16? 0

10. What is the probability of rolling each of the following sums?

**a.** 10 $\frac{6}{36}$ **b.** 15 $\frac{1}{36}$ **c.** 5 $\frac{1}{36}$



## 3 Reflect

5

### Guided Discussion REASONING

Whole Group

Have students think about a new version of the Roll-a-Sum Race. In this version, the first of two players gets a point when a sum of 8, 9, 10, or 11 is rolled. The second player gets a point when a sum of 5, 6, 7, 12, 13, 14, or 15 is rolled. The first player to get 10 points will be the winner. Have students discuss if the game is fair and what a fair game would be. Guide students to see that in a fair game both players should have an equal chance of winning. Ask students if they know a way to change the rules to make the game fair to both players. Lead the discussion with questions such as the following:

- **If there are 36 possible outcomes, how might it be possible for each player to have the same chance of winning?** If each player had the same number of chances to win (18).
- **What are some ways the sums could be reassigned to each player to make it fair?** Any arrangement where there are 18 possible outcomes for each player will be valid. One example is 8, 9, 11, 12 for one player and the remaining sums for the other.

**Cumulative Review:** For review of relation signs, assign Problems 10–11 on student page 351.

**Family Involvement:** Assign the ***Practice, Reteach,*** or ***Enrichment*** activities depending on the needs of your students. Encourage students to play the **Fracto I** or **Fracto II Game Mat** or **Fracto eGame** with a friend or relative.

**Concept/Question Board:** Encourage students to continue to look for real-world examples of fractions and post them on the Concept/Question Board.

**Math Puzzler:** Think about how this picture would look if you removed a triangle from each side of the balance. Which is heavier, a square or a triangle? How can you tell? One square weighs the same as one triangle and one circle, so a square is heavier than a triangle.

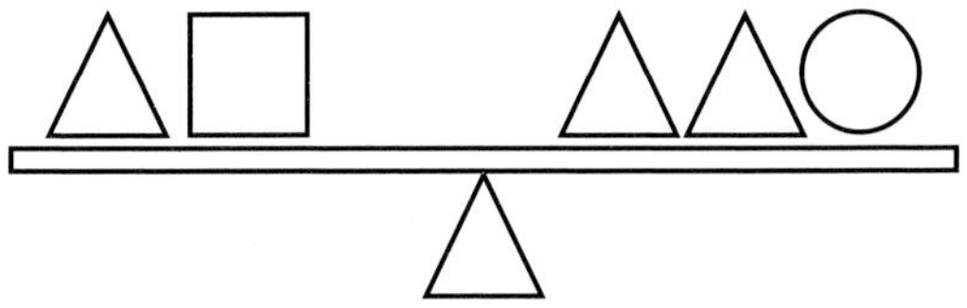

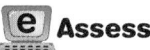

# 4 Assess and Differentiate

**e Assess** Use ***eAssess*** to record and analyze evidence of student understanding.

## A Gather Evidence

Use the Daily Class Assessment Records in ***Assessment*** or ***eAssess*** to record daily observations.

### Informal Assessment
**Games**

Did the student ENGAGING
- ❑ pay attention to others' contributions?
- ❑ contribute information and ideas?
- ❑ improve on a strategy?
- ❑ reflect on and check the accuracy of his or her work?

### Informal Assessment
**Guided Discussion**

Did the student UNDERSTANDING
- ❑ make important observations?
- ❑ extend or generalize learning?
- ❑ provide insightful answers?
- ❑ pose insightful questions?

## B Summarize Findings

Analyze and summarize assessment data for each student. Determine which Assessment Follow-Up is appropriate for each student. Use the Student Assessment Record in ***Assessment*** or ***eAssess*** to update assessment records.

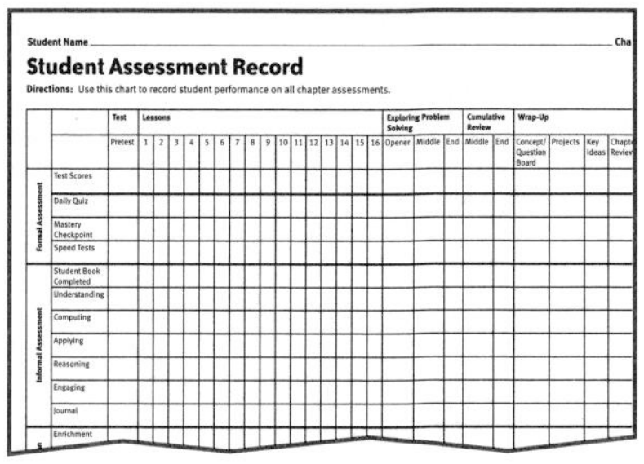
Student Name
Student Assessment Record

**Assessment Page T41**

## C Assessment Follow-Up • DIFFERENTIATE INSTRUCTION

Based on your observations, use these teaching strategies for assessment follow-up.

### INTERVENTION

Review student performance on ***Intervention*** Lesson 8.B to see if students have mastered prerequisite skills for this lesson.

### ENGLISH LEARNER

**Review**

Use Lesson 8.5 in ***English Learner Support Guide*** to review lesson concepts and vocabulary.

### ENRICH

**If . . .** students are proficient in the lesson concepts,

**Then . . .** encourage them to work on the chapter projects or ***Enrichment*** Lesson 8.5.

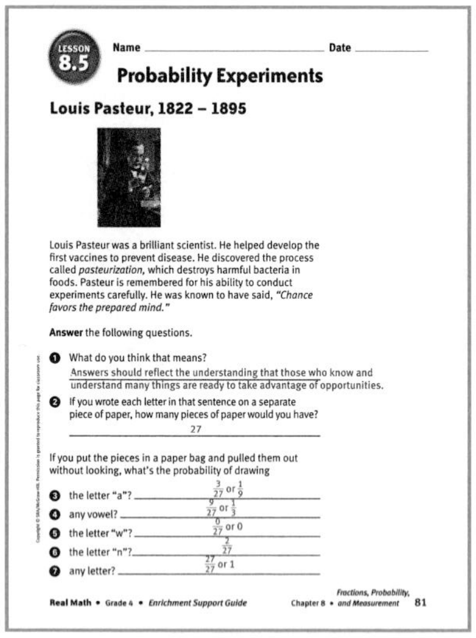
LESSON 8.5 Name ________ Date ________

**Probability Experiments**

**Louis Pasteur, 1822 – 1895**

Louis Pasteur was a brilliant scientist. He helped develop the first vaccines to prevent disease. He discovered the process called *pasteurization*, which destroys harmful bacteria in foods. Pasteur is remembered for his ability to conduct experiments carefully. He was known to have said, *"Chance favors the prepared mind."*

**Answer** the following questions.

1. What do you think that means? Answers should reflect the understanding that those who know and understand many things are ready to take advantage of opportunities.
2. If you wrote each letter in that sentence on a separate piece of paper, how many pieces of paper would you have? 27

If you put the pieces in a paper bag and pulled them out without looking, what's the probability of drawing

3. the letter "a"? $\frac{3}{27}$ or $\frac{1}{9}$
4. any vowel? $\frac{9}{27}$ or $\frac{1}{3}$
5. the letter "w"? $\frac{0}{27}$ or 0
6. the letter "n"? $\frac{2}{27}$
7. any letter? $\frac{27}{27}$ or 1

**Real Math** • Grade 4 • *Enrichment Support Guide* Chapter 8 • *Fractions, Probability, and Measurement* 81

Enrichment Lesson 8.5

### PRACTICE

**If . . .** students would benefit from additional practice,

**Then . . .** assign ***Practice*** Lesson 8.5.

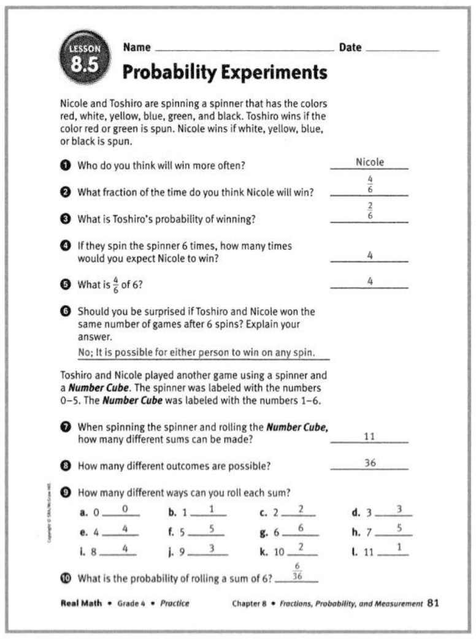
LESSON 8.5 Name ________ Date ________

**Probability Experiments**

Nicole and Toshiro are spinning a spinner that has the colors red, white, yellow, blue, green, and black. Toshiro wins if the color red or green is spun. Nicole wins if white, yellow, blue, or black is spun.

1. Who do you think will win more often? Nicole
2. What fraction of the time do you think Nicole will win? $\frac{4}{6}$
3. What is Toshiro's probability of winning? $\frac{2}{6}$
4. If they spin the spinner 6 times, how many times would you expect Nicole to win? 4
5. What is $\frac{4}{6}$ of 6? 4
6. Should you be surprised if Toshiro and Nicole won the same number of games after 6 spins? Explain your answer. No; It is possible for either person to win on any spin.

Toshiro and Nicole played another game using a spinner and a ***Number Cube***. The spinner was labeled with the numbers 0–5. The ***Number Cube*** was labeled with the numbers 1–6.

7. When spinning the spinner and rolling the ***Number Cube***, how many different sums can be made? 11
8. How many different outcomes are possible? 36
9. How many different ways can you roll each sum?
   a. 0 __0__ b. 1 __1__ c. 2 __2__ d. 3 __3__
   e. 4 __4__ f. 5 __5__ g. 6 __6__ h. 7 __5__
   i. 8 __4__ j. 9 __3__ k. 10 __2__ l. 11 __1__
10. What is the probability of rolling a sum of 6? $\frac{6}{36}$

**Real Math** • Grade 4 • *Practice* Chapter 8 • *Fractions, Probability, and Measurement* 81

Practice Lesson 8.5

### RETEACH

**If . . .** students are having difficulty understanding probability experiments,

**Then . . .** have students model a probability experiment, such as pulling a cube from a bag that contains three red and three blue cubes. Ask questions about what they expect to happen. Have them note the color of each draw and repeat this many times, recording their information in a chart. Ask follow-up questions about what is likely to come out next, about changing the ratio of red to blue cubes, changing the number of cubes, etc.

## Objectives
- To provide an opportunity to apply probability concepts to a real-world situation
- To provide practice with mental addition
- To provide an informal introduction to equivalent fractions

## NCTM Standards
**Number and Operations**
Compute fluently and make reasonable estimates

**Connections**
Recognize and apply mathematics in contexts outside of mathematics

## Materials
*Number Cubes (0–5 and 5–10)

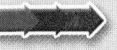

## Technology
**Presentation** Lesson 8.6
**Games** Anything but 10

## Test Prep
**Cumulative Review**
- Mental Math reviews informal comparison of fractions (Lesson 7.2).
- The **Anything but 10 Game** reviews basic addition facts (Lesson 1.5).

**Extended Response**
Problem 12

*Manipulative Kit Item

# Applying Fractions

**Context of the Lesson** This lesson assesses what students have learned about fractions in the early part of the chapter before continuing concepts such as equivalent fractions and mixed numbers.

See page 328B for Math Background for teachers for this lesson.

## Planning for Learning • DIFFERENTIATE INSTRUCTION

### INTERVENTION

**If . . .** students lack the prerequisite skill of finding the fraction of a number,

**Then . . .** teach Intervention Lesson 8.B.

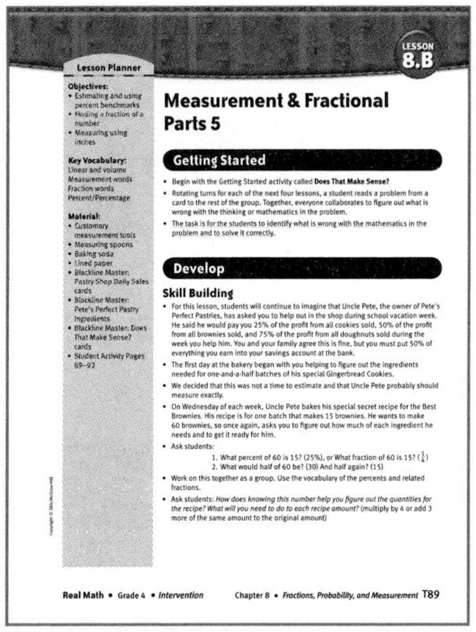
Lesson Planner
LESSON 8.B
Measurement & Fractional Parts 5
Getting Started
Develop
Skill Building
Real Math • Grade 4 • Intervention Chapter 8 • Fractions, Probability, and Measurement T89

Intervention Lesson 8.B

### ENGLISH LEARNER

Preview

**If . . .** students need language support,

**Then . . .** use Lesson 8.6 in English Learner Support Guide to preview lesson concepts and vocabulary.

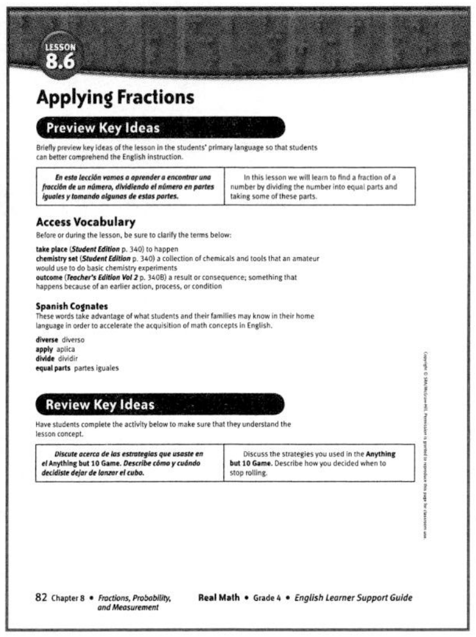
LESSON 8.6
Applying Fractions
Preview Key Ideas
Access Vocabulary
Spanish Cognates
Review Key Ideas
82 Chapter 8 • Fractions, Probability, and Measurement Real Math • Grade 4 • English Learner Support Guide

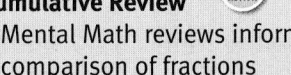

English Learner Lesson 8.6

### ENRICH

**If . . .** students are proficient in the lesson concepts,

**Then . . .** encourage them to devise new strategies for the Anything but 10 game.

### PRACTICE

**If . . .** students would benefit from additional practice,

**Then . . .** extend the probability investigations in small group Strategy Building.

### RETEACH

**If . . .** students are having difficulty taking the fractional part of a number,

**Then . . .** have them model the process with graph paper or manipulatives before assigning the student pages.

### Access Vocabulary

**a vote to take place** a vote will happen. The members will vote or take a vote.
**chemistry set** a collection of chemicals and tools that an amateur would use to do basic chemistry experiments.

**Spanish Cognates**
**to apply** aplicar
**divide** dividir
**equal parts** partes iguales

## Mental Math

5

Review THUMBS UP Provide practice with informal comparison of fractions of the same whole, such as the following. Students should respond with thumbs-up if the answers represent the same amount or thumbs-down if they don't. Write pairs of fractions on the board and say them aloud.

**a.** $\frac{1}{4}, \frac{1}{2}$ down **b.** $\frac{5}{10}, \frac{6}{12}$ up **c.** $\frac{4}{6}, \frac{2}{3}$ up

**d.** $\frac{1}{8}, \frac{4}{16}$ down **e.** $\frac{2}{6}, \frac{1}{3}$ up **f.** $\frac{10}{15}, \frac{2}{5}$ down

## 1 Develop

25

### Tell Students In Today's Lesson They Will

solve problems using fractions

### Strategy Building UNDERSTANDING

Whole Group

1. Tell students that the class is going to perform another probability experiment. In this experiment, they will roll one 0–5 ***Number Cube*** and one 5–10 ***Number Cube*** many times and keep track of whether both numbers rolled are even. Ask students questions such as the following about the possible outcomes:
   - **If you use two cubes, what is the greatest number of even numbers you can roll?** 2
   - **What is the greatest possible number of odd numbers?** 2
   - **What other possible outcomes are there?** one even and one odd cube
2. Make sure students understand that an odd number on the 0–5 ***Number Cube*** with an even number on the 5–10 ***Number Cube*** is considered a separate outcome from an even number on the 0–5 ***Number Cube*** cube and an odd number on the 5–10 ***Number Cube*** even though both outcomes have one odd and one even number. Ask students how many possible outcomes there are. 4

   Demonstrate this by making a grid on the board.

Ask students questions about probability, such as the following, and write the answers on the board:

- **What is the probability of rolling two odd numbers?** $\frac{1}{4}$
- **What is the probability of rolling two even numbers?** $\frac{1}{4}$
- **What is the probability of rolling one odd and one even number?** $\frac{2}{4}$ or $\frac{1}{2}$
- **How many times would you expect to roll two even numbers if we tried this experiment twelve times?** about 3
- **How could we calculate the answer?** Possible answer: The probability is $\frac{1}{4}$; 12 divided into 4 equal parts is 3.
- **If the experiment was done repeatedly (with 12 rolls each time), would two even numbers be rolled exactly three times, for each repetition of the experiment?** probably not

3. Now expand the prediction for rolling two even numbers to greater and greater numbers of trials. Write exercises, such as the following, on the board and have the class answer them as a group:

   $\frac{1}{4}$ of 20 = 5 $\frac{1}{4}$ of 60 = 15

   $\frac{1}{4}$ of 80 = 20 $\frac{1}{4}$ of 800 = 200

Based on these calculations, have students predict how many times two even numbers will appear in 8,000 trials. 2,000

Ask a student to explain how she or he found their answer. One method would be to multiply the answer for $\frac{1}{4}$ of 800 by 10.

### Strategy Building ENGAGING

Small Group

Have students work in small groups to test the prediction for twelve rolls. Have each group write *yes* (two even numbers) or *no* (zero or one even number) for each of their twelve rolls. Have each group report their number of yes tallies back to the class when they are finished.

### Skill and Strategy Building

Whole Group

Game **Anything but 10 Game**

Discuss the rules for the **Anything but 10 Game** on page 341. This game reinforces addition facts and mathematical reasoning. Encourage students to come up with their own strategies and intuitive concepts of probability. Refer to the sum of 10 as the "anything but" number. Make sure that students understand that when they give up their turn willingly (without having rolled a sum of 10), the points gained on that turn are safe and cannot be lost.

## 2 Assign Student Pages

20

### Pages 340–341 APPLYING

Have students work on page 340 independently.

#### Monitoring Student Progress

| If . . . | Then . . . |
| --- | --- |
| students are having trouble finding fractions of whole numbers | suggest that they need to focus on the denominator alone. Once the whole number has been divided into the correct number of equal parts, counting how many of the parts they need to work with (using the numerator) should be more straightforward. |

### As Students Finish

Game **Anything but 10 Game**

## LESSON 8.6 Applying Fractions

### Key Ideas

**Fractions are used in many diverse situations.**
One example is finding a fraction of a number.

Let's review. What is $\frac{2}{3}$ of 24?

Divide 24 into 3 equal parts. $3)\overline{24}$  Then take 2 parts. $2 \times 8 = 16$

★ ★ ★ ★ ★ ★ ★ ★ ★ ★ ★ ★ : ★ ★ ★ ★ ★ ★ ★ ★ ★ ★ ★ ★
★ ★ ★ ★ ★ ★ ★ ★ ★ ★ ★ ★ : ★ ★ ★ ★ ★ ★ ★ ★ ★ ★ ★ ★

**Use** your understanding of how to find fractions of numbers to solve these problems.

① The city council can vote only if at least $\frac{5}{6}$ of its members are present. The city council has 18 members. How many members must be present for a vote to take place?    at least 15

② Winston has 9 cousins, and $\frac{2}{3}$ of them are boys. How many of his cousins are girls?   3

③ Tasha can save $\frac{1}{4}$ of the cost of a chemistry set if she waits until it goes on sale. How much will a $28 chemistry set cost if it is on sale?  $21

### Solve.

④ $\frac{2}{3}$ of 30 = ☐  20  ⑤ $\frac{3}{3}$ of 30 = ☐  30  ⑥ $\frac{0}{3}$ of 30 = ☐  0

⑦ $\frac{1}{6}$ of 30 = ☐  5  ⑧ $\frac{3}{6}$ of 30 = ☐  15  ⑨ $\frac{4}{6}$ of 30 = ☐  20

⑩ $\frac{5}{6}$ of 30 = ☐  25  ⑪ $\frac{6}{6}$ of 30 = ☐  30

⑫ **Extended Response** Compare your answers to Problems 4 and 9. Are they the same or different? Explain your reasoning by drawing a picture using 30 stars for each answer.   See Reflect in *Teacher's Edition.*

340        ☒ **Textbook** This lesson is available in the *eTextbook.*

---

## Game

### Probability and Strategies Practice

# Anything But 10 Game

**Players:** Two or more

**Materials:** Number Cubes (one 0–5, one 5–10)

**Object:** To score a total sum of 100 or more

**Math Focus:** Addition and mathematical reasoning

**HOW TO PLAY**

❶ Roll both cubes. Find the sum of the two numbers rolled.

❷ If the sum is not 10, add the number of points rolled to your running score. Keep your turn and roll again, or stop and add the total of your running score to your permanent score.

❸ On each turn, you may have as many rolls as you like until you either roll a sum of 10 or choose to stop. If you choose to stop, add your running score to your permanent score.

❹ When you roll a sum of 10, you lose your turn and you lose any points in your running score. You add 0 to your permanent score. (NOTE: You never lose the points in your permanent score.)

❺ The first player to score 100 or more is the winner.

### SAMPLE GAME

| Round | Janice Rolls: | Sum | Score | Austin Rolls: | Sum | Score |
|-------|---------------|-----|-------|---------------|-----|-------|
| 1 |  7 5 | 12 | | 9 4 | 13 | |
| | 5 4 | 9 | | 6 2 | 8 | 21 |
| | 10 5 | 15 | 36 | Stops | | |
| 2 | 8 3 | 11 | | 10 4 | 14 | |
| | 7 0 | 7 | | 8 3 | 11 | |
| | 6 4 | 10 | 36 | 7 1 | 8 | 54 |
| | Loses turn | | | Stops | | |

After two rounds, Austin is ahead 54 to 36.

☒ **Games** This game is available as an *eGame.*        341

---

## Applying Fractions LESSON 8.6

### 3 Reflect                                                    5

## Guided Discussion REASONING                    Whole Group

Discuss students' strategies for the **Anything but 10 Game** by asking questions such as the following:

■ **Did you feel you had a good chance to get anything but 10?** Yes. The actual probability is $\frac{30}{36}$ or $\frac{5}{6}$

■ **Is it possible to roll anything but 10 twenty times in a row?** yes

■ **Is it likely?** No; while students are not expected to know the actual answer (the probability is less than 3% or $\frac{5}{6}$ used as a factor 20 times), hopefully they will have begun to develop an intuitive understanding of this.

■ **How did you decide when to stop rolling?**

### Extended Response ✔

**Problem 12** Correctly drawn pictures will show that $\frac{2}{3}$ of 30 (two groups of 10 stars) and $\frac{4}{6}$ of 30 (four groups of 5 stars) are each 20.

---

 **Curriculum Connection:** Students discussed voting of city council members in this lesson. Discuss voting of the local city council and any issues being discussed at this time.

 **Cumulative Review:** For review of percent benchmarks, assign Problems 12–13 on student page 351.

 **Family Involvement:** Assign the *Practice, Reteach,* or *Enrichment* activities depending on the needs of your students.

Encourage students to play the **Anything but 10 Game** with a friend or relative or **Anything but 10 ☒ Games.**

 **Concept/Question Board:** Encourage students to continue to look for real-world examples of fractions and post them on the Concept/Question Board.

 **Math Puzzler:** Before lunch David set out a row of 6 glasses. The first 3 were full of juice, and the next 3 were empty. How could David move just one glass so that every full glass would be next to an empty one? He could pour juice from the second glass into the fifth glass and return the second glass to its original spot.

# 4 Assess and Differentiate

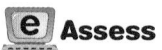

**e Assess** Use ***eAssess*** to record and analyze evidence of student understanding.

## A Gather Evidence

Use the Daily Class Assessment Records in ***Assessment*** or ***eAssess*** to record daily observations.

### Informal Assessment

**✓ Strategy Building**

Did the student UNDERSTANDING

- ❑ make important observations?
- ❑ extend or generalize learning?
- ❑ provide insightful answers?
- ❑ pose insightful questions?

### Portfolio Assessment

**✓ Extended Response**

Did the student REASONING

- ❑ provide a clear explanation?
- ❑ communicate reasons and strategies?
- ❑ choose appropriate strategies?
- ❑ argue logically?

## B Summarize Findings

Analyze and summarize assessment data for each student. Determine which Assessment Follow-Up is appropriate for each student. Use the Student Assessment Record in ***Assessment*** or ***eAssess*** to update assessment records.

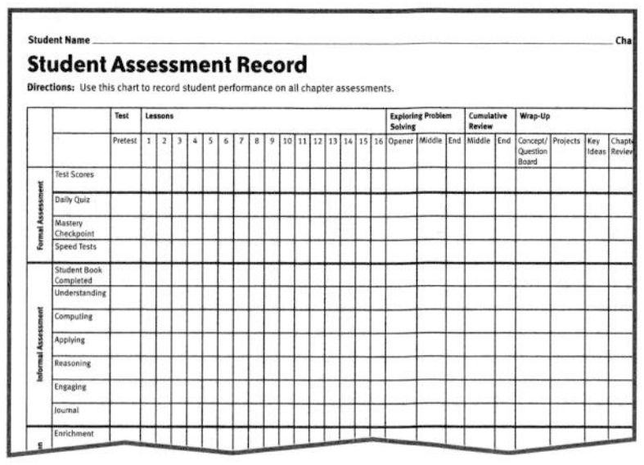
Student Name
Student Assessment Record

**Assessment Page T41**

## C Assessment Follow-Up • DIFFERENTIATE INSTRUCTION

Based on your observations, use these teaching strategies for Assessment follow-up.

### INTERVENTION

Review student performance on ***Intervention*** Lesson 8.B to see if students have mastered prerequisite skills for this lesson.

### ENGLISH LEARNER

**Review**

Use Lesson 8.6 in ***English Learner Support Guide*** to review lesson concepts and vocabulary.

### ENRICH

**If . . .** students are proficient in the lesson concepts,

**Then . . .** encourage them to work on the chapter projects or ***Enrichment*** Lesson 8.6.

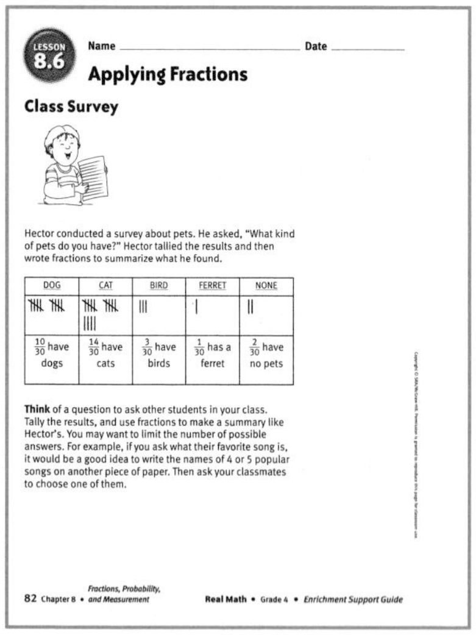
LESSON 8.6 Name ____ Date ____

**Applying Fractions**

**Class Survey**

Hector conducted a survey about pets. He asked, "What kind of pets do you have?" Hector tallied the results and then wrote fractions to summarize what he found.

| DOG | CAT | BIRD | FERRET | NONE |
|---|---|---|---|---|
| 卌 卌 | 卌 卌 \|\|\|\| | \|\|\| | \| | \|\| |
| $\frac{10}{30}$ have dogs | $\frac{14}{30}$ have cats | $\frac{3}{30}$ have birds | $\frac{1}{30}$ has a ferret | $\frac{2}{30}$ have no pets |

**Think** of a question to ask other students in your class. Tally the results, and use fractions to make a summary like Hector's. You may want to limit the number of possible answers. For example, if you ask what their favorite song is, it would be a good idea to write the names of 4 or 5 popular songs on another piece of paper. Then ask your classmates to choose one of them.

82 Chapter 8 • Fractions, Probability, and Measurement — Real Math • Grade 4 • Enrichment Support Guide

Enrichment Lesson 8.6

### PRACTICE

**If . . .** students would benefit from additional practice,

**Then . . .** assign ***Practice*** Lesson 8.6.

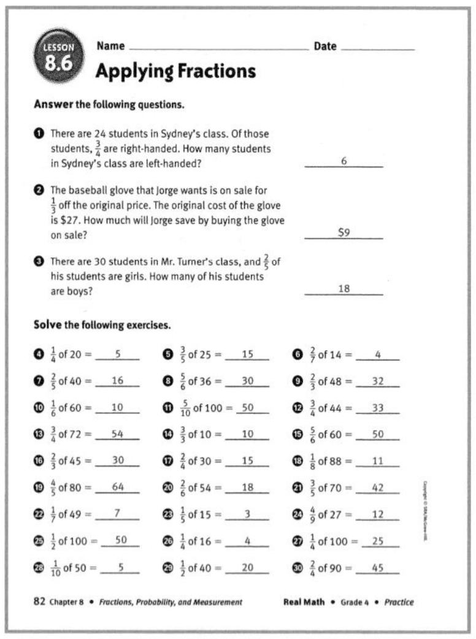
LESSON 8.6 Name ____ Date ____

**Applying Fractions**

**Answer the following questions.**

1. There are 24 students in Sydney's class. Of those students, $\frac{3}{4}$ are right-handed. How many students in Sydney's class are left-handed? 6
2. The baseball glove that Jorge wants is on sale for $\frac{1}{3}$ off the original price. The original cost of the glove is \$27. How much will Jorge save by buying the glove on sale? \$9
3. There are 30 students in Mr. Turner's class, and $\frac{2}{5}$ of his students are girls. How many of his students are boys? 18

**Solve the following exercises.**

4. $\frac{1}{4}$ of 20 = 5
5. $\frac{3}{5}$ of 25 = 15
6. $\frac{2}{7}$ of 14 = 4
7. $\frac{2}{5}$ of 40 = 16
8. $\frac{5}{6}$ of 36 = 30
9. $\frac{2}{3}$ of 48 = 32
10. $\frac{1}{6}$ of 60 = 10
11. $\frac{5}{10}$ of 100 = 50
12. $\frac{3}{4}$ of 44 = 33
13. $\frac{3}{4}$ of 72 = 54
14. $\frac{3}{3}$ of 10 = 10
15. $\frac{5}{6}$ of 60 = 50
16. $\frac{2}{3}$ of 45 = 30
17. $\frac{2}{4}$ of 30 = 15
18. $\frac{1}{8}$ of 88 = 11
19. $\frac{4}{5}$ of 80 = 64
20. $\frac{2}{6}$ of 54 = 18
21. $\frac{3}{5}$ of 70 = 42
22. $\frac{1}{7}$ of 49 = 7
23. $\frac{1}{5}$ of 15 = 3
24. $\frac{4}{9}$ of 27 = 12
25. $\frac{1}{2}$ of 100 = 50
26. $\frac{1}{4}$ of 16 = 4
27. $\frac{1}{4}$ of 100 = 25
28. $\frac{1}{10}$ of 50 = 5
29. $\frac{1}{2}$ of 40 = 20
30. $\frac{2}{4}$ of 90 = 45

82 Chapter 8 • Fractions, Probability, and Measurement — Real Math • Grade 4 • Practice

Practice Lesson 8.6

### RETEACH

**If . . .** students are having difficulty taking a fractional part of a number,

**Then . . .** students can also find fractional parts of a whole number by multiplying the whole number by the fraction. A whole number can be written as a fraction by writing it as a fraction with a denominator of 1.

For example, $24 = \frac{24}{1}$. So $\frac{2}{3}$ of 24 = $\frac{2}{3} \times \frac{24}{1} = \frac{(2 \times 24)}{(3 \times 1)} = \frac{48}{3} = 16$.

## Lesson Planner

**OBJECTIVES**
- To provide practice solving simple probability problems
- To provide practice finding fractions of whole numbers
- To demonstrate that there are many ways to shade a fractional part of a geometric figure

**NCTM STANDARDS**

**Number and Operations**
Compute fluently and make reasonable estimates

**Geometry**
Use visualizations, spatial reasoning, and geometric modeling to solve problems

**Data Analysis and Probability**
Understand and apply basic concepts of probability

**MATERIALS**
- ***Number Cubes**
- Graph paper (optional)
- ***Fracto I or Fracto II Game Mats** (optional)

**TECHNOLOGY**
**e Presentation** Lesson 8.7
**e Games** Fracto, or **Anything but 10**

**TEST PREP**
**Cumulative Review**
Mental Math reviews informal comparison of fractions (Lesson 8.1).

*Manipulative Kit Item

# Probability and Fractions

**Context of the Lesson** This lesson continues the informal introduction to equivalent fractions that started in Lesson 8.6. Equivalent fractions will be formally introduced in the next lesson.
See page 328B for Math Background for teachers for this lesson.

## Planning for Learning • DIFFERENTIATE INSTRUCTION

### INTERVENTION

**If . . .** students lack the prerequisite skill of finding a fraction of a number,

**Then . . .** teach ***Intervention*** Lesson 8.B.

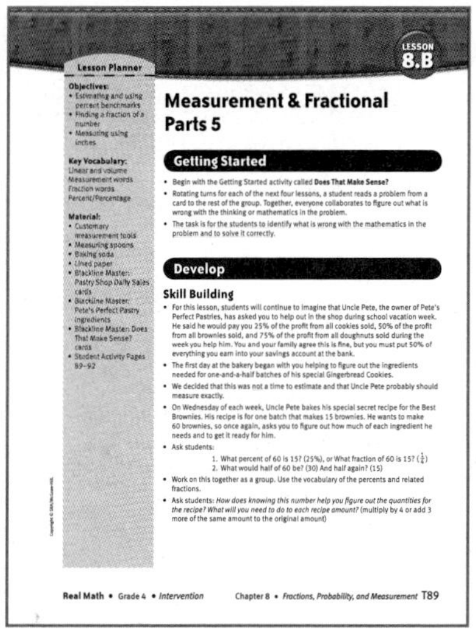
Lesson 8.B
Measurement & Fractional Parts 5
Getting Started
Develop

Intervention Lesson 8.B

### ENGLISH LEARNER

Preview

**If . . .** students need language support,

**Then . . .** use Lesson 8.7 in ***English Learner Support Guide*** to preview lesson concepts and vocabulary.

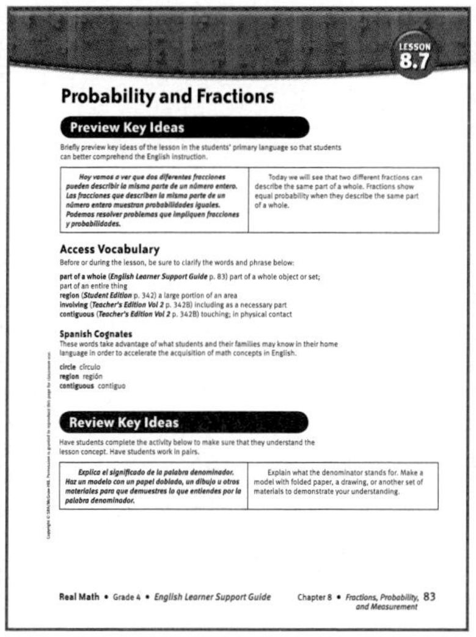
Lesson 8.7
Probability and Fractions
Preview Key Ideas
Access Vocabulary
Spanish Cognates
Review Key Ideas

English Learner Lesson 8.7

### ENRICH

**If . . .** students are proficient in the lesson concepts,

**Then . . .** encourage them to devise variations for the **Fracto Game.**

### PRACTICE

**If . . .** students would benefit from additional practice,

**Then . . .** extend Guided Discussion with additional examples before assigning the student pages.

### RETEACH

**If . . .** students are having difficulty understanding the intro activity,

**Then . . .** have students compare the activity to portions of pizza before assigning the student pages.

**Access Vocabulary**
**part of a whole** part of a whole object or set; an entire thing

**Spanish Cognates**
**circle** círculo
**region** región

# Teaching Lesson 8.7

## Mental Math
5

Review THUMBS UP Provide practice with comparing fractions of the same whole number. Students should respond with thumbs-up if the answers represent the same amount or thumbs-down if they don't. Write pairs of fractions, such as the following, on the board and say them aloud:

**a.** $\frac{1}{8}, \frac{2}{16}$ up **b.** $\frac{2}{10}, \frac{1}{5}$ up **c.** $\frac{4}{8}, \frac{1}{4}$ down

**d.** $\frac{6}{8}, \frac{3}{4}$ up **e.** $\frac{2}{3}, \frac{3}{6}$ down **f.** $\frac{2}{4}, \frac{3}{6}$ up

## 1 Develop
25

### Tell Students In Today's Lesson They Will
solve problems involving fractions and probability

### Guided Discussion
REASONING Whole Group

1. Work a sample problem, such as the following, with the class that uses fractions of a whole and probability concurrently.
   - Draw a circle on the board and divide it into quarters. Shade the left half of the circle. Ask students to name a fraction that describes how much of the circle is shaded. $\frac{2}{4}$ or $\frac{1}{2}$
   - Review the meaning of *denominator* (the bottom number that tells us how many equal parts to divide something into) and *numerator* (the top number that tells us how many of those equal-sized parts we are dealing with).
   - Draw a second circle on the board that is the same size as the first. Divide this circle into eighths. Shade the left half of the circle as before. Again ask students to name a fraction that describes how much of the circle is shaded. $\frac{4}{8}, \frac{2}{4}$, or $\frac{1}{2}$
   - Ask students if one circle has more shaded area than the other. Students should see that although there are a different number of parts shaded, the total shaded area of each circle is equal.
2. Now have the students consider the circles as two spinners. Ask questions such as the following:
   - **In how many different sections can the spinner land on the first circle?** 4
   - **Since two of those sections are shaded, what fraction would describe the probability of the spinner stopping on a shaded section?** $\frac{2}{4}$ or $\frac{1}{2}$
   - **If we spun the first spinner 12 times, about how many times would you expect the spinner to stop on a shaded section?** 6
   - **In how many different areas can the spinner land on the second circle?** 8.
   - **Since 4 of the areas are shaded, what fraction would describe the probability of landing on a shaded section?** $\frac{4}{8}$ or $\frac{1}{2}$
   - **If we spun the second spinner 12 times, how many times would you expect the spinner to stop on a shaded section?** 6
   - **Which spinner is more likely to land on a shaded section?** The probability of each spinner landing on a shaded section is equal.
3. Draw a third circle that is bigger than the other two.

   Divide this circle into 8 sections and shade 4 of them as before, but now alternate shaded regions with regions that are not shaded. Ask students if this bigger spinner has a greater chance of stopping on a shaded region than the other two circle spinners. no

   Have a volunteer explain the reasoning for their answer. Guide students to see that, although the size and location of the shaded regions on the third circle are different from those on the second circle, the relationship of the number of shaded sections (4) to the total number of sections (8) is the same. The probability of the spinner stopping on a shaded section is the same for each ($\frac{4}{8}$).

## 2 Assign Student Pages
25

### Page 342–343
APPLYING

Have students complete pages 342 and 343 independently.

### Monitoring Student Progress

| | |
|---|---|
| **If . . .** students have trouble with general probability concepts | **Then . . .** they might benefit from extra concrete experience with probability, such as acting out the exercise in the student book (roll a 0–5 cube several times and decide about what fraction of the time it will land on specific numbers). |
| **If . . .** students make incorrect denominators for probability fractions | **Then . . .** clarify that the denominator represents the total number of equal possible outcomes for an experiment. For example, for Problem 1 in the student book, the denominator is the total number of ways the cube can land (6), not the number of ways that Andre can win (4). |

### As Students Finish

Game **Fracto I** or **Fracto II Game** or **Anything but 10 Game**

e **Games Fracto** or **Anything but 10 Game**

Student Page

## LESSON 8.7 Probability and Fractions

### Key Ideas

**Two fractions can describe the same probability.**

Shade $\frac{1}{2}$ of a circle.

Shade $\frac{2}{4}$ of the same circle.

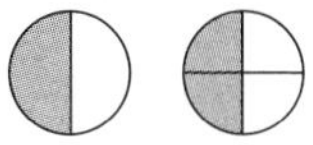

We can see that $\frac{1}{2}$ and $\frac{2}{4}$ of the same circle represent the same amount of that circle. $\frac{1}{2} = \frac{2}{4}$

If the first circle was a spinner, we would expect to land on a shaded region $\frac{1}{2}$ of the time. If the second circle was also a spinner, we would expect to land on a shaded region $\frac{2}{4}$ of the time. On which spinner do we expect to land on a shaded region more frequently?

The answer is neither one. The two spinners would have an equal probability of landing on a shaded region.

**Solve** these problems.

Andre and Emma are rolling a 0–5 ***Number Cube.*** When the cube shows 0, 1, or 2, Andre wins. When it shows 3, 4, or 5, Emma wins.

1. What is the probability that Emma will win? $\frac{3}{6}$ or $\frac{1}{2}$
2. What is the probability that Andre will win? $\frac{3}{6}$ or $\frac{1}{2}$
3. Suppose they play the game 120 times.
   - **a.** About how many times would you expect Emma to win? 60
   - **b.** About how many times would you expect Andre to win? 60
   - **c.** Would you be surprised if Emma did not win exactly 60 times? no

Skyler and Mackenzie flip a coin. Skyler will win if it lands heads up. Mackenzie will win if it lands tails up.



Student Page

4. What is the probability that Skyler will win? $\frac{1}{2}$
5. If they play 120 times, about how many games would you expect Skyler to win? 60
6. Compare your answers for Problems 3 and 5. (Compare $\frac{3}{6}$ of 120 and $\frac{1}{2}$ of 120.) Are they the same or different? They are the same.
7. Explain which probability is greater, $\frac{3}{6}$ or $\frac{1}{2}$.
   The probabalities are the same: $\frac{3}{6} = \frac{1}{2}$.

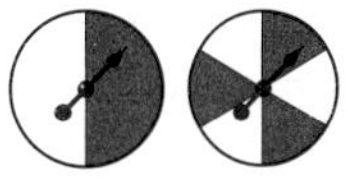

spinner A spinner B

8. What is the probability of landing on red if you use
   - **a.** Spinner A? $\frac{1}{2}$ **b.** Spinner B? $\frac{3}{6}$ or $\frac{1}{2}$
9. Which spinner gives you a better chance of landing on red? They give you the same chance.

**Write** a fraction that describes the shaded portion of each of the following circles.

10. $\frac{1}{4}$ 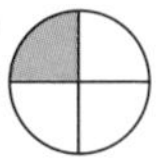
11. $\frac{1}{2}$ 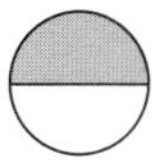
12. $\frac{2}{4}$ or $\frac{1}{2}$ 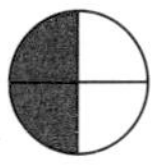

13. Which is greater, $\frac{1}{4}$ of the circle or $\frac{1}{2}$ of the circle? $\frac{1}{2}$
14. Which is greater, $\frac{3}{4}$ of the circle or $\frac{1}{2}$ of the circle? $\frac{3}{4}$
15. Which is greater, $\frac{4}{8}$ of the circle or $\frac{1}{2}$ of the circle? They are equal.

**Write** a fraction that describes the shaded portion of each of the following rectangles.

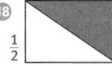

16. $\frac{1}{2}$ 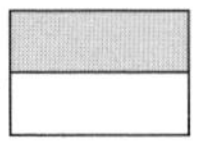
17. $\frac{2}{4}$ or $\frac{1}{2}$ 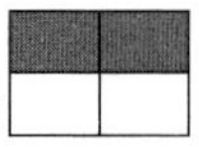
18. $\frac{1}{2}$ 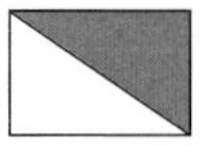



## 3 Reflect

5

### Guided Discussion APPLYING

Whole Group

Ask students the probability of various outcomes when a coin is successfully flipped 3 times. Ask questions such as:

- **What combinations of 3 coin flips would give 0 heads?** TTT
- **What combinations would give 1 head?** HTT, THT, TTH
- **2 heads?** HHT, HTH, THH
- **3 heads?** HHH
- **Knowing this information, what is the probability of flipping three heads?** $\frac{1}{8}$
- **Probability of 2 heads? 1 head? 0 heads?** $\frac{3}{8}, \frac{3}{8}, \frac{1}{8}$

**Cumulative Review:** For review of 10% and $\frac{1}{10}$, assign Problems 14–15 on student page 351.

**Family Involvement:** Assign the ***Practice, Reteach,*** or ***Enrichment*** activities depending on the needs of your students.

Encourage students to play the **Fracto I** or **Fracto II Game Mat** with a friend or relative or **Fracto e Games.**

**Concept/Question Board:** Encourage students to continue to look for real-world examples of fractions and post them on the Concept/Question Board.

**Math Puzzler:** Each fall, the softball league holds its annual championship playoff tournament. This year, 32 teams are competing. According to the rules, a team is eliminated after one loss. How many games will be played to find the tournament champion? 31

# 4 Assess and Differentiate

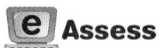

**e Assess** Use ***eAssess*** to record and analyze evidence of student understanding.

## A Gather Evidence

Use the Daily Class Assessment Records in ***Assessment*** or ***eAssess*** to record daily observations.

### Informal Assessment

**Guided Discussion**

Did the student REASONING

- ❑ provide a clear explanation?
- ❑ communicate reasons and strategies?
- ❑ choose appropriate strategies?
- ❑ argue logically?

### Informal Assessment

**Guided Discussion**

Did the student APPLYING

- ❑ apply learning in new situations?
- ❑ contribute concepts?
- ❑ contribute answers?
- ❑ connect mathematics to real-world situations?

## B Summarize Findings

Analyze and summarize assessment data for each student. Determine which Assessment Follow-Up is appropriate for each student. Use the Student Assessment Record in ***Assessment*** or ***eAssess*** to update assessment records.

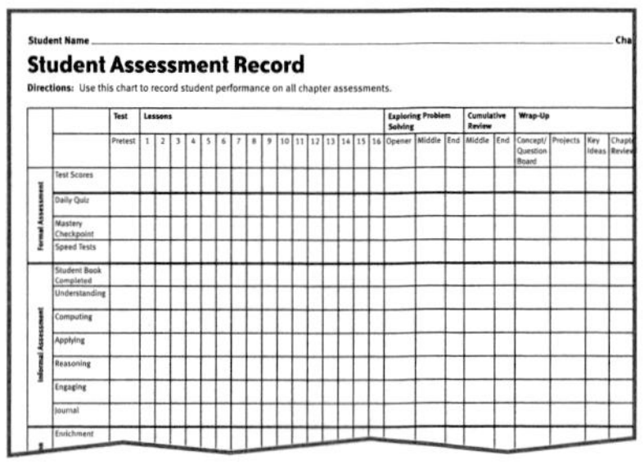
Student Name

**Student Assessment Record**

Directions: Use this chart to record student performance on all chapter assessments.

Assessment Page T41

## C Assessment Follow-Up • DIFFERENTIATE INSTRUCTION

Based on your observations, use these teaching strategies for assessment follow-up.

### INTERVENTION

Review student performance on ***Intervention*** Lesson 8.B to see if students have mastered prerequisite skills for this lesson.

### ENGLISH LEARNER

**Review**

Use Lesson 8.7 in ***English Learner Support Guide*** to review lesson concepts and vocabulary.

### ENRICH

**If . . .** students are proficient in the lesson concepts,

**Then . . .** encourage them to work on the chapter projects or ***Enrichment*** Lesson 8.7.

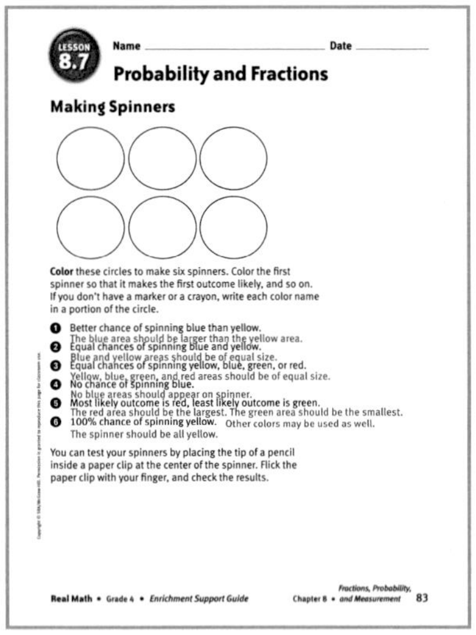
LESSON 8.7 Name ________ Date ________

**Probability and Fractions**

**Making Spinners**

**Color** these circles to make six spinners. Color the first spinner so that it makes the first outcome likely, and so on. If you don't have a marker or a crayon, write each color name in a portion of the circle.

1. Better chance of spinning blue than yellow. The blue area should be larger than the yellow area.
2. Equal chances of spinning blue and yellow. Blue and yellow areas should be of equal size.
3. Equal chances of spinning yellow, blue, green, or red. Yellow, blue, green, and red areas should be of equal size.
4. No chance of spinning blue. No blue areas should appear on spinner.
5. Most likely outcome is red, least likely outcome is green. The red area should be the largest. The green area should be the smallest.
6. 100% chance of spinning yellow. Other colors may be used as well. The spinner should be all yellow.

You can test your spinners by placing the tip of a pencil inside a paper clip at the center of the spinner. Flick the paper clip with your finger, and check the results.

Real Math • Grade 4 • *Enrichment Support Guide* Chapter 8 • *Fractions, Probability, and Measurement* 83

Enrichment Lesson 8.7

### PRACTICE

**If . . .** students would benefit from additional practice

**Then . . .** assign ***Practice*** Lesson 8.7.

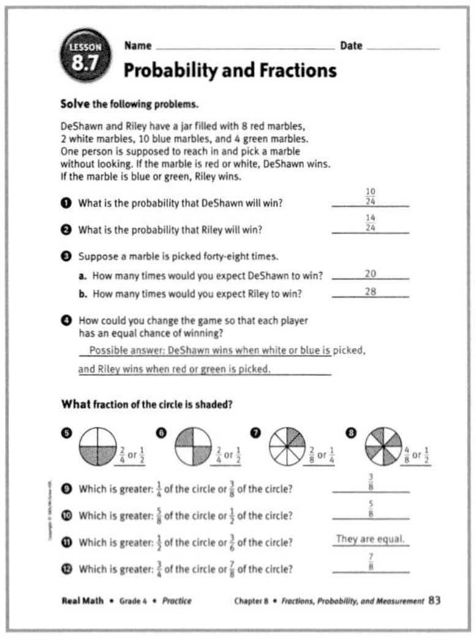
LESSON 8.7 Name ________ Date ________

**Probability and Fractions**

**Solve the following problems.**

DeShawn and Riley have a jar filled with 8 red marbles, 2 white marbles, 10 blue marbles, and 4 green marbles. One person is supposed to reach in and pick a marble without looking. If the marble is red or white, DeShawn wins. If the marble is blue or green, Riley wins.

1. What is the probability that DeShawn will win? $\frac{10}{24}$
2. What is the probability that Riley will win? $\frac{14}{24}$
3. Suppose a marble is picked forty-eight times.
   a. How many times would you expect DeShawn to win? 20
   b. How many times would you expect Riley to win? 28
4. How could you change the game so that each player has an equal chance of winning? Possible answer: DeShawn wins when white or blue is picked, and Riley wins when red or green is picked.

**What fraction of the circle is shaded?**

5. $\frac{2}{4}$ or $\frac{1}{2}$
6. $\frac{2}{4}$ or $\frac{1}{2}$
7. $\frac{2}{8}$ or $\frac{1}{4}$
8. $\frac{4}{8}$ or $\frac{1}{2}$
9. Which is greater: $\frac{1}{4}$ of the circle or $\frac{3}{8}$ of the circle? $\frac{3}{8}$
10. Which is greater: $\frac{5}{8}$ of the circle or $\frac{1}{2}$ of the circle? $\frac{5}{8}$
11. Which is greater: $\frac{1}{2}$ of the circle or $\frac{3}{6}$ of the circle? They are equal.
12. Which is greater: $\frac{3}{4}$ of the circle or $\frac{7}{8}$ of the circle? $\frac{7}{8}$

Real Math • Grade 4 • *Practice* Chapter 8 • *Fractions, Probability, and Measurement* 83

Practice Lesson 8.7

### RETEACH

**If . . .** students are having difficulty with probability concepts,

**Then . . .** students may benefit from acting out the seven problems on the first page of the lesson. They can use 0–5 Number Cubes and a coin. Be sure to help them understand any discrepancy between the theoretical probability and the actual outcomes.

Lesson Planner

**OBJECTIVES**
- To provide practice in finding equivalent fractions

**NCTM STANDARDS**
**Number and Operations**
Understand numbers, ways of representing numbers, relationships among numbers, and number systems

**MATERIALS**
- ***Response Wheels**
- Colored pencils or crayons (5 different colors per student, if possible)
- Standard 8.5″ × 11″ unlined white paper (one sheet per student)

**TECHNOLOGY**
e **Presentation** Lesson 8.8
e **MathTools** Fractions
e **Games** Fracto

**TEST PREP**
**Cumulative Review**
Mental Math reviews fractions of numbers (Lesson 8.6).

**LOOKING AHEAD**
You will need folded paper to use in Lesson 8.9.

*Manipulative Kit Item

# Equivalent Fractions

**Context of the Lesson** In this lesson, the concept of equivalent fractions is formally introduced. Students will use equivalent fractions as a method for comparing fractions of the same quantity that have unlike denominators in Lesson 8.9. NOTE: This lesson may take more than one day to complete.

See page 328B for Math Background for teachers for this lesson.

## Planning for Learning • DIFFERENTIATE INSTRUCTION

### INTERVENTION

**If . . .** students lack the prerequisite skill of estimating using percent benchmarks,

**Then . . .** teach ***Intervention*** Lesson 8.A.

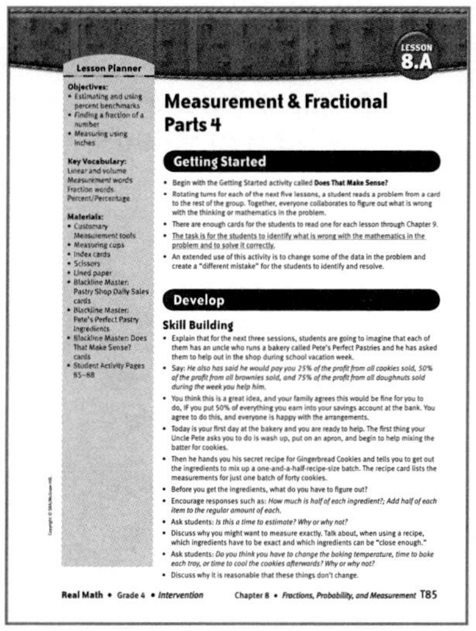
Lesson 8.A
Measurement & Fractional Parts 4

Intervention Lesson 8.A

### ENGLISH LEARNER

Preview

**If . . .** students need language support,

**Then . . .** use Lesson 8.8 in ***English Learner Support Guide*** to preview lesson concepts and vocabulary.

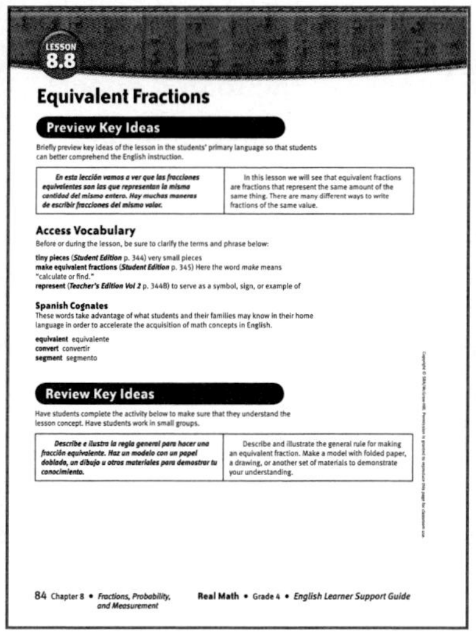
Lesson 8.8
Equivalent Fractions

English Learner Lesson 8.8

### ENRICH

**If . . .** students are proficient in the lesson concepts,

**Then . . .** encourage them to work on the chapter projects.

### PRACTICE

**If . . .** students would benefit from additional practice,

**Then . . .** create additional equivalent fractions in the Guided Discussion.

### RETEACH

**If . . .** students are having difficulty understanding equivalent fractions,

**Then . . .** model equivalent fractions with fraction tiles.

**Access Vocabulary**
**tiny pieces** very small pieces
**free to divide it again** here the word free means able to, not restricted. In this usage it does not mean the opposite of expensive

**Spanish Cognates**
**equivalent** equivalente
**convert** convertir
**segment** segmento

## Mental Math

5

Review | RESPONSE WHEEL

Provide students with "fraction-of" number exercises such as the following:

a. $\frac{1}{2}$ of 50 is ____ 25

b. $\frac{2}{3}$ of 60 is ____ 40

c. $\frac{1}{10}$ of 70 is ____ 7

d. $\frac{1}{5}$ of 25 is ____ 5

e. $\frac{1}{4}$ of 16 is ____ 4

f. $\frac{2}{5}$ of 40 is ____ 16

g. $\frac{5}{6}$ of 30 is ____ 25

h. $\frac{3}{8}$ of 24 is ____ 9

## 1 Develop

30

### Tell Students In Today's Lesson They Will

practice finding equivalent fractions.

### Skill Building UNDERSTANDING

Whole Group

1. Distribute an 8.5″ × 11″ sheet of paper to each student. Ask the students not to write on or crease the paper because they will be folding and labeling it in a particular way for today's lesson.

   Starting with the paper vertical, fold it down into halves. Have students do the same.

   - **What fraction of the original paper is the folded sheet?** $\frac{1}{2}$

2. Have students open their paper to its full size. Instruct them to lightly shade one of the halves and write the label $\frac{1}{2}$ in that area. Refold the paper along the existing crease, so it is again in halves. Fold this halved sheet in halves again. Have students do the same with their papers.

   - **What fraction of the original paper is this folded sheet?** $\frac{1}{4}$

   Ask students to open their paper to its full size again, undoing both folds, so that the half they shaded and labeled $\frac{1}{2}$ is facing up. There will now be a crease dividing the uncolored half into quarters. Have students lightly shade one of the quarters with a different color, and label it $\frac{1}{4}$.

3. Repeat the above procedure, continuing to fold each iteration in halves again, to make $\frac{1}{8}$, $\frac{1}{16}$, and $\frac{1}{32}$ of the original paper.

   This entire process will take five folds to complete. Have the students write what fraction of the entire page the remaining uncolored portion would be. $\frac{1}{32}$

   The final sheet should look something like this.

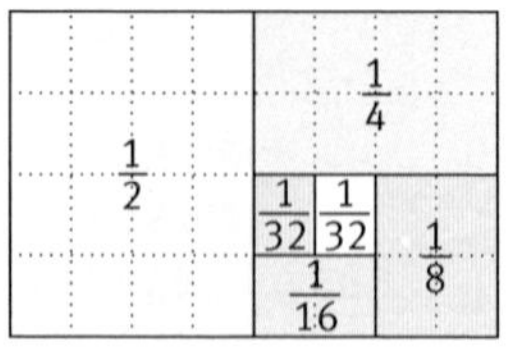


### Strategy Building REASONING

Small Group

Divide the class into groups of 3–5 students. Have students devise ways to express these relationships. Students might discuss doubling and/or halving, or say that two of one sized fraction is the same size as another fraction that is one size bigger.

Have students focus on relationships between fractions that represent equal amounts of the paper by comparing the "$\frac{1}{2}$" square with the other fractions. Ask question such as the following:

- **How many quarters equal the same area as $\frac{1}{2}$?** 2
- **How many eighths equal the same area as $\frac{1}{2}$?** 4
- **How many $\frac{1}{32}$ squares would it take to fill the $\frac{1}{2}$ portion of the sheet?** 16

### Guided Discussion UNDERSTANDING

Whole Group

Ask students to share pairs of fractions that represent the same amount of the paper and write them on the board.

Introduce the term equivalent fractions by explaining that when two fractions represent the same amount, they are called equivalent fractions. One way to find equivalent fractions is to multiply the fraction by 1, or in this case by a fraction equal to 1. Ask the students questions such as the following:

- **How many halves equal 1 whole?** 2
- **How many fourths equal 1 whole?** 4
- **How many eighths equal 1 whole?** 8

Write each of the fractions equal to 1 on the board (e.g., $\frac{2}{2}$).

Multiplying a number or fraction by 1 does not change its value.

Write $\frac{1}{2}$ on the board. Ask students to find a fraction equal to 1 (for example $\frac{3}{3}$).

Extend the above math statement to read $\frac{1}{2} \times \frac{3}{3} = ?$

- **Since we are multiplying by 1, is the answer going to be a different value?** no

Finish the math sentence so it reads: $\frac{1}{2} \times \frac{3}{3} = \frac{3}{6}$. Ask the students to describe how this answer is possible. $1 \times 3 = 3$, $2 \times 3 = 6$

Practice creating other equivalent fractions with a given denominator using examples such as the following:

$\frac{1}{4} = \frac{?}{8}$ 2

$\frac{2}{4} = \frac{?}{8}$ 4

## 2 Assign Student Pages

15

### Pages 344–345 APPLYING

Have students work independently or in small groups. For Problems 5–14 students should figure out what number the denominator needs to be multiplied by to get 12 (divide 12 by the denominator), and multiply the numerator by that number.

### As Students Finish

Game *Fracto Game Mat*

eGames *Fracto*

eMathTools *Fractions* Have students explore finding equivalent fractions and making comparisons.

Student Page

LESSON 8.8 Equivalent Fractions

## Key Ideas

**Fractions that represent the same rational number are called equivalent fractions.**

Marc and Chet bought a pizza. It was cut into 8 equal pieces. Marc ate 2 of the pieces. Chet said, "You ate $\frac{2}{8}$ of the pizza."

Marc said, "No, I ate only $\frac{1}{4}$ of the pizza."

Who is right?

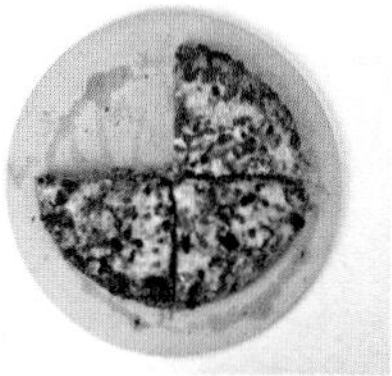

There are many different fractions that describe the same amount. In this example, *both* Marc and Chet are right. Marc ate 2 of the 8 equal pieces, so he ate $\frac{2}{8}$ of the pizza. But if the pizza had been cut into only 4 equal pieces, Marc could have eaten just 1 of those pieces and still have eaten the same amount. He would have eaten $\frac{1}{4}$ of the pizza.

We call $\frac{1}{4}$ and $\frac{2}{8}$ equivalent fractions since they describe the same amount, and we can write $\frac{1}{4} = \frac{2}{8}$.

**Answer** these questions.

1. If the pizza had been cut into 12 equal pieces, how many would Marc have had to eat to equal $\frac{1}{4}$ of the pizza? Is $\frac{3}{12} = \frac{1}{4}$? 3; yes
2. If the pizza had been cut into 40 equal pieces, how many would Marc have had to eat to equal $\frac{1}{4}$ of the pizza? Is $\frac{10}{40} = \frac{1}{4}$? 10; yes

You might not think that 10 tiny pieces, each $\frac{1}{40}$ of the pizza, are as satisfying as $\frac{2}{8}$ of the pizza. Still, the fractions $\frac{10}{40}$ and $\frac{2}{8}$ are equal, and you would be eating the same amount of pizza.

344 eTextbook This lesson is available in the *eTextbook*.

Student Page

The fraction $\frac{3}{4}$ indicates we have 3 of 4 equal sections. We would get the same amount if we divided each of the 4 sections into 5 equal parts and took 15 of the 20 total parts.

Multiplying a number by 1 will not change the value of that number. A fraction can also be multiplied by 1 without changing its value.

Multiplying our original fraction, $\frac{3}{4}$, by a fraction equal to 1 will result in an equivalent fraction.

Remember, a fraction with a numerator equal to its denominator equals 1.

In our example, we could multiply $\frac{3}{4}$ by $\frac{5}{5}$

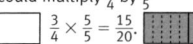

 $\frac{3}{4} \times \frac{5}{5} = \frac{15}{20}$. 

We can make equivalent fractions by multiplying any fraction by a fraction equal to 1; that is, by multiplying the numerator and denominator by the same number.

**Solve.**

3. Write a fraction with a denominator of 20 that is equivalent to $\frac{3}{4}$. In other words, $\frac{3}{4} = \frac{?}{20}$. $\frac{15}{20}$
4. Write a fraction with a denominator of 60 that is equivalent to $\frac{5}{12}$. $\frac{25}{60}$

**Convert** each fraction to one that has a denominator of 12 and is equivalent. For example, $\frac{2}{3}$ is equivalent to $\frac{8}{12}$.

5. $\frac{1}{2}$ $\frac{6}{12}$
6. $\frac{3}{4}$ $\frac{9}{12}$
7. $\frac{4}{6}$ $\frac{8}{12}$
8. $\frac{1}{3}$ $\frac{4}{12}$
9. $\frac{5}{6}$ $\frac{10}{12}$
10. $\frac{1}{4}$ $\frac{3}{12}$
11. $\frac{3}{6}$ $\frac{6}{12}$
12. $\frac{2}{6}$ $\frac{4}{12}$
13. $\frac{1}{6}$ $\frac{2}{12}$
14. $\frac{2}{4}$ $\frac{6}{12}$

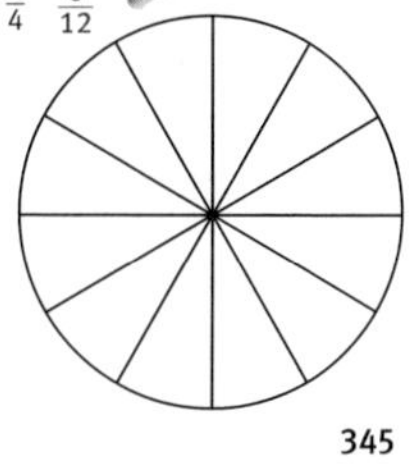

Chapter 8 • Lesson 8 345

## 3 Reflect 5

### Guided Discussion REASONING

Whole Group

Ask the students if they can use the patterns they have noticed from the paper folding activity to predict what fraction would come after $\frac{1}{32}$. $\frac{1}{64}$, then $\frac{1}{128}$, then $\frac{1}{256}$, and so on

Ask students to explain their thinking. Can they describe a general rule that might explain how we progress from one fraction to the next during the paper folding activity? for example, the bottom number is doubled each time the paper is folded in half—twice as many pieces indicate a piece that is half as big.

**Cumulative Review:** For review of rounding, assign Problem 16 on student page 351.

**Family Involvement:** Assign the ***Practice, Reteach,*** or ***Enrichment*** activities depending on the needs of your students. Encourage students to explain how their folded sheet of paper shows equivalent fractions with a friend or relative.

**Concept/Question Board:** Encourage student to continue to look for real-world examples of fractions and post them on the Concept/Question Board.

**Math Puzzler:** Granny gave $10 to her five grandchildren. She said, "I want you to divide the money so that my oldest grandchild gets 25¢ more than my next-oldest grandchild, who should get 25¢ more than my next-oldest grandchild, and so on." If the five grandchildren follow Granny's instructions, how much money will the youngest grandchild get? $1.50

# 4 Assess and Differentiate

e Assess Use ***eAssess*** to record and analyze evidence of student understanding.

## A Gather Evidence

Use the Daily Class Assessment Records in ***Assessment*** or ***eAssess*** to record daily observations.

### Informal Assessment
**Concept Question Board**

Did the student APPLYING
- ❑ apply learning in new situations?
- ❑ contribute concepts?
- ❑ contribute answers?
- ❑ connect mathematics to real-world situations?

### Informal Assessment
**Strategy Building**

Did the student UNDERSTANDING
- ❑ make important observations?
- ❑ extend or generalize learning?
- ❑ provide insightful answers?
- ❑ pose insightful questions?

## B Summarize Findings

Analyze and summarize assessment data for each student. Determine which Assessment Follow-Up is appropriate for each student. Use the Student Assessment Record in ***Assessment*** or ***eAssess*** to update assessment records.

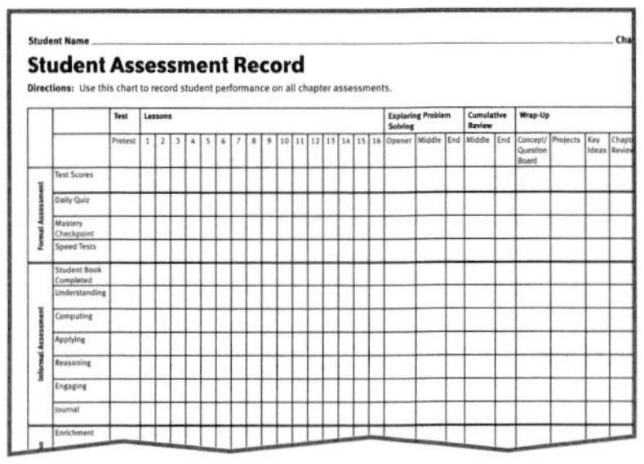
Student Name
Student Assessment Record
Directions: Use this chart to record student performance on all chapter assessments.

Assessment Page T41

## C Assessment Follow-Up • DIFFERENTIATE INSTRUCTION

Based on your observations, use these teaching strategies for assessment follow-up.

### INTERVENTION

Review student performance on ***Intervention*** Lesson 8.A to see if students have mastered prerequisite skills for this lesson.

### ENGLISH LEARNER

**Review**

Use Lesson 8.8 in ***English Learner Support Guide*** to review lesson concepts and vocabulary.

### ENRICH

**If . . .** students are proficient in the lesson concepts,

**Then . . .** encourage them to work on the chapter projects or ***Enrichment*** Lesson 8.8.

LESSON 8.8 Name ______ Date ______

Equivalent Fractions

**Fraction Dominoes**

Carly and Bianca are playing dominoes with equivalent fractions.

**Ring** all the correct matches.

| | | | |
|---|---|---|---|
| $\frac{3}{8}$ | $\frac{1}{4}$ | $\frac{2}{8}$ | $\frac{2}{3}$ |
| $\frac{3}{4}$ | $\frac{3}{8}$ | $\frac{5}{10}$ | $\frac{1}{2}$ |
| $\frac{5}{8}$ | $\frac{1}{3}$ | $\frac{4}{12}$ | $\frac{3}{9}$ |
| $\frac{6}{8}$ | $\frac{1}{3}$ | $\frac{3}{9}$ | $\frac{1}{5}$ |
| $\frac{4}{8}$ | $\frac{3}{4}$ | $\frac{6}{8}$ | $\frac{4}{9}$ |
| $\frac{5}{8}$ | $\frac{6}{7}$ | $\frac{5}{8}$ | $\frac{3}{8}$ |
| $\frac{2}{10}$ | $\frac{3}{8}$ | $\frac{1}{4}$ | $\frac{3}{7}$ |
| $\frac{2}{3}$ | $\frac{1}{5}$ | $\frac{2}{10}$ | $\frac{3}{4}$ |

84 Chapter 8 • *Fractions, Probability, and Measurement* **Real Math** • Grade 4 • *Enrichment Support Guide*

Enrichment Lesson 8.8

### PRACTICE

**If . . .** students would benefit from additional practice,

**Then . . .** assign ***Practice*** Lesson 8.8.

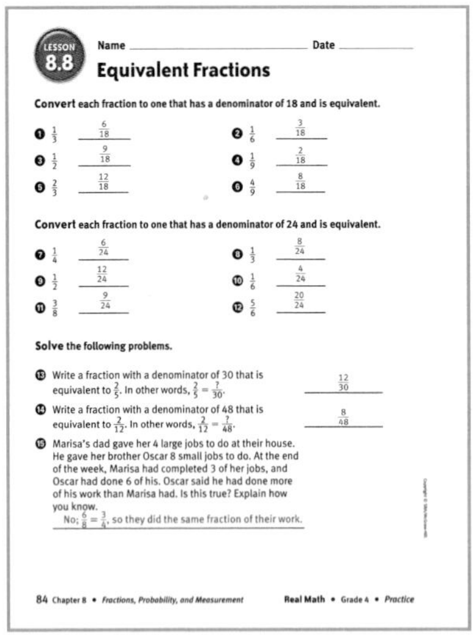
LESSON 8.8 Name ______ Date ______

Equivalent Fractions

**Convert** each fraction to one that has a denominator of 18 and is equivalent.

1. $\frac{1}{3}$ $\frac{6}{18}$
2. $\frac{1}{6}$ $\frac{3}{18}$
3. $\frac{1}{2}$ $\frac{9}{18}$
4. $\frac{1}{9}$ $\frac{2}{18}$
5. $\frac{2}{3}$ $\frac{12}{18}$
6. $\frac{4}{9}$ $\frac{8}{18}$

**Convert** each fraction to one that has a denominator of 24 and is equivalent.

7. $\frac{1}{4}$ $\frac{6}{24}$
8. $\frac{1}{3}$ $\frac{8}{24}$
9. $\frac{1}{2}$ $\frac{12}{24}$
10. $\frac{1}{6}$ $\frac{4}{24}$
11. $\frac{3}{8}$ $\frac{9}{24}$
12. $\frac{5}{6}$ $\frac{20}{24}$

**Solve** the following problems.

13. Write a fraction with a denominator of 30 that is equivalent to $\frac{2}{5}$. In other words, $\frac{2}{5} = \frac{?}{30}$. $\frac{12}{30}$
14. Write a fraction with a denominator of 48 that is equivalent to $\frac{2}{12}$. In other words, $\frac{2}{12} = \frac{?}{48}$. $\frac{8}{48}$
15. Marisa's dad gave her 4 large jobs to do at their house. He gave her brother Oscar 8 small jobs to do. At the end of the week, Marisa had completed 3 of her jobs, and Oscar had done 6 of his. Oscar said he had done more of his work than Marisa had. Is this true? Explain how you know.
No; $\frac{6}{8} = \frac{3}{4}$, so they did the same fraction of their work.

84 Chapter 8 • *Fractions, Probability, and Measurement* **Real Math** • Grade 4 • *Practice*

Practice Lesson 8.8

### RETEACH

**If . . .** students are having difficulty understanding equivalent fractions,

**Then . . .** reteach the lesson concept.

## Lesson Planner

**OBJECTIVES**
To introduce the use of equivalent fractions to compare fractions with unlike denominators

**NCTM STANDARDS**
**Connections**
Understand how mathematical ideas interconnect and build on one another to produce a coherent whole

**MATERIALS**
*Response Wheels

**TECHNOLOGY**
e **Presentation** Lesson 8.9
e **MathTools** Fractions
e **Games** Fracto

**TEST PREP**
**Cumulative Review**
Mental Math reviews fractions of numbers (Lesson 8.6).

*Manipulative Kit Item

# Comparing Fractions

**Context of the Lesson** In Lesson 8.8, the concept of equivalent fractions was formally introduced. In this lesson, students will use equivalent fractions as a method for comparing fractions of the same quantity that have unlike denominators.

See page 328B for Math Background for teachers for this lesson.

## Planning for Learning • DIFFERENTIATE INSTRUCTION

### INTERVENTION

**If . . .** students lack the prerequisite skill of finding a fraction of a number,

**Then . . .** teach ***Intervention*** Lesson 8.B.

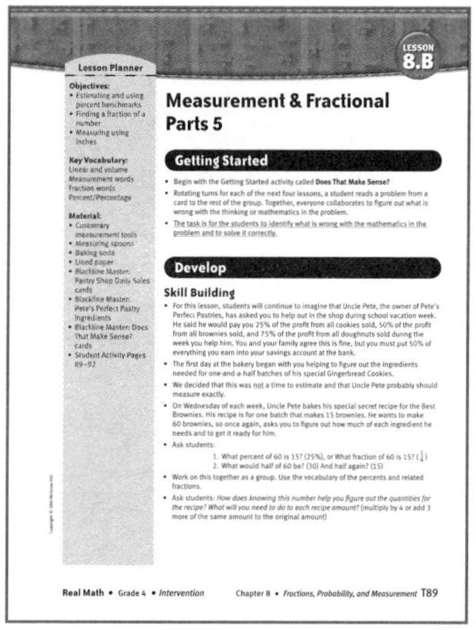
LESSON 8.B
Lesson Planner
Objectives:
- Estimating and using percent benchmarks
- Finding a fraction of a number
- Measuring using inches

Key Vocabulary:
Linear and volume
Measurement words
Fraction words
Percent/Percentage

Material:
- Customary measurement tools
- Measuring spoons
- Baking soda
- Lined paper
- Blackline Master: Pastry Shop Daily Sales cards
- Blackline Master: Pete's Perfect Pastry Ingredients
- Blackline Master: Does That Make Sense? cards
- Student Activity Pages 89–92

Measurement & Fractional Parts 5

Getting Started
- Begin with the Getting Started activity called **Does That Make Sense?**
- Rotating turns for each of the next four lessons, a student reads a problem from a card to the rest of the group. Together, everyone collaborates to figure out what is wrong with the thinking or mathematics in the problem.
- The task is for the students to identify what is wrong with the mathematics in the problem and to solve it correctly.

Develop
Skill Building
- For this lesson, students will continue to imagine that Uncle Pete, the owner of Pete's Perfect Pastries, has asked you to help out in the shop during school vacation week. He said he would pay you 25% of the profit from all cookies sold, 50% of the profit from all brownies sold, and 75% of the profit from all doughnuts sold during the week you help him. You and your family agree this is fine, but you must put 50% of everything you earn into your savings account at the bank.
- The first day at the bakery began with you helping to figure out the ingredients needed for one-and-a-half batches of his special Gingerbread Cookies.
- We decided that this was not a time to estimate and that Uncle Pete probably should measure exactly.
- On Wednesday of each week, Uncle Pete bakes his special secret recipe for the Best Brownies. His recipe is for one batch that makes 15 brownies. He wants to make 60 brownies, so once again, asks you to figure out how much of each ingredient he needs and to get it ready for him.
- Ask students:
  1. What percent of 60 is 15? (25%), or What fraction of 60 is 15? ($\frac{1}{4}$)
  2. What would half of 60 be? (30) And half again? (15)
- Work on this together as a group. Use the vocabulary of the percents and related fractions.
- Ask students: *How does knowing this number help you figure out the quantities for the recipe? What will you need to do to each recipe amount?* (multiply by 4 or add 3 more of the same amount to the original amount)

Real Math • Grade 4 • *Intervention* Chapter 8 • *Fractions, Probability, and Measurement* T89

Intervention Lesson 8.B

### ENGLISH LEARNER

Preview

**If . . .** students need language support,

**Then . . .** use Lesson 8.9 in ***English Learner Support Guide*** to preview lesson concepts and vocabulary.

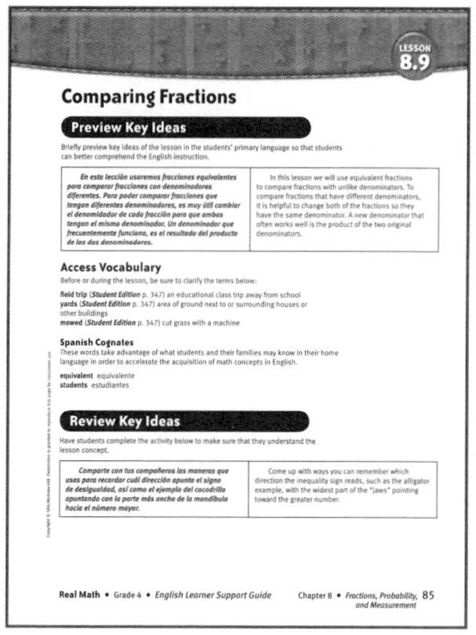
LESSON 8.9
Comparing Fractions

Preview Key Ideas
Briefly preview key ideas of the lesson in the students' primary language so that students can better comprehend the English instruction.

| | |
|---|---|
| *En esta lección usaremos fracciones equivalentes para comparar fracciones con denominadores diferentes. Para poder comparar fracciones que tengan diferentes denominadores, es muy útil cambiar el denomidador de cada fracción para que ambas tengan el mismo denominador. Un denominador que frecuentemente funciona, es el resultado del producto de los dos denominadores.* | In this lesson we will use equivalent fractions to compare fractions with unlike denominators. To compare fractions that have different denominators, it is helpful to change both of the fractions so they have the same denominator. A new denominator that often works well is the product of the two original denominators. |

Access Vocabulary
Before or during the lesson, be sure to clarify the terms below:
**field trip** (*Student Edition* p. 347) an educational class trip away from school
**yards** (*Student Edition* p. 347) area of ground next to or surrounding houses or other buildings
**mowed** (*Student Edition* p. 347) cut grass with a machine

Spanish Cognates
These words take advantage of what students and their families may know in their home language in order to accelerate the acquisition of math concepts in English.
**equivalent** equivalente
**students** estudiantes

Review Key Ideas
Have students complete the activity below to make sure that they understand the lesson concept.

| | |
|---|---|
| *Comparte con tus compañeros las maneras que usas para recordar cuál dirección apunta el signo de desigualdad, así como el ejemplo del cocodrilo apuntando con la parte más ancha de la mandíbula hacia el número mayor.* | Come up with ways you can remember which direction the inequality sign reads, such as the alligator example, with the widest part of the "jaws" pointing toward the greater number. |

Real Math • Grade 4 • *English Learner Support Guide* Chapter 8 • *Fractions, Probability, and Measurement* 85

English Learner Lesson 8.9

### ENRICH

**If . . .** students are proficient in the lesson concepts,

**Then . . .** encourage them to work on the chapter projects.

### PRACTICE

**If . . .** students would benefit from additional practice,

**Then . . .** extend Skill Building to compare additional fractions.

### RETEACH

**If . . .** students are having difficulty understanding comparing fractions,

**Then . . .** extend Guided Discussion using fraction tiles or other manipulatives.

# Teaching Lesson 8.9

## Mental Math 5

Review THUMBS UP Have students show the correct signal to make each statement correct. Students should show thumbs-up for greater than, thumbs-down for less than, and an open hand for equal to. Use exercises such as the following:

**a.** $\frac{1}{2}$ of 12 ____ $\frac{2}{3}$ of 18 thumbs-down

**b.** $\frac{3}{4}$ of 80 ____ $\frac{3}{10}$ of 100 thumbs-up

**c.** $\frac{6}{8}$ of 48 ____ $\frac{5}{10}$ of 48 thumbs-up

**d.** $\frac{8}{10}$ of 80 ____ $\frac{7}{10}$ of 100 thumbs-down

## 1 Develop 25

### Tell Students In Today's Lesson They Will

use equivalent fractions to compare fractions with unlike denominators.

### Guided Discussion REASONING

Whole Group

Have students get out their folded papers from Lesson 8.8.

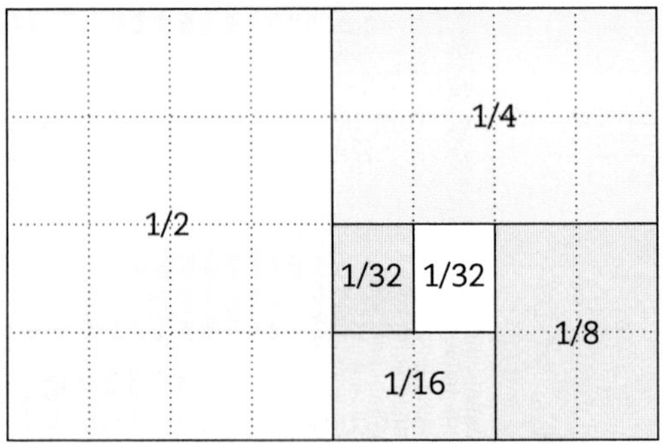


1. Have students discuss what fraction of the page represents the greatest area $\frac{1}{2}$.
   Which fraction of the paper represents the least area? $\frac{1}{32}$
   - **If the fraction $\frac{1}{2}$ is the greatest amount of the paper's area and the fraction $\frac{1}{32}$ is the least amount of the paper's area, is it possible to say that $\frac{1}{2}$ of the page is bigger than $\frac{1}{32}$ of the page?** yes

   Ask questions such as the following:
   - **When talking about the area of the paper, how might you write a number sentence to say that $\frac{1}{2}$ is bigger than $\frac{1}{32}$?** $\frac{1}{2} > \frac{1}{32}$
   - **How would you write a number sentence to say that $\frac{1}{32}$ is smaller than $\frac{1}{2}$?** $\frac{1}{32} < \frac{1}{2}$

2. Discuss easy ways to remember which direction the inequality sign reads. possible answers include: The big end of the arrow goes next to the greater number, the little end next to the smaller number; the "jaws" of the hungry "alligator" want to eat the greater number
   - **When discussing the area of the paper, what symbol would we use to describe equivalent fractions?** =

### Skill Building APPLYING

Small Group

Break the students into groups of two or three. Have them use their folded papers to answer questions such as the following. Have students write their answers on a separate sheet of paper with the correct symbol (<, >, =)

- $\frac{1}{2}$ ____ $\frac{1}{4}$ >
- $\frac{1}{4}$ ____ $\frac{1}{8}$ >
- $\frac{1}{8}$ ____ $\frac{1}{2}$ <
- $\frac{4}{8}$ ____ $\frac{1}{2}$ =
- $\frac{4}{32}$ ____ $\frac{1}{2}$ <
- $\frac{1}{2}$ ____ 1 <

## 2 Assign Student Pages 20

### Pages 346–347 ENGAGING

Have students complete pages 346–347 independently. You may suggest that one new denominator that always works is the product of the two original denominators, although the product of the two denominators is not necessarily the *smallest* appropriate denominator.

### As Students Finish

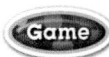

Game ***Fracto Game Mat***

e Games ***Fracto***

e MathTools ***Fractions*** Have students explore finding equivalent fractions and making comparisons.

Student Page

# LESSON 8.9 Comparing Fractions

## Key Ideas

**When we compare fractions that have different denominators, it is helpful to change them so they have the same denominators.**

A new denominator that often works well is the product of the two original denominators.

For example, which is bigger, $\frac{2}{4}$ or $\frac{1}{3}$?

To compare these fractions, write them as equivalent fractions with the denominator of 12 (since $4 \times 3 = 12$). To do this, we multiply $\frac{2}{4}$ by $\frac{3}{3}$ (a fraction equal to 1), and multiply $\frac{1}{3}$ by $\frac{4}{4}$ (a fraction equal to 1).

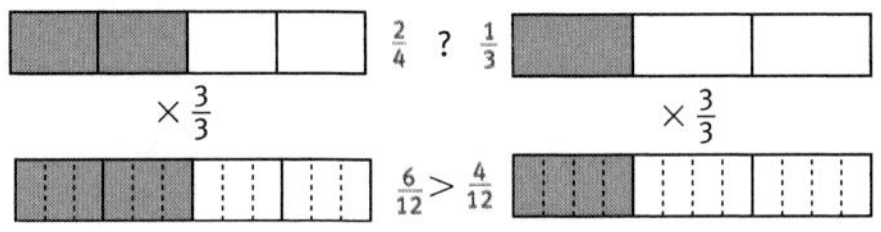


Since we know $\frac{6}{12} > \frac{4}{12}$, we also know $\frac{2}{4} > \frac{1}{3}$.

**Show** which fraction of the circle is larger or show that they are the same. Replace ▒ with <, >, or =.

1. $\frac{1}{6} < \frac{1}{4}$
2. $\frac{5}{6} > \frac{2}{4}$
3. $\frac{1}{2} = \frac{6}{12}$
4. $\frac{3}{4} > \frac{1}{2}$
5. $\frac{5}{12} < \frac{1}{2}$
6. $\frac{2}{4} < \frac{3}{4}$
7. $\frac{1}{3} = \frac{2}{6}$
8. $\frac{4}{8} < \frac{2}{3}$

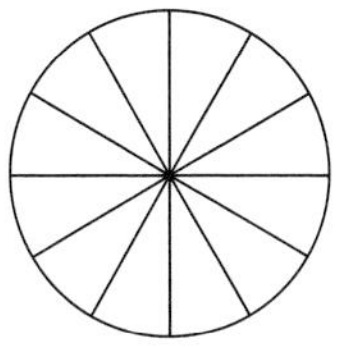

346

Textbook This lesson is available in the ***eTextbook***.

Student Page

**Solve.**

9. Ricky read $\frac{2}{3}$ of a 250-page book, and Ella read $\frac{2}{3}$ of a 150-page book.
   **a.** Who read more pages? Ricky
   **b.** Who read more words? can't tell
10. Jeremy and Linda have yards that are the same size. If Linda mowed $\frac{1}{2}$ of her yard, and Jeremy mowed $\frac{2}{3}$ of his yard, who mowed more? Jeremy
11. Rachel and Jaime want to share a pizza that has been sliced into 12 equal pieces. If Rachel eats 5 pieces, will she have eaten more or less than $\frac{1}{2}$ of the pizza? less

Two of the third-grade classes at Wooster Woods Elementary went on a field trip. Each class had 24 people going.

12. $\frac{1}{3}$ of Ms. Beshley's class packed peanut butter and jelly sandwiches for lunch. $\frac{1}{4}$ of Mr. Kahn's class packed peanut butter and jelly sandwiches for lunch. Which class packed more peanut butter and jelly sandwiches? Ms. Beshley's class
13. In Mr. Kahn's class, $\frac{1}{2}$ of the class had apple juice to drink. $\frac{3}{4}$ of the students in Ms. Beshley's class brought apple juice to drink. Which class had fewer students with apple juice? Mr. Kahn's class
14. How many people went on the field trip total? 48

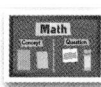

Chapter 8 • Lesson 9 347

# 3 Reflect

10

## Guided Discussion

Discuss the lesson by pointing out that in most practical situations one denominator will be a multiple of the other. For example: $\frac{5}{8}$ and $\frac{21}{32}$

- **Is 32 a multiple of 8?** yes
- **What number when multiplied by 8 equals 32?** 4
- **If we multiply $\frac{5}{8}$ by $\frac{4}{4}$, what is the equivalent fraction?** $\frac{20}{32}$
- **Which fraction is greater?** $\frac{21}{32}$

When comparing a fraction to $\frac{1}{2}$ multiply the numerator of the fraction by 2 (from the denominator of $\frac{1}{2}$) and compare it to the denominator of the fraction.

For example: $\frac{1}{2}$ and $\frac{31}{63}$

Multiply $2 \times 31 = 62$

Compare 62 and 63

$62 < 63$

Therefore, $\frac{31}{63} < \frac{1}{2}$.

**Cumulative Review:** For review of rounding, assign Problem 17 on student page 351.

**Family Involvement:** Assign the ***Practice, Reteach,*** or ***Enrichment*** activities depending on the needs of your students. Encourage students to explain how their folded sheet of paper shows equivalent fractions with a friend or relative.

**Concept/Question Board:** Encourage students to continue to look for real-world examples of fractions and post them on the Concept/Question Board.

**Math Puzzler:** Put the following four fractional amounts of money in order from greatest to least value: $\frac{4}{5}$ of a nickel, $\frac{3}{5}$ of a quarter, $\frac{1}{2}$ of a half dollar, and $\frac{7}{20}$ of a dollar. $\frac{7}{20}$ of a dollar = 35¢, $\frac{1}{2}$ of a half dollar = 25¢, $\frac{3}{5}$ of a quarter = 15¢, and $\frac{4}{5}$ of a nickel = 4¢

# 4 Assess and Differentiate

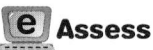

e Assess Use ***eAssess*** to record and analyze evidence of student understanding.

## A Gather Evidence

Use the Daily Class Assessment Records in ***Assessment*** or ***eAssess*** to record daily observations.

### Informal Assessment
**✓ Guided Discussion**

Did the student REASONING
- ❑ provide a clear explanation?
- ❑ communicate reasons and strategies?
- ❑ choose appropriate strategies?
- ❑ argue logically?

### Informal Assessment
**✓ Games**

Did the student COMPUTING
- ❑ respond accurately?
- ❑ respond quickly?
- ❑ respond with confidence?
- ❑ self-correct?

## B Summarize Findings

Analyze and summarize assessment data for each student. Determine which Assessment Follow-Up is appropriate for each student. Use the Student Assessment Record in ***Assessment*** or ***eAssess*** to update assessment records.

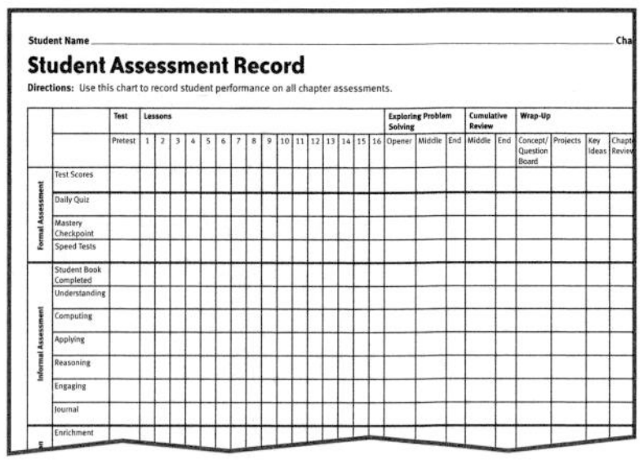

Student Name

Student Assessment Record

Directions: Use this chart to record student performance on all chapter assessments.

**Assessment Page T41**

## C Assessment Follow-Up • DIFFERENTIATE INSTRUCTION

Based on your observations, use these teaching strategies for assessment follow-up.

### INTERVENTION

Review student performance on ***Intervention*** Lesson 8.B to see if students have mastered prerequisite skills for this lesson.

### ENGLISH LEARNER

**Review**

Use Lesson 8.9 in ***English Learner Support Guide*** to review lesson concepts and vocabulary.

### ENRICH

**If . . .** students are proficient in the lesson concepts,

**Then . . .** encourage them to work on the chapter projects or ***Enrichment*** Lesson 8.9.

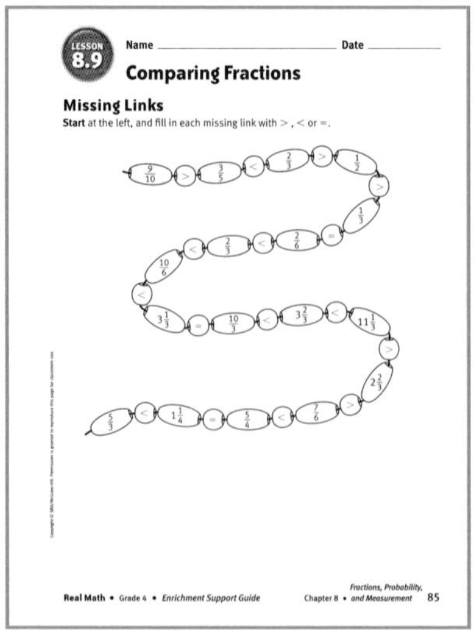

LESSON 8.9 Name ______ Date ______

Comparing Fractions

Missing Links

Start at the left, and fill in each missing link with >, <, or =.

Real Math • Grade 4 • Enrichment Support Guide    Chapter 8 • Fractions, Probability, and Measurement 85

**Enrichment Lesson 8.9**

### PRACTICE

**If . . .** students would benefit from additional practice,

**Then . . .** assign ***Practice*** Lesson 8.9.

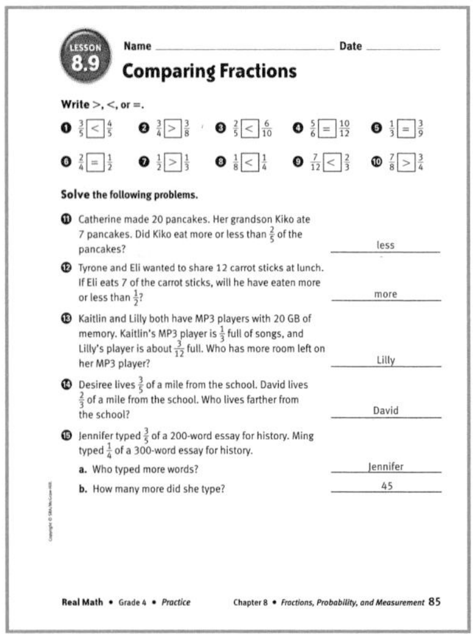

LESSON 8.9 Name ______ Date ______

Comparing Fractions

Write >, <, or =.

Solve the following problems.

Catherine made 20 pancakes. Her grandson Kiko ate 7 pancakes. Did Kiko eat more or less than $\frac{1}{2}$ of the pancakes? less

Tyrone and Eli wanted to share 12 carrot sticks at lunch. If Eli eats 7 of the carrot sticks, will he have eaten more or less than $\frac{1}{2}$? more

Kaitlin and Lilly both have MP3 players with 20 GB of memory. Kaitlin's MP3 player is $\frac{1}{2}$ full of songs, and Lilly's player is about $\frac{7}{12}$ full. Who has more room left on her MP3 player? Lilly

Desiree lives $\frac{1}{3}$ of a mile from the school. David lives $\frac{2}{3}$ of a mile from the school. Who lives farther from the school? David

Jennifer typed $\frac{1}{2}$ of a 200-word essay for history. Ming typed $\frac{1}{4}$ of a 300-word essay for history.
a. Who typed more words? Jennifer
b. How many more did she type? 45

Real Math • Grade 4 • Practice    Chapter 8 • Fractions, Probability, and Measurement 85

**Practice Lesson 8.9**

### RETEACH

**If . . .** students are having difficulty comparing two fractions,

**Then . . .** reteach the concept using ***Reteach*** Lesson 8.9.

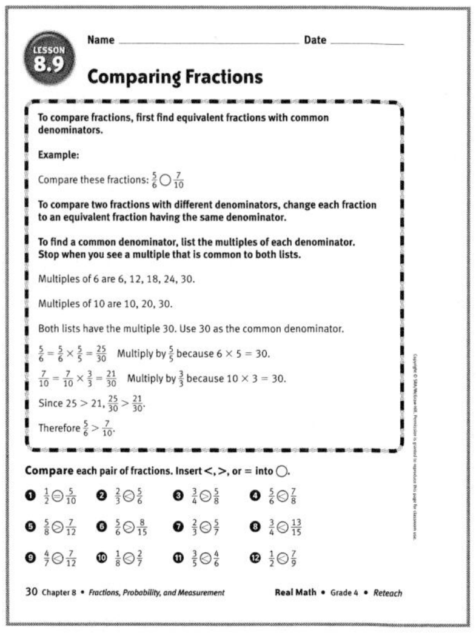

LESSON 8.9 Name ______ Date ______

Comparing Fractions

To compare fractions, first find equivalent fractions with common denominators.

Example:

Compare these fractions: $\frac{5}{6} \bigcirc \frac{7}{10}$

To compare two fractions with different denominators, change each fraction to an equivalent fraction having the same denominator.

To find a common denominator, list the multiples of each denominator. Stop when you see a multiple that is common to both lists.

Multiples of 6 are 6, 12, 18, 24, 30.

Multiples of 10 are 10, 20, 30.

Both lists have the multiple 30. Use 30 as the common denominator.

$\frac{5}{6} = \frac{5}{6} \times \frac{5}{5} = \frac{25}{30}$ Multiply by $\frac{5}{5}$ because 6 × 5 = 30.

$\frac{7}{10} = \frac{7}{10} \times \frac{3}{3} = \frac{21}{30}$ Multiply by $\frac{3}{3}$ because 10 × 3 = 30.

Since 25 > 21, $\frac{25}{30} > \frac{21}{30}$.

Therefore $\frac{5}{6} > \frac{7}{10}$.

Compare each pair of fractions. Insert <, >, or = into ◯.

30 Chapter 8 • Fractions, Probability, and Measurement    Real Math • Grade 4 • Reteach

**Reteach Lesson 8.9**

CHAPTER 8 **Problem Solving**

# Exploring Problem Solving

## Objectives
- To compare two sales by comparing their fractional discounts
- To use proportional reasoning to make generalizations when relative amounts are known but absolute amounts are not
- To analyze the Use Simple Numbers and Make a Diagram strategies

## Materials
- Graph paper
- Rulers
- Scissors

**Context of the Lesson** In this lesson, students use what they have learned about fractions to compare advertised sales and decide if an advertisement delivers what it seems to promise.

## 1 Develop 5

### Tell Students In Today's Lesson They Will
- read a challenging problem about DVDs on sale.
- look at how two students try two different strategies to solve the same problem.
- solve the problem with their group and share how they solved it.

## Guided Discussion
Have students talk about the kinds of sales they have seen advertised, such as $\frac{1}{3}$ off, 20% off, or buy 2 get 1 free. Make sure they understand fractional savings by asking questions such as the following:

- **Suppose you buy some video games that usually cost \$100. You get them on sale for \$50. How much did you save?** \$50
- **What fraction of the regular price did you save?** $\frac{50}{100}$, or $\frac{1}{2}$

Tell students they are going to use what they know about fractions to examine a common type of sale.

Student Page

### Exploring Problem Solving

What fraction do you save at each sale? Which sale is better? Why?

The
DISC Pile
1/2 off Sale!!!
Buy 1 DVD at regular price…
Get a 2nd DVD for 1/2 off!

Wild Will's
HUGE DVD SALE
Buy 2 DVDs at regular price,
get a 3rd for FREE!

**Laura solved the problem this way:**

*I Tried Simple Numbers to solve the problem.*

*My Plan*
*A. First I'll choose a simple number for the price of a DVD.*
*B. Then I'll see what fraction I save at each sale.*
*C. I'll use a price of 1 cent. That's the simplest price I can think of.*

**Think** about Laura's strategy. Answer these questions. Answers are in the *Teacher's Edition.*

1. What do you think of Laura's choice for a simple number?
2. If you were using Laura's strategy, would you try more than one number?
3. What number or numbers would you use?
4. Do you think Laura's strategy will work?

 Textbook This lesson is available in the *eTextbook.*

Student Page

**Steve solved the problem this way:**

*I Made a Diagram to solve the problem.*

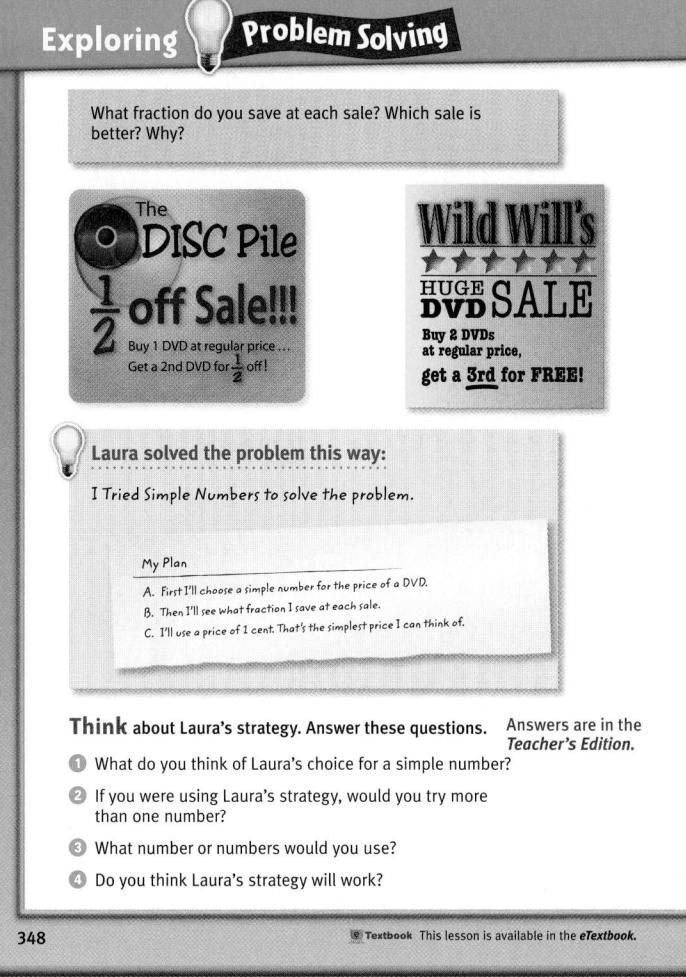

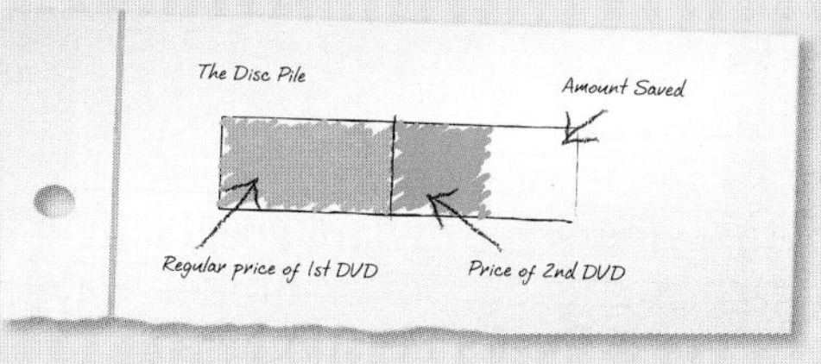

The Disc Pile
Amount Saved
Regular price of 1st DVD
Price of 2nd DVD

**Think** about Steve's strategy. Answer these questions.

5. What did Steve use to represent the regular price of a DVD? a rectangle
6. What did Steve use to represent the price of the 2nd DVD at The Disc Pile? a rectangle half the size of the first
7. Should you compare the amount saved to the regular price of 1 DVD or 2 DVDs? Why? To the price of 2 DVDs, because you have to buy 2 to get the savings.
8. What fraction do you save when you buy 2 DVDs at The Disc Pile? You save $\frac{1}{4}$, because the discount is $\frac{1}{4}$ of what you would pay for 2 DVDs.
9. Do you agree that this is a $\frac{1}{2}$*-off Sale*? Why or why not?
10. Finish solving the problem. Use Laura's strategy, Steve's strategy, or a strategy of your own. What strategy did you use? Why?

9. Students should at least agree that the use of $\frac{1}{2}$ is misleading.
10. Answers will vary. No matter which strategy students use, they should discover that you save $\frac{1}{4}$ at The Disc Pile and $\frac{1}{3}$ at Wild Will's. Although Wild Will's is a bigger fractional discount, students may discuss other factors involved in determining the better sale.

## 2 Exploring Problem Solving 20

### Using Student Pages

Have students study the advertisements on page 348. Make sure they understand them. Ask questions such as the following:

- **To take advantage of the sale at The Disc Pile, at least how many DVDs must you buy?** 2
- **What does *Get a 2nd DVD for* $\frac{1}{2}$*-off* mean?** If you pay the regular price for one DVD, you pay only half the regular price for the next DVD you buy.
- **Does the advertisement tell you the regular price of a DVD?** no

Discuss Laura's strategy. Ask questions such as the following:

- **Why is Laura making up the price of a DVD?** The price is not given.
- **Can Laura use any price, even if it is nowhere close to the real price?** Laura can use any price since she is trying to find out the fraction she will save. The fraction will not depend on what price she uses, but the higher the price, the more money she will save.
- **If Laura uses one cent as the regular price of a DVD, how much will the second DVD cost at The Disc Pile?** half of a cent

Give students time to think about Problems 1–4, then discuss them.

### Answers to Problems 1–4

**Problem 1**

Although one cent is a simple amount, it is not easy to work with in this problem. When you take half of 1, you end up with a fraction. If Laura started with a larger number, she might not have any fractions.

**Problem 2**

Trying more than one number is a good way to reduce the chance that the numbers you try are special in some way. In some situations, trying only one number may lead to a conclusion that is not true for all numbers.

**Problem 3**

Any rounded whole number should work, as long as it is even. For example, if the regular price were $10, then the second DVD would cost $5.

**Problem 4**

Students can try different numbers to see if they always get the same result. At The Disc Pile, for example, no matter what price students use, the savings will be $\frac{1}{4}$ of what the regular price for 2 DVDs would be.

Examine Steve's strategy by giving students time to think about Problems 5–9 and then discussing them.

Assign Problem 10. Have students work individually or in small groups to solve the problem.

## 3 Reflect 15

**Knowledge Age Skills**

**Effective Communication** Call on several groups to explain how they found the fractional savings for the two DVD sales. After each method is presented, ask questions such as the following:

- **Did this method show that the answer is true no matter what the regular price is? How?**
- **What did you like about this method or the way it was presented?**

Discuss the following points:

- Fractions can sometimes be used in misleading or confusing ways. It is important to be clear about what a fraction refers to. If customers get half off the price of only one of several items, their savings are less than if they get half off everything they buy.
- Even if customers do not know the regular price of a DVD, they can still figure out how much they save *relative to what they would have paid.*
- Students may disagree on which sale is better. For one thing, the regular price may be much less at one store than at the other. Also, although the sale at Wild Will's offers a greater fractional savings, you have to buy more to take advantage of it.

## 4 Assess 10

When evaluating student work, focus not only on the correctness of the answer, but also on whether students thought rationally about the problem and the various solutions presented. Some questions to consider include the following:

- Did the student understand the problem?
- Did the student show all the steps that the group took in solving the problem?
- Did the student recognize when a strategy would not work and try something else?
- Did the student check to see if the reasoning and the answer made sense?

### Sample Solutions Strategies

**Make a Model**

Students might use graph paper to draw and cut out models similar to the diagrams on page 349.

**Use Number Sense**

Students should see that savings of $\frac{1}{2}$ of 1 DVD is the same as $\frac{1}{4}$ of 2 DVDs.

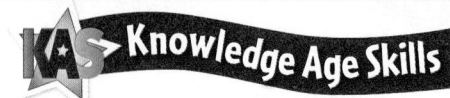

# Cumulative Review

## Assign Pages 350–351

Use this Cumulative Review as a review of concepts and skills that students have previously learned.

Here are different ways you can assign these problems to your students as they work through the chapter:

- For each lesson in the chapter, assign a set of Cumulative Review problems to be completed as practice or for homework.
  - Lesson 8.1—Problems 1–2
  - Lesson 8.2—Problems 3–4
  - Lesson 8.3—Problems 5–7
  - Lesson 8.4—Problems 8–9
  - Lesson 8.5—Problems 10–11
  - Lesson 8.6—Problems 12–13
  - Lesson 8.7—Problems 14–15
  - Lesson 8.8—Problem 16
  - Lesson 8.9—Problem 17
- At any point during the chapter, assign part or all of the Cumulative Review problems to be completed as practice or for homework.

### Cumulative Review

**Problems 1–2** review math vocabulary, Lessons 1.1, 1.7, 1.8, and 2.8.

**Problems 3–4** review multidigit addition and subtraction, Lesson 2.3.

**Problems 5–7** review addition and subtraction with hidden digits, Lesson 2.5.

**Problems 8–9** review perimeter, Lesson 1.8.

**Problems 10–11** review relation signs, Lesson 2.4.

**Problems 12–13** review percent benchmarks, Lesson 7.2.

**Problems 14–15** review 10% and $\frac{1}{10}$, Lesson 7.8.

**Problem 16** reviews rounding, Lessons 1.4 and 1.8.

**Problem 17** reviews rounding, Lessons 1.4 and 1.8.

### Monitoring Student Progress

**If . . .** students miss more than one problem in a section, **Then . . .** refer to the indicated lesson for remediation suggestions.

Student Page

## Cumulative Review

**Vocabulary** Lessons 1.1, 1.7, 1.8, and 2.8

**Fill** in each sentence with the appropriate vocabulary word.

| |
|---|
| integers |
| perimeter |

1. The ___ around the island was 54 miles. perimeter
2. The number 20 and −20 are both ___. integers

**Multidigit Addition and Subtraction** Lesson 2.3

**Choose** the correct answer.

3. 2673 − 1492
   a. 3,645
   b. 1,221
   (c.) 1,181
4. 649 + 281
   a. 448
   (b.) 930
   c. 820

**Addition and Subtraction with Hidden Digits** Lesson 2.5

**Solve** to find the missing digits.

5. 463 + 63__ = 6798 35
6. __74 − 596 = 278 8
7. __4 − 389 = 375 76

**Perimeter** Lesson 1.8

**Find** the perimeter.

8. The standard size for a volleyball court is 60 feet long and 30 feet wide. What is the perimeter? 180 feet
9. Standard paper size is about 9 inches by 11 inches. What is the perimeter? 40 inches

350

eTextbook This lesson is available in the *eTextbook*.

Student Page

**Using Relation Signs** Lesson 2.4

**What** is the correct sign? Write <, >, or =.

10. 100 __ 73 + 10 >
11. 24 − 6 __ 16 + 8 <

**Percent Benchmarks** Lesson 7.2

**Solve.**

12. 50% of 44 = __ 22
13. 75% of 180 = __ 135

**Understanding 10% and $\frac{1}{10}$** Lesson 7.8

**Complete** the following problems.

14. 30% of 90 = __ 27
15. 60% of 90 = __ 54

**Rounding** Lesson 1.4, 1.8

**Solve** the following problems.

16. A rectangle has a length of 10 inches and a width of 6 inches. Find the perimeter of this rectangle. Draw two new rectangles that have the same perimeter but different measurements. 32; Possible answer: 8 × 8 rectangle and 12 × 4 rectangle
17. (Multistep) The city baseball team had an attendance of 6,858 at the first game of the season and 5,923 at the second game. Round each game's attendance to the nearest hundred, and estimate the total number of fans in attendance for both games. 6,900 + 5,900 is about 13,000.

Real Math • Chapter 8 351

## Mid-Test

# Individual Oral Assessment

## Purpose of the Test

The Individual Oral Assessment is designed to measure students' growing knowledge of chapter concepts. It is administered to each student individually, and it requires oral responses from each student. The test takes about five minutes to complete.

See ***Assessment*** for detailed instructions for administering and interpreting the test, and record students' answers on the Student Assessment Recording Sheet.

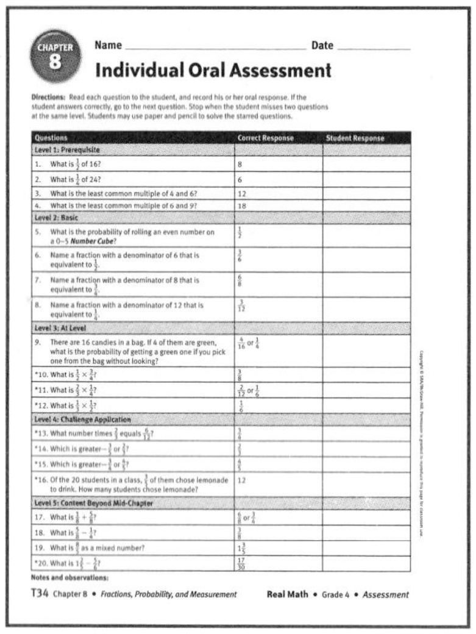
Name Date
Individual Oral Assessment

Assessment Page T34

### Directions

Read each question to the student, and record his or her oral response. If the student answers correctly, go to the next question. Stop when the student misses two questions at the same level. Students may use paper and pencil to solve the starred questions.

## Questions

### Level 1: Prerequisite

1. What is $\frac{1}{2}$ of 16? 8
2. What is $\frac{1}{4}$ of 24? 6
3. What is the least common multiple of 4 and 6? 12
4. What is the least common multiple of 6 and 9? 18

### Level 2: Basic

5. What is the probability of rolling an even number on a 0–5 ***Number Cube?*** $\frac{1}{2}$
6. Name a fraction with a denominator of 6 that is equivalent to $\frac{1}{2}$. $\frac{3}{6}$
7. Name a fraction with a denominator of 8 that is equivalent to $\frac{3}{4}$. $\frac{6}{8}$
8. Name a fraction with a denominator of 12 that is equivalent to $\frac{1}{4}$. $\frac{3}{12}$

### Level 3: At Level

9. There are 16 candies in a bag. If 4 of them are green, what is the probability of getting a green one if you pick one from the bag without looking? $\frac{4}{16}$ or $\frac{1}{4}$

*10. What is $\frac{1}{2} \times \frac{3}{4}$? $\frac{3}{8}$

*11. What is $\frac{2}{3} \times \frac{1}{4}$? $\frac{2}{12}$ or $\frac{1}{6}$

*12. What is $\frac{1}{3} \times \frac{1}{2}$? $\frac{1}{6}$

### Level 4: Challenge Application

*13. What number times $\frac{2}{3}$ equals $\frac{6}{12}$? $\frac{3}{4}$

*14. Which is greater—$\frac{3}{5}$ or $\frac{2}{3}$? $\frac{2}{3}$

*15. Which is greater—$\frac{3}{4}$ or $\frac{4}{5}$? $\frac{4}{5}$

*16. Of the 20 students in a class, $\frac{3}{5}$ of them chose lemonade to drink. How many students chose lemonade? 12

### Level 5: Content Beyond Mid-Chapter

17. What is $\frac{1}{8} + \frac{5}{8}$? $\frac{6}{8}$ or $\frac{3}{4}$
18. What is $\frac{5}{8} - \frac{1}{4}$? $\frac{3}{8}$
19. What is $\frac{8}{5}$ as a mixed number? $1\frac{3}{5}$

*20. What is $1\frac{2}{5} - \frac{5}{6}$? $\frac{17}{30}$

## Lesson Planner

### Objectives
- To introduce students to mixed numbers and improper fractions
- To provide practice converting between mixed numbers and improper fractions

### NCTM Standards
**Number and Operations**
Understand numbers, ways of representing numbers, relationships among numbers, and number systems

**Connections**
Recognize and use connections among mathematical ideas

### Technology
**Presentation** Lesson 8.10
**MathTools** Fractions
**Games** Fracto

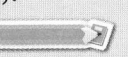

### Test Prep
**Cumulative Review**
Mental Math reviews equivalent fractions (Lesson 8.8).

**Writing + Math**
Journal

# Fractions Greater than 1

**Context of the Lesson** Within Grade 4 of ***Real Math,*** students have worked only informally with mixed numbers. However, Grade 3 provided an opportunity for students to work with decimal and fractions greater than 1.

See page 328B for Math Background for teachers for this lesson.

## Planning for Learning • DIFFERENTE INSTRUCTION

### INTERVENTION
**If . . .** students lack the prerequisite skill of estimating using percent benchmarks,

**Then . . .** teach ***Intervention*** Lesson 8.A.

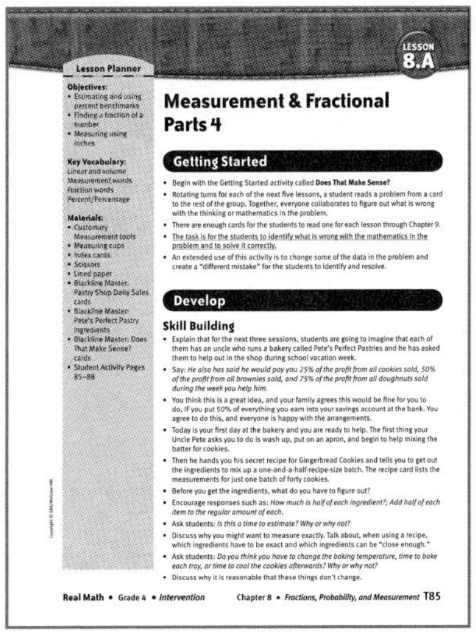
Lesson 8.A
Measurement & Fractional Parts 4

Intervention Lesson 8.A

### ENGLISH LEARNER
**Preview**

**If . . .** students need language support,

**Then . . .** use Lesson 8.10 in ***English Learner Support Guide*** to preview lesson concepts and vocabulary.

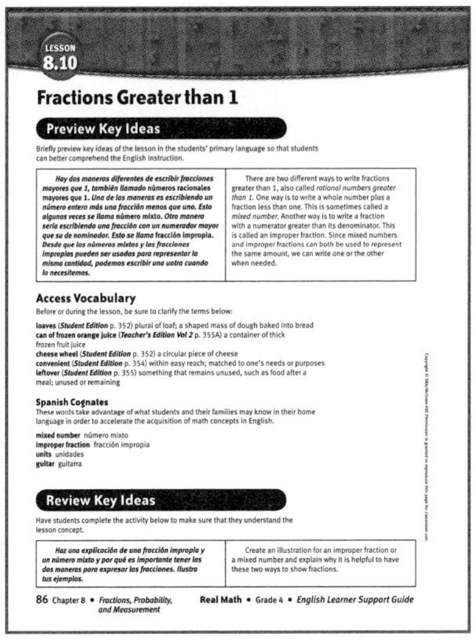
Lesson 8.10
Fractions Greater than 1

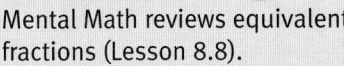

English Learner Lesson 8.10

### ENRICH
**If . . .** students are proficient in the lesson concepts,

**Then . . .** encourage them to work on the chapter projects.

### PRACTICE
**If . . .** students would benefit from additional practice,

**Then . . .** extend Skill Practice before assigning the student pages.

### RETEACH
**If . . .** students are having difficulty understanding mixed numbers,

**Then . . .** extend Guided Discussion about converting mixed numbers and improper fractions

### Vocabulary
**mixed number** ***n.*** a number consisting of a whole number and a fraction
**improper fraction** ***n.*** a fraction whose numerator is greater than its denominator

### Access Vocabulary
**loaves of bread** the plural of loaf of bread. A loaf is a shaped mass of dough baked into bread.
**obey the rules** do what they are told, follow the rules

### Spanish Cognates
**mixed number** número mixto
**improper fraction** fracción impropia
**units** unidades

# Teaching the Lesson

## Mental Math 5

Review THUMBS UP

Provide practice with equivalent fractions, such as the following. Show thumbs-up to represent greater than, thumbs-down to represent less than, and an open hand to represent equal to.

**a.** $\frac{1}{2}$ ___ $\frac{4}{8}$ open hand **b.** $\frac{6}{10}$ ___ $\frac{2}{5}$ thumbs-up

**c.** $\frac{12}{20}$ ___ $\frac{3}{4}$ thumbs-down **d.** $\frac{1}{8}$ ___ $\frac{1}{4}$ thumbs-down

**e.** $\frac{2}{4}$ ___ $\frac{3}{6}$ open hand **f.** $\frac{7}{10}$ ___ $\frac{3}{5}$ thumbs-up

## 1 Develop 25

### Tell Students In Today's Lesson They Will

be introduced to fractions greater than 1 and practice converting between mixed numbers and improper fractions.

### Guided Discussion UNDERSTANDING

Whole Group

**Mixed Numbers and Improper Fractions**

1. Ask students questions such as the following:
   - **Can we have $3\frac{1}{2}$ of something?** yes
   - **Where have you used or heard numbers like $3\frac{1}{2}$?** possible answers: time; measuring length; weight; quantities of food
   - **What do you think $3\frac{1}{2}$ means?** 3 wholes and $\frac{1}{2}$ of 1 whole
2. Draw the following image of blocks on the board for students to see. Ask students how much area is shaded and how they know. $1\frac{1}{4}$ (or $\frac{5}{4}$) for the first Write the fraction $1\frac{1}{4}$ on the board next to the diagram. Stress that the diagram is *one whole shaded bar plus a partially shaded second bar.*

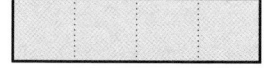

3. Explain how to name the shaded area as a mixed number. There is 1 shaded whole plus 1 shaded fourth of another whole. We say the total shaded amount is $1\frac{1}{4}$. Although we read this as *one and one fourth,* it is more convenient to write it without the "and."
   - **What does it mean when the numerator of a fraction is equal to its denominator?** The fraction represents 1, the whole.
4. To make a fraction that represents a quantity larger than 1, called an improper fraction, we need to have a numerator that is *greater* than the denominator. To describe the set of bars drawn on the board, we need to talk in fourths (since that's how many parts 1 whole has been divided into). The picture of the bars shows us that there are clearly 5 shaded fourths. The improper fraction describing this would be $\frac{5}{4}$. Write this improper fraction on the board next to $1\frac{1}{4}$. Any time we use a mixed number to describe an amount, we could also use an improper fraction. Point out to students that $1\frac{1}{4}$ and $\frac{5}{4}$ both represent the same number.

### Guided Discussion UNDERSTANDING

Whole Group

**Converting Between Mixed Numbers and Improper Fractions**

1. Draw the number of wholes on the board plus the fractional piece. Ask the students to name this illustration and write the mixed number on the board near the illustration. $2\frac{1}{3}$
   - **How many thirds are in 2?** 6
2. Remind students that the fraction's denominator is 3, so you will be dividing the 2 whole bars into thirds. It might be instructive to show this step visually by drawing lines through the 2 whole bars to divide them into thirds, and writing $\frac{3}{3}$ next to each one.
   - **How many more thirds do we have?** $\frac{1}{3}$
   - **How many thirds are there in all?** 7
3. Write on the board the improper fraction $\frac{7}{3}$ so you have the statement $2\frac{1}{3} = \frac{7}{3}$. The mixed number $2\frac{1}{3}$ is equivalent to the improper fraction $\frac{7}{3}$.
   Teacher note: To change a mixed number to an improper fraction, you multiply the whole number by the amount of equal-sized parts in the fraction (the fraction's denominator) and then add any extra parts from the fraction (the fraction's numerator).

### Skill Practice COMPUTING

Small Group

**Converting Between Improper Fractions and Mixed Numbers**

Divide the class into groups of three or four. Have them work the examples together as a group.

1. Work through an example, such as $\frac{9}{4}$, using an illustration. Draw 9 pie pieces on the board.
   - **How many pieces are there?** 9
   - **If each piece is $\frac{1}{4}$ of a circle, what improper fraction is represented here?** $\frac{9}{4}$
   - **How many whole circles do we have, if each piece is $\frac{1}{4}$ of a circle?** 2

   Draw a line around each group of 4 shapes; label each of the two sets with a 1. Students might see that this process is the same as dividing the numerator by the denominator (without, for the time being, focusing on the remainder).

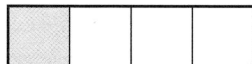

**2.** Ask how many more pieces are left. 1

The important thing for students to note is that the remaining part is a part of a whole and needs to be recorded as such. In this case, the remaining part is not just "1" but "$\frac{1}{4}$." Write the mixed number $2\frac{1}{4}$ on the board so you have the statement $\frac{9}{4} = 2\frac{1}{4}$. The improper fraction $\frac{9}{4}$ is equivalent to the mixed number $2\frac{1}{4}$.

Teacher note: To change an improper fraction to a mixed number you do the reverse of the above procedure—ask how many whole units there are (divide the numerator by the denominator) Then, if there is a remainder, that becomes the fraction in the new mixed number.

Have the groups of students write the following mixed numbers as improper fractions. Use fraction manipulatives if necessary.

**a.** $1\frac{1}{2}$ $\frac{3}{2}$ **b.** $1\frac{3}{7}$ $\frac{10}{7}$ **c.** $2\frac{4}{5}$ $\frac{14}{5}$ **d.** $2\frac{7}{8}$ $\frac{23}{8}$ **e.** $10\frac{1}{10}$ $\frac{101}{10}$; should be done without a manipulative

Have the groups write improper fractions, such as the following, as mixed numbers. Use fraction manipulatives if necessary.

**a.** $\frac{4}{3}$ $1\frac{1}{3}$ **b.** $\frac{5}{2}$ $2\frac{1}{2}$ **c.** $\frac{8}{4}$ 2 **d.** $\frac{10}{8}$ $1\frac{2}{8}$ or $1\frac{1}{4}$ **e.** $\frac{12}{10}$ $1\frac{2}{10}$ or $1\frac{1}{5}$

## 2 Assign Student Pages 25

### Page 352–353 APPLYING

Small Group

Have students work on pages 352 and 353 independently or in small groups. Although the word problems on page 353 involve adding and subtracting mixed numbers, the context and numbers have been chosen so that students can do them without learning an algorithm. Therefore, discuss these problems using diagrams or concrete objects, but do not teach a general step-by-step procedure.

Student Page

LESSON 8.10 **Fractions Greater than 1**

**Key Ideas**

**There are different ways to write fractions greater than 1 or rational numbers greater than 1.**

One way is to write a whole number plus a fraction less than 1. This is sometimes called a mixed number. For example, $2\frac{1}{8}$ is a mixed number that means 2 whole quantities plus $\frac{1}{8}$.

Another way is to write a fraction with a top number (numerator) greater than its bottom number (denominator). This is sometimes called an improper fraction. An example of an improper fraction is $\frac{17}{8}$.

Here is an example of how to use a mixed number.

Mr. Cheng baked 4 loaves of bread.

His children ate half of one loaf. Mr. Cheng had three and one-half loaves left.

We can write three and one half as $3\frac{1}{2}$.

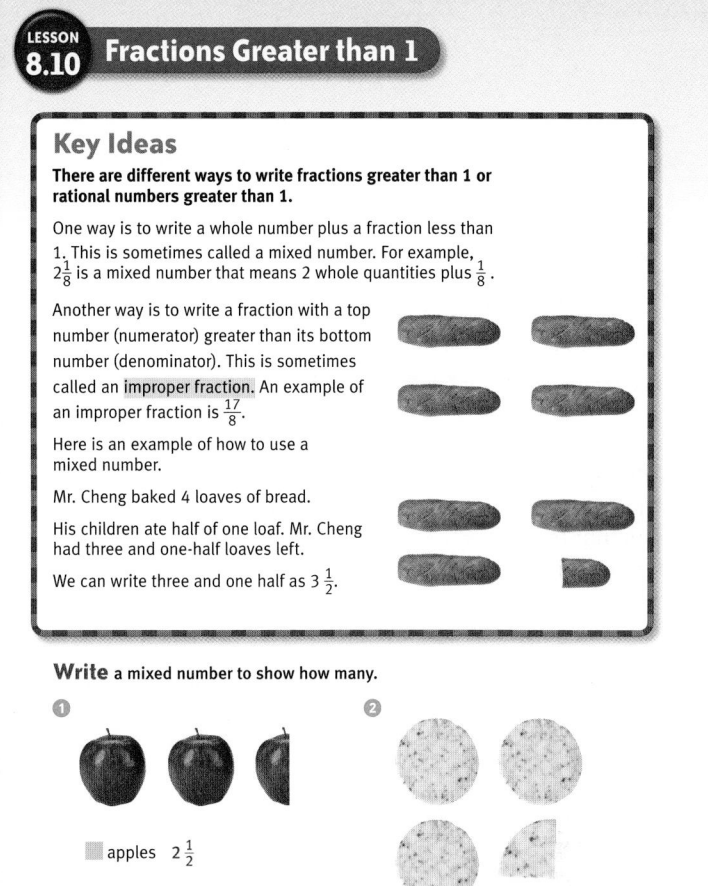

**Write** a mixed number to show how many.

1

apples $2\frac{1}{2}$

2

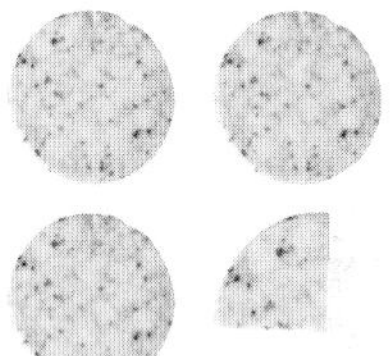

cheese wheels $3\frac{1}{4}$



Textbook This lesson is available in the ***eTextbook***.

Student Page

Mr. Cheng cut the remaining loaves of bread into half-loaves and told his children they were allowed to eat one half-loaf per day. Mr. Cheng now has 7 half-loaves left.

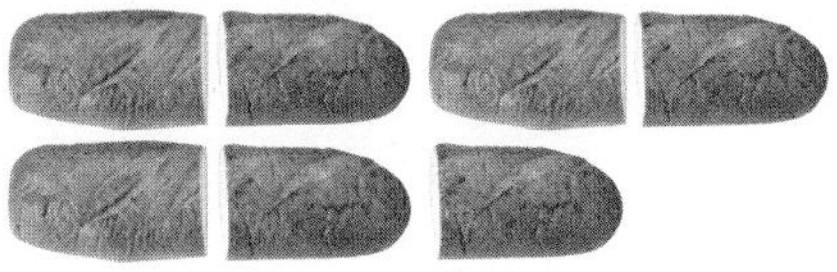

We can write seven halves as $\frac{7}{2}$.

If Mr. Cheng's children do as he asked, how long will the bread last?

7 days or 1 week

**Write** an improper fraction to show how many.

3

apples $\frac{5}{2}$

4

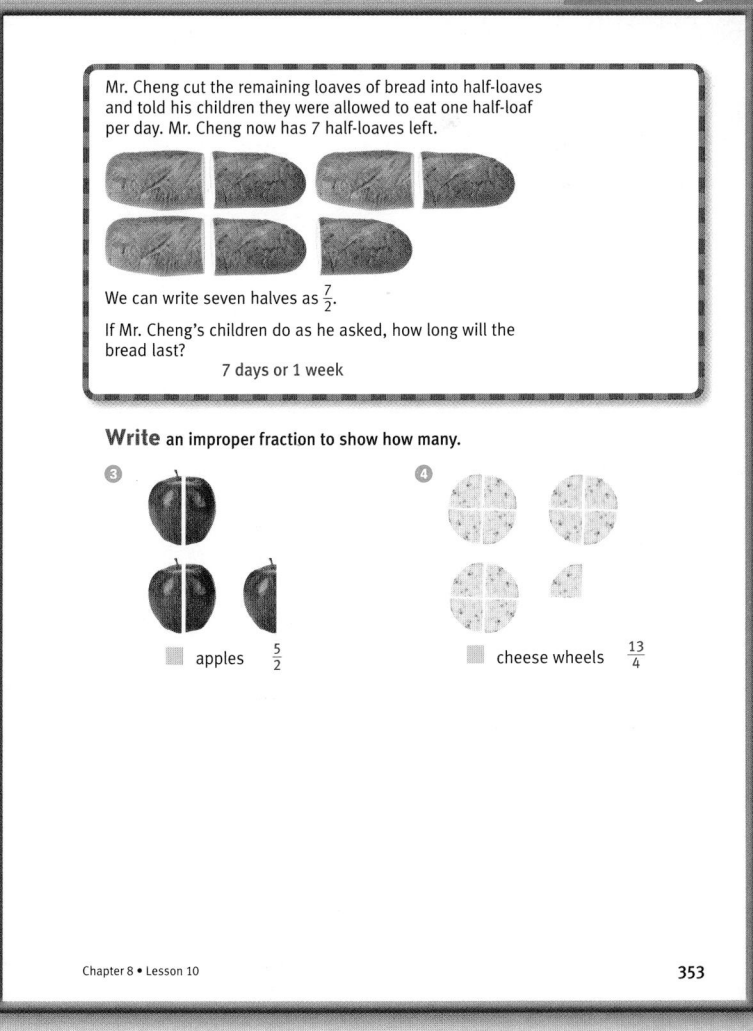

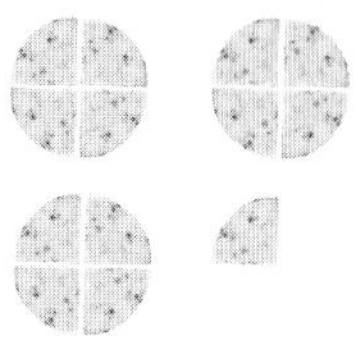

cheese wheels $\frac{13}{4}$

# Assign Student Pages, continued

### Pages 354–355 APPLYING

Have students complete pages 354 and 355 independently.

## Monitoring Student Progress

| | |
|---|---|
| **If . . .** students have difficulty understanding general concepts about fractions that represent amounts larger than 1, | **Then . . .** extra work with concrete objects (e.g., fraction bars, counters, and so on.) might help them gain understanding. |
| **If . . .** students have trouble understanding mixed number notation, | **Then . . .** explain that 2 and $\frac{1}{2}$ can be written in a shorter form ($2\frac{1}{2}$). Then say some mixed numbers and have students write them. |

### As Students Finish

**Game** **Fracto Game Mat**

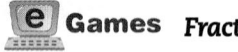

**e Games** *Fracto*

**e MathTools** *Fractions* Have students explore combinations of fractions that are greater than 1.

Student Page



Since mixed numbers and improper fractions can both be used to represent the same amount, you can use whichever form is most convenient.

Look at the following example of how to write $2\frac{3}{5}$ as an improper fraction:

- The denominator of the new improper fraction will be the same as the denominator of the fraction in the mixed number. In this example, the denominator is 5 (fifths).
- Determine how many fifths there are in the whole number part (the 2) of the mixed number. Count the number of parts in the picture below or multiply 2 by 5. The answer is 10. $\frac{10}{5}$ is equivalent to 2 whole units.

Can you see that $2\frac{3}{5}$ and $\frac{13}{5}$ represent the same amount in the picture below?

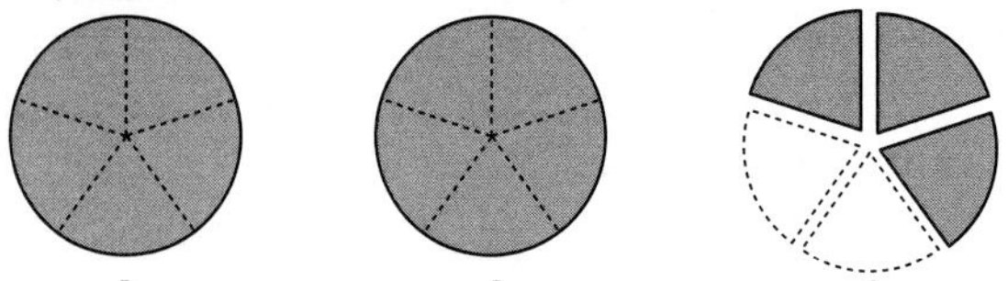

$\frac{5}{5}$ + $\frac{5}{5}$ + $\frac{3}{5}$ = $\frac{13}{5}$

$\frac{10}{5}$ (the whole-number part) + $\frac{3}{5}$ (the fraction part) = $\frac{13}{5}$

**Write** each mixed number as an improper fraction.

5. $2\frac{5}{6}$ $\frac{17}{6}$
6. $4\frac{1}{3}$ $\frac{13}{3}$
7. $3\frac{1}{6}$ $\frac{19}{6}$
8. $4\frac{3}{5}$ $\frac{23}{5}$
9. $6\frac{5}{9}$ $\frac{59}{9}$
10. $2\frac{5}{7}$ $\frac{19}{7}$
11. $3\frac{1}{4}$ $\frac{13}{4}$
12. $3\frac{5}{6}$ $\frac{23}{6}$
13. $5\frac{3}{8}$ $\frac{43}{8}$
14. $2\frac{3}{8}$ $\frac{19}{8}$
15. $4\frac{3}{4}$ $\frac{19}{4}$
16. $1\frac{2}{5}$ $\frac{7}{5}$



Textbook This lesson is available in the ***eTextbook.***

Student Page

Look at the following example of how to write the improper fraction $\frac{13}{5}$ as a mixed number:

- How many whole units are there in $\frac{13}{5}$, or how many groups of 5 are in 13? The answer is 2 whole units.
- Notice the leftover amount is $\frac{3}{5}$.
- The improper fraction $\frac{13}{5}$ can be rewritten as 2 whole units and $\frac{3}{5}$, or $2\frac{3}{5}$.

Can you see that $\frac{13}{5}$ and $2\frac{3}{5}$ represent the same number in the picture below?

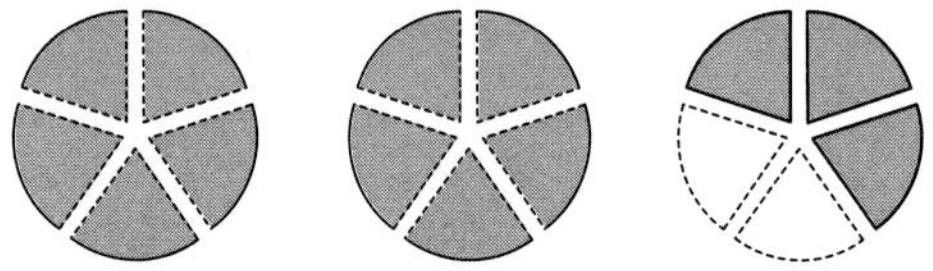

1 + 1 + $\frac{3}{5}$ = $2\frac{3}{5}$

**Write** each improper fraction as a mixed number or a whole number.

17. $\frac{5}{2}$ $2\frac{1}{2}$
18. $\frac{5}{4}$ $1\frac{1}{4}$
19. $\frac{8}{6}$ $1\frac{2}{6}$ or $1\frac{1}{3}$
20. $\frac{7}{5}$ $1\frac{2}{5}$
21. $\frac{21}{3}$ 7
22. $\frac{15}{7}$ $2\frac{1}{7}$
23. $\frac{29}{3}$ $9\frac{2}{3}$
24. $\frac{8}{7}$ $1\frac{1}{7}$
25. $\frac{7}{4}$ $1\frac{3}{4}$
26. $\frac{11}{6}$ $1\frac{5}{6}$
27. $\frac{20}{5}$ 4
28. $\frac{28}{5}$ $5\frac{3}{5}$

Writing + Math **Journal**

Find the improper fraction that is equal to the mixed number $4\frac{5}{6}$. Draw a picture that shows what it means.

See Reflect in the *Teacher's Edition.*

# 3 Reflect

5

## Guided Discussion REASONING

Whole Group

Read statements such as the following. Have the students answer *yes* if the last sentence is true or *no* if it is not true. If it is not true, have the students explain why.

- **Dustin has a guitar lesson at 5:30 P.M. At 3:00 P.M. he said, "My guitar lesson starts in $2\frac{1}{2}$ hours."** yes
- **A can of frozen orange juice makes enough juice for 6 glasses. Deborah used 1 can to make a pitcher of orange juice. She drank $3\frac{1}{2}$ glasses for breakfast. There are now $3\frac{1}{2}$ glasses of orange juice left.** no; $3\frac{1}{2} + 3\frac{1}{2} = 7$
- **Dee Dee works a total of $3\frac{3}{4}$ hours every day at a hardware store. Today she worked 2 hours before dinner and $1\frac{3}{4}$ hours after dinner.** yes
- **Sonia told Jay to meet her in $1\frac{1}{2}$ hours. Jay showed up on time 90 minutes later.** yes

### Writing + Math Journal REASONING

Discuss students' pictures. Pictures should be a representation of any fraction equivalent to $4\frac{5}{6}$ such as $4\frac{10}{12}$.

**Cumulative Review:** For review of percents, assign Problems 1–4 on student page 373.

**Family Involvement:** Assign the ***Practice, Reteach,*** or ***Enrichment*** activities depending on the needs of your students. Encourage students to play the **Fracto I** or **Fracto II Game Mat** or **Fracto eGames** with a friend or relative.

**Concept/Question Board:** Encourage students to continue looking for real-world examples of fractions and post them on the Concept/Question Board.

**Math Puzzler:** Fill in the boxes, using the digits 1, 2, 3, and 4 to form as many true fraction statements as you can.

$\frac{\square}{\square} > \frac{\square}{\square}$

$\frac{3}{4} > \frac{1}{2}, \frac{2}{4} > \frac{1}{3}, \frac{2}{3} > \frac{1}{4}$

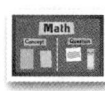

# 4 Assess and Differentiate

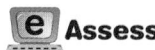

**e Assess** Use ***eAssess*** to record and analyze evidence of student understanding.

## A Gather Evidence

Use the Daily Class Assessment Records in ***Assessment*** or ***eAssess*** to record daily observations.

### Informal Assessment

**✓ Skill Practice**

Did the student COMPUTING

- ❑ respond accurately?
- ❑ respond quickly?
- ❑ respond with confidence?
- ❑ self-correct?

### Portfolio Assessment

**✓ Journal**

Did the student ENGAGING

- ❑ provide a clear explanation?
- ❑ communicate reasons and strategies?
- ❑ choose appropriate strategies?
- ❑ argue logically?

## B Summarize Findings

Analyze and summarize assessment data for each student. Determine which Assessment Follow-Up is appropriate for each student. Use the Student Assessment Record in ***Assessment*** or ***eAssess*** to update assessment records.

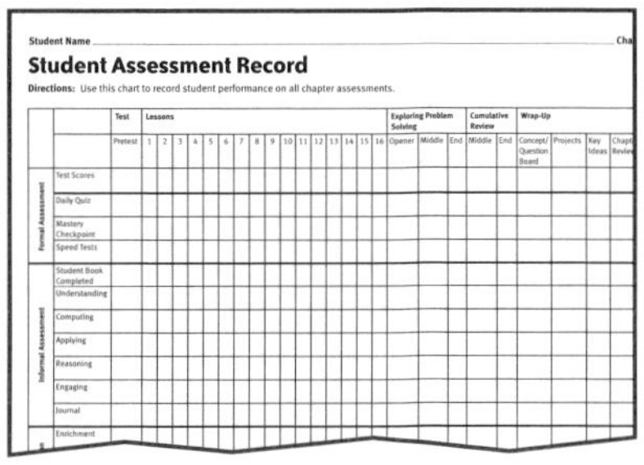


**Assessment Page T41**

## C Assessment Follow-Up • DIFFERENTIATE INSTRUCTION

Based on your observations, use these teaching strategies for assessment follow-up.

### INTERVENTION

Review student performance on ***Intervention*** Lesson 8.A to see if students have mastered prerequisite skills for this lesson.

### ENGLISH LEARNER

**Review**

Use Lesson 8.10 in ***English Learner Support Guide*** to review lesson concepts and vocabulary.

### ENRICH

**If . . .** students are proficient in the lesson concepts,

**Then . . .** encourage them to work on the chapter projects or ***Enrichment*** Lesson 8.10.

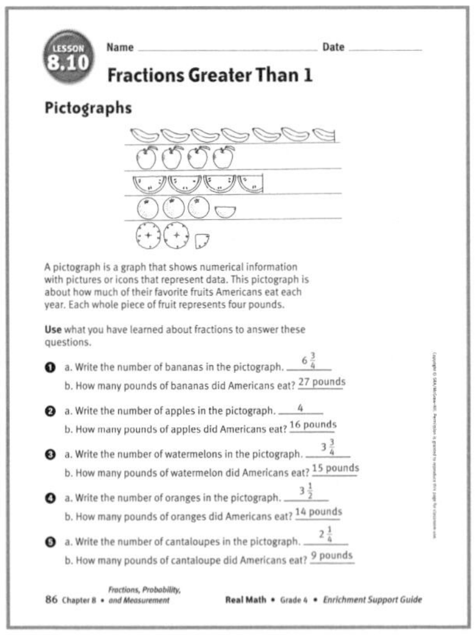

LESSON 8.10 Name ______ Date ______

**Fractions Greater Than 1**

**Pictographs**

A pictograph is a graph that shows numerical information with pictures or icons that represent data. This pictograph is about how much of their favorite fruits Americans eat each year. Each whole piece of fruit represents four pounds.

**Use** what you have learned about fractions to answer these questions.

1. a. Write the number of bananas in the pictograph. $6\frac{3}{4}$
   b. How many pounds of bananas did Americans eat? 27 pounds
2. a. Write the number of apples in the pictograph. 4
   b. How many pounds of apples did Americans eat? 16 pounds
3. a. Write the number of watermelons in the pictograph. $3\frac{3}{4}$
   b. How many pounds of watermelon did Americans eat? 15 pounds
4. a. Write the number of oranges in the pictograph. $3\frac{1}{2}$
   b. How many pounds of oranges did Americans eat? 14 pounds
5. a. Write the number of cantaloupes in the pictograph. $2\frac{1}{4}$
   b. How many pounds of cantaloupe did Americans eat? 9 pounds

86 Chapter 8 • *Fractions, Probability, and Measurement* **Real Math** • Grade 4 • *Enrichment Support Guide*

**Enrichment Lesson 8.10**

### PRACTICE

**If . . .** students would benefit from additional practice,

**Then . . .** assign ***Practice*** Lesson 8.10.

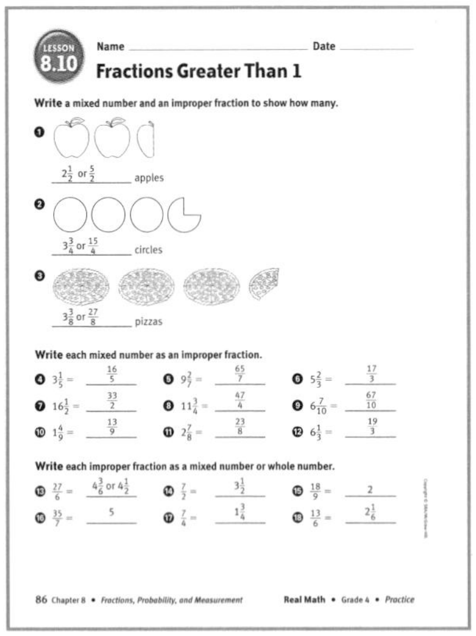

LESSON 8.10 Name ______ Date ______

**Fractions Greater Than 1**

**Write** a mixed number and an improper fraction to show how many.

1. $2\frac{1}{2}$ or $\frac{5}{2}$ apples
2. $3\frac{3}{4}$ or $\frac{15}{4}$ circles
3. $3\frac{3}{8}$ or $\frac{27}{8}$ pizzas

**Write** each mixed number as an improper fraction.

4. $3\frac{1}{5} = \frac{16}{5}$
5. $9\frac{2}{7} = \frac{65}{7}$
6. $5\frac{2}{3} = \frac{17}{3}$
7. $16\frac{1}{2} = \frac{33}{2}$
8. $11\frac{3}{4} = \frac{47}{4}$
9. $6\frac{7}{10} = \frac{67}{10}$
10. $1\frac{4}{9} = \frac{13}{9}$
11. $2\frac{7}{8} = \frac{23}{8}$
12. $6\frac{1}{3} = \frac{19}{3}$

**Write** each improper fraction as a mixed number or whole number.

13. $\frac{27}{6} = 4\frac{3}{6}$ or $4\frac{1}{2}$
14. $\frac{7}{2} = 3\frac{1}{2}$
15. $\frac{18}{9} = 2$
16. $\frac{35}{7} = 5$
17. $\frac{7}{4} = 1\frac{3}{4}$
18. $\frac{13}{6} = 2\frac{1}{6}$

86 Chapter 8 • *Fractions, Probability, and Measurement* **Real Math** • Grade 4 • *Practice*

**Practice Lesson 8.10**

### RETEACH

**If . . .** students are having difficulty understanding fractions greater than 1,

**Then . . .** reteach the lesson concept.

# Representing Fractions Greater than 1

**OBJECTIVES**
- To review multiple ways to name rational numbers greater than 1
- To provide practice finding equivalent fractions for rational numbers greater than 1

**NCTM STANDARDS**
**Number and Operations**
Understanding numbers, ways of representing numbers, relationships among numbers, and number systems

**MATERIALS**
*Response Wheels

**TECHNOLOGY**
**e Presentation** Lesson 8.11
**e MathTools** Fraction
**e Games** Fracto

**TEST PREP**
**Cumulative Review**
Mental Math reviews the estimated placement of fractions on a number line.

*Manipulative Kit Item

**Context of the Lesson** Students learned how to convert fractions greater than 1, using improper fractions and mixed numbers in Lesson 8.10. In this lesson, students will expand their knowledge of fractions greater than 1 to increase their understanding of different representations of rational numbers.

See page 328B for Math Background for teachers for this lesson.

## Planning for Learning • DIFFERENTIATE INSTRUCTION

### INTERVENTION

**If . . .** students lack the prerequisite skill of finding a fraction of a number,

**Then . . .** teach ***Intervention*** Lesson 8.B.

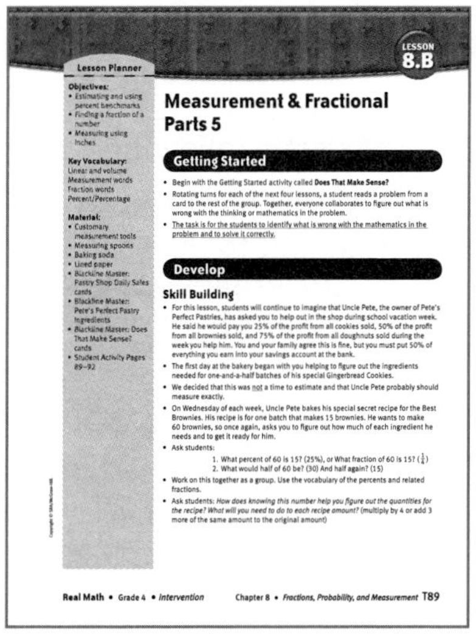
Measurement & Fractional Parts 5

Intervention Lesson 8.B

### ENGLISH LEARNER

Preview

**If . . .** students need language support,

**Then . . .** use Lesson 8.11 in ***English Learner Support Guide*** to preview lesson concepts and vocabulary.

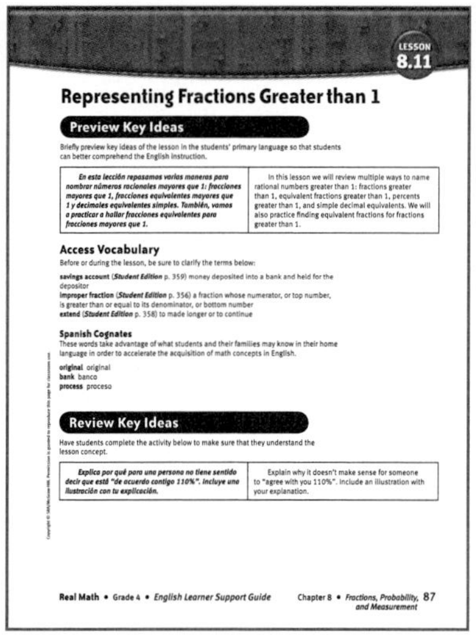
Representing Fractions Greater than 1

English Learner Lesson 8.11

### ENRICH

**If . . .** students are proficient in the lesson concepts,

**Then . . .** encourage them to work on the chapter projects.

### PRACTICE

**If . . .** students would benefit from additional practice,

**Then . . .** extend Skill Practice before assigning the student pages.

### RETEACH

**If . . .** students are having difficulty understanding different forms of fractions greater than 1,

**Then . . .** extend Guided Discussion before assigning the student pages.

**Review Vocabulary**
Review from Lesson 8.3: **Rational Number**
Review from Lesson 8.3: **Equivalent**

**Access Vocabulary**
**science fair** an event where science projects are displayed around a large room and students explain their work

**Spanish Cognates**
**original** original
**bank** banco
**process** proceso

## Mental Math

5

RESPONSE WHEEL

Give students exercises such as the following that require them to estimate fractions. Students should use their percent sliders on the Response Wheel to show the percent of 1 the fraction is closer to: 0%, 50%, or 100%.

**a.** $\frac{12}{20}$ 50% **b.** $\frac{1}{50}$ 0% **c.** $\frac{2}{10}$ 0%

**d.** $\frac{8}{9}$ 100% **e.** $\frac{3}{5}$ 50% **f.** $\frac{6}{7}$ 100%

**g.** $\frac{1}{25}$ 0% **h.** $\frac{15}{32}$ 50% **i.** $\frac{5}{16}$ 50%

**j.** $\frac{6}{15}$ 50% **k.** $\frac{99}{100}$ 100%

## 1 Develop

[TK]

### Tell Students In Today's Lesson They Will

review ways to name rational numbers greater than 1 and find equivalent fractions for rational numbers greater than 1.

## Guided Discussion

UNDERSTANDING

Whole Group

1. Draw a representation of a fraction greater than 1 on the board. For example, $\frac{5}{4}$ can be shown like this.

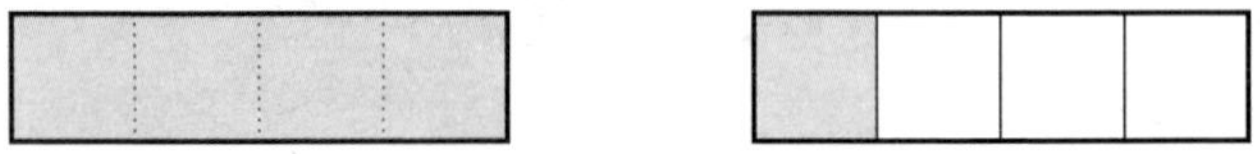

- **What fraction is represented by this picture?** $\frac{5}{4}$ or $1\frac{1}{4}$

Label the picture $\frac{5}{4}$ or $1\frac{1}{4}$.

- **What will be the result if each quarter piece is divided in halves again?** each sections will be eighths, and there will be eight parts in each of the bars.
- **How many of these eighths would now be shaded?** 10

Modify the original picture to show this and add the new label.

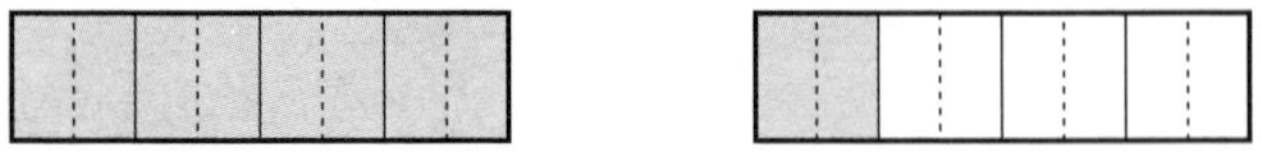

$\frac{5}{4}$ or $1\frac{1}{4} = \frac{10}{8}$

3. Ask students if they know how to get $\frac{10}{8}$ from $\frac{5}{4}$ without having to use a picture. (e.g., Can they use multiplication? What did they learn previously about making equivalent fractions?) Students should see that they can multiply by a fraction equal to 1 to make an equivalent fraction. In this example, since they cut each quarter in halves, they will double the number of squares. Multiplying $\frac{5}{4}$ by $\frac{2}{2}$ will give the equivalent fraction $\frac{10}{8}$. Explain to students that they may convert a mixed number to an improper fraction before they find an equivalent fraction.

4. On the board write $1\frac{1}{2}$.
   - **What would the improper fraction for this mixed number be?** $\frac{3}{2}$
   - **What is an equivalent fraction for $\frac{3}{2}$?** Possible answers: $\frac{6}{4}$ (if multiplied by $\frac{2}{2}$), $\frac{9}{6}$ (if multiplied by $\frac{3}{3}$), $\frac{12}{8}$ (if multiplied by $\frac{4}{4}$) and so on.

## Skill Practice

COMPUTING

Small Group

Have the students work with one or two partners to find equivalent fractions. Remind students to multiply by a fraction equal to 1. Use fractions such as the following:

- $\frac{4}{3}$ Possible answers: $\frac{8}{6}, \frac{12}{9}, \frac{16}{12}$
- $\frac{3}{2}$ Possible answers: $\frac{6}{4}, \frac{9}{6}, \frac{12}{8}$
- $\frac{5}{2}$ Possible answers: $\frac{10}{4}, \frac{15}{6}, \frac{20}{8}$
- $\frac{7}{3}$ Possible answers: $\frac{14}{6}, \frac{21}{9}, \frac{28}{12}$
- $\frac{9}{4}$ Possible answers: $\frac{18}{8}, \frac{27}{12}, \frac{36}{16}$
- $\frac{100}{3}$ Possible answers: $\frac{200}{6}, \frac{300}{9}, \frac{400}{12}$

For each equivalent fraction, have students list the fraction equal to 1 that they used.

## Guided Discussion

REASONING

Whole Group

- **How can $1\frac{1}{4}$ be written as a decimal?** 1.25

Explain to the students that if a mixed number is a whole number plus a fraction, then the decimal number will be the whole number plus the decimal equivalent of the fraction (if the fraction has a decimal equivalent). In Lesson 8.3, students learned the decimal equivalent of $\frac{1}{4}$ is 0.25; therefore, $1\frac{1}{4}$ is the same as 1 + .25 or 1.25.

Ask the following question about percents.

- **How would $1\frac{1}{4}$ be written as a percent?** 125%

Explain to the students that, if a mixed number is a whole number plus a fraction, then the percent will be 100% plus the percent equivalent of the fraction in the mixed number. In Chapter 7 the students discovered $\frac{1}{4}$ is equivalent to 25%. Since 1 is equivalent to 100% and $\frac{1}{4}$ is equivalent to 25%, the mixed number $1\frac{1}{4}$ would be the same quantity as 125% of the whole.

A word of caution about percents greater than 100%: in cases where you use percent, it still has to be a percent *of* something—even if that something is not mentioned. People sometimes say *I agree with you 110%*. This means that they agree absolutely. However, if you agree with someone as much as is possible, it couldn't be any more than 100%!

Read statements such as the following, and ask the students whether or not they are possible. If not, explain why.

- **Lauren is 125% of her little brother's height.** possible
- **Phinneaus is a hard worker; he gives 150%.** not possible; giving his most would be equivalent to 100%
- **Liam ate 200% of the pumpkin pie.** not possible; the maximum percentage of one pie is 100%
- **Walter's hamster now weighs 175% of its birth weight.** possible

## 2 Assign Student Pages 20

### Pages 356–357 UNDERSTANDING

Have students complete pages 356 and 357 independently. Remind them that a fraction is equal to 1 when the numerator and denominator are the same.

Student Page

LESSON 8.11 **Representing Fractions Greater than 1**

### Key Ideas

**There are many ways to name rational numbers greater than 1.**

- Fractions greater than 1
- Decimal equivalents greater than 1
- Percents greater than 100%

To find a fraction that is equivalent to another, multiply the starting fraction by another fraction that is equal to 1. Remember, a fraction is equal to 1 when the numerator and denominator are the same.

$\frac{3}{4} \times \frac{2}{2} = \frac{6}{8}$

The process is the same for an improper fraction.

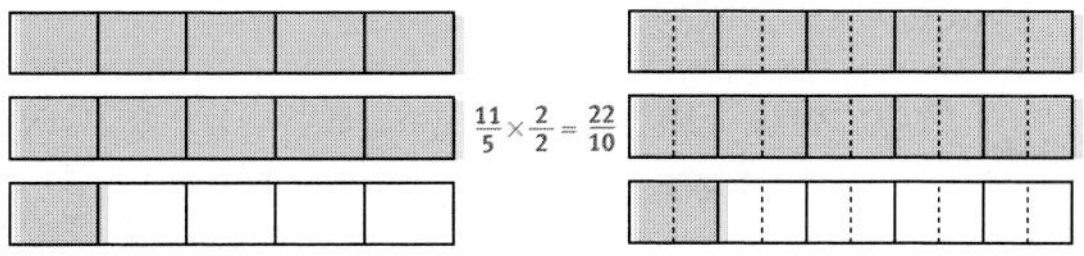

$\frac{11}{5} \times \frac{2}{2} = \frac{22}{10}$

The fractions $\frac{11}{5}$ and $\frac{22}{10}$ are equivalent fractions and represent the same amount. The fractions are different ways to express the same rational number.

**Fill** in the missing information to make the following statements true.

1. $\frac{7}{3} = \frac{\square}{12}$ 28
2. $\frac{5}{2} = \frac{20}{\square}$ 8
3. $\frac{9}{4} = \frac{\square}{20}$ 45
4. $\frac{13}{6} = \frac{\square}{18}$ 39
5. $\frac{8}{5} = \frac{24}{\square}$ 15
6. $\frac{\square}{8} = \frac{44}{32}$ 11



eTextbook This lesson is available in the *eTextbook*.

Student Page

To find an equivalent fraction for a mixed number, you would first write it as an improper fraction. You may then multiply the improper fraction by a fraction that is equal to 1. Look at the following example:

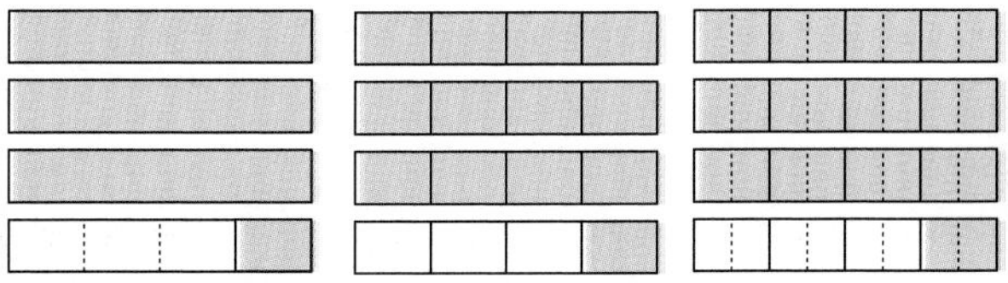

$3\frac{1}{4} \longrightarrow \frac{13}{4} \times \frac{2}{2} = \frac{26}{8}$

The mixed number $3\frac{1}{4}$ can be written as the equivalent improper fraction $\frac{13}{4}$. It may then be multiplied by a fraction equal to 1 (in this example, $\frac{2}{2}$ was used). So another equivalent fraction for $3\frac{1}{4}$ is $\frac{26}{8}$, which also can be written as $3\frac{2}{8}$.

**Fill** in the missing information to make the following statements true.

7. $\frac{9}{8} = \frac{\square}{64}$ 72
8. $\frac{7}{1} = \frac{\square}{7}$ 49
9. $\frac{\square}{2} = \frac{48}{32}$ 3
10. $\frac{18}{\square} = \frac{36}{14}$ 7
11. $1\frac{9}{10} = \frac{\square}{100}$ 190
12. $2\frac{2}{5} = \frac{36}{\square}$ 15

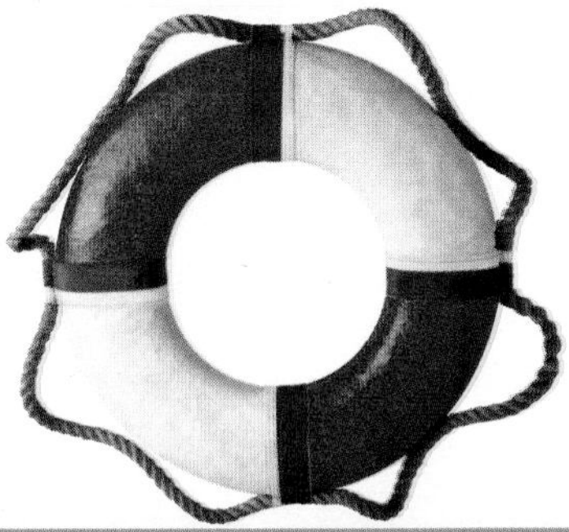

# Teaching Lesson 8.11

## Assign Student Pages, continued

### Pages 358–359  UNDERSTANDING

Have students work on pages 358 and 359 independently.

### As Students Finish

 **Game** Fracto Game Mat

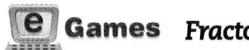

 **Games** *Fracto*

**MathTools** *Fractions* Have students explore equivalent forms of fractions greater than 1.

---

We have already learned that we can use fractions less than 1 to name locations on the number line between 0 and 1. In exactly the same way as we did for fractions less than 1, we are able to name locations on the number line using fractions greater than 1.

We can extend our number line by using either mixed numbers or improper fractions. Let's look at the following example of a number line from 1 to 3:

| $\frac{10}{10}$ | $\frac{12}{10}$ | $\frac{14}{10}$ | $\frac{16}{10}$ | $\frac{18}{10}$ | $\frac{20}{10}$ | $\frac{22}{10}$ | $\frac{24}{10}$ | $\frac{26}{10}$ | $\frac{28}{10}$ | $\frac{30}{10}$ |
|---|---|---|---|---|---|---|---|---|---|---|
| $\frac{5}{5}$ | $\frac{6}{5}$ | $\frac{7}{5}$ | $\frac{8}{5}$ | $\frac{9}{5}$ | $\frac{10}{5}$ | $\frac{11}{5}$ | $\frac{12}{5}$ | $\frac{13}{5}$ | $\frac{14}{5}$ | $\frac{15}{5}$ |
| 1 | $1\frac{1}{5}$ | $1\frac{2}{5}$ | $1\frac{3}{5}$ | $1\frac{4}{5}$ | 2 | $2\frac{1}{5}$ | $2\frac{2}{5}$ | $2\frac{3}{5}$ | $2\frac{4}{5}$ | 3 |

1.0  1.2  1.4  1.6  1.8  2.0  2.2  2.4  2.6  2.8  3.0

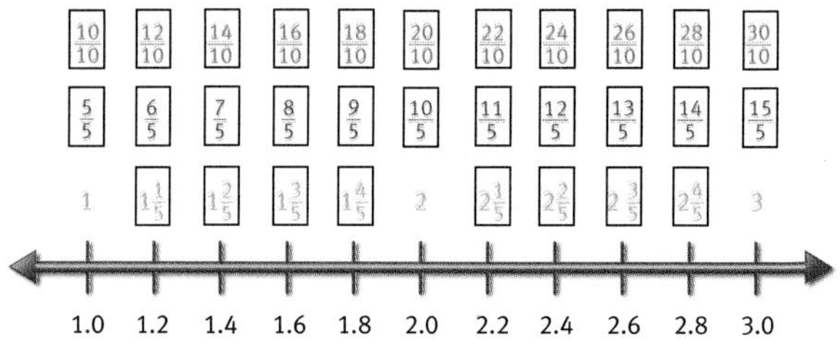

**Use** what you have learned about finding equivalent fractions and about decimal equivalents to solve the following exercises. Use the number line to help you.

What is the decimal equivalent of

13. $\frac{6}{5}$   1.2
14. $\frac{26}{10}$   2.6
15. $2\frac{3}{5}$   2.6
16. $\frac{14}{10}$   1.4
17. $1\frac{2}{5}$   1.4

18. $\frac{30}{15}$   2
19. $\frac{36}{20}$   1.8
20. $\frac{18}{15}$   1.2
21. $2\frac{2}{10}$   2.2
22. $\frac{36}{10}$   3.6

Remember that rational numbers can be graphed on the number line. Therefore, $\frac{24}{10}$, $\frac{12}{5}$, $2\frac{2}{5}$, and 2.4 are all names for the same rational number, and they are graphed at the same point on the number line.

Textbook This lesson is available in the *eTextbook*.

---

We know from earlier lessons that percents are fractions with denominators of 100. If we can make improper fractions with denominators of 100, then it makes sense that we could also make percents greater than 100.

Evan is saving extra money for his family's vacation next summer. He started a savings account with $100, and now has a total of $150 in his account.

23. By what amount did his money increase?   $50

24. **a.** What percent is the increase of the original $100?   50%

    **b.** What fraction is it?   $\frac{1}{2}$

25. What percent of the original $100 is $150? (Hint: He has more money than when he started, so the percent will be greater than 100%.)   150%

26. Rewrite Evan's $150 as a fraction of the original $100.   $\frac{150}{100}$ or $1\frac{50}{100}$ or $1\frac{1}{2}$ or $\frac{3}{2}$

# 3 Reflect

5

## Guided Discussion REASONING

Whole Group

Create a small chart showing ways to represent rational numbers greater than 1. Give students a quantity, such as $2\frac{3}{10}$, and have them fill in the chart with the other names. (Possible answers: $\frac{23}{10}$, 2.30, 2.3, $\frac{46}{20}$, and 230%)

**Cumulative Review:** For review of multidigit addition and subtraction, assign Problems 5–8 on student page 373.

**Family Involvement:** Assign the ***Practice, Reteach,*** or ***Enrichment*** activities depending on the needs of your students. Encourage students to play the **Fracto I** or **Fracto II Game Mat** or **Fracto** **eGames** with a friend or relative.

**Concept/Question Board:** Have students attempt to answer any unanswered questions on the Concept/Question Board.

**Math Puzzler:** Give each letter of the alphabet a numerical value (A = 1, B = 2, C = 3, and so on). Which has the greater value, the sum of the letters in your first name or the sum of the letters in your last name? By how much? (NOTE: You might prepare a list of the numerical value of each letter in advance.) Answers will vary depending on the students' names.

# 4 Assess and Differentiate

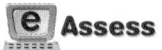

e Assess Use ***eAssess*** to record and analyze evidence of student understanding.

## A Gather Evidence

Use the Daily Class Assessment Records in ***Assessment*** or ***eAssess*** to record daily observations.

### Informal Assessment

**Mental Math**

Did the student COMPUTING

- ❑ respond accurately?
- ❑ respond quickly?
- ❑ respond with confidence?
- ❑ self-correct?

### Informal Assessment

**Student Pages**

Did the student UNDERSTANDING

- ❑ make important observations?
- ❑ extend or generalize learning?
- ❑ provide insightful answers?
- ❑ pose insightful questions?

## B Summarize Findings

Analyze and summarize assessment data for each student. Determine which Assessment Follow-Up is appropriate for each student. Use the Student Assessment Record in ***Assessment*** or ***eAssess*** to update assessment records.

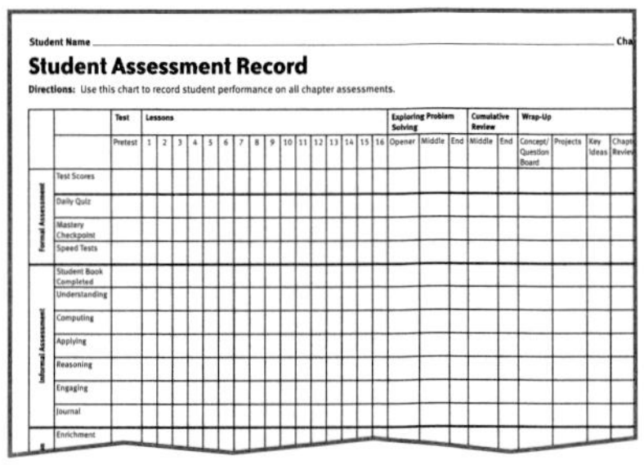
Student Assessment Record

**Assessment Page T41**

## C Assessment Follow-Up • DIFFERENTIATE INSTRUCTION

Based on your observations, use these teaching strategies for assessment follow-up.

### INTERVENTION

Review student performance on ***Intervention*** Lesson 8.B to see if students have mastered prerequisite skills for this lesson.

### Review

Use Lesson 8.11 in ***English Learner Support Guide*** to review lesson concepts and vocabulary.

### ENRICH

**If . . .** students are proficient in the lesson concepts,

**Then . . .** encourage them to work on the chapter projects or ***Enrichment*** Lesson 8.11.

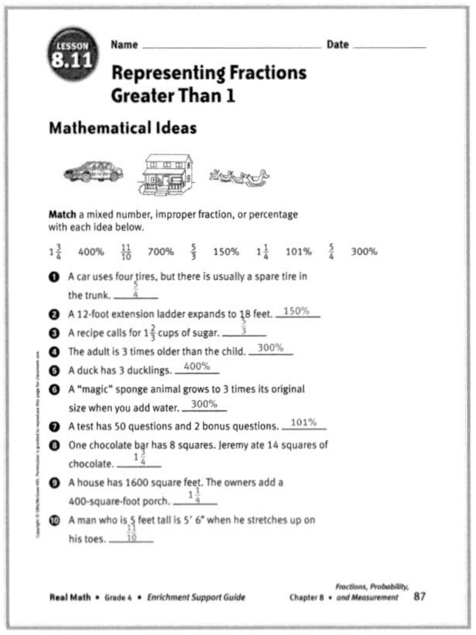
LESSON 8.11 Name ____ Date ____

**Representing Fractions Greater Than 1**

**Mathematical Ideas**

**Match** a mixed number, improper fraction, or percentage with each idea below.

$1\frac{3}{4}$ 400% $\frac{11}{10}$ 700% $\frac{5}{3}$ 150% $1\frac{1}{4}$ 101% $\frac{5}{4}$ 300%

1. A car uses four tires, but there is usually a spare tire in the trunk. $\frac{5}{4}$
2. A 12-foot extension ladder expands to 18 feet. 150%
3. A recipe calls for $1\frac{2}{3}$ cups of sugar. $\frac{5}{3}$
4. The adult is 3 times older than the child. 300%
5. A duck has 3 ducklings. 400%
6. A "magic" sponge animal grows to 3 times its original size when you add water. 300%
7. A test has 50 questions and 2 bonus questions. 101%
8. One chocolate bar has 8 squares. Jeremy ate 14 squares of chocolate. $1\frac{3}{4}$
9. A house has 1600 square feet. The owners add a 400-square-foot porch. $1\frac{1}{4}$
10. A man who is 5 feet tall is 5′ 6″ when he stretches up on his toes. $\frac{11}{10}$

Real Math • Grade 4 • Enrichment Support Guide Chapter 8 • Fractions, Probability, and Measurement 87

Enrichment Lesson 8.11

### PRACTICE

**If . . .** students would benefit from additional practice,

**Then . . .** assign ***Practice*** Lesson 8.11.

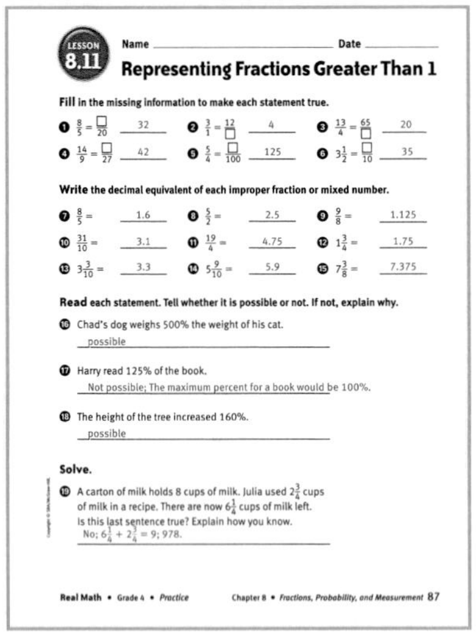
LESSON 8.11 Name ____ Date ____

**Representing Fractions Greater Than 1**

**Fill** in the missing information to make each statement true.

1. $\frac{8}{5} = \frac{\square}{20}$ 32
2. $\frac{3}{1} = \frac{12}{\square}$ 4
3. $\frac{13}{4} = \frac{65}{\square}$ 20
4. $\frac{14}{9} = \frac{\square}{27}$ 42
5. $\frac{5}{4} = \frac{\square}{100}$ 125
6. $3\frac{1}{2} = \frac{\square}{10}$ 35

**Write** the decimal equivalent of each improper fraction or mixed number.

7. $\frac{8}{5} =$ 1.6
8. $\frac{5}{2} =$ 2.5
9. $\frac{9}{8} =$ 1.125
10. $\frac{31}{10} =$ 3.1
11. $\frac{19}{4} =$ 4.75
12. $1\frac{3}{4} =$ 1.75
13. $3\frac{3}{10} =$ 3.3
14. $5\frac{9}{10} =$ 5.9
15. $7\frac{3}{8} =$ 7.375

**Read** each statement. Tell whether it is possible or not. If not, explain why.

16. Chad's dog weighs 500% the weight of his cat. possible
17. Harry read 125% of the book. Not possible; The maximum percent for a book would be 100%.
18. The height of the tree increased 160%. possible

**Solve.**

19. A carton of milk holds 8 cups of milk. Julia used $2\frac{3}{4}$ cups of milk in a recipe. There are now $6\frac{1}{4}$ cups of milk left. Is this last sentence true? Explain how you know. No; $6\frac{1}{4} + 2\frac{3}{4} = 9$; 978.

Real Math • Grade 4 • Practice Chapter 8 • Fractions, Probability, and Measurement 87

Practice Lesson 8.11

### RETEACH

**If . . .** students are having difficulty understanding representations of fractions greater than 1,

**Then . . .** have them draw a number line and mark where each of the representations is located. Additionally, students may benefit from working in small groups to write word problems using rational numbers greater than 1. Encourage them to use the newspaper and grocery ads to come up with ideas for their word problems.

## Lesson Planner

### Objectives
- To review the inch, foot, and yard as customary units for measuring length
- To provide practice in estimating length and in measuring objects using customary units
- To provide practice using mixed numbers

### NCTM Standards
**Measurement**
Understand measurable attributes of objects and the units, systems, and processes of measurement

**Connections**
Recognize and use connections among mathematical ideas

### Materials
- *Response Wheels
- Rulers and/or tape measures

### Technology
**e Presentation** Lesson 8.12
**e MathTools** Electronic Ruler
**e Games** Fracto or Anything But 10

### Test Prep
**Cumulative Review**
Mental Math reviews converting mixed numbers to improper fractions (Lesson 8.10).

*Manipulative Kit Item

# Reading a Ruler

**Context of the Lesson** Measurement is a familiar application in which fractions may be used. This lesson allows students to review measuring skills before beginning the addition and subtraction of measurements, which is an informal introduction to the addition and subtraction of fractions.

See page 328B for Math Background for teachers for this lesson.

## Planning for Learning • DIFFERENTIATE INSTRUCTION

### INTERVENTION

**If . . .** students lack the prerequisite skill of measuring using inches,

**Then . . .** teach ***Intervention*** Lesson 8.C.

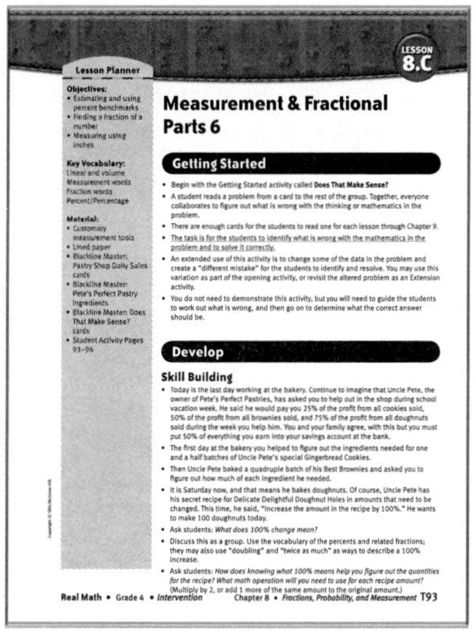
LESSON 8.C
Lesson Planner
Measurement & Fractional Parts 6
Getting Started
Develop
Skill Building
Real Math • Grade 4 • Intervention Chapter 8 • Fractions, Probability, and Measurement T93

Intervention Lesson 8.C

### ENGLISH LEARNER

Preview

**If . . .** students need language support,

**Then . . .** use Lesson 8.12 in ***English Learner Support Guide*** to preview lesson concepts and vocabulary.

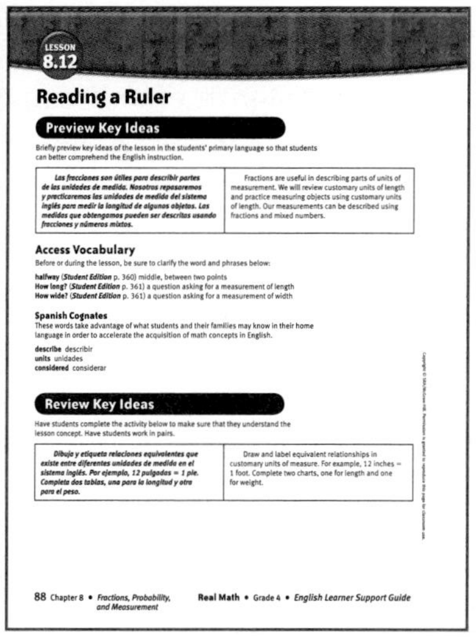
LESSON 8.12
Reading a Ruler
Preview Key Ideas
Access Vocabulary
Spanish Cognates
Review Key Ideas
88 Chapter 8 • Fractions, Probability, and Measurement Real Math • Grade 4 • English Learner Support Guide

English Learner Lesson 8.12

### ENRICH

**If . . .** students are proficient in the lesson concepts,

**Then . . .** encourage them to work on the chapter projects.

### PRACTICE

**If . . .** students would benefit from additional practice,

**Then . . .** have students measure objects in the classroom.

### RETEACH

**If . . .** students are having difficulty understanding measuring,

**Then . . .** review the scale and zero point on their rulers.

### Access Vocabulary
**halfway** middle, between two points
**how long** asks for a measurement of length
**how wide** asks for a measurement of width
**how heavy** asks for a measurement of weight

**Spanish Cognates**
**describe** describir

## Mental Math

5

Review | Response Wheel

Provide practice converting mixed numbers to improper fractions. Write examples such as the following on the board:

a. $1\frac{1}{2}$ $\frac{3}{2}$ b. $1\frac{1}{3}$ $\frac{4}{3}$ c. $2\frac{1}{4}$ $\frac{9}{4}$

d. $3\frac{2}{3}$ $\frac{11}{3}$ e. $4\frac{3}{5}$ $\frac{23}{5}$ f. $8\frac{1}{2}$ $\frac{17}{2}$

g. $10\frac{1}{10}$ $\frac{101}{10}$ h. $9\frac{4}{9}$ $\frac{85}{9}$ i. $7\frac{2}{5}$ $\frac{37}{5}$

j. $6\frac{6}{7}$ $\frac{48}{7}$

## 1 Develop

20

### Tell Students In Today's Lesson They Will

review customary units of length and practice measuring objects using customary units of length.

### Guided Discussion

UNDERSTANDING — Whole Group

1. Use a physical ruler or ***eMathTools: Electronic Ruler*** to practice measuring simple objects with the class. Review where to place the beginning of the ruler and how to read halves, fourths, eighths, and sixteenths of an inch (depending on the ruler). Review measuring to the nearest eighth of an inch.
2. Point out equivalent relationships among customary units of length and write them on the board. Examples include: 12 inches = 1 foot, 3 feet = 1 yard, 36 inches = 1 yard.
3. Review with the students how to convert between each of the customary units of length (inches, feet, and yards). Ask questions such as the following:
   - **How many inches are in 2 feet?** 24 inches
   - **How many feet are in 3 yards?** 9 feet
   - **How many feet are in 48 inches?** 4 feet
   - **How many inches are in 1 yard?** 36 inches
4. Introduce students to the concept of parts of a customary unit of length. Ask questions such as the following:
   - **If there are 12 inches in 1 foot, 1 inch = ______ foot** $\frac{1}{12}$
   - **If there are 12 inches in 1 foot, 2 inches = ______ foot** $\frac{2}{12}$
   - **If there are 12 inches in 1 foot, 3 inches = ______ foot** $\frac{3}{12}$
   - **If there are 12 inches in 1 foot, 6 inches = ______ foot** $\frac{6}{12}$ or $\frac{1}{2}$

## 2 Assign Student Pages

25

### Pages 360–361

APPLYING — Small Group

Have students work on page 360 and Problems 7–12 on page 361 independently. Remind students to estimate their answer first and record their estimate as well as the actual measurement on page 361. When students have finished the first half of page 361, have them work in small groups on the measuring activity at the bottom of page 361.

### As Students Finish

Game — **Anything But 10** or **Fracto Game Mat**

eGames — ***Fracto*** or ***Anything But 10***

eMathTools — ***Electronic Ruler*** Have students explore aspects of measurement.

#### RESEARCH IN ACTION

"Measurement is one of the main real-world applications of mathematics...counting is a type of measurement—it measures how many items in a collection. Measurement of continuous quantities involves assigning a number to attributes such as length, area, and weight. Together, number and measurements are components of quantitative reasoning. In this vein, measurement helps connect the two realms of number and geometry, each providing conceptual support to the other."

Clements, Douglas and Sarama, J. eds. *Engaging Young Children in Mathematics: Standards for Early Childhood Mathematics Education.* Mahwah, NJ: Lawrence Erlbaum Associates, Publishers, 2004. pp. 43–50.

Student Page

LESSON 8.12 **Reading a Ruler**

## Key Ideas

**Fractions can be useful when describing parts of units of measurement.**

This pencil is between 3 and 4 inches long.

It is almost halfway between 3 and 4 inches.
It is about $3\frac{1}{2}$ inches long.

This piece of chalk is between 2 and 3 inches long.
It is about $2\frac{3}{4}$ inches long.

This highlighter is between 4 and 5 inches long.
It is about $4\frac{7}{8}$ inches long.

Remember: 12 inches = 1 foot
36 inches = 3 feet = 1 yard

**Answer** these questions.

1. How many feet is 1 inch? $\frac{1}{12}$
2. How many yards is 1 foot? $\frac{1}{3}$
3. How many yards is 1 inch? $\frac{1}{36}$
4. How many inches are there in 16 yards? 576
5. How many inches are there in 10 feet? 120
6. How many feet are there in 84 inches? 7

360 eTextbook This lesson is available in the ***eTextbook.***

Student Page

**Estimate** the length first. Then measure to the nearest $\frac{1}{8}$ inch. Write down both your estimate and the actual measurement. Answers $\frac{1}{8}$ inch greater or less should be considered correct.

7.  $2\frac{7}{8}$ in.

8.  $1\frac{7}{8}$ in.

9. 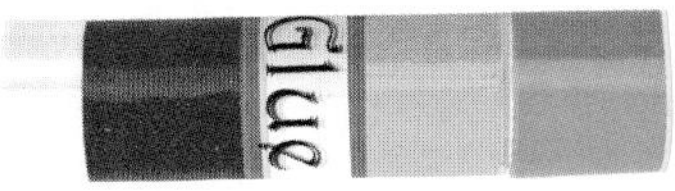

$3\frac{3}{4}$ in.

10.  1 in.

11.  4 in.

12.  $5\frac{3}{8}$ in.

**Measure.** Answers to the last four questions will vary based on the measurement of each classroom.

13. How long is the cover of your mathematics book in inches? $11\frac{1}{8}$ in. or $11\frac{1}{4}$ in.
14. How wide is the cover of your mathematics book in inches? $8\frac{3}{4}$ in.
15. How long is your desk in feet and inches? In inches only?
16. How wide is your desk in feet and inches? In inches only?
17. How long is your classroom in yards and feet? In feet only?
18. How wide is your classroom in yards and feet? In feet only?

Chapter 8 • Lesson 12 361

# 3 Reflect

5

## Guided Discussion APPLYING

Whole Group

Using the answer from Problem 13 of student page 361, have the students find the width and length of their classroom in inches. Have the students explain how they got their answers. Most students should determine the number of book lengths they will need and then multiply that number by their answer from Problem 13.

**Cumulative Review:** For review of number lines, assign Problems 9–12 on student page 373.

**Family Involvement:** Assign the ***Practice, Reteach,*** or ***Enrichment*** activities depending on the needs of your students.

Encourage students to play the **Fracto I** or **Fracto II Game Mat** or **Fracto *eGames*** with a friend or relative.

**Concept/Question Board:** Have students attempt to answer any unanswered questions on the Concept/Question Board.

**Math Puzzler:** Duncan is the best player on his after-school basketball team. He holds three season records: he made 156 two-point shots, 47 three-point shots, and 132 one-point free throws. How many points did Duncan score altogether during his record-setting season? 585 points

# 4 Assess and Differentiate

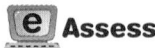

e Assess Use ***eAssess*** to record and analyze evidence of student understanding.

## A Gather Evidence

Use the Daily Class Assessment Records in ***Assessment*** or ***eAssess*** to record daily observations.

### Informal Assessment

**Concept/Question Board**

Did the student ENGAGING

- ❑ pay attention to others' contributions?
- ❑ contribute information and ideas?
- ❑ improve on a strategy?
- ❑ reflect on and check the accuracy of his or her work?

### Informal Assessment

**Games**

Did the student APPLYING

- ❑ apply learning in new situations?
- ❑ contribute concepts?
- ❑ contribute answers?
- ❑ connect mathematics to real-world situations?

## B Summarize Findings

Analyze and summarize assessment data for each student. Determine which Assessment Follow-Up is appropriate for each student. Use the Student Assessment Record in ***Assessment*** or ***eAssess*** to update assessment records.

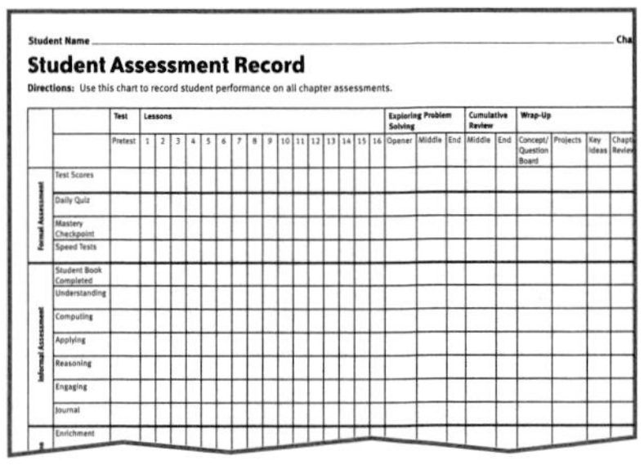


**Assessment Page T41**

## C Assessment Follow-Up • DIFFERENTIATE INSTRUCTION

Based on your observations, use these teaching strategies for assessment follow-up.

### INTERVENTION

Review student performance on ***Intervention*** Lesson 8.C to see if students have mastered prerequisite skills for this lesson.

### ENGLISH LEARNER

**Review**

Use Lesson 8.12 in ***English Learner Support Guide*** to review lesson concepts and vocabulary.

### ENRICH

**If . . .** students are proficient in the lesson concepts,

**Then . . .** encourage them to work on the chapter projects or ***Enrichment*** Lesson 8.12.

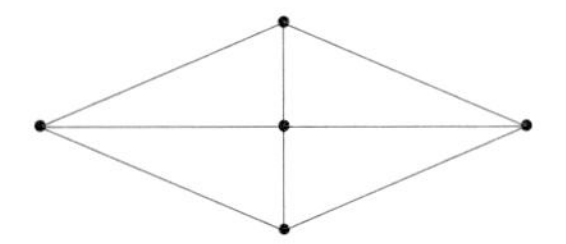

LESSON 8.12 Name ______ Date ______

**Reading a Ruler**

**Connect the Dots**

**Use** a ruler to measure distances and draw straight lines to follow these directions.

1. Connect the dots that are $2\frac{7}{8}$ inches apart. There are four.
2. Draw a vertical line to connect the dots that are $1\frac{1}{8}$ inches apart. There are two.
3. Draw a horizontal line to connect the dots that are $2\frac{3}{4}$ inches apart. There are two.
4. What is the name of the shape you have drawn? rhombus
5. How many triangles did you make? eight
6. How many right triangles did you make? four

88 Chapter 8 • *Fractions, Probability, and Measurement* **Real Math** • Grade 4 • *Enrichment Support Guide*

Enrichment Lesson 8.12

### PRACTICE

**If . . .** students would benefit from additional practice,

**Then . . .** assign ***Practice*** Lesson 8.12.

LESSON 8.12 Name ______ Date ______

**Reading a Ruler**

**Estimate the length first. Then measure the length to the nearest $\frac{1}{8}$ inch.** Check students' estimates for reasonable answers close to actual measure.

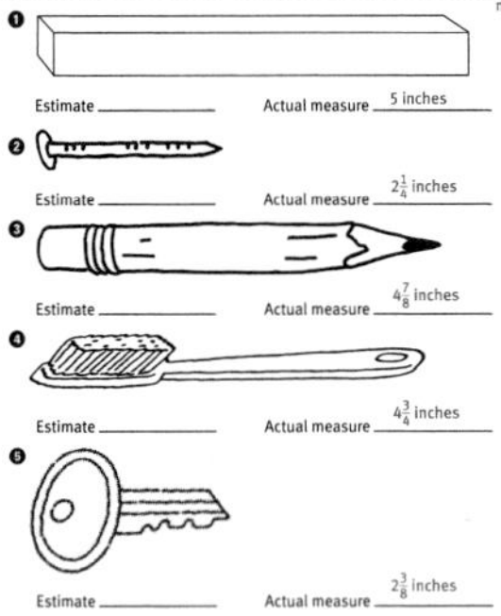

1. Estimate ______ Actual measure 5 inches
2. Estimate ______ Actual measure $2\frac{1}{4}$ inches
3. Estimate ______ Actual measure $4\frac{7}{8}$ inches
4. Estimate ______ Actual measure $4\frac{3}{4}$ inches
5. Estimate ______ Actual measure $2\frac{3}{8}$ inches

88 Chapter 8 • *Fractions, Probability, and Measurement* **Real Math** • Grade 4 • *Practice*

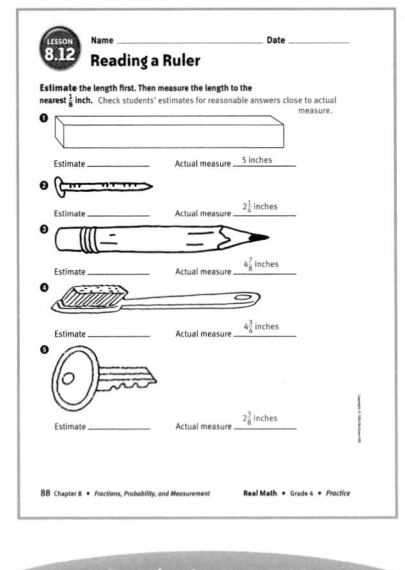

Practice Lesson 8.12

### RETEACH

**If . . .** students are having difficulty making measurements,

**Then . . .** provide additional opportunities for students to estimate and measure lengths in the classroom, on the playground, or at home and to express these lengths in inches, feet, and yards.

# Adding and Subtracting Measurements

### Objectives
- To provide an intuitive introduction to, and practice with, addition and subtraction of simple fractions and mixed numbers without an algorithm
- To provide practice solving word problems involving addition and subtraction of simple fractions and mixed numbers

### NCTM Standards
**Number and Operations**
Compute fluently and make reasonable estimates

**Problem Solving**
Build new mathematical knowledge through problem solving

### Materials
- Inch rulers
- Paper strips (optional)
- *Overhead projector fraction tiles

### Technology
e **Presentation** Lesson 8.13
e **MathTools** Fractions
e **Games** Fracto or *Anything But 10*

### Test Prep
**Cumulative Review** Review
Mental Math reviews addition with common fractions.

*Manipulative Kit Item

**Context of the Lesson** This lesson uses measurement skills as an informal introduction to the addition and subtraction of fractions. At this point, it is important to develop the students' familiarity and confidence with simple fractions and their ability to solve practical problems with fractions. A formal algorithm for the addition and subtraction of fractions will be introduced in Lesson 8.14.

See page 328B for Math Background for teachers for this lesson.

## Planning for Learning • DIFFERENTIATE INSTRUCTION

### INTERVENTION
**If . . .** students lack the prerequisite skill of measuring in inches,

**Then . . .** teach ***Intervention*** Lesson 8.C.

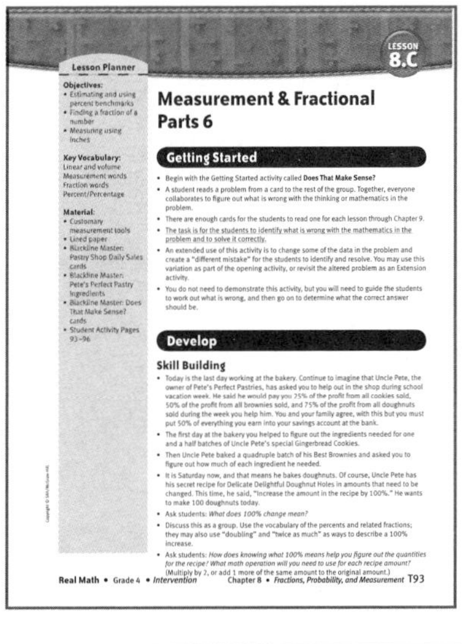
Lesson Planner
LESSON 8.C
Measurement & Fractional Parts 6
Getting Started
Develop
Skill Building

Intervention Lesson 8.C

### ENGLISH LEARNER
**Preview**

**If . . .** students need language support,

**Then . . .** use Lesson 8.13 in ***English Learner Support Guide*** to preview lesson concepts and vocabulary.

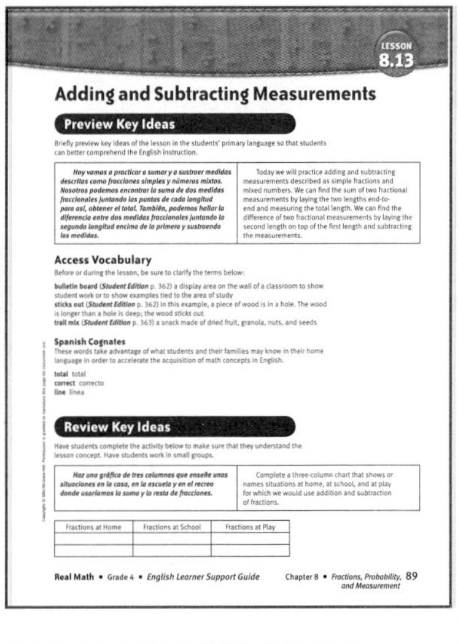
LESSON 8.13
Adding and Subtracting Measurements
Preview Key Ideas
Access Vocabulary
Spanish Cognates
Review Key Ideas

English Learner Lesson 8.13

### ENRICH
**If . . .** students are proficient in the lesson concepts,

**Then . . .** encourage them to work on the chapter projects.

### PRACTICE
**If . . .** students would benefit from additional practice,

**Then . . .** do additional student page examples using different lengths.

### RETEACH
**If . . .** students are having difficulty understanding addition and subtraction of measurements,

**Then . . .** model the process with fraction tiles.

### Access Vocabulary
**side by side** next to each other; the side of one object is touching the side of another object

**figure out the answer** solve, think of the solution to a problem

**Spanish Cognates**
**total** total
**correct** correcto

# Teaching Lesson 8.13

## Mental Math

5

Review RESPONSE WHEEL Present simple addition exercises, such as the following, using common fractions. Have the class respond with thumbs-up if they think the sum is greater than 1, thumbs-down if it is less than 1, or an open hand if they think the sum equals 1.

**a.** $\frac{1}{4} + \frac{1}{4} =$ down **b.** $\frac{1}{3} + \frac{1}{3} =$ down

**c.** $\frac{3}{4} + \frac{1}{2} =$ up **d.** $\frac{1}{5} + \frac{1}{3} =$ down

**e.** $\frac{2}{3} + \frac{1}{3} =$ open hand **f.** $\frac{4}{5} + \frac{2}{3} =$ up

**g.** $\frac{6}{8} + \frac{1}{8} =$ down **h.** $\frac{5}{7} + \frac{3}{7} =$ up

**i.** $\frac{4}{12} + \frac{1}{3} =$ down **j.** $\frac{1}{2} + \frac{3}{6} =$ open hand

## 1 Develop

25

### Tell Students In Today's Lesson They Will

practice addition and subtraction of measurements that involve simple fractions.

### Guided Discussion APPLYING

Whole Group

1. Using the overhead projector fraction tiles, lay out a $\frac{1}{8}$ tile and a $\frac{1}{2}$ tile. Ask questions such as the following:
   - **What fractions do each of these tiles represent?** $\frac{1}{8}$ and $\frac{1}{2}$
   - **Which fraction is greater/which fraction is smaller** $\frac{1}{2}, \frac{1}{8}$
   - **What is the sum of the two fractions?** $\frac{5}{8}$

   Demonstrate this equation using fractions tiles.
2. Use fraction tiles to demonstrate two or three more examples. Use tiles such as $\frac{1}{4}, \frac{1}{2}, \frac{1}{3}, \frac{1}{6}$, and $\frac{1}{8}$. Be sure to always verify the answer by laying the total number of tiles out for the students to see. One example should include a whole fraction bar (e.g., $1\frac{1}{6} + \frac{1}{6}$). Using the electronic ruler, measure distances equivalent to the amount on the fraction tiles to demonstrate the similarity.
3. Using the fraction tiles, lay out a $\frac{3}{4}$ and a $\frac{1}{2}$ tile.
   - **Are these tiles equivalent?** no
   - **What is the difference between these two fractions?** $\frac{1}{4}$

   Students should easily see that there is $\frac{1}{4}$ remaining when the $\frac{1}{2}$ tile is compared to the $\frac{3}{4}$ tile.

   Use fraction tiles to demonstrate two or three mores examples of finding the difference between fractions. Be sure to always verify the answer using the tiles so the students can see it.

   One example should include a whole faction bar (e.g., $1\frac{1}{2} - \frac{1}{2}$). This concept can also be demonstrated using line segments. Measure the line segments to the nearest $\frac{1}{2}, \frac{1}{4}$, and $\frac{1}{8}$ inch and add or subtract the measured amounts.

   Go over examples, such as the one on student page 362, carefully with the class. Help students see how to add and subtract fractions, using fractions of an inch as a model.

## 2 Assign Student Pages

25

### Page 363 APPLYING

Have students complete page 363 independently. Make sure that students understand the illustration at the top of the page. This illustration is a general diagram to help them understand how to approach the exercises, but the actual length of the line segments will vary in each exercise.

#### Monitoring Student Progress

| | |
|---|---|
| **If . . .** students have difficulty adding and subtracting simple fractions, | **Then . . .** allow them to use fraction tiles, cardboard fraction strips, or other fraction manipulatives. |
| **If . . .** students have difficulty using a ruler to check Problems 1–6, | **Then . . .** consider having students make cardboard strips calibrated in eighths; the larger size of these nonstandard units may make it easier for them to check their answers. |
| **If . . .** students have trouble recognizing equivalent fractions while doing simple fraction arithmetic, | **Then . . .** have them work with one cardboard ruler calibrated in eighths and another strip of the same size calibrated in twelfths. Work with them to help them see that $\frac{1}{4}$ of the strip, $\frac{2}{8}$ of the strip, and $\frac{3}{12}$ of the strip are all the same length. |

### As Students Finish

Game **Anything But 10** or **Fracto Game Mat**

e Games *Anything But 10* or *Fracto*

e MathTools *Fractions* Have students model today's activity.

Student Page

LESSON 8.13 Adding and Subtracting Measurements

## Key Ideas

**We can find the sum of two fractional measurements by laying the two lengths end to end and measuring the total length.**

**We can find the difference of two fractional measurements by laying the second length on top of the first length and subtracting the measurements.**

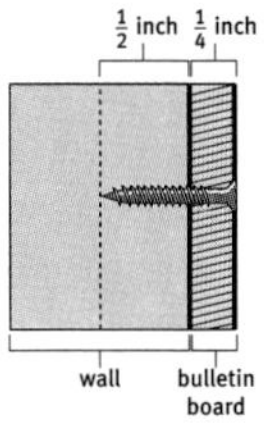


Conrad is putting a bulletin board on his wall. The bulletin board is $\frac{1}{4}$ of an inch thick. He wants the screws to go through the bulletin board and about $\frac{1}{2}$ inch into the wall. How long does each screw need to be? $\frac{3}{4}$ in.

Measure to check.

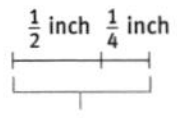

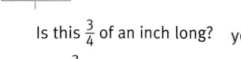

Is this $\frac{3}{4}$ of an inch long? yes

Conrad has a $\frac{3}{4}$-inch wooden plug to fill a hole that is $\frac{1}{2}$ of an inch deep. How much must be cut off so that no wood sticks out of the hole? $\frac{1}{4}$ in.

Measure to check.

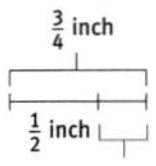


Is this $\frac{1}{4}$ inch? yes



Textbook This lesson is available in the ***eTextbook***.

Student Page

In the problems below, the lengths of two of the segments are given. Calculate the length of the third segment. Then use a ruler to draw line segments of the correct length on your paper and check your answer.

### Solve.

Imagine a line with points *A*, *B*, and *C*:

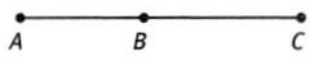

1. $AB = \frac{1}{4}$ inch, $BC = \frac{1}{4}$ inch. $AC =$ ■ $\frac{2}{4}$ or $\frac{1}{2}$ inch
2. $AB = \frac{3}{8}$ inch, $BC = \frac{3}{8}$ inch. $AC =$ ■ $\frac{6}{8}$ or $\frac{3}{4}$ inch
3. $AC = 2$ inches, $AB = \frac{1}{4}$ inch. $BC =$ ■ $1\frac{3}{4}$ inches
4. $BC = \frac{5}{8}$ inch, $AC = 1$ inch. $AB =$ ■ $\frac{3}{8}$ inch
5. $AB = 1\frac{1}{2}$ inches, $BC = 1\frac{1}{8}$ inches. $AC =$ ■ $2\frac{5}{8}$ inches
6. $AC = \frac{3}{4}$ inch, $BC = \frac{1}{2}$ inch. $AB =$ ■ $\frac{1}{4}$ inch

Check students' drawings.

**Solve** **these problems. Be sure to label your answers correctly.**

7. Kurt rode his horse for 2 hours yesterday and $\frac{3}{4}$ of an hour today. How many hours did he ride during the two days? $2\frac{3}{4}$ hours
8. Dinah placed a box that is $\frac{3}{4}$ of a foot tall on another box that is $\frac{1}{4}$ of a foot tall. How tall are the two boxes together? 1 foot
9. Pauline had $1\frac{1}{2}$ pounds of trail mix. She gave her sister $\frac{1}{4}$ of a pound. How much does she have left? $1\frac{1}{4}$ pounds
10. Andrea ran 2 miles on Monday and $2\frac{1}{2}$ miles on Wednesday. How many miles did she run altogether in those two days? $4\frac{1}{2}$ miles



## 3 Reflect 5

### Guided Discussion REASONING

Whole Group

When measuring, we can round to the nearest whole inch, foot, and so on.

- **Why might it be better to measure to the nearest half, quarter, or even eighth-inch?** it is a more precise measurement
- **When might we need to measure to the nearest half-, quarter-, or eighth-inch?** measuring carpet, tiling, building most things, for comparing purposes

SOCIAL STUDIES **Curriculum Connection:** Students discussed running in this lesson. Read *Wilma Unlimited: How Wilma Rudolph Became the World's Fastest Woman,* a story about one of America's most beloved runners who fought back serious illness to become an Olympian.

Review **Cumulative Review:** For review of maps and charts, assign Problems 13–14 on student page 374.

**Family Involvement:** Assign the ***Practice, Reteach,*** or ***Enrichment*** activities depending on the needs of your students. Encourage students to play the **Fracto I** or **Fracto II Game Mat** or **Fracto *eGames*** with a friend or relative.

**Concept/Question Board:** Have students attempt to answer any unanswered questions on the Concept/Question Board.

**Math Puzzler:** Miyoshi has two fast-growing plants. When she bought them, both were $\frac{1}{2}$ foot tall. One plant grows 3 inches per week, and the other grows 5 inches per week. In what amount of time will one plant be 1 foot taller than the other? Six weeks

# 4 Assess and Differentiate

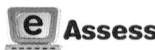

**e Assess** Use ***eAssess*** to record and analyze evidence of student understanding.

## A Gather Evidence

Use the Daily Class Assessment Records in ***Assessment*** or ***eAssess*** to record daily observations.

### Informal Assessment

**Guided Discussion**

Did the student APPLYING

- ❑ apply learning in new situations?
- ❑ contribute concepts?
- ❑ contribute answers?
- ❑ connect mathematics to real-world situations?

### Informal Assessment

**Games**

Did the student ENGAGING

- ❑ pay attention to others' contributions?
- ❑ contribute information and ideas?
- ❑ improve on a strategy?
- ❑ reflect on and check the accuracy of his or her work?

## B Summarize Findings

Analyze and summarize assessment data for each student. Determine which Assessment Follow-Up is appropriate for each student. Use the Student Assessment Record in ***Assessment*** or ***eAssess*** to update assessment records.

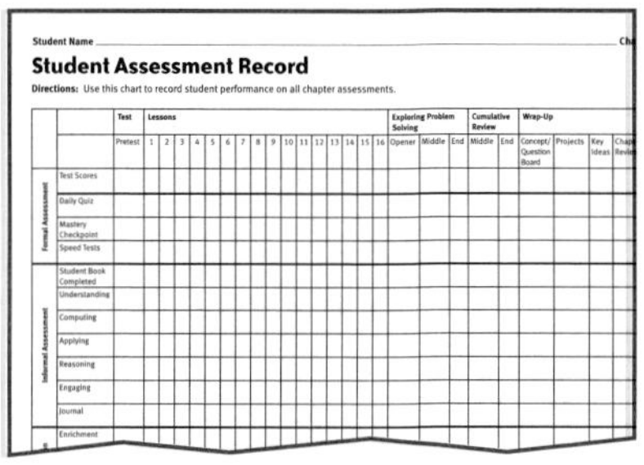


**Assessment Page T41**

## C Assessment Follow-Up • DIFFERENTIATE INSTRUCTION

Based on your observations, use these teaching strategies for assessment follow-up.

### INTERVENTION

Review student performance on ***Intervention*** Lesson 8.C to see if students have mastered prerequisite skills for this lesson.

### ENGLISH LEARNER

**Review**

Use Lesson 8.13 in ***English Learner Support Guide*** to review lesson concepts and vocabulary.

### ENRICH

**If . . .** students are proficient in the lesson concepts,

**Then . . .** encourage them to work on the chapter projects or ***Enrichment*** Lesson 8.13.

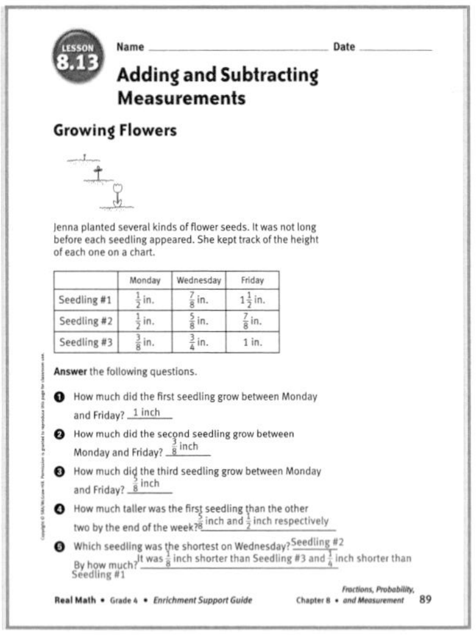

LESSON 8.13 Name ______ Date ______

**Adding and Subtracting Measurements**

**Growing Flowers**

Jenna planted several kinds of flower seeds. It was not long before each seedling appeared. She kept track of the height of each one on a chart.

| | Monday | Wednesday | Friday |
|---|---|---|---|
| Seedling #1 | $\frac{1}{2}$ in. | $\frac{7}{8}$ in. | $1\frac{1}{2}$ in. |
| Seedling #2 | $\frac{1}{2}$ in. | $\frac{5}{8}$ in. | $\frac{7}{8}$ in. |
| Seedling #3 | $\frac{3}{8}$ in. | $\frac{3}{4}$ in. | 1 in. |

**Answer** the following questions.

1. How much did the first seedling grow between Monday and Friday? 1 inch
2. How much did the second seedling grow between Monday and Friday? $\frac{3}{8}$ inch
3. How much did the third seedling grow between Monday and Friday? $\frac{5}{8}$ inch
4. How much taller was the first seedling than the other two by the end of the week? $\frac{5}{8}$ inch and $\frac{1}{2}$ inch respectively
5. Which seedling was the shortest on Wednesday? Seedling #2 By how much? It was $\frac{1}{8}$ inch shorter than Seedling #3 and $\frac{1}{4}$ inch shorter than Seedling #1

Real Math • Grade 4 • Enrichment Support Guide — Chapter 8 • Fractions, Probability, and Measurement 89

Enrichment Lesson 8.13

### PRACTICE

**If . . .** students would benefit from additional practice,

**Then . . .** assign ***Practice*** Lesson 8.13.

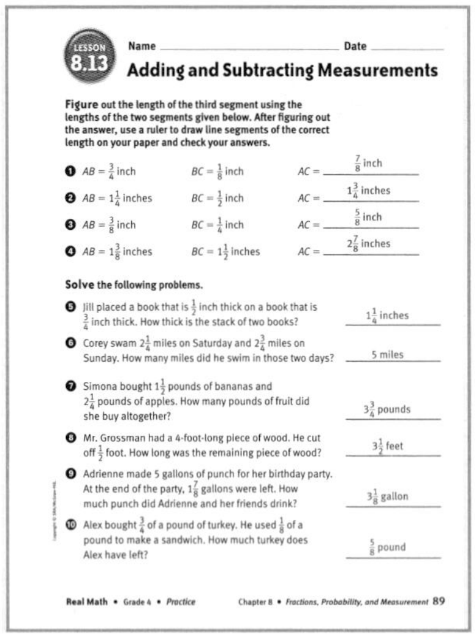

LESSON 8.13 Name ______ Date ______

**Adding and Subtracting Measurements**

**Figure** out the length of the third segment using the lengths of the two segments given below. After figuring out the answer, use a ruler to draw line segments of the correct length on your paper and check your answers.

1. $AB = \frac{3}{4}$ inch   $BC = \frac{1}{8}$ inch   $AC =$ $\frac{7}{8}$ inch
2. $AB = 1\frac{1}{4}$ inches   $BC = \frac{1}{2}$ inch   $AC =$ $1\frac{3}{4}$ inches
3. $AB = \frac{3}{8}$ inch   $BC = \frac{1}{4}$ inch   $AC =$ $\frac{5}{8}$ inch
4. $AB = 1\frac{3}{8}$ inches   $BC = 1\frac{1}{2}$ inches   $AC =$ $2\frac{7}{8}$ inches

**Solve** the following problems.

5. Jill placed a book that is $\frac{1}{2}$ inch thick on a book that is $\frac{3}{4}$ inch thick. How thick is the stack of two books? $1\frac{1}{4}$ inches
6. Corey swam $2\frac{1}{4}$ miles on Saturday and $2\frac{3}{4}$ miles on Sunday. How many miles did he swim in those two days? 5 miles
7. Simona bought $1\frac{1}{2}$ pounds of bananas and $2\frac{1}{4}$ pounds of apples. How many pounds of fruit did she buy altogether? $3\frac{3}{4}$ pounds
8. Mr. Grossman had a 4-foot-long piece of wood. He cut off $\frac{1}{2}$ foot. How long was the remaining piece of wood? $3\frac{1}{2}$ feet
9. Adrienne made 5 gallons of punch for her birthday party. At the end of the party, $1\frac{7}{8}$ gallons were left. How much punch did Adrienne and her friends drink? $3\frac{1}{8}$ gallon
10. Alex bought $\frac{3}{4}$ of a pound of turkey. He used $\frac{1}{8}$ of a pound to make a sandwich. How much turkey does Alex have left? $\frac{5}{8}$ pound

Real Math • Grade 4 • Practice — Chapter 8 • Fractions, Probability, and Measurement 89

Practice Lesson 8.13

### RETEACH

**If . . .** students are having difficulty adding and subtracting measurements,

**Then . . .** have students make a model that shows common equivalent fractions. They can use strips of paper of equal lengths that they fold or mark off to show halves, thirds, fourths, sixths, eighths, twelfths, and sixteenths. Students can use these models to help them add and subtract fractions and to recognize common equivalent fractions.

## Lesson Planner

### Objectives
- To review adding and subtracting fractions with like denominators
- To demonstrate how to use equivalent fractions to add fractions with unlike denominators
- To demonstrate how to use equivalent fractions to subtract fractions with unlike denominators

### NCTM Standards
**Number and Operations**
Compute fluently and make reasonable estimates

### Materials
- *Response Wheels
- Fraction tiles
- Fraction circles
- Overhead projector fraction tiles

### Technology
**e Presentation** Lesson 8.14
**e Games** Fracto

### Test Prep
**Cumulative Review**
Mental Math reviews converting mixed numbers to improper fractions (Lesson 8.10).

*Manipulative Kit Item

Overview **LESSON 8.14**

# Adding and Subtracting Fractions

**Context of the Lesson** This lesson introduces the use of common denominators as a formal algorithm for the addition and subtraction of fractions. It also builds on the informal work with addition and subtraction of fractions using measurements in Lesson 8.13. The method of finding common denominators will be applied to the addition and subtraction of fractions greater than 1 in Lessons 8.15 and 8.16. This lesson contains a Mastery Checkpoint.

See page 328B for Math Background for teachers for this lesson.

## Planning for Learning • DIFFERENTIATE INSTRUCTION

### INTERVENTION
**If . . .** students lack the prerequisite skill of finding a fraction of a number,

**Then . . .** teach ***Intervention*** Lesson 8.B.

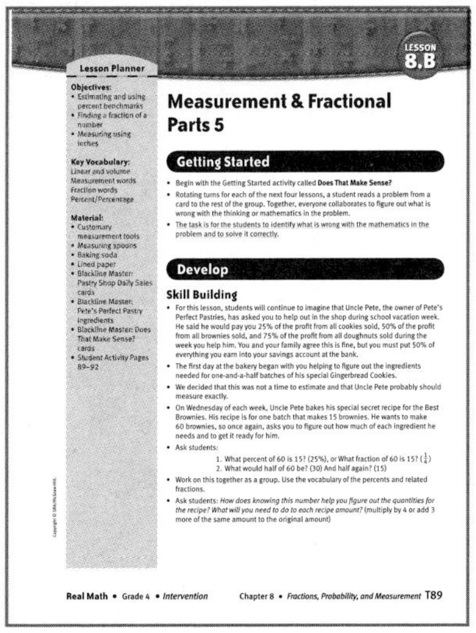
LESSON 8.B
Lesson Planner
Measurement & Fractional Parts 5
Getting Started
Develop
Skill Building
Real Math • Grade 4 • Intervention Chapter 8 • Fractions, Probability, and Measurement T89

Intervention Lesson 8.B

### ENGLISH LEARNER
**Preview**

**If . . .** students need language support,

**Then . . .** use Lesson 8.14 in ***English Learner Support Guide*** to preview lesson concepts and vocabulary.

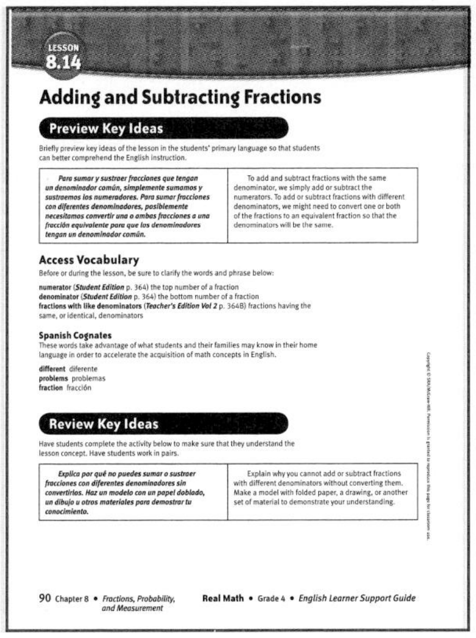
LESSON 8.14
Adding and Subtracting Fractions
Preview Key Ideas
Access Vocabulary
Spanish Cognates
Review Key Ideas
90 Chapter 8 • Fractions, Probability, and Measurement Real Math • Grade 4 • English Learner Support Guide

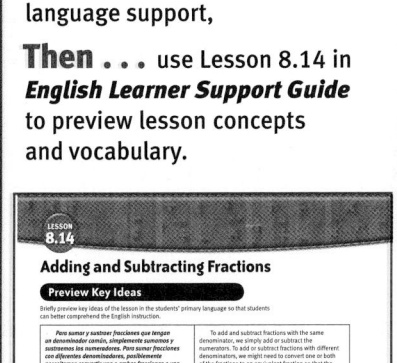

English Learner Lesson 8.14

### ENRICH
**If . . .** students are proficient in the lesson concepts,

**Then . . .** encourage them to work on the chapter projects.

### PRACTICE
**If . . .** students would benefit from additional practice,

**Then . . .** extend the examples in the Guided Discussion.

### RETEACH
**If . . .** students are having difficulty understanding addition and subtraction of fractions,

**Then . . .** model the process with fraction tiles.

### Access Vocabulary
**figure out the answer** solve

**Spanish Cognates**
**total** total
**correct** correcto

# Teaching Lesson 8.14

## Mental Math 5

Review RESPONSE WHEEL Provide students with exercises such as the following that practice converting between different forms of fractions greater than 1. Have students convert each mixed number to an improper fraction.

a. $1\frac{1}{4}$ $\frac{5}{4}$ b. $1\frac{2}{5}$ $\frac{7}{5}$ c. $1\frac{3}{7}$ $\frac{10}{7}$
d. $1\frac{5}{6}$ $\frac{11}{6}$ e. $3\frac{1}{3}$ $\frac{10}{3}$ f. $4\frac{1}{2}$ $\frac{9}{2}$
g. $3\frac{2}{5}$ $\frac{17}{5}$ h. $3\frac{1}{7}$ $\frac{22}{7}$ i. $2\frac{5}{8}$ $\frac{21}{8}$

## 1 Develop 20

### Tell Students In Today's Lesson They Will

- learn how to use equivalent fractions to add and subtract fractions with unlike denominators.
- review adding and subtracting fractions with like denominators.

## Guided Discussion UNDERSTANDING Whole Group

### Adding and Subtracting Fractions with the Same Denominators

1. Present a basic addition problem, such as the following, using common fraction tiles.
   - **What is the sum of $\frac{1}{3}$ and $\frac{1}{3}$?** $\frac{2}{3}$
   - **What is the sum of $\frac{1}{4}$ and $\frac{3}{4}$?** 1

   This concept was introduced and extended in previous lessons.
2. Continue with addition problems like these until you are sure the students can add fractions with common denominators. Then provide subtraction problems with common denominators, such as the following:
   - **What is $\frac{3}{4} - \frac{1}{4}$?** $\frac{2}{4}$ or $\frac{1}{2}$
   - **What is $\frac{5}{6} - \frac{2}{6}$?** $\frac{3}{6}$ or $\frac{1}{2}$

   Have students practice reducing their answers into lowest terms (e.g., $\frac{4}{6}$ is equivalent to $\frac{2}{3}$).

   Describe the process for subtracting fractions with the same denominator.

### Adding and Subtracting Fractions with Different Denominators

1. Students should know that multiplying a number or fraction by 1 will not change its value. Review this idea with the class and demonstrate it by using fraction tiles and written examples. Show $\frac{1}{2}$ with fraction tiles and write the fraction on the board. Ask for a fraction equal to 1 (e.g., $\frac{2}{2}, \frac{3}{3}, \frac{4}{4}, \frac{5}{5}$, and so on) Choosing an equivalent fraction for 1, write the multiplication process for finding an equivalent fraction on the board. For example, $\frac{1}{2} \times \frac{2}{2} = \frac{2}{4}$.
2. Take the $\frac{2}{4}$ fraction tiles and align them with the $\frac{1}{2}$ fraction tiles. Demonstrate that these are equivalent fractions. Continue this process until the students are comfortable.
3. Now, write $\frac{1}{4} + \frac{1}{3}$ on the board.
   - **Can these fractions be added as they are?** no
   - **What do you think we need to do before adding?** they need the same denominators
4. Write $\frac{1}{4} \times \frac{3}{3}$ and $\frac{1}{3} \times \frac{4}{4}$ on the board. Have the students find the equivalent fractions ($\frac{3}{12}$; $\frac{4}{12}$). Show these new equivalent fractions with the corresponding fractions tiles (e.g., place $\frac{3}{12}$ above $\frac{1}{4}$ and $\frac{4}{12}$ above $\frac{1}{3}$). Demonstrate that these are indeed equivalent fractions.
   - **How many twelfths are there?** 7
5. Continue solving addition problems like these until the students are familiar with the concept. Then provide subtraction problems with different denominators such as the following:
   - **What is $\frac{3}{4} - \frac{1}{2}$?** $\frac{1}{4}$
   - **What is $\frac{5}{6} - \frac{2}{3}$?** $\frac{1}{6}$
   - **What at is $\frac{7}{8} - \frac{1}{2}$?** $\frac{3}{8}$

   Also have the students practice reducing their answers into lowest terms.

## 2 Assign Student Pages 20

### Pages 364–365 APPLYING

Have students complete the problems on pages 364–365 individually.

**Monitoring Student Progress**

| If . . . | Then . . . |
|---|---|
| students are having difficulty adding and subtracting fractions with different denominators, | have them use fraction manipulatives to find like denominators. |

### As Students Finish

Game **Fracto Game Mat**

e Games **Fracto**

Student Page

LESSON 8.14 Adding and Subtracting Fractions

## Key Ideas

**To add or subtract fractions with the *same* denominators, we simply add or subtract the numerators.**

Since the denominator is common to both, it will stay the same. All we need to do is add or subtract the numerators.

For instance, $\frac{5}{8} - \frac{3}{8} = \frac{2}{8}$.

To add or subtract fractions with *different* denominators, we might need to replace one or both of the fractions with an equivalent fraction so that both fractions will have the same denominator.

What is $\frac{1}{3} + \frac{1}{6}$?

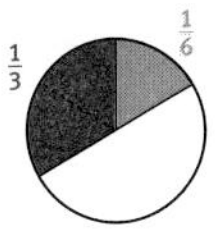


In the figure, $\frac{1}{6}$ of the circle is shaded blue, and $\frac{1}{3}$ of the circle is shaded red. If you divide the $\frac{1}{3}$ into 2 equal parts, each is $\frac{1}{6}$. We know that $\frac{1}{3}$ is the same as $\frac{2}{6}$. How many sixths are shaded altogether?

$\frac{1}{3} + \frac{1}{6} = (\frac{1}{3} \times \frac{2}{2}) + \frac{1}{6} = \frac{2}{6} + \frac{1}{6} = \frac{3}{6}$ (or $\frac{1}{2}$)

**Add or subtract the following fractions. Write all improper fractions as mixed numbers or whole numbers.**

1. $\frac{1}{4} + \frac{3}{4} =$ ▢ $\frac{4}{4}$ or 1
2. $\frac{2}{3} + \frac{2}{3} =$ ▢ $\frac{4}{3}$ or $1\frac{1}{3}$
3. $\frac{16}{21} - \frac{5}{21} =$ ▢ $\frac{11}{21}$
4. $\frac{5}{9} + \frac{1}{9} =$ ▢ $\frac{6}{9}$ or $\frac{2}{3}$
5. $\frac{6}{7} - \frac{2}{7} =$ ▢ $\frac{4}{7}$
6. $1\frac{1}{4} - \frac{1}{4} =$ ▢ 1



eTextbook This lesson is available in the ***eTextbook.***

Student Page

If we want to subtract $\frac{1}{4}$ from $\frac{2}{3}$ we would proceed in the same way.

$\frac{2}{3} - \frac{1}{4} = ?$

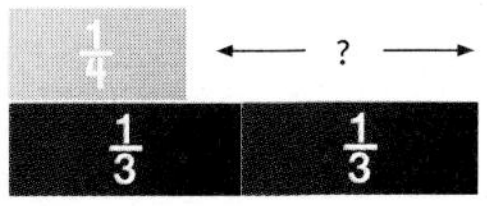


It is hard to tell what is remaining when we subtract $\frac{1}{4}$ from $\frac{2}{3}$. However, both the $\frac{1}{4}$ and $\frac{2}{3}$ can be divided into twelfths.

$\frac{2}{3} - \frac{1}{4} = \frac{8}{12} - \frac{3}{12} = \frac{5}{12}$

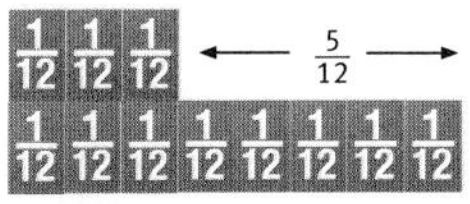


Instead of drawing pictures, you can replace fractions with equivalent fractions that have a common denominator. Remember, if you multiply a number or fraction by 1, it does not change the value of the number or fraction.

Another way to write 1 is $\frac{4}{4}$. $\frac{2}{3} \times \frac{4}{4} = \frac{8}{12}$

Another way to write 1 is $\frac{3}{3}$. $\frac{1}{4} \times \frac{3}{3} = \frac{3}{12}$

$\frac{2}{3} - \frac{1}{4} = (\frac{2}{3} \times \frac{4}{4}) - (\frac{1}{4} \times \frac{3}{3}) = \frac{8}{12} - \frac{3}{12} = \frac{5}{12}$

**Solve the following exercises.**

7. $\frac{1}{8} + \frac{3}{8} =$ ▢ $\frac{4}{8}$ or $\frac{1}{2}$
8. $\frac{3}{4} - \frac{1}{2} =$ ▢ $\frac{1}{4}$
9. $\frac{3}{8} + \frac{5}{8} =$ ▢ $\frac{8}{8}$ or 1
10. $\frac{5}{16} + \frac{1}{4} =$ ▢ $\frac{9}{16}$
11. $\frac{1}{3} + \frac{1}{8} =$ ▢ $\frac{11}{24}$
12. $\frac{1}{2} - \frac{3}{8} =$ ▢ $\frac{1}{8}$
13. $\frac{7}{16} - \frac{3}{16} =$ ▢ $\frac{4}{16}$ or $\frac{1}{4}$
14. $\frac{3}{4} - \frac{2}{3} =$ ▢ $\frac{1}{12}$
15. $\frac{5}{6} - \frac{1}{4} =$ ▢ $\frac{14}{24}$ or $\frac{7}{12}$



## 3 Reflect

5

### Guided Discussion REASONING

Whole Group

Have students discuss strategies for finding like denominators. How do they decide which number to choose as the common denominator? One simple method is to multiply the two denominators together. Often one of the denominators is a multiple of the other and can be used as the common denominator (e.g., $\frac{3}{4}$ and $\frac{3}{12}$ can be converted into $\frac{9}{12}$ and $\frac{3}{12}$ instead of $\frac{36}{48}$ and $\frac{12}{48}$).

Use Mastery Checkpoint 17 found in ***Assessment*** to evaluate student mastery of adding and subtracting simple fractions. By this time students should be able to correctly answer eighty percent of the Mastery Checkpoint items.

**Cumulative Review:** For review of three-digit by two-digit multiplication, assign Problems 15–19 on student page 374.

**Family Involvement:** Assign the ***Practice, Reteach,*** or ***Enrichment*** activities depending on the needs of your students.

Encourage students to play the **Fracto I** or **Fracto II** or **Game Mat** or **Fracto *eGames*** with a friend or relative.

**Concept/Question Board:** Have students attempt to answer any unanswered questions on the Concept/Question Board.

**Math Puzzler:** The floor of Mr. Gill's toolshed is a square. He covered it with 81 square paving stones. What fraction of the stones forms the border of the floor? (Suggestion: draw a picture to solve) $\frac{32}{81}$

# 4 Assess and Differentiate

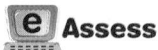

**e Assess** Use ***eAssess*** to record and analyze evidence of student understanding.

## A Gather Evidence

Use the Daily Class Assessment Records in ***Assessment*** or ***eAssess*** to record daily observations.

### Formal Assessment

**Mastery Checkpoint**

Did the student
- ❑ use correct procedures?
- ❑ respond with at least 80% accuracy?

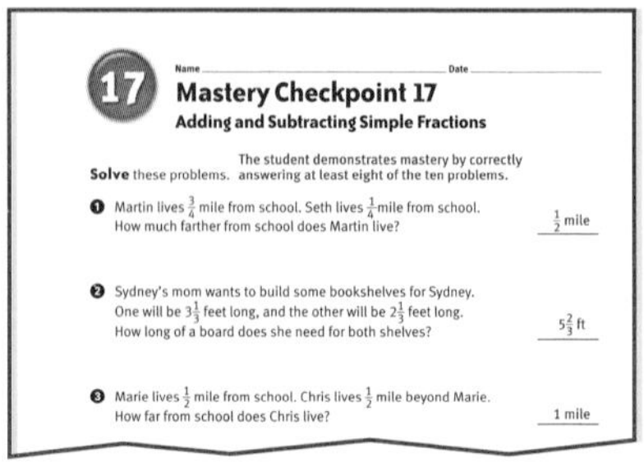
17 Mastery Checkpoint 17
Adding and Subtracting Simple Fractions

Solve these problems. The student demonstrates mastery by correctly answering at least eight of the ten problems.

1. Martin lives $\frac{3}{4}$ mile from school. Seth lives $\frac{1}{4}$ mile from school. How much farther from school does Martin live? $\frac{1}{2}$ mile
2. Sydney's mom wants to build some bookshelves for Sydney. One will be $3\frac{1}{3}$ feet long, and the other will be $2\frac{1}{3}$ feet long. How long of a board does she need for both shelves? $5\frac{2}{3}$ ft
3. Marie lives $\frac{1}{2}$ mile from school. Chris lives $\frac{1}{2}$ mile beyond Marie. How far from school does Chris live? 1 mile

Assessment Page T69

## B Summarize Findings

Analyze and summarize assessment data for each student. Determine which Assessment Follow-Up is appropriate for each student. Use the Student Assessment Record in ***Assessment*** or ***eAssess*** to update assessment records.

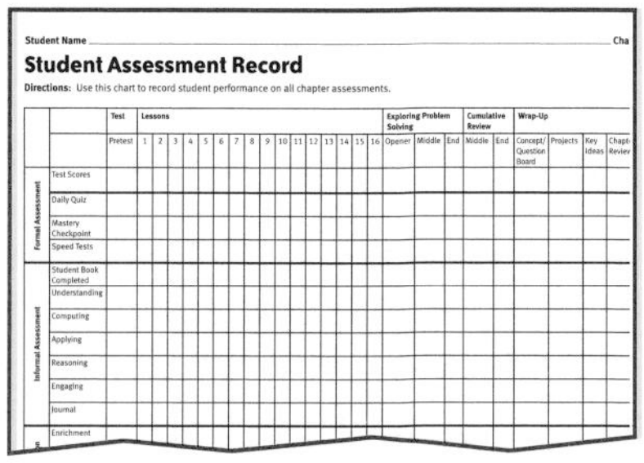
Student Assessment Record

Assessment Page T41

## C Assessment Follow-Up • DIFFERENTIATE INSTRUCTION

Based on your observations, use these teaching strategies for assessment follow-up.

### INTERVENTION

Review student performance on ***Intervention*** Lesson 8.B to see if students have mastered prerequisite skills for this lesson.

### ENGLISH LEARNER

**Review**

Use Lesson 8.14 in ***English Learner Support Guide*** to review lesson concepts and vocabulary.

### ENRICH

**If . . .** students are proficient in the lesson concepts,

**Then . . .** encourage them to work on the chapter projects or ***Enrichment*** Lesson 8.14.

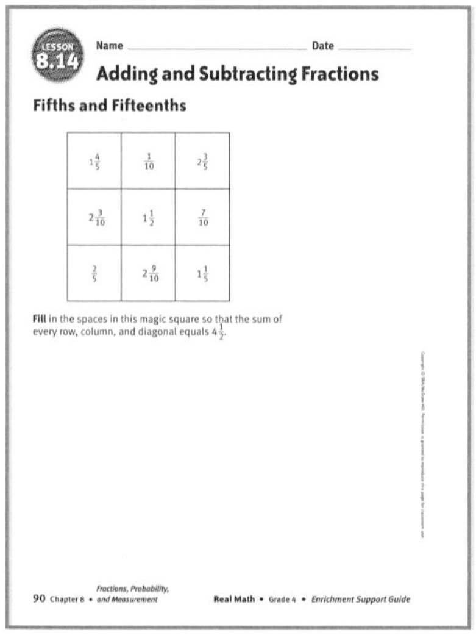
LESSON 8.14 Adding and Subtracting Fractions
Fifths and Fifteenths

Enrichment Lesson 8.14

### PRACTICE

**If . . .** students would benefit from additional practice,

**Then . . .** assign ***Practice*** Lesson 8.14.

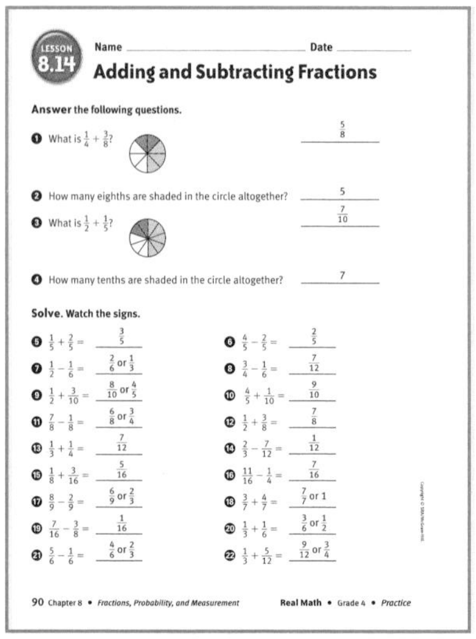
LESSON 8.14 Adding and Subtracting Fractions

Practice Lesson 8.14

### RETEACH

**If . . .** students are having difficulty understanding adding and subtracting fractions,

**Then . . .** reteach the concept using ***Reteach*** Lesson 8.14.

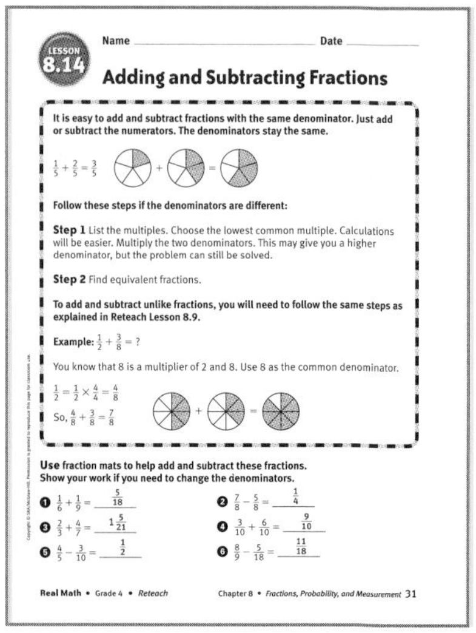
LESSON 8.14 Adding and Subtracting Fractions

Reteach Lesson 8.14

## Lesson Planner

**OBJECTIVES**
- To demonstrate how to add mixed numbers with like denominators
- To demonstrate how to use equivalent fractions to add mixed numbers with unlike denominators
- To provide some realistic situations in which adding fractions may be useful

**NCTM STANDARDS**
**Number and Operations**
Compute fluently and make reasonable estimates

**MATERIALS**
*Response Wheels

**TECHNOLOGY**
**Presentation** Lesson 8.15
**MathTools** Fractions
**Games** Fracto or Anything but 10

**TEST PREP**
**Cumulative Review**
Mental Math reviews converting mixed numbers to improper fractions (Lesson 8.10).

**Writing + Math**
Journal

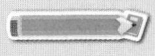

*Manipulative Kit Item

# Adding Fractions Greater than 1

**Context of the Lesson** This lesson builds on the algorithm for addition and subtraction of fractions that was developed in Lesson 8.14. In this lesson, students use the method of finding common denominators to add fractions greater than 1.

See page 328B for Math Background for teachers for this lesson.

## Planning for Learning • DIFFERENTIATE INSTRUCTION

### INTERVENTION

**If . . .** students lack the prerequisite skill of finding a fraction of a number,

**Then . . .** teach ***Intervention*** Lesson 8.B.

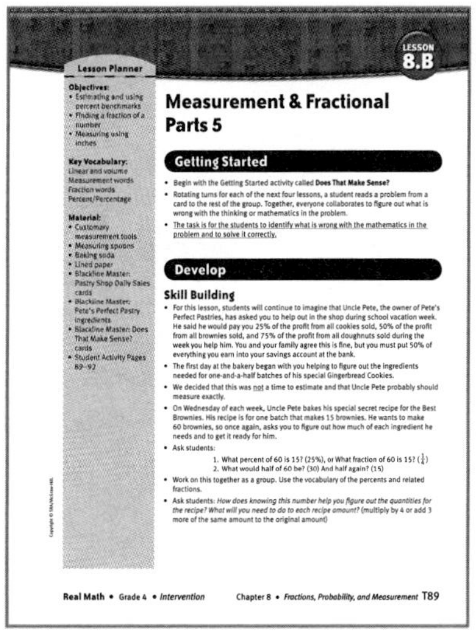
LESSON 8.B
Lesson Planner
Measurement & Fractional Parts 5
Getting Started
Develop
Skill Building

Intervention Lesson 8.B

### ENGLISH LEARNER

Preview

**If . . .** students need language support,

**Then . . .** use Lesson 8.15 in ***English Learner Support Guide*** to preview lesson concepts and vocabulary.

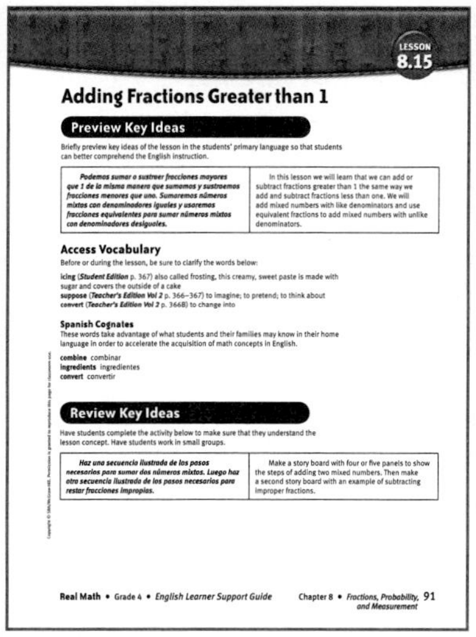
LESSON 8.15
Adding Fractions Greater than 1
Preview Key Ideas
Access Vocabulary
Spanish Cognates
Review Key Ideas

English Learner Lesson 8.15

### ENRICH

**If . . .** students are proficient in the lesson concepts,

**Then . . .** encourage them to work on the chapter projects.

### PRACTICE

**If . . .** students would benefit from additional practice,

**Then . . .** extend the Skill Practice before assigning the student pages.

### RETEACH

**If . . .** students are having difficulty adding fractions greater than 1,

**Then . . .** extend Guided Discussion before assigning the student pages.

### Access Vocabulary

**makes sense** seems to be the right choice, seems closest without working out the exact answer

**frosting** also called icing this sweet paste is made of sugar and covers the outside of a cake

**Spanish Cognates**
**substitute** substituir
**combine** combine

## Mental Math 5

Review | RESPONSE WHEEL

Present students with exercises, such as the following, that practice converting mixed numbers to improper fractions:

a. $3\frac{1}{2}$ $\frac{7}{2}$
b. $4\frac{1}{4}$ $\frac{17}{4}$
c. $5\frac{1}{3}$ $\frac{16}{3}$
d. $6\frac{1}{5}$ $\frac{31}{5}$
e. $2\frac{2}{3}$ $\frac{8}{3}$
f. $7\frac{1}{2}$ $\frac{15}{2}$
g. $3\frac{1}{9}$ $\frac{28}{9}$
h. $8\frac{1}{5}$ $\frac{41}{5}$

## 1 Develop 25

### Tell Students In Today's Lesson They Will

add mixed numbers with like denominators and use equivalent fractions to add mixed numbers with unlike denominators.

### Guided Discussion UNDERSTANDING

Whole Group

Adding fractions greater than 1 is a small step from adding fractions less than 1.

1. Draw circles on the board that represent $2\frac{1}{3}$ and label them. Next to this illustration draw circles that represent $2\frac{2}{3}$ and label them.
   - **What is the value of the first set of circles?** $2\frac{1}{3}$
   - **What is the value of the second set of circles?** $2\frac{2}{3}$
   - **What is the total amount shown on the board?** 5

   For demonstration purposes, move the $\frac{1}{3}$ from the first illustration to the missing circle section of the second illustration. This should clearly show students a total of 5 circles.

   Write the math sentence $2\frac{1}{3} + 2\frac{2}{3} = 5$ on the board. Have the students explain how they found this answer.
2. Draw circles on the board that represent $1\frac{1}{4}$ and label them. Draw circles representing $2\frac{1}{2}$ next to the illustration and label them.
   - **What is the value of each set of circles?** $1\frac{1}{4}$; $2\frac{1}{2}$
   - **Can the mixed numbers be added as they are? If not, what must be done?** no; they need to have like denominators

   Write $2\frac{1}{2}$ as $2\frac{2}{4}$, demonstrating with fraction tiles if needed. Many students will recognize this equivalency from previous lessons.

   The new math sentence should be $1\frac{1}{4} + 2\frac{2}{4} = ?$
   - **What is the total?** $3\frac{3}{4}$
3. Continue working on adding fractions greater than 1. Remind the students to write any improper fractions as mixed numbers. Ask questions such as the following:
   - $2\frac{1}{2} + 3\frac{1}{3} = ?$ $5\frac{5}{6}$
   - $4\frac{2}{5} + 3\frac{1}{10} = ?$ $7\frac{1}{2}$
   - $10\frac{1}{10} + 4\frac{9}{10} = ?$ 15
   - $5\frac{4}{6} + 1\frac{1}{2} = ?$ $6\frac{7}{6}$ or $7\frac{1}{6}$

### Skill Practice COMPUTING

Small Group

Another way to help students add fractions greater than 1 is to have them first convert the mixed number to an improper fraction and then solve.

1. Review how to convert a mixed number to an improper fraction.
2. Explain to students that once they have turned their problem into one involving improper fractions, the process of adding is the same as it is for fractions less than 1. Students will need to find like denominators as before, but the number on the top of the fraction will be greater than the number on the bottom.
3. Have students complete examples, such as the following in, small groups. Have the students first change the mixed numbers to improper fractions. The first problem is a good example of this concept ($1\frac{2}{3}$ has already been converted to $\frac{5}{3}$).
   - $\frac{1}{3} + \frac{5}{3} = n$ $n = 2$
   - $4\frac{1}{5} + 2\frac{3}{10} = n$ $n = 6\frac{5}{10} = 6\frac{1}{2}$
   - $\frac{5}{4} + 7\frac{1}{4} = n$ $n = 8\frac{2}{4} = 8\frac{1}{2}$
   - $2\frac{1}{2} + 7\frac{5}{8} = n$ $n = 10\frac{1}{8}$
   - $2 + 1\frac{3}{7} = n$ $n = 3\frac{3}{7}$
   - $1\frac{2}{3} + \frac{1}{3} = n$ $n = 2$

## 2 Assign Student Pages 20

### Pages 366–367 APPLYING

Have students complete pages 366 and 367 independently.

#### Monitoring Student Progress

**If . . .** students are having difficulty adding and subtracting fractions with different denominators,

**Then . . .** have them use fraction manipulatives to find common denominators.

### As Students Finish

Game **Fracto** or **Anything But 10 Game Mat**

e Games *Fracto* or *Anything But 10*

e MathTools *Fractions* Have students explore addition of fractions.

## LESSON 8.15 Adding Fractions Greater Than 1

### Key Ideas

**You can add fractions greater than 1 the same way you add fractions less than 1.**

To add with *different* denominators, remember to convert one or both of the fractions to an equivalent fraction so that the denominators will be the same.

Look at this example.    $4\frac{1}{3} + 6\frac{7}{8} \rightarrow 4\frac{8}{24} + 6\frac{21}{24}$

$4\frac{8}{24}$
$+ 6\frac{21}{24}$
$\overline{\quad\frac{29}{24}}$

Now that the denominators are the same, you may add the numerators as before to get the sum of the fractional part.

$4\frac{8}{24}$
$+ 6\frac{21}{24}$
$\overline{10\frac{29}{24}}$

Then add the whole units together.

You may wish to rewrite $10\frac{29}{24}$ by converting the improper fraction: $10\frac{29}{24} = 10 + \left(1\frac{5}{24}\right) = 11\frac{5}{24}$

$$4\frac{1}{3} + 6\frac{7}{8} = 11\frac{5}{24}$$

**Solve** the following addition exercises.

① $\frac{1}{3} + \frac{5}{3} = n$    $n = 2$
② $\frac{1}{3} + 1\frac{2}{3} = n$    $n = 2$
③ $4\frac{1}{5} + 2\frac{3}{10} = n$    $n = 6\frac{5}{10}$
④ $\frac{5}{4} + 7\frac{1}{4} = n$    $n = 8\frac{2}{4}$
⑤ $2\frac{1}{2} + 7\frac{5}{8} = n$    $n = 10\frac{1}{8}$
⑥ $2 + 1\frac{3}{7} = n$    $n = 3\frac{3}{7}$
⑦ $\frac{4}{5} + 3\frac{4}{5} = n$    $n = 4\frac{3}{5}$
⑧ $2\frac{2}{3} + 3\frac{1}{6} = n$    $n = 5\frac{5}{6}$
⑨ $10 + 8\frac{1}{7} = n$    $n = 18\frac{1}{7}$

366                Textbook  This lesson is available in the *eTextbook.*

---

Raoul decided to bake cupcakes for his little sister's birthday.

**Chocolate Cupcakes**

Dry Ingredients
2 cups all-purpose flour
$1\frac{3}{4}$ cups granulated sugar
$\frac{2}{3}$ cup baking cocoa
$1\frac{1}{2}$ teaspoons baking powder
$1\frac{1}{2}$ teaspoons baking soda
$\frac{1}{2}$ teaspoon salt

Wet Ingredients
1 cup milk
$\frac{1}{8}$ cup water
$\frac{1}{2}$ cup vegetable oil
2 large eggs
$\frac{3}{4}$ teaspoon vanilla extract

Dry Ingredients
$3\frac{1}{8}$ cups sifted powdered sugar
$\frac{1}{2}$ stick butter or margarine

Icing

Wet Ingredients
$\frac{1}{4}$ cup milk
$\frac{1}{4}$ cup water
$1\frac{1}{3}$ teaspoons vanilla extract

⑩ How much flour will Raoul need?
    2 cups
⑪ How much vanilla extract will Raoul need?  $1\frac{13}{12}$ or $2\frac{1}{12}$ teaspoons
⑫ How much sugar (both granulated and powdered) will he need? $4\frac{7}{8}$ cups
⑬ How much milk will he need? $1\frac{1}{4}$ cups
⑭ How much water will Raoul need? $\frac{3}{8}$ cup
⑮ If this recipe is for 24 cupcakes, how many eggs will Raoul need for 48 cupcakes?  4 large eggs

Writing + Math  Journal

What process might Raoul use to determine the amount of ingredients for 36 cupcakes?

See Reflect in the *Teacher's Edition.*

---

## 3 Reflect                                      5

### Guided Discussion                          Small Group

Referring to the answers for Problems 10–15 on page 367, have the students determine how much of each ingredient Raoul will need if he wants to make 48 cupcakes. Ask questions such as the following:

■ **How much flour will he need?** 4 cups
■ **How much sugar (both regular and powdered) will he need?**
   $9\frac{6}{8}$ cups or $9\frac{3}{4}$ cups
■ **How much baking cocoa will Raoul need?** $\frac{4}{3}$ cups or $1\frac{1}{3}$ cups
■ **How much milk will he need?** $2\frac{1}{2}$ cups
■ **How much water will Raoul need?** $\frac{6}{8}$ cup or $\frac{3}{4}$ cup

Writing + Math  Journal  ✓

Raoul has the information he needs to make 24 or 48 cupcakes. In order to make 36 cupcakes, students should find the amount of ingredients between 24 and 36 cupcakes. Another approach is to find half of the amount of each ingredient needed to make 24 cupcakes and add those results to the amount of ingredients needed for 24 cupcakes. For example, 2 eggs are needed for 24, half of that is 1 egg, so for 36 cupcakes Raoul would need 3 eggs (2 + 1 = 3). Modeling with fraction tiles and circles would help in either scenario.

 **Curriculum Connection:** Students discussed recipes in this lesson. Have students create or research a recipe of their favorite foods.

 **Cumulative Review:** For review of exponents, assign Problems 20–22 on student page 374.

 **Family Involvement:** Assign the *Practice, Reteach,* or *Enrichment* activities depending on the needs of your students.

Encourage students to play the **Fracto I** or **Fracto II Game Mat** or **Fracto *eGames*** with a friend or relative.

 **Concept/Question Board:** Have students attempt to answer any unanswered questions on the Concept/Question Board.

 **Math Puzzler:** Suppose you have a piece of paper, and you fold it in half, then in half again, then in half one more time. Then you unfold the paper completely. How many sections will you see? 8

# 4 Assess and Differentiate

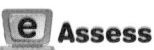

**e Assess** Use ***eAssess*** to record and analyze evidence of student understanding.

## A Gather Evidence

Use the Daily Class Assessment Records in ***Assessment*** or ***eAssess*** to record daily observations.

### Informal Assessment
**Journal**

Did the student ENGAGING
- ❑ pay attention to others' contributions?
- ❑ contribute information and ideas?
- ❑ improve on a strategy?
- ❑ reflect on and check the accuracy of his or her work?

### Informal Assessment
**Skill Practice**

Did the student COMPUTING
- ❑ respond accurately?
- ❑ respond quickly?
- ❑ respond with confidence?
- ❑ self-correct?

## B Summarize Findings

Analyze and summarize assessment data for each student. Determine which Assessment Follow-Up is appropriate for each student. Use the Student Assessment Record in ***Assessment*** or ***eAssess*** to update assessment records.

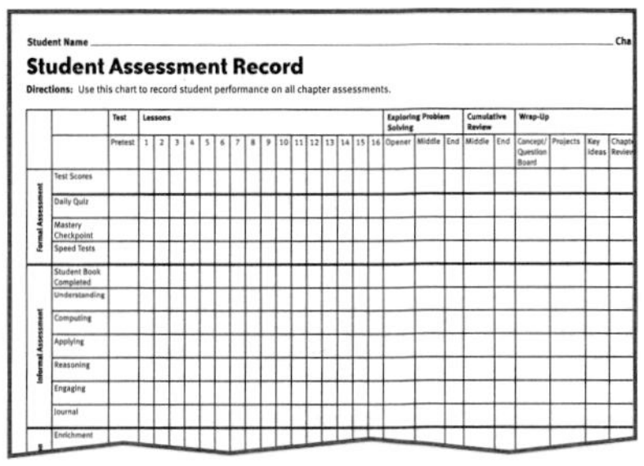
Student Assessment Record

**Assessment Page T41**

## C Assessment Follow-Up • DIFFERENTIATE INSTRUCTION

Based on your observations, use these teaching strategies for assessment follow-up.

### INTERVENTION

Review student performance on ***Intervention*** Lesson 8.B to see if students have mastered prerequisite skills for this lesson.

### ENGLISH LEARNER

Review

Use Lesson 8.15 in ***English Learner Support Guide*** to review lesson concepts and vocabulary.

### ENRICH

**If . . .** students are proficient in the lesson concepts,

**Then . . .** encourage them to work on the chapter projects or ***Enrichment*** Lesson 8.15.

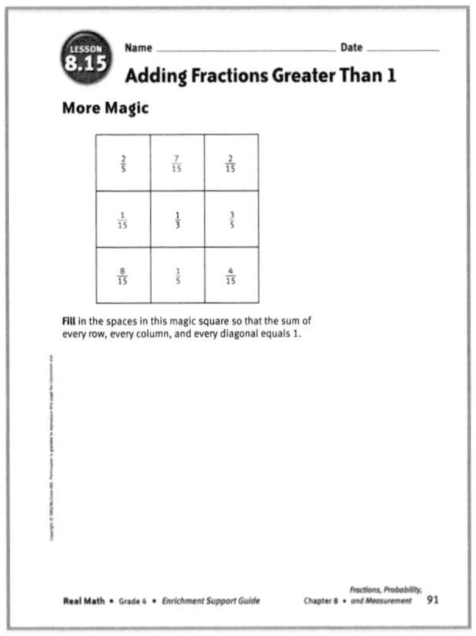
LESSON 8.15 Adding Fractions Greater Than 1

More Magic

Fill in the spaces in this magic square so that the sum of every row, every column, and every diagonal equals 1.

Enrichment Lesson 8.15

### PRACTICE

**If . . .** students would benefit from additional practice,

**Then . . .** assign ***Practice*** Lesson 8.15.

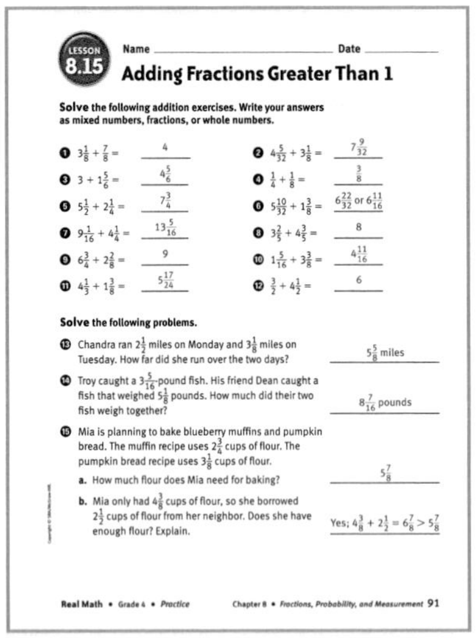
LESSON 8.15 Adding Fractions Greater Than 1

Solve the following addition exercises. Write your answers as mixed numbers, fractions, or whole numbers.

Solve the following problems.

Practice Lesson 8.15

### RETEACH

**If . . .** students are having difficulty adding fractions greater than 1,

**Then . . .** reteach the concept using ***Reteach*** Lesson 8.15

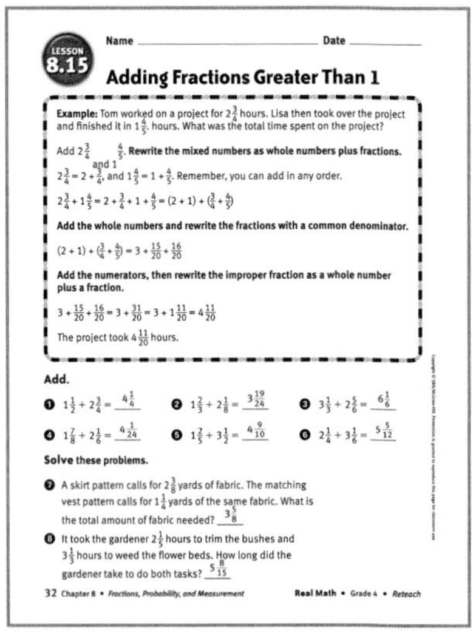
LESSON 8.15 Adding Fractions Greater Than 1

Add.

Solve these problems.

Reteach Lesson 8.15

### Objectives
- To demonstrate how to subtract mixed numbers with like denominators
- To demonstrate how to use equivalent fractions to subtract mixed numbers with unlike denominators

### NCTM Standards
**Number and Operations**
Compute fluently and make reasonable estimates

### Materials
*Response Wheels

### Technology
**e Presentation** Lesson 8.16
**e Games** Fracto
**e MathTools** Fractions

### Test Prep
**Cumulative Review**
Mental Math reviews adding mixed numbers as well as adding and subtracting fractions (Lessons 8.14 and 8.15).

*Manipulative Kit Item

# Subtracting Fractions Greater than 1

**Context of the Lesson** This lesson builds on the algorithm for the subtraction of fractions that was developed in Lesson 8.14. In this lesson, students use the method of finding common denominators to subtract fractions greater than 1.

See page 328B for Math Background for teachers for this lesson.

## Planning for Learning • DIFFERENTIATE INSTRUCTION

### INTERVENTION

**If . . .** students lack the prerequisite skill of finding a fraction of a number,

**Then . . .** teach ***Intervention*** Lesson 8.B.

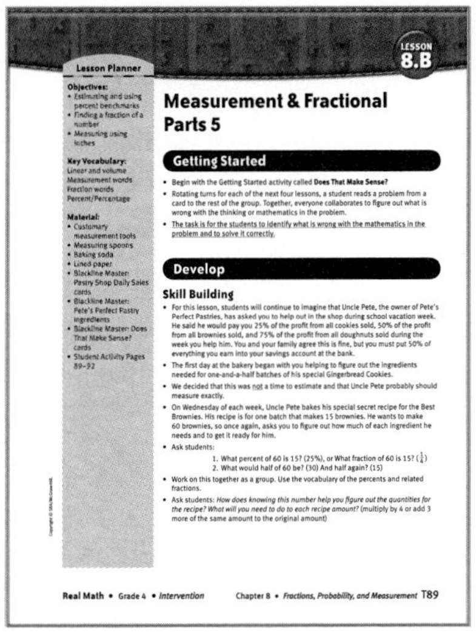
Lesson Planner
LESSON 8.B
Measurement & Fractional Parts 5
Getting Started
Develop
Skill Building

Intervention Lesson 8.B

### ENGLISH LEARNER

Preview

**If . . .** students need language support,

**Then . . .** use Lesson 8.16 in ***English Learner Support Guide*** to preview lesson concepts and vocabulary.

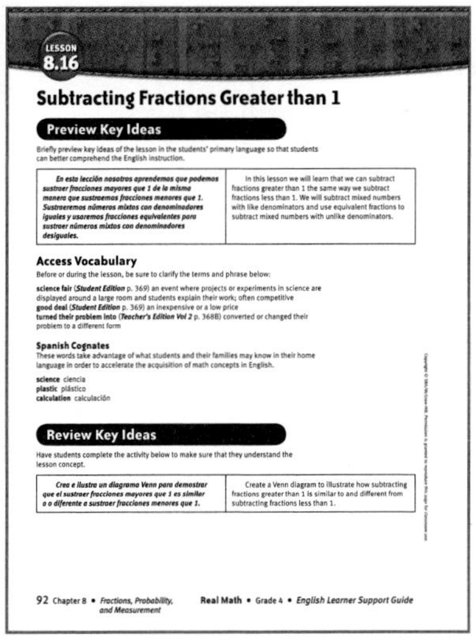
LESSON 8.16
Subtracting Fractions Greater than 1
Preview Key Ideas
Access Vocabulary
Spanish Cognates
Review Key Ideas

English Learner Lesson 8.16

### ENRICH

**If . . .** students are proficient in the lesson concepts,

**Then . . .** encourage them to work on the chapter projects.

### PRACTICE

**If . . .** students would benefit from additional practice,

**Then . . .** extend Skill Building before assigning the student pages.

### RETEACH

**If . . .** students are having difficulty subtracting fractions greater than 1,

**Then . . .** extend Guided Discussion.

**Review Vocabulary**
Review from Lesson 7.3 **equivalent**
Review from Lesson 8.10 **mixed number**
Review from Lesson 8.10 **improper fraction**

**Spanish Cognates**
**convert** converter
**calculation** calculación

## Mental Math 5

Review RESPONSE WHEEL

Present students with exercises, such as the following, that practice adding mixed numbers and adding and subtracting fractions:

a. $\frac{1}{4} + \frac{2}{4}$ $\frac{3}{4}$
b. $\frac{1}{2} + \frac{1}{2}$ 1
c. $1\frac{1}{3} + \frac{1}{3}$ $1\frac{2}{3}$
d. $\frac{5}{8} - \frac{2}{8}$ $\frac{3}{8}$
e. $\frac{8}{9} - \frac{7}{9}$ $\frac{1}{9}$
f. $7\frac{1}{2} + \frac{1}{2}$ 8
g. $4\frac{3}{4} + \frac{1}{4}$ 5
h. $8\frac{4}{5} - \frac{3}{5}$ $8\frac{1}{5}$

## 1 Develop 25

### Tell Students In Today's Lesson They Will

subtract mixed numbers with like denominators and use equivalent fractions to subtract mixed numbers with unlike denominators.

### Guided Discussion REASONING

Whole Group

Subtracting fractions greater than 1 is a small step from subtracting fractions less than 1.

1. Write a math sentence, such as $3\frac{2}{3} - 1\frac{1}{3}$, on the board. Also draw circles representing $3\frac{2}{3}$ and label them.
   - **What is the value of the set of circles?** $3\frac{2}{3}$
   - **If we take away $1\frac{1}{3}$ circles, how many will be left?** $2\frac{1}{3}$

   To demonstrate this answer, erase $1\frac{1}{3}$ of the circles. Show students there are $2\frac{1}{3}$ circles left.
2. Draw circles representing $2\frac{1}{2}$ with no label on the board.
   - **What is the value of these circles?** $2\frac{1}{2}$

   Write $2\frac{1}{2} - 1\frac{1}{4}$ on the board.
   - **Can the mixed numbers be subtracted as they are? If not, what must be done so you can subtract them?** no; we must find like denominators

   Write $2\frac{1}{2}$ as $2\frac{2}{4}$, demonstrating with fraction tiles if needed. Many students will recognize this equivalency from previous lessons.

   The new math sentence should be $2\frac{2}{4} - 1\frac{1}{4} = ?$
   - **What is the answer to the math sentence?** $1\frac{1}{4}$
3. Continue working on subtracting fractions greater than 1, using problems such as the following. Have students respond using response cards:
   - $6\frac{4}{5} - 2\frac{2}{5}$ $4\frac{2}{5}$
   - $2\frac{8}{9} - 2\frac{2}{9}$ $\frac{6}{9}$ or $\frac{2}{3}$
   - $5\frac{3}{4} - 2\frac{1}{2}$ $3\frac{1}{4}$
   - $10\frac{7}{10} - \frac{2}{5}$ $10\frac{3}{10}$
   - $8 - \frac{1}{2}$ $7\frac{1}{2}$

### Skill Building COMPUTING

Small Group

Another way to help students subtract fractions greater than 1 is to have them first convert the mixed number to an improper fraction and then solve.

1. Review how to convert a mixed number to an improper fraction.
2. Explain to students that once they have turned their problem into one involving improper fractions, the process of subtracting is the same as it is for fractions less than 1. The students will need to find like denominators as before, but the numerator will be greater than the denominator.
3. Provide examples such as the following. Have the students first change the mixed numbers to improper fractions.
   - $n = 6\frac{2}{3} - 4\frac{1}{6}$ $n = \frac{20}{3} - \frac{25}{6} = \frac{40}{6} - \frac{25}{6} = \frac{15}{6} = 2\frac{3}{6} = 2\frac{1}{2}$
   - $n = 7\frac{5}{12} - 2\frac{1}{4}$ $n = \frac{89}{12} - \frac{9}{4} = \frac{89}{12} - \frac{27}{12} = \frac{62}{12} = 5\frac{2}{12}$
   - $3\frac{5}{16} - 1\frac{1}{4} = n$ $n = \frac{53}{16} - \frac{5}{4} = \frac{53}{16} - \frac{20}{16} = \frac{33}{16} = 2\frac{1}{16}$

## 2 Assign Student Pages 25

**Pages 368–369** UNDERSTANDING

Have students complete pages 368 and 369 independently. Students may want to use fraction circles or fraction tiles to assist with Problems 10–18.

### Monitoring Student Progress

| | |
|---|---|
| **If . . .** students are having difficulty adding and subtracting fractions with unlike denominators, | **Then . . .** have them use fraction manipulatives to find like denominators. |
| **If . . .** students are having difficulty converting mixed numbers to improper fractions, | **Then . . .** have them demonstrate their answers with fraction tiles or fraction circles. |

### As Students Finish

Game **Fracto Game Mat**

e Games *Fracto*

e MathTools *Fractions* Have students explore subtraction problems.

Student Page

LESSON 8.16 Subtracting Fractions Greater Than 1

## Key Ideas

**You can subtract fractions greater than 1 in much the same way you subtract fractions less than 1.**

To subtract fractions with *different* denominators, remember to replace one or both of the fractions with an equivalent fraction so that the denominators will be the same.

Look at this example: $5\frac{2}{3} - 3\frac{1}{4} \longrightarrow 5\frac{8}{12} - 3\frac{3}{12}$

$$\begin{array}{r} 5\frac{8}{12} \\ -\,3\frac{3}{12} \\ \hline 2\frac{5}{12} \end{array}$$

Now that the denominators are the same, you may subtract the fractions and then subtract the whole numbers.

$5\frac{2}{3} - 3\frac{1}{4} = 2\frac{5}{12}$

If the fractional part of the number you are subtracting is greater than the fractional part of the number you are subtracting from, there will be an extra step of regrouping before doing the subtraction.

Look at this example: $7\frac{2}{5} - 4\frac{3}{4} \longrightarrow 7\frac{8}{20} - 4\frac{15}{20}$

$$\begin{array}{r} {}^{6\frac{20}{20}}\not{7}\frac{8}{20} \\ -\,4\frac{15}{20} \\ \hline \end{array}$$

Since $\frac{20}{20} = 1$, we can regroup 7 as $6\frac{20}{20}$. The $\frac{20}{20}$ is added to the $\frac{8}{20}$, so that $7\frac{8}{20}$ is regrouped as $6\frac{28}{20}$. Then subtract the fractional parts and whole numbers as before.

$7\frac{2}{5} - 4\frac{3}{4} = 2\frac{13}{20}$

**Solve** the following subtraction exercises.

1. $\square = 4\frac{4}{16} - 3\frac{1}{4}$ 1
2. $4\frac{12}{16} - 3\frac{3}{4} = \square$ 1
3. $7\frac{1}{3} - 2\frac{1}{2} = \square$ $4\frac{5}{6}$
4. $3\frac{5}{12} - 2\frac{1}{6} = \square$ $1\frac{3}{12}$
5. $\square = \frac{1}{2} - \frac{1}{3}$ $\frac{1}{6}$
6. $5\frac{3}{8} - 3\frac{1}{2} = \square$ $1\frac{7}{8}$
7. $\square = 6\frac{2}{3} - 4\frac{1}{7}$ $2\frac{11}{21}$
8. $7\frac{1}{2} - 4\frac{1}{4} = \square$ $3\frac{1}{4}$
9. $12\frac{3}{4} - \frac{1}{4} = \square$ $12\frac{2}{4}$

368 Textbook This lesson is available in the ***eTextbook.***

Student Page

Four students working on projects for the Science Fair need different lengths of plastic tubing. Mr. Krump says he can get a good deal on the tubing, but it only comes in 6-foot lengths. Each student has a homework assignment to determine how much of their plastic tubing will be left after they cut off what they need.

**Solve** the following problems.

Haley needs 3 pieces that are $1\frac{1}{2}$ feet each.

10. The total length she needs is $\square$ feet. $4\frac{1}{2}$
11. She will have $\square$ feet left. $1\frac{1}{2}$

Bertram needs 4 pieces that are 12 inches each.

12. The total length he needs is $\square$ feet. 4
13. He will have $\square$ feet left. 2

Chloe needs 2 pieces that are 2 feet 6 inches each.

14. The total length she needs is $\square$ feet. 5
15. She will have $\square$ feet left. 1

Gamba needs 1 piece that is $5\frac{1}{2}$ feet.

16. The total length he needs is $\square$ feet. $5\frac{1}{2}$
17. He will have $\square$ feet left. $\frac{1}{2}$
18. **a.** Who will have the most piping left over? Bertram
    **b.** Who will have the least? Gamba

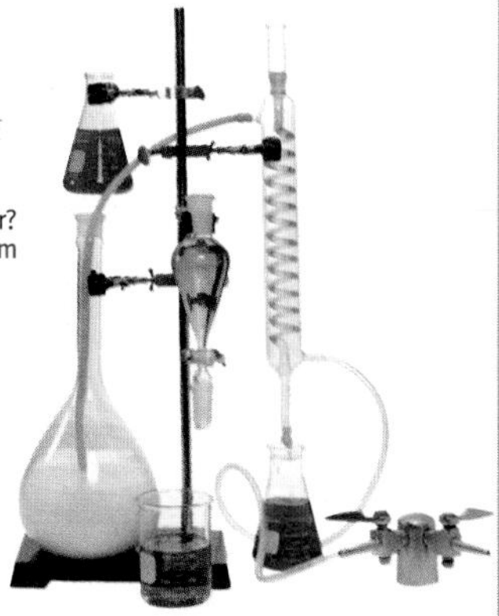

Chapter 8 • Lesson 16 369

## 3 Reflect

5

## Guided Discussion REASONING

Whole Group

Looking at answers from student page 369, how much piping would Haley, Bertram, Chloe, and Gamba need altogether? How many 6 foot lengths would Mr. Krump need to purchase? If each 6 foot pipe cost $4, what would be the total cost? 19 feet; 4; $16

SCIENCE

**Curriculum Connection:** Students discussed science fairs in this lesson. Have students create or research a science project they could do at school.

Review

**Cumulative Review:** For review of exponents, assign Problems 23–27 on student page 374.

**Family Involvement:** Assign the ***Practice, Reteach,*** or ***Enrichment*** activities depending on the needs of your students.

Encourage students to play the **Fracto I** or **Fracto II Game Mat** or **Fracto *eGames*** with a friend or relative.

**Concept/Question Board:** Have students attempt to answer any unanswered questions on the Concept/Question Board.

**Math Puzzler:** Omar is making a calendar for the month of March. How many times will he write the digit 1 on the calendar? 14, not counting any 1s he might write for the year

# 4 Assess and Differentiate

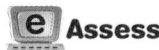

eAssess Use ***eAssess*** to record and analyze evidence of student understanding.

## A Gather Evidence

Use the Daily Class Assessment Records in ***Assessment*** or ***eAssess*** to record daily observations.

### Informal Assessment
**Student Pages**

Did the student UNDERSTANDING
- make important observations?
- extend or generalize learning?
- provide insightful answers?
- pose insightful questions?

### Informal Assessment
**Games**

Did the student COMPUTING
- respond accurately?
- respond quickly?
- respond with confidence?
- self-correct?

## B Summarize Findings

Analyze and summarize assessment data for each student. Determine which Assessment Follow-Up is appropriate for each student. Use the Student Assessment Record in ***Assessment*** or ***eAssess*** to update assessment records.

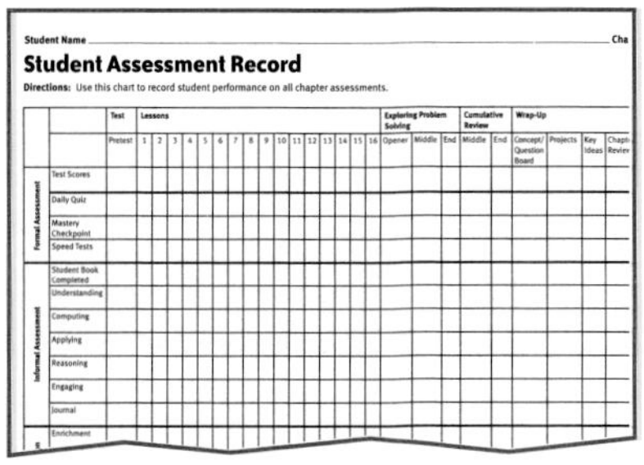


**Assessment Page T41**

## C Assessment Follow-Up • DIFFERENTIATE INSTRUCTION

Based on your observations, use these teaching strategies for assessment follow-up.

### INTERVENTION

Review student performance on ***Intervention*** Lesson 8.B to see if students have mastered prerequisite skills for this lesson.

### ENGLISH LEARNER

**Review**

Use Lesson 8.16 in ***English Learner Support Guide*** to review lesson concepts and vocabulary.

### ENRICH

**If . . .** students are proficient in the lesson concepts,

**Then . . .** encourage them to work on the chapter projects or ***Enrichment*** Lesson 8.16.

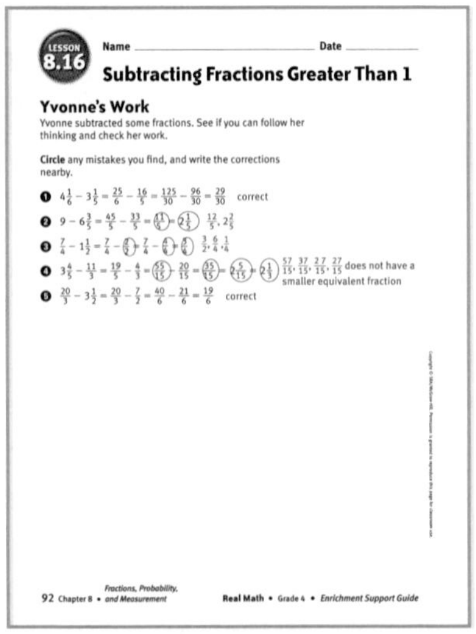

LESSON 8.16 Name ______ Date ______

**Subtracting Fractions Greater Than 1**

**Yvonne's Work**

Yvonne subtracted some fractions. See if you can follow her thinking and check her work.

**Circle** any mistakes you find, and write the corrections nearby.

1. $4\frac{1}{6} - 3\frac{1}{5} = \frac{25}{6} - \frac{16}{5} = \frac{125}{30} - \frac{96}{30} = \frac{29}{30}$ correct
2. $9 - 6\frac{3}{5} = \frac{45}{5} - \frac{33}{5} = \frac{11}{5} = 2\frac{1}{5}$ $\frac{12}{5}, 2\frac{2}{5}$
3. $\frac{7}{4} - 1\frac{1}{2} = \frac{7}{4} -$ [illegible] $= \frac{7}{4} -$ [illegible] $=$ [illegible] $\frac{3}{2}, \frac{6}{4}, \frac{1}{4}$
4. $3\frac{4}{5} - \frac{11}{3} = \frac{19}{5} - \frac{4}{3} = \frac{55}{15} - \frac{20}{15} = \frac{35}{15} = 2\frac{5}{15} = 2\frac{1}{3}$ $\frac{57}{15}, \frac{37}{15}, 2\frac{7}{15}, \frac{27}{15}$ does not have a smaller equivalent fraction
5. $\frac{20}{3} - 3\frac{1}{2} = \frac{20}{3} - \frac{7}{2} = \frac{40}{6} - \frac{21}{6} = \frac{19}{6}$ correct

92 Chapter 8 • *Fractions, Probability, and Measurement* **Real Math** • Grade 4 • *Enrichment Support Guide*

Enrichment Lesson 8.16

### PRACTICE

**If . . .** students would benefit from additional practice,

**Then . . .** assign ***Practice*** Lesson 8.16.

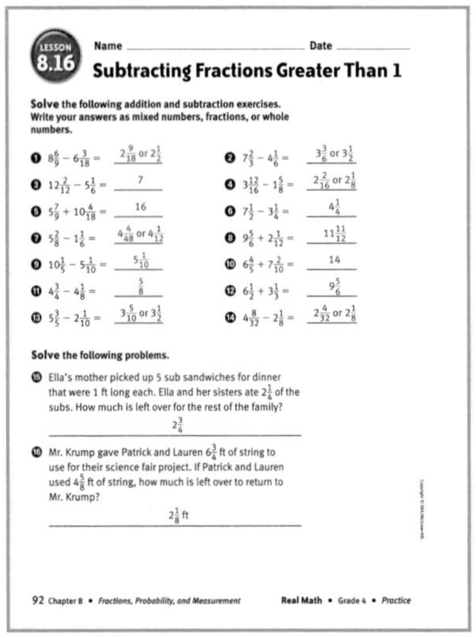

LESSON 8.16 Name ______ Date ______

**Subtracting Fractions Greater Than 1**

**Solve** the following addition and subtraction exercises. Write your answers as mixed numbers, fractions, or whole numbers.

1. $8\frac{6}{9} - 6\frac{3}{18} =$ $2\frac{9}{18}$ or $2\frac{1}{2}$
2. $7\frac{2}{3} - 4\frac{1}{6} =$ $3\frac{3}{6}$ or $3\frac{1}{2}$
3. $12\frac{2}{12} - 5\frac{1}{6} =$ 7
4. $3\frac{12}{16} - 1\frac{5}{8} =$ $2\frac{2}{16}$ or $2\frac{1}{8}$
5. $5\frac{7}{9} + 10\frac{4}{18} =$ 16
6. $7\frac{1}{2} - 3\frac{1}{4} =$ $4\frac{1}{4}$
7. $5\frac{2}{8} - 1\frac{1}{6} =$ $4\frac{4}{48}$ or $4\frac{1}{12}$
8. $9\frac{5}{6} + 2\frac{1}{12} =$ $11\frac{11}{12}$
9. $10\frac{1}{5} - 5\frac{1}{10} =$ $5\frac{1}{10}$
10. $6\frac{4}{5} + 7\frac{2}{10} =$ 14
11. $4\frac{3}{4} - 4\frac{1}{8} =$ $\frac{5}{8}$
12. $6\frac{1}{2} + 3\frac{1}{3} =$ $9\frac{5}{6}$
13. $5\frac{3}{5} - 2\frac{1}{10} =$ $3\frac{5}{10}$ or $3\frac{1}{2}$
14. $4\frac{8}{32} - 2\frac{1}{8} =$ $2\frac{4}{32}$ or $2\frac{1}{8}$

**Solve** the following problems.

15. Ella's mother picked up 5 sub sandwiches for dinner that were 1 ft long each. Ella and her sisters ate $2\frac{1}{4}$ of the subs. How much is left over for the rest of the family? $2\frac{3}{4}$
16. Mr. Krump gave Patrick and Lauren $6\frac{3}{4}$ ft of string to use for their science fair project. If Patrick and Lauren used $4\frac{5}{8}$ ft of string, how much is left over to return to Mr. Krump? $2\frac{1}{8}$ ft

92 Chapter 8 • *Fractions, Probability, and Measurement* **Real Math** • Grade 4 • *Practice*

Practice Lesson 8.16

### RETEACH

**If . . .** students are having difficulty subtracting fractions greater than 1,

**Then . . .** reteach the concept using ***Reteach*** Lesson 8.16.

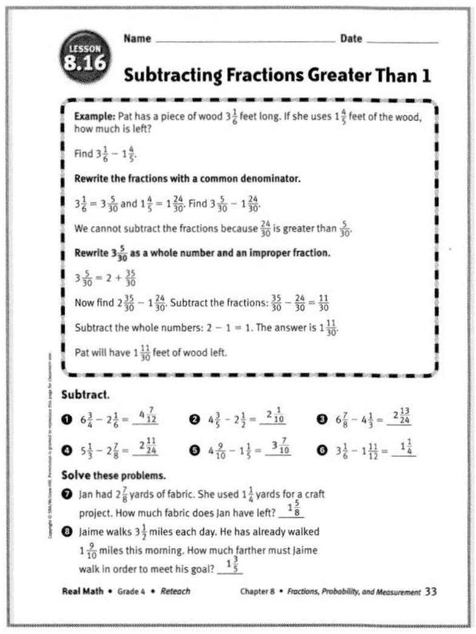

LESSON 8.16 Name ______ Date ______

**Subtracting Fractions Greater Than 1**

**Example:** Pat has a piece of wood $3\frac{1}{6}$ feet long. If she uses $1\frac{4}{5}$ feet of the wood, how much is left?

Find $3\frac{1}{6} - 1\frac{4}{5}$.

**Rewrite the fractions with a common denominator.**

$3\frac{1}{6} = 3\frac{5}{30}$ and $1\frac{4}{5} = 1\frac{24}{30}$. Find $3\frac{5}{30} - 1\frac{24}{30}$.

We cannot subtract the fractions because $\frac{24}{30}$ is greater than $\frac{5}{30}$.

**Rewrite $3\frac{5}{30}$ as a whole number and an improper fraction.**

$3\frac{5}{30} = 2 + \frac{35}{30}$

Now find $2\frac{35}{30} - 1\frac{24}{30}$. Subtract the fractions: $\frac{35}{30} - \frac{24}{30} = \frac{11}{30}$

Subtract the whole numbers: $2 - 1 = 1$. The answer is $1\frac{11}{30}$.

Pat will have $1\frac{11}{30}$ feet of wood left.

**Subtract.**

1. $6\frac{3}{4} - 2\frac{1}{6} =$ $4\frac{7}{12}$
2. $4\frac{3}{5} - 2\frac{1}{2} =$ $2\frac{1}{10}$
3. $6\frac{7}{8} - 4\frac{1}{3} =$ $2\frac{13}{24}$
4. $5\frac{1}{3} - 2\frac{7}{8} =$ $2\frac{11}{24}$
5. $4\frac{9}{10} - 1\frac{1}{5} =$ $3\frac{7}{10}$
6. $3\frac{1}{6} - 1\frac{11}{12} =$ $1\frac{1}{4}$

**Solve these problems.**

7. Jan had $2\frac{7}{8}$ yards of fabric. She used $1\frac{1}{4}$ yards for a craft project. How much fabric does Jan have left? $1\frac{5}{8}$
8. Jaime walks $3\frac{1}{2}$ miles each day. He has already walked $1\frac{9}{10}$ miles this morning. How much farther must Jaime walk in order to meet his goal? $1\frac{3}{5}$

**Real Math** • Grade 4 • *Reteach* Chapter 8 • *Fractions, Probability, and Measurement* 33

Reteach Lesson 8.16

# Exploring Problem Solving

### Objectives

- To estimate fractions in order to analyze data
- To use spatial sense to eliminate unreasonable choices
- To explore solving and presenting solutions to nonroutine problems that involve fractions and measurement

**Context of the Lesson** This lesson builds on what the students have learned about fractions and customary units of measure. Students estimate the fraction of an area on a circle graph and the fraction of a set on a map. The lesson also leads into the topic of the next chapter—geometry.

## 1 Develop

5

### Tell Students In Today's Lesson They Will

- read about the first time a satellite was used to rescue people.
- compare the use of two kinds of signals that satellites have used to help rescue people.
- go on a search-and-rescue mission.

## Guided Discussion

With the class, read the news article on student page 370, which recounts the first time a satellite was used to rescue someone who was lost.

Help the class understand the workings of the SARSAT system, which is illustrated on the page. Consider having students act out the rescue described in the news article, with different students taking on the different roles depicted in the diagram.

- pilot and passengers
- satellite
- local user terminal
- mission control center
- rescue coordination center
- search-and-rescue party

Student Page

**Exploring Problem Solving**

C1

~ September, 1982 ~

**HISTORY WAS MADE TODAY!**

History was made today when a satellite in orbit helped to rescue a pilot and two passengers whose plane had crashed in the mountains of British Columbia, Canada. As the satellite passed overhead, it received a signal from the aircraft and relayed it to the Victoria Rescue Coordination Center, which then sent a search team that rescued and saved the stranded trio.

*The downed aircraft is in the approximate center of the photo.*

*The crash site.*

SARSAT (Search and Rescue Satellite Assisted Tracking System) uses a network of satellites and ground stations to send aid quickly to anyone who sends out a special emergency signal. Even a lost hiker can use a small device called a PLB (Personal Locator Beacon) to send out a signal for help.

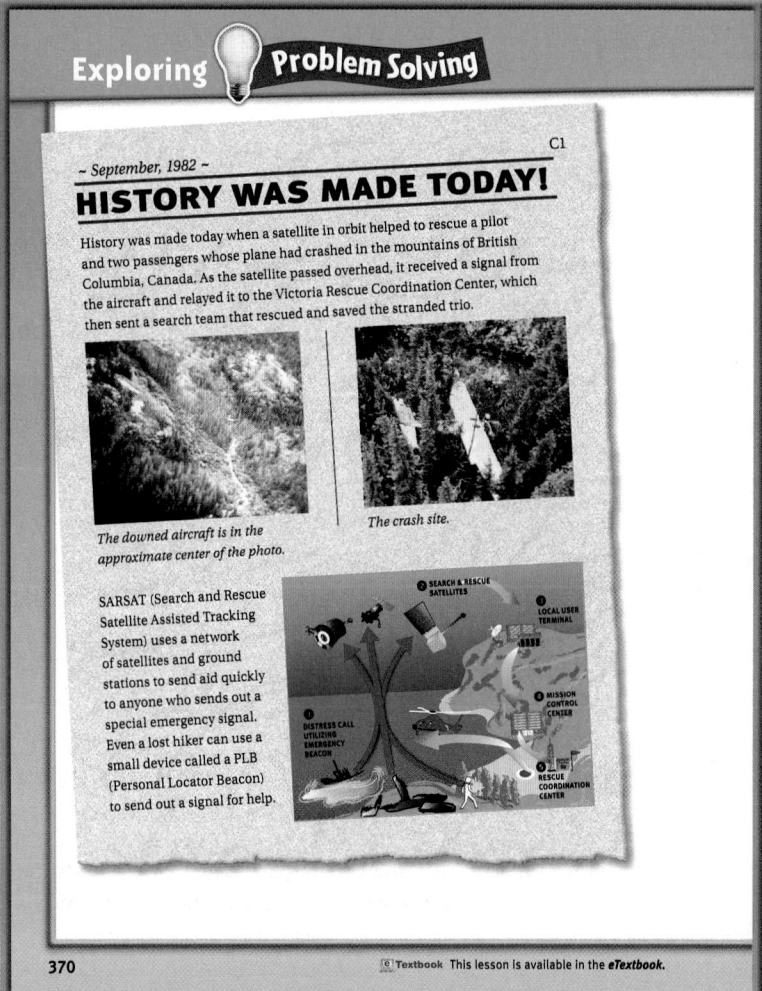

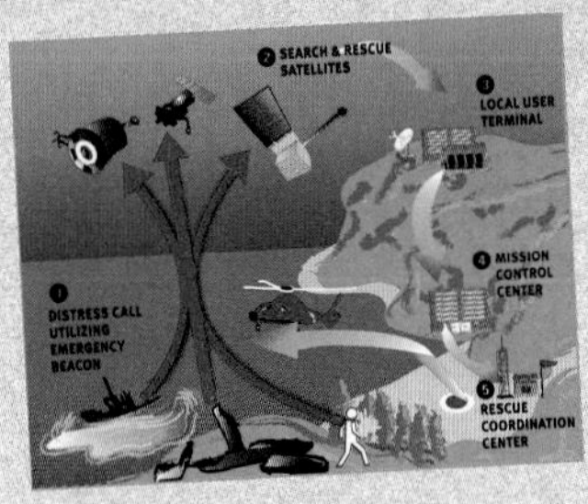


370 Textbook This lesson is available in the *eTextbook*.

## 2 Exploring Problem Solving 30

### Using Student Pages

Read the top of student page 371 with the class. If students ask about the two signals, you can explain that the old signal was set at a frequency of 121.5 megahertz, an international standard for maritime distress signals. Because of problems with that frequency, a new one, 406 megahertz, was used. The receiving satellites were built to recognize both frequencies.

To make sure students understand the circle graph and the map, ask questions such as the following:

- **In the year shown, how many people who used the old signal were rescued?** 488
- **Exactly what fraction of the people rescued by satellite that year used the old signal?** $\frac{488}{1,414}$
- **What does each red dot on the map stand for?** a location where a SARSAT-aided rescue initiated by an old signal type took place
- **If the map showed the whole world, do you think there would be more than, less than, or exactly 1,414 dots? Why? (Remember, the map shows locations, but the graph shows numbers of people.)** There would be less, because a single rescue often saves more than one person.

Read, discuss, and answer Problems 1–3 with the class. The main point of these problems is to give students an opportunity to use real data to estimate and compare a fraction of an area and a fraction of a set. The students' explanations in Problem 3 can be speculative.

### Answer

#### Problem 3

One reason could be that a greater fraction of people in the United States used the new signal. Another reason could be that rescues involving the old signal may have involved more people on average than rescues involving the new signal.

Student Page

Over the last two decades, satellites helped rescue over 15,000 people. The SARSAT system was designed to recognize two kinds of signals: old and new. The graph shows which signals were used by people who were rescued by satellite in a recent year.

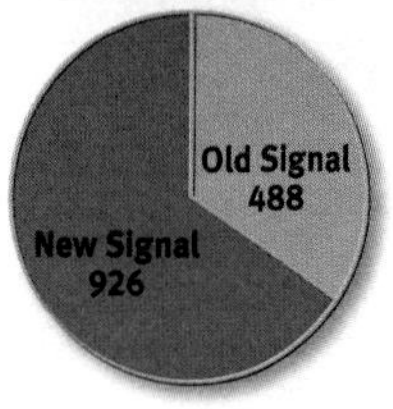


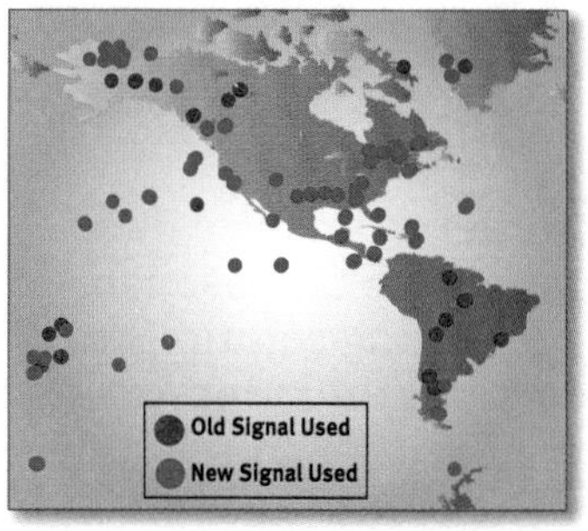


This map shows the locations of SARSAT rescue missions in and around North and South America for the same year as the circle graph. The color of the dot shows whether the rescued party used the old or the new signal.

2 Reasonable estimates are $\frac{1}{4}$, $\frac{1}{5}$, or $\frac{1}{6}$. Estimation methods may include "eyeballing" and making a rough count of the two kinds of dots.

**Solve** the following problems. Use the map and the graph.

1. For the year shown, about what fraction of the people rescued by SARSAT worldwide used the old signal? about $\frac{1}{3}$
2. For that same year, about what fraction of the SARSAT rescue missions in and around North and South America used the old signal? How did you estimate?
3. How can you explain why the fractions in Problems 1 and 2 are different? See the *Teacher's Edition.*

Chapter 8 371

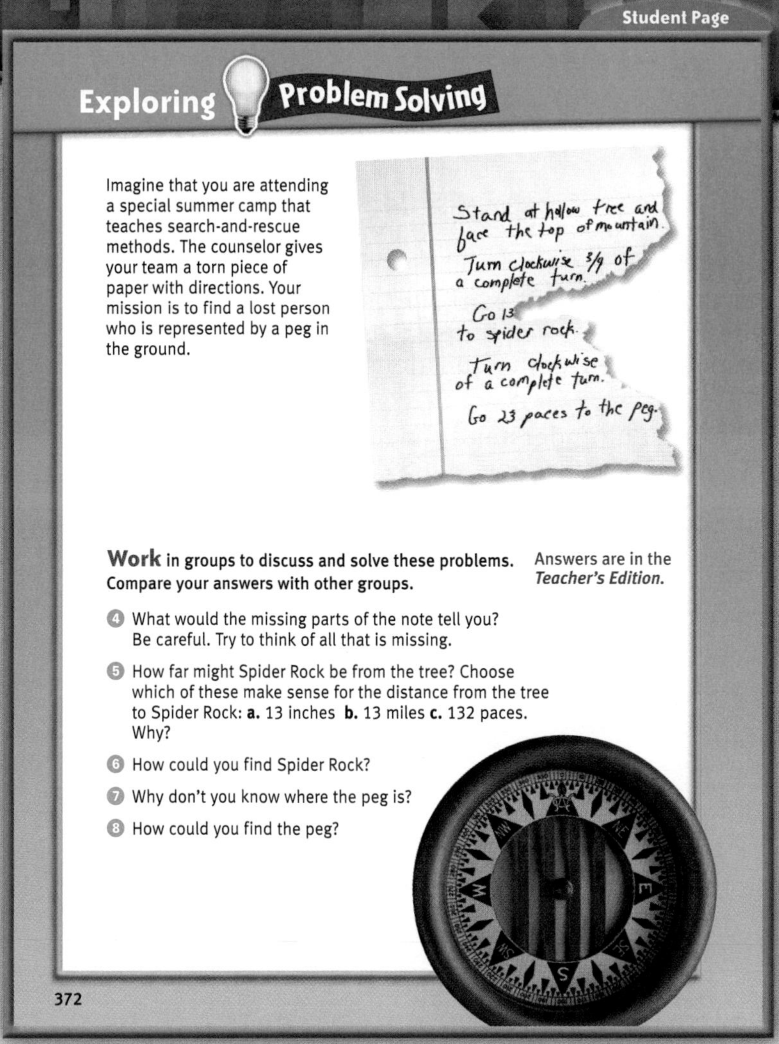
Student Page

Exploring Problem Solving

Imagine that you are attending a special summer camp that teaches search-and-rescue methods. The counselor gives your team a torn piece of paper with directions. Your mission is to find a lost person who is represented by a peg in the ground.

Stand at hollow tree and face the top of mountain.
Turn clockwise 3/4 of a complete turn.
Go 13
to spider rock.
Turn clockwise
of a complete turn.
Go 23 paces to the peg.
W
E
S



**Work** in groups to discuss and solve these problems. Compare your answers with other groups.

Answers are in the *Teacher's Edition.*

4. What would the missing parts of the note tell you? Be careful. Try to think of all that is missing.
5. How far might Spider Rock be from the tree? Choose which of these make sense for the distance from the tree to Spider Rock: **a.** 13 inches **b.** 13 miles **c.** 132 paces. Why?
6. How could you find Spider Rock?
7. Why don't you know where the peg is?
8. How could you find the peg?

372

With the class, read and discuss the information on student page 372. Then have students work in groups on Problems 4–8.

## Answers to Problems 4–8

### Problem 4

The missing part of the note would give the complete number instead of just the first two digits (13), and it would tell whether the number referred to paces, yards, or some other unit.

### Problem 5

Among various possibilities, Spider Rock could be 13, approximately 130, or approximately 1,300 paces from the tree. Also, the unit could be feet, yards, or meters.

**a.** 13 inches makes little sense because it would put Spider Rock right next to the tree.
**b.** 132 miles is unreasonable for this type of search exercise.
**c.** 132 paces would be a reasonable distance. It is far enough that a person would not see the rock without knowing in what direction to look, yet close enough that a person could walk to it in a reasonable amount of time.

### Problem 6

Start walking in the correct direction from the hollow tree and keep going until you find the rock.

### Problem 7

It is not known what direction the peg is from the rock.

### Problem 8

Go 23 paces away from the rock and then walk in a circle around the rock, thus covering all the possible directions.

## 3 Reflect

10

**Knowledge Age Skills**

**Effective Communication** Have groups present and explain their answers to selected problems from page 372. Ask questions such as the following:

- **Do you understand the reasoning?**
- **Do you agree with the reasoning? Why or why not?**

## 4 Assess

15

When evaluating student work, focus not only on the correctness of the answer, but also on students' thinking and communication. Some questions to consider include the following:

- Did the student understand the data and interpret it in reasonable ways?
- Did the student make reasonable estimates of fractions?
- Did the student use ideas about measurement and geometry to support a conclusion?

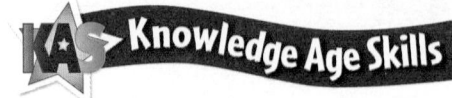

# Cumulative Review

## Assign Pages 373–374

Use this Cumulative Review as a review of concepts and skills that students have previously learned.

Here are different ways you can assign these problems to your students as they work through the chapter:

- For each lesson in the chapter, assign a set of Cumulative Review problems to be completed as practice or for homework.
  - Lesson 8.10—Problems 1–4
  - Lesson 8.11—Problems 5–8
  - Lesson 8.12—Problems 9–12
  - Lesson 8.13—Problems 13–14
  - Lesson 8.14—Problems 15–19
  - Lesson 8.15—Problems 20–22
  - Lesson 8.16—Problems 23–27
- At any point during the chapter, assign part or all of the Cumulative Review problems to be completed as practice or for homework.

### Cumulative Review

**Problems 1–4** review percentages, Lesson 7.1.

**Problems 5–8** review multidigit addition and subtraction, Lesson 2.3.

**Problems 9–12** review number lines, Lesson 7.7.

**Problems 13–14** review maps and charts, Lesson 1.9.

**Problems 15–19** review three-digit by two-digit multiplication, Lesson 6.5.

**Problems 20–22** review exponents, Lesson 5.11.

**Problems 23–27** review exponents, Lesson 5.11.

### Monitoring Student Progress

**If . . .** students miss more than one problem in a section, **Then . . .** refer to the indicated lesson for remediation suggestions.

Student Page

## Cumulative Review

**Learning about Percents** Lesson 7.1

**Pretend** that these rectangles are pieces of wood. Each piece will be cut, and the white piece will be used. Estimate what percentage of each piece will be used and explain how you got your answer.

1. 25%
2. 90%
3. 75%
4. 25%

**Multidigit Addition and Subtraction** Lesson 2.3

**Choose** the correct answer.

5. 370 + 825 + 564 + 231
   Ⓐ 1,890 **Ⓑ 1,990** Ⓒ 9,110
6. 800 − 355
   Ⓐ 554 Ⓑ 555 **Ⓒ 445**
7. 2893417 + 6484385
   Ⓐ 9,376,800 **Ⓑ 9,377,802** Ⓒ 9,387,208
8. 5,500 − 3,400 =
   Ⓐ 2,000 **Ⓑ 2,100** Ⓒ 2,200

**Number Lines** Lesson 7.7

**Place** the following decimals on the number line.

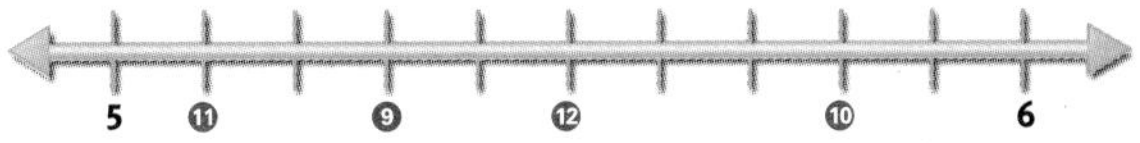


9. 5.3
10. 5.8
11. 5.1
12. 5.5



Student Page

## Cumulative Review

**Using Maps and Charts** Lesson 1.9

**Use** the map to answer the questions.

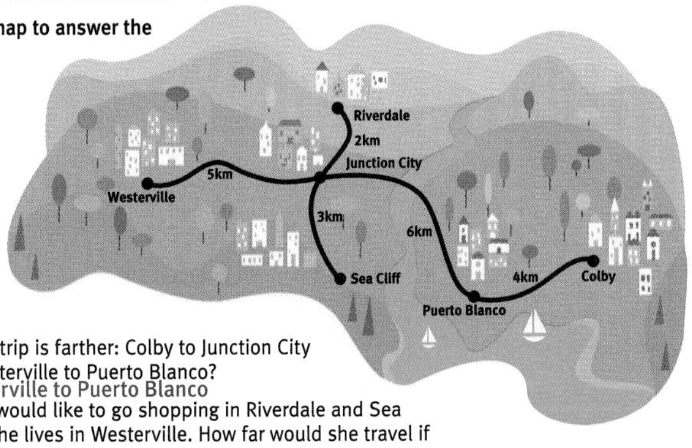


13. Which trip is farther: Colby to Junction City or Westerville to Puerto Blanco? Westerville to Puerto Blanco
14. Maria would like to go shopping in Riverdale and Sea Cliff. She lives in Westerville. How far would she travel if her route was from Westerville to Riverdale to Sea Cliff and back to Westerville? 20 km

**Multiplication: Three-Digit by Two-Digit** Lesson 6.5

**Multiply.**

15. 124 × 32 = ▢ 3,968
16. 602 × 43 = ▢ 25,886
17. 387 × 57 = ▢ 22,059
18. 299 × 68 = ▢ 20,332
19. 400 × 77 = ▢ 30,800

**Exponents** Lesson 5.11

**Write** these problems as exponents.

20. 8 × 8 = ▢ $8^2$
21. 3 × 3 × 3 × 3 × 3 × 3 = ▢ $3^6$
22. 7 × 7 × 7 × 7 = ▢ $7^4$

**Solve** these exponent equations.

23. $4^5$ = ▢ 1,024
24. $2^7$ = ▢ 128
25. $7^2$ = ▢ 49
26. $5^2$ = ▢ 25
27. $3^3$ = ▢ 27



eTextbook This lesson is available in the *eTextbook*.

CHAPTER 8 Review

# Wrap-Up

## 1 Discuss

5

### Concept/Question Board

Review the Concept/Question Board with students.

- Discuss students' contributions to the Concept side of the Board.
- Have students repose their questions, and lead a discussion to find satisfactory answers.

## Chapter Projects

Provide an opportunity for students who have worked on one or more of the chapter projects outlined on page 329C to share their work with the class. Allow each student or student group five minutes to present or discuss their projects. For formal assessment, use the rubrics found in ***Across the Curriculum Math Connections;*** the rubric for **Create a Sculpture as a Memorial** is on page 87, and the rubric for **Make a Slide Show about Surviving a Natural Disaster** is on page 91. For informal assessment, use the following rubric and questions.

| | Exceeds Expectations | Meets Expectations | Minimally Meets Expectations |
|---|---|---|---|
| Applies mathematics in real-world situations: | ❑ | ❑ | ❑ |
| Demonstrates strong engagement in the activity: | ❑ | ❑ | ❑ |

### Create a Sculpture as a Memorial

ART WebQuest

- What images did you sketch from the information about the Great Chicago Fire of 1871?
- What design did your group select for your sculpture?
- How did you select a scale for your model? What scale did you select?
- Do you think your sculpture makes a good memorial? Why or why not?
- If you were able to choose another drawing or image to create a model, which one would you choose? Why?
- Why do you think citizens of a city might want a sculpture to remind them of a tragic event?
- How could changes to the sculpture's form make it communicate your idea even more effectively?

### Make a Slide Show about Surviving a Natural Disaster

SOCIAL STUDIES

- Which natural disaster did you select? Why?
- What statistics did you include in your slide show?
- How did you turn statistical information into fractions?
- What other information could you have included in your slide show?
- How can cooperation help people solve problems?
- If you had to choose another disaster, what would you select? Why? Could you use the same information to survive that disaster? Why or why not?

# 2 Assign Student Pages 25

## Key Ideas Review ✓ UNDERSTANDING

Have students complete the Review questions independently or in small groups. Then discuss each question as a class.

### Possible Answers

**Problem 1** Problems 1–4 involve addition, subtraction, and multiplication of fractions and also the equivalence of fractions. The answer is $\frac{4}{54}$ or $\frac{2}{27}$.

**Problem 2** The answer is $6\frac{10}{12}$ or $6\frac{5}{6}$.

**Problem 3** The answer is $\frac{3}{9}$ or $\frac{1}{3}$.

**Problem 4** The answer is 16.

**Problem 5** Problems 5–7 involve fractions on a number line. This is a very important skill to understand because students are beginning to comprehend fractions as numbers as they are being placed on number lines. The answer is $2\frac{5}{10}$ or $2\frac{1}{2}$.

**Problem 6** This problem involves knowing that $\frac{1}{2}$ as a decimal is 0.5. The answer is 2.5.

**Problem 7** There are a number of equivalent answers to the fraction that is at point C on the number line, such as the following:

- $2\frac{4}{5}$
- $2\frac{32}{40}$
- $2\frac{16}{20}$

Extended Response

**Problem 8** To change an improper fraction to a mixed number, the numerator is divided by the denominator. The number that would be the remainder is then set as the numerator of a new fraction with the divisor as the denominator. For example, in $\frac{14}{4}$, 14 is divided by 4 to get 3 R2. The 3 is the whole number in the mixed number, and $\frac{2}{4}$ is the fraction.

Extended Response

**Problem 9** This problem allows students to explain how they know one fraction is greater than another. Students may say $\frac{1}{6}$ is smaller because 6 represents how many parts the whole figure is divided into. Since there are more slices when there are 6 pieces, each piece is smaller than it would be if cut into fourths.

Extended Response

**Problem 10** This probability question uses the idea of *fairness* during an event. The game is not fair because Raphael has a probability of $\frac{3}{5}$ of landing on a number to give him a point. Janice has a probability of only $\frac{2}{5}$ of earning a point. One way to make it fair is to say that if the spinner lands on 2, they will spin again.

Student Page

## CHAPTER 8 Key Ideas Review

**In this chapter you explored various features of fractions.**

You learned about fractional equivalents and how to add and subtract fractions.

You learned how to use fractions to demonstrate probabilities.

**Solve** each problem.

1. $\frac{1}{6}$ of $\frac{4}{9}$ = ■ $\frac{4}{54}$ or $\frac{2}{27}$
2. $4\frac{2}{4} + 2\frac{1}{3}$ = ■ $6\frac{10}{12}$ or $6\frac{5}{6}$
3. $\frac{6}{9} - \frac{1}{3}$ = ■ $\frac{3}{9}$ or $\frac{1}{3}$
4. $\frac{4}{6}$ of 24 = ■ 16

**Use** the number line to answer the questions.

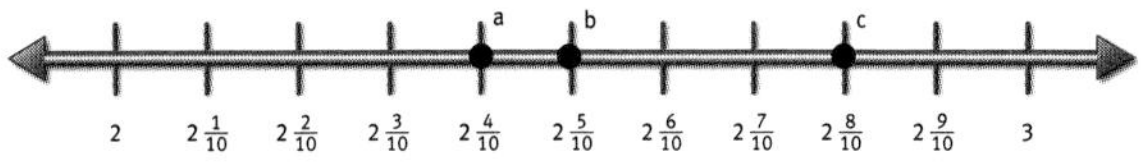


5. What value is *b* at? $2\frac{5}{10}$
6. What would that value be as a decimal? 2.5
7. Write an equivalent fraction for *c*. Possible answers: $2\frac{4}{5}$, $2\frac{16}{20}$, or $2\frac{32}{40}$.

**Provide** a detailed answer for the following exercises. Extended Response

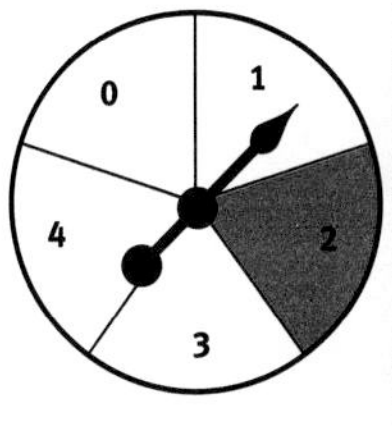


8. Explain how to change an improper fraction to a mixed number, and provide an example.
9. Explain why $\frac{1}{6}$ is smaller than $\frac{1}{4}$.
10. Raphael and Janice were playing with a spinner when Raphael suggested a game. If the spinner landed on numbers 0–2, Raphael got a point, and if it landed on 3 or 4, Janice got a point. Was this game fair? If not, explain what would make it fair. See *Teacher's Edition* for the answer.

375

# CHAPTER 8 Review

## Chapter Review

Use this Chapter 8 Review as a preliminary chapter test to identify areas in which each student is having difficulty or in which the class may need help. If students do well on the Chapter 8 Review, you may wish to skip directly to the next chapter. If not, you may want to spend time helping students overcome their individual difficulties before they take the Chapter Test.

Each set of problems reviews concepts from one or more lessons in the chapter. Students can refer to a specific lesson for additional instruction if they need help. You can also use this information to assign additional practice based on the previous lesson concepts.

Have students complete pages 376–377 on their own. For review purposes, you may want to do some of the word problems on page 377 as a class.

### Monitoring Student Progress

**Game** **Problems 1–3 Lesson 8.1**

**If . . .** students miss any of these problems about fractions of geometric figures,

**Then . . .** check to see whether the errors are from carelessness or whether students do not understand the concept of a fraction of a shape. Students who do not understand may require special help and might benefit by playing the **Fracto Game Mats,** which provide practice with recognizing fractions of circles and rectangles.

**Problems 4–6 Lesson 8.2**

**If . . .** students miss more than one of these fraction of a fraction problems,

**Then . . .** check to be sure they understand the process. If students are making mistakes in multiplication or division, give them extra practice with facts.

**Problems 7–9 Lesson 8.5**

**If . . .** students miss more than one of these probability problems,

**Then . . .** have the students work with manipulatives to act out the problems.

**Problems 10–13 Lesson 8.6**

**If . . .** students have difficulty completing these fraction problems,

**Then . . .** give students opportunities to use manipulatives to act out the situations.

**Problems 14–19 Lessons 8.8–8.9**

**If . . .** students miss more than one of these equivalent fraction and fraction comparison problems,

**Then . . .** give students more practice with these two concepts.

**Problems 20–27 Lessons 8.10–8.11**

**If . . .** students miss more than one of these problems that involve working with fractions greater than 1,

**Then . . .** assess to see whether the difficulty is with the arithmetic or the conversion steps.

**Problems 28–29 Lesson 8.12**

**If . . .** students have difficulty with these simple measurements,

**Then . . .** provide opportunities for students to use a ruler and measure objects around the room, outside, and at home.

**Problems 30–33 Lessons 8.15–8.16**

**If . . .** students miss more than one of these problems involving adding and subtracting fractions greater than 1,

**Then . . .** assess to see if the difficulty is with the arithmetic or with the concept. Provide more opportunities for practice.

## CHAPTER 8 Chapter Review

Lesson 8.1 **What** fraction of each figure is shaded?

1. 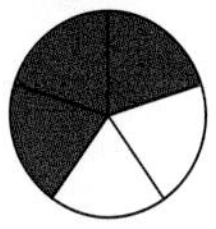 $\frac{3}{5}$

2. 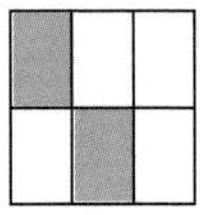 $\frac{2}{6}$ or $\frac{1}{3}$

3. 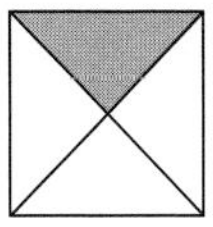 $\frac{1}{4}$

Lesson 8.2 **Complete** the following to make correct statements.

4. $\frac{2}{3}$ of $\frac{3}{4}$ is $\frac{6}{12}$ or $\frac{1}{2}$
5. $\frac{3}{4} \times \frac{1}{3} =$ $\frac{3}{12}$ or $\frac{1}{4}$
6. $\frac{4}{5}$ of $\frac{3}{7}$ is $\frac{12}{35}$

Lesson 8.5 **Solve** these problems.

Ben has a plaid shirt, a striped shirt, and a plain shirt, all with long sleeves. He also has the same styles with short sleeves. He has a pair of jeans, a pair of khakis, and a pair of dress slacks.

7. How many possible outfits can he get? 18 combinations
8. Ben's mother chose an outfit for him to wear. What is the probability that she chose a long sleeved, plaid shirt along with khaki pants? $\frac{1}{18}$
9. Ben's younger brother spilled grape juice on Ben's dress slacks and short-sleeved, striped shirt. What fraction of Ben's wardrobe is now ruined? $\frac{8}{18}$ or $\frac{4}{9}$

Lesson 8.6 **Write** the correct amount.

10. $\frac{1}{4}$ of 100 = ▒ 25
11. $\frac{2}{3}$ of 90 = ▒ 60
12. $\frac{3}{4}$ of 36 = ▒ 27

**Solve** the following problem. Explain your answer.

13. Extended Response Lucas's teacher asked the class of 24 students the following question: If $\frac{2}{3}$ of our class walks home and $\frac{1}{4}$ of our class takes the bus, how many students are left? 2 students



eTextbook This lesson is available in the *eTextbook*.

Student Page

Lesson 8.8

**List** two equivalent fractions for the following.

14. $\frac{1}{3}$ ▒, ▒ possible answers: $\frac{2}{6}$ and $\frac{3}{9}$
15. $\frac{4}{5}$ ▒, ▒ possible answers: $\frac{8}{10}$ and $\frac{12}{15}$
16. $\frac{1}{2}$ ▒, ▒ possible answers: $\frac{2}{4}$ and $\frac{50}{100}$
17. $\frac{15}{50}$ ▒, ▒ possible answers: $\frac{3}{10}$ and $\frac{30}{100}$

**Write** these fractions in order from smallest to largest.

18. $\frac{1}{3}, \frac{1}{5}, \frac{1}{100}, \frac{1}{4}, \frac{1}{25}$ ▒ ▒ ▒ ▒ ▒ $\frac{1}{100}, \frac{1}{25}, \frac{1}{5}, \frac{1}{4}, \frac{1}{3}$
19. $\frac{3}{10}, \frac{9}{10}, \frac{6}{10}, \frac{7}{10}, \frac{2}{10}$ ▒ ▒ ▒ ▒ ▒ $\frac{2}{10}, \frac{3}{10}, \frac{6}{10}, \frac{7}{10}, \frac{9}{10}$

Lessons 8.10 and 8.11

**Convert** mixed numbers to improper fractions or improper fractions to mixed numbers.

20. $\frac{13}{2}$ ▒ $6\frac{1}{2}$
21. $5\frac{1}{2}$ ▒ $\frac{11}{2}$
22. $7\frac{2}{3}$ ▒ $\frac{23}{3}$
23. $\frac{52}{5}$ ▒ $10\frac{2}{5}$

**What** is the decimal equivalent of

24. $2\frac{1}{4}$ ▒ 2.25
25. $1\frac{5}{8}$ ▒ 1.625
26. $\frac{35}{4}$ ▒ 8.75
27. $\frac{27}{2}$ ▒ 13.5

Lesson 8.12

**Solve.**

28. What fractional part of 1 foot is 1 inch? ▒ $\frac{1}{12}$
29. What fractional part of 1 yard is 1 inch? ▒ $\frac{1}{36}$

Lessons 8.15 and 8.16

**Solve** for *n*.

30. $5\frac{7}{8} + 2\frac{3}{4} = n$ $n = 8\frac{5}{8}$
31. $3\frac{5}{12} - 2\frac{1}{6} = n$ $n = 1\frac{1}{4}$
32. $n = 3\frac{1}{2} + 7\frac{3}{8}$ $n = 10\frac{7}{8}$
33. $n = 4\frac{13}{16} - 3\frac{3}{4}$ $n = 1\frac{1}{16}$

# CHAPTER 8 Assessment

## 3 Chapter Tests

40

### Practice Test

**Student Pages 378–381**

- The Chapter 8 Practice Test on ***Student Edition*** pages 378–381 provides an opportunity to formally evaluate students' proficiency with concepts developed in this chapter.
- The content is similar to the Chapter 8 Review in standardized format.

**Problem 22** Extended Response

Students can solve Problem 22 by making use of the table that they complete in part a. All possible outcomes will be presented in the table. Students can then tally the occurrences of different events for parts b, c, and d.

Student Page

## CHAPTER 8 Practice Test

**Solve** the problems below.

1. Sarah and Stewart are sharing a pizza. If Sarah eats $\frac{1}{6}$ of the pizza, and Stewart eats $\frac{1}{2}$ of the pizza, what fraction of the pizza is left over? $\frac{1}{3}$
2. Convert the fractions in the table to an equivalent fraction with a denominator of 36.

| Fraction | equivalent |
|---|---|
| $\frac{1}{2}$ | $\frac{18}{36}$ |
| $\frac{1}{3}$ | ■ $\frac{12}{36}$ |
| $\frac{4}{6}$ | ■ $\frac{24}{36}$ |
| $\frac{7}{12}$ | ■ $\frac{21}{36}$ |

3. Which fraction is bigger, $\frac{7}{12}$ or $\frac{4}{6}$? $\frac{4}{6}$ or $\frac{8}{12}$

**Solve** the problems below.

4. Kelley practiced the piano for $2\frac{1}{2}$ hours on Saturday and for $1\frac{1}{6}$ hours on Sunday. How much time did she spend practicing this weekend? $3\frac{4}{6}$ or $3\frac{2}{3}$ hours
5. If Kelley has to spend at least 3 hours practicing each weekend, how much more time did she practice than she needed to? $\frac{2}{3}$ hour or 40 minutes
6. Donna wants to buy a guitar that costs $400. So far, she has saved $\frac{1}{2}$ of what she needs to buy the guitar. How much has Donna saved so far? $200

378 eTextbook This lesson is available in the *eTextbook*.

Student Page

**Select** the correct answer.

7. What is $\frac{1}{2}$ of $\frac{6}{8}$?
   Ⓐ $\frac{1}{8}$ ● $\frac{3}{8}$
   Ⓒ $\frac{4}{10}$ Ⓓ $\frac{2}{10}$
8. Dakota can save $\frac{1}{4}$ of the cost of a tennis racket when it goes on sale. How much will she save on a racket that regularly costs $70?
   Ⓐ $7.00 Ⓑ $12.50
   Ⓒ $17.00 ● $17.50
9. Which fraction is equivalent to $\frac{4}{9}$?
   Ⓐ $\frac{4}{16}$ Ⓑ $\frac{12}{32}$
   ● $\frac{8}{18}$ Ⓓ $\frac{2}{3}$
10. Which decimal is equivalent to $\frac{4}{5}$?
    Ⓐ 0.3 Ⓑ 0.5
    Ⓒ 0.6 ● 0.8
11. Which answer shows $\frac{19}{5}$ written as a mixed number?
    Ⓐ $1\frac{9}{5}$ Ⓑ $2\frac{2}{3}$
    ● $3\frac{4}{5}$ Ⓓ $5\frac{4}{6}$
12. About how long is the crayon?
    ● $2\frac{1}{4}$ inches Ⓑ $2\frac{1}{2}$ inches
    Ⓒ $3\frac{4}{5}$ inches Ⓓ $5\frac{4}{6}$ inches

13. Jennie has 12 cousins, and 2/3 of them are girls. How many of her cousins are girls?
    Ⓐ 2 Ⓑ 3
    ● 8 Ⓓ 5
14. Craig ran 2 miles on Wednesday and $3\frac{1}{4}$ miles on Saturday. How many miles did he run altogether?
    Ⓐ $1\frac{1}{4}$ ● $5\frac{1}{4}$
    Ⓒ $5\frac{1}{2}$ Ⓓ 5

Real Math • Chapter 8 379

# CHAPTER 8 · Practice Test

**Solve for n.**

15. $\frac{2}{3} \times \frac{1}{8} = n$
   Ⓐ $n = \frac{1}{12}$    Ⓑ $n = \frac{6}{12}$
   Ⓒ $n = \frac{6}{7}$    Ⓓ $n = \frac{8}{9}$

16. $\frac{4}{7} \times \frac{1}{2} = n$
   Ⓐ $n = \frac{1}{2}$    Ⓑ $n = \frac{3}{7}$
   ● $n = \frac{2}{7}$    Ⓓ $n = \frac{3}{10}$

17. What is 20% of 80?
   Ⓐ 8    Ⓑ 10
   ● 16    Ⓓ 24

18. What is 5% of 80?
   Ⓐ 12    ● 4
   Ⓒ 3    Ⓓ 2

**Use the graph to answer questions 19 through 21.**

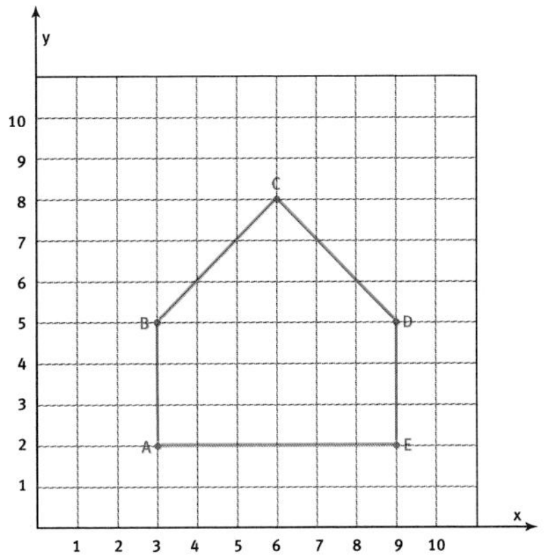

19. What are the coordinates of point D?
   Ⓐ (2, 9)    Ⓑ (3, 2)
   Ⓒ (9, 2)    ● (9, 5)

20. What point is at (3, 5)?
   Ⓐ A    ● B
   Ⓒ D    Ⓓ C

21. What is the length of segment AE?
   Ⓐ 5    ● 6
   Ⓒ 9    Ⓓ 12

380    Textbook This lesson is available in the *eTextbook*.

**Extended Response Solve the problems below.**

22. In a game, each player rolls two cubes numbered 0 to 5. The player adds the value of each cube and records the score. After 10 rolls, the player with the most points wins.

   a. Complete the table to show all the possible sums of the two cubes.

|   | 0 | 1 | 2 | 3 | 4 | 5 |
|---|---|---|---|---|---|---|
| 0 | 0 | 1 | 2 | 3 | 4 | 5 |
| 1 | 1 | 2 | 3 | 4 | 5 | 6 |
| 2 | 2 | 3 | 4 | 5 | 6 | 7 |
| 3 | 3 | 4 | 5 | 6 | 7 | 8 |
| 4 | 4 | 5 | 6 | 7 | 8 | 9 |
| 5 | 5 | 6 | 7 | 8 | 9 | 10 |

   b. How many possible outcomes are there?

   c. What is the highest sum a player can roll? 10

   d. What is the probability that a player will roll the sum of 5?

   e. What is the probability that a player will get no points on a given turn?

   b. There are thirty-six possible outcomes. There are six numbers on each cube. 6 × 6 = 36

   d. $\frac{6}{36}$; there are six combinations that will give a sum of 5.

   e. $\frac{1}{36}$; of the thirty-six possible outcomes, one gives a sum of zero

# Chapter Test ✓ COMPUTING

● For further evaluation instead of or in addition to this test, you may wish to have students take the Chapter 8 Test provided in **Assessment**.

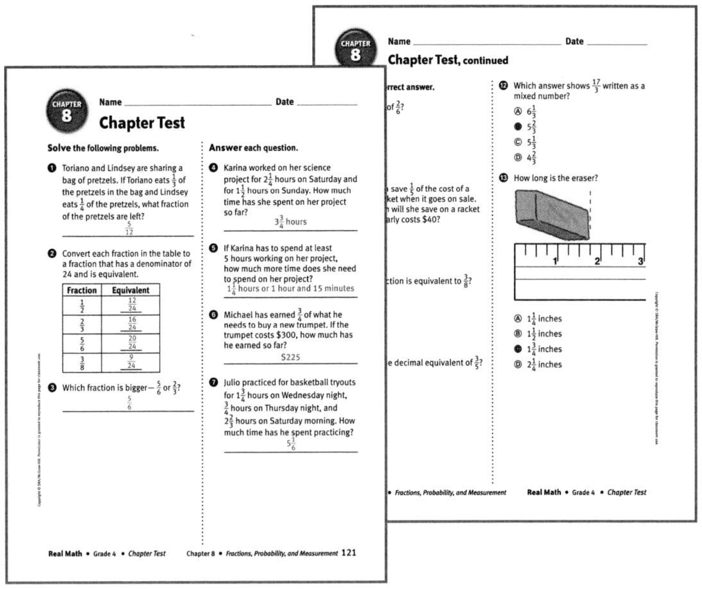

**Assessment, pages 121–122**

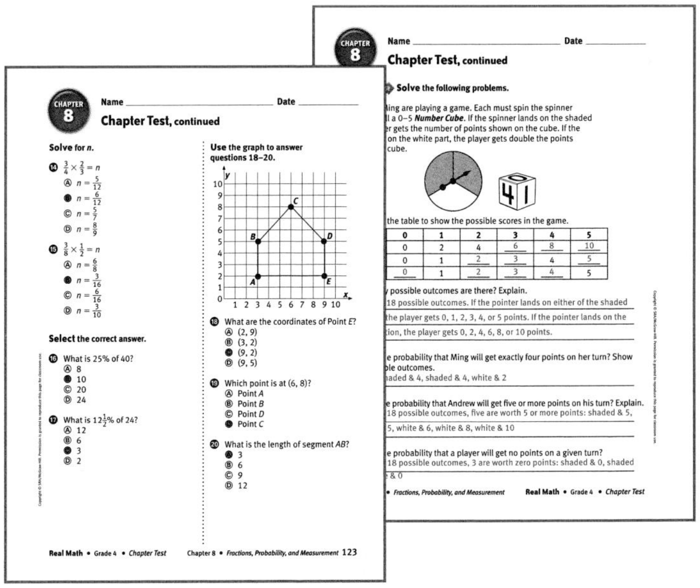

**Assessment, pages 123–124**

# CHAPTER 8 Assessment

## 4 Assess and Differentiate

**eAssess** Use ***eAssess*** to record and analyze evidence of student understanding.

## A Gather Evidence

Use the Daily Class Assessment Records in ***Assessment*** or ***eAssess*** to record Informal and Formal Assessments.

### Informal Assessment

**Key Ideas Review** UNDERSTANDING

Did the student
- ❑ answer questions?
- ❑ pose new questions?
- ❑ extend the discussion?
- ❑ provide insight?

### Informal Assessment

**Project** APPLYING

Did the student
- ❑ meet the project objectives?
- ❑ communicate clearly?
- ❑ complete the project accurately?
- ❑ connect mathematics to real-world situations?

### Formal Assessment

**Chapter Test** COMPUTING

Score the test, and record the results.

## B Summarize Findings

Analyze and summarize assessment data for each student. Determine which Chapter Follow-Up is appropriate for each student. Use the Student Assessment Record in ***Assessment*** or ***eAssess*** to update assessment records.

## C Chapter Follow-Up • DIFFERENTIATE INSTRUCTION

Based on your observations, use these teaching strategies for chapter follow-up.

| ENRICH | PRACTICE | RETEACH | INTERVENTION |
|---|---|---|---|
| **If . . .** students demonstrate **secure understanding** of chapter concepts, **Then . . .** have them move on to the next chapter. | **If . . .** students exhibit **competent understanding** of chapter concepts, **Then . . .** have them move on to the next chapter. | **If . . .** students demonstrate **emerging understanding** of chapter concepts, **Then . . .** move on to the next chapter, but continue to provide cumulative review. | **If . . .** students demonstrate **minimal understanding** of chapter concepts, **Then . . .** intensive intervention is needed before they start the next chapter. |

CHAPTER 8

# Teacher Reflection

## Lesson Study

Reflect on each of the lessons you taught in this chapter. Rate each one on the following scale, then consider ways to maintain or improve positive teaching experiences in the future.

| Lessons | Very Effective | Effective | Less Effective | What Worked | Ways to Improve |
|---|---|---|---|---|---|
| 8.1 Writing Appropriate Fractions | | | | | |
| 8.2 Fractions of Fractions | | | | | |
| 8.3 Fractions and Rational Numbers | | | | | |
| 8.4 Probability | | | | | |
| 8.5 Probability Experiments | | | | | |
| 8.6 Applying Fractions | | | | | |
| 8.7 Probability and Fractions | | | | | |
| 8.8 Equivalent Fractions | | | | | |
| 8.9 Comparing Fractions | | | | | |
| 8.10 Fractions Greater Than 1 | | | | | |
| 8.11 Representing Fractions Greater Than 1 | | | | | |
| 8.12 Reading a Ruler | | | | | |
| 8.13 Adding and Subtracting Measurements | | | | | |
| 8.14 Adding and Subtracting Fractions | | | | | |
| 8.15 Adding Fractions Greater Than 1 | | | | | |
| 8.16 Subtracting Fractions Greater Than 1 | | | | | |

CHAPTER 9 Overview

# Decimals

## Lessons



## Teaching for Understanding

***This chapter focuses on introducing and honing strategies for working with decimals.*** The objective for students is to compare decimals, compute decimals across operations, and see decimals as practical numbers in society. These lessons bridge the gap for students to move on to more developed mathematical logic, and it is crucial for students to comprehend these concepts for math classes in the future.

## Prerequisite Skills and Concepts

- Comparing Numbers through 1,000
- Multiplying and Dividing by Powers of 10
- Multiplying Any Two Numbers

## Decimal and Measurement Skills Trace

| Before Grade 4 | Grade 4 | After Grade 4 |
|---|---|---|
| **Grade 3** Formally introduced to decimals and computing with decimals | **Chapter 7** introduced percentages and reviewed decimals and fractions. **This chapter** develops strategies for learning to use decimals as numbers. | Mastery of basic computation of decimals and use of decimals in various real-world situations |

## Problem Solving

Problem solving is in every lesson. This chapter includes the following:

**CHAPTER INTRODUCTION** Students solve a problem that uses decimals in comparing parts of wholes (pp. 382I–383C).

**EXPLORING PROBLEM SOLVING** The first lesson provides practice using decimals and metric units (pp. 414–415A). The second lesson provides actual television ratings to explore fractions, decimals, and proportional reasoning (pp. 434–436A).

## Games

Develop reasoning skills, and provide extensive practice.

**Roll a Decimal Game** (Lesson 9.5), **Find the Distance Game I and II** (Lesson 9.8), **Harder Roll a Decimal Game** (Lesson 9.10), **Checkbook Game and Harder Checkbook Game** (Lesson 9.11), **Decimal Roll a Problem Game** (Lesson 9.12), **Metric Unit Game** (Lesson 9.15)

# Math Background

## Decimals

### About Decimals

*Most students do not develop sufficient meanings for decimal symbols when they are introduced. Soon students are asked to learn rules for manipulating decimals. Because they do not know what the symbols mean, they have no way of figuring out why the rules work. . . . Without knowing what the symbols mean, students are unable to judge whether their answers are reasonable or whether they are on the right track. Because decimals are the last number system with which many students work, the initial errors they make persist and are difficult to remediate.*

Hiebert, James. "Decimal Fractions" *Arithmetic Teacher* March 1987.

- In decimals, as in whole numbers, the place value of each digit is ten times the value of the digit to its right.
- Calculation with decimals can generally be taught as an extension of calculation with whole numbers. Emphasizing the similarities helps students understand that decimal arithmetic does not really require a completely new set of rules.
- The algorithm for multiplying a decimal by a whole number is similar to the algorithm for multiplying two whole numbers, with the additional step of placing the decimal point in the product

### Decimals Less than 1

Decimals less than 1 are typically written with a 0 in the ones place for the following three reasons:

- It is the Standard International (SI) convention.
- It makes it clearer that there is a decimal point in the number. For example, it is less likely for .7 to be read as 7 if the zero is included (0.7).
- Most calculators display numbers less than 1 with a 0 in the ones place.

You might explain these points to students, especially if they ask about the 0.

In those cases, however, where the ones-place 0 might confuse rather than clarify, as in some problems involving multiplication of decimals, we will omit the 0. Also, to parallel real life, we sometimes show money amounts without the zero. In any event, a student should not be marked wrong for giving a correct answer with the zero omitted.

### Precision

- Zeroes can be written to the right of a decimal without changing the value of the decimal. For example, 4.3 is the same number as 4.30 and 4.300. However, writing 0s after a measurement can change the meaning of the measurement.
- The number of decimal places in a measurement generally indicates the amount of precision in the measurement. For example, if the length of a board is given as 4 meters, the board was probably measured to the nearest meter. If the length is given as 4.3 meters, it was probably measured to the nearest tenth of a meter, or decimeter. Similarly, 4.30 meters indicates a measurement to the nearest hundredth of a meter, or centimeter, and 4.300 meters indicates a measurement to the nearest thousandth of a meter, or millimeter.
- A length given as 4.3 meters could actually be anywhere between 4.25 meters and 4.35 meters. A length given as 4.300 meters should be between 4.2995 meters and 4.3005 meters. Writing a measurement of 4.3 meters as 4.300 meters implies that the writer knows the measurement is more precise than it really is.

### Weight and Mass

- For simplicity, ***Real Math*** follows the common convention of measuring both weight and mass in kilograms.
- Technically, the pound is a unit of weight and a kilogram is a unit of mass. Weight is the amount of heaviness of an object; mass is the amount of matter an object contains. Mass is measured on a balance scale in kilograms (or slugs, in the customary system), whereas weight is measured on a spring scale in newtons (or pounds, in the customary system).
- As long as gravity remains constant, there is a direct relationship between weight and mass (weight = mass × gravity). However, mass is independent of gravity and weight is not. For example, someone who weighs 75 pounds on Earth has a mass of about 34 kilograms. On the moon, that person's mass remains about 34 kilograms, but his or her weight decreases to about 12 pounds.

CHAPTER 9 Overview

# What Research Says

## About Decimal Numbers

### How Children Learn Decimal Numbers

Fourth-grade students' development of number sense should continue with a focus on the structure of numbers and the relationships among numbers. Students need opportunities to recognize and generate equivalent representations and approximations for the same number. By studying fractions, decimals, and percentages simultaneously, students can learn to move among equivalent forms, flexibly choosing and using appropriate and convenient forms of a number to solve problems and express quantities.

In fourth grade students will use models and other strategies to represent and study decimal numbers. Students need to be exposed to a variety of activities to help them develop a rich understanding of decimal numbers and equivalence among the many representations of fractional parts of a whole. For example, calculator activities can help expose students to counting and place-value patterns for decimal numbers as they count. Similarly, involving students in an exploration of metric conversions while working with various metric units of measure provides students with meaningful and practical contexts of common uses of decimal numbers in their world.

Having students study and compare fractions, decimals, and percentages simultaneously encourages them to become familiar and comfortable working with either decimals, fractions, or percent forms of a number, choosing and using the form of the number that is best suited for the context of the problem they are solving. Students will develop an understanding of equivalence and approximations among fractions, decimals, and percentages and the information each type of representation conveys, and with these understandings and skills, they should be able to develop strategies for computing with familiar fractions and decimals.

(Adapted from the National Council of Teachers of Mathematics. *Principles and Standards for School Mathematics*. Reston, VA: NCTM, 2000, pp. 148–150)

### Research-Based Teaching Strategies

*Some important changes must be made in the way decimals are commonly taught if we hope to improve students' understanding and performance.*

1. *More time must be devoted to developing the meaning of decimal fractions symbols when they are introduced.*
2. *Many of the rules students are taught for working with decimal numbers should be developed from the meaning of the symbols.*
3. *Students should be asked to estimate the answers to decimal computation problems before calculating, especially those for which the algorithm is more complicated—multiplication and division. Estimation helps students understand what the algorithm is doing for them and judge the reasonableness of their calculated answers.*

*Fourth-grade students should build their understanding of fractions as parts of a whole and as one representation of division. This understanding will develop as the children are given opportunities to see and explore a variety of models of fractions, focusing primarily on familiar fractions such as halves, thirds, fourths, fifths, sixths, eighths, and tenths. Students will see how fractions are related to a unit whole, compare fractional parts of a whole, and find equivalent fractions.*

(Hiebert, James. "Decimal Fractions" *Arithmetic Teacher* March 1987.)

### RESEARCH IN ACTION

**Decimal Numbers** Chapter 9 continues to reinforce the development of part–whole number concepts and develops an understanding of how decimal numbers represent fractional parts of a whole.

**Metric Units of Measure** Throughout Chapter 9 students will develop an awareness and appreciation of the role that *ten* plays in metric units of measure and metric conversions.

**Equivalence** Chapter 9 will provide students with a variety of activities and contexts for thinking about part–whole relationships with numbers as represented by decimals, fractions, and percentages.

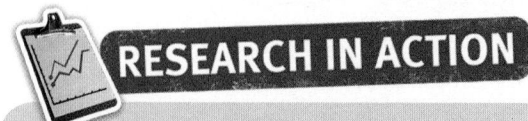

## Vocabulary

**coordinates** (Lesson 4.2) a pair of numbers that give the location of a point on a graph; also called ordered pairs of numbers

**cubic centimeter** (Lesson 9.15) a unit of volume equal to the volume of a rectangular solid that is 1 centimeter long, 1 centimeter wide, and 1 centimeter deep

**decimal point** (Lesson 9.1) a dot used to separate the ones digit from the tenths digit

**deposit** (Lesson 9.11) to put into a checking or savings account

**difference** (Lesson 2.2) remainder left after subtracting one quantity from another

**equation** (Lesson 3.9) a mathematical statement showing that one quantity or expression is equal to another quantity or expression

**equivalent** (Lesson 7.3) having the same value

**metric system** (Lesson 9.7) a decimal system of measurement that uses the meter as the fundamental unit of length

**power** (Lesson 5.1) the number of times a given number or expression is multiplied by itself

**precision** (Lesson 9.4) the state of being precise or exact

**product** (Lesson 3.1) the result of multiplying two or more numbers (factors)

**rounding** (Lesson 9.3) changing a number to another number that is easier to work with and that is close enough for the purpose of a particular problem

**sum** (Lesson 2.1) a result obtained from addition

**volume** (Lesson 6.6) the amount of space an object can hold

**withdraw** (Lesson 9.11) to remove from a checking or savings account

## English Learner

### Cognates

For English learners, a quick way to acquire new English vocabulary words is to build on what is known in the primary language.

| English | Spanish |
|---|---|
| cents | centavos |
| decimal point | punto decimal |
| equal | igual |
| metric | métrica |

### Access Vocabulary

English learners may understand words in different contexts or not understand idioms. Review chapter vocabulary for this concern. For example:

| | |
|---|---|
| value | worth |
| to convert | to change one thing for another |
| plot | to locate the point on a graph where two coordinates intersect |

CHAPTER 9 Overview

# Chapter Planner

| Lessons | Objectives | NCTM Standards | State Standards |
|---|---|---|---|
| **9.1 Parts of a Whole** pages 384A–387B 60 minutes | **Review the concepts of decimals** by demonstrating their relationships to corresponding fractions | Number and Operations | |
| **9.2 Decimals and Fractions** Pages 388A–391B 60 minutes | **Begin to develop concepts of comparing decimals** by understanding tenths, hundredths, and thousandths | Number and Operations | |
| **9.3 Comparing Decimals** Pages 392A–393A 60 minutes | **Explore strategies for comparing decimals** through understanding the relative magnitude of decimals | Number and Operations | |
| **9.4 Ordering Decimals** Pages 394A–397B 60 minutes | **Explore strategies for ordering a set of decimals** by building on the basic decimal comparisons made in Lesson 9.3 | Number and Operations | |
| **9.5 Rounding Decimals** Pages 398A–399A 60 minutes | **Explore strategies for rounding decimals to a specified degree** by applying knowledge of the relative magnitude of decimals | Number and Operations | |
| **9.6 Multiplying and Dividing by Powers of 10** Pages 400A–403B 60 minutes | **Begin to develop concepts for multiplying and dividing** by powers of 10 through the conversion of metric measurements | Number and Operations | |
| **9.7 Metric Units** Pages 404A–405A 60 minutes | **Explore the relationships among metric units** by applying the multiplication and division skills learned in Lesson 9.6 | Number and Operations<br>Measurement | |
| **9.8 Metric Measurements of Length** Pages 406A–409B 60 minutes | **Express metric units as decimals in a common unit** by recalling multiplication and division by powers of 10 | Number and Operations<br>Measurement | |
| **9.9 Adding and Subtracting Decimals** Pages 410A–413B 60 minutes | **Explore strategies for adding and subtracting decimals** by solving practical problems | Number and Operations<br>Problem Solving | |
| **9.10 Using Decimals** Pages 418A–419A 60 minutes | **Explore strategies for adding and subtracting decimals** by solving word problems based on real-life situations | Number and Operations<br>Problem Solving | |
| **9.11 Balancing a Checkbook** Pages 420A–423B 60 minutes | **Practice adding and subtracting decimals** by using a checkbook scenario | Number and Operations<br>Problem Solving | |
| **9.12 Multiplying a Decimal by a Whole Number** Pages 424A–427B 60 minutes | **Explore strategies for finding a product from a decimal and a whole number** while being introduced to multiplying a decimal by another decimal | Number and Operations | |
| **9.13 Graphing and Applying Decimals** Pages 428A–429A 60 minutes | **Practice multiplying decimals by whole numbers** by applying decimals to the measurement of metric weight and volume | Number and Operations | |
| **9.14 Metric Units of Weight and Volume** Pages 430A–431A 60 minutes | **Practice multiplication of decimals** by reflecting the metric units of weight and volume of liquids | Measurement | |
| **9.15 Cubic Centimeters** Pages 432A–433A 60 minutes | **Practice multiplication of decimals** by extending knowledge learned in Lesson 9.14 to volume of solids | Measurement<br>Problem Solving | |

# Additional Resources

| Vocabulary | Manipulatives and Materials | Games to reinforce skills and concepts |
|---|---|---|
| decimal point | • Response Wheels<br>• Base-Ten blocks (optional)<br>• Play money (optional) | |
| equivalent | • Response Wheels<br>• Overhead projector transparencies of a hundredths grid from *Practice*<br>• Base-Ten blocks | |
| rounding | • Response Wheels<br>• Stopwatches<br>• Play money | |
| precision | • Number Cubes<br>• Calculators (optional) | Roll a Decimal Game (New) |
| rounding | • Number Cubes | Roll a Decimal Game (Lesson 9.4) |
| decimal point | • Response Wheels | |
| metric system | • Metersticks<br>• Metric rulers<br>• Base-Ten blocks (optional) | |
| precision | • Response Wheels<br>• Chart paper<br>• Graph paper<br>• Metric rulers<br>• Find the Distance I and II Game Mats<br>• Number Cubes | Find the Distance I and II Game Mats (New) |
| sum<br>difference | • Play money (optional)<br>• Graph paper (optional) | |
| equation | • Number Cubes<br>• Graph paper (optional) | Harder Roll a Decimal Game (New) |
| deposit<br>withdrawal | • Response Wheels<br>• Counters (optional)<br>• Sample check stubs (optional)<br>• Sample check registers (optional) | Checkbook Game (New)<br>Harder Checkbook Game (New) |
| product | • Response Wheels<br>• Calculators<br>• Number Cubes | Decimal Roll a Problem Game (New) |
| coordinates | • Graph paper<br>• Play money (optional)<br>• Number Cubes | Decimal Roll a Problem Game (Lesson 9.12) |
| volume | • Response Wheels<br>• Graph Paper<br>• Metric scale or balance and metric weights<br>• Litter containers<br>• Index cards (optional) | Metric Unit Game (New) |
| cubic centimeter | • Response Wheels<br>• Measuring tools (optional)<br>• Number Cubes | |

## Differentiated Instruction

*Intervention Support Guide* provides instruction for the following prerequisite skills:

- Lesson 9.A Comparing Numbers through 1,000
- Lesson 9.B Multiplying and Dividing by Powers of 10
- Lesson 9.C Multiplying Any Two Numbers

*Enrichment Support Guide*

*Practice*

*Reteach Support Guide*

*English Learner Support Guide*

## Technology

The following electronic resources are available:

**Planner** Lessons 9.1–9.15

**Presentation** Lessons 9.1–9.15

**Textbook** Lessons 9.1–9.15

**Assess** Lessons 9.1–9.15

**MathTools** **Base-Ten Blocks** Lessons 9.1, 9.15; **Number Line** Lessons 9.1–9.6; **Metric and Customary Units Tool** Lessons 9.7–9.8, 9.14; **Electronic Ruler** Lessons 9.7–9.8; **Calculator** Lessons 9.9–9.10, 9.12; **Spreadsheet** Lesson 9.11

CHAPTER 9 Overview

# Chapter Planner, continued

| Problem Solving | When to Use | Objectives | NCTM Standards | Skills Covered |
|---|---|---|---|---|
| **Chapter Introduction** pages 382I–383C 15–30 minutes | Use after the Chapter 9 Pretest | Introduce chapter concepts in a problem-solving setting | Communicating<br>Reasoning and Proof | Reading Charts<br>Fractions |
| **Exploring Problem Solving** pages 414–415A 30–45 minutes | Use any time during the chapter | Explore methods of solving nonroutine problems | Measurement<br>Representation<br>Connections | Making Diagrams, Ratios, Decimals, Metric Units |
| **Exploring Problem Solving** pages 434–436A 45–60 minutes | Use any time after the first Exploring Problem Solving | Develop logical reasoning while integrating reading skills with mathematics | Algebra<br>Data Analysis and Probablity | Fractions, Decimals, Reading Charts |

| Review | | | | |
|---|---|---|---|---|
| **Cumulative Review** pages 416–417 15–30 minutes | Use any time after Lesson 9.7 | Review concepts and skills taught earlier in the year | Algebra<br>Problem Solving<br>Number and Operations | Fractions, Multiplication, Percents, Multiples, Factors |
| **Cumulative Review** pages 437–438 15–30 minutes | Use any time after Lesson 9.15 | Review concepts and skills taught earlier in the year | Measurement, Number and Operations, Algebra, Reasoning | Measurement, Division, Multiplication, Reasoning |
| **Chapter 9 Review** pages 440–441 30–45 minutes | Use after Lesson 9.15 | Review concepts and skills taught in the chapter | Measurement, Number and Operations, Problem Solving | Decimals, Fractions, Metric Systems |

| Assessment | | | | |
|---|---|---|---|---|
| **Informal Assessment** (pp. 384A–433A) Rubrics | Use at the end of the lesson | Provide daily evaluation of math proficiency | Problem Solving<br>Reasoning and Proof<br>Communication | Computing, Understanding, Reasoning, Applying, Engaging |
| **Pretest** (*Assessment* p. 126) 15–30 minutes | Use after or in place of the Chapter 8 Review | Provide assessment or additional practice of the chapter concepts | Number and Operations<br>Measurement | Comparing Numbers, Multidigit Addition and Subtraction, Converting Metric Measurements |
| **Individual Oral Assessment** (p. 417A) 5 minutes per student | Begin after Lesson 9.7 | Provide alternate means of assessing students' progress | Numbers and Operations<br>Measurement<br>Problem Solving | Decimals |
| **Mastery Checkpoint** (*Assessment* pp. T71–T74) 5 minutes per student | Use after or in place of the Chapter 9 Review | Provide assessment or additional practice of the chapter concepts | Measurement<br>Number and Operations | Comparing Decimals, Multiplying and Dividing of Multiples of 10, Adding and Subtracting Decimals, Measurement |
| **Chapter 9 Practice Test** (pp. 442–445A) 30–45 minutes | Use after or in place of the Chapter 9 Review | Provide assessment or additional practice of the chapter concepts | Measurement<br>Number and Operations<br>Problem Solving | Decimal, Fractions, Metric System |
| **Chapter 9 Test** (*Assessment* pp. 136–139) 30–45 minutes | Use after or in place of the Chapter 9 Review | Provide assessment or additional practice of the chapter concepts | Measurement<br>Number and Operations<br>Problem Solving | Decimals, Fractions, Metric System |

# Technology Resources and Support

Visit SRAonline.com for online versions of the ***Real Math eSuite.***

## Technology for Teachers

| | |
|---|---|
| **e Presentation** | Lessons 9.1–9.15 Use the ***ePresentation*** to interactively present chapter content. |
| **e Planner** | Use the Chapter and Lesson Planners to outline activities and time frames for Chapter 9. |
| **e Assess** | Students can take the following assessment in ***eAssess:***<br>• Chapter Pretest<br>• Mastery Checkpoint Lessons 9.4, 9.7, 9.9, and 9.14<br>• Chapter Test<br>Teachers can record results and print reports for all assessments in this chapter. |
| **e MathTools** | **Base-Ten Blocks** Lessons 9.1, 9.15; **Number Line** Lessons 9.1–9.6; **Metric and Customary Unit Tool** Lessons 9.7–9.8, 9.14; **Electronic Ruler** Lessons 9.7–9.8; **Calculator** Lessons 9.9–9.10, 9.12; **Spreadsheet** Lessons 9.11 |

## Technology for Students

| | |
|---|---|
| **e Textbook** | An electronic, interactive version of the ***Student Edition*** is available for all lessons in Chapter 9. |
| **e MathTools** | **Base-Ten Blocks** Lessons 9.1, 9.15; **Number Line** Lessons 9.1–9.6; **Metric and Customary Units Tool** Lessons 9.7–9.8, 9.14; **Electronic Ruler** Lessons 9.7–9.8; **Calculator** Lessons 9.9–9.10, 9.12; **Spreadsheet** Lesson 9.11 |
| SRA TECH KNOWLEDGE | ***TechKnowledge*** Level 4 provides lessons that specifically teach the Unit 10 Internet, Unit 9 Electronic Reference, and Unit 7 Spreadsheet applications that students can use while working on this chapter's projects. |

# Decimals and Measurement

## 1 Introduce Chapter 9 5

### Chapter Objectives

Explain to students that in this chapter they will build on what they already know about decimals. They will

- learn strategies for comparing decimals.
- learn about the relationships among metric units.
- add, subtract, and multiply decimals.

### Pretest COMPUTING

Administer the Pretest in ***Assessment.***

The Pretest for Chapter 9 covers the following prerequisite skills:

- Rounding (Problems 1–2)
- Using relation signs (Problems 3–4)
- Multidigit addition and subtraction (Problems 5–8)
- Multiplying by powers of 10 (Problems 9–10)
- Converting metric units (Problems 11–12)

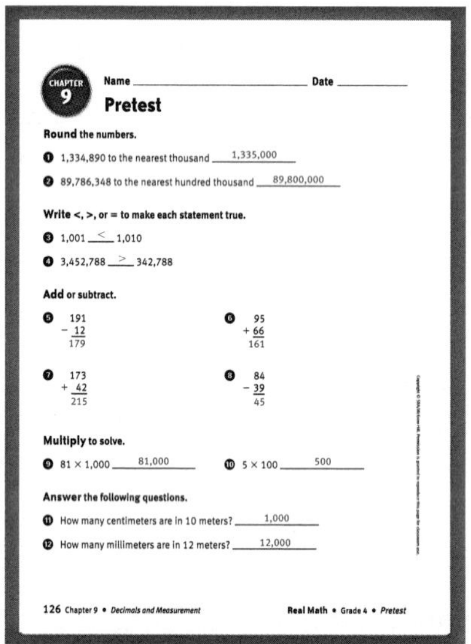
CHAPTER 9 Name ________ Date ________

**Pretest**

**Round the numbers.**

1. 1,334,890 to the nearest thousand 1,335,000
2. 89,786,348 to the nearest hundred thousand 89,800,000

**Write <, >, or = to make each statement true.**

3. 1,001 < 1,010
4. 3,452,788 > 342,788

**Add or subtract.**

5. 191 − 12 = 179
6. 95 + 66 = 161
7. 173 + 42 = 215
8. 84 − 39 = 45

**Multiply to solve.**

9. 81 × 1,000 81,000
10. 5 × 100 500

**Answer the following questions.**

11. How many centimeters are in 10 meters? 1,000
12. How many millimeters are in 12 meters? 12,000

126 Chapter 9 • *Decimals and Measurement* — **Real Math** • Grade 4 • *Pretest*

Chapter 9 Pretest

The Pretest also covers the following topics from this chapter:

- Converting fractions to decimals (Problems 13–14)
- Comparing the value of decimals (Problems 15–17)
- Ordering and adding decimals (Problems 18–19)
- Metric units of length (Problems 20–21)
- Multiplying numbers with decimals by whole numbers (Problem 22)

### Access Prior Knowledge UNDERSTANDING

Have students discuss the television industry. Ask questions such as the following:

- Have you or anyone you know ever been on a television program?
- What is your favorite television show?
- What kind of commercials appear during your favorite show?

## 2 Exploring Problem Solving 20

### Tell Students In Today's Lesson They Will

- look at a survey about the television shows watched by some fourth graders.
- discuss which television show is most popular.
- choose a television show during which students will air their commercial.

### Using Student Pages

Read with students the survey information on page 383. Ask questions such as the following:

- **How many students were surveyed?** 100
- **How many of the students surveyed watched *Halftime?*** 21
- **How many of the students surveyed were not watching television when *Halftime* was on?** 17
- **How many of the students surveyed were watching other shows when *Halftime* was on?** 62

### Answers to Problems 1–3

**Problem 1**

*My Friend Max:* $\frac{19}{100}$ or about $\frac{1}{5}$; *Halftime:* $\frac{21}{100}$ or about $\frac{1}{5}$; *Space Kids:* $\frac{5}{100}$ or $\frac{1}{20}$

**Problem 2**

*My Friend Max:* $\frac{19}{54}$ or about $\frac{1}{3}$; *Halftime:* $\frac{21}{83}$ or about $\frac{1}{4}$; *Space Kids:* $\frac{5}{10}$ or $\frac{1}{2}$

**Problem 3**

Students may not agree on how to interpret the term *most popular*. Some may say that *Halftime* was the most popular show because more students watched *Halftime* than either of the other two shows. Some may say that it is not a fair comparison because *Halftime* is on when a lot of students watch television. They might argue that if *My Friend Max* had been shown at a better time more students would have watched it. Encourage students to explore these issues, because these are the kinds of issues that networks and advertisers deal with.

You need not go into the details about television ratings. In the next Problem Solving lesson, students will learn the basics of how television ratings are calculated and solve problems related to ratings. Also, students will learn more about ratings as they explore the CyberSolver on page 382–383.

Student Page

# Chapter 9 Decimals and Measurement

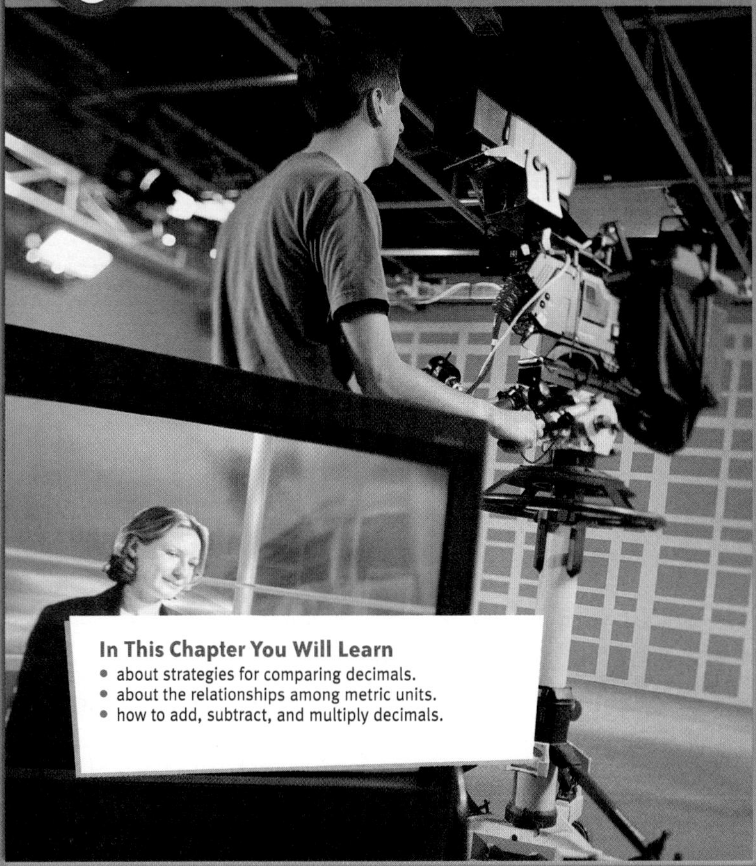

**In This Chapter You Will Learn**

- about strategies for comparing decimals.
- about the relationships among metric units.
- how to add, subtract, and multiply decimals.

Student Page

## Problem Solving

John took a survey to see which television shows students in his grade watched. He picked three of his favorite shows. He asked all 100 fourth graders in his school whether they watched these shows last week. He also asked if they watched any show during those times. He recorded his results in a table.

REAL WORLD

| TV Show | Day | Time | Number Who Watched This Show | Number Who Watched TV at this Time |
|---|---|---|---|---|
| My Friend Max | Sat. | 9:00 – 9:30 a.m. | 19 | 54 |
| Halftime | Tues. | 7:30 – 8:00 p.m. | 21 | 83 |
| Space Kids | Sun. | 1:00 – 1:30 p.m. | 5 | 10 |

**Work with a group to answer these questions.**

1. What fraction of all fourth graders watched each show?
2. About what fraction of fourth graders who were watching television watched each show?
3. Which show do you think is most popular? Why?
4. If a company wants to put a commercial on television, it pays the station or the network. The price depends on the show. Why do you think it costs so much more to put on a commercial during *Halftime* than during *Space Kids?*

**Prices for a 30-Second Commercial**

| TV Show | Price |
|---|---|
| *My Friend Max* | $50,000 |
| *Halftime* | $100,000 |
| *Space Kids* | $5,000 |

5. If you were putting a commercial on television, which show would you choose in order to get the most value for your money? Explain.

383

Use Problem 4 to initiate a discussion about television advertising. Help students understand that sponsors pay to put a commercial on the air to help their business advertise. If a greater number of potential customers see an advertisement, an advertiser will be willing to pay a greater amount to run the advertisement.

Have students work in groups on Problem 5. Provide help as needed. Encourage students to use whatever problem-solving strategy or strategies they think will work. Encourage students to estimate and to use proportional reasoning.

## Answers to Problems 4–5

### Problem 4

More people watch *Halftime* than *Space Kids.*

### Problem 5

One way to approach the value of an ad is to look at the cost of reaching each viewer. On that basis, *Space Kids* is the best value. Students can compare the value of advertising during these three shows by asking themselves a question such as: *Since an ad on* Halftime *costs twice as much as an ad on* My Friend Max, *will it be seen by twice as many kids?* The answer is clearly no if the survey is indicative of the general population, because about the same number of students watched each show.

You may want to discuss other factors that advertisers consider, such as reaching the intended audience. A company advertising a children's toy may want to make sure its advertisement is seen by children who would want the toy *and* by adults who would buy the toy for a child. You might also point out that companies use their advertising budget to run their commercials during more than one show and in other media besides television, such as newspapers, magazines, and radio.

## CyberSolver

To extend problem solving, have students use the Internet to find the answers to the following questions:

- **How do we know how many people watched a television show?**
- **Why is it important for television stations to know how many people watch each show?**
- **What are television ratings?**
- **What are the ratings for some of your favorite shows?**

Students can find information about television ratings by searching the Internet using key phrases such as *Nielsen ratings, television ratings,* and *ratings of television shows*. They can get ratings for recent weeks on the Web site http://www.televisionweek.com/page.cms?pageId=10.

CHAPTER 9

# Introduction

## Exploring Problem Solving, continued

### Concept/Question Board APPLYING

**Questions**

Have students write three questions they have about decimals and measurement and how they can be used. Then have them select one question to post on the Question side of the Board.

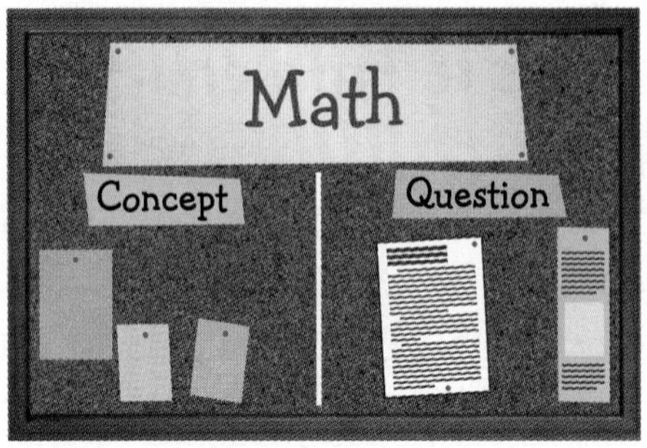


**Concepts**

As students work through the chapter, have them collect examples of how decimals and measurement are used in everyday situations. For each example, have students write problems that relate to the item(s). Have them display their examples on the Concept side of the Board.

Suggest the following:

- batting average
- box of cereal
- ruler

**Answers**

Throughout the chapter, have students post answers to the questions and solutions to the problems on the Board.

## 3 Reflect 5

### Knowledge Age Skills

**Effective Communication** Have groups present their answers and reasoning for Problem 5. After each group presents, ask questions such as the following:

- **Did you give valid reasons for your decision?**
- **What other factors might you have considered?**

### Home Connection

At this time, you may want to send home the letter on pages 34–37 of ***Home Connection.*** This letter describes what students will be learning and what activities they can do at home to support their work in school.

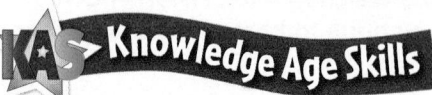

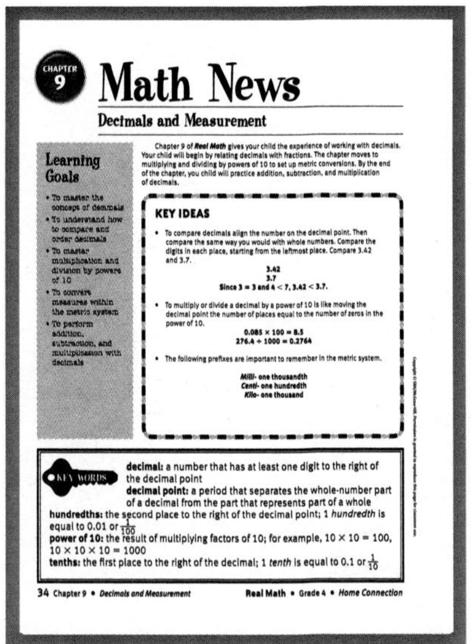

CHAPTER 9 **Math News**

**Decimals and Measurement**

**Learning Goals**

- To master the concept of decimals
- To understand how to compare and order decimals
- To master multiplication and division by powers of 10
- To convert measures within the metric system
- To perform addition, subtraction, and multiplication with decimals

Chapter 9 of ***Real Math*** gives your child the experience of working with decimals. Your child will begin by relating decimals with fractions. The chapter moves to multiplying and dividing by powers of 10 to set up metric conversions. By the end of the chapter, you child will practice addition, subtraction, and multiplication of decimals.

**KEY IDEAS**

- To compare decimals align the number on the decimal point. Then compare the same way you would with whole numbers. Compare the digits in each place, starting from the leftmost place. Compare 3.42 and 3.7.

  **3.42**
  **3.7**
  **Since 3 = 3 and 4 < 7, 3.42 < 3.7.**

- To multiply or divide a decimal by a power of 10 is like moving the decimal point the number of places equal to the number of zeros in the power of 10.

  **$0.085 \times 100 = 8.5$**
  **$276.4 \div 1000 = 0.2764$**

- The following prefixes are important to remember in the metric system.

  ***Milli-*** **one thousandth**
  ***Centi-*** **one hundredth**
  ***Kilo-*** **one thousand**

KEY WORDS

**decimal:** a number that has at least one digit to the right of the decimal point
**decimal point:** a period that separates the whole-number part of a decimal from the part that represents part of a whole
**hundredths:** the second place to the right of the decimal point; 1 *hundredth* is equal to 0.01 or $\frac{1}{100}$
**power of 10:** the result of multiplying factors of 10; for example, $10 \times 10 = 100$, $10 \times 10 \times 10 = 1000$
**tenths:** the first place to the right of the decimal; 1 *tenth* is equal to 0.1 or $\frac{1}{10}$

34 Chapter 9 • *Decimals and Measurement* **Real Math** • Grade 4 • *Home Connection*

Home Connection page 34

# 4 Assess and Differentiate

**e Assess** Use ***eAssess*** to record and analyze evidence of student understanding.

## A Gather Evidence

Use the Daily Class Assessment Records in ***Assessment*** or ***eAssess*** to record daily observations.

### Informal Assessment

**Access Prior Knowledge**

Did the student UNDERSTANDING

- ❑ make important observations?
- ❑ extend or generalize learning?
- ❑ provide insightful answers?
- ❑ pose insightful questions?

### Informal Assessment

**Concept/Question Board**

Did the student APPLYING

- ❑ apply learning in new situations?
- ❑ contribute concepts?
- ❑ contribute answers?
- ❑ connect mathematics to real-world situations?

### Formal Assessment

**Pretest** COMPUTING

Review student answers in each problem set.

- ❑ Rounding (Problems 1–2)
- ❑ Using relation signs (Problems 3–4)
- ❑ Multidigit addition and subtraction (Problems 5–8)
- ❑ Multiplying by powers of 10 (Problems 9–10)
- ❑ Converting metric units (Problems 11–12)
- ❑ Converting fractions to decimals (Problems 13–14)
- ❑ Comparing the value of decimals (Problems 15–17)
- ❑ Ordering and adding decimals (Problems 18–19)
- ❑ Metric units of length (Problems 20–21)
- ❑ Multiplying numbers with decimals by whole numbers (Problem 22)

## B Summarize Findings

Analyze and summarize assessment data for each student. Determine which Assessment Follow-Up is appropriate for each student. Use the Student Assessment Record on ***Assessment*** or ***eAssess*** to update assessment records.

## C Assessment Follow-Up • DIFFERENTIATE INSTRUCTION

### ENRICH

**If . . .** students demonstrate a secure understanding of chapter concepts,

**Then . . .** move quickly through the chapter or use ***Enrichment*** Lessons 9.1–9.15 as assessment follow-up to extend and apply understanding.

### PRACTICE

**If . . .** students grasp chapter concepts with competent understanding,

**Then . . .** use ***Practice*** Lessons 9.1–9.15 as lesson follow-up to develop fluency.

### RETEACH

**If . . .** students have prerequisite understanding but demonstrate emerging understanding of chapter concepts,

**Then . . .** use ***Reteach*** Lessons 9.1, 9.5, 9.6, 9.7, and 9.12 to reteach lesson concepts.

### INTERVENTION

**If . . .** students are not competent with prerequisite skills,

**Then . . .** use ***Intervention*** Lessons 9.A–9.C before each lesson to develop fluency with prerequisite skills.

### ENGLISH LEARNER

Use ***English Learner Support Guide*** Lessons 9.1–9.15 for strategies to preteach lesson vocabulary and concepts.

# Math Across the Curriculum

Preview the chapter projects with students. Assign or have students choose from the projects to extend and enrich concepts in this chapter.

## Design a Set Using Metric Units

1–2 weeks

**Math Objective**
To reinforce studies of metric measurements by creating a scale model of a theatrical set

**Fine Arts Objective**
To reinforce studies of design by creating a set design based upon a theatrical script

**Technology Objective**
To use gadgets such as scanners and printers to design a theatrical set

Have students use mathematics to design and create a scale model of a theatrical set. To broaden the fine arts concepts, have students choose a play script which you are currently studying.

As part of the project, students should consider the following issues:

- whether the design will be realistic or abstract
- the time, place, and mood of the play
- the actors' movements
- the scale of objects within the set
- the colors to be used

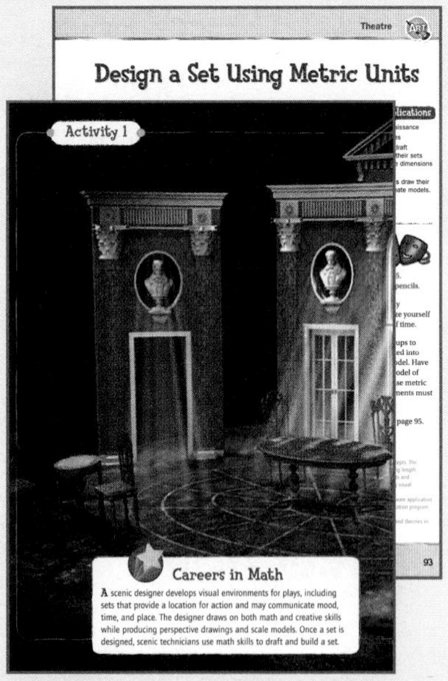


For specific step-by-step instructions for this project, see ***Across the Curriculum Math Connections*** pages 92–95.

### Knowledge Age Skills

**Teamwork** Students work in groups to determine the best design to model.

**Problem Formulation, Planning, and Strategizing** Students plan and strategize to design a set and build the three-dimensional model.

## Research Television Ratings

1–2 weeks

**Math Objective**
To reinforce studies of decimals as parts of a whole

**Social Studies Objective**
To reinforce studies of services

**Technology Objective**
To use electronic reference sources to search for information

While considering how television ratings could be used to plan a television commercial for a product, have students use technology to

- select a product to advertise on television.
- gather information about television ratings, demographics, and top-rated television shows.
- discover what other ratings research is available.

For this project, students use the Internet and electronic reference sources to investigate the following:

- advertising categories
- U.S. demographics
- Nielsen ratings
- the relationship of television ratings to demographics

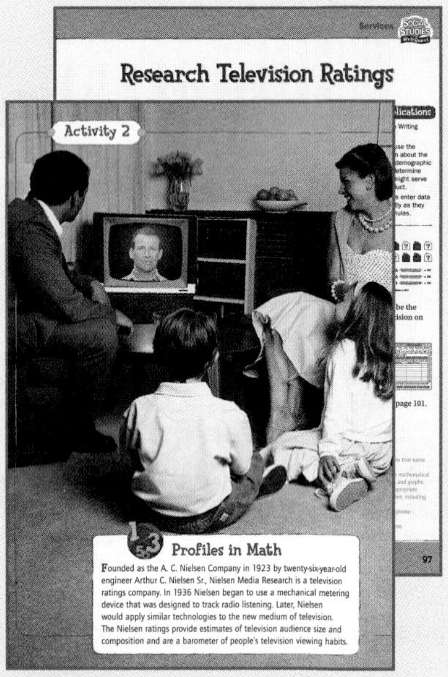


For specific step-by-step instructions for this project, see ***Across the Curriculum Math Connections*** pages 96–101.

### Knowledge Age Skills

**Creative Work with Ideas** Students explore the information within the role of an advertising executive.

**Problem Formulation, Planning, and Strategizing** Students choose strategies to plan an effective television commercial.

*TechKnowledge* Level 4 provides lessons that specifically teach the Unit 10 Internet, Unit 9 Electronic Reference, and Unit 7 Spreadsheet applications that students can use in this project.

## Lesson Planner

### OBJECTIVES
- To reintroduce the meaning of standard notation for decimals
- To demonstrate the relationship of decimals to corresponding fractions
- To review the concept of decimal place value

### NCTM STANDARDS
**Number and Operations**
Understand numbers, ways of representing numbers, relationships among numbers, and number systems

**Connections**
Understand how mathematical ideas interconnect and build on one another to produce a coherent whole

### MATERIALS
- ***Response Wheels**
- *Base-ten blocks (optional)
- *Play money (optional)

### TECHNOLOGY
**e Presentation** Lesson 9.1
**e MathTools Base-Ten Blocks; Number Lines (Converting between Percents, Decimals, and Fractions)**
**e Games Cube 100**

### TEST PREP
**Cumulative Review**
Mental Math reviews comparing decimal values (Lesson 7.5).

### Looking Ahead
In Lesson 9.2, you will need transparency copies of page 146 from ***Practice*** (tenths and hundredths grids for class discussion).

*Manipulative Kit Item

# Parts of a Whole

**Context of the Lesson** Students have worked with decimals used to represent monetary amounts throughout the year. Students worked with decimals in the context of time measurements and centiseconds in Chapter 7. Chapter 10 of Grade 3 also focused on decimals. The first five lessons in this sequence provide opportunities to build an understanding of decimals before moving on to metric measurement and arithmetic with decimals.

See page 382B for Math Background for teachers for this lesson.

## Planning for Learning • DIFFERENTIATE INSTRUCTION

### INTERVENTION
**If . . .** students lack the prerequisite skill of comparing numbers through 1,000,

**Then . . .** teach ***Intervention*** Lesson 9.A.

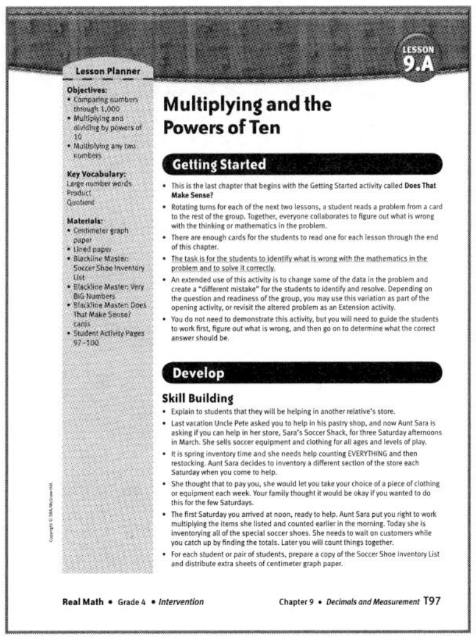
Lesson Planner
LESSON 9.A
Multiplying and the Powers of Ten
Getting Started
Develop

Intervention Lesson 9.A

### ENGLISH LEARNER
**Preview**

**If . . .** students need language support,

**Then . . .** use Lesson 9.1 in ***English Learner Support Guide*** to preview lesson concepts and vocabulary.

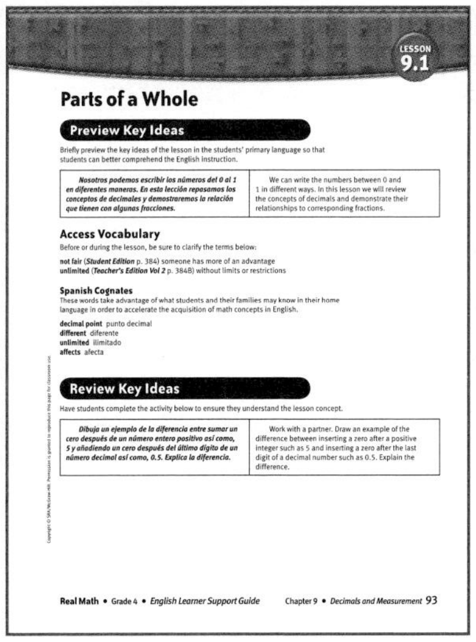
LESSON 9.1
Parts of a Whole
Preview Key Ideas
Access Vocabulary
Spanish Cognates
Review Key Ideas

English Learner Lesson 9.1

### ENRICH
**If . . .** students are proficient in the lesson concepts,

**Then . . .** emphasize chapter projects.

### PRACTICE
**If . . .** students would benefit from additional practice,

**Then . . .** extend Guided Discussion before assigning the student pages.

### RETEACH
**If . . .** students are having difficulty understanding parts of a whole,

**Then . . .** extend Guided Discussion before assigning the student pages.

### Vocabulary
**decimal point** ***n.*** a dot used in separating the ones digit from the tenths digit

### Access Vocabulary
**"That's not fair"** When we feel someone has more of an advantage, we might say this.

### Spanish Cognates
**decimal points** punto decimal
**different** diferente

# Teaching Lesson 9.1

## Mental Math

5

THUMBS UP

Write the number 4 on the board. Then read a series of decimals such as the following aloud. Students should respond by showing thumbs-up if the decimal is greater than 4, thumbs-down if it is less than 4, or an open hand if the decimal is equal to 4.

**a.** 7.00 up
**b.** 0.6 down
**c.** 4.00 open hand
**d.** 4.1 up
**e.** 3.09 down
**f.** 5.0 up
**g.** 8.0 up
**h.** 0.73 down
**i.** 0.0958 down
**J.** 4.001 up

## 1 Develop

25

### Tell Students In Today's Lesson They Will

review the concepts of decimals, and demonstrate their relationships to corresponding fractions.

### Guided Discussion

UNDERSTANDING

Whole Group

Tell students they are going to have a contest to find out who can think of the least number that is still greater than zero. Once students start giving fractional or decimal answers, they might give successively smaller answers, such as one-thousandth, one-millionth, and so on. Guide students to realize that there is an unlimited quantity of small numbers that are greater than zero.

Review the meaning of decimal numbers less than 1 and how to write them. Start with fractions that students are familiar with from Chapter 8, and ask them if they remember their decimal equivalents. Write decimal equivalents on the board, and review how they are read. For example, if a volunteer gave the decimal equivalent of $\frac{1}{10}$ as 0.1, explain that it is read *one-tenth* or *zero point one.* This can also be demonstrated using the ***eMathTools: Number Line.***

**NOTE:** This program follows the convention of writing 0 in the ones place for decimals less than 1, except in cases where it might be confusing. This is especially true in the course of a calculation such as $0.1 \times 4$ or $3 \div 0.1$. However, written answers and oral responses that omit the 0 should be accepted. Students should understand that many people write decimals without the 0. The reason the 0 is there is to reduce the probability that a reader will fail to notice the decimal point.

Review fractions and decimal equivalents of smaller and smaller quantities (for example, hundredths, thousandths) and how to write and name them. Discuss the decimal system of writing numbers and how it is based on 10. Draw a chart on the board or overhead projector similar to the one on page 386. If further clarification is needed, use play money, base-ten blocks, or ***eMathTools: Base-Ten Blocks.***

Ask questions such as the following:

- **How many times greater is \$3 than \$0.30?** 10 times greater
- **How many times greater is \$0.30 than \$0.03?** 10 times greater
- **What does moving to the left in a number do for the value of the digit?** Each place is worth ten times as much as the one to its right. Hundreds are 10 times the tens, which are in turn 10 times the ones.
- **What does moving to the right do for the worth of the digit?** Each place is one tenth as much. Ones are a tenth of tens, which are in turn a tenth of hundreds.
- **If this is always true in the decimal system, what should happen when we go to the right of the ones place?** It's value will be a tenth of that in the ones place.
- **Would it be more or less than 1?** less
- **If you write 0.999. . . (9 with a million nines), is the number greater than or less than 1?** less than 1

Emphasize the importance of the decimal point as an indication of the break between the whole number part and the fractional part represented by the decimal. The decimal point tells us where the ones digit is—to the left of the point.

Review how to read different decimal numbers. For example, 6 tens, 9 ones, 4 tenths, and 2 hundredths can be written 69.42 and would be read as *sixty-nine and forty-two hundredths* or *sixty-nine point four two.* The naming convention for decimals involves naming the least unit. Discourage the use of decimals read as *point forty-two.* A better option is *point four two*, because students may think point forty-two is greater than zero point five (0.5).

**NOTE:** Fractions and decimals are both names for rational numbers, but not all fractions have decimal names. For example; $\frac{1}{3}$ as a decimal is 0.333. . . .

### Skill Practice

APPLYING

Whole Group

1. Say a decimal with the class. For example, if you chose the decimal 3.06, you should say *three and six hundredths.*
2. Students should then show the decimal on their ***Response Wheels.*** Use examples such as the following:

**a.** 4.65
**b.** 0.36
**c.** 20.2
**d.** 5.05
**e.** 94.23
**f.** 0.94

We can approximate $\frac{1}{3}$ as a decimal as precisely as we wish but we cannot find an exact decimal equivalent. Only rational numbers that can be represented by fractions whose denominators have prime factors of 2 and 5 can be represented as decimals.

# 2 Assign Student Pages 25

## Pages 384–385 APPLYING

Have students complete page 385 independently. You may want to complete several problems with the class.

### RESEARCH IN ACTION

"Most students do not develop sufficient meanings for decimal symbols when they are introduced. Soon students are asked to learn rules for manipulating decimals. Because they do not know what the symbols mean, they have no way of figuring out why the rules work. They must memorize each rule and hope that they remember on which problems to use them, a method that works for the simplest routine problems that are practiced heavily but not for problems that are even a little different. Without knowing what the symbols mean, students are unable to judge whether their answers are reasonable or whether they are on the right track. Because decimals are the last number system with which many students work, the initial errors they make persist and are difficult to remediate."

Hiebert, James. "Decimal Fractions" *Arithmetic Teacher*. March 1987.

Student Page

## LESSON 9.1 Parts of a Whole

### Key Ideas

**You can write numbers between 0 and 1 in different ways.**

"I just made up a game," said June. "What's the least number greater than 0 that you can make?"

"I know," shouted Andy. "It's 1."

"I can do better than that," said Rico. "I say $\frac{1}{2}$."

"That's not fair," said Andy. "We can't use that kind of number."

"It's my game," said June. "Any kind of number is all right. And I'm going to say $\frac{1}{10}$."

"Well," said Andy, "I can make a number that's even less."

Which of the following might Andy use as an example?

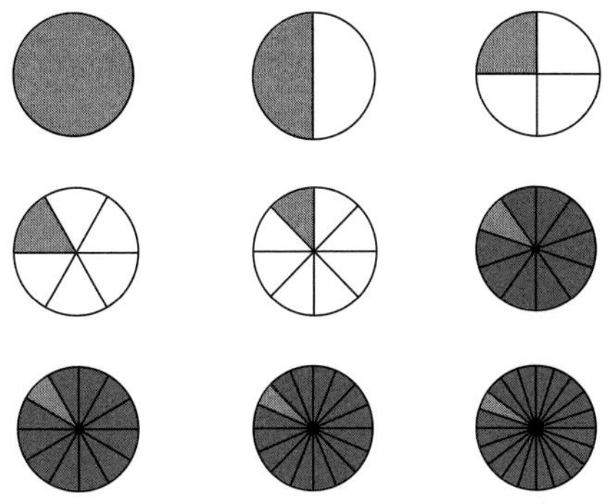

The last three figures ($\frac{1}{12}$, $\frac{1}{16}$, and $\frac{1}{20}$) are examples of numbers less than $\frac{1}{10}$.

384 eTextbook This lesson is available in the *eTextbook*.

Student Page

If you divide a whole into ten equal parts, each part is one-tenth of the whole.

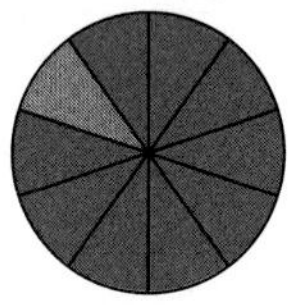

We can write one-tenth in different ways:

As a fraction: $\frac{1}{10}$

As a decimal: 0.1

$\frac{1}{10} = 0.1$

When you read 0.1, you say "one tenth" or "zero point one."

If you divide a whole number into one hundred equal parts, each part is one-hundredth of the whole.

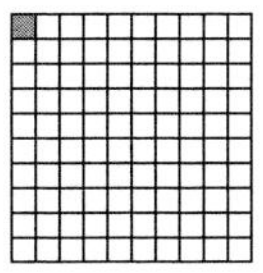

We can write one-hundredth in two ways:

As a fraction: $\frac{1}{100}$

As a decimal: 0.01

$\frac{1}{100} = 0.01$

When you read 0.01, you say "one one-hundredth" or "zero point zero one."

**Answer** these questions.

1. Suppose you divide 1 into 1,000 equal parts. What would each part be? Write it in two ways. $\frac{1}{1{,}000}$; 0.001
2. Suppose you divide 1 into 10,000 equal parts. Show two ways to write what each part would be. $\frac{1}{10{,}000}$; 0.0001
3. Suppose you divide 1 into 100,000 equal parts. Show two ways to write what each part would be. $\frac{1}{100{,}000}$; 0.00001
4. Suppose you divide 1 into 1,000,000 equal parts. Show two ways to write what each part would be. $\frac{1}{1{,}000{,}000}$; 0.000001
5. Which is greater, $\frac{1}{10}$ or $\frac{1}{100}$? $\frac{1}{10}$
6. Which is greater, 0.1 or 0.01? 0.1
7. Which is greater, 0.1 or 0.001? 0.1

Chapter 9 • Lesson 1 385

# Assign Student Pages, continued

## Pages 386–387

Small Group

Have students complete page 387 independently or in pairs.

### As Students Finish

Game *Cube 100* (Lesson 3.5)

eGames *Cube 100*

Student Page



Our system of writing numbers is based on 10. Look at the number 3,333.

The red 3 stands for 3 ones.

- What does the orange 3 stand for? 3 tens
- What does the green 3 stand for? 3 hundreds
- What does the blue 3 stand for? 3 thousands

As we move to the left, each place is worth 10 times as much.

A 3 in the tens place is worth 10 times the value of a 3 in the ones place.

A 3 in the hundreds place is worth 10 times a 3 in the tens place.

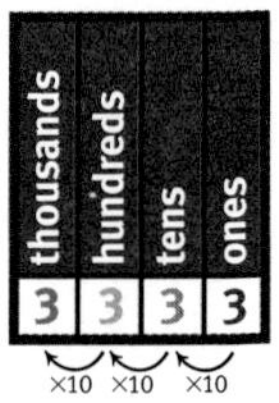


If you move to the right, it's just the opposite. Each place is worth one-tenth as much.

A 3 in the tens place is worth one-tenth of a 3 in the hundreds place.

A 3 in the ones place is worth one-tenth of a 3 in the tens place.

- What happens if you keep going to the right?

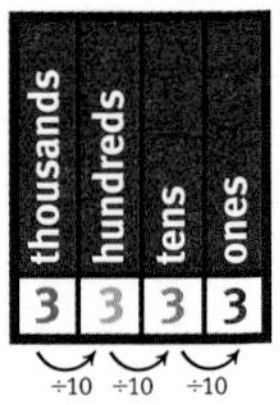


The next place is worth one-tenth of 1. That's the tenths place.

- What happens if you keep going to the right?

The next place is worth one-tenth of one-tenth. That's the hundredths place.

- How do you know what place you are in? The decimal point tells where the ones place is and you can determine the value of the placeholder by counting the digits to the right or left of the ones place.

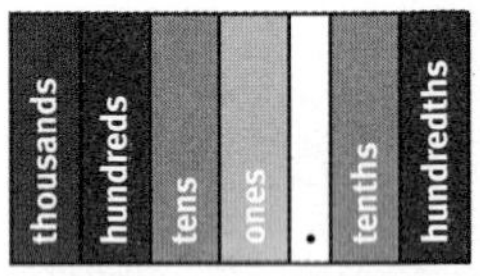




Textbook This lesson is available in the *eTextbook*.

Student Page

Use a point between the ones place and the tenths place.

The point is called a decimal point.

Suppose you want to write 4 tens, 3 ones, 5 tenths, and 4 hundredths.

You would write it like this: 43.54

When written in this form the number is called a decimal.

When you read it, you would say "forty-three and fifty-four hundredths" or "forty-three point fifty four."

**Tell** the value of the bold digit in each of the following numbers.

8. 0.0**5** 5 hundredths
9. 1.**6**3 6 tenths
10. **2**0.37 2 tens
11. 62.**7**6 7 tenths
12. 74.3**5** 5 hundredths
13. 0.**5**7 5 tenths
14. **2**.59 2 ones
15. 91.3**5** 5 hundredths
16. **5**3.47 5 tens
17. 22.**2**2 2 tenths
18. **1**.6 1 one
19. 83.5**6** 6 hundredths
20. 21.**4**2 4 tenths
21. 1**7**.52 7 ones
22. 15.**0**6 0 tenths

**Write** each number in standard decimal form.

23. 5 ones, 2 tenths, 4 hundredths 5.24
24. 7 hundreds, 2 tens, 6 ones, 3 tenths 726.3
25. 3 tens, 3 ones, 3 tenths, 3 hundredths 33.33
26. 9 hundreds, 0 tens, 3 ones, 4 tenths, 5 hundredths 903.45
27. 4 tens, 9 ones, 0 tenths, 7 hundredths 49.07

**Write** each number in standard decimal form. The first one has been done for you.

28. 30 + 4 + 0.6 + 0.04 34.64
29. 16 + 0.8 + 0.05 16.85
30. 60 + 0 + 0.7 + 0.03 60.73
31. 80 + 2 + 0.06 82.06
32. 50 + 9 + 0.3 + 0.07 59.37
33. 90 + 1 + 0.7 + 0.02 91.72
34. 10 + 3 + 0.9 + 0.06 13.96
35. 20 + 4 + 0.8 + 0.06 24.86

## 3 Reflect

5

### Guided Discussion REASONING

Whole Group

Students often have trouble understanding how writing extra zeros affects quantities when they begin to study decimals. Have students discuss the purpose of the decimal point in decimal numbers. It tells you where the ones place is.

Ask students questions such as the following:

- **If we put 0 after 8, we get a new number, 80. But what happens with a decimal number if we write 0 at the end?** If we write 0s only after the last digit to the right of the decimal point, the number keeps the same value (the extra zeros generally indicate greater precision in measurement).
- **If you have the decimal 0.5 and you write 0 to the right of 5, you get 0.50. Is 0.50 a different quantity from 0.5? Why or why not?** No; $\frac{5}{10}$ and $\frac{50}{100}$ are equivalent fractions—they are names for the same rational number.
- **What is the difference in value of 6 in 46, 4.6, and 4.06?** 6 ones in 46, 6 tenths in 4.6, 6 hundredths in 4.06

Inform students that when measurements (or calculations) are made to the nearest tenth, they should write the number to the nearest tenth (0.5), and when measurements (or calculations) are made to the nearest hundredth, they should write the number to the nearest hundredth (0.05).

**Cumulative Review:** For review of multidigit addition and subtraction, assign Problems 1–2 on student page 416.

**Family Involvement:** Assign the ***Practice, Reteach,*** or ***Enrichment*** activities depending on the needs of your students.

Encourage students to experiment with ***eMathTools: Number Lines (Converting between Percents, Decimals, and Fractions)*** with a friend or relative.

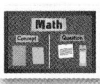

**Concept/Question Board:** Have students look for additional examples of decimals and post them on the Concept/Question Board.

**Math Puzzler:** Aksana and Yakov are twins. They began earning money babysitting when they were 12 years old. Aksana started out charging \$2.50 per hour and got a raise of \$0.40 per hour on her birthday each year. Yakov began charging \$2.90 per hour and got a \$0.30 raise on his birthday each year. How old were the twins when they both charged the same hourly rate? What was that amount? They were both 16, and each charged \$4.10 per hour.

# 4 Assess and Differentiate

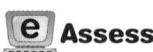

**e Assess** Use ***eAssess*** to record and analyze evidence of student understanding.

## A Gather Evidence

Use the Daily Class Assessment Records in ***Assessment*** or ***eAssess*** to record daily observations.

### Informal Assessment
**✓ Mental Math**

Did the student COMPUTING
- ❑ respond accurately?
- ❑ respond quickly?
- ❑ respond with confidence?
- ❑ self-correct?

### Informal Assessment
**✓ Guided Discussion**

Did the student UNDERSTANDING
- ❑ make important observations?
- ❑ extend or generalize learning?
- ❑ provide insightful answers?
- ❑ pose insightful questions?

## B Summarize Findings

Analyze and summarize assessment data for each student. Determine which Assessment Follow-Up is appropriate for each student. Use the Student Assessment Record in ***Assessment*** or ***eAssess*** to update assessment records.

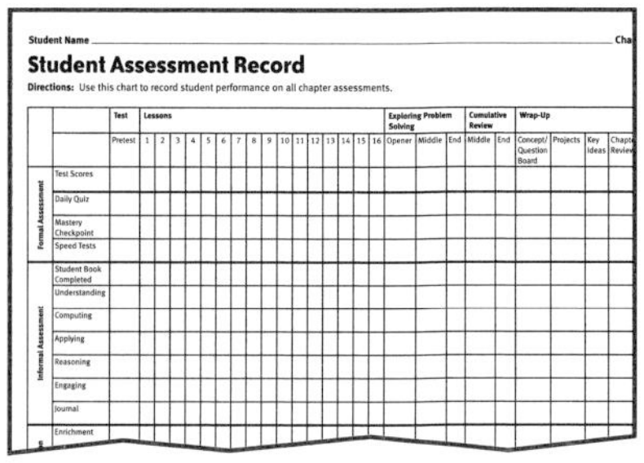


## C Assessment Follow-Up • DIFFERENTIATE INSTRUCTION

Based on your observations, use these teaching strategies for assessment follow-up.

### INTERVENTION

Review student performance on ***Intervention*** Lesson 9.A to see if students have mastered prerequisite skills for this lesson.

### ENGLISH LEARNER

**Review**

Use Lesson 9.1 in ***English Learner Support Guide*** to preview lesson concepts and vocabulary.

### ENRICH

**If . . .** students are proficient in the lesson concepts,

**Then . . .** encourage them to work on the chapter projects or ***Enrichment*** Lesson 9.1.

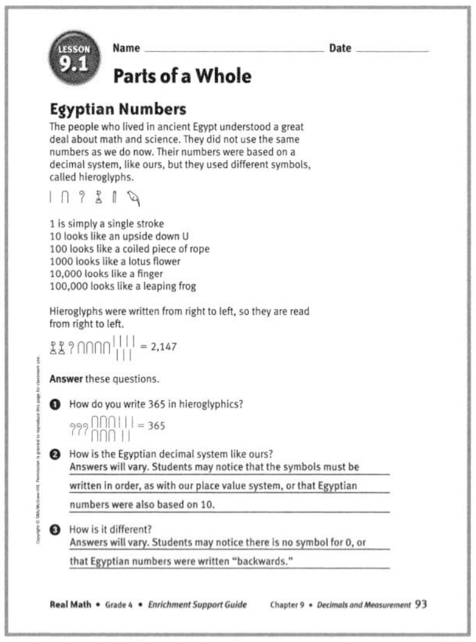

LESSON 9.1 Name ______ Date ______

**Parts of a Whole**

**Egyptian Numbers**

The people who lived in ancient Egypt understood a great deal about math and science. They did not use the same numbers as we do now. Their numbers were based on a decimal system, like ours, but they used different symbols, called hieroglyphs.

1 is simply a single stroke
10 looks like an upside down U
100 looks like a coiled piece of rope
1000 looks like a lotus flower
10,000 looks like a finger
100,000 looks like a leaping frog

Hieroglyphs were written from right to left, so they are read from right to left.

= 2,147

**Answer** these questions.

1. How do you write 365 in hieroglyphics? = 365
2. How is the Egyptian decimal system like ours? Answers will vary. Students may notice that the symbols must be written in order, as with our place value system, or that Egyptian numbers were also based on 10.
3. How is it different? Answers will vary. Students may notice there is no symbol for 0, or that Egyptian numbers were written "backwards."

Real Math • Grade 4 • *Enrichment Support Guide* Chapter 9 • *Decimals and Measurement* 93

Enrichment Lesson 9.1

### PRACTICE

**If . . .** students would benefit from additional practice,

**Then . . .** assign ***Practice*** Lesson 9.1.

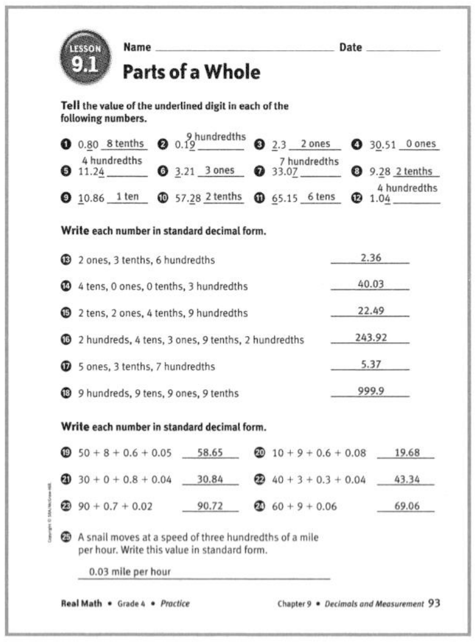

LESSON 9.1 Name ______ Date ______

**Parts of a Whole**

**Tell** the value of the underlined digit in each of the following numbers.

1. 0.80 8 tenths
2. 0.19 9 hundredths
3. 2.3 2 ones
4. 30.51 0 ones
5. 11.24 4 hundredths
6. 3.21 3 ones
7. 33.07 7 hundredths
8. 9.28 2 tenths
9. 10.86 1 ten
10. 57.28 2 tenths
11. 65.15 6 tens
12. 1.04 4 hundredths

**Write each number in standard decimal form.**

13. 2 ones, 3 tenths, 6 hundredths 2.36
14. 4 tens, 0 ones, 0 tenths, 3 hundredths 40.03
15. 2 tens, 2 ones, 4 tenths, 9 hundredths 22.49
16. 2 hundreds, 4 tens, 3 ones, 9 tenths, 2 hundredths 243.92
17. 5 ones, 3 tenths, 7 hundredths 5.37
18. 9 hundreds, 9 tens, 9 ones, 9 tenths 999.9

**Write each number in standard decimal form.**

19. 50 + 8 + 0.6 + 0.05 58.65
20. 10 + 9 + 0.6 + 0.08 19.68
21. 30 + 0 + 0.8 + 0.04 30.84
22. 40 + 3 + 0.3 + 0.04 43.34
23. 90 + 0.7 + 0.02 90.72
24. 60 + 9 + 0.06 69.06
25. A snail moves at a speed of three hundredths of a mile per hour. Write this value in standard form. 0.03 mile per hour

Real Math • Grade 4 • *Practice* Chapter 9 • *Decimals and Measurement* 93

Practice Lesson 9.1

### RETEACH

**If . . .** students are having difficulty understanding parts of a whole,

**Then . . .** reteach the concept using ***Reteach*** Lesson 9.1.

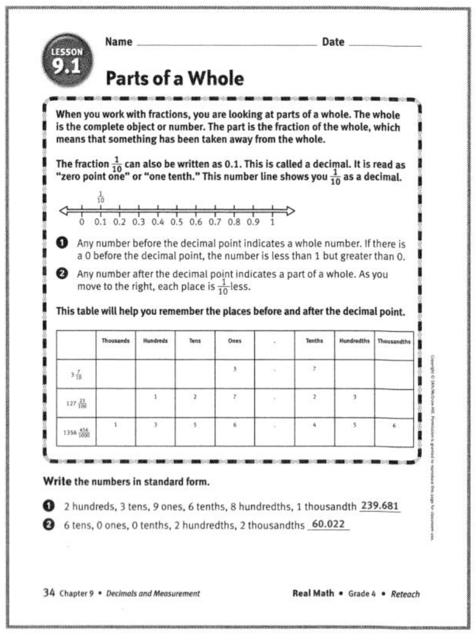

LESSON 9.1 Name ______ Date ______

**Parts of a Whole**

When you work with fractions, you are looking at parts of a whole. The whole is the complete object or number. The part is the fraction of the whole, which means that something has been taken away from the whole.

The fraction $\frac{1}{10}$ can also be written as 0.1. This is called a decimal. It is read as "zero point one" or "one tenth." This number line shows you $\frac{1}{10}$ as a decimal.

1. Any number before the decimal point indicates a whole number. If there is a 0 before the decimal point, the number is less than 1 but greater than 0.
2. Any number after the decimal point indicates a part of a whole. As you move to the right, each place is $\frac{1}{10}$ less.

This table will help you remember the places before and after the decimal point.

| | Thousands | Hundreds | Tens | Ones | . | Tenths | Hundredths | Thousandths |
|---|---|---|---|---|---|---|---|---|
| $3\frac{7}{10}$ | | | | 3 | . | 7 | | |
| $127\frac{23}{100}$ | | 1 | 2 | 7 | . | 2 | 3 | |
| $1356\frac{456}{1000}$ | 1 | 3 | 5 | 6 | . | 4 | 5 | 6 |

**Write the numbers in standard form.**

1. 2 hundreds, 3 tens, 9 ones, 6 tenths, 8 hundredths, 1 thousandth 239.681
2. 6 tens, 0 ones, 0 tenths, 2 hundredths, 2 thousandths 60.022

34 Chapter 9 • *Decimals and Measurement* Real Math • Grade 4 • *Reteach*

Reteach Lesson 9.1

## Lesson Planner

### Objectives
- To develop students' understanding of the relationship among tenths, hundredths, and thousandths
- To review and practice comparing decimals and using relation signs
- To explain the relationship of decimals to corresponding fractions

### NCTM Standards
**Number and Operations**
Understand numbers, ways of representing, numbers, relationships among numbers, and number systems

### Materials
- ***Response Wheels**
- Overhead transparency of page 146 from ***Practice***
- *Base-ten blocks
- ***Inequality Game*** (optional)

### Technology
**ePresentation** Lesson 9.2
**eMathTools Number Lines (Converting Percents, Decimals, and Fractions)**

### Test Prep
**Cumulative Review**
Mental Math reviews percents and fractions of wholes (Lesson 7.4).

*Manipulative Kit Item

# Decimals and Fractions

**Context of the Lesson** This lesson and Lesson 9.1 involve a minimal number of decimals greater than 1, allowing students to focus on the places to the right of the decimal point. This lesson provides opportunities for students to visualize tenths, hundredths, and thousandths, which can give them a sense of the value of different decimal place values in relation to each other. Beginning in Lesson 9.3, we include decimals greater than 1, which is a natural and common use of decimals.

See page 382B for Math Background for teachers for this lesson.

## Planning for Learning • DIFFERENTIATE INSTRUCTION

### INTERVENTION
**If . . .** students lack the prerequisite skill of comparing numbers through 1,000,

**Then . . .** teach ***Intervention*** Lesson 9.A.

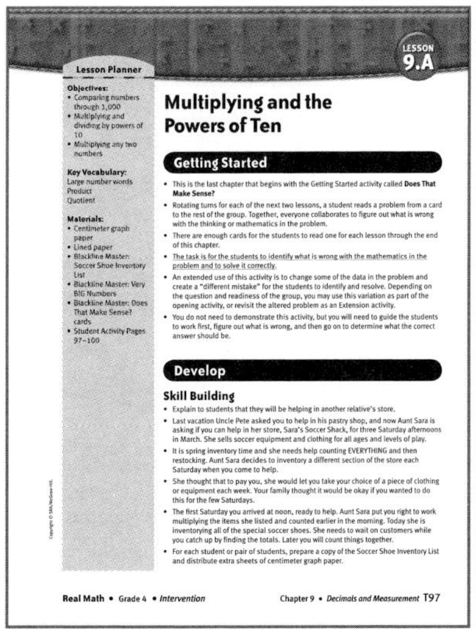
Lesson 9.A
Multiplying and the Powers of Ten
Getting Started
Develop

Intervention Lesson 9.A

### ENGLISH LEARNER
**Preview**

**If . . .** students need language support,

**Then . . .** use Lesson 9.2 in ***English Learner Support Guide*** to preview lesson concepts and vocabulary.

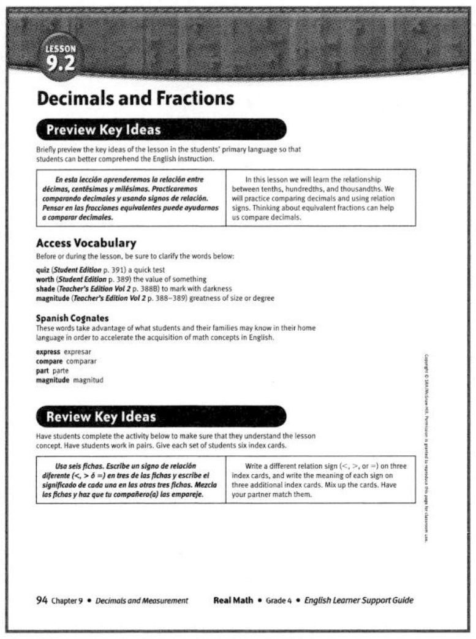
Lesson 9.2
Decimals and Fractions
Preview Key Ideas
Access Vocabulary
Review Key Ideas

English Learner Lesson 9.2

### ENRICH
**If . . .** students are proficient in the lesson concepts,

**Then . . .** emphasize chapter projects.

### PRACTICE
**If . . .** students would benefit from additional practice,

**Then . . .** extend Guided Discussion before assigning the student pages.

### RETEACH
**If . . .** students are having difficulty understanding how to compare decimals,

**Then . . .** extend Guided Discussion before assigning the student pages.

**Vocabulary**
Review from Lesson 7.3:
**equivalent**

**Access Vocabulary**
**quiz** short test

**Spanish Cognates**
**express** expresar

## Mental Math 5

Review RESPONSE WHEEL Present exercises that review percentages and fractions, such as the following:

**a.** What is 50% of 12? 6
**b.** What is 75% of 8? 6
**c.** What is $\frac{1}{2}$ of 50? 25
**d.** What is $\frac{1}{4}$ of 80? 20
**e.** What is 25% of 16? 4
**f.** What is 25% of 100? 25
**g.** What is $\frac{3}{4}$ of 40? 30
**h.** What is 20% of 100? 20

## 1 Develop 25

**Tell Students In Today's Lesson They Will**
develop an understanding of tenths, hundredths, and thousandths by comparing decimals.

### Guided Discussion UNDERSTANDING

Whole Group

**1.** Discuss with the class the many different ways to look at decimals. First remind students that percentages of 1 can be represented by two-place decimals, which are equivalent to hundredths of quantities. Write 45% of 1 on the board and show how it can be written as a fraction ($\frac{45}{100}$) and as a decimal (0.45). The meaning of 45% is $\frac{45}{100}$ because a percentage is a way to write a fraction whose denominator is 100.

Tell the class that you can also think about decimals using a grid. Show the overhead projector transparency of the hundredths grid and fill in three of the squares.

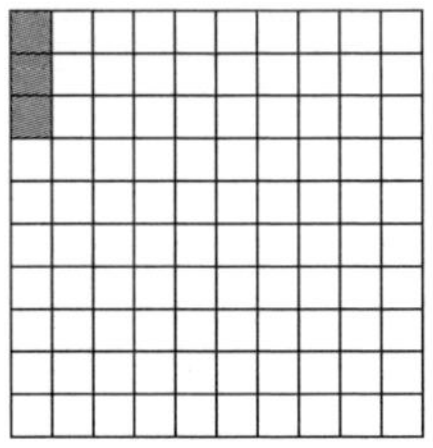

Ask questions such as the following:

- **What is the total number of squares in this grid?** 100
- **How many are filled in?** 3
- **What is that as a fraction?** $\frac{3}{100}$
- **What is that as a percentage?** 3%
- **How would we represent it as a decimal?** 0.03

You can use ***eMathTools: Number Lines (Converting Percents, Decimals, and Fractions)*** to demonstrate these conversions.

**2.** On the board, create a chart showing percentages, fractions, and decimals such as the following:

| Fraction (Denominator of 100) | Percentage | Decimal |
|---|---|---|
| $\frac{3}{100}$ | 3% | 0.03 |

Now shade nine squares on the hundredths grid. Ask a volunteer to come and fill in the fraction, percent, and decimal amounts for nine shaded squares. The answers are $\frac{9}{100}$, 9%, and 0.09.

Next shade forty-three squares on the grid. Ask a volunteer to come and fill in the amounts in the chart on the board. The answers are $\frac{43}{100}$, 43%, and 0.43.

Finally, shade seventy squares on the hundredths grid. Again, ask a volunteer to fill in the amounts in the chart on the board. The answers are $\frac{70}{100}$, 70%, and 0.70.

**3.** Lay the transparency of the tenths grid over the transparency of the hundredths grid.

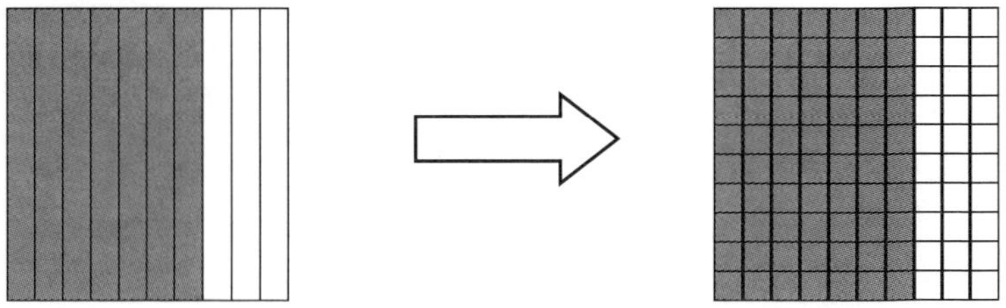

Show the students that there is an equivalency— $\frac{70}{100}$ represents the same amount as $\frac{7}{10}$. Therefore, the decimal equivalents of the two fractions are equal: 0.70 = 0.7.

**4.** Quickly review the meaning of the relation signs (<, >, =). Remind students that they can use base-ten blocks or draw and shade their own grids to get a sense of the relative size of decimals.

Help students understand that, when comparing decimals, lining up the decimal points will ensure comparing quantities of like magnitude. Demonstrate this with examples such as 0.20 and 0.080. Without drawing a picture, students can see that 0.20 is greater if the decimal points are aligned properly—0.080 has 0 tenths and therefore cannot be larger than 0.2 no matter how many digits follow the tenths place.

When comparing decimals—particularly decimals with thousandths and ten thousandths—remind students to count places carefully. To make it easier to compare decimals, students might use zeros to equate the number of digits both numbers have to the right of the decimal point. For example, it might be easier to compare 0.0321 and 0.040 by rewriting the problem as 0.0321 and 0.0400.

# 2 Assign Student Pages 25

## Pages 388–389 APPLYING

Have students complete pages 388 and 389 independently. Provide base-ten blocks as needed to help students get a sense of the magnitude of tenths in relation to hundredths.

### RESEARCH IN ACTION

"Students often view the study of whole numbers, decimal fractions, common fractions, and integers as disconnected topics. One tool that may be useful in developing numerical understanding and in making connection across number systems is the number line, a geometric representation of numbers that gives each number a unique point on the line and an oriented distance from the origin. . . .The number line may become particularly useful as students are learning about integers and rational numbers, for it may help students develop a sense of the magnitudes and relationships of those numbers in a way that is less clear in other representations.

Kilpatrick, J. Swafford, J. and Findell, B. eds. *Adding It Up: Helping Children Learn Mathematics*. Washington, D.C.: National Research Council/National Academy Press, 2001, p. 418.

Student Page

## LESSON 9.2 Decimals and Fractions

### Key Ideas

**Decimals make numbers easy to compare.**

Remember, if a whole is divided into 10 equal parts, 1 part would be $\frac{1}{10}$, or 0.1.

So, 3 parts would be $\frac{3}{10}$, or 0.3.

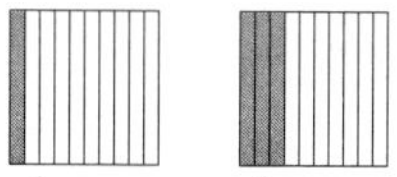

$\frac{1}{10} = 0.1$ $\frac{3}{10} = 0.3$

If a whole is divided into 100 equal parts, 1 part would be $\frac{1}{100}$, or 0.01.

So, 3 parts would be $\frac{3}{100}$, or 0.03.

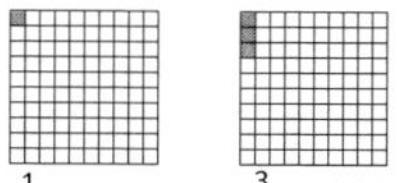

$\frac{1}{100} = 0.01$ $\frac{3}{100} = 0.03$

Suppose you divided a whole into 1,000 equal parts.

- What would 1 part be? $\frac{1}{1,000}$ or 0.001
- What would 3 parts be? $\frac{3}{1,000}$ or 0.003
- What would 7 parts be? $\frac{7}{1,000}$ or 0.007

Here is one way to compare the decimals 0.007 and 0.03.

| | |
|---|---|
| 0.007<br>0.03**0** | Write a 0 after the last digit so the numbers have the same number of digits to the right of the decimal point. |
| So 0.007 < 0.03 (as $\frac{7}{1,000} < \frac{30}{100}$). | Line up the decimal points. |

**Replace** ■ with <, >, or =.

1. 0.1 < 0.3
2. 0.03 < 0.1
3. 0.007 < 0.08
4. 0.01 < 0.03
5. 0.7 > 0.08
6. 0.2 > 0.09
7. 0.01 < 0.07
8. 0.1 > 0.001
9. 0.3 > 0.03



Textbook This lesson is available in the ***eTextbook***.

Student Page

10. How are 0.1 and 0.10 related (<, >, or =)? =

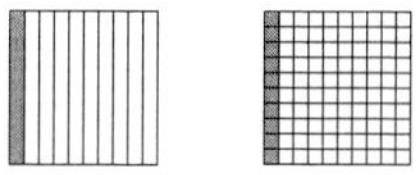

$\frac{1}{10} = 0.1$ $\frac{10}{100} = 0.10$

11. Which is greater, 0.2 or 0.27? 0.27

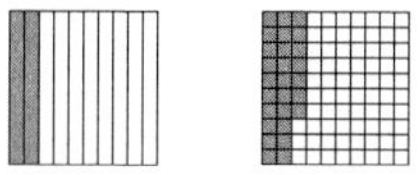

$\frac{2}{10} = 0.2$ $\frac{27}{100} = 0.27$

Remember, a dime is $\frac{1}{10}$ of a dollar, and a penny, or cent, is $\frac{1}{100}$ of a dollar.

Ten cents has the same value as 1 dime. So 1 dime has a greater value than 9 cents.

**Choose** the amount that is worth more money.

12. 3 dimes or 33 cents (circled: 33 cents)
13. 6 cents or 1 dime (circled: 1 dime)
14. 11 cents or 1 dime (circled: 11 cents)
15. 8 dimes or 80 cents same
16. 10 cents or 1 dime same
17. 7 dimes or 8 cents (circled: 7 dimes)

**Write** each amount of money as a decimal of a dollar. The first one has been done for you.

18. 3 dimes and 7 cents = $0.37
19. 9 dimes and 8 cents = ■ $0.98
20. 6 dimes and 4 cents = ■ $0.64
21. 64 cents = ■ $0.64
22. 0 dimes and 8 cents = ■ $0.08
23. 7 dimes and 3 cents = ■ $0.73
24. 2 dimes and 9 cents = ■ $0.29

# Assign Student Pages, continued

**Pages 390–391** APPLYING

Have students complete pages 390 and 391 independently.

## Monitoring Student Progress

**If . . .** students do not have a feel for magnitude when it is expressed in decimal notation,

**Then . . .** give them extra work using concrete base-ten materials that relate to the decimal notation for the amount involved (for example, have students choose an amount of play money then write that amount in decimal notation).

### As Students Finish

Game ***Inequality Game*** (introduced in Lesson 2.4)

Student Page

LESSON 9.2 • Decimals and Fractions

**For** each figure, show what portion is shaded by writing a fraction and a decimal. The first one has been done for you.

25 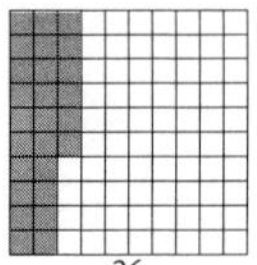

$\frac{26}{100}$, 0.26

26 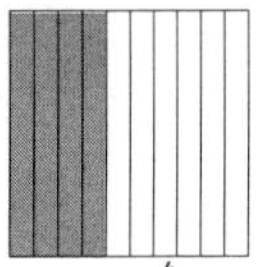

$\frac{4}{10}$, 0.4

27 

$\frac{4}{100}$, 0.04

28 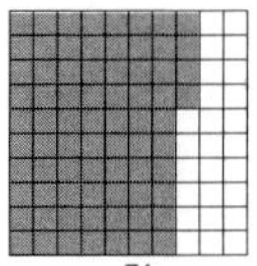

$\frac{74}{100}$, 0.74

29 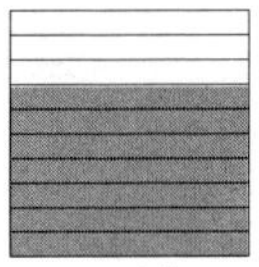

$\frac{7}{10}$, 0.7

30 

$\frac{7}{100}$, 0.07

31 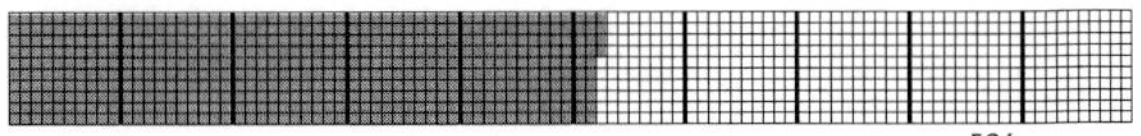

$\frac{524}{1,000}$, 0.524

32 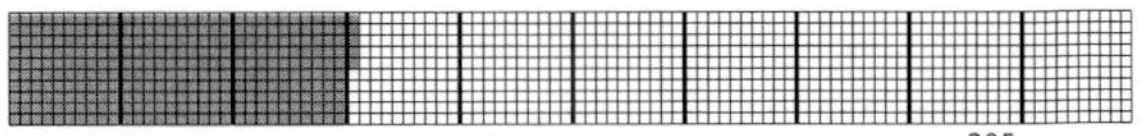

$\frac{305}{1,000}$, 0.305

390

Textbook This lesson is available in the ***eTextbook***.

Student Page

**Write** each of these fractions as a decimal.

**Examples:** $\frac{3}{100} = 0.03$ $\frac{7}{10,000} = 0.0007$

33 $\frac{2}{10} =$ 0.2

34 $\frac{4,783}{10,000} =$ 0.4783

35 $\frac{478}{10,000} =$ 0.0478

36 $\frac{11}{100} =$ 0.11

37 $\frac{10}{100} =$ 0.1

38 $\frac{700}{1,000} =$ 0.700

39 $\frac{70}{1,000} =$ 0.070

40 $\frac{4}{100} =$ 0.04

41 $\frac{7}{10} =$ 0.7

42 $\frac{74}{100} =$ 0.74

**Copy** each pair of numbers. Replace the ■ with <, >, or =.

43 0.02 < 0.3

44 0.406 < 0.407

45 0.83 > 0.80

46 0.8 = 0.80

47 0.8 < 0.83

48 0.62 < 0.90

49 0.9 = 0.90

50 0.62 < 0.9

**Solve** these problems.

51 Eric correctly answered 8 out of 10 questions on his English quiz. Write a fraction to show how much of the quiz he got right. $\frac{8}{10}$ or $\frac{4}{5}$

52 Jessica spent \$16 for a watch and \$4 for a pair of earrings. Write a fraction to show the cost of the earrings compared to the cost of the watch. $\frac{4}{16}$ or $\frac{1}{4}$

Chapter 9 • Lesson 2

391

## 3 Reflect 5

### Guided Discussion REASONING

Whole Group

Have students discuss what kind of picture they could draw that would compare the decimals 0.24 and 0.3 to determine which is greater. From the drawing, students should see that 0.3 is greater than 0.24.

**Cumulative Review:** For review of fractions and rational numbers, assign Problems 3–5 on student page 416.

**Family Involvement:** Assign the ***Practice, Reteach,*** or ***Enrichment*** activities depending on the needs of your students. Encourage students to experiment with ***eMathTools: Number Lines (Converting Percents, Decimals and Fractions)*** with a friend or relative.

**Concept/Question Board:** Have students look for additional examples of fractions and decimals and post them on the Concept/Question Board.

**Math Puzzler:** Use each of the digits 5, 3, 1, and 0 to form the greatest and least possible decimal numbers. Then use any of the same four digits to form two decimals with the same value. 5,310.0; 0.0135; one possible pair of equivalent decimals is 15.30, 15.3

# 4 Assess and Differentiate

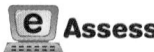

**e Assess** Use ***eAssess*** to record and analyze evidence of student understanding.

## A Gather Evidence

Use the Daily Class Assessment Records in ***Assessment*** or ***eAssess*** to record daily observations.

### Formal Assessment

**✓ Student Pages**

Did the student UNDERSTANDING

- ❑ make important observations?
- ❑ extend or generalize learning?
- ❑ provide insightful answers?
- ❑ pose insightful questions?

### Informal Assessment

**✓ Guided Discussion**

Did the student REASONING

- ❑ provide a clear explanation?
- ❑ communicate reasons and strategies?
- ❑ choose appropriate strategies?
- ❑ argue logically?

## B Summarize Findings

Analyze and summarize assessment data for each student. Determine which Assessment Follow-Up is appropriate for each student. Use the Student Assessment Record in ***Assessment*** or ***eAssess*** to update assessment records.

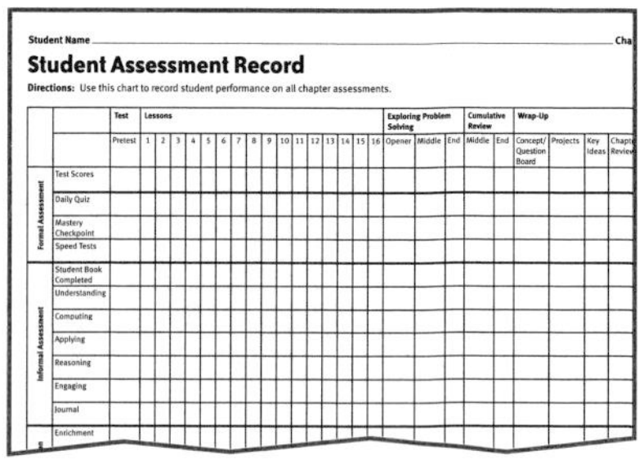

## C Assessment Follow-Up • DIFFERENTIATE INSTRUCTION

Based on your observations, use these teaching strategies for assessment follow-up.

### INTERVENTION

Review student performance on ***Intervention*** Lesson 9.A to see if students have mastered prerequisite skills for this lesson.

### ENGLISH LEARNER

**Review**

Use Lesson 9.2 in ***English Support Guide*** to preview lesson concepts and vocabulary.

### ENRICH

**If . . .** students are proficient in the lesson concepts,

**Then . . .** encourage them to work on the chapter projects or ***Enrichment*** Lesson 9.2.

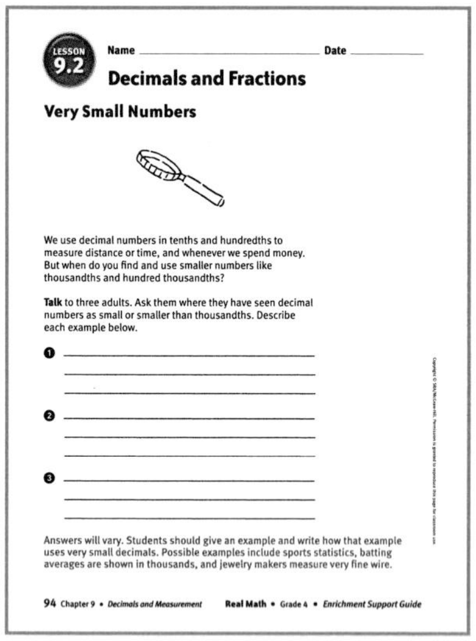

LESSON 9.2 Name ______ Date ______

Decimals and Fractions

Very Small Numbers

We use decimal numbers in tenths and hundredths to measure distance or time, and whenever we spend money. But when do you find and use smaller numbers like thousandths and hundred thousandths?

**Talk** to three adults. Ask them where they have seen decimal numbers as small or smaller than thousandths. Describe each example below.

1. ______
2. ______
3. ______

Answers will vary. Students should give an example and write how that example uses very small decimals. Possible examples include sports statistics, batting averages are shown in thousands, and jewelry makers measure very fine wire.

94 Chapter 9 • Decimals and Measurement Real Math • Grade 4 • Enrichment Support Guide

Enrichment Lesson 9.2

### PRACTICE

**If . . .** students would benefit from additional practice,

**Then . . .** assign ***Practice*** Lesson 9.2.

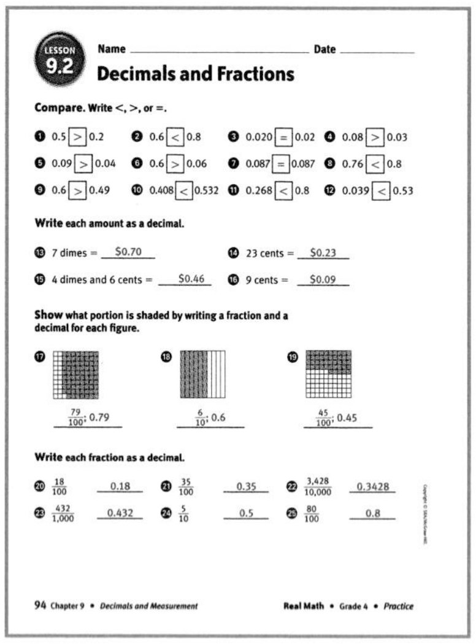

LESSON 9.2 Name ______ Date ______

Decimals and Fractions

Compare. Write <, >, or =.

1. $0.5 > 0.2$
2. $0.6 < 0.8$
3. $0.020 = 0.02$
4. $0.08 > 0.03$
5. $0.09 > 0.04$
6. $0.6 > 0.06$
7. $0.087 = 0.087$
8. $0.76 < 0.8$
9. $0.6 > 0.49$
10. $0.408 < 0.532$
11. $0.268 < 0.8$
12. $0.039 < 0.53$

Write each amount as a decimal.

13. 7 dimes = $0.70
14. 23 cents = $0.23
15. 4 dimes and 6 cents = $0.46
16. 9 cents = $0.09

Show what portion is shaded by writing a fraction and a decimal for each figure.

17. $\frac{79}{100}$; 0.79
18. $\frac{6}{10}$; 0.6
19. $\frac{45}{100}$; 0.45

Write each fraction as a decimal.

20. $\frac{18}{100}$ 0.18
21. $\frac{35}{100}$ 0.35
22. $\frac{3,428}{10,000}$ 0.3428
23. $\frac{432}{1,000}$ 0.432
24. $\frac{5}{10}$ 0.5
25. $\frac{80}{100}$ 0.8

94 Chapter 9 • Decimals and Measurement Real Math • Grade 4 • Practice

Practice Lesson 9.2

### RETEACH

**If . . .** students are having difficulty understanding how to compare decimals,

**Then . . .** have them shade in a grid for each number and compare the grids. You can make a class set of reusable number grids by laminating a photocopied sheet between two layers of clear adhesive plastic. Then students can use erasable markers to shade in their grids and wipe them clean when they are done.

## Lesson Planner

### OBJECTIVES
- To assess students' understanding of the relative magnitude of decimals
- To provide problems involving coin combinations to compare decimals in a real-world context

### NCTM STANDARDS
**Number and Operations**
Understand numbers, ways of representing numbers, relationships among numbers, and number systems

**Connections**
Recognize and apply mathematics in contexts outside of mathematics

### MATERIALS
- ***Response Wheels**
- *Stopwatches
- *Play coins (optional)
- **Baseball Game** (optional)

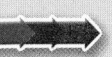

### TECHNOLOGY
**e Presentation** Lesson 9.3
**e MathTools Coins and Money** and **Stopwatch**
**e Games Baseball Game** (optional)

### TEST PREP
**Cumulative Review**
Mental Math reviews percentages and fractional parts of whole numbers (Lessons 7.2 and 7.4).

**Extended Response**
Problems 25–28

*Manipulative Kit Item

# Comparing Decimals

**Context of the Lesson** This lesson provides practice in comparing two decimal numbers before students are required to order multiple decimal quantities in Lesson 9.4. After being introduced to the place values of the decimal, students need to be able to distinguish their worth. The use of cents can help students visualize the value of decimals to the hundredths place.

See page 382B for Math Background for teachers for this lesson.

## Planning for Learning • DIFFERENTIATE INSTRUCTION

### INTERVENTION

**If . . .** students lack the prerequisite skill of comparing numbers through 1,000,

**Then . . .** teach ***Intervention*** Lesson 9.A.

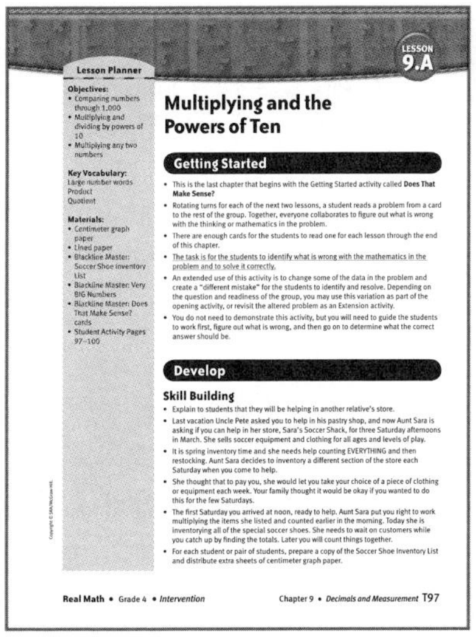


Intervention Lesson 9.A

### ENGLISH LEARNER

**Preview**

**If . . .** students need language support,

**Then . . .** use Lesson 9.3 in ***English Learner Support Guide*** to preview lesson concepts and vocabulary.

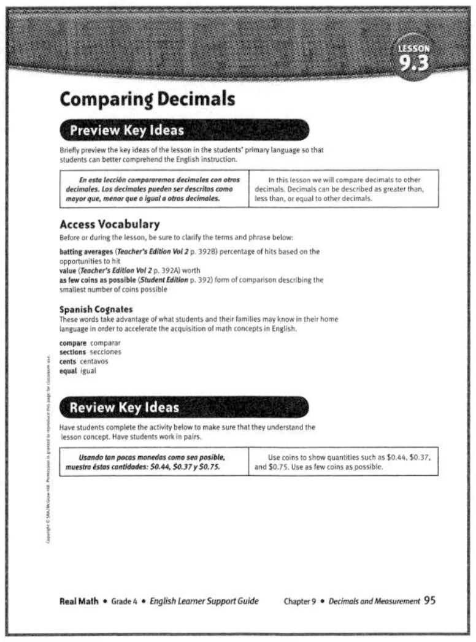


English Learner Lesson 9.3

### ENRICH

**If . . .** students are proficient in the lesson concepts,

**Then . . .** emphasize chapter projects.

### PRACTICE

**If . . .** students would benefit from additional practice,

**Then . . .** extend Guided Discussion before assigning the student pages.

### RETEACH

**If . . .** students are having difficulty understanding how to order decimals,

**Then . . .** extend Guided Discussion before assigning the student pages.

### Vocabulary
**rounding \round ing\ *v.*** changing a number to another number that is easier to work with and that is close enough for the purpose

### Access Vocabulary
**value** worth
**as few as possible** smallest amount possible

### Spanish Cognates
**compar** comparar
**sections** secciones
**eliminate** eliminar

# Teaching Lesson 9.3

## Mental Math 5

Present problems, such as the following, to the class. Have students use the slide measurement strip on their ***Response Wheels*** to estimate how much is demonstrated by the statement.

a. $\frac{2}{8}$ of 100 Students should show about $\frac{1}{4}$ of strip.
b. 50% of 26 Students should show about $\frac{1}{2}$ of strip.
c. 33% of 21 Students should show about $\frac{1}{3}$ of strip.
d. $\frac{3}{24}$ of 48 Students should show about $\frac{1}{8}$ of strip.
e. $\frac{9}{18}$ of 36 Students should show about $\frac{1}{2}$ of strip.
f. 20% of 40 Students should show about $\frac{1}{5}$ of strip.

## 1 Develop 30

**Tell Students In Today's Lesson They Will**
compare decimals to other decimals.

### Strategy Building ENGAGING

Small Group

1. Draw a chart on the board or overhead projector with the headings *Task*, *First Student's Time*, *Second Student's Time*, and *Comparison of Times*. Explain to the students that they will be comparing the times for a number of tasks today.
2. Provide students a quick refresher on the stopwatch, including how it works and how to read the screen. You may also need to include a comment on proper stopwatch etiquette. For example, the person timing the actions, should wear the stopwatch around his or her neck at all times. Stopwatch examples can be done using the ***eMathTools: Stopwatch***.
3. Have students find a partner with whom to complete an assortment of tasks to be timed to the nearest hundredth of a second. One student will keep time while the other completes the task. Then they will trade jobs. Have students record their results on their chart as they finish each task.

   Some activities students can time include the following:
   - write your name 5 times
   - do 8 jumping jacks
   - say the alphabet

   **NOTE:** Remind students that it is the person with the *least* time that has completed the task faster.

### Guided Discussion UNDERSTANDING

Whole Group

1. Describe a situation such as the following to the class:

   Joe DiMaggio and Jackie Robinson were two of the greatest baseball players of all time. During their careers they had batting averages of 0.325 and 0.311, respectively. (A batting average is actually a percentage, written as a decimal to the nearest thousandth, of how many times a batter gets a hit based on their opportunities at the plate.)

   Explain that we need to find the differences to compare these decimals. To find the differences, line up the decimal points to clarify which place values are represented. Ask questions such as the following:
   - **Which place, in the two batting averages, has a different digit?** the hundredths place
   - **Which of those two digits is greater?** 2
   - **Whose batting average is greater?** Joe DiMaggio's
2. Write a whole number, such as 1, on the board or overhead projector. Then write 0.999999999999. Ask for a volunteer to align the decimals of these numbers. Ask students questions such as the following:
   - **In which placeholder are the numbers different?** the ones column
   - **Which number is greater?** 1

## 2 Assign Student Pages 20

**Pages 392–393** APPLYING

Small Group

Have students complete pages 392–393 with a partner. Provide play coins to help them solve the problems. Encourage students to try all the possibilities they can think of before deciding that a problem is impossible.

### As Students Finish

Game **Baseball Game** (introduced in Lesson 4.15)

e Games ***Baseball Game***

Student Page

## LESSON 9.3 Comparing Decimals

**Key Ideas**

**Decimals, like whole numbers, can be described as greater than, less than, or equal to other decimals.**

**Replace** the ▒ with <, >, or = to make the statement true.

| | | | |
|---|---|---|---|
| 1 0.32 < 3.2 | 2 1.01 > 1.001 | 3 0.07 < 0.3 | 4 26.37 > 2.84 |
| 5 0.5 < 1.0 | 6 1.28 = 1.280 | 7 0.06 < 0.2 | 8 0.6 > 0.02 |
| 9 3.89 > 3.809 | 10 0.73 = 0.73 | 11 0.215 = 0.215 | 12 21.2 > 18.0 |
| 13 0.973 > 0.839 | 14 0.973 < 8.39 | 15 51.24 < 204.1 | 16 9.7 > 6.8 |
| 17 5.5555 < 40.7 | 18 1.4 > 0.8 | 19 0.0104 < 0.104 | 20 4.083 > 4.07 |

**Use** pennies, nickels, dimes, quarters, and half-dollars to form each amount. Try to use as few coins as possible. The first one has been done for you.

21 $0.57 (50) (5) (1) (1)

22 $0.80 (50) (25) (5)

23 $0.74 (50) (10) (10) (1) (1) (1) (1)

24 $1.05 (50) (50) (5)

392

Textbook This lesson is available in the *eTextbook*.

Student Page

Extended Response **Which** of the following are possible? For those that are possible, write the coins needed and explain how you came up with an answer.

25 Make 35 cents with 3 coins. How did you get your answer? 1 quarter, 2 nickels.

26 Make 54 cents with 4 coins. Not possible.

27 Make 87 cents with 11 coins. Refer to the *Teacher's Edition* for all possible combinations.

28 Make 86 cents with 10 coins. Refer to the Teacher's Edition for all possible combinations.

**Work** in groups to solve the next four problems.

29 Write 6 different coin combinations to create 25 cents.

30 David has 4 coins. They are worth 46¢ altogether. Tell which of the following statements are reasonable and explain your answer.

a. David has 2 dimes.
reasonable, because 10¢ + 10¢ + 25¢ + 1¢ = 46¢

b. David has 2 quarters.
not reasonable, because 25¢ + 25¢ = 50¢

c. David has 6 pennies.
not reasonable; he has only 4 coins

29 Answers may vary. Sample answers: 1 quarter; 2 dimes, 1 nickel; 1 dime, 3 nickels; 1 dime, 2 nickels, 5 pennies; 1 dime, 15 pennies; 5 nickels

Chapter 9 • Lesson 3 393

# 3 Reflect

5

## Guided Discussion REASONING

Whole Group

Have students discuss when it is better to have a smaller decimal, and when it is better to have a greater decimal. For example, students might mention that a decimal must be smaller to be the winner when racing, and it is better to have a larger decimal when dealing with money.

### Extended Response

**Problem 27:** 8 dimes, 1 nickel, 2 pennies or 3 quarters, 1 nickel, 7 pennies

**Problem 28:** Same as Problem 27 with one fewer penny.

SOCIAL STUDIES **Curriculum Connection:** Students may be interested in researching baseball statistics of past players. They may also find it interesting that women played major league baseball during the 1940s. Students can compare the statistics of men and women online or at the library.

Review **Cumulative Review:** For review of multiplication and division, assign Problems 6–10 on student page 416.

**Family Involvement:** Assign the ***Practice, Reteach,*** or ***Enrichment*** activities depending on the needs of your students. Encourage students to experiment with ***eMathTools: Number Lines (Converting Percents, Decimals, and Fractions)*** with a friend or relative.

**Concept/Question Board:** Have students look for additional examples of decimals and post them on the Concept/Question Board.

**Math Puzzler:** The five-word sentence *Tina is at Anitra's House* contains exactly twenty letters. Tally them to find out which letter represents the largest part of the sentence and which letters represent equal parts of the sentence. Express the size of the parts in decimal form. A = 0.2, which is the greatest decimal part of the sentence; N = 0.1; T, I, and S each represent 0.15; R, H, O, U, and E each represent 0.05 of the whole sentence.

# 4 Assess and Differentiate

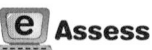

e Assess Use ***eAssess*** to record and analyze evidence of student understanding.

## A Gather Evidence

Use the Daily Class Assessment Records in ***Assessment*** or ***eAssess*** to record daily observations.

### Informal Assessment

**✓ Mental Math**

Did the student COMPUTING

- ❑ respond accurately?
- ❑ respond quickly?
- ❑ respond with confidence?
- ❑ self-correct?

### Informal Assessment

**✓ Strategy Building**

Did the student ENGAGING

- ❑ pay attention to others' contributions?
- ❑ contribute information and ideas?
- ❑ improve on a strategy?
- ❑ reflect on and check the accuracy of his or her work?

## B Summarize Findings

Analyze and summarize assessment data for each student. Determine which Assessment Follow-Up is appropriate for each student. Use the Student Assessment Record in ***Assessment*** or ***eAssess*** to update assessment records.

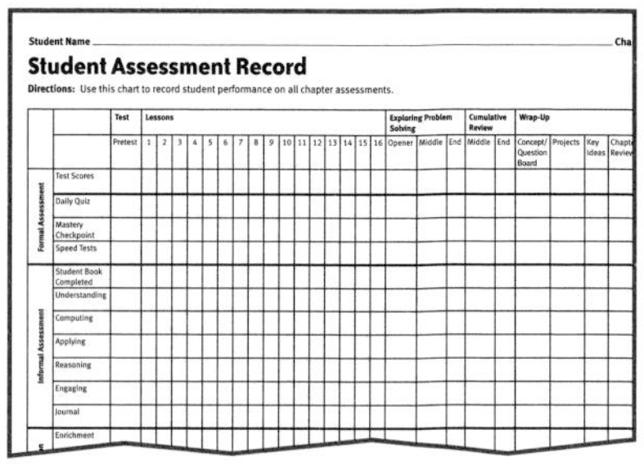


**Assessment Page T41**

## C Assessment Follow-Up • DIFFERENTIATE INSTRUCTION

Based on your observations, use these teaching strategies for assessment follow-up.

### INTERVENTION

Review student performance on ***Intervention*** Lesson 9.A to see if students have mastered prerequisite skills for this lesson

### ENGLISH LEARNER

**Review**

Use Lesson 9.3 in ***English Learner Support Guide*** to preview lesson concepts and vocabulary.

### ENRICH

**If . . .** students are proficient in the lesson concepts,

**Then . . .** encourage them to work on the chapter projects or ***Enrichment*** Lesson 9.3.

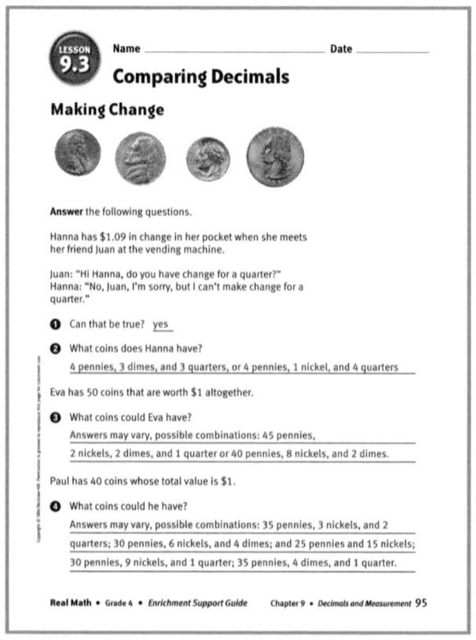

LESSON 9.3 Name ______ Date ______

**Comparing Decimals**

**Making Change**

**Answer** the following questions.

Hanna has $1.09 in change in her pocket when she meets her friend Juan at the vending machine.

Juan: "Hi Hanna, do you have change for a quarter?"
Hanna: "No, Juan, I'm sorry, but I can't make change for a quarter."

1. Can that be true? yes
2. What coins does Hanna have? 4 pennies, 3 dimes, and 3 quarters, or 4 pennies, 1 nickel, and 4 quarters

Eva has 50 coins that are worth $1 altogether.

3. What coins could Eva have? Answers may vary, possible combinations: 45 pennies, 2 nickels, 2 dimes, and 1 quarter or 40 pennies, 8 nickels, and 2 dimes.

Paul has 40 coins whose total value is $1.

4. What coins could he have? Answers may vary, possible combinations: 35 pennies, 3 nickels, and 2 quarters; 30 pennies, 6 nickels, and 4 dimes; and 25 pennies and 15 nickels; 30 pennies, 9 nickels, and 1 quarter; 35 pennies, 4 dimes, and 1 quarter.

**Real Math** • Grade 4 • *Enrichment Support Guide* Chapter 9 • *Decimals and Measurement* 95

Enrichment Lesson 9.3

### PRACTICE

**If . . .** students would benefit from additional practice,

**Then . . .** assign ***Practice*** Lesson 9.3.

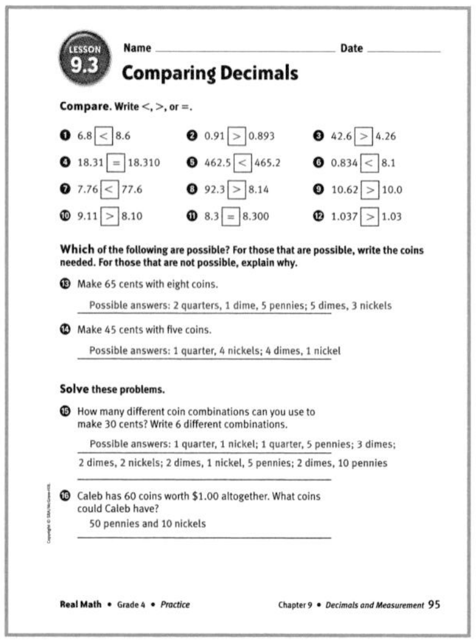

LESSON 9.3 Name ______ Date ______

**Comparing Decimals**

**Compare.** Write <, >, or =.

1. 6.8 [<] 8.6
2. 0.91 [>] 0.893
3. 42.6 [>] 4.26
4. 18.31 [=] 18.310
5. 462.5 [<] 465.2
6. 0.834 [<] 8.1
7. 7.76 [<] 77.6
8. 92.3 [>] 8.14
9. 10.62 [>] 10.0
10. 9.11 [>] 8.10
11. 8.3 [=] 8.300
12. 1.037 [>] 1.03

**Which of the following are possible? For those that are possible, write the coins needed. For those that are not possible, explain why.**

13. Make 65 cents with eight coins. Possible answers: 2 quarters, 1 dime, 5 pennies; 5 dimes, 3 nickels
14. Make 45 cents with five coins. Possible answers: 1 quarter, 4 nickels; 4 dimes, 1 nickel

**Solve these problems.**

15. How many different coin combinations can you use to make 30 cents? Write 6 different combinations. Possible answers: 1 quarter, 1 nickel; 1 quarter, 5 pennies; 3 dimes; 2 dimes, 2 nickels; 2 dimes, 1 nickel, 5 pennies; 2 dimes, 10 pennies
16. Caleb has 60 coins worth $1.00 altogether. What coins could Caleb have? 50 pennies and 10 nickels

**Real Math** • Grade 4 • *Practice* Chapter 9 • *Decimals and Measurement* 95

Practice Lesson 9.3

### RETEACH

**If . . .** students are having difficulty understanding how to compare decimals,

**Then . . .** have them compare sums of money. Start with the largest coin that is smaller than the total. Then keep adding as many of the next larger coins as possible. Keep going until they reach pennies.

## Lesson Planner

**OBJECTIVES**
- To demonstrate how to annex zeros to help compare decimal amounts with different numbers of digits to the right of the decimal point
- To demonstrate that there is always another number between any two given numbers, no matter how close the numbers seem
- To demonstrate the use of decimals to calibrate a number line

**NCTM STANDARDS**

**Number and Operations**
Understand numbers, ways of representing numbers, relationships among numbers, and number systems

**Algebra**
Understand patterns, relations, and functions

**Communication**
Use the language of mathematics to express mathematical ideas precisely

**MATERIALS**
- ***Number Cubes**
- ***Calculators**
- **Assessment** Page T71

**TECHNOLOGY**

**ePresentation** Lesson 9.4
**eMathTools Number Lines (Converting between Percents, Decimals, and Fractions); Calculator**

**TEST PREP**

**Cumulative Review**
Mental Math reviews comparing decimals (Lesson 9.2).

*Manipulative Kit Item

# Ordering Decimals

**Context of the Lesson** This lesson builds on the basic decimal comparisons made in Lesson 9.3 to show students how to order a set of decimal numbers. Students will need to understand the order of decimals to help with Lesson 9.5, Rounding Decimals, which calls for students to know place values of decimals and the numeration of decimals. This lesson includes a Mastery Checkpoint.

See page 382B for Math Background for teachers for this lesson.

## Planning for Learning • DIFFERENTIATE INSTRUCTION

### INTERVENTION

**If . . .** students lack the prerequisite skill of comparing numbers through 1,000,

**Then . . .** teach ***Intervention*** Lesson 9.A.

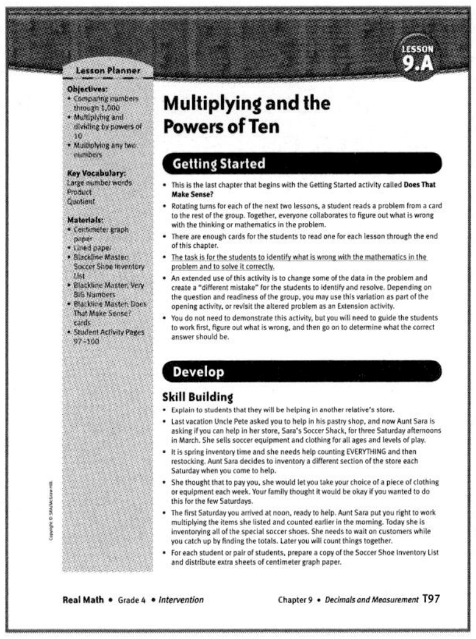
Lesson Planner
LESSON 9.A
Multiplying and the Powers of Ten
Getting Started
Develop
Skill Building

Intervention Lesson 9.A

### ENGLISH LEARNER

**If . . .** students need language support,

**Then . . .** use Lesson 9.2 in ***English Learner Support Guide*** to preview lesson concepts and vocabulary.

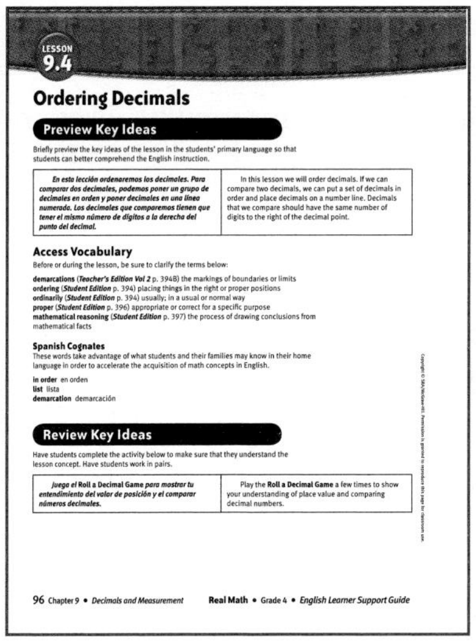
LESSON 9.4
Ordering Decimals
Preview Key Ideas
Access Vocabulary
Spanish Cognates
Review Key Ideas

English Learner Lesson 9.4

### ENRICH

**If . . .** students are proficient in the lesson concepts,

**Then . . .** emphasize additional game time.

### PRACTICE

**If . . .** students would benefit from additional practice,

**Then . . .** extend Strategy Building before assigning the student pages.

### RETEACH

**If . . .** students are having difficulty understanding how to order decimals,

**Then . . .** extend Guided Discussion before assigning the student pages.

**Vocabulary**
**precision \pri sizh´ ən\ *n.*** the state of being precise or exact

**Access Vocabulary**
**ordering** putting in order or sequence

**Spanish Cognates**
**in order** en orden

## Mental Math

5

Review THUMBS UP

Provide practice comparing decimals less than 1, using exercises such as the following. Have students show thumbs-up for numbers that are greater than, thumbs-down for numbers that are less than, and an open hand for number that are equal to.

| | |
|---|---|
| **a.** 0.02 _____ 0.05 down | **h.** 0.02 _____ 0.001 up |
| **b.** 0.05 _____ 0.02 up | **i.** 0.4 _____ 0.04 up |
| **c.** 0.70 _____ 0.7 open | **j.** 0.05 _____ 0.2 down |
| **d.** 0.8 _____ 0.009 up | **k.** 0.03 _____ 0.09 down |
| **e.** 0.09 _____ 0.1 down | **l.** 0.09 _____ 0.03 up |
| **f.** 0.45 _____ 0.4 up | **m.** 0.02 _____ 0.0200 open |
| **g.** 0.06 _____ 0.6 down | **n.** 0.08 _____ 0.5 down |

## 1 Develop

25

**Tell Students In Today's Lesson They Will**
learn to order decimals.

### Using Student Pages UNDERSTANDING

Whole Group

Discuss with students that writing one or more extra zeros to the right of the last digit after a decimal point does not change the value of that number. Ask questions such as the following:

- **Is 0.4 equal to 0.40?** yes
- **Is 0.4 equal to 0.04?** no

Point out that writing extra zeros after a number without a decimal point, such as 3, does change the value of that number, because it moves the digit to a different place (for example, tens instead of ones) unless there is a decimal point to the left of the 3. Ask questions such as the following:

- **Is 4 equal to 40?** no
- **Is 4 equal to 04?** Yes, but we usually don't write it as 04.
- **Is 4 equal to 4.0?** Yes, but 4.0 implies a greater degree of precision.

Ask students where in a number they can write zero without affecting the value of the number. before the leftmost, or greatest, place value of a whole number (for example, 50 = 050) or rightmost, or least, place value after the decimal point (for example, 5.5 = 5.50) Emphasize that the decimal point establishes place value that will not change if you write more zeros on either end of the existing number. Complete some examples with the class.

**NOTE:** It is also important to emphasize that it is customary to write a single zero before a decimal to indicate there are no ones in that number (for example, 0.4).

Read the story on page 395 with the class. Discuss Alia's method for finding a number between two other numbers. Ask students if they think her method will always work. yes

Try this method with the class using several different decimals.

Discuss a number line like the one on page 396. This number line can be demonstrated using ***eMathTools: Number Lines.*** Review with students how to read the demarcations on the number line. For example, if there are nine marks between 0 and 1, the distance between two adjacent marks should be read as 0.1 or 0.10. Have students place decimal numbers on the line and explain their reasoning for placing the numbers where they did.

### Strategy Building ENGAGING

Small Group

Game

**Roll a Decimal Game**

Demonstrate the **Roll a Decimal Game** two or three times by having two students play it in front of the class. This game provides practice with place value, comparing decimal numbers, and probability. Announce what the players roll after each turn so that other students can play along in their seats. Make sure students place each digit permanently before the next digit is rolled.

# 2 Assign Student Pages 25

## Pages 394–395 APPLYING

Part of page 395 was discussed earlier in the Using Student Pages section. Have students complete pages 394 and 395 independently.

### RESEARCH IN ACTION

Some important changes must be made in the way decimals are commonly taught if we hope to improve students' understanding and performance.

1. More time must be devoted to developing the meaning of decimal fractions symbols *when they are introduced.*
2. Many of the rules students are taught for working with decimal numbers should be developed from the meaning of the symbols.
3. Students should be asked to estimate the answers to decimal computation problems before calculating, especially those for which the algorithm is more complicated—multiplication and division. Estimation helps students understand what the algorithm is doing for them and judge the reasonableness of their calculated answers.

Hiebert, James. "Decimal Fractions" *Arithmetic Teacher* March 1987.

Student Page

LESSON 9.4 **Ordering Decimals**

### Key Ideas

**If you can compare two decimals, you can put a set of decimals in order and place them on a number line.**

Ordinarily, decimals that you compare should have the same number of digits to the right of the decimal point. However, when people measure they sometimes forget to write the extra zeros at the end of the number.

For example, if you measure the length of a table to the nearest centimeter, you could report it as 1.34 meters. If the measurement came out to be 2 meters, you should report it as 2.00 meters. This shows how much precision you believe is in your measurement.

3, 3.5, 3.4073, 3.48, 3.408, 3.02, 3.40729

We can write each number with five decimal places to make comparing easier.

3.00000, 3.50000, 3.40730, 3.48000, 3.40800, 3.02000, 3.40729

If we list the numbers in order from least to greatest the list will look like this:

3, 3.02, 3.40729, 3.4073, 3.408, 3.48, 3.5

**Rewrite** each of the following sets of numbers from least to greatest.

1. 24, 19, 20, 23.9, 20.7, 23.97 — 19, 20, 20.7, 23.9, 23.97, 24
2. 2.4, 1.9, 2, 2.39, 2.07, 2.397 — 1.9, 2, 2.07, 2.39, 2.397, 2.4
3. 0.0024, 0.0019, 0.002, 0.00239, 0.00207, 0.002397
   0.0019, 0.002, 0.00207, 0.00239, 0.002397, 0.0024
4. 0.1, 0.02, 0.003, 0.0004, 0.00005, 0.000006
   0.000006, 0.00005, 0.0004, 0.003, 0.02, 0.1
5. 8.82, 8.12, 8.0, 8.01, 8.6, 8.10
   8.0, 8.01, 8.10, 8.12, 8.6, 8.82



Textbook This lesson is available in the *eTextbook.*

Student Page

Mel asked, "Could there be two numbers so close together that there is no number in between them?"

"I don't think so," said June. "Why don't we try to find out?"

Mel tried 0.001 and 0.002. Alia said, "I can find a number between them. I can think of those numbers as 0.0010 and 0.0020. Then 0.0015 must be exactly halfway between them."

"And 0.0014, 0.0013, and a lot of other numbers are between them too, but those numbers are closer to 0.001 than to 0.002," said Mel.

"We can also find lots of numbers between the two original numbers that are closer to 0.002, like 0.0016 and 0.0017," said June. "I think we can always find a lot of numbers between any two numbers."

**For** each of the following pairs of numbers:

**a.** Find a number that is exactly halfway between the two numbers shown.

**b.** Find a number that is closer to the smaller number.

**c.** Find a number that is closer to the greater number.

**d.** Write your three answers in order from least to greatest.

Watch your numbering. The first and last number in each set may vary.

6. 0.2 and 0.3
   0.22, 0.25, 0.29
7. 0.02 and 0.1
   0.03, 0.06, 0.09
8. 1.7 and 1.8
   1.71, 1.75, 1.79
9. 0 and 0.00000001
   0.0000000029, 0.000000005, 0.0000000099
10. 1.7 and 2.1
    1.71, 1.9, 2.0
11. 5 and 5.1
    5.01, 5.05, 5.09
12. 1.7 and 2.2
    1.71, 1.95, 2.1
13. 5 and 5.00000001
    5.000000001, 5.000000005, 5.000000006
14. 0.003 and 0.004
    0.0031, 0.0035, 0.0039
15. 4.9 and 5
    4.91, 4.95, 4.99
16. 3.003 and 3.004
    3.0031, 3.0035, 3.0039
17. 4.99 and 5
    4.991, 4.995, 4.999
18. 9.003 and 9.004
    9.0031, 9.0035, 9.0039
19. 4.9999999 and 5
    4.999999910, 4.99999995, 4.99999999
20. 0 and 0.1
    0.01, 0.05, 0.09
21. 1 and 2
    1.1, 1.5, 1.9

# Assign Student Pages, continued

## Pages 396–397 APPLYING

Discuss the number line on page 396. Have students continue working on page 396 independently.

### As Students Finish

**Game** Roll a Decimal Game



Student Page



**Look** at the number line shown below.

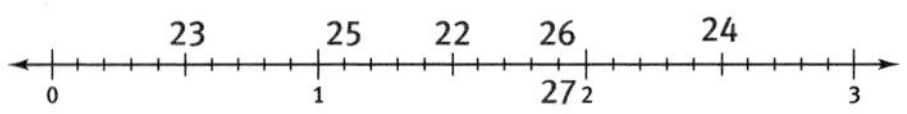


22. Where would you put the number 1.5 so that it would be in the proper place?
23. Where would you place 0.5 (or .5)?
24. Where would you place 2.5?
25. Where would you place 1.1?
26. Where would you place 1.9?
27. Where would you place 1.9307? The only answer is an estimate.

**For** each of the following sets of numbers, draw a number line and write the numbers where they belong. Be sure to draw your number line so that all the numbers listed in the exercise will fit.

28. 2.11111, 2.01, 2.1, 3.704, 4.06, 4.6 Check students' work.
29. 0.73, 1.8, 0.099, 0.99, 2.05, 2.1
30. 1.8, 2.1, 1.9, 2.01, 1.79, 2.001

**For** each of the following number lines, tell what number should be placed where the letter is shown.

31.
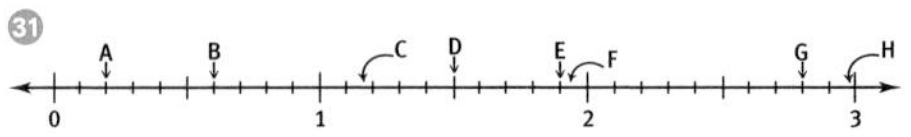


31. A 0.2; B 0.6; C 1.14; D 1.5; E 1.9; F 1.92; G 2.8; H 2.99; Values for C, F, and H may vary slightly.

32.
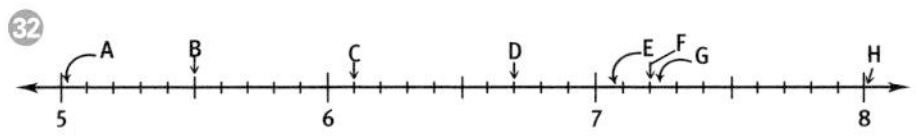


32. A 5.03; B 5.5; C 6.1; D 6.7; E 7.08; F 7.1; G 7.12; H 8.01; Values for A, E, G, and H may vary slightly.


eTextbook This lesson is available in the *eTextbook.*

Student Page

**Game**

# Roll a Decimal Game

**Players:** Two

**Materials:** ***Number Cubes:*** one 0–5 (red), one 5–10 (blue)

**Object:** To make the greater decimal

**Math Focus:** Place value, comparing decimal numbers, and mathematical reasoning

## HOW TO PLAY

1. Roll the 0–5 ***Number Cube.*** If you roll a 0, roll that ***Number Cube*** again.
2. Write a decimal point followed by as many blanks as the number rolled. If you rolled a 3, you would write: 0.___
3. Roll the 5–10 ***Number Cube*** as many times as there are blanks in your decimal. If you roll a 10, roll that cube again.
4. Each time you roll the ***Number Cube,*** write that number in one of your blanks.
5. The player with the greater decimal is the winner.

**SAMPLE GAME**

| Sara rolled: | Sara wrote: | David rolled: | David wrote: |
|---|---|---|---|
| 0 rolled again | | 3 | 0. ___ |
| 2 | 0. __ | 6 | 0. _6_ |
| 6 | 0. _6 | 9 | 0.96_ |
| 7 | 0.76 | 10 rolled again | |
| | | 10 rolled again | |
| | | 6 | 0.966 |

David was the winner.


eGames This game is available in *eGames.*

## 3 Reflect

5

### Guided Discussion REASONING

Whole Group

Have students explain why extra zeros can be written to the right of some numbers without changing their value but can change the value of other numbers. Ask questions such as the following:

- **How do you write 0.2 as a fraction?** $\frac{2}{10}$
- **How do you write 0.20 as a fraction?** $\frac{20}{100}$
- **Are $\frac{2}{10}$ and $\frac{20}{100}$ equivalent fractions?** yes
- **How is 0.54 written as a fraction?** $\frac{54}{100}$
- **What about 0.5400?** $\frac{5,400}{10,000}$
- **Are $\frac{54}{100}$ and $\frac{5,400}{10,000}$ equivalent?** yes
- **Will writing zeros after the last digit of a decimal always create equivalent fractions?** yes

After establishing this logic, ask questions such as the following:

- **How do you write 0.73 as a fraction?** $\frac{73}{100}$
- **What about 0.073?** $\frac{73}{1,000}$
- **Are $\frac{73}{100}$ and $\frac{73}{1,000}$ equivalent?** no
- **So why can we write zeros in some decimal places without changing the number's value but not in others?** Writing zeros in certain places will create equivalent decimals, while doing so in other places will not.

Use Mastery Checkpoint 18 found in ***Assessment*** to evaluate student mastery of understanding decimals. By this time students should be able to correctly answer eighty percent of the Mastery Checkpoint items.

**Cumulative Review:** For review of multidigit multiplication, assign Problems 11–15 on student page 416.

**Family Involvement:** Assign the ***Practice, Reteach,*** or ***Enrichment*** activities depending on the needs of your students.

Encourage students to play the **Roll a Decimal Game** with a friend or relative.

**Concept/Question Board:** Have students look for additional examples of decimals and post them on the Concept/Question Board.

**Math Puzzler:** Suppose you want to display 43.012 on your calculator, but you may press only the 0, the 1, the decimal point, and the addition sign keys. How can you do this? (Provide calculators for students to use to solve this problem.) Enter 10 + 10 + 10 + 10 + 1 + 1 + 1 + 0.01 + 0.001 + 0.001.

# 4 Assess and Differentiate

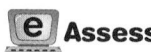

e Assess Use *eAssess* to record and analyze evidence of student understanding.

## A Gather Evidence

Use the Daily Class Assessment Records in ***Assessment*** or ***eAssess*** to record daily observations.

### Formal Assessment

**Mastery Checkpoint**

Did the student
- ❑ use correct procedures?
- ❑ respond with at least eighty percent accuracy?

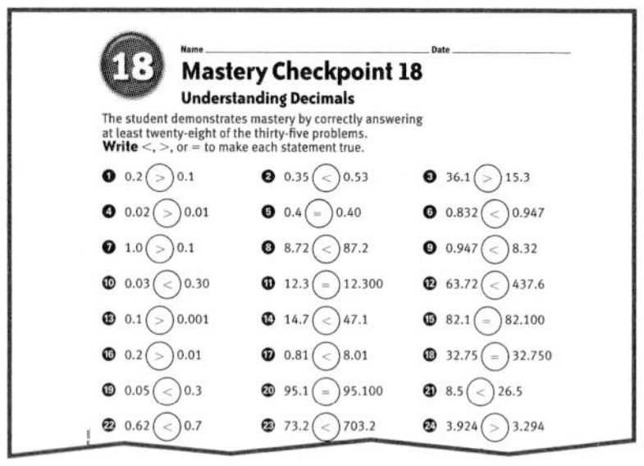

Name ______ Date ______

**18 Mastery Checkpoint 18**

**Understanding Decimals**

The student demonstrates mastery by correctly answering at least twenty-eight of the thirty-five problems.
**Write** <, >, or = to make each statement true.

| | | |
|---|---|---|
| 1 0.2 (>) 0.1 | 2 0.35 (<) 0.53 | 3 36.1 (>) 15.3 |
| 4 0.02 (>) 0.01 | 5 0.4 (=) 0.40 | 6 0.832 (<) 0.947 |
| 7 1.0 (>) 0.1 | 8 8.72 (<) 87.2 | 9 0.947 (<) 8.32 |
| 10 0.03 (<) 0.30 | 11 12.3 (=) 12.300 | 12 63.72 (<) 437.6 |
| 13 0.1 (>) 0.001 | 14 14.7 (<) 47.1 | 15 82.1 (=) 82.100 |
| 16 0.2 (>) 0.01 | 17 0.81 (<) 8.01 | 18 32.75 (=) 32.750 |
| 19 0.05 (<) 0.3 | 20 95.1 (=) 95.100 | 21 8.5 (<) 26.5 |
| 22 0.62 (<) 0.7 | 23 73.2 (<) 703.2 | 24 3.924 (>) 3.294 |

Assessment Page T71

## B Summarize Findings

Analyze and summarize assessment data for each student. Determine which Assessment Follow-Up is appropriate for each student. Use the Student Assessment Record in ***Assessment*** or ***eAssess*** to update assessment records.

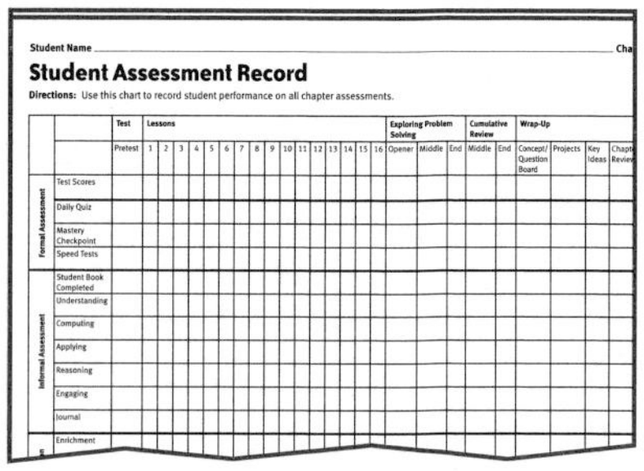

Student Name ______

**Student Assessment Record**

Directions: Use this chart to record student performance on all chapter assessments.

Assessment Page T41

## C Assessment Follow-Up • DIFFERENTIATE INSTRUCTION

Based on your observations, use these teaching strategies for assessment follow-up.

### INTERVENTION

Review student performance on ***Intervention*** Lesson 9.A to see if students have mastered prerequisite skills for this lesson.

### ENGLISH LEARNER

**Review**

Use Lesson 9.4 in ***English Learner Support Guide*** to preview lesson concepts and vocabulary.

### ENRICH

**If . . .** students are proficient in the lesson concepts,

**Then . . .** encourage them to work on the chapter projects or ***Enrichment*** Lesson 9.4.

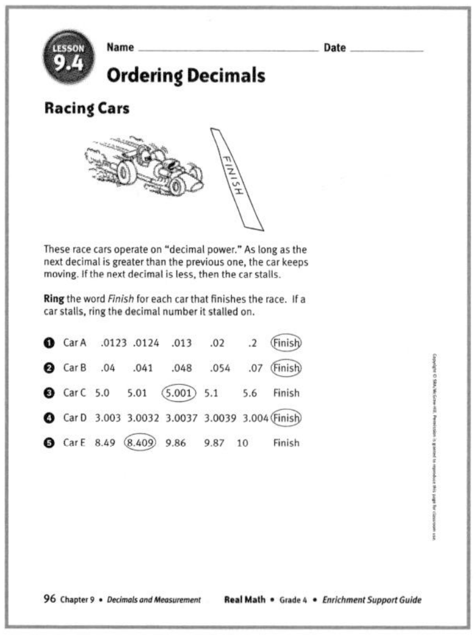

LESSON 9.4 Name ______ Date ______

**Ordering Decimals**

**Racing Cars**

These race cars operate on "decimal power." As long as the next decimal is greater than the previous one, the car keeps moving. If the next decimal is less, then the car stalls.

**Ring** the word *Finish* for each car that finishes the race. If a car stalls, ring the decimal number it stalled on.

1. Car A .0123 .0124 .013 .02 .2 (Finish)
2. Car B .04 .041 .048 .054 .07 (Finish)
3. Car C 5.0 5.01 (5.001) 5.1 5.6 Finish
4. Car D 3.003 3.0032 3.0037 3.0039 3.004 (Finish)
5. Car E 8.49 (8.409) 9.86 9.87 10 Finish

96 Chapter 9 • *Decimals and Measurement* **Real Math** • Grade 4 • *Enrichment Support Guide*

Enrichment Lesson 9.4

### PRACTICE

**If . . .** students would benefit from additional practice,

**Then . . .** assign ***Practice*** Lesson 9.4.

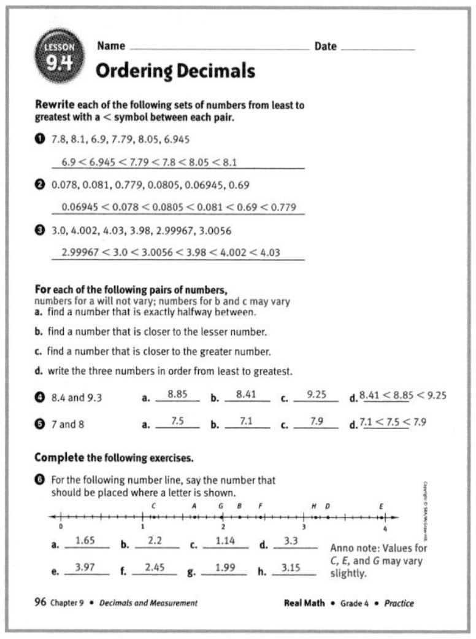

LESSON 9.4 Name ______ Date ______

**Ordering Decimals**

**Rewrite each of the following sets of numbers from least to greatest with a < symbol between each pair.**

1. 7.8, 8.1, 6.9, 7.79, 8.05, 6.945
   6.9 < 6.945 < 7.79 < 7.8 < 8.05 < 8.1
2. 0.078, 0.081, 0.779, 0.0805, 0.06945, 0.69
   0.06945 < 0.078 < 0.0805 < 0.081 < 0.69 < 0.779
3. 3.0, 4.002, 4.03, 3.98, 2.99967, 3.0056
   2.99967 < 3.0 < 3.0056 < 3.98 < 4.002 < 4.03

**For each of the following pairs of numbers,**
numbers for a will not vary; numbers for b and c may vary
a. find a number that is exactly halfway between.
b. find a number that is closer to the lesser number.
c. find a number that is closer to the greater number.
d. write the three numbers in order from least to greatest.

4. 8.4 and 9.3 a. 8.85 b. 8.41 c. 9.25 d. 8.41 < 8.85 < 9.25
5. 7 and 8 a. 7.5 b. 7.1 c. 7.9 d. 7.1 < 7.5 < 7.9

**Complete the following exercises.**

6. For the following number line, say the number that should be placed where a letter is shown.

a. 1.65 b. 2.2 c. 1.14 d. 3.3
e. 3.97 f. 2.45 g. 1.99 h. 3.15

Anno note: Values for *C*, *E*, and *G* may vary slightly.

96 Chapter 9 • *Decimals and Measurement* **Real Math** • Grade 4 • *Practice*

Practice Lesson 9.4

### RETEACH

**If . . .** students are having difficulty understanding how to order decimals,

**Then . . .** reteach the concept using ***Reteach*** Lesson 9.4.

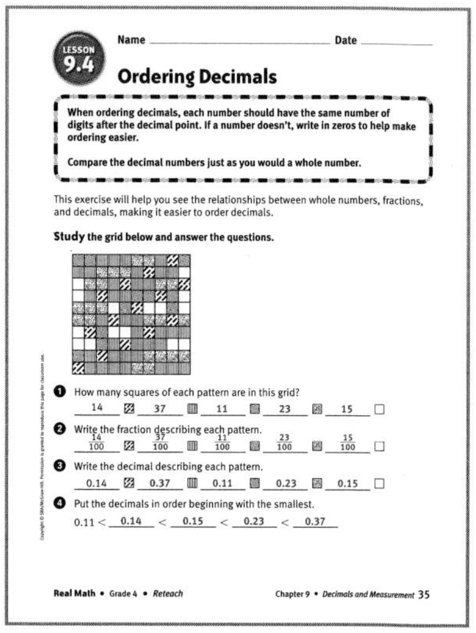

LESSON 9.4 Name ______ Date ______

**Ordering Decimals**

**When ordering decimals, each number should have the same number of digits after the decimal point. If a number doesn't, write in zeros to help make ordering easier.**

**Compare the decimal numbers just as you would a whole number.**

This exercise will help you see the relationships between whole numbers, fractions, and decimals, making it easier to order decimals.

**Study the grid below and answer the questions.**

1. How many squares of each pattern are in this grid?
   14 ▨ 37 ▥ 11 ▩ 23 ▦ 15 □
2. Write the fraction describing each pattern.
   $\frac{14}{100}$ ▨ $\frac{37}{100}$ ▥ $\frac{11}{100}$ ▩ $\frac{23}{100}$ ▦ $\frac{15}{100}$ □
3. Write the decimal describing each pattern.
   0.14 ▨ 0.37 ▥ 0.11 ▩ 0.23 ▦ 0.15 □
4. Put the decimals in order beginning with the smallest.
   0.11 < 0.14 < 0.15 < 0.23 < 0.37

**Real Math** • Grade 4 • *Reteach* Chapter 9 • *Decimals and Measurement* 35

## Lesson Planner

**OBJECTIVES**
- To provide practice with rounding numbers to a specified degree of precision
- To help students develop judgment about rounding numbers in specific realistic situations

**NCTM STANDARDS**

**Number and Operations**
Understand numbers, ways of representing numbers, relationships among numbers, and number systems.

**Connections**
Recognize and use connections among mathematical ideas.

**Communication**
Use the language of mathematics to express mathematical ideas precisely

**MATERIALS**
- *Number Cubes
- Calculator (optional)

**TECHNOLOGY**
**Presentation** Lesson 9.5
**MathTools** Number Lines (Converting between Percents, Decimals, and Fractions) and Calculator

**TEST PREP**
**Cumulative Review**
Mental Math reviews equivalent decimals (Lesson 9.3).

*Manipulative Kit Item

# Rounding Decimals

**Context of the Lesson** Rounding decimals is an important skill because computations often give decimal results that must be rounded in order to be meaningful. Rounding is also useful for approximating answers when computing to give students an idea as to whether or not their answer is correct. For students to comprehend how to round decimals, they will need to have the knowledge on decimals from Lessons 9.1 through 9.4. Students rounded whole numbers in Lesson 1.4.

See page 382B for Math Background for teachers for this lesson.

## Planning for Learning • DIFFERENTIATE INSTRUCTION

### INTERVENTION

**If . . .** students lack the prerequisite skill of comparing numbers through 1,000,

**Then . . .** teach ***Intervention*** Lesson 9.A.

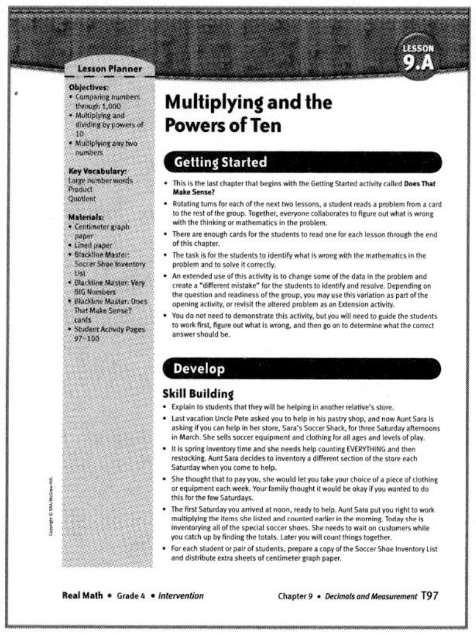


Intervention Lesson 9.A

### ENGLISH LEARNER

**If . . .** students need language support,

**Then . . .** use Lesson 9.5 in ***English Learner Support Guide*** to preview lesson concepts and vocabulary.

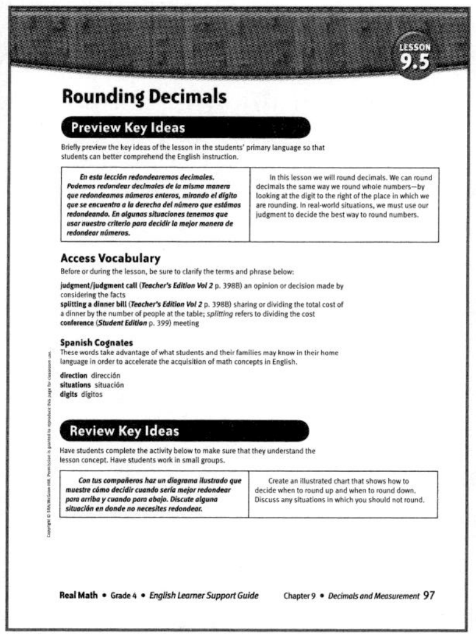


English Learner Lesson 9.5

### ENRICH

**If . . .** students are proficient in the lesson concepts,

**Then . . .** emphasize game strategies.

### PRACTICE

**If . . .** students would benefit from additional practice,

**Then . . .** extend Guided Discussion before assigning the student pages.

### RETEACH

**If . . .** students are having difficulty understanding how to round decimals,

**Then . . .** extend Guided Discussion before assigning the student pages.

**Access Vocabulary**
**realistic** like real life
**judgment call** a decision made by considering the facts

**Spanish Cognates**
**direction** dirección
**practical** práctica
**situations** situaciones

## Mental Math

5

THUMBS UP

Write a decimal, such as 4.07, on the board. As you say other numbers, such as the following, students should show thumbs-up if the number is greater than 4.07, thumbs-down if less than 4.07, or an open hand if the number is equal to 4.07.

**a.** 4.008 down
**b.** 4.073 up
**c.** 7 up
**d.** 4.707 up
**e.** 4.05889 down
**f.** 4.08 up
**g.** 4.0089 down
**h.** 4.070 open hand
**i.** 4.069 down
**j.** 4.7 up

## 1 Develop

25

**Tell Students In Today's Lesson They Will**
learn to round decimals.

### Guided Discussion UNDERSTANDING

Whole Group

1. Ask students if they know any real-life situations where rounding a decimal number can be helpful. One example could be splitting a dinner bill equally among a group of people.

   Give students an example, such as the following: 4 people are splitting the cost of a lunch that costs a total of $16.77. This can be demonstrated using ***eMathTools: Calculator,*** or have a student use a calculator to divide this total by 4 and read the result. 4.1925 Ask questions such as the following:

   - **What is the smallest monetary denomination that is used in the United States?** cent
   - **What fraction of a dollar is this?** $\frac{1}{100}$
   - **What is the place value of 5 in 4.1925?** ten-thousandths
   - **Will any of the people at lunch be able to pay to this level of precision?** No; the cent is the limiting factor at $\frac{1}{100}$ of a dollar.

   Any decimal number with more than two digits after the decimal point will not correspond to a real amount of money. In cases like this, people will often round the numbers.

2. Review the guidelines for rounding a number. Ask questions such as the following:

   - **What is 4,530 rounded to the nearest hundred?** 4,500
   - **Why is 4,500 the answer?** The 3 in the tens place is closer to zero (4,500) than 10 (4,600).
   - **What, then, is 4,570 rounded to the nearest hundred?** 4,600
   - **Why is 4,600 the answer?** The 7 in the tens place is closer to 10 (4,600) than 0 (4,500).

   Remind students that to round any number, we make our decision by looking at the place value that is to the right of the place value of interest.

   Ask students if they remember what to do if the digit to the right of the place value of interest is 5, a number that falls exactly in the middle. Ask questions such as the following:

   - **How would you round 4,557 to the nearest hundred?** 4,600
   - **What about 4,550?** It would be correct to round this to either 4,500 or 4,600.

   Explain that we usually round up if we know there are more nonzero digits after the 5. But if the last digit is 5 and there are only 0s after that, then there is no reason to round in either direction. It is a judgment call at that point.

3. Place special emphasis on the fact that, in practical situations, people apply their judgment about how to round.

   Ask students to suggest examples of realistic situations in which they might have to round decimal numbers (for example, rounding money, rounding time that goes into centiseconds, rounding metric measurements, etc.).

## 2 Assign Student Pages

25

**Pages 398–399** APPLYING

Have students complete page 399 independently.

Game **Roll a Decimal Game** (introduced in Lesson 9.4)

Student Page

LESSON 9.5 Rounding Decimals

### Key Ideas

**You can round decimals the same way you round whole numbers—look to the right of the final digit you want to keep to decide whether to round up or down. Whenever you round, you should also consider the situation.**

Let's look at an example. To round 3.5943295 to the nearest hundredth, we look at the digit to the right of the hundredths place. Because 4 is less than 5, the number is closer to 3.59 than to 3.60, so we round to 3.59.

**3.59**43295 ⟶ 3.59

If the next digit is 5, and we know there are more nonzero digits, we usually round up. But what if the last digit is 5 and it is the last nonzero digit? Then we may round in either direction. For example, 2.85 is equally close to 2.8 and 2.9.

If we are adding a group of numbers, we should probably round such numbers up half the time and down half the time.

See how each of the following numbers are rounded to the nearest thousandth.

- 2.03450012 rounds to 2.035
- 2.0345 can be rounded to either 2.034 or 2.035

In real-world situations, you must use your judgment to decide the best way to round numbers. For example, suppose 7 people went out to eat. The total bill was $36.77, and each person wants to pay the same amount.

If you divide 36.77 by 7, you get 5.2528571. But people cannot pay part of a penny. If we round to the nearest penny, we will get an answer of $5.25 for each person. But 7 times 5.25 is 36.75, which is 2 cents short. In this case, we could ask two people to pay an extra penny.

398 eTextbook This lesson is available in the *eTextbook*.

Student Page

**Round** each of the following numbers to the nearest hundredth.

1. 4.7380389 4.74
2. 45.92800003 45.93
3. 4.73501001 4.74
4. 3.451 3.45
5. 4.735 4.73 or 4.74
6. 3.541999999 3.54
7. 0.007 0.01
8. 0.051 0.05
9. 1.003 1.00
10. 1.294 1.29
11. 0.003 0.00
12. 10.609 10.61
13. 45.928 45.93
14. 8.543 8.54

**Round** each of the following numbers to the nearest thousandth.

15. 1.23456 1.235
16. 0.0075 0.007 or 0.008
17. 1.2345 1.234 or 1.235
18. 0.148762 0.149
19. 1.234500001 1.235
20. 19.417023 19.417
21. 1.234499999 1.234
22. 4.0012 4.001

**For** each of the following, use a calculator and round in a way that makes sense.

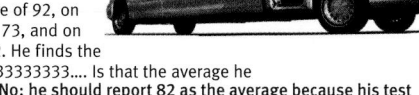

23. Philip has taken 3 tests. On the first one he got a score of 92, on the second he scored 73, and on the third he scored 82. He finds the average to be 82.33333333333.... Is that the average he should report? Why? **No; he should report 82 as the average because his test scores consist of only 2 digits.**
24. Bonita needs 1 bag of fertilizer to fertilize 200 square feet of her garden. The length of the garden is 73.5 feet and the width is 19 feet. How many bags of fertilizer should she buy? **7, the total area of her yard is 1,396.5 sq. ft.**
25. Ms. Goldberg runs a limousine service. Each bus can carry 16 people. She has been asked to supply buses to take 175 people to a conference. She divides 175 by 16 and gets 10.9375. How many buses does she need? **11**

Chapter 9 • Lesson 5 399

# 3 Reflect

5

## Guided Discussion REASONING

Whole Group

Lead a discussion on rounding rules. Ask questions such as the following:

- **Why can we say that 4.735 rounded to the nearest hundredth is either 4.73 or 4.74?** It is equally close to both.
- **Why do we say that 4.73501 rounded to the nearest hundredth is 4.74, and not 4.73?** Since there is a nonzero digit after the 5, we can say that it is closer to 4.74 than 4.73.
- **Why do we round 5s up if there are more digits after the 5, and round either way if there are no more (nonzero) digits?** If there are no nonzero digits, the number will be equidistant from both rounded numbers; if there are more nonzero digits, the number will be closer to the greater rounded number.

**Cumulative Review:** For review of fractions greater than 1, assign Problems 16–22 on student page 416.

**Family Involvement:** Assign the ***Practice, Reteach,*** or ***Enrichment*** activities depending on the needs of your students. Encourage students to play the **Roll a Decimal Game** with a friend or relative.

**Concept/Question Board:** Have students look for additional examples of decimals and post them on the Concept/Question Board.

**Math Puzzler:** Keisha and her dad have the same birthday. This year, Keisha's dad is 5 times older than Keisha. In three years, Keisha's dad will be only 4 times older than she is. How old are Keisha and her dad now, and how old will they be in 3 years? 9 and 45; 12 and 48

# 4 Assess and Differentiate

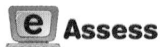

**e Assess** Use ***eAssess*** to record and analyze evidence of student understanding.

## A Gather Evidence

Use the Daily Class Assessment Records in ***Assessment*** or ***eAssess*** to record daily observations.

### Informal Assessment
**✓ Mental Math**

Did the student **COMPUTING**
- ❑ respond accurately?
- ❑ respond quickly?
- ❑ respond with confidence?
- ❑ self-correct?

### Informal Assessment
**✓ Student Pages**

Did the student **UNDERSTANDING**
- ❑ make important observations?
- ❑ extend or generalize learning?
- ❑ provide insightful answers?
- ❑ pose insightful questions?

## B Summarize Findings

Analyze and summarize assessment data for each student. Determine which Assessment Follow-Up is appropriate for each student. Use the Student Assessment Record in ***Assessment*** or ***eAssess*** to update assessment records.

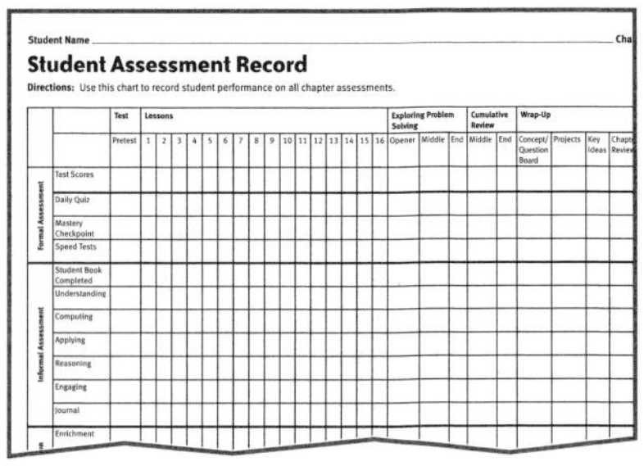


**Assessment Page T41**

## C Assessment Follow-Up • DIFFERENTIATE INSTRUCTION

Based on your observations, use these teaching strategies for assessment follow-up.

### INTERVENTION

Review student performance on ***Intervention*** Lesson 9.A to see if students have mastered prerequisite skills for this lesson.

### ENGLISH LEARNER

**Review**

Use Lesson 9.1 in ***English Learner Support Guide*** to preview lesson concepts and vocabulary.

### ENRICH

**If . . .** students are proficient in the lesson concepts,

**Then . . .** encourage them to work on the chapter projects or ***Enrichment*** Lesson 9.5.

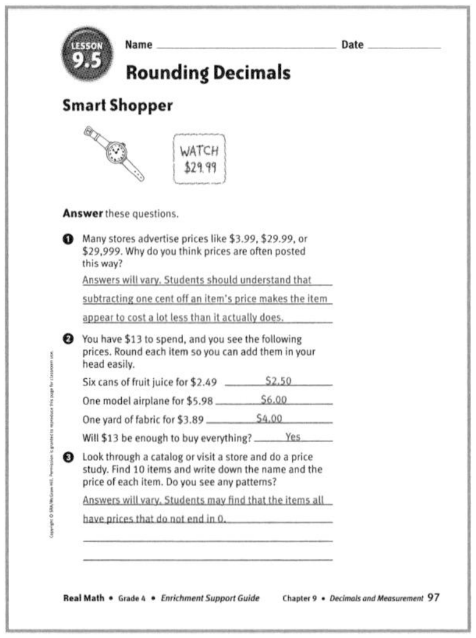

LESSON 9.5 Name ______ Date ______

Rounding Decimals

Smart Shopper



**Answer** these questions.

1. Many stores advertise prices like $3.99, $29.99, or $29,999. Why do you think prices are often posted this way?
   Answers will vary. Students should understand that subtracting one cent off an item's price makes the item appear to cost a lot less than it actually does.
2. You have $13 to spend, and you see the following prices. Round each item so you can add them in your head easily.
   Six cans of fruit juice for $2.49 $2.50
   One model airplane for $5.98 $6.00
   One yard of fabric for $3.89 $4.00
   Will $13 be enough to buy everything? Yes
3. Look through a catalog or visit a store and do a price study. Find 10 items and write down the name and the price of each item. Do you see any patterns?
   Answers will vary. Students may find that the items all have prices that do not end in 0.

Real Math • Grade 4 • *Enrichment Support Guide* Chapter 9 • *Decimals and Measurement* 97

Enrichment Lesson 9.5

### PRACTICE

**If . . .** students would benefit from additional practice,

**Then . . .** assign ***Practice*** Lesson 9.5.

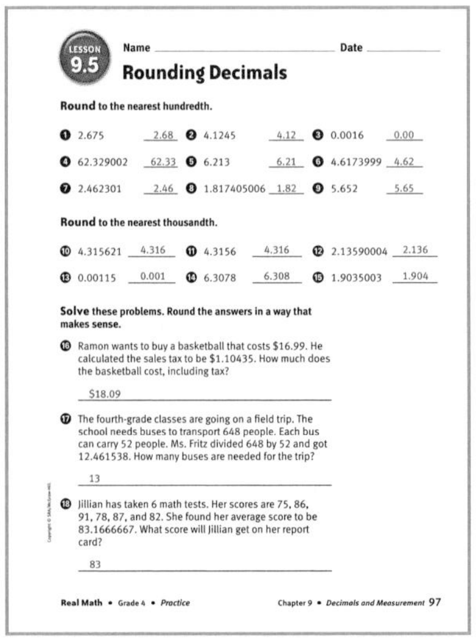

LESSON 9.5 Name ______ Date ______

Rounding Decimals

**Round** to the nearest hundredth.

1. 2.675 2.68
2. 4.1245 4.12
3. 0.0016 0.00
4. 62.329002 62.33
5. 6.213 6.21
6. 4.6173999 4.62
7. 2.462301 2.46
8. 1.817405006 1.82
9. 5.652 5.65

**Round** to the nearest thousandth.

10. 4.315621 4.316
11. 4.3156 4.316
12. 2.13590004 2.136
13. 0.00115 0.001
14. 6.3078 6.308
15. 1.9035003 1.904

**Solve** these problems. Round the answers in a way that makes sense.

16. Ramon wants to buy a basketball that costs $16.99. He calculated the sales tax to be $1.10435. How much does the basketball cost, including tax?
    $18.09
17. The fourth-grade classes are going on a field trip. The school needs buses to transport 648 people. Each bus can carry 52 people. Ms. Fritz divided 648 by 52 and got 12.461538. How many buses are needed for the trip?
    13
18. Jillian has taken 6 math tests. Her scores are 75, 86, 91, 78, 87, and 82. She found her average score to be 83.1666667. What score will Jillian get on her report card?
    83

Real Math • Grade 4 • *Practice* Chapter 9 • *Decimals and Measurement* 97

Practice Lesson 9.5

### RETEACH

**If . . .** students are having difficulty understanding how to round decimals,

**Then . . .** reteach the concept using ***Reteach*** Lesson 9.5.

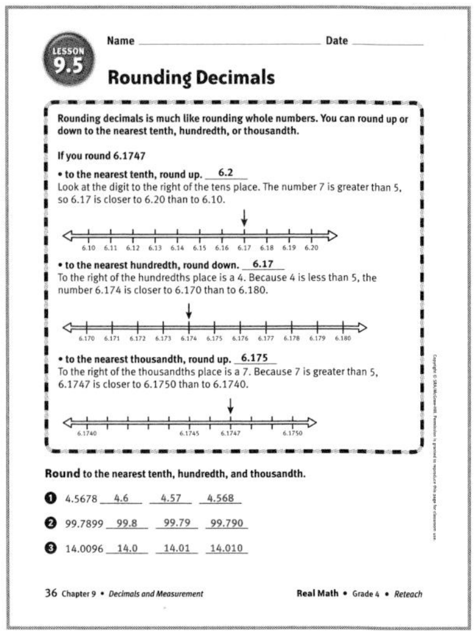

LESSON 9.5 Name ______ Date ______

Rounding Decimals

Rounding decimals is much like rounding whole numbers. You can round up or down to the nearest tenth, hundredth, or thousandth.

If you round 6.1747

- to the nearest tenth, round up. 6.2
  Look at the digit to the right of the tens place. The number 7 is greater than 5, so 6.17 is closer to 6.20 than to 6.10.
  
- to the nearest hundredth, round down. 6.17
  To the right of the hundredths place is a 4. Because 4 is less than 5, the number 6.174 is closer to 6.170 than to 6.180.
  
- to the nearest thousandth, round up. 6.175
  To the right of the thousandths place is a 7. Because 7 is greater than 5, 6.1747 is closer to 6.1750 than to 6.1740.
  

**Round** to the nearest tenth, hundredth, and thousandth.

1. 4.5678 4.6 4.57 4.568
2. 99.7899 99.8 99.79 99.790
3. 14.0096 14.0 14.01 14.010

36 Chapter 9 • *Decimals and Measurement* Real Math • Grade 4 • *Reteach*

Reteach Lesson 9.5

# Multiplying and Dividing by Powers of 10

**Context of the Lesson** Students have multiplied and divided whole numbers by powers of 10 in various contexts throughout the year. The skills taught in this lesson will help students move decimal points appropriately when placed within specific contexts.

See page 382B for Math Background for teachers for this lesson.

## OBJECTIVES

- To introduce procedures for multiplying and dividing decimals by 10, 100, and 1,000
- To provide practice in converting between metric measurements

## NCTM STANDARDS

**Number and Operations**
Understand meanings of operations and how they relate to one another

**Measurement**
Understand measurable attributes of objects and the units, systems, and processes of measurement

## MATERIALS

*Response Wheels

## TECHNOLOGY

**Presentation** Lesson 9.6
**MathTools Number Lines (Converting between Percents, Decimals, and Fractions)**

## TEST PREP

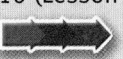

**Cumulative Review**
Mental Math reviews multiplying and dividing by powers of 10 (Lesson 5.1).

**Extended Response**
Problem 28

*Manipulative Kit Item

## Planning for Learning • DIFFERENTIATE INSTRUCTION

### INTERVENTION

**If . . .** students lack the prerequisite skill of multiplying and dividing by powers of 10,

**Then . . .** teach ***Intervention*** Lesson 9.B.

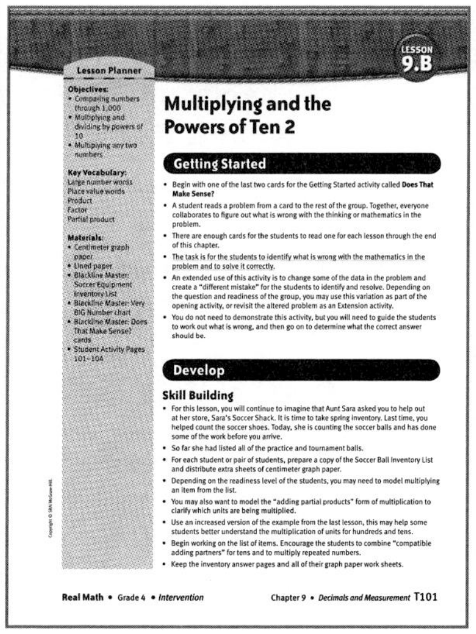


Intervention Lesson 9.B

### ENGLISH LEARNER

**Preview**

**If . . .** students need language support,

**Then . . .** use Lesson 9.6 in ***English Learner Support Guide*** to preview lesson concepts and vocabulary.

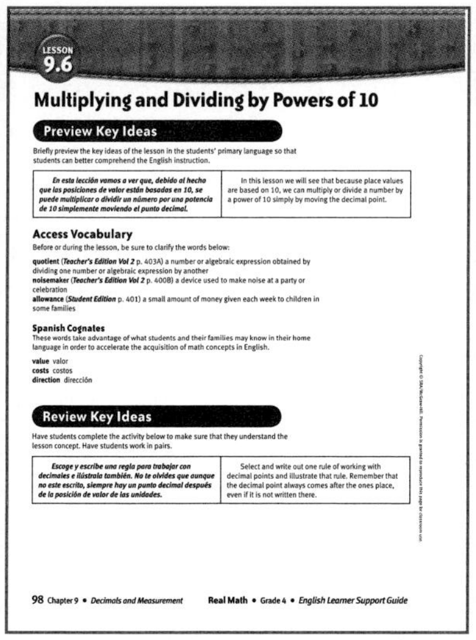


English Learner Lesson 9.6

### ENRICH

**If . . .** students are proficient in the lesson concepts,

**Then . . .** emphasize chapter projects.

### PRACTICE

**If . . .** students would benefit from additional practice,

**Then . . .** extend Guided Discussion before assigning the student pages.

### RETEACH

**If . . .** students are having difficulty understanding multiplication and division by powers of 10,

**Then . . .** extend Strategy Building before assigning the student pages.

**Access Vocabulary**
**watch the signs** pay attention or be aware of the operation symbols

**Spanish Cognates**
**value** valor
**extra** extra

# Teaching Lesson 9.6

## Mental Math

5

Review · RESPONSE WHEEL

Provide problems, such as the following, that involve multiplying and dividing whole numbers by 10 and multiples of 10.

**a.** 900 ÷ 10 = 90
**b.** 9 × 10 = 90
**c.** 45 × 100 = 4,500
**d.** 4,500 ÷ 10 = 450
**e.** 6,600 ÷ 10 = 660
**f.** 660 × 100 = 66,000
**g.** 90 × 100 = 9,000
**h.** 450 ÷ 10 = 45
**i.** 4,500 ÷ 100 = 45
**j.** 45 × 10 = 450
**k.** 600 × 10 = 6,000
**l.** 6,600 ÷ 100 = 66

## 1 Develop

25

### Tell Students In Today's Lesson They Will

practice multiplying and dividing by powers of 10 within the context of decimals.

### Strategy Building

UNDERSTANDING

Small Group

Write the chart on the board and have each group of students copy it and complete the last two rows. Present a scenario, such as the following, to the class.

- Olivia is buying supplies for a birthday party. There will be ten people at the party. She made a chart to show prices in cents and in dollars and cents. Help Olivia complete the last two rows of the chart.

| Item | Price in cents for 1 | Price in cents for 10 | Price in Dollars and Cents for 1 | Price in Dollars and Cents for 10 |
|---|---|---|---|---|
| Balloon | 7¢ | 70¢ | \$0.07 | \$0.70 |
| Noisemaker | 29¢ | 290¢ | \$0.29 | \$2.90 |
| Hat | 63¢ | 630¢ | \$0.63 | \$6.30 |
| Sticker | 37¢ | 370¢ | \$0.37 | \$3.70 |

Compare the two cents columns and then compare the two dollars columns. What can we say about the movement of the decimal point? It appears to move to the right in the second column.

Write a chart such as the following on the board and have each pair copy it and complete the last three rows. Present a second scenario, such as the following, to the class.

- Ten people are sharing the cost of the food for Olivia's birthday party. They made a chart to show the prices in both cents and dollars. Help them complete the chart.
- Examine the two dollars-and-cents columns. What do you notice about the decimal point? It shifts one place to the left across the columns.

| Item | Total Cost in Cents | Total Cost for Each Person in Cents | Total Cost in Dollars and Cents | Total Cost for Each Person in Dollars and Cents |
|---|---|---|---|---|
| Cupcakes | 380¢ | 38¢ | \$3.80 | \$0.38 |
| Ice Cream | 980¢ | 98¢ | \$9.80 | \$0.98 |
| Granola Bars | 470¢ | 47¢ | \$4.70 | \$0.47 |
| Milk | 260¢ | 26¢ | \$2.60 | \$0.26 |

### Guided Discussion

UNDERSTANDING

Whole Group

1. Remind students that a "power of 10" is a number that results from multiplying 10 by itself a certain number of times. For example, $10 \times 10 = 10^2$. Discuss multiplying a decimal by a power of 10. Ask questions such as the following:
   - **If a decimal point is not written in a number, where is it located?** The decimal point always comes after the ones place, even if it is not written there.
   - **In which direction do you move the decimal point if you are multiplying by a power of 10?** You move the decimal point that many places to the right.
   - **What is 10 × 7.6?** 76
   - **What is 4.05 × 10?** 40.5
   - **What is 2 × 10?** 20
   - **What happens when you multiply a decimal by 100 or $10^2$?** The decimal point moves two places to the right.
   - **What is 37 × 100?** 3,700
   - **What happens when you multiply a decimal by 1,000 or $10^3$?** The decimal point moves three places to the right.
   - **What is 8.26597 × 1,000?** 8,265.97
2. Discuss dividing a decimal by a power of 10. Ask questions such as the following:
   - **Which direction do you move the decimal point if you are dividing by a power of 10?** You move the decimal point to the left.
   - **What is 36 ÷ 10?** 3.6
   - **What is 0.8 ÷ 10?** 0.08
   - **What happens when you divide a decimal by 100?** The decimal point moves two places to the left.
   - **What is 46.4 ÷ 100?** 0.464
   - **What happens when you divide a decimal by 1,000?** The decimal point moves three places to the left.
   - **What is 96 ÷ 1,000?** 0.096

# 2 Assign Student Pages

25

### Pages 400–401 APPLYING

Pages 400–401 involve multiplying by powers of 10. Have students complete these pages on their own.

Student Page

LESSON 9.6

## Multiplying and Dividing by Powers of 10

### Key Ideas

**Because place values are based on 10, you can multiply or divide a number by a power of 10 by moving the decimal point to the right or left.**

The value of a digit in its place in a number is ten times as great as the value of the digit in the place to its right. So you can multiply by 10 by moving the decimal point one place to the right, which has the same effect as moving each digit one place to the left.

**Examples:**

$10 \times 4.5 = ?$ 4.5. $10 \times 4.5 = 45$

$3.06 \times 10 = ?$ 3.0.6 $3.06 \times 10 = 30.6$

Remember, the decimal point always comes after the ones place, even if it is not written there. Sometimes you need to write a 0 after the decimal point.

$8 \times 10 = ?$ 8.0. $8 \times 10 = 80$

$100 = 10 \times 10 = 10^2$. To multiply by 100, move the decimal point two places to the right.

**Examples:**

$100 \times 17.15 = ?$ 17.1 5. $100 \times 17.15 = 1715$

$6.7 \times 100 = ?$ 6.7 0. $6.7 \times 100 = 670$

$1{,}000 = 10 \times 10 \times 10 = 10^3$. To multiply by 1,000, move the decimal point three places to the right.

**Examples:**

$1.9396 \times 1{,}000 = ?$ 1.9 3 9.6 $1.9396 \times 10^3 = 1{,}939.6$

$1.07 \times 1{,}000 = ?$ 1.0 7 0. $1.07 \times 10^3 = 1{,}070$



Textbook This lesson is available in the ***eTextbook***.

Student Page

### Multiply.

1. $10 \times 7$ 70
2. $12 \times 10$ 120
3. $10 \times 60$ 600
4. $10 \times 59$ 590
5. $100 \times 7$ 700
6. $12 \times 10^2$ 1,200
7. $60 \times 100$ 6,000
8. $100 \times 59$ 5,900
9. $1{,}000 \times 8$ 8,000
10. $1{,}000 \times 0.798$ 798
11. $1{,}000 \times 73$ 73,000
12. $1{,}000 \times 7.23$ 7,230
13. $10 \times 7.2$ 72
14. $10 \times 81.34$ 813.4
15. $10^3 \times 74.82$ 74,820
16. $10^2 \times 7.2$ 720
17. $86.29 \times 10$ 862.9
18. $100 \times 86.29$ 8,629
19. $47.28 \times 10$ 472.8
20. $42 \times 10^3$ 42,000
21. $100 \times 81.34$ 8,134
22. $50 \times 1{,}000$ 50,000
23. $100 \times 47.28$ 4,728
24. $10^3 \times 68.92$ 68,920

### Answer the following questions.

25. How many cents are in $330.29? 33,029 cents
26. Ahmed wants to buy 10 crickets. Each cricket costs $0.10. How much will the crickets cost altogether? $1.00
27. If Debbie saves $0.50 a week from her allowance, how much money will she have in 100 weeks? $50.00
28. Extended Response Suki has $2.75. She wants to buy 10 apples at 25¢ each. Does she have enough money? Explain how you found the answer. Yes; 10 apples at $0.25 would cost $2.50.

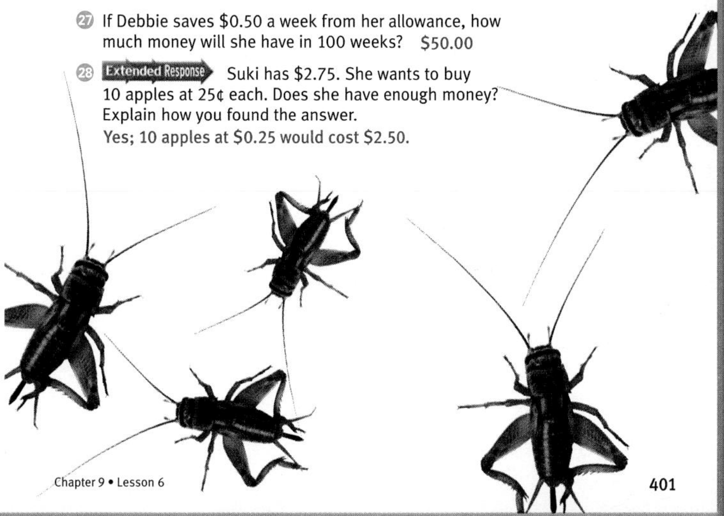

# Assign Student Pages, continued

### Pages 402–403 APPLYING

Pages 402–403 deal with division by powers of 10. You may want to stop students after they complete pages 400–401 to remind them the decimal point will be moving to the left as they divide.

## Monitoring Student Progress

**If . . .** students are having trouble multiplying or dividing by 10, 100, or 1,000,

**Then . . .** have them decide whether the answer will be greater than or less than the number they are multiplying or dividing. Then call their attention to the fact that the number of zeros—one in 10, two in 100, three in 1,000—tells how many places to move the decimal point. Showing the exponential notation may also help.

### As Students Finish

Game **Roll a Decimal Game** (introduced in Lesson 9.4)

Student Page

LESSON 9.6 • Multiplying and Dividing by Powers of 10

The value of a digit is one-tenth the value it would have if it was in the place to its left. So you can divide by 10 by moving the decimal point one place to the left.

**Examples:**

| | | |
|---|---|---|
| 47 ÷ 10 = ? | 4.7 | 47 ÷ 10 = 4.7 |
| 0.7 ÷ 10 = ? | .0.7 | 0.7 ÷ 10 = 0.07 |
| 38.6 ÷ 10 = ? | 3.8.6 | 38.6 ÷ 10 = 3.86 |

100 = 10 × 10. To divide by 100, move the decimal point two places to the left.

**Examples:**

| | | | |
|---|---|---|---|
| 545 ÷ 100 = ? | 5.4 5. | 545 ÷ 100 = 5.45 | 545 ÷ $10^2$ = 5.45 |
| 65 ÷ 100 = ? | .6 5. | 65 ÷ 100 = 0.65 | 65 ÷ $10^2$ = 0.65 |

Sometimes you need to write in 0.

0.73 ÷ 100 = ? .0 0.73 0.73 ÷ $10^2$ = 0.0073

1,000 = 10 × 10 × 10. To divide by 1,000, move the decimal point three places to the left.

**Examples:**

| | | | |
|---|---|---|---|
| 45 ÷ 1,000 = ? | .0 4 5. | 45 ÷ $10^3$ = 0.045 | 45 ÷ 1,000 = 0.045 |
| 22 ÷ 1,000 = ? | .0 2 2. | 22 ÷ $10^3$ = 0.022 | 45 ÷ 1,000 = 0.022 |

402 Textbook This lesson is available in the *eTextbook*.

Student Page

**Divide.**

| | | |
|---|---|---|
| 29 38 ÷ 10 3.8 | 30 0.8 ÷ 10 0.08 | 31 0.9 ÷ 10 0.09 |
| 32 5.9 ÷ 10 0.59 | 33 75 ÷ 100 0.75 | 34 8,390 ÷ 100 83.90 |
| 35 7.5 ÷ 100 0.075 | 36 0.98 ÷ 100 0.0098 | 37 2,500 ÷ $10^3$ 2.5 |
| 38 351 ÷ 1,000 0.351 | 39 14.76 ÷ $10^3$ 0.01476 | 40 16 ÷ 1,000 0.016 |
| 41 3.8 ÷ 10 0.38 | 42 147.6 ÷ 1,000 0.1476 | 43 279 ÷ 1,000 0.279 |
| 44 6.8 ÷ $10^2$ 0.068 | 45 43.2 ÷ 10 4.32 | 46 1,116 ÷ $10^2$ 11.16 |
| 47 0.756 ÷ 100 0.00756 | 48 8 ÷ 1,000 0.008 | 49 0.78 ÷ 10 0.078 |
| 50 48.27 ÷ 10 4.827 | 51 183 ÷ 100 1.83 | 52 125.7 ÷ 1,000 0.1257 |

**Do** the following calculations.

| | | |
|---|---|---|
| 53 765.4321 × 10 7654.321 | 54 765.4321 ÷ 10 76.54321 | 55 765.4321 ÷ $10^2$ 7.654321 |
| 56 765.4321 ÷ 1,000 0.7654321 | 57 765.4321 × $10^3$ 765,432.1 | 58 765.4321 ÷ 100,000 0.007654321 |
| 59 765.4321 × 100,000 76,543,210 | | |

You know that there are 100 centimeters in a meter and 1,000 meters in a kilometer. So, to find out how many centimeters there are in 73.2 meters, you multiply 73.2 by 100 or move the decimal point two places to the right, after writing the extra 0.

**Solve** the following problems.

60 How many centimeters are in 56.24 meters? 5,624

61 How many meters are in 7.24 kilometers? 7,240

62 How many centimeters are in 7.24 kilometers? 724,000

63 How many meters are in 2,435 centimeters? 24.35

64 How many kilometers are in 2,435 centimeters? 0.02435

Chapter 9 • Lesson 6 403

## 3 Reflect

5

### Guided Discussion REASONING

Whole Group

Have students explain which direction the decimal point needs to move when multiplying or dividing by a power of 10. Ask questions such as the following:

- **In general, which direction do you move the decimal point when dividing by a power of 10?** to the left
- **In general, which direction do you move the decimal point when multiplying by a power of 10?** to the right

### Extended Response

**Problem 28** Encourage students to estimate before multiplying, but to actually multiply to answer the question.

**Cumulative Review:** For review of fractions, assign Problems 23–27 on student page 417.

**Family Involvement:** Assign the ***Practice, Reteach,*** or ***Enrichment*** activities depending on the needs of your students.
Encourage students to play the **Roll a Decimal Game** with a friend or relative.

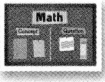

**Concept/Question Board:** Encourage students to continue to post questions, answers, and examples on the Concept/Question Board.

**Math Puzzler:** Using the digits 2, 3, 4, and as many 0s as you want, create a division problem with a quotient of 800. (There are many possible answers to this problem.) One possible answer is $2,400 \div 3 = 800$.

# 4 Assess and Differentiate

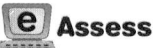

**e Assess** Use ***eAssess*** to record and analyze evidence of student understanding.

## A Gather Evidence

Use the Daily Class Assessment Records in ***Assessment*** or ***eAssess*** to record daily observations.

### Informal Assessment
**☑ Strategy Building**

Did the student UNDERSTANDING
- ❑ make important observations?
- ❑ extend or generalize learning?
- ❑ provide insightful answers?
- ❑ pose insightful questions?

### Informal Assessment
**☑ Concept/Question Board**

Did the student APPLYING
- ❑ apply learning in new situations?
- ❑ contribute concepts?
- ❑ contribute answers?
- ❑ connect mathematics to real-world situations?

## B Summarize Findings

Analyze and summarize assessment data for each student. Determine which Assessment Follow-Up is appropriate for each student. Use the Student Assessment Record in ***Assessment*** or ***eAssess*** to update assessment records.

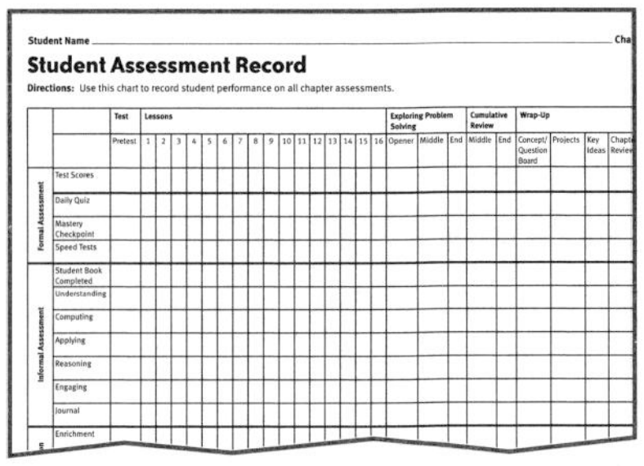
Student Name
Student Assessment Record
Directions: Use this chart to record student performance on all chapter assessments.

Assessment Page T41

## C Assessment Follow-Up • DIFFERENTIATE INSTRUCTION

Based on your observations, use these teaching strategies for assessment follow-up.

### INTERVENTION

Review student performance on ***Intervention*** Lesson 9.B to see if students have mastered prerequisite skills for this lesson.

### ENGLISH LEARNER

**Review**

Use Lesson 9.6 in ***English Learner Support Guide*** to review lesson concepts and vocabulary.

### ENRICH

**If . . .** students are proficient in the lesson concepts,

**Then . . .** encourage them to work on the chapter projects or ***Enrichment*** Lesson 9.6.

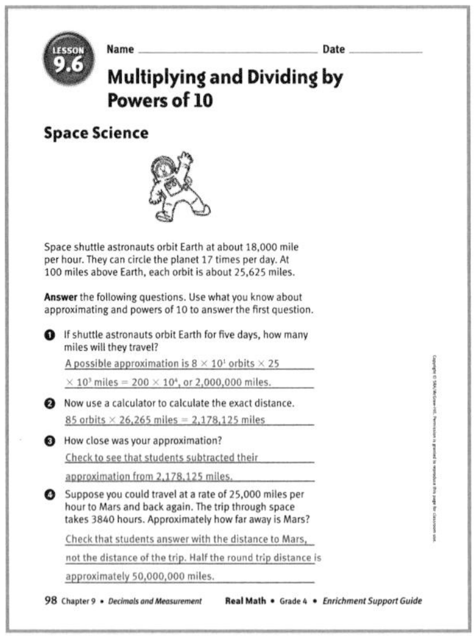
LESSON 9.6 Name ______ Date ______
Multiplying and Dividing by Powers of 10
Space Science
Space shuttle astronauts orbit Earth at about 18,000 mile per hour. They can circle the planet 17 times per day. At 100 miles above Earth, each orbit is about 25,625 miles.
Answer the following questions. Use what you know about approximating and powers of 10 to answer the first question.
1. If shuttle astronauts orbit Earth for five days, how many miles will they travel? A possible approximation is 8 × 10¹ orbits × 25 × 10³ miles = 200 × 10⁴, or 2,000,000 miles.
2. Now use a calculator to calculate the exact distance. 85 orbits × 26,265 miles = 2,178,125 miles
3. How close was your approximation? Check to see that students subtracted their approximation from 2,178,125 miles.
4. Suppose you could travel at a rate of 25,000 miles per hour to Mars and back again. The trip through space takes 3840 hours. Approximately how far away is Mars? Check that students answer with the distance to Mars, not the distance of the trip. Half the round trip distance is approximately 50,000,000 miles.
98 Chapter 9 • Decimals and Measurement Real Math • Grade 4 • Enrichment Support Guide

Enrichment Lesson 9.6

### PRACTICE

**If . . .** students would benefit from additional practice,

**Then . . .** assign ***Practice*** Lesson 9.6.

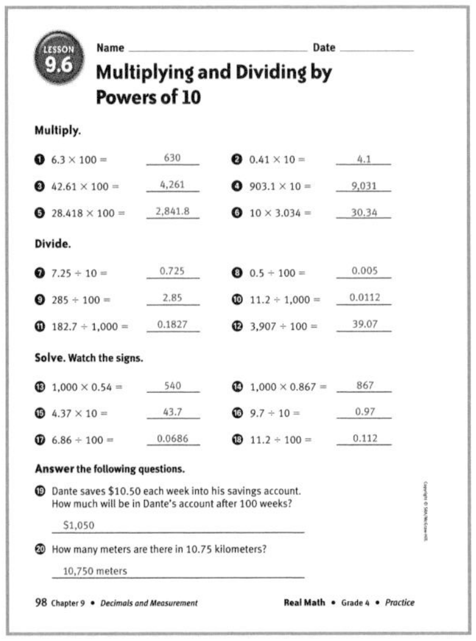
LESSON 9.6 Name ______ Date ______
Multiplying and Dividing by Powers of 10
Multiply.
1. 6.3 × 100 = 630
2. 0.41 × 10 = 4.1
3. 42.61 × 100 = 4,261
4. 903.1 × 10 = 9,031
5. 28.418 × 100 = 2,841.8
6. 10 × 3.034 = 30.34
Divide.
7. 7.25 ÷ 10 = 0.725
8. 0.5 ÷ 100 = 0.005
9. 285 ÷ 100 = 2.85
10. 11.2 ÷ 1,000 = 0.0112
11. 182.7 ÷ 1,000 = 0.1827
12. 3,907 ÷ 100 = 39.07
Solve. Watch the signs.
13. 1,000 × 0.54 = 540
14. 1,000 × 0.867 = 867
15. 4.37 × 10 = 43.7
16. 9.7 ÷ 10 = 0.97
17. 6.86 ÷ 100 = 0.0686
18. 11.2 ÷ 100 = 0.112
Answer the following questions.
19. Dante saves $10.50 each week into his savings account. How much will be in Dante's account after 100 weeks? $1,050
20. How many meters are there in 10.75 kilometers? 10,750 meters
98 Chapter 9 • Decimals and Measurement Real Math • Grade 4 • Practice

Practice Lesson 9.6

### RETEACH

**If . . .** students are having difficulty understanding multiplication and division by powers of 10,

**Then . . .** reteach the concept using ***Reteach*** Lesson 9.6.

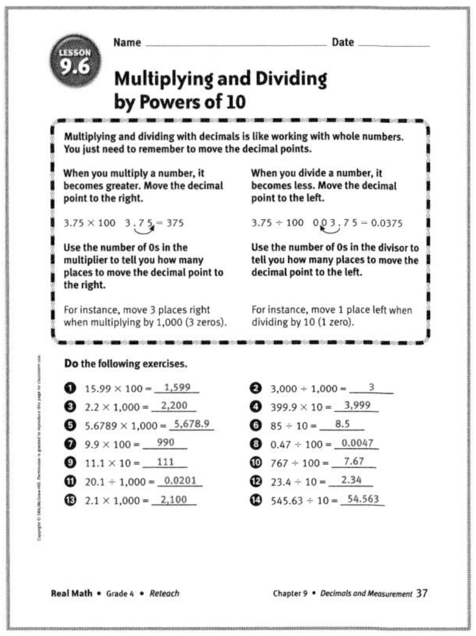
LESSON 9.6 Name ______ Date ______
Multiplying and Dividing by Powers of 10
Multiplying and dividing with decimals is like working with whole numbers. You just need to remember to move the decimal points.
When you multiply a number, it becomes greater. Move the decimal point to the right. 3.75 × 100 3.75 = 375
When you divide a number, it becomes less. Move the decimal point to the left. 3.75 ÷ 100 003.75 = 0.0375
Use the number of 0s in the multiplier to tell you how many places to move the decimal point to the right.
Use the number of 0s in the divisor to tell you how many places to move the decimal point to the left.
For instance, move 3 places right when multiplying by 1,000 (3 zeros).
For instance, move 1 place left when dividing by 10 (1 zero).
Do the following exercises.
1. 15.99 × 100 = 1,599
2. 3,000 ÷ 1,000 = 3
3. 2.2 × 1,000 = 2,200
4. 399.9 × 10 = 3,999
5. 5.6789 × 1,000 = 5,678.9
6. 85 ÷ 10 = 8.5
7. 9.9 × 100 = 990
8. 0.47 ÷ 100 = 0.0047
9. 11.1 × 10 = 111
10. 767 ÷ 100 = 7.67
11. 20.1 ÷ 1,000 = 0.0201
12. 23.4 ÷ 10 = 2.34
13. 2.1 × 1,000 = 2,100
14. 545.63 ÷ 10 = 54.563
Real Math • Grade 4 • Reteach Chapter 9 • Decimals and Measurement 37

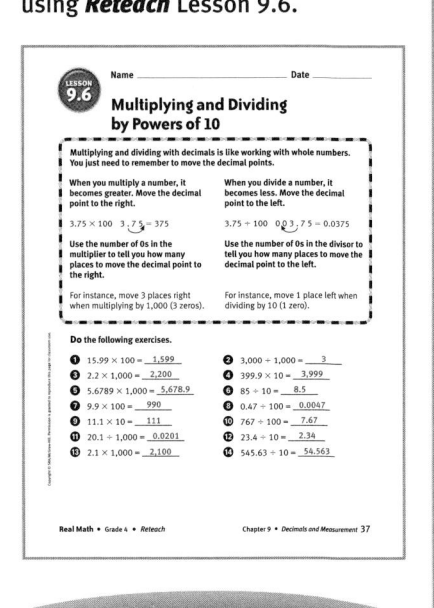

Reteach Lesson 9.6

## Lesson Planner

### Objectives
- To review measuring length with metric units
- To review the relationship among metric units of length and to provide practice converting from one metric unit of length to another
- To provide practical applications of decimals

### NCTM Standards
**Measurement**
Understand measurable attributes of objects and the units, systems, and processes of measurement

**Connections**
Recognize and apply mathematics in contexts outside of mathematics

**Measurement**
Practice measuring lengths within the metric system

### Materials
- *Metersticks
- *Metric rulers
- **Assessment** Page T72

### Technology
**Presentation** Lesson 9.6
**MathTools Metric and Customary Units Tool**

### Test Prep
**Cumulative Review**
Mental Math reviews multiplying and dividing by powers of 10 (Lesson 9.6).

### Looking Ahead
Measure an object in the classroom that is approximately four decimeters long in preparation for the Reflect section in Lesson 9.8.

*Manipulative Kit Item

# Metric Units

**Context of the Lesson** This lesson provides an application for the multiplication and division skills covered in Lesson 9.6. Students have worked with the metric system in previous lessons this year, and they measured length in nonstandard units in Grade 1 and in meters and centimeters in Grades 2 and 3. Upcoming lessons will review metric units of weight and volume. This lesson includes a Mastery Checkpoint.

See page 382B for Math Background for teachers for this lesson.

## Planning for Learning • DIFFERENTIATE INSTRUCTION

### INTERVENTION
**If . . .** students lack the prerequisite skill of multiplying and dividing by powers of 10,

**Then . . .** teach ***Intervention*** Lesson 9.B.

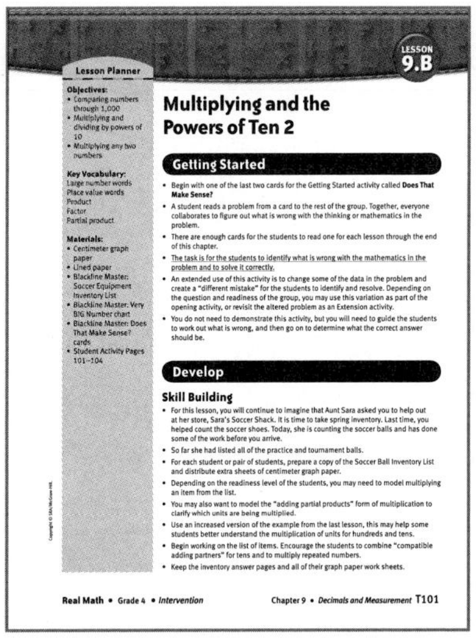
Lesson Planner
LESSON 9.B
Multiplying and the Powers of Ten 2
Getting Started
Develop
Skill Building
Real Math • Grade 4 • Intervention    Chapter 9 • Decimals and Measurement T101

Intervention Lesson 9.B

### ENGLISH LEARNER
Preview

**If . . .** students need language support,

**Then . . .** use Lesson 9.7 in ***English Learner Support Guide*** to preview lesson concepts and vocabulary.

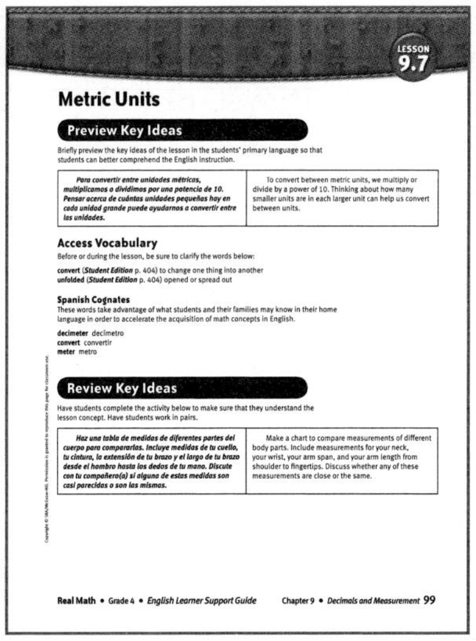
LESSON 9.7
Metric Units
Preview Key Ideas
Access Vocabulary
Spanish Cognates
decimeter decímetro
convert convertir
meter metro
Review Key Ideas
Real Math • Grade 4 • English Learner Support Guide    Chapter 9 • Decimals and Measurement 99

English Learner Lesson 9.7

### ENRICH
**If . . .** students are proficient in the lesson concepts,

**Then . . .** emphasize chapter projects.

### PRACTICE
**If . . .** students would benefit from additional practice,

**Then . . .** extend Guided Discussion before assigning the student pages.

### RETEACH
**If . . .** students are having difficulty understanding how to convert metric units,

**Then . . .** extend Guided Discussion before assigning the student pages.

### Vocabulary
**metric system *n.*** a decimal system of measurement that uses the meter as the fundamental unit of length

### Access Vocabulary
**to convert** to change one thing for another

### Spanish Cognates
**decimeter** decímetro
**value** valor

# Teaching Lesson 9.7

## Mental Math 5

Review RESPONSE WHEEL Provide problems, such as the following, that involve multiplying and dividing whole numbers by 10 and powers of 10.

| | |
|---|---|
| **a.** 700 ÷ 10 = 70 | **g.** 70 × 100 = 7,000 |
| **b.** 7 × 10 = 70 | **h.** 250 ÷ 10 = 25 |
| **c.** 25 × 100 = 2,500 | **i.** 5,500 ÷ 100 = 55 |
| **d.** 5,500 ÷ 10 = 550 | **j.** 65 × 10 = 650 |
| **e.** 9,900 ÷ 10 = 990 | **k.** 990 × 10 = 9,900 |
| **f.** 990 × 100 = 99,000 | **l.** 9,900 ÷ 100 = 99 |

## 1 Develop 25

### Tell Students In Today's Lesson They Will

review the conversion of measurements and how to measure lengths within the metric system.

### Guided Discussion UNDERSTANDING

Whole Group

If possible, use a meterstick during the discussion, or refer to the illustration of a folded meterstick on page 404.

1. Review the base-ten nature of the metric system. Each unit conversion for a particular aspect of something (length, weight, volume, and so on) in the metric system will be a multiplication or division operation by a power of 10.
2. Introduce the word *decimeter* to the class. Ask questions such as the following:
   - **What is a decimeter?** 10 cm or $\frac{1}{10}$ of a meter
   - **What do you think *deci*- means?** one-tenth
   - **How many decimeters are in 1 meter?** 10
   - **What fraction of a meter is 1 decimeter?** $\frac{1}{10}$
   - **How is the fraction of a meter equal to 1 decimeter written as a decimal?** 0.1
3. Go over the information about metric equivalencies. Ask students questions such as the following:
   - **How many centimeters are on a meterstick?** 100
   - **Do you remember what *centi*- refers to?** Centi refer s to "hundredths" as in *centimeters* and *cents*, or hundreds as in *century* or *centipede*.
   - **One centimeter is what fraction of a meterstick?** $\frac{1}{100}$
   - **What is the decimal equivalent of $\frac{1}{100}$?** 0.01
4. Review what a millimeter is by asking questions such as the following:
   - **How many millimeters equal 1 centimeter?** 10
   - **How many millimeters are in 1 meter?** 1,000
   - **What fraction is 1 millimeter of 1 centimeter?** $\frac{1}{10}$

### Skill Practice ENGAGING

Small Group

Draw a chart on the board or overhead projector similar to the one below.

| Item | Millimeter Measurements | Centimeter Measurements | Decimeter Measurements |
|---|---|---|---|
| cover of a book | 263 mm × 205 mm | 26.3 cm × 20.5 cm | 2.63 dm × 2.05 dm |

Have students, in small groups or on their own, find ten objects to name, measure, and convert to fill in the chart.

Another variation to this activity is to provide the students with ten measurements of various metric lengths and have them measure or estimate to find objects of those sizes. Once they find the objects, they can record the converted measurements. This can be demonstrated using the ***eMathTools: Metric and Customary Units Tool***.

## 2 Assign Student Pages 20

### Page 405 APPLYING

Complete the first few problems as a class before having students complete page 405 on their own, using a meterstick or the illustration of a meterstick as needed.

#### Monitoring Student Progress

**If . . .** students have trouble remembering the relationships between metric units,

**Then . . .** encourage them to create a chart showing equivalencies.

### As Students Finish

Game **Roll a Decimal Game** (introduced in Lesson 9.4)

Student Page

LESSON 9.7 **Metric Units**

## Key Ideas

**To convert between metric units, you multiply or divide by a power of 10.**

When this ruler is unfolded, it is 1 meter long.

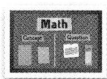

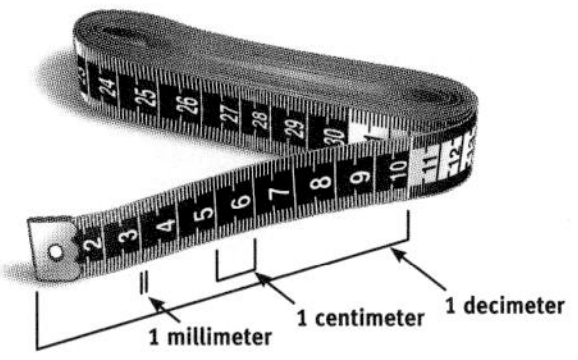


1 meter = 10 decimeters = 100 centimeters = 1,000 millimeters

About how long is a meter? Most doors are about 2 meters tall. A meterstick is 1 meter long. Most classroom doors are a little less than 1 meter wide.

If a meter is divided into 10 equal parts, each part is 0.1 meter. That's also called 1 decimeter (dm).

1 dm = 0.1 m

Two of the parts (2 dm) would be 0.2 meter.

2 dm = 0.2 m

To convert between units, think about how many smaller units are in each larger unit.

To convert from a smaller unit to a larger unit, divide by a power of 10.

| Unit | Operation | New Unit |
|---|---|---|
| dm | ÷10 | m |
| cm | ÷100 | m |

To convert from a larger unit to a smaller unit, multiply by a power of 10.

| Unit | Operation | New Unit |
|---|---|---|
| m | ×10 | dm |
| m | ×100 | cm |



Textbook This lesson is available in the *eTextbook*.

Student Page

**Find** the value of the missing number.

1. 3 dm = ___ m 0.3
2. 8 dm = ___ m 0.8
3. ___ dm = 6 m 60
4. 5 dm = ___ m 0.5
5. ___ dm = 9 m 90
6. ___ dm = 1.0 m 10

If a meter is divided into 100 equal parts, each part is 0.01 meter. This is also called 1 centimeter (cm).

1 cm = 0.01 m

Two of the parts (2 cm) would be 0.02 meter.

2 cm = 0.02 m

**Find** the value of the missing number.

7. 7 cm = ___ m 0.07
8. 8 cm = ___ m 0.08
9. ___ cm = 0.04 m 4
10. 27 cm = ___ m 0.27
11. ___ cm = 0.31 m 31
12. ___ cm = 1.00 m 100

If a meter is divided into 1,000 equal parts, each part is 0.001 meter. This is also called 1 millimeter (mm).

1 mm = 0.001 m

Two of the parts (2 mm) would be 0.002 meter.

2 mm = 0.002 m

**Find** the value of the missing number.

13. ___ mm = 1.000 m 1,000
14. 6 mm = ___ m 0.006
15. 709 mm = ___ m 0.709
16. ___ mm = 0.300 m 300
17. 66 mm = ___ m 0.066
18. ___ mm = 0.305 m 305

**Measure.** Write each measurement in two ways.
Answers will vary according to measurements of each classroom.

19. Top of student desk Length: ___ mm = ___ cm Width: ___ mm = ___ c
20. Classroom Length: ___ cm = ___ m Width: ___ cm = ___ m





# 3 Reflect

5

## Guided Discussion REASONING

Whole Group

Explore how conversion can always be done using multiplication. Ask questions such as the following:

- **How do we convert centimeters to meters?** divide by 100
- **How many meters are 253 centimeters equal to?** 253 ÷ 100 = 2.53

Review what students learned about conversions by asking questions such as the following:

- **What part of a meter is equal to 1 centimeter?** 0.01
- **If 1 centimeter = 0.01 meter, can we say (253 × 1) centimeters = (253 × 0.01) meters?** yes

We already know that 253 centimeters = 2.53 meters, confirming that 253 × 0.01 is the same as 253 ÷ 100.

- **How many centimeters are in a kilometer?** 100,000
- **How many inches are in a mile?** 63,360
- **Is the ease with which you did the first calculation sufficient reason to convert to the metric system?** Probably not; nobody really cares that there are 63,360 inches in a mile or 100,000 centimeters in a kilometer. If you did care, you could figure it out fairly quickly.

Use Mastery Checkpoint 19 found in ***Assessment*** to evaluate student mastery of multiplying and dividing decimals by powers of 10. By this time students should be able to correctly answer eighty percent of the Mastery Checkpoint items.

**Curriculum Connection:** Many European countries, such as Ireland, use the metric system in everyday life. *Artemis Fowl* is a book set in Ireland. Students may be interested in reading this or other stories set in Ireland.

**Cumulative Review:** For review of relation signs, assign Problems 28–32 on student page 417.

**Family Involvement:** Assign the ***Practice, Reteach,*** or ***Enrichment*** activities depending on the needs of your students.

Encourage students to play the **Roll a Decimal Game** with a friend or relative.

**Concept/Question Board:** Encourage students to continue to post questions, answers, and examples on the Concept/Question Board.

**Math Puzzler:** Shaquan wrote down each decimal as he counted aloud by tenths from 3.3 to 6.6. How many times did he write the digit 5? 14 times if both fives in 5.5 are counted

# 4 Assess and Differentiate

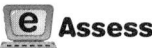

**e Assess** Use ***eAssess*** to record and analyze evidence of student understanding.

## A Gather Evidence

Use the Daily Class Assessment Records in ***Assessment*** or ***eAssess*** to record daily observations.

### Formal Assessment

**Mastery Checkpoint**

Did the student

- ❑ use correct procedures?
- ❑ respond with at least eighty percent accuracy?

19 Name ______ Date ______

**Mastery Checkpoint 19**

**Multiplying and Dividing Decimals by Powers of 10**

The student demonstrates mastery by correctly answering at least thirty-two of the forty problems.

**Multiply.**

1. 7.2 × 10 = 72
2. 100 × 902.3 = 90,230
3. 100 × 80 = 8,000
4. 88 × 1,000 = 88,000
5. 10 × 376.05 = 3,760.5
6. 473.01 × 100 = 47,301
7. 1,000 × 49.6 = 49,600
8. 28.1 × 100 = 2,810
9. 7.9 × 1,000 = 7,900
10. 79.3 × 1,000 = 79,300

**Divide.**

11. 52.5 ÷ 10 = 5.25
12. 2.007 ÷ 10 = 0.2007
13. 80.05 ÷ 100 = 0.8005
14. 4,387.2 ÷ 10 = 438.72
15. 7.36 ÷ 10 = 0.736
16. 563.71 ÷ 100 = 5.6371
17. 487.3 ÷ 100 = 4.873
18. 291.43 ÷ 1,000 = 0.29143
19. 79.5 ÷ 1,000 = 0.0795
20. 64.8 ÷ 1,000 = 0.0648

**Assessment Page T72**

## B Summarize Findings

Analyze and summarize assessment data for each student. Determine which Assessment Follow-Up is appropriate for each student. Use the Student Assessment Record in ***Assessment*** or ***eAssess*** to update assessment records.

**Student Assessment Record**

Directions: Use this chart to record student performance on all chapter assessments.

**Assessment Page T41**

## C Assessment Follow-Up • DIFFERENTIATE INSTRUCTION

Based on your observations, use these teaching strategies for assessment follow-up.

### INTERVENTION

Review student performance on ***Intervention*** Lesson 9.B to see if students have mastered prerequisite skills for this lesson.

### ENGLISH LEARNER

**Review**

Use Lesson 9.7 in ***English Learner Support Guide*** to review lesson concepts and vocabulary.

### ENRICH

**If . . .** students are proficient in the lesson concepts

**Then . . .** encourage them to work on the chapter projects or ***Enrichment*** Lesson 9.7.

LESSON 9.7 Name ______ Date ______

**Metric Units**

**Micrometers**

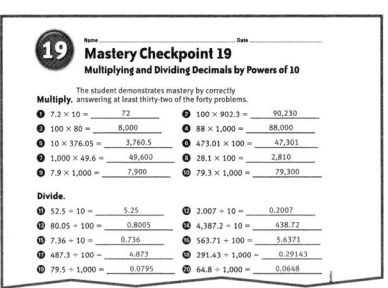

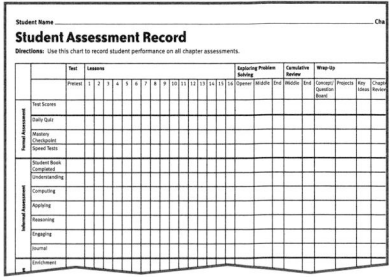

mi•cro•me•ter \mi' kro me ter\ 1. A unit of length equal to one thousandth of a millimeter, or one millionth of a meter. \mi krom' e ter\ 2. A tool used for measuring very small distances or objects.

**Think** about rulers you have seen. Rulers are used to measure many things in inches or centimeters. An average human hair is about 50 microns, or .05 millimeters wide.

1. Could you measure the width of a strand of hair with a ruler? No, not accurately
2. List at least three other objects that you could use a micrometer to measure. Answers will vary. Possible answers include the thickness of a sheet of paper, plastic or foil, and the width of grooves on woodscrews, tools, or automotive parts.

**Change** these micron measurements to millimeters.

3. 76 microns = .076 mm
4. 30 microns = .03 mm
5. 12 microns = .012 mm
6. 5 microns = .005 mm

Real Math • Grade 4 • Enrichment Support Guide   Chapter 9 • Decimals and Measurement 99

**Enrichment Lesson 9.7**

### PRACTICE

**If . . .** students would benefit from additional practice

**Then . . .** assign ***Practice*** Lesson 9.7.

LESSON 9.7 Name ______ Date ______

**Metric Units**

**Find the value of the missing number.**

1. 6 dm = 0.6 m
2. 4 dm = 0.4 m
3. 7 m = 70 dm
4. 90 dm = 9 m
5. 1 m = 10 dm
6. 6 m = 60 dm
7. 70 m = 700 dm
8. 21 cm = 0.21 m
9. 9 cm = 0.09 m
10. 0.42 m = 42 cm
11. 9 cm = 0.09 m
12. 100 cm = 1 m
13. 4 mm = 0.004 m
14. 127 mm = 0.127 m
15. 37 mm = 0.037 m
16. 1,000 mm = 1 m
17. 810 mm = 0.810 m
18. 0.7 m = 700 mm
19. 2 km = 2,000 m
20. 12 km = 12,000 m
21. 60 m = 0.06 km
22. 910 m = 0.91 km

**Solve the following problems.**

23. Each curtain panel in Jamila's front window measures 120 cm. Write this value in meters. 1.2 m
24. Yesterday, Sheryl hiked 5.7 km. How many meters did she hike? 5,700 m

Real Math • Grade 4 • Practice   Chapter 9 • Decimals and Measurement 99

**Practice Lesson 9.7**

### RETEACH

**If . . .** students are having difficulty understanding metric units

**Then . . .** reteach the concept using ***Reteach*** Lesson 9.7.

LESSON 9.7 Name ______ Date ______

**Metric Units**

The metric system is based on units of 10. Each unit of measure is 10 times less or 10 times greater than the next unit.

This chart shows the relationships among units of length in the metric system. Notice that each unit is greater or less than another by 10 or a multiple of 10.

**Metric Units of Length**

1 meter (m) = 1,000 millimeters (mm); 1 millimeter = $\frac{1}{1000}$ meter
1 meter = 100 centimeters (cm); 1 centimeter = $\frac{1}{100}$ meter
1 meter = 10 decimeters (dm); 1 decimeter = $\frac{1}{10}$ meter

$1.00 = 100 pennies. One penny can be expressed as • $\frac{1}{100}$ of $1. • $0.01

1 meter = 100 centimeters. One centimeter can be expressed as • $\frac{1}{100}$ of 1 meter. • 0.01 meter.

$1 = 10 dimes. One dime can be expressed as • $\frac{1}{10}$ of $1. • $0.1

1 meter = 10 decimeters. One decimeter can be expressed as • $\frac{1}{10}$ of 1 meter. • 0.1 meter.

Here are some hints to help convert greater units of length to lesser units.

- To convert meters to decimeters, multiply by 10. 3 m × 10 = 30 dm
- To convert meters to centimeters, multiply by 100. 4 m × 100 = 400 cm
- To convert meters to millimeters, multiply by 1,000. 2 m × 1000 = 2000 mm; 200 mm ÷ 1000 = 0.2 m

**Measure these items. Write each measurement two ways.** Answers will vary. Possible answers:

1. Length of foot 18 cm = 1.8 dm
2. Length of desk 32 cm = 320 mm
3. Length of pencil 14 cm = 0.14 m

38 Chapter 9 • Decimals and Measurement   Real Math • Grade 4 • Reteach

**Reteach Lesson 9.7**

# Metric Measurements of Length

**OBJECTIVES**
- To provide practice with measuring
- To demonstrate how to express metric measurements as decimals in a common unit
- To review methods of organizing data and making a bar graph

**NCTM STANDARDS**

**Measurement**
Understand measurable attributes of objects and the units, systems, and processes of measurement

**Data Analysis and Probability**
Formulate questions that can be addressed with data, and collect, organize, and display relevant data to answer them.

**Measurement**
Measure the lengths of objects using the metric system

**MATERIALS**
- *Response Wheels
- Chart paper
- Graph paper
- *Metric rulers
- *Copies of the **Find the Distance 1 & 2 Game Mats**
- **Number Cubes*

**TECHNOLOGY**
**Presentation** Lesson 9.8
**MathTools Metric and Customary Units Tool**

**TEST PREP**
**Cumulative Review**
Mental Math reviews basic facts of the four operations (Lessons 1.5 and 3.10).

*Manipulative Kit Item

**Context of the Lesson** This lesson extends learning about metric units from the previous lesson. Students will need to recall multiplication and division by powers of 10 and how to read a metric ruler. This lesson will guide students into Lesson 9.9, Adding and Subtracting Decimals, by teaching students to align decimals, a crucial step in adding and subtracting decimals.

See page 382B for Math Background for teachers for this lesson.

## Planning for Learning • DIFFERENTIATE INSTRUCTION

### INTERVENTION

**If . . .** students lack the prerequisite skill of multiplying and dividing by powers of 10,

**Then . . .** teach ***Intervention*** Lesson 9.B.

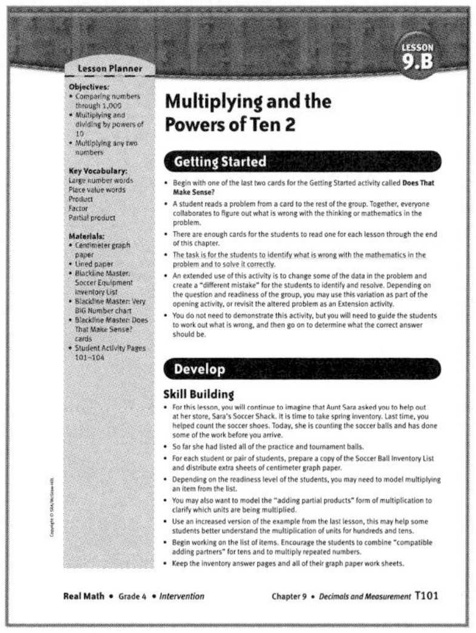


Intervention Lesson 9.B

### ENGLISH LEARNER

**Preview**

**If . . .** students need language support,

**Then . . .** use Lesson 9.8 in ***English Learner Support Guide*** to preview lesson concepts and vocabulary.

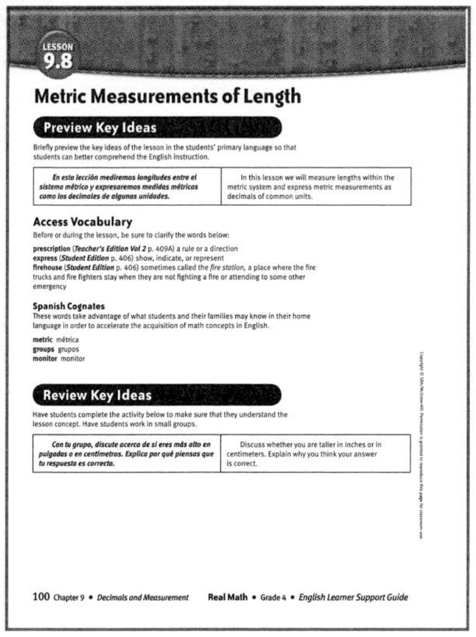


English Learner Lesson 9.8

### ENRICH

**If . . .** students are proficient in the lesson concepts,

**Then . . .** emphasize additional game time.

### PRACTICE

**If . . .** students would benefit from additional practice,

**Then . . .** extend Guided Discussion before assigning the student pages.

### RETEACH

**If . . .** students are having difficulty understanding how to convert metric units of length,

**Then . . .** extend Guided Discussion before assigning the student pages.

**Access Vocabulary**
**firehouse** the place where firefighters and fire trucks stay when they are not helping at an emergency

**Spanish Cognates**
**metric** métrica
**groups** grupos

## Mental Math

5

RESPONSE WHEEL Present practice problems, such as the following, that involve the basic facts in all four operations.

| | | |
|---|---|---|
| **a.** 4 + 7 = 11 | **g.** 8 + 6 = 14 | **m.** 7 × 7 = 49 |
| **b.** 15 − 10 = 5 | **h.** 28 ÷ 7 = 4 | **n.** 12 − 9 = 3 |
| **c.** 72 ÷ 8 = 9 | **i.** 4 × 8 = 32 | **o.** 40 ÷ 10 = 4 |
| **d.** 5 × 8 = 40 | **j.** 3 + 7 = 10 | **p.** 9 × 7 = 63 |
| **e.** 10 − 5 = 5 | **k.** 10 × 10 = 100 | **q.** 32 ÷ 4 = 8 |
| **f.** 6 + 6 = 12 | **l.** 27 ÷ 9 = 3 | **r.** 9 + 2 = 11 |

## 1 Develop

20

### Tell Students In Today's Lesson They Will

express metric measurements as decimals of common units and measure lengths within the metric system.

### Strategy Building ENGAGING

Small Group

Game **Find the Distance 1 and Find the Distance 2 Game Mats**

You may wish to demonstrate the ***Find the Distance 1 and 2 Game Mats*** before beginning the lesson so students may play the game when they are finished. The game provides practice with estimating distances and comparing lengths. Ask several volunteers to play a demonstration game as others watch to be sure everyone understands the rules. After students play the game once or twice, encourage them to try the harder version.

### Guided Discussion UNDERSTANDING

Whole Group

Have students look around the room for something that is approximately 1 meter long, such as the width of a door. Next have them find something that is about 1 centimeter long. Then ask questions such as the following:

- **How many centimeters are in 1 meter?** 100
- **What percent of 1 meter is 1 centimeter?** 1%
- **What fraction of 1 meter is 1 centimeter?** $\frac{1}{100}$
- **If you had something that was 200 centimeters long, how many meters long is it?** 2 meters
- **If you had something that was 35 centimeters long, how could you show that as a fraction of a meter?** $\frac{35}{100}$ of a meter
- **How would you say that as a decimal?** 0.35 meter

1. Have a volunteer point to where $\frac{25}{100}$ of a meter is located on a meterstick or demonstrate using ***eMathTools: Metric and Customary Units Tool.*** Check to see if the estimate is correct. Then have another volunteer estimate where 0.65 of a meter is located. Check this estimate. Have students explain how they made their estimations.

Have pairs of students look around the room and find something they estimate to be between 0.25 of a meter and 0.65 of a meter. Have each pair first write their estimate of the object as a fraction of a meter in decimal notation. Then allow them to check their estimates by measuring the objects while nobody is watching.

Have each pair announce the decimal measurements of their object, then have the other students try to guess what the object is.

2. Ask students if they remember how long a decimeter is in terms of meters. 0.1 m

   Ask for a volunteer to come to the board to see if they can draw a line that is approximately one decimeter long. Using the meterstick, check the length of the line and adjust it, if necessary.

Have students make a connection between decimeters, centimeters, millimeters, and meters. Ask questions such as the following:

- **There are 10 decimeters in 1 meter and 10 centimeters in 1 decimeter. How many millimeters are in 1 centimeter?** 10
- **What fraction of 1 centimeter is 1 millimeter?** $\frac{1}{10}$
- **What fraction of 1 decimeter is 1 millimeter?** $\frac{1}{100}$
- **Can anyone tell what fraction of 1 meter 1 millimeter is? The word *milli-* means "thousandth."** $\frac{1}{1,000}$

Have students measure the lengths of small objects, such as pencil erasers, to the nearest millimeter. Have them express the measurement as part of a meter using fractions and using decimals. Estimation is acceptable, as every fraction cannot always be expressed as a decimal.

# 2 Assign Student Pages 30

## Pages 406–407 APPLYING

Have students complete pages 406–407 independently. You may wish to remind students to measure in millimeters for precision on page 407.

### RESEARCH IN ACTION

"Accurate measuring procedures such as placing manipulative units without leaving spaces between them can be developed through many experiences. Similarly, with rulers, teachers can help children develop concepts and procedures such as accurate alignment, starting at zero, and focusing on the points rather than only the numbers on the ruler. Counting points rather than line segments is more likely in ruler activities and partitioning tasks. That is, accepting earlier use of rulers is *not* the same as believing that such use implies mastery either of the tool or of measurement concepts. Rather, it is an additional way to present experiences and problems that will help childen develop understanding."

(Clements, Douglas and Sarama, J., eds. *Engaging Young Children in Mathematics: Standards for Early Childhood Mathematics Education.* Mahwah, NJ: Lawrence Erlbaum Associates, Publishers, 2004. p. 52.)

Student Page

LESSON 9.8 **Metric Measurements of Length**

### Key Ideas

**You can express the same length using different metric units.**

Angel measured a table that is 2 meters, 3 decimeters, 8 centimeters, and 5 millimeters long. There is a shorter way to report this measurement.

Change each unit to meters:
2 m = 2 m
3 dm = 0.3 m
8 cm = 0.08 m
5 mm = 0.005 m

Then add:
2.**000** m
0.3**00** m
0.08**0** m
+ 0.005 m
2.385 m

2 m, 3 dm, 8 cm, 5 mm = 2.385 m

**Write** each measurement in meters only.

1. 6 m, 3 dm, 8 cm, 5 mm — 6.385 m
2. 9 m, 3 cm, 6 mm — 9.036 m
3. 4 m, 0 dm, 2 cm, 6 mm — 4.026 m
4. 3 m, 2 dm, 5 mm — 3.205 m
5. 4 m, 2 cm, 6 mm — 4.026 m
6. 7 m, 1 dm, 4 cm, 0 mm — 7.140 m
7. 2 m, 0 dm, 9 cm, 8 mm — 2.098 m
8. 7 m, 1 dm, 4 cm — 7.14 m

The distance from the library to the firehouse was measured. It was 2 kilometers, 415 meters. Write the measurement in kilometers only (1 m = 0.001 km).

2 km = 2 km
415 m = 0.415 km

2.000 km
+ 0.415 km
2.415 km

2 km, 415 m = 2.415 km

**Write** these measurements in kilometers only.

9. 1 km, 210 m — 1.210 km
10. 4 km, 50 m — 4.050 km
11. 4 km, 500 m — 4.500 km
12. 2,200 m — 2.200 km

406 eTextbook This lesson is available in the *eTextbook*.

Student Page

**Give** the length of each bug first in millimeters, then in centimeters. Answers 1 mm greater or lesser should be accepted as correct.

13. 
21 mm, 2.1 cm

14. 
50 mm, 5.0 cm

15. 
33 mm, 3.3 cm

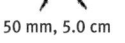

16. 
23 mm, 2.3 cm

17. 
50 mm, 5.0 cm

18. 
17 mm, 1.7 cm

19. 
37 mm, 3.7 cm

20. 
36 mm, 3.6 cm

21. 
36 mm, 3.6 cm

22. 
77 mm, 7.7 cm

Chapter 9 • Lesson 8 407

# Assign Student Pages, continued

### Pages 408–409 APPLYING

Small Group

Have students complete pages 408 and 409 in small groups in order to assist one another with measurements.

### As Students Finish

Game  Find the Distance Game Mat

Student Page



Ramona measured the height of each student in her class. She made a chart to show the height of each person:

| Height (cm) | Number of People |
|---|---|
| 118 | \|\| |
| 119 | |
| 120 | \|\| |
| 121 | \|\|\| |
| 122 | 𝍸 \| |
| 123 | 𝍸 \|\| |
| 124 | \|\|\|\| |
| 125 | |
| 126 | \|\| |
| 127 | \| |

Ramona discovered that the most common height in her class is 123 cm.

Then Ramona made a bar graph so people could see the results more easily.

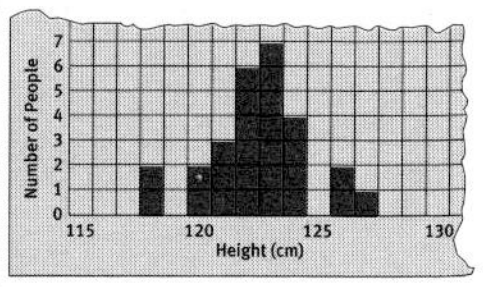


**Work** in groups. Measure the height of each person.

Stand up straight, with your back to the wall.

Put a book on your head.

Step away from the wall.

Make a mark on the wall with tape where the book touches the wall.

Measure in centimeters.

23 Make a chart and a bar graph to show your results.



Textbook This lesson is available in the ***eTextbook***.

Student Page

**Copy** the chart below and complete it by measuring various items. First measure the items in millimeters to find the most precise measurement possible, then use what you know about the metric system to fill in the measurements for centimeters and meters.

24

| Object | Millimeters | Centimeters | Meters |
|---|---|---|---|
| Height of a desk | ■ | ■ | ■ |
| Length of a chalkboard | ■ | ■ | ■ |
| Perimeter of the cover of this math book | ■ | ■ | ■ |
| Diagonal length of a computer monitor screen | ■ | ■ | ■ |
| Width of a doorway | ■ | ■ | ■ |
| Choose your own object | ■ | ■ | ■ |

## 3 Reflect

5

### Guided Discussion REASONING

Whole Group

Measure a classroom object in advance of this discussion. Choose an object that is approximately four decimeters long.

Tell students there is an object in the room that is approximately four decimeters long.

Have students discuss which objects might be four decimeters in length.

Have a student measure the secret object, and tell the class what the measurement is. If the object is slightly bigger than four decimeters, then any extra centimeters should be included. Have each student write the measurement of the object in decimeters, in centimeters, and as a decimal of 1 meter. Then ask questions such as the following:

- **Why do we need to have different units of measurement?** Answers may include that it is inconvenient to have units that are very small or very large. For example, imagine expressing the distance from Earth to the sun in millimeters or expressing the weight of a grain of sand in kilograms.

**Cumulative Review:** For review of percent benchmarks, assign Problems 33–37 on student page 417.

**Family Involvement:** Assign the ***Practice, Reteach,*** or ***Enrichment*** activities depending on the needs of your students.

Encourage students to play ***Roll a Decimal Game*** with a friend or relative.

**Concept/Question Board:** Have students look for additional examples of using the metric system and post them on the Concept/Question Board.

**Math Puzzler:** Use the digits 0, 1, 4, and 8 to create a decimal that fits each prescription without repeating digits in the same number.

**a.** This decimal is more than half of 1. Possible answers: 0.8, 0.81, 0.814, and 0.84

**b.** This decimal is between 1 and 2. Possible answers: 1.4, 1.8, and 1.048

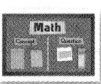

# 4 Assess and Differentiate

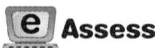

**e Assess** Use ***eAssess*** to record and analyze evidence of student understanding.

## A Gather Evidence

Use the Daily Class Assessment Records in ***Assessment*** or ***eAssess*** to record daily observations.

### Informal Assessment

**Mental Math**

Did the student **COMPUTING**

- ❑ respond accurately?
- ❑ respond quickly?
- ❑ respond with confidence?
- ❑ self-correct?

### Performance Assessment

**Games**

Did the student **ENGAGING**

- ❑ pay attention to others' contributions?
- ❑ contribute information and ideas?
- ❑ improve on a strategy?
- ❑ reflect on and check the accuracy of his or her work?

## B Summarize Findings

Analyze and summarize assessment data for each student. Determine which Assessment Follow-Up is appropriate for each student. Use the Student Assessment Record in ***Assessment*** or ***eAssess*** to update assessment records.

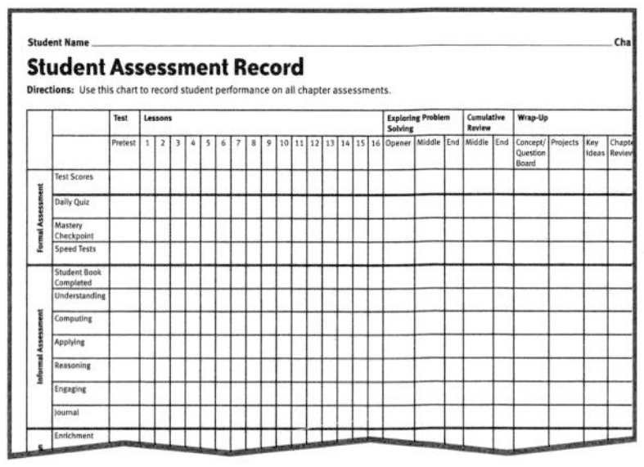
Student Assessment Record

**Assessment Page T41**

## C Assessment Follow-Up • DIFFERENTIATE INSTRUCTION

Based on your observations, use these teaching strategies for assessment follow-up.

### INTERVENTION

Review student performance on ***Intervention*** Lesson 9.B to see if students have mastered prerequisite skills for this lesson.

### ENGLISH LEARNER

**Review**

Use Lesson 9.8 in ***English Learner Support Guide*** to preview lesson concepts and vocabulary.

### ENRICH

**If . . .** students are proficient in the lesson concepts,

**Then . . .** encourage them to work on the chapter projects or ***Enrichment*** Lesson 9.8.

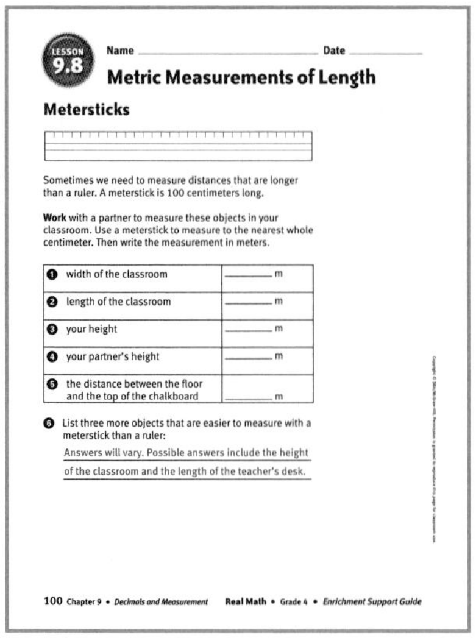
LESSON 9.8 Name ______ Date ______

**Metric Measurements of Length**

**Metersticks**

Sometimes we need to measure distances that are longer than a ruler. A meterstick is 100 centimeters long.

**Work** with a partner to measure these objects in your classroom. Use a meterstick to measure to the nearest whole centimeter. Then write the measurement in meters.

| | |
|---|---|
| 1 width of the classroom | ____ m |
| 2 length of the classroom | ____ m |
| 3 your height | ____ m |
| 4 your partner's height | ____ m |
| 5 the distance between the floor and the top of the chalkboard | ____ m |

6 List three more objects that are easier to measure with a meterstick than a ruler:
Answers will vary. Possible answers include the height of the classroom and the length of the teacher's desk.

100 Chapter 9 • *Decimals and Measurement* **Real Math** • Grade 4 • *Enrichment Support Guide*

Enrichment Lesson 9.8

### PRACTICE

**If . . .** students would benefit from additional practice,

**Then . . .** assign ***Practice*** Lesson 9.8.

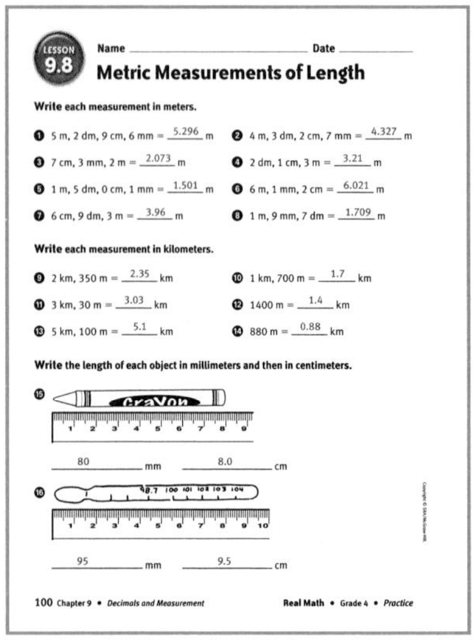
LESSON 9.8 Name ______ Date ______

**Metric Measurements of Length**

**Write each measurement in meters.**

1 5 m, 2 dm, 9 cm, 6 mm = 5.296 m
2 4 m, 3 dm, 2 cm, 7 mm = 4.327 m
3 7 cm, 3 mm, 2 m = 2.073 m
4 2 dm, 1 cm, 3 m = 3.21 m
5 1 m, 5 dm, 0 cm, 1 mm = 1.501 m
6 6 m, 1 mm, 2 cm = 6.021 m
7 6 cm, 9 dm, 3 m = 3.96 m
8 1 m, 9 mm, 7 dm = 1.709 m

**Write each measurement in kilometers.**

9 2 km, 350 m = 2.35 km
10 1 km, 700 m = 1.7 km
11 3 km, 30 m = 3.03 km
12 1400 m = 1.4 km
13 5 km, 100 m = 5.1 km
14 880 m = 0.88 km

**Write the length of each object in millimeters and then in centimeters.**

15 80 mm 8.0 cm

16 95 mm 9.5 cm

100 Chapter 9 • *Decimals and Measurement* **Real Math** • Grade 4 • *Practice*

Practice Lesson 9.8

### RETEACH

**If . . .** students are having difficulty understanding how to express metric measurements as decimals of a common unit,

**Then . . .** provide extra measuring practice by taking advantage of regular classroom situations that lend themselves to measuring, such as construction or crafts projects, athletic contests that involve distance, and so on.

# Adding and Subtracting Decimals

**Context of the Lesson** Adding and subtracting decimals was taught in Grade 3. Students worked with adding and subtracting decimals in the context of time measurements in Chapter 7. Lessons 9.9 through 9.11 provide practice in adding and subtracting decimals to solve practical problems. This lesson includes a Mastery Checkpoint.

See page 382B for Math Background for teachers for this lesson.

## Objectives

- To provide practice for, and assess mastery of, addition and subtraction of decimals by relating these skills to monetary amounts
- To provide practice in solving word problems that involve adding and subtracting decimals

## NCTM Standards

**Number and Operations**
Understand the meaning of operations and how they relate to one another

**Problem Solving**
Solve problems that arise in mathematics and in other contexts

**Connections**
Recognize and apply mathematics in contexts outside of mathematics

## Materials

- *Play money (optional)
- Graph paper (optional)
- ***Store Game Mat (optional)**
- **Assessment Page T73**

## Technology

**e Presentation** Lesson 9.9
**e MathTools** Calculator

## Test Prep

**Cumulative Review**
Mental Math reviews multiplying and dividing by powers of 10 (Lesson 9.6).

**Extended Response**
Problem 25

**Writing + Math**
Journal

## Looking Ahead

Create price tags to be placed on various items around the classroom. You may also bring in items from areas outside of the classroom. The price tags need to range in price from 5¢ to $5. Make many items with decimal number prices (for example, $1.49, $2.99, $3.25). You may create some price tags that are, for example, 2 for $1, allowing the students to purchase items at 50¢ each.

*Manipulative Kit Item

## Planning for Learning • DIFFERENTIATE INSTRUCTION

### INTERVENTION

**If . . .** students lack the prerequisite skill of multiplying and dividing by powers of 10,

**Then . . .** teach ***Intervention*** Lesson 9.B.

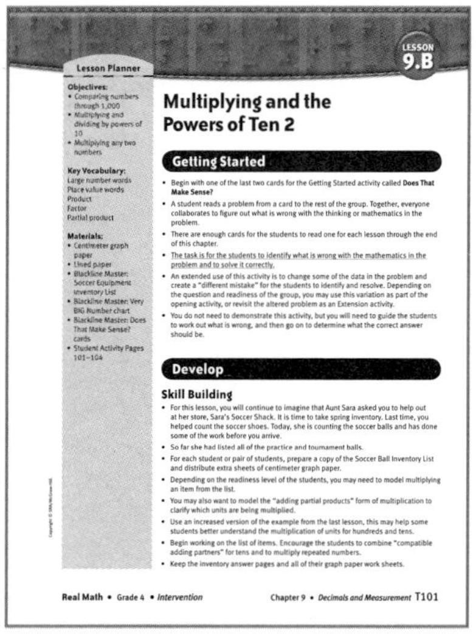


Intervention Lesson 9.B

### ENGLISH LEARNER

Preview

**If . . .** students need language support,

**Then . . .** use Lesson 9.9 in ***English Learner Support Guide*** to preview lesson concepts and vocabulary.

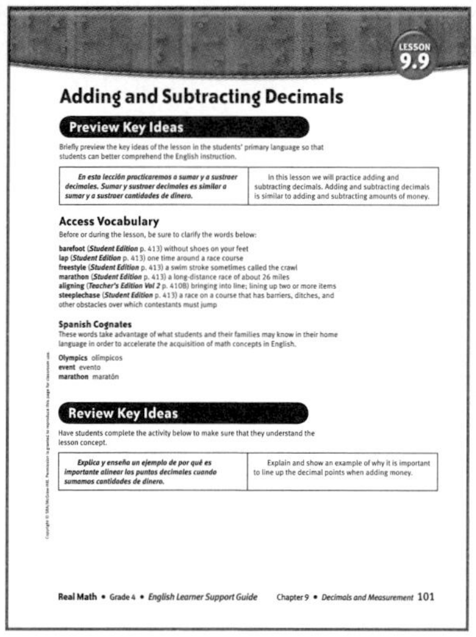


English Learner Lesson 9.9

### ENRICH

**If . . .** students are proficient in the lesson concepts,

**Then . . .** have them play the **Store Game Mat.**

### PRACTICE

**If . . .** students would benefit from additional practice,

**Then . . .** extend Skill Practice before assigning the student pages.

### RETEACH

**If . . .** students have difficulty understanding how to add and subtract decimals,

**Then . . .** extend Guided Discussion before assigning the student pages.

### Vocabulary

Review from Lesson 2.1: **sum**
Review from Lesson 2.2: **difference**

### Access Vocabulary

**marathon** a long running race of approximately 26 miles

### Spanish Cognates

**Olympics** Olímpicos
**marathon** maratón

## Mental Math

5

Review RESPONSE WHEEL Provide problems, such as the following, to practice multiplying and dividing decimals by powers of 10:

**a.** 421.02 × 10 = 4,210.2
**b.** 8.06 × 10 = 80.6
**c.** 384.71 × 100 = 38,471
**d.** 10 × 59.3 = 593
**e.** 0.06 ÷ 100 = 0.0006
**f.** 475 ÷ 100 = 4.75
**g.** 0.43 ÷ 10 = 0.043
**h.** 1.003 ÷ 10 = 0.1003
**i.** 1,000 × 0.301 = 301
**j.** 3.45 ÷ 100 = 0.0345
**k.** 1,000 × 0.062 = 62
**l.** 10 × 8.06 = 80.6

## 1 Develop

25

### Tell Students In Today's Lesson They Will

practice addition and subtraction of decimals by relating these skills to adding and subtracting monetary amounts and by solving word problems.

## Guided Discussion UNDERSTANDING

Whole Group

1. Ask students if they remember how to add two sums of money. Remind them that it is important to line up the decimal points so that the answer makes sense. Cents should be added to cents, and dollars to dollars. By estimation, students know that $5 + $1.31, for example, will add to an amount between $6 and $7. Clearly, a sum of $1.36 (one example of a misalignment of place values) would not be correct.

   Explain that subtracting one monetary amount from another requires the same consideration as adding them. Again, the important point is that the same digit can have different values depending on its place value. So, when subtracting, you want to subtract things of like magnitude. Aligning the decimal points helps us assure this.

   Work through an example such as $6 − $2.17. $3.83 Students know by estimation that the difference will be between $4 and $3. So, clearly a difference of $2.11 (one example of a misalignment of place values) would not be correct.

   Tell students that adding and subtracting decimals involves similar rules. Remind students that writing a zero at the end of a decimal number does not change its value. Therefore, if it is helpful to put in a zero to reinforce how to align the digits of a problem, they should feel free to do so. For example:

$$37.27 + 4.6 = ?$$

$$\begin{array}{r} 37.27 \\ +\ 4.60 \\ \hline 41.87 \end{array}$$

**NOTE:** As students increase their understanding of measurement, money, and rational numbers, they will develop a sense of precision with decimals. For example, a table could measure about 2 meters in length. If, however, someone measured to the nearest centimeter, they might find that the table is actually 203 centimeters. A third person could measure the length of the table as 2,035 millimeters. Writing out new millimeters measurement in meters, we could say the table is actually 2.035 meters in length. Mastery of this concept is not required at this time.

## Skill Practice COMPUTING

Whole Group

Give students examples, such as the following, to practice adding and subtracting decimal amounts:

6.40 − 0.05 = 6.35
8.92 − 2.39 = 6.53
7.04 − 2.06 = 4.98
13.3 + 4.11 = 17.41
25.01 + 0.6 = 25.61

## 2 Assign Student Pages 25

**Page 411**

Have students complete page 411 independently.

Student Page

LESSON 9.9 Adding and Subtracting Decimals

### Key Ideas

**Adding and subtracting decimals is similar to adding and subtracting amounts of money.**

Linda has \$0.97. If she earns \$3.75 for washing Mr. Lomaki's dog, how much money will she have?

Do you remember how to add amounts of money?

$$\begin{array}{r} \$3.75 \\ +\ 0.97 \\ \hline \$4.72 \end{array}$$

Line up the decimal points so you can add pennies to pennies, dimes to dimes, dollars to dollars, and so on.

Felipe has \$4.72. He needs \$10 to buy a flashlight. How much more does he need?

Do you remember how to subtract amounts of money?

$$\begin{array}{r} \$10.00 \\ -\ 4.72 \\ \hline \$5.28 \end{array}$$

Line up the decimal points so you can subtract pennies from pennies, dimes from dimes, dollars from dollars, and so on.

Cameron timed himself running the perimeter of the playground. He got halfway around in 13.35 seconds. It took Cameron 16.8 seconds to run the second half. How long did it take him to run all the way around?

When you add or subtract decimals, line up the decimal points. This will allow you to add or subtract tenths with tenths, hundredths with hundredths, and thousandths with thousandths.

$16.8 + 13.35 = ?$ Line up the decimal points.

$$\begin{array}{r} 16.80 \\ +\ 13.35 \\ \hline 30.15 \end{array}$$

Add.

It took Cameron 30.15 seconds to run the perimeter of the playground.



eTextbook This lesson is available in the *eTextbook*.

Student Page

**Example:** 8.6 – 3.25

$$\begin{array}{r} 8.6 \\ -\ 3.25 \\ \hline \end{array}$$ Line up the decimal points.

$$\begin{array}{r} 8.6\mathbf{0} \\ -\ 3.25 \\ \hline \end{array}$$ If it helps, include 0 (because 8.6 and 8.60 have the same value).

$$\begin{array}{r} 8.60 \\ -\ 3.25 \\ \hline 5.35 \end{array}$$ Subtract.

**Add** or subtract.

1. $6.72 + 11.09$ = 17.81
2. $9.5 + 8.63$ = 18.13
3. $5.2 + 3.15$ = 8.35
4. $8.2 + 3.01$ = 11.21
5. $1.7 - 0.9$ = 0.8
6. $8.03 - 7.04$ = 0.99
7. $3.07 + 0.96$ = 4.03
8. $4.07 - 3.10$ = 0.97
9. $5.33 - 4.03$ = 1.30
10. $8.4 + 2.7$ = 11.1
11. $2.96 - 1.09$ = 1.87
12. $7.43 + 2.99$ = 10.42

**Solve** for *n*.

13. $2.36 + 6.5 = n$ $n = 8.86$
14. $2.34 - 2.09 = n$ $n = 0.25$
15. $6.07 + 3.03 = n$ $n = 9.10$
16. $4.64 + 6 = n$ $n = 10.64$
17. $10.9 - 9.01 = n$ $n = 1.89$
18. $8.26 - 8.19 = n$ $n = 0.07$
19. $5.4 - 3.3 = n$ $n = 2.1$

**Solve.**

20. Kendra lives 1.25 kilometers from the library. She has walked 0.62 kilometers toward the library. How much farther does she have to walk? 0.63 km

# Assign Student Pages, continued

### Pages 412–413

Small Group

Have students work in small groups on pages 412 and 413. The problems on these pages provide realistic applications for adding and subtracting decimals. If students have trouble with Problem 28, remind them there are 60 seconds in 1 minute.

#### Monitoring Student Progress

| **If . . .** | **Then . . .** |
|---|---|
| students continue to have trouble aligning decimal points, | have them use graph paper to better align their numbers. Use one column of the graph paper for decimal points. Reinforce estimating answers by using play money to show when answers don't make sense. |

### As Students Finish

**Game** **Roll a Decimal Game** (introduced in Lesson 9.4)

Student Page



**Solve** these problems. SOCIAL STUDIES

21 In the 1900 Olympics, Irving Baxter jumped 1.90 meters in the running high jump. In 2004, Matt Hemingway jumped 2.34 meters in the running high jump.

**a.** Which man jumped higher? Matt Hemingway

**b.** How much higher did he jump? 0.44 meters

22 In the 1896 Olympic games, Thomas Burke ran 100 meters in 12 seconds. In the 1900 Olympic Games, Francis W. Jarvis ran 100 meters in 10.8 seconds.

**a.** What was the difference in their times? 1.2 seconds

**b.** Who ran faster? Francis W. Jarvis

23 In the 2004 Olympics, Justin Gatlin ran 100 meters in 9.85 seconds. By how much time did he beat 10 seconds? 0.15 seconds

24 In the 2004 Olympics, Lauren Williams ran 100 meters in 10.96 seconds. If she had run that fast for another 100 meters, how long would it have taken her to run a total distance of 200 meters? 21.92 seconds

25 Extended Response In the 1996 Olympics, Veronica Campbell ran 200 meters in 22.05 seconds. She also ran 100 meters in 10.97 seconds. Was her average speed for the 200-meter run faster or slower than her average speed for the 100-meter run? Why do you think there was a difference? slower; possible answer: she might need to run slower at the beginning of the longer 200-meter race to conserve energy for the sprint at the finish line.

eTextbook This lesson is available in the *eTextbook.*

Student Page

26 In the 1900 Olympics, J. W. B. Tewksbury ran the 400-meter hurdle in 57.6 seconds. In 1992 Kevin Young had a time of 46.78 seconds in the same event. How much faster was Young? 10.82 seconds

27 The 10,000-meter run is an Olympic event. How many kilometers is 10,000 meters? 10

28 In the 2004 Olympics, Kaitlin Sandeno swam the 400-meter freestyle in 4 minutes and 6.19 seconds. In the 1924 Olympics, John Weissmuller swam the 400-meter freestyle in 5 minutes and 4.2 seconds. By how much did Kaitlin Sandeno beat John Weissmuller's time? 58.01 seconds

29 In the 1964 Olympics, Abebe Bikila ran the marathon *barefoot* in 2 hours, 12 minutes, and 11.2 seconds. (The marathon is 42,195 m—about 26 miles!) In the 1948 Olympics, Delfo Cabrera ran the marathon in 2 hours, 34 minutes, and 51.6 seconds. In how much less time did Abebe Bikila run the marathon barefoot? 22 minutes and 40.4 seconds

30 In the 1932 Olympics, Volmari Iso-Hollo ran an extra lap by mistake in the 3,000-meter steeplechase. His time for the race was 10 minutes and 33.4 seconds. In the 1936 Olympics, he ran the same race in 9 minutes and 3.8 seconds. About how long do you think it took Iso-Hollo to run the extra lap? A reasonable estimate is about 90 seconds.

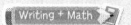

Writing + Math **Journal**

When adding whole numbers such as 123 + 45, are the decimals aligned? Explain your answer. Yes. See *Teacher's Edition* for possible explanations.

## 3 Reflect

5.

### Guided Discussion REASONING

Whole Group

When might the average time for runners in the 4 × 100 meter relay be faster than their best time for the 100-meter dash? The slowest part of the 100-meter dash is at the beginning when the runner is just getting started. In the relay, the runner to whom the baton is being handed is already accelerating.

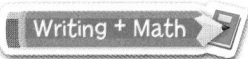

### Extended Response

**Problem 25** Her time for the 100-meter run was faster than for the 200-meter run. One possible answer is that she had to conserve energy for the sprint at the finish.

Writing + Math **Journal**

Students' answers should mention that when adding whole numbers, the decimal points are aligned because the decimal point comes after the ones column, even if they are not explicitly printed.

Use Mastery Checkpoint 20 found in ***Assessment*** to evaluate student mastery of addition and subtraction of decimal numbers. By this time students should be able to correctly answer eighty percent of the Mastery Checkpoint items.

**Curriculum Connection:** Students may be interested in studying various Olympiads, some of which may have been referenced in the ***Student Edition.***

**Cumulative Review:** For review of comparing fractions, assign Problems 38–43 on student page 417.

**Family Involvement:** Assign the ***Practice, Reteach,*** or ***Enrichment*** activities depending on the needs of your students.

Encourage students to play the **Roll a Decimal Game** with a friend or relative.

**Concept/Question Board:** Have students look for additional examples of decimals and post them on the Concept/Question Board.

**Math Puzzler:** Find a decimal number that is equally greater than 1.7 and less than 7.1. 4.4

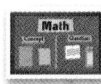

# 4 Assess and Differentiate

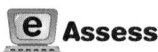

**eAssess** Use ***eAssess*** to record and analyze evidence of student understanding.

## A Gather Evidence

Use the Daily Class Assessment Records in ***Assessment*** or ***eAssess*** to record daily observations.

### Formal Assessment

**Mastery Checkpoint**

Did the student

- ❑ use correct procedures?
- ❑ respond with at least eighty percent accuracy?

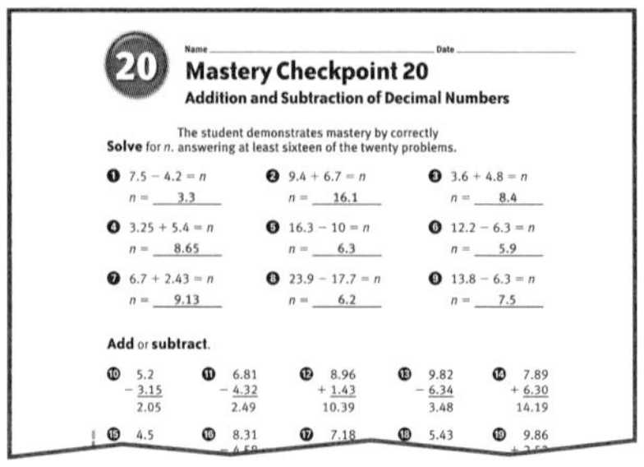


Assessment Page T73

## B Summarize Findings

Analyze and summarize assessment data for each student. Determine which Assessment Follow-Up is appropriate for each student. Use the Student Assessment Record in ***Assessment*** or ***eAssess*** to update assessment records.

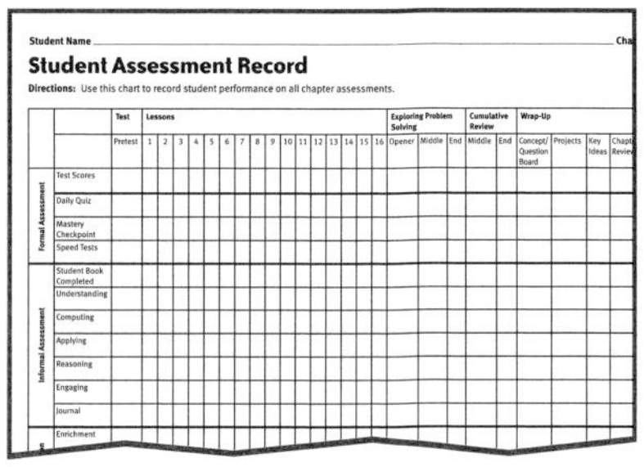


Assessment Page T41

## C Assessment Follow-Up • DIFFERENTIATE INSTRUCTION

Based on your observations, use these teaching strategies for assessment follow-up.

### INTERVENTION

Review student performance on ***Intervention*** Lesson 9.B to see if students have mastered prerequisite skills for this lesson.

### ENGLISH LEARNER

**Review**

Use Lesson 9.9 in ***English Learner Support Guide*** to preview lesson concepts and vocabulary.

### ENRICH

**If . . .** students are proficient in the lesson concepts,

**Then . . .** encourage them to work on the chapter projects or ***Enrichment*** Lesson 9.9.

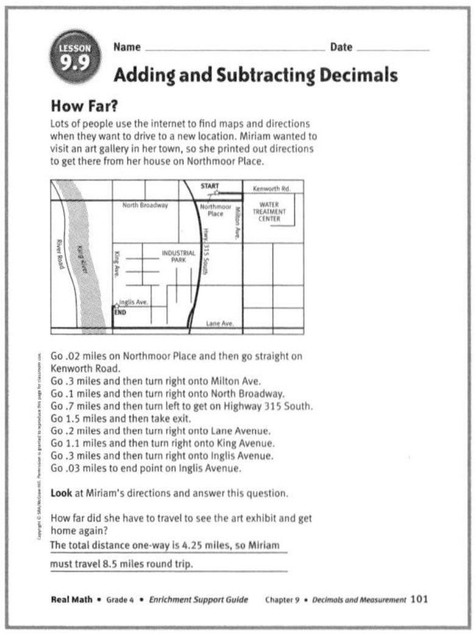


Enrichment Lesson 9.9

### PRACTICE

**If . . .** students would benefit from additional practice,

**Then . . .** assign ***Practice*** Lesson 9.9.

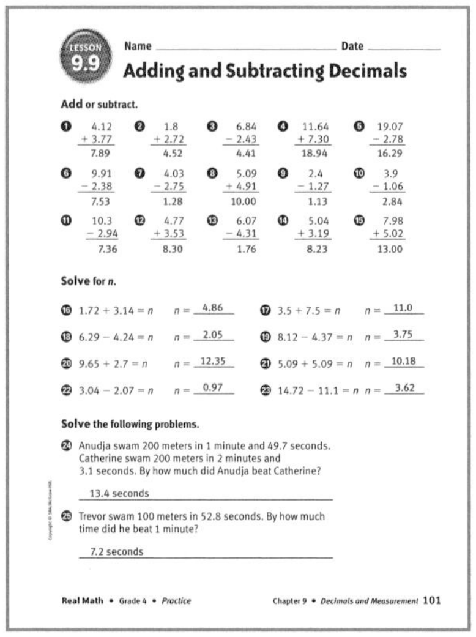


Practice Lesson 9.9

### RETEACH

**If . . .** students have difficulty understanding adding and subtracting decimals,

**Then . . .** reteach the concept using ***Reteach*** Lesson 9.9.

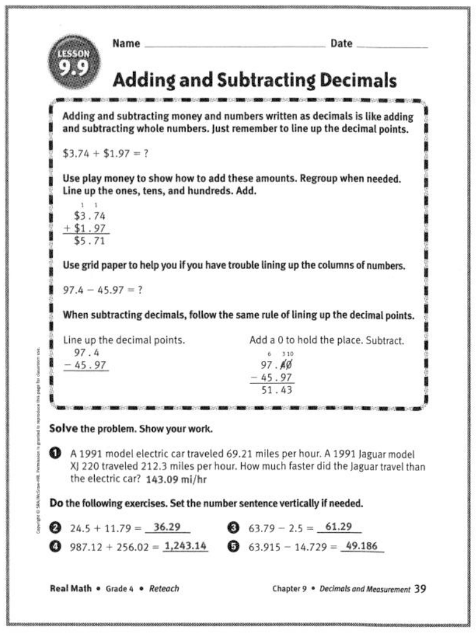


Reteach Lesson 9.9

# Exploring Problem Solving

## Objectives

- To analyze combining the Use Simple Numbers and Make a Table strategies
- To analyze combining the Make a Diagram and Look For a Pattern strategies
- To provide practice using ratios that contain decimals
- To provide practice using decimals and metric units in a realistic situation

**Context of the Lesson** In this lesson, students apply what they have learned about decimals and metric measurement to solve a challenging problem. The lesson also continues the television theme begun in the Chapter Introduction. This theme will appear again in the Problem Solving Lesson on page 434.

## 1 Develop

5

### Tell Students In Today's Lesson They Will

- read a challenging problem about designing a television screen.
- look at two methods for solving the problem.
- use one of the methods presented or their own method to solve the problem with their group and share their strategy.

## Guided Discussion

Have students talk about different types, sizes, and shapes of television screens. You may wish to talk about what it means for two figures to be mathematically similar, but keep in mind that similarity and congruence will be taught in the next chapter. Ask questions such as the following:

- **What shape are most television screens?** rectangles
- **Do all the rectangular television screens have the same shape?** Help students see that some are more square and some are more elongated.

Student Page

### Exploring Problem Solving

IN THE 1940s

*In the 1940s,* when television first came out, companies decided to make television screens the same shape as movie screens.

Years later, movie screens became wider. Eventually, the shape of television screens changed, too.

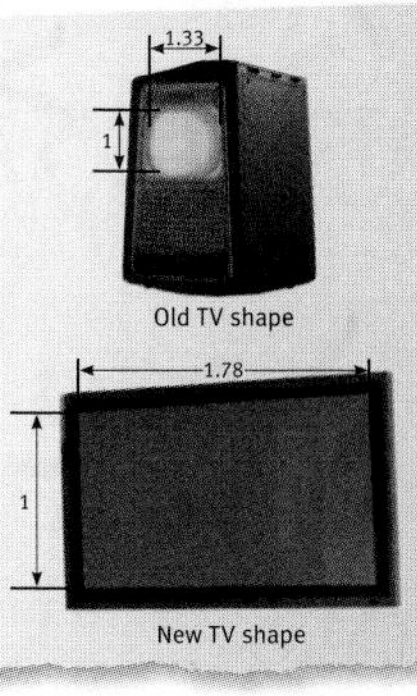


Imagine that you are designing a portable movie player. You want to use the widescreen format. You want the screen to be 5.00 centimeters high. How wide should it be?

**Ken solved the problem this way:**

I Used Simpler Numbers and Made a Table to solve the problem.

How would I solve the problem if the numbers were simpler? What if the ratio were 2 to 1 instead of 1.78 to 1?

I could make a table to show the widths for different heights.

| Height | 1 cm | 2 cm | 3 cm |
|---|---|---|---|
| Width | 2 cm | 4 cm | 6 cm |

I can use the same kind of table with the actual ratio 1.78 to 1.

| Height | 1.00 cm | 2.00 cm | 3.00 cm |
|---|---|---|---|
| Width | 1.78 cm | 3.56 cm | |



Textbook This lesson is available in the ***eTextbook***.

Student Page

❶ He is showing what the widths would be if the ratio were 2 to 1.

**Think about Ken's strategy. Answer these questions.**

❷ It shows what the widths would be using the actual ratio of 1.78 to 1.

1. Why does Ken's first table show a width of 2 centimeters for a height of 1 centimeter?
2. Why does the second table show a width of 1.78 centimeters for a height of 1 centimeter?
3. In the second table, what is the meaning of 3.56 centimeters? How do you think Ken got that figure?

❸ 3.56 cm is how wide the screen would be if it were 2 cm high. He added 1.78 + 1.78.

**Beverly solved the problem this way:**

I Made a Diagram and Used a Pattern to solve the problem.

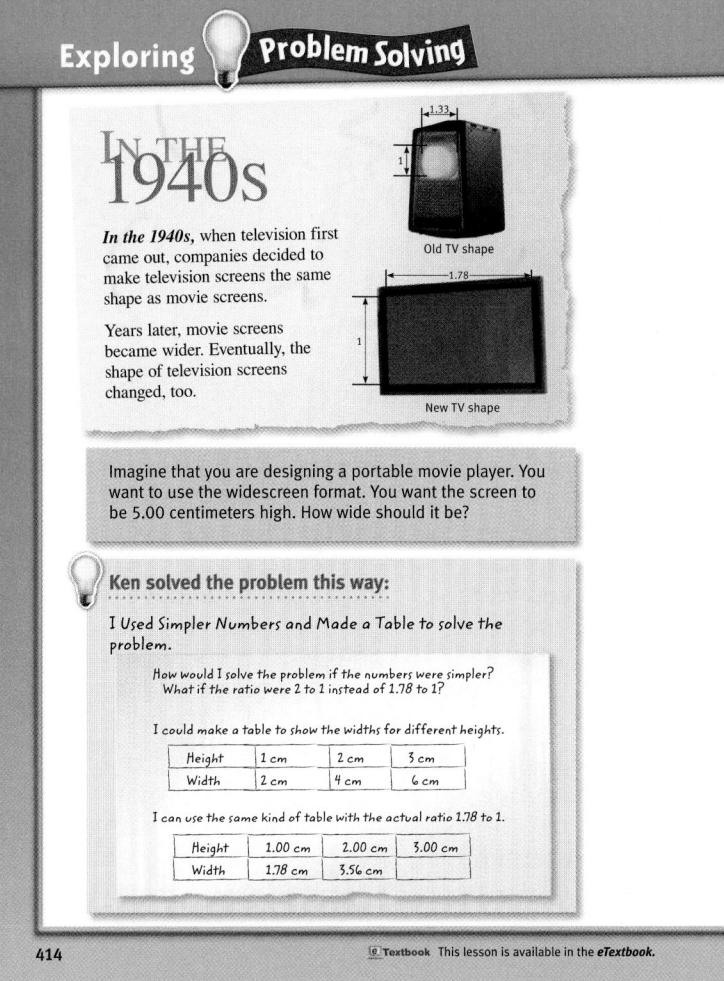

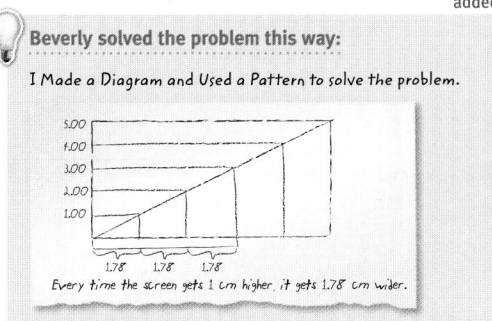

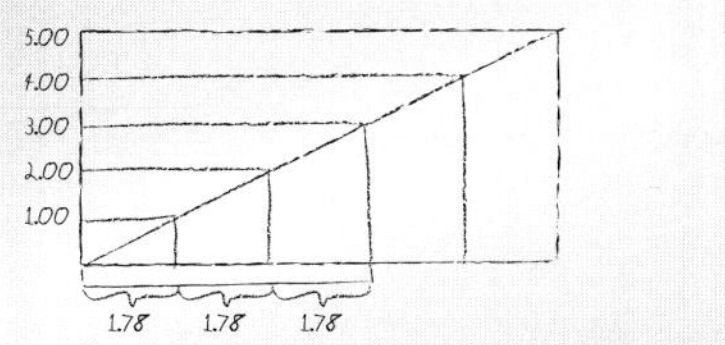


Every time the screen gets 1 cm higher, it gets 1.78 cm wider.

**Think about Beverly's strategy. Answer these questions.**

4. What does Beverly's diagram show? what the screen would look like if it was 1 cm high, 2 cm high, and so on
5. Why did Beverly draw all the rectangles with the same shape? no matter how big the screen, the width is always 1.78 times greater than the height.
6. What pattern do you see for the width of the screens? Each screen is 1.78 cm wider than the one before.
7. How can Beverly finish solving the problem? She can add 1.78 five times.
8. How is Beverly's strategy like Ken's strategy? How is it different? See the *Teacher's Edition.*
9. Solve the problem. What strategy did you use? Why? The width should be 8.90 cm.

## 2 Exploring Problem Solving 20

### Using Student Pages

Read and discuss the information and the problem on page 414 with the class. Make sure students understand that each screen format can come in many sizes. Ask questions such as the following:

- **Do the two screens shown on page 414 have the same exact shape?** no
- **Which shape will you be using for the screen you are designing?** the wider one
- **Why would you want your movie player to have this exact shape?** So it can show most movies without cutting off any of the image. Students may have seen the black bars on the top and bottom of a television screen when a widescreen movie is shown on a standard television.

The ratio of screen width to height is called *aspect ratio.* Although 1:78 to 1 is a common aspect ratio for movies, many movies are produced in other formats as well. Illustrated examples can be found on the Internet.

Discuss Ken's method for solving the problem. Give students time to think about Problems 1–3 on page 415, then discuss them.

Have the class examine Beverly's method. Give students time to think about Problems 4–7, then discuss them.

### Answer

#### Problem 8

Students may see that both strategies involve adding 1.78 cm five times to get the final width. However, Ken and Beverly arrived at this calculation in different ways. Ken thought about how he would solve the problem if the ratio were a simpler 2 to 1, and Beverly drew a diagram.

Have students work in pairs or small groups to solve Problem 9.

## 3 Reflect 15

Knowledge Age Skills

**Effective Communication** Have groups present their solutions and methods to Problem 9. After each method is presented, ask questions such as the following:

- **Did the group check its results?**
- **What did you like about the method or the way it was presented?**

#### Extending the Problem

Students may be interested in solving one or both of these problems that relate to showing a movie in one format on a television screen that uses a different format.

- **When a widescreen movie (1.78 to 1) is shown on a standard television screen without black bars, what fraction or percent of the image is cut off to make it fit?** $\frac{1.78 - 1.33}{1.78} = \frac{178 - 133}{178} = \frac{45}{178}$, or about $\frac{1}{4}$ or 25%

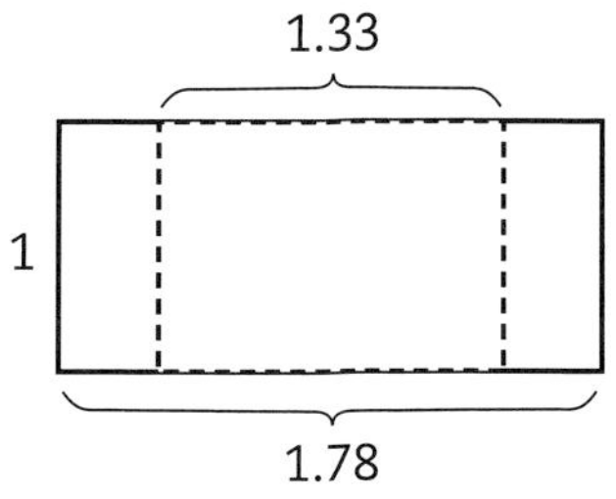


- **When a widescreen movie is shown on a standard television screen with black bars, what fraction or percent of the screen do the black bars take up?** This problem involves shrinking the widescreen image proportionally until it fits onto the old-format screen. Students might make scale diagrams or models to see that the height of the letterboxed image is about 75 percent of the screen, and therefore about 25 percent of the screen is taken up by the black bars.

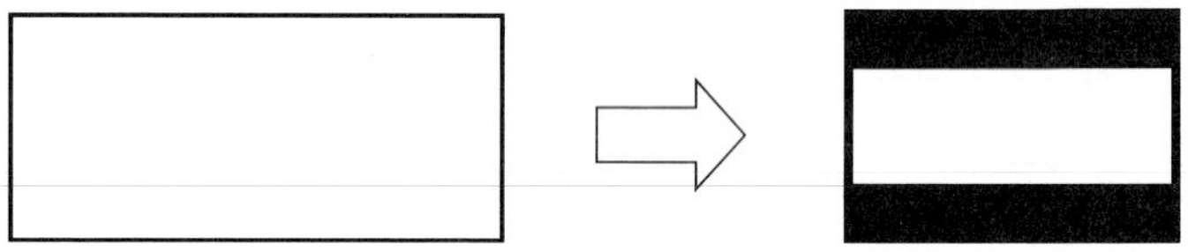

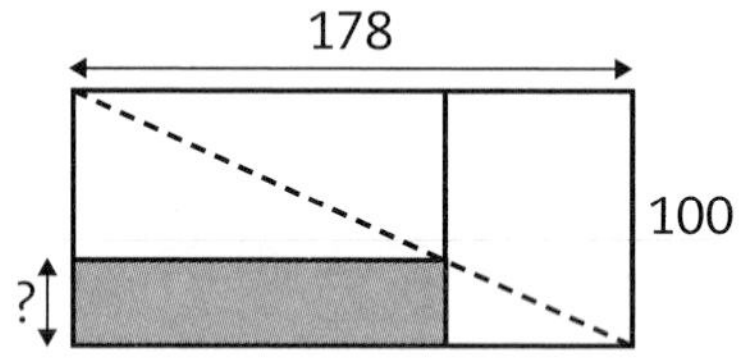


## 4 Assess 10

When evaluating student work, focus not only on the correctness of the answer but also on whether students thought rationally about the problem and the various solutions presented. Some questions to consider include the following:

- Did the student understand the problem?
- Did the student show all the steps the group took in solving the problem?
- Did the student check to see if the reasoning and the answer made sense?

# Cumulative Review

## Assign Pages 416–417

Use this Cumulative Review as a review of concepts and skills that students have previously learned.

Here are different ways you can assign these problems to your students as they work through the chapter:

- For each lesson in the chapter, assign a set of Cumulative Review problems to be completed as practice or for homework.
  - Lesson 9.1—Problems 1–2
  - Lesson 9.2—Problems 3–5
  - Lesson 9.3—Problems 6–10
  - Lesson 9.4—Problems 11–15
  - Lesson 9.5—Problems 16–22
  - Lesson 9.6—Problems 23–27
  - Lesson 9.7—Problems 28–32
  - Lesson 9.8—Problems 33–37
  - Lesson 9.9—Problems 38–43
- At any point during the chapter, assign part or all of the Cumulative Review problems to be completed as practice or for homework.

### Cumulative Review

**Problems 1–2** review multidigit addition and subtraction, Lesson 2.3.

**Problems 3–5** review fractions and rational numbers, Lesson 8.3.

**Problems 6–10** review multiplication and division, Lesson 3.10.

**Problems 11–15** review multidigit multiplication, Lessons 6.2 and 6.5.

**Problems 16–22** review fractions greater than 1, Lessons 8.15–8.16.

**Problems 23–27** review fractions, Lesson 8.6.

**Problems 28–32** review relation signs, Lesson 2.4.

**Problems 33–37** review percent benchmarks, Lesson 7.2.

**Problems 38–43** review comparing fractions, Lesson 8.9.

### Monitoring Student Progress

**If . . .** students miss more than one problem in a section, **Then . . .** refer to the indicated lesson for remediation suggestions.

---

## Cumulative Review

**Multidigit Addition and Subtraction** Lesson 2.3

**Solve** each problem.

① 
$$\begin{array}{r} 364165 \\ + 381632 \\ \hline \end{array}$$  745,797

② 
$$\begin{array}{r} 10000 \\ - 854 \\ \hline \end{array}$$  9,146

**Fractions and Rational Numbers** Lesson 8.3    ③④⑤ Answers will vary. Possible answers:

**Write** two equivalent fractions for the following.

③ $\frac{4}{10}$   $\frac{2}{5}, \frac{8}{20}, \frac{12}{30}$

④ $\frac{3}{15}$   $\frac{1}{5}, \frac{6}{30}, \frac{18}{90}$

⑤ $\frac{6}{7}$   $\frac{12}{14}, \frac{18}{21}, \frac{24}{28}$

**Composite Function Rules** Lesson 4.10

⑥ $36 \div 3 =$ ▩   12

⑦ $8 \times 6 =$ ▩   48

⑧ $0 \div 144 =$ ▩   0

⑨ $8 \times 7 =$ ▩   56

⑩ $10 \times 20 =$ ▩   200

**Two- and Three-Digit Multiplication** Lessons 6.2 and 6.5

⑪ 
$$\begin{array}{r} 58 \\ \times 16 \\ \hline \end{array}$$  928

⑫ 
$$\begin{array}{r} 411 \\ \times 64 \\ \hline \end{array}$$  26,304

⑬ 
$$\begin{array}{r} 800 \\ \times 15 \\ \hline \end{array}$$  12,000

⑭ 
$$\begin{array}{r} 616 \\ \times 812 \\ \hline \end{array}$$  500,192

⑮ 
$$\begin{array}{r} 393 \\ \times 127 \\ \hline \end{array}$$  49,911

**Adding and Subtracting Fractions Greater than 1** Lesson 8.15–8.16

**Solve** the following exercises. Write answers greater than 1 as mixed numbers or whole numbers.

⑯ $3\frac{1}{3} + 7\frac{1}{3} = n$   $n = 10\frac{2}{3}$

⑰ $4\frac{13}{16} - 3\frac{3}{4} = n$   $n = 1\frac{1}{16}$

⑱ $\frac{1}{5} + 2\frac{3}{10} = n$   $n = 2\frac{1}{2}$

⑲ $n = 4\frac{2}{3} - 3\frac{1}{7}$   $n = 1\frac{11}{21}$

⑳ $\frac{5}{4} + 3\frac{1}{4} = n$   $n = 4\frac{1}{2}$

㉑ $6\frac{5}{9} - \frac{13}{9} = n$   $n = 5\frac{1}{9}$

㉒ $8 + 2\frac{3}{7} = n$   $n = 10\frac{3}{7}$

---

**Applying Fractions** Lesson 8.6

**Solve.**

㉓ $\frac{2}{6}$ ▩ $=$ ▩   8

㉔ $\frac{1}{5}$ ▩ $=$ ▩   7

㉕ $\frac{6}{12}$ ▩ $=$ ▩   25 of 50

㉖ $\frac{1}{7}$ of 24 $=$ ▩   4   of 28

㉗ $\frac{1}{9}$ of 35 $=$ ▩   6   of 54

**Using Relations Signs** Lesson 2.4

**What** is the correct sign, <, >, or =?

㉘ $54 \div 9 + 3$ ▩ $1 \times 10$   <

㉙ $15 \times 15 - 30$ ▩ $35$   >

㉚ $6 \times 8 + 12$ ▩ $12 \times 5$   =

㉛ $92 - 20 \div 8$ ▩ $3$   >

㉜ $64 \div 4 - 12$ ▩ $5$   <

**Percent Benchmarks** Lesson 7.2

**Solve.**

㉝ 75% of 80 $=$ ▩   60

㉞ 25% of 25 $=$ ▩   $6\frac{1}{4}$

㉟ 30% of 50 $=$ ▩   15

㊱ 15% of \$120 $=$ ▩   \$18

㊲ Vivian bought 1 new CD at the mall today. The price tag on the CD read \$15.00 (including tax). However, when she gave the sales clerk \$15.00, the clerk said, "Oh, these are on sale today." She gave Vivian \$2.25 in change. Figure out what the percentage off the price was.   15%

**Comparing Fractions** Lesson 8.9

**Place** the fractions on the number line.

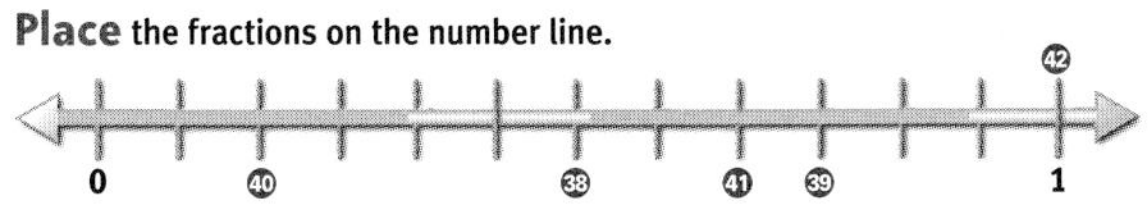

㊳ $\frac{1}{2}$

㊴ $\frac{3}{4}$

㊵ $\frac{1}{6}$

㊶ $\frac{2}{3}$

㊷ $\frac{12}{12}$

# Mid-Test
# Individual Oral Assessment

## Purpose of the Test

The Individual Oral Assessment is designed to measure students' growing knowledge of chapter concepts. It is administered to each student individually, and it requires oral responses from each student. The test takes about five minutes to complete.

See **Assessment** for detailed instructions for administering and interpreting the test, and record students' answers on the Student Assessment Recording Sheet.

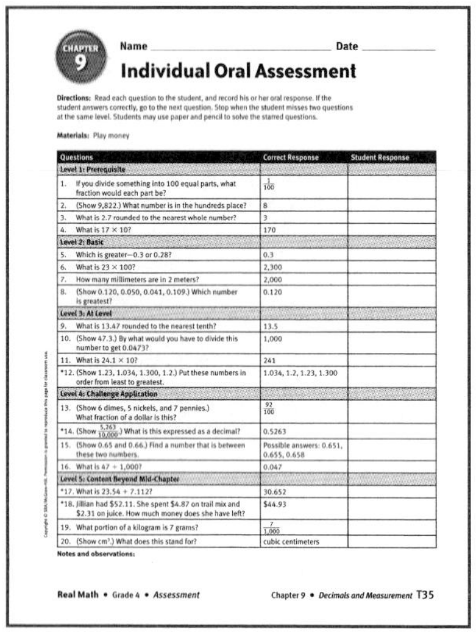

**Assessment Page T35**

## Directions

Read each question to the student, and record his or her oral response. If the student answers correctly, go to the next question. Stop when the student misses two questions at the same level. Students may use paper and pencil to solve the starred questions.

**Materials:** Play money

## Questions

### Level 1: Prerequisite

1. If you divide something into 100 equal parts, what fraction would each part be? $\frac{1}{100}$

2. (Show 9,822.) What number is in the hundreds place? 8

3. What is 2.7 rounded to the nearest whole number? 3

4. What is 17 × 10? 170

### Level 2: Basic

5. Which is greater—0.3 or 0.28? 0.3

6. What is 23 × 100? 2,300

7. How many millimeters are in 2 meters? 2,000

8. (Show 0.120, 0.050, 0.041, 0.109.) Which number is greatest? 0.120

### Level 3: At Level

9. What is 13.47 rounded to the nearest tenth? 13.5

10. (Show 47.3.) By what would you have to divide this number to get 0.0473? 1,000

11. What is 24.1 × 10? 241

*12. (Show 1.23, 1.034, 1.300, 1.2.) Put these numbers in order from least to greatest. 1.034, 1.2, 1.23, 1.300

### Level 4: Challenge Application

13. (Show 6 dimes, 5 nickels, and 7 pennies.) What fraction of a dollar is this? $\frac{92}{100}$

*14. (Show $\frac{5,263}{10,000}$.) What is this expressed as a decimal? 0.5263

15. (Show 0.65 and 0.66.) Find a number that is between these two numbers. Possible answers: 0.651, 0.655, 0.658

16. What is 47 ÷ 1,000? 0.047

### Level 5: Content Beyond Mid-Chapter

*17. What is 23.54 + 7.112? 30.652

*18. Jillian had $52.11. She spent $4.87 on trail mix and $2.31 on juice. How much money does she have left? $44.93

19. What portion of a kilogram is 7 grams? $\frac{7}{1,000}$

20. (Show cm³.) What does this stand for? cubic centimeters

## Lesson Planner

**OBJECTIVES**
- To provide practice in solving word problems involving the addition and subtraction of decimals
- To provide practice in adding and subtracting decimals

**NCTM STANDARDS**

**Number and Operations**
Compute silently and make reasonable estimates

**Problem Solving**
Solve problems that arise in mathematics and in other contexts

**MATERIALS**
- ***Number Cubes** (one 0–5, one 5–10)
- Graph paper (optional)

**TECHNOLOGY**

**Presentation** Lesson 9.10
**MathTools** Calculator

**TEST PREP**

**Cumulative Review**
Mental Math reviews adding and subtracting decimals (Lesson 9.9).

**Multistep Problems**
Problems 2 and 3

**Extended Response**
Problem 2

**Writing + Math**
Journal

*Manipulative Kit Item

# Using Decimals

**Context of the Lesson** This is the second of three lessons on adding and subtracting decimals. This lesson provides application through word problems based on real-life situations. The **Harder Roll a Decimal Game** gives students the opportunity to add and subtract many decimal numbers.

See page 382B for Math Background for teachers for this lesson.

## Planning for Learning • DIFFERENTIATE INSTRUCTION

### INTERVENTION

**If . . .** students lack the prerequisite skill of multiplying any two numbers,

**Then . . .** teach ***Intervention*** Lesson 9.C.

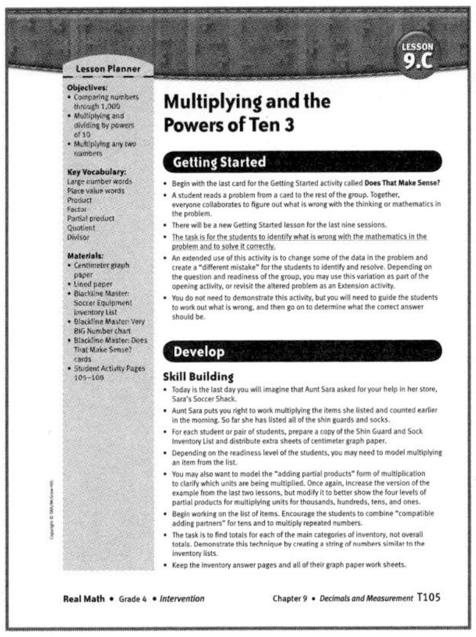
Lesson Planner
LESSON 9.C
Multiplying and the Powers of Ten 3
Getting Started
Develop
Skill Building
Real Math • Grade 4 • Intervention Chapter 9 • Decimals and Measurement T105

Intervention Lesson 9.C

### ENGLISH LEARNER

Preview

**If . . .** students need language support,

**Then . . .** use Lesson 9.10 in ***English Learner Support Guide*** to preview lesson concepts and vocabulary.

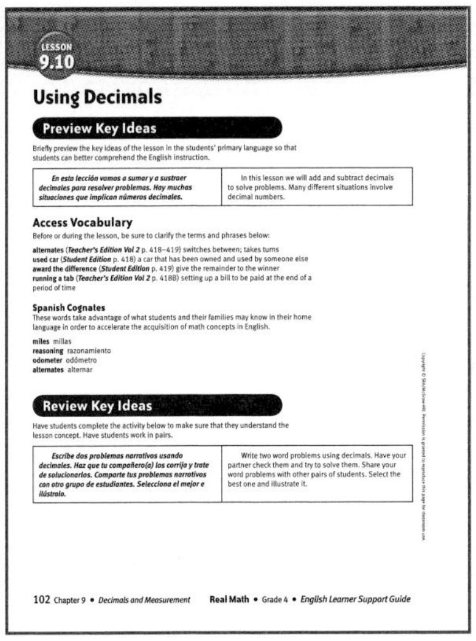
LESSON 9.10
Using Decimals
Preview Key Ideas
Access Vocabulary
Spanish Cognates
Review Key Ideas
102 Chapter 9 • Decimals and Measurement Real Math • Grade 4 • English Learner Support Guide

English Learner Lesson 9.10

### ENRICH

**If . . .** students are proficient in the lesson concepts,

**Then . . .** emphasize additional game time.

### PRACTICE

**If . . .** students would benefit from additional practice,

**Then . . .** extend Skill Practice before assigning the student pages.

### RETEACH

**If . . .** students have difficulty understanding addition and subtraction of decimals in word problems,

**Then . . .** extend Strategy Building before assigning the student pages.

**Vocabulary**
Review from Lesson 3.9: **equation**

**Access Vocabulary**
**award the difference** give the amount obtained by subtracting

**Spanish Cognates**
**odometer** odómetro
**reasoning** razonamiento

# Teaching Lesson 9.10

## Mental Math 5

Review THUMBS UP

Write the numbers 0 and 2 on the board. Present problems, such as the following, in which students show thumbs-up when answers fall within these boundaries and thumbs-down when answers fall outside these boundaries.

**a.** 0.05 + 1.9 up
**b.** 3.01 − 1.02 up
**c.** 8.6 − 7.3 up
**d.** 6.67 − 5.07 up
**e.** 8.66 − 3.04 down
**f.** 0.15 + 0.98 up
**g.** 0.11 + 0.09 up
**h.** 5.07 − 2.50 down

## 1 Develop 20

**Tell Students In Today's Lesson They Will**
add and subtract decimals to solve word problems.

### Skill Practice ENGAGING

Small Group

Game

Model the **Harder Roll a Decimal Game** by having two students play two or three rounds in front of the class. This game provides practice with place value, subtracting and adding decimal numbers, and mathematical reasoning. It provides a legitimate reason to subtract numbers with a different number of decimal places. At first, suggest that games last three rounds. Students may play longer games later on, if they wish.

### Strategy Building UNDERSTANDING

Whole Group

**1.** In order to review adding and subtracting money, create a store within your classroom by placing price tags on various items around the room. The price tags should range from 50¢ to $5. The students will bring the price tags to the "cash register" (a designated area) for each purchase. Write the prices of many of the items as decimals (for example, $1.49, $2.99, $3.25). If items are, for example, 2 for $1, give the students the option of buying 1 item for 50¢. NOTE: There is a "no returns" policy on items purchased.

**2.** Give students a $15 spending limit. Tell them they should try to spend as much as possible as long as it is less than or equal to $15. They will be running a tab at the cash register under their name. The tab sheets should resemble a checkbook register, but should be much simpler.

| Kenya's Tab Sheet | | | |
|---|---|---|---|
| Item | Cost of Item | Balance | Computations |
| Book | $2.25 | $12.75 | 15.00<br>− 2.25<br>12.75 |

As students bring price tags to the cash register, have them write the item name and the cost on their tab sheet. Each student should find their remaining balance before leaving the cash register area to shop. Help students with the arithmetic when needed. Students should take each price tag back to the item it came from so other students can buy that item.

Allow students to purchase whatever they desire as long as they don't run out of credit on their tabs.

**3.** After each student has spent all of his or her money or after a designated time limit, have students take their tab sheets back to their desks. Ask questions such as the following:

- **How did you decide which items to buy?**
- **Knowing what you know now, would you make any changes? Explain.**
- **Were you able to spend your entire tab?**
- **Who came within $1 of spending their entire tab?**

Review any lingering difficulties students might be having with decimal place value and decimal arithmetic.

## 2 Assign Student Pages 30

**Pages 418–419** APPLYING

Small Group

Have students complete page 418 independently or in small groups.

### Monitoring Student Progress

**If . . .** a student is having difficulty adding and subtracting decimal numbers,

**Then . . .** have them use graph paper to help keep place values aligned.

### As Students Finish

Game **Harder Roll a Decimal Game**

Student Page

LESSON 9.10 **Using Decimals**

**Key Ideas**

**Many different situations involve decimal numbers.**

**Use** your skills for working with decimals to solve the following problems.

1. A year ago Jake bought a used car that had traveled 48,927.8 miles. Now the car has traveled 75,485.2 miles.
   a. How many miles has the car traveled in the past year? 26,557.4
   b. How many miles does the car need to travel to reach 100,000 miles? 24,514.8

2. Multistep **Extended Response** Donna wants to ride her bike at least 50 miles every week. At the beginning of the week the odometer on her bike showed 143.6 miles. Now it shows she has ridden 184.8 miles.
   a. How many more miles does she have to ride this week to meet her goal? 8.8
   b. After this week, how many weeks will it take for her odometer to show 300 miles? Explain how you found your answer. 3; $3 \times 50 = 150$; $193.6 + 150 = 343.6$

3. Multistep Steve started with $25.81. Last week he spent $7.50, and he earned $12.75 washing cars. How much money does he have now? $31.06

4. A movie ticket costs $7.25.
   a. How much will 2 tickets cost? $14.50
   b. What will the change be if the 2 tickets were paid for with a $20 bill? $5.50
   c. How much will 4 tickets cost? $29.00

5. Melissa needs 6 pounds of cheese to make queso dip for her party. She bought a package of cheese that weighs 2.2 pounds and one that weighs 2.6 pounds.
   a. How many more pounds of cheese does she need? What number sentences did you use to solve the problem? 1.2; $2.2 + 2.6 = 4.8$, $6.0 - 4.8 = 1.2$
   b. If she buys another package of cheese and it weighs 2.1 pounds, how much will be left over? 0.9 pound

418 eTextbook This lesson is available in the *eTextbook*.

Student Page

# Game

## Harder Roll a Decimal Game

**Players:** Two

**Materials:** ***Number Cubes:*** one 0–5 (red), one 5–10 (blue)

**Object:** To get the greater total score

**Math Focus:** Place value, subtracting decimal numbers, and mathematical reasoning

**HOW TO PLAY**

1. Follow rules 1 through 4 for the **Roll a Decimal Game** on page 397.
2. Subtract the lesser decimal from the greater decimal, and award the difference to the player with the greater decimal.
3. After an agreed upon number of rounds, add your scores.
4. The player with the greater total is the winner.

**SAMPLE GAME**

| Round | Devonte | Airlea | Devonte's score | Airlea's score |
|---|---|---|---|---|
| 1 | 0.76 | 0.966 | | 0.206 |
| 2 | 0.957 | 0.676 | 0.281 | |
| 3 | 0.97775 | 0.9665 | 0.01125 | |
| 4 | 0.8 | 0.9576 | | 0.1576 |
| 5 | 0.99 | 0.866 | 0.124 | |
| 6 | 0.86855 | 0.8875 | | 0.01895 |
| | | Total | 0.41625 | 0.38255 |

After six rounds, Devonte was the winner.

Writing + Math **Journal**

Create a word problem that involves using addition and subtraction of decimals to find the answer.

Answers will vary. See *Teacher's Edition* for possible answers.

Chapter 9 • Lesson 10 eGames This game is available in *eGames*. 419



# 3 Reflect

5

## Guided Discussion REASONING

Whole Group

Discuss the **Harder Roll a Decimal Game** with students. Ask questions such as the following:

- **What is the greatest possible score for one turn in the game?** 0.49999 if one player rolls 0.99999 and the second player rolls 0.5.
- **What is the least possible score that is greater than 0?** 0.00001
- **What strategies did you use for deciding which number to put in a blank?** Answers will vary. One possible answer: the number rolled on the 5–10 *Number Cube* was the number always placed in the tenths place.

## Extended Response REASONING

**Problem 2** Students may mention that, by the end of the week, Donna should have ridden her bike 193.6 miles ($143.6 + 50$). In an additional 3 weeks, Donna should travel a minimum of 343.6 miles ($193.6 + 50 + 50 + 50$).

### Writing + Math Journal

Any word problem involving the addition or subtraction of decimals is acceptable. Have students estimate before solving their problems and check their answers after solving.

**Cumulative Review:** For review of length measurement and addition and subtraction of fractions, assign Problems 1–4 on student page 437.

**Family Involvement:** Assign the ***Practice, Reteach,*** or ***Enrichment*** activities depending on the needs of your students.

Encourage students to play the **Harder Roll a Decimal Game** with a friend or relative.

**Concept/Question Board:** Have students attempt to answer any unanswered questions on the Concept/Question Board.

**Math Puzzler:** Find the pattern in the following sequence of numbers. Then determine the next four numbers to continue the pattern: 1.2, 1.45, 1.15, 1.4, 1.1, 1.35, 1.05, . . . . The pattern alternates from adding 0.25 to subtracting 0.3. The next four numbers are 1.3, 1.0, 1.25, and 0.95.

# 4 Assess and Differentiate

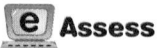

e Assess Use ***eAssess*** to record and analyze evidence of student understanding.

## A Gather Evidence

Use the Daily Class Assessment Records in ***Assessment*** or ***eAssess*** to record daily observations.

### Performance Assessment

**Game**

Did the student ENGAGING

- ❑ pay attention to others' contributions?
- ❑ contribute information and ideas?
- ❑ improve on a strategy?
- ❑ reflect on and check the accuracy of his or her work?

### Informal Assessment

**Concept/Question Board**

Did the student APPLYING

- ❑ apply learning in new situations?
- ❑ contribute concepts?
- ❑ contribute answers?
- ❑ connect mathematics to real-world situations?

## B Summarize Findings

Analyze and summarize assessment data for each student. Determine which Assessment Follow-Up is appropriate for each student. Use the Student Assessment Record in ***Assessment*** or ***eAssess*** to update assessment records.

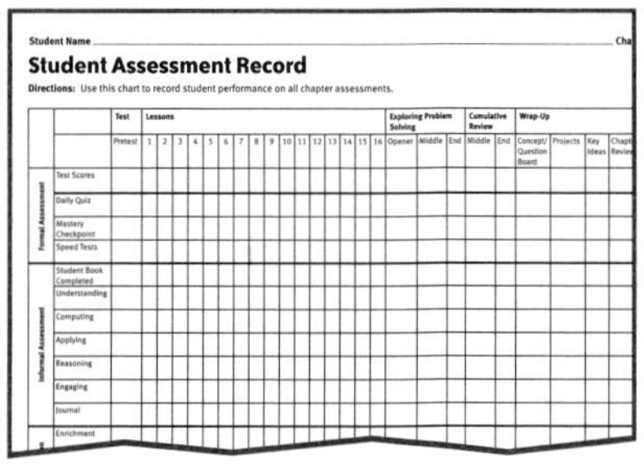


**Assessment Page T41**

## C Assessment Follow-Up • DIFFERENTIATE INSTRUCTION

Based on your observations, use these teaching strategies for assessment follow-up.

### INTERVENTION

Review student performance on ***Intervention*** Lesson 9.C to see if students have mastered prerequisite skills for this lesson.

### ENGLISH LEARNER

**Review**

Use Lesson 9.10 in ***English Learner Support Guide*** to review lesson concepts and vocabulary.

### ENRICH

**If . . .** students are proficient in the lesson concepts,

**Then . . .** encourage them to work on the chapter projects or ***Enrichment*** Lesson 9.10.

LESSON 9.10 Name ______ Date ______

**Using Decimals**

**Continents and Oceans**

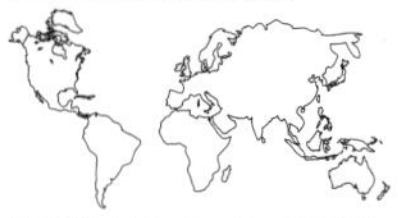

**Use** this information to answer the questions below.

Asia contains 29.5% of Earth's land.
Africa contains 20% of Earth's land.
North America contains 16.3% of Earth's land.
South America contains 11.8% of Earth's land.
Europe contains 6.5% of Earth's land.
Australia contains 5.2% of Earth's land.
Antarctica contains 9.6% of Earth's land.

1. What is the sum of all the percentages listed above? 98.9%
2. Why isn't the total 100% Large islands are missing.
3. What percentage is missing? 1.1%
4. Use an almanac, map, or globe to find the names of two of the many big islands that are missing. Answers will vary. Possible answers include Greenland, New Guinea, Borneo, Madagascar, Honshu, Great Britain, Ellesmere, and Victoria.
5. If land covers 29.2% of Earth's surface, how much of our planet is covered by water? 100 − 29.2 = 70.8%

102 Chapter 9 • *Decimals and Measurement* **Real Math** • Grade 4 • *Enrichment Support Guide*

**Enrichment Lesson 9.10**

### PRACTICE

**If . . .** students would benefit from additional practice,

**Then . . .** assign ***Practice*** Lesson 9.10.

LESSON 9.10 Name ______ Date ______

**Using Decimals**

**Solve the following problems.**

1. A 24-ounce jar of peanut butter costs $3.49. A 16-ounce jar of peanut butter costs $2.69. How much more does the 24-ounce jar cost than the 16-ounce jar? $0.80
2. Ms. Williamson bought a skirt for $34.98 and a blouse for $19.99. How much did Ms. Williamson spend altogether? $54.97
3. The DiFlorio family planned to drive 482 kilometers the first day of their vacation. They drove 135.6 kilometers before breakfast and 189.8 kilometers after breakfast. How much farther do they have to drive? 156.6 kilometers
4. On his first try, Bryce threw a softball 20.38 meters. On his second try he threw it 24.67 meters. How much farther did Bryce throw the softball on the second try? 4.29 meters
5. Marjan had $4,136.78 in her checking account. She then wrote a check for $23.45 and made a deposit of $135.75. How much is in Marjan's checking account now? $4,249.08
6. Before Ms. Diaz went on a business trip, the odometer on her car showed 27,274.9 kilometers. After her trip it showed 28,109.4 kilometers. How many kilometers did she drive? 834.5 kilometers

102 Chapter 9 • *Decimals and Measurement* **Real Math** • Grade 4 • *Practice*

**Practice Lesson 9.10**

### RETEACH

**If . . .** students have difficulty understanding addition and subtraction of decimals submerged in word problems,

**Then . . .** have them turn notebook paper sideways so that the lines form columns. Have students use grocery ads for local stores to make out a shopping list. Then have them add the total cost of all the items. They can also try to limit themselves to a $50 or $100 budget and determine how close they came to their limit.

# Balancing a Checkbook

**Context of the Lesson** This is the third of three lessons on decimals and their applications. The most common example of addition and subtraction of decimals is the ledger in a checking account. Most students are familiar with the basics of checking accounts, although they may not know the terminology.

See page 382B for Math Background for teachers for this lesson.

## Objectives

- To provide realistic problems and practice in adding and subtracting monetary amounts
- To introduce the skill of maintaining and balancing a checking account

## NCTM Standards

**Connections**
Recognize and apply mathematics in contexts outside of mathematics

**Representation**
Create and use representation to organize, record, and communicate mathematical ideas

**Word Problems**
Solve word problems

## Materials

- *Play money (optional)
- *Counters (optional)
- Sample check stubs (optional)
- Sample check registers (optional)
- Sample checking account statements (optional)
- **Checkbook** and **Harder Checkbook Game Mats**
- **Transaction Game Mat (optional)**

## Technology

**Presentation** Lesson 9.11
**MathTools** Spreadsheet

## Test Prep

**Cumulative Review**
Mental Math reviews adding and subtracting decimal numbers as money (Lesson 9.9).

**Multistep Problems**
Problems 5, 11, and 14

**Extended Response**
Problem 13

**Writing + Math**
Journal

*Manipulative Kit Item

## Planning for Learning • DIFFERENTIATE INSTRUCTION

### INTERVENTION

**If . . .** students lack the prerequisite skill of multiplying any two numbers,

**Then . . .** teach ***Intervention*** Lesson 9.C.

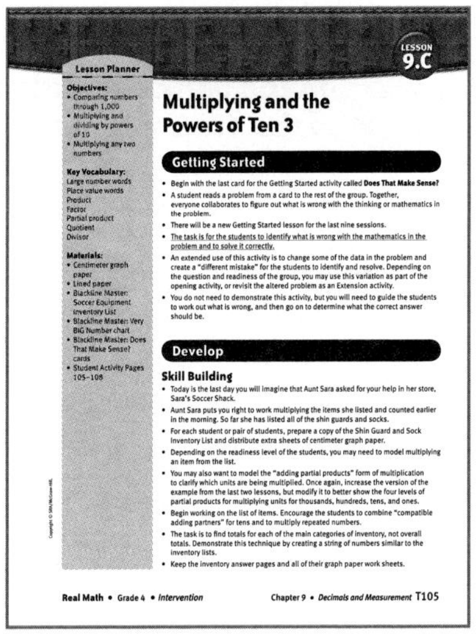


Intervention Lesson 9.C

### ENGLISH LEARNER

Preview

**If . . .** students need language support

**Then . . .** use Lesson 9.11 in ***English Learner Support Guide*** to preview lesson concepts and vocabulary.

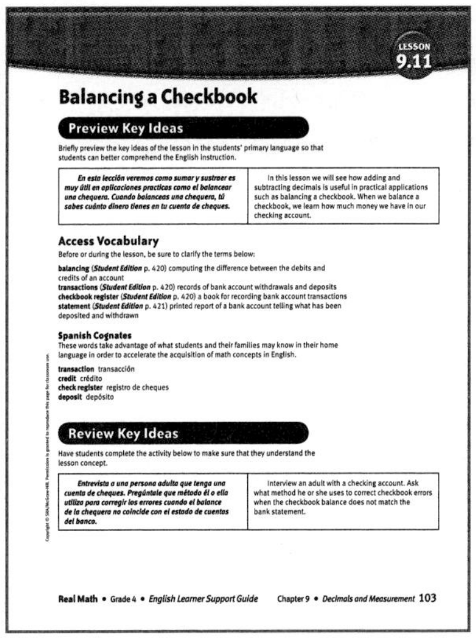


English Learner Lesson 9.11

### ENRICH

**If . . .** students are proficient in the lesson concepts,

**Then . . .** have them play the **Transaction Game Mat.**

### PRACTICE

**If . . .** students would benefit from additional practice,

**Then . . .** extend Strategy Building before assigning student pages.

### RETEACH

**If . . .** students have difficulty understanding addition and subtraction of decimals,

**Then . . .** extend Using Student Pages before assigning the student pages.

### Vocabulary

**deposit \di pä′ zət\ *v.*** to place money in a bank
**withdraw \with drô′\ *v.*** to remove money from a bank

### Access Vocabulary

**balance** compute the difference between the debits and credits of an account
**statement** printed report of a bank account

### Spanish Cognates

**transaction** transacción
**credit** crédito
**check register** regístro de cheques
**deposit** depósito

## Mental Math

5

THUMBS UP

Present exercises, such as the following, that involve monetary amounts. Have students respond with thumbs-down if the answer is obviously wrong and thumbs-up if it is possibly correct.

**a.** $3.16 + $4.37 = $9.53 down
**b.** $4.99 − $2.49 = $2.50 up
**c.** $2.08 + $0.83 = $10.15 down
**d.** $3.98 + $2.00 = $5.98 up
**e.** $4.16 − $0.45 = $1.03 down
**f.** $8.64 − $3.22 = $11.17 down

## 1 Develop

20

### Tell Students In Today's Lesson They Will

learn to maintain a checkbook register by adding and subtracting decimals.

### Strategy Building

ENGAGING

Small Group

Demonstrate the **Checkbook** and **Harder Checkbook Game Mats** by asking two or three students to play in front of the class. These games provide practice with adding and subtracting multidigit numbers and with maintaining a record of monetary transactions.

### Using Student Pages

UNDERSTANDING

Whole Group

Since students will need to be clear on the generic format of a checkbook register, this lesson should be taught with student books open to pages 420 and 421.

#### Student Page 420

Discuss page 420 with the class. Confirm that students understand what a checking account is and how it works. Go over the meaning of each entry on page 420, and have students verify that each calculation on the sample check register is correct. Ask questions such as the following:

- **A deposit means money is added to the account. Should Ms. Taylor add or subtract the deposit from her previous balance?** add
- **Did she add correctly?** yes
- **Should the rent payment be added or subtracted?** subtracted
- **Did she subtract correctly?** yes

Work through the problems on page 420 with the students, making note that Problem 3 is for an entry that is not recorded on this checkbook register.

#### Student Page 421

Explain that the bank also keeps records of Ms. Taylor's account and sends her a summary or statement of these records each month.

Show students sample checks, stubs, or checkbook registers, if possible. Review Ms. Taylor's checkbook on page 421. Ask questions such as the following:

- **What is the difference in the end-of-month balances shown on the bank's records and Ms. Taylor's records?** $166.38
- **Is the error in the number of dollars or cents?** both
- **Is it necessary to check all the arithmetic to find the error?** It is not necessary but may often be the first choice people use to find errors in their checkbooks.
- **Can anyone think of a shortcut?** Possible answers: Check to see if the last digit is correct because that may indicate the error; estimate answers to look for one that is obviously wrong; use a calculator.

# 2 Assign Student Pages

30

## Pages 420–421

UNDERSTANDING

Have students find the error in Ms. Taylor's checkbook on page 421, using estimation or another method to help them avoid doing more work than necessary. Also, have the students complete the rest of the problems on page 421.

| CHECK # | DATE | TRANSACTION | DEBIT | CREDIT | BALANCE |
|---|---|---|---|---|---|
| | | | | | 907.13 |
| D | 1-3 | Deposit | | 649.39 | +649.39 |
| | | | | | 1556.52 |
| 109 | 1-3 | Star Realty Co. | 475.00 | | –475.00 |
| | | Rent | | | 1081.52 |
| ATM | 1-8 | CASH | 50.00 | | –50.00 |
| | | | | | 1031.52 |
| 110 | 1-12 | Watts Power Co. | 83.19 | | –83.19 |
| | | Electrictity | | | 948.33 |
| 111 | 1-14 | Betty's Boutique | 34.26 | | –34.26 |
| | | Pants | | | 914.07 |
| 112 | 1-16 | Clothing Mart | 110.85 | | –110.85 |
| | | Jacket | | | 803.22 |
| 113 | 1-28 | Terrific Travel Agency | 107.00 | | –107.00 |
| | | Bus tickets | | | 696.22 |
| D | 1-30 | Deposit | | 649.39 | +649.39 |
| | | | | | 1345.61 |
| 114 | 2-3 | Star Realty Co. | 475.00 | | –475.00 |
| | | Rent | | | 870.61 |
| D | 2-6 | Watts Power Co. | | 23.78 | +23.78 |
| | | Refund for Overcharge | | | 894.39 |

Student Page

LESSON 9.11

# Balancing a Checkbook

## Key Ideas

**Adding and subtracting decimals is useful in practical applications, such as balancing a checkbook.**

Many people keep money in personal checking accounts. They use addition and subtraction after each transaction to record how much money they have in their account.

Whenever Ms. Taylor pays with a check or debit card, or makes a withdrawal from her checking account, she keeps a record of the transaction in her checkbook register. This helps her keep track of how much money she has in her checking account.

Ms. Taylor keeps the record of each transaction in a check register. Look at this check register to see what information is on it.

| CHECK | DATE | TRANSACTION | DEBIT | CREDIT | BALANCE |
|---|---|---|---|---|---|
| | | | | | 907 13 |
| D | 1-3-06 | Deposit | | 649 39 | + 649 39 |
| | | | | | 1556 52 |
| 109 | 1-3 | Star Realty Co. | 475 00 | | −475 00 |
| | | Rent | | | 1081 52 |

**Solve** the following.

1. Why did Ms. Taylor use a *D* in the Check column? deposit
2. What does the word *debit* mean? something paid out
3. How much was Ms. Taylor's deposit on February 21, 2006? Unknown; her only credit was on 1–3–06
4. On what date was Ms. Taylor's only deposit made? January 3, 2006



Textbook This lesson is available in the *eTextbook*.

Student Page

Every month Ms. Taylor gets a statement from her bank. The statement shows the bank's records of her account.

Her statement for January said that Ms. Taylor had $907.13 in her account on January 3, and $1,345.61 at the end of the month. This did not agree with her records.

| CHECK | DATE | TRANSACTION | DEBIT | CREDIT | BALANCE |
|---|---|---|---|---|---|
| | | | | | 907 13 |
| D | 1-3 | Deposit | | 649 39 | + 649 39 |
| | | | | | 1556 52 |
| 109 | 1-3 | Star Realty Co. | 475 00 | | − 475 00 |
| | | Rent | | | 1081 52 |
| ATM | 1-8 | CASH | 50 00 | | − 50 00 |
| | | | | | 1031 52 |
| 110 | 1-12 | Watts Power Co. | 83 19 | | − 83 19 |
| | | electricity | | | 1114 71 |
| 111 | 1-14 | Betty's Boutique | 34 26 | | − 34 26 |
| | | Pants | | | 1080 45 |
| 112 | 1-16 | Clothing Mart | 110 85 | | − 110 85 |
| | | Jacket | | | 969 60 |
| 113 | 1-28 | Terrific Travel Agency | 107 00 | | − 107 00 |
| | | bus tickets | | | 862 60 |
| D | 1-30 | Deposit | | 649 39 | + 649 39 |
| | | | | | 1511 99 |

**Refer** to Ms. Taylor's checkbook register above to solve the following problem.

Multistep

5. Did Ms. Taylor make an error in her calculations? If she did, correct the error and all following entries so that her records show the same balance at the end of the month as the bank statement shows. Check #110 has the error.
6. If Ms. Taylor's new balance is $1345.61 and the next transaction is her rent for February, what will her new balance be? (Assume the rent has not increased or decreased since January.) $870.61
7. On February 6, Ms. Taylor received a check in the mail from Watts Power Company stating that she had overpaid on her gas and electric bill. Ms. Taylor deposited the check for $23.78 into her checking account. What is her new balance? $894.39

# Teaching Lesson 9.11

## Assign Student Pages, continued

### Pages 422–423 UNDERSTANDING

Have students complete pages 422–423 independently. For Problem 14, it might help to have students create their own register to keep track of each transaction. Be sure to allow at least 10–15 minutes for students to play the **Checkbook** or **Harder Checkbook Game Mat.**

#### Monitoring Student Progress

**If . . .** students have difficulty deciding whether to add or subtract,

**Then . . .** have each student create a two-column chart listing examples of credits and debits.

### As Students Finish

Game **Checkbook** or **Harder Checkbook Game Mats**

Student Page

LESSON 9.11 • Balancing a Checkbook

**Solve** each problem.

8. Karen opened a new checking account with $150. She wrote a check for $57.14 to pay her satellite television bill. Then she wrote a check for $67.09 to pay for groceries. Does she have enough money left in her checking account to withdraw $30 in cash? no
9. Dr. Xiang made a deposit of $215.81 to her checking account. That gave her a balance of $403.05. How much money did Dr. Xiang have in her account before she made the deposit? $187.24
10. Jared wrote a check in the amount of $28.46 for two CDs. He wrote another check for $42.69 to pay for a new sweatshirt. Jared's original balance was $116.39. What is his new balance? $45.24
11. Multistep Michael had $507.08 in his checking account. He made a deposit for $325.00 and then wrote one check for $106.88 and another check for $75. What is his new balance? $650.20
12. Yesterday Phillipe wrote a check for $18.45. This morning he withdrew $40.00. His new balance is $97.88.
    a. What was his balance before both of these transactions? $156.33
    b. If Phillipe wants to bring his new balance to $100, how much money should he deposit into his checking account? $2.12

422

eTextbook This lesson is available in the *eTextbook.*

Student Page

When writing entries in his checkbook, Bill always rounds the entries by dropping the cents. For example, when he needs to make a payment of $43.98, he records $43 as the amount for the check in his checkbook. Bill would record a deposit to his account of $97.01 as $97.

13. Extended Response Because Bill does this both for deposits to his account and for checks he writes, he thinks that his account should balance out in the end. Do you think it should? Why or why not?

13. No; he probably makes fewer deposits than payments or withdrawals; his cents won't be the same for the deposits and withdrawals.

One month Bill made deposits in the following amounts: $416.20, $416.20, and $98.80.

He also wrote checks in the following amounts: $7.83, $59.46, $12.50, $25.00, $241.10, $17.69, $50.00, $28.54, $25.00, $16.58, $57.43, $247.56, $73.12, $57.34, and $10.00.

14. Multistep Assume Bill started with a balance of $100 in his checking account.
    a. What should his balance be at the end of the month? $102.05
    b. What would Bill think his balance is? $106
15. If Bill continues this process for the entire year, what problem situations might he encounter?

15. Possible answer: he may not have the money he thought was in his account and may overdraw.

Writing + Math **Journal**

Explain why it is a good idea to record transactions in a checkbook. Answers will vary. Refer to the *Teacher's Edition* for possible answers.

Chapter 9 • Lesson 11 423

## 3 Reflect

5

### Guided Discussion REASONING

Whole Group

Discuss the **Harder Checkbook Game Mat** with students. Ask questions such as the following:

- **What is the greatest possible score you could get playing this game without going backward?** 1,362.21, which can be arrived at by landing on the following squares: 4, 8, 13, 16, 20, 25, 27, and Finish
- **What is the least amount of turns you could take before losing all $1,000?** 10 turns will exhaust the $1,000 by landing on the following squares: 2, 5, 9, 10, 12, 15, 17, 22, 26, and 30.
- **How did the checkbook register help you in adding and subtracting numbers?** Answers will vary. One possibility is that it helped keep the numbers organized.

### Extended Response

**Problem 13** The balance at the end of the month will probably not be correct. Students' answers will vary as to why this is; one possible answer is the amount of cents that are dropped from the deposits will likely not equal the amount of cents taken from a withdrawal.

### Writing + Math Journal

Students' answers will vary. One possibility is that it is a good way to keep track of the amount of money you have.

---

SOCIAL STUDIES **Curriculum Connection:** Students interested in money may enjoy researching money from other countries or the history of money. (Paper currency was first used in 806 A.D. in China.)

Review **Cumulative Review:** For review of division with remainders, assign Problems 5–10 on student page 437.

**Family Involvement:** Assign the ***Practice, Reteach,*** or ***Enrichment*** activities depending on the needs of your students.

Encourage students to play the **Harder Roll a Decimal Game** with a friend or relative.

**Concept/Question Board:** Have students attempt to answer any unanswered questions on the Concept/Question Board.

**Math Puzzler:** In the equation $4.AB + A.99 = 1B.A2$, $A$ and $B$ stand for different digits. Find the value of $A$ and $B$ so that the equation is correct. A = 8 and B = 3

# 4 Assess and Differentiate

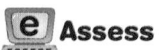

**eAssess** Use ***eAssess*** to record and analyze evidence of student understanding.

## A Gather Evidence

Use the Daily Class Assessment Records in ***Assessment*** or ***eAssess*** to record daily observations.

### Informal Assessment
**Mental Math**

Did the student COMPUTING
- ❑ respond accurately?
- ❑ respond quickly?
- ❑ respond with confidence?
- ❑ self-correct?

### Informal Assessment
**Student Pages**

Did the student UNDERSTANDING
- ❑ make important observations?
- ❑ extend or generalize learning?
- ❑ provide insightful answers?
- ❑ pose insightful questions?

## B Summarize Findings

Analyze and summarize assessment data for each student. Determine which Assessment Follow-Up is appropriate for each student. Use the Student Assessment Record in ***Assessment*** or ***eAssess*** to update assessment records.

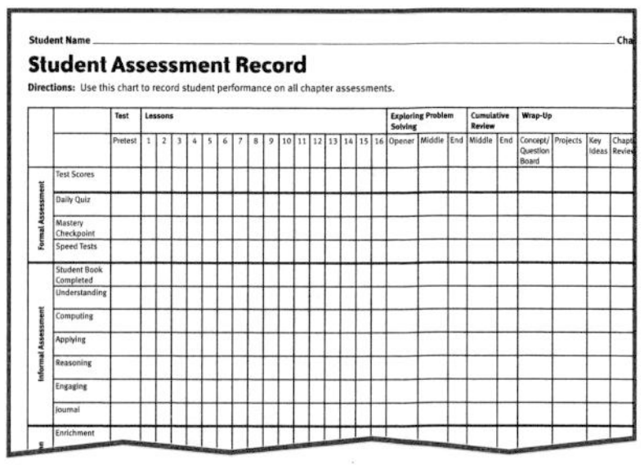


**Assessment Page T41**

## C Assessment Follow-Up • DIFFERENTIATING INSTRUCTION

Based on your observations, use these teaching strategies for assessment follow-up.

### INTERVENTION

Review student performance on ***Intervention*** Lesson 9.C to see if students have mastered prerequisite skills for this lesson.

### ENGLISH LEARNER

**Review**

Use Lesson 9.11 in ***English Learner Support Guide*** to preview lesson concepts and vocabulary.

### ENRICH

**If . . .** students are proficient in the lesson concepts,

**Then . . .** encourage them to work on the chapter projects or ***Enrichment*** Lesson 9.11.

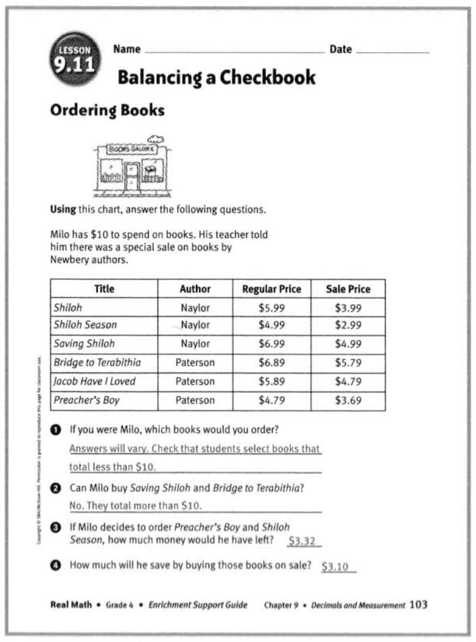

LESSON 9.11 Name ______ Date ______

**Balancing a Checkbook**

**Ordering Books**

**Using** this chart, answer the following questions.

Milo has $10 to spend on books. His teacher told him there was a special sale on books by Newbery authors.

| Title | Author | Regular Price | Sale Price |
|---|---|---|---|
| *Shiloh* | Naylor | $5.99 | $3.99 |
| *Shiloh Season* | Naylor | $4.99 | $2.99 |
| *Saving Shiloh* | Naylor | $6.99 | $4.99 |
| *Bridge to Terabithia* | Paterson | $6.89 | $5.79 |
| *Jacob Have I Loved* | Paterson | $5.89 | $4.79 |
| *Preacher's Boy* | Paterson | $4.79 | $3.69 |

1. If you were Milo, which books would you order? Answers will vary. Check that students select books that total less than $10.
2. Can Milo buy *Saving Shiloh* and *Bridge to Terabithia*? No. They total more than $10.
3. If Milo decides to order *Preacher's Boy* and *Shiloh Season*, how much money would he have left? $3.32
4. How much will he save by buying those books on sale? $3.10

Real Math • Grade 4 • *Enrichment Support Guide* Chapter 9 • *Decimals and Measurement* 103

Enrich Lesson 9.11

### PRACTICE

**If . . .** students would benefit from additional practice,

**Then . . .** assign ***Practice*** Lesson 9.11.

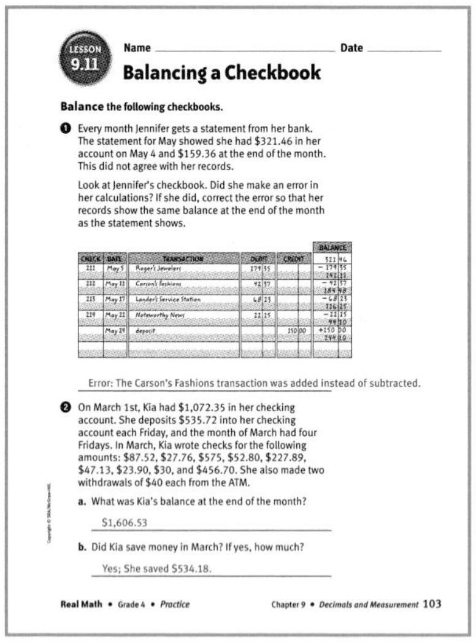

LESSON 9.11 Name ______ Date ______

**Balancing a Checkbook**

**Balance** the following checkbooks.

1. Every month Jennifer gets a statement from her bank. The statement for May showed she had $321.46 in her account on May 4 and $159.36 at the end of the month. This did not agree with her records.

   Look at Jennifer's checkbook. Did she make an error in her calculations? If she did, correct the error so that her records show the same balance at the end of the month as the statement shows.

| CHECK | DATE | TRANSACTION | DEBIT | CREDIT | BALANCE |
|---|---|---|---|---|---|
| | | | | | 321.46 |
| 211 | May 5 | Roger's Jewelers | 179.35 | | − 179.35 / 142.11 |
| 212 | May 11 | Carson's Fashions | 42.37 | | − 42.37 / 184.48 |
| 213 | May 17 | Lander's Service Station | 68.23 | | − 68.23 / 116.25 |
| 214 | May 22 | Noteworthy News | 22.15 | | − 22.15 / 94.10 |
| | May 29 | deposit | | 150.00 | + 150.00 / 244.10 |

   Error: The Carson's Fashions transaction was added instead of subtracted.

2. On March 1st, Kia had $1,072.35 in her checking account. She deposits $535.72 into her checking account each Friday, and the month of March had four Fridays. In March, Kia wrote checks for the following amounts: $87.52, $27.76, $575, $52.80, $227.89, $47.13, $23.90, $30, and $456.70. She also made two withdrawals of $40 each from the ATM.
   a. What was Kia's balance at the end of the month? $1,606.53
   b. Did Kia save money in March? If yes, how much? Yes; She saved $534.18.

Real Math • Grade 4 • *Practice* Chapter 9 • *Decimals and Measurement* 103

Practice Lesson 9.11

### RETEACH

**If . . .** students have difficulty understanding addition and subtraction of decimals,

**Then . . .** consider inviting a local bank employee to present banking information to the class, including how to fill out a ledger.

## Lesson Planner

**OBJECTIVES**
- To demonstrate how to find the product of a decimal and a whole number
- To provide practice with multiplying a decimal by a whole number

**NCTM STANDARDS**

**Number and Operations**
Understand meanings of operations and how they relate to one another

**Connections**
Understand how mathematical ideas interconnect and build on one another to produce a coherent whole

**TECHNOLOGY**

**e Presentation** Lesson 9.12
**e MathTools** Calculator

**MATERIALS**
- ***Response Wheels**
- *Calculators
- Graph paper (optional)
- ***Number Cubes** (one 0–5, one 5–10)

**TEST PREP**

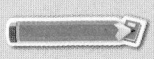

**Cumulative Review**
Mental Math reviews rational number equivalents (Lessons 9.1 and 9.2).

**Extended Response**
Problem 18

**Writing + Math**
Journal

*Manipulative Kit Item

# Multiplying by a Whole Number

**Context of the Lesson** This lesson teaches students the steps to take when multiplying a decimal by a whole number. Students have multiplied multidigit numbers in Grade 3 as well as earlier in this grade. Multiplication of two decimals will be introduced in Grade 5.

See page 382B for Math Background for teachers for this lesson.

## Planning for Learning • DIFFERENTIATE INSTRUCTION

### INTERVENTION

**If . . .** students lack the prerequisite skill of multiplying any two numbers,

**Then . . .** teach ***Intervention*** Lesson 9.C.

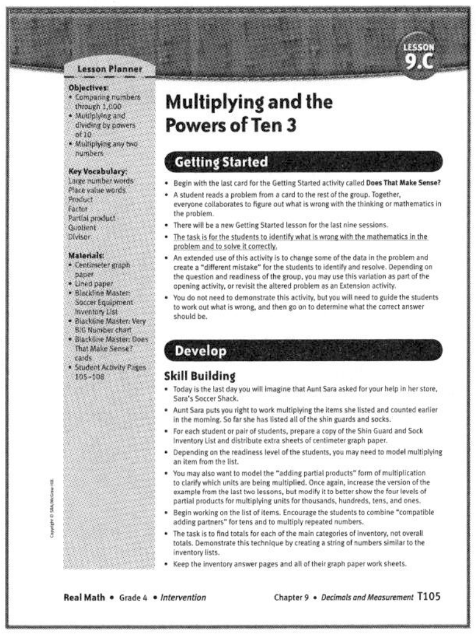


Intervention Lesson 9.C

### ENGLISH LEARNER

Preview

**If . . .** students need language support,

**Then . . .** use Lesson 9.12 in ***English Learner Support Guide*** to preview lesson concepts and vocabulary.

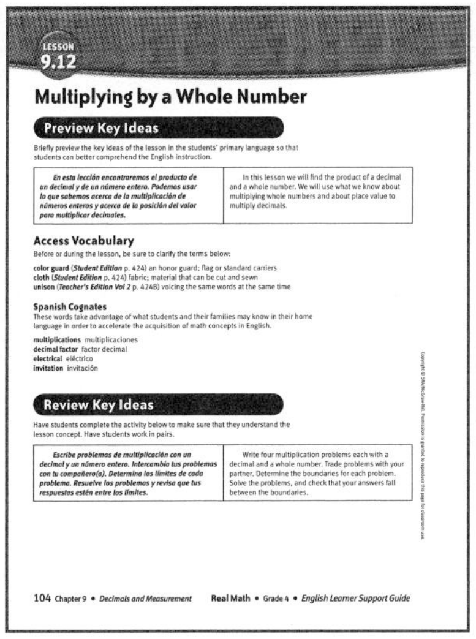


English Learner Lesson 9.12

### ENRICH

**If . . .** students are proficient in the lesson concepts,

**Then . . .** emphasize additional game time.

### PRACTICE

**If . . .** students would benefit from additional practice,

**Then . . .** extend Using Student Pages before assigning the student pages.

### RETEACH

**If . . .** students have difficulty understanding multiplication of a decimal by a whole number,

**Then . . .** extend Using Student Pages before assigning the student pages.

**Vocabulary**
Review from Lesson 3.1:
**product**

**Access Vocabulary**
**cloth** fabric that can be cut and sewn into clothes or other things

**Spanish Cognates**
**multiplication** multiplicación
**decimal factor** factor decimal

# Teaching Lesson 9.12

## Mental Math 5

Review · RESPONSE WHEEL

Present students with problems such as the following. Have them estimate if the decimal or fraction is closer to 0, 50% ($\frac{1}{2}$), or 1 by using the slide wheel on their ***Response Wheels.***

**a.** 0.79 1
**b.** 0.44 50%
**c.** 0.55 50%
**d.** 0.09 0
**e.** $\frac{3}{8}$ 50%
**f.** $\frac{9}{10}$ 1
**g.** 0.15 0
**h.** 0.006 0
**i.** $\frac{1}{2}$ 50%
**j.** $\frac{99}{100}$ 1

## 1 Develop 20

**Tell Students In Today's Lesson They Will**
find the product of a decimal and a whole number.

### Strategy Building ENGAGING

Small Group

Game

Model how to play the **Decimal Roll a Problem Game** by having two students play two or three rounds in front of the class. This game provides practice in multiplying a decimal by a whole number and in mathematical reasoning. Review any lingering difficulties students might have with the multiplication of a decimal by a whole number.

### Skill Practice COMPUTING

Whole Group

Review · RESPONSE WHEEL

Have students find the product to multidigit multiplication problems such as the following:

**a.** 12 × 11 = 132
**b.** 48 × 24 = 1,152
**c.** 88 × 16 = 1,408
**d.** 89 × 17 = 1,513
**e.** 60 × 31 = 1,860
**f.** 36 × 27 = 972

### Using Student Pages UNDERSTANDING

Whole Group

Review page 424 carefully with the class.

It is an excellent idea to first start with students estimating any time they need to find the product of two or more numbers, especially if any of the numbers are decimals.

For example, in Key Ideas the students need to find the product of 1.3 and 21. The boundaries for the product are 20 (1 × 20) and 60 (2 × 30), so the answer should fall somewhere between 20 and 60 (closer to 20). This will allow the students to see *obviously* wrong answers (for example, 273, which is 13 × 21).

Find the boundaries of examples such as the following:

- 1.23 × 5 Possible boundaries are 5 and 10.
- 1.23 × 23 Possible boundaries are 20 and 60.
- 1.23 × 358 Possible boundaries are 300 and 800.
- 7,198 × 0.09 Possible boundaries are 630 and 270; 0.09 is close to $\frac{1}{10}$ so it would be 7,198 × $\frac{1}{10}$.
- 82 × 0.48 An estimate would be about 41 because 0.48 is almost 50%.

**NOTE:** It is also important to remind the students of the Commutative Law of Multiplication. Sometimes students can find a solution more easily when they are able to arrange the factors in a different order.

Have students state a rule for deciding where to place the decimal point in the product. Make sure everyone grasps the rule. Have students tell how many places to move the decimal point in the answers in examples such as the following:

- 0.23 × 78 2
- 14 × 1.2 1
- 584 × 0.007 3
- 7,198 × 0.9 1
- 1,000 × 0.01 2

Work through Examples 1 and 2 on page 425 with the class. Move your finger along each product from right to left as students count off in unison the number of places to determine where the decimal point belongs.

# 2 Assign Student Pages 30

## Pages 424–425 APPLYING

Have students complete the bottom of page 425 independently. Remind them to estimate the product first. This will help them detect obviously wrong answers.

### Monitoring Student Progress

| If . . . | Then . . . |
|---|---|
| **If . . .** students commit frequent errors in multiplication due to misalignment of digits, | **Then . . .** have them perform their calculations on graph paper so that they may use the grid to align their partial products. |
| **If . . .** students get unreasonable answers to decimal multiplication problems, | **Then . . .** have them get a sense of the magnitude of the potential answer by rounding the decimal numbers and then multiplying the resulting whole numbers. |

Student Page

LESSON 9.12 **Multiplying by a Whole Number**

### Key Ideas

**You can use what you know about place value and multiplying whole numbers and decimals.**

Jenny is making 21 flags for her school's Color Guard. Each flag takes 1.3 meters of cloth. What is the total length of cloth Jenny needs?

To find out, you would multiply 1.3 by 21.

Chad told Jenny that $1.3 \times 21$ was 27.3.

Can that be right? Why or why not?

You could do the problem using decimeters. Multiply 13 by 21.

$$\begin{array}{r} 13 \\ \times\ 21 \\ \hline 13 \\ 26\ \ \\ \hline 273 \end{array}$$

273 dm = 27.3 m

So Jenny needs 27.3 meters of cloth. Chad was right.
$21 \times 1.3 = 27.3$

Let's look at the two multiplications side by side.

$$\begin{array}{r} 13 \\ \times\ 21 \\ \hline 13 \\ 26\ \ \\ \hline 273 \end{array} \qquad \begin{array}{r} 1.3 \\ \times\ 21 \\ \hline 13 \\ 26\ \ \\ \hline 27.3 \end{array}$$

The problems and the answers are the same except for the decimal point.

Can you figure out a simple rule for deciding where to put the decimal point in the answer?

Put the decimal point in the answer as many places from the right as it is in the decimal factor.

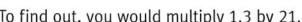

Textbook This lesson is available in the *eTextbook*.

Student Page

To multiply a decimal by a whole number:

1. Estimate the product.
2. Multiply as you would with two whole numbers.
3. Put the decimal point in the answer as many places from the right as it is in the decimal factor.

**Example 1:** $514 \times 2.3$

If we estimate the product we know the answer will be between 1,000 ($500 \times 2$) and 1,800 ($600 \times 3$).

$$\begin{array}{r} 5\ 1\ 4 \\ \times\ 2.3 \\ \hline 1542 \\ +\ 1028\ \ \\ \hline 1182.2 \end{array}$$

Multiply as you would with two whole numbers.

The decimal point is one place from the right. So, place the decimal point one place from the right in the answer.

**Example 2:** $0.24 \times 79$

If we estimate the product, we know the answer will be approximately 20 (estimate about 25% of 80).

$$\begin{array}{r} 0.24 \\ \times\ 79 \\ \hline 216 \\ +\ 168\ \ \\ \hline 18.96 \end{array}$$

Multiply as you would with two whole numbers.

The decimal point is two places from the right in 0.24. So, in the answer, place the decimal point two places from the right.

**Estimate** the product, then multiply.

1. $3.07 \times 11$ 33.77
2. $0.83 \times 22$ 18.26
3. $7{,}198 \times 0.09$ 647.82
4. $385 \times 1.2$ 462
5. $82 \times 0.03$ 2.46
6. $97.8 \times 79$ 7,726.2
7. $6.8 \times 13$ 88.4
8. $39 \times 2.25$ 87.75
9. $2.36 \times 1{,}528$ 3,606.08
10. $0.25 \times 12$ 3

# Assign Student Pages, continued

### Pages 426–427 APPLYING

Have students complete page 426 independently.

### As Students Finish

Games ✓ **Decimal Roll a Problem Game**

Student Page



Remember, if we estimate the product we know the answer will be between 40 (4 × 10) and 100 (5 × 20).

$$\begin{array}{r} 4.07 \\ \times\ 12 \\ \hline 814 \\ +\ 407\ \\ \hline 48.84 \end{array}$$

4.07 — The decimal point is two places from the right.

48.84 — Place the decimal point two places from the right.

**Estimate** the product, then multiply.

11. 256 × 1.2 307.2
12. 617 × 2.5 1,542.5
13. 451 × 82.3 37,117.3
14. 112 × 4.92 551.04
15. 673 × 5.6 3,768.8

**Solve** these problems.

16. Bart is the manager of a baseball team. His team needs 13 new shirts. Each shirt costs $7.29. Bart has $75.
    a. Does he have enough money? no
    b. If not, how much more money does Bart need? $19.77
17. Myrna wants to buy 2 shelves. One is 3 meters long, and the other is 4 meters long. Each shelf costs $4.05 per meter. How much will the 2 shelves cost? $28.35
18. Extended Response Mr. Washington is building a house. He needs 27 electrical outlets. Each outlet costs $2.71. Will the 27 outlets cost more than $100 altogether? Explain how you found your answer.
19. The Omega Publishing Company ships an average of 751 books each week. It costs 48¢ to mail each book. How much does mailing cost, on average, each week? $360.48
20. Eric needs to buy stamps to send 21 party invitations. Each stamp costs 37¢. Eric has $7.75. Does he have enough money to buy stamps for all of the invitations? no

18. No; explanations will vary. See *Teacher's Edition* for possible answers.

Writing + Math **Journal**

Will the product of a decimal number less than one and a whole number be greater than or less than the original numbers? Why? Give an example to support your answer.

The number will be less. See *Teacher's Edition* for possible answers.



Textbook This lesson is available in the ***eTextbook***.

Student Page

Game

## Decimal Roll a Problem Game

**Players:** Two

**Materials:** ***Number Cube:*** one 0–5 (red)

**Object:** To get the greatest product

**Math Focus:** Multiplication of one- and two-digit decimal numbers and whole numbers, place value, and mathematical reasoning.

**HOW TO PLAY**

1. Use blanks to outline a multiplication problem on your paper, like this:

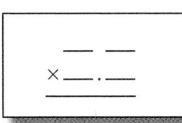

   __ __
   × __ . __
   _______

2. The first player will roll the ***Number Cube*** four times.
3. Each time the ***Number Cube*** is rolled, write that number in one of the blanks on your outline.
4. When all of the blanks have been filled in, find the product of the two numbers.
5. The player with the greatest product wins the round.

**Other Ways To Play the Game:**

- Try to get the least product.
- Move the decimal so the second number is a decimal number in the hundredths place.
- Use a 5–10 ***Number Cube***. If you roll a 10, roll again.



Games This game is available in ***eGames.***

## 3 Reflect

5

### Guided Discussion

Have students find the product of problems such as the following:

**a.** $127 \times 0.007 = 0.889$

**b.** $1{,}008 \times 0.009 = 9.072$

**c.** $10{,}000 \times 0.0004 = 4$

**d.** $894 \times 0.00006 = 0.05364$

Discuss why students were able to find the product even though they have not practiced working with problems beyond the hundredths. Without the decimal point, the problems are the same as multiplying multidigit numbers by single-digit numbers.

### Extended Response

**Problem 18** One possibility is that we know Mr. Washington will not spend $100 for 27 electrical outlets because if we round $2.71 to $3 and round 27 to 30, we know the product would be $3 \times 30 = 90 < 100$

Writing + Math **Journal**

Students should see that the product of a decimal that is less than 1 and a whole number is less than the whole number in the equation. The reason, just like when multiplying fractions, is that a decimal is less than a whole. Thus when multiplying by a part of a whole number, the product will result in a number less than the whole number in the equation. Notice that when a whole number is multiplied by 1, the product is always going to be that number. If a number is multiplied by a number less than 1, the product must be less than the number. Students' examples will vary; one possibility could be $16 \times 0.25 = 4$.

**Cumulative Review:** For review of common multiples and common factors, assign Problems 11–18 on student page 438.

**Family Involvement:** Assign the ***Practice, Reteach,*** or ***Enrichment*** activities depending on the needs of your students. Encourage students to play the **Decimal Roll a Problem Game** with a friend or relative.

**Concept/Question Board:** Have students attempt to answer any unanswered questions on the Concept/Question Board.

**Math Puzzler:** Zhang, Jill, and Winton are friends of different ages. Jill, the friend whose age is in the middle, is the only one whose age is an even number. Zhang is the oldest. The friends' age range is eight years. Their average age is 12, but none of the friends are that age this year. Use the clues to find the age of each friend. Zhang is 17 years old, Jill is 10 years old, and Winton is 9 years old. Another answer is Zhang is 15 years old, Jill is 14 years old, and Winton is 7 years old.

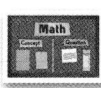

# 4 Assess and Differentiate

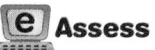

e Assess Use ***eAssess*** to record and analyze evidence of student understanding.

## A Gather Evidence

Use the Daily Class Assessment Records in ***Assessment*** or ***eAssess*** to record daily observations.

### Informal Assessment

**Skill Practice**

Did the student COMPUTING

- ❑ respond accurately?
- ❑ respond quickly?
- ❑ respond with confidence?
- ❑ self-correct?

### Performance Assessment

**Game**

Did the student ENGAGING

- ❑ pay attention to others' contributions?
- ❑ contribute information and ideas?
- ❑ improve on a strategy?
- ❑ reflect on and check the accuracy of his or her work?

## B Summarize Findings

Analyze and summarize assessment data for each student. Determine which Assessment Follow-Up is appropriate for each student. Use the Student Assessment Record in ***Assessment*** or ***eAssess*** to update assessment records.

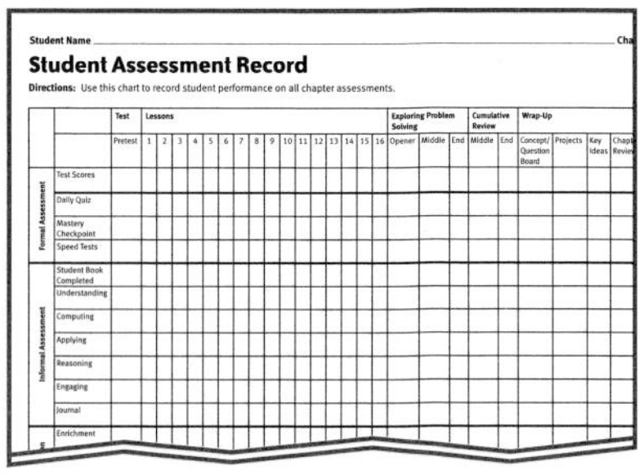


Assessment Page T41

## C Assessment Follow-Up • DIFFERENTIATE INSTRUCTION

Based on your observations, use these teaching strategies for assessment follow-up.

### INTERVENTION

Review student performance on ***Intervention*** Lesson 9.C to see if students have mastered prerequisite skills for this lesson.

### ENGLISH LEARNER

**Review**

Use Lesson 9.12 in ***English Learner Support Guide*** to preview lesson concepts and vocabulary.

### ENRICH

**If . . .** students are proficient in the lesson concepts,

**Then . . .** encourage them to work on the chapter projects or ***Enrichment*** Lesson 9.12.

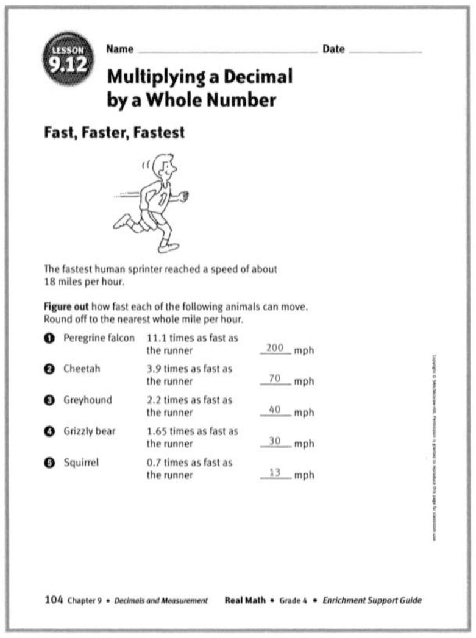

LESSON 9.12 Name ______ Date ______

**Multiplying a Decimal by a Whole Number**

**Fast, Faster, Fastest**

The fastest human sprinter reached a speed of about 18 miles per hour.

**Figure out** how fast each of the following animals can move. Round off to the nearest whole mile per hour.

1. Peregrine falcon — 11.1 times as fast as the runner — 200 mph
2. Cheetah — 3.9 times as fast as the runner — 70 mph
3. Greyhound — 2.2 times as fast as the runner — 40 mph
4. Grizzly bear — 1.65 times as fast as the runner — 30 mph
5. Squirrel — 0.7 times as fast as the runner — 13 mph

104 Chapter 9 • *Decimals and Measurement* **Real Math** • Grade 4 • *Enrichment Support Guide*

Enrichment Lesson 9.12

### PRACTICE

**If . . .** students would benefit from additional practice,

**Then . . .** assign ***Practice*** Lesson 9.12.

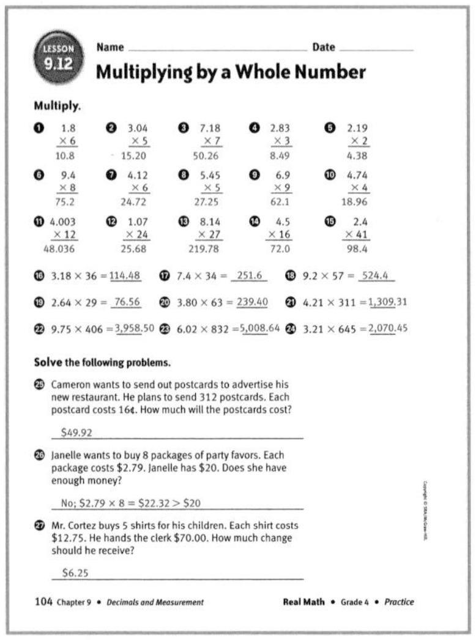

LESSON 9.12 Name ______ Date ______

**Multiplying by a Whole Number**

**Multiply.**

1. 1.8 × 6 = 10.8
2. 3.04 × 5 = 15.20
3. 7.18 × 7 = 50.26
4. 2.83 × 3 = 8.49
5. 2.19 × 2 = 4.38
6. 9.4 × 8 = 75.2
7. 4.12 × 6 = 24.72
8. 5.45 × 5 = 27.25
9. 6.9 × 9 = 62.1
10. 4.74 × 4 = 18.96
11. 4.003 × 12 = 48.036
12. 1.07 × 24 = 25.68
13. 8.14 × 27 = 219.78
14. 4.5 × 16 = 72.0
15. 2.4 × 41 = 98.4
16. 3.18 × 36 = 114.48
17. 7.4 × 34 = 251.6
18. 9.2 × 57 = 524.4
19. 2.64 × 29 = 76.56
20. 3.80 × 63 = 239.40
21. 4.21 × 311 = 1,309.31
22. 9.75 × 406 = 3,958.50
23. 6.02 × 832 = 5,008.64
24. 3.21 × 645 = 2,070.45

**Solve the following problems.**

25. Cameron wants to send out postcards to advertise his new restaurant. He plans to send 312 postcards. Each postcard costs 16¢. How much will the postcards cost? $49.92
26. Janelle wants to buy 8 packages of party favors. Each package costs $2.79. Janelle has $20. Does she have enough money? No; $2.79 × 8 = $22.32 > $20
27. Mr. Cortez buys 5 shirts for his children. Each shirt costs $12.75. He hands the clerk $70.00. How much change should he receive? $6.25

104 Chapter 9 • *Decimals and Measurement* **Real Math** • Grade 4 • *Practice*

Practice Lesson 9.12

### RETEACH

**If . . .** students are having difficulty understanding multiplication of a decimal by a whole number,

**Then . . .** reteach the concept using ***Reteach*** Lesson 9.12.

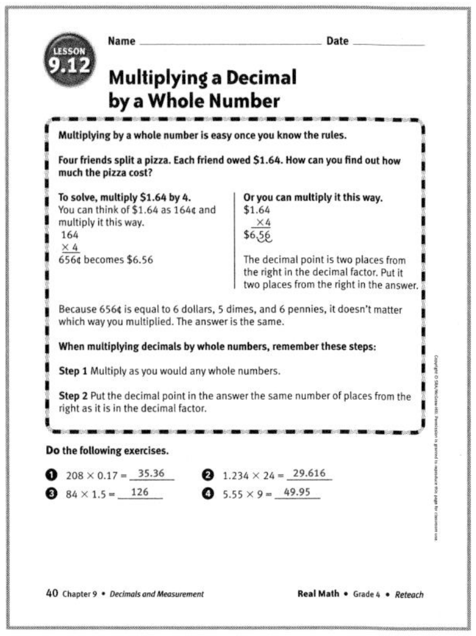

LESSON 9.12 Name ______ Date ______

**Multiplying a Decimal by a Whole Number**

**Multiplying by a whole number is easy once you know the rules.**

**Four friends split a pizza. Each friend owed $1.64. How can you find out how much the pizza cost?**

**To solve, multiply $1.64 by 4.** You can think of $1.64 as 164¢ and multiply it this way. 164 × 4 = 656¢ becomes $6.56

**Or you can multiply it this way.** $1.64 × 4 = $6.56. The decimal point is two places from the right in the decimal factor. Put it two places from the right in the answer.

Because 656¢ is equal to 6 dollars, 5 dimes, and 6 pennies, it doesn't matter which way you multiplied. The answer is the same.

**When multiplying decimals by whole numbers, remember these steps:**

**Step 1** Multiply as you would any whole numbers.

**Step 2** Put the decimal point in the answer the same number of places from the right as it is in the decimal factor.

**Do the following exercises.**

1. 208 × 0.17 = 35.36
2. 1.234 × 24 = 29.616
3. 84 × 1.5 = 126
4. 5.55 × 9 = 49.95

40 Chapter 9 • *Decimals and Measurement* **Real Math** • Grade 4 • *Reteach*

Reteach Lesson 9.12

## Lesson Planner

**OBJECTIVES**
- To provide practice applying function rules and graphing decimals and fractions
- To provide practice estimating products to solve problems involving the multiplication of decimals and whole numbers

**NCTM STANDARDS**

**Data Analysis and Probability**
Formulate questions that can be addressed with data and collect, organize, and display relevant data to answer them

**Algebra**
- Understand patterns, relations, and functions
- Analyze change in various contexts

**MATERIALS**
- Graph paper
- *Play money (optional)
- ***Number Cubes** (one 0–5, one 5–10)
- ***Checkbook Game Mat** (optional)

**TECHNOLOGY**
**e Presentation** Lesson 9.13
**e MathTools** Graphing Tool

**TEST PREP**
**Cumulative Review**
Mental Math reviews multiplication of a decimal by a whole number (Lesson 9.12).

### Looking Ahead
Lesson 9.14 has an option to measure the weights of various volumes of water in grams using a set of containers and a balance. Have these items available.

*Manipulative Kit Item

# Graphing and Applying Decimals

**Context of the Lesson** This lesson provides an opportunity to practice the skill of multiplying a decimal by a whole number, which was introduced in Lesson 9.12. Lessons 9.14 and 9.15 cover applying decimals to the measurement of metric weight and volume.

See page 382B for Math Background for teachers for this lesson.

## Planning for Learning • DIFFERENTIATE INSTRUCTION

### INTERVENTION

**If . . .** students lack the prerequisite skill of multiplying any two numbers,

**Then . . .** teach ***Intervention*** Lesson 9.C.

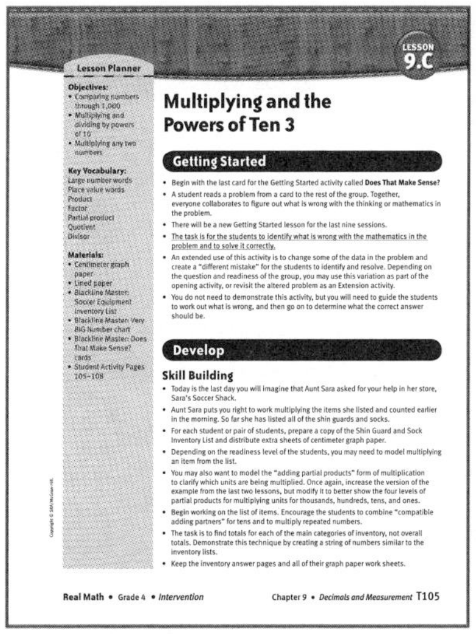


Intervention Lesson 9.C

### ENGLISH LEARNER

**Preview**

**If . . .** students need language support,

**Then . . .** use Lesson 9.13 in ***English Learner Support Guide*** to preview lesson concepts and vocabulary.

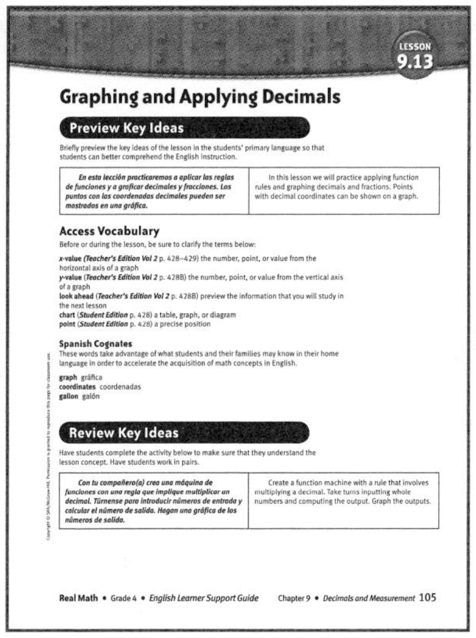


English Learner Lesson 9.13

### ENRICH

**If . . .** students are proficient in the lesson concepts,

**Then . . .** emphasize chapter projects.

### PRACTICE

**If . . .** students would benefit from additional practice,

**Then . . .** extend Guided Discussion before assigning the student pages.

### RETEACH

**If . . .** students have difficulty understanding graphing or computing decimals,

**Then . . .** extend Guided Discussion before assigning the student pages.

**Vocabulary**
Review from Lesson 4.2:
**coordinates**

**Spanish Cognates**
**graph** gráfica
**coordinates** coordenadas

## Mental Math 5

THUMBS UP

Provide number sentences involving multiplication of a decimal by a whole number with products that are either reasonable or not reasonable. Students should respond with thumbs-up if the product is reasonable, and thumbs-down if it is not.

**a.** 2.5 × 12 = 300 down
**b.** 1.3 × 17 = 2.30 down
**c.** 6.4 × 7 = 28.4 down
**d.** 7.8 × 3 = 23.4 up or down
**e.** 0.3 × 25 = 50.5 down
**f.** 8.2 × 5 = 56.8 down
**g.** 3.8 × 4 = 15.62 up
**h.** 4.4 × 8 = 35.72 up
**i.** 5.2 × 6 = 38.2 down
**j.** 2.6 × 45 = 90.2 down
**k.** 7.7 × 11 = 84.7 up

## 1 Develop 20

### Tell Students In Today's Lesson They Will

practice applying function rules and graphing decimals and fractions.

### Guided Discussion UNDERSTANDING

Whole Group

Briefly review function rules and graphing ordered pairs. Explain that the same rules apply to functions and graphs of decimals as to whole numbers. Write an example of a function rule on the board such as the following:

$x \Rightarrow (\times 4) \Rightarrow n \Rightarrow (-3) \Rightarrow y$

First have the class work as a group to complete a coordinate table for whole number values. Examples include the following:

| | 1 | 2 | 3 | 4 |
|---|---|---|---|---|
| y | 1 | 5 | 9 | 13 |

Ask questions such as the following:

- **What will these points look like when we graph them?** They will all lie on a line.
- **Will this be true for any whole number we enter into our function machine?** yes

Plot the sample points on the board or use ***eMathTools: Graphing Tools*** to verify this statement.

Review how to estimate answers by rounding a decimal number both up and down to get a range. For example, 9 × 3.7 will have a product between 27 (9 × 3) and 36 (9 × 4). A quick estimation of the answer to a decimal multiplication problem can be helpful to find solutions that make sense.

Ask students questions such as the following:

- **What will happen if we enter a decimal number, like 1.4, into the function machine?** One possibility is that we will compute with decimals.
- **Without even calculating, what can we say about the y-value when x equals 1.4?** We could expect the y-value for 1.4 to fall between the y-values for x equal to 1 and x equal to 2.
- **Looking at the graph on the board, can we say what range the y- value will fall in?** 1–5
- **What about the y-values for 1.3, 1.7, or 1.9?** They will also be in the range of 1–5.

Guide students through the step for calculating the y-value of 1.4.

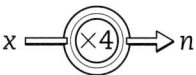

$x \Rightarrow (\times 4) \Rightarrow n$

Multiply, and then place the decimal point as many places to the right as in the factors.

$$\begin{array}{r} 1.4 \\ \times 4 \\ \hline 5.6 \end{array}$$

We can check this by repeated addition: 1.4 + 1.4 + 1.4 + 1.4 = 5.6

$n \Rightarrow (-3) \Rightarrow y$

$$\begin{array}{r} 5.6 \\ -3.0 \\ \hline 2.6 \end{array}$$

Therefore, when x = 1.4, y = 2.6. Review the procedure with other decimal numbers as needed, and make another chart.

| x | 1.4 | 2.2 | 3.6 | 4.4 |
|---|---|---|---|---|
| y | 2.6 | 5.8 | 11.4 | 14.6 |

Show students how to draw these points on the existing graph on the board or using ***eMathTools: Graphing Tools.*** Ask questions such as the following:

- **Do the decimal numbers fall on the same line?** yes

## 2 Assign Student Pages 30

### Pages 428–429 APPLYING

Have students complete pages 428 and 429 independently. You may need to tell the students to look ahead so that they select a scale that will accommodate the decimal number for the graph in Problem 2. Have graph paper available for Problems 2 and 4. You may wish to allow students to use calculators for Problem 4 so the points they need to graph are more likely to be correct.

### As Students Finish

Game **Checkbook** or **Harder Checkbook Game Mat** (introduced in Lesson 9.11)

Student Page

LESSON 9.13 **Graphing and Applying Decimals**

**Key Ideas**

Points with decimal coordinates can be shown on a graph.

**Solve** these problems. Draw and complete the charts.

1. Use the function rule to complete the chart.

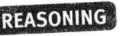

$x \rightarrow (\times 3) \rightarrow (-2) \rightarrow y$

| x | y |
|---|---|
| 1 | 1 |
| 2 | 4 |
| 3 | 7 |
| 4 | 10 |
| 5 | 13 |

2. Now plot the points on a sheet of graph paper. Points should be plotted on (1, 1), (2, 4), (3, 7), (4, 10), and (5, 13)
3. Do all five points seem to be on the same straight line? yes
4. Fill in the following chart for the function rule in Problem 1. Then plot all of these points on the same graph you used for Problem 2. Do these points also seem to lie on the same straight line? yes

| x | y |
|---|---|
| 1.1 | 1.3 |
| 1.2 | 1.6 |
| 1.3 | 1.9 |
| 1.9 | 3.7 |
| 2.3 | 4.9 |
| 2.6 | 5.8 |
| 3.2 | 7.6 |
| 3.7 | 9.1 |
| 4.1 | 10.3 |
| 4.5 | 11.5 |
| 4.8 | 12.4 |
| 4.9 | 12.7 |

428 Textbook This lesson is available in the *eTextbook*.

Student Page

**Solve** the following problems.

5. Mr. Becker bought 12.2 gallons of gasoline on Sunday. On Thursday he bought 8.3 gallons of gasoline.
   a. How much gasoline did Mr. Becker buy altogether? 20.5 gallons
   b. How much more gasoline did he buy on Sunday than he bought on Thursday? 3.9 gallons
6. If a snail can crawl 0.6 meters in one day, how far can it crawl in one week? In one month (31 days)? In one year (365 days)? 4.2 m; 18.6 m; 219 m
7. Ahmad wants to tile his kitchen floor. He ordered 60 tiles. Each tile costs $1.46. How much did Ahmad pay for the tiles? $87.60
8. Mrs. Khan bought 15 bags of pretzels for a party. Each bag cost $4.89. How much did she pay altogether? $73.35
9. Alberto wants to call his mother long distance from a pay phone. Each minute will cost 31¢. If he has $4, can he talk for 15 minutes? no

**In** each problem, two of the answers are clearly wrong, and one is correct. Choose the correct answer.

10. 8 × 1.7
    a. 19.6
    (b.) 13.6
    c. 7.6
11. 6 × 2.4
    a. 10.4
    b. 22.4
    (c.) 14.4
12. 4.9 × 5
    a. 28.67
    b. 259.7
    (c.) 24.5
13. 0.5 × 9
    a. 34.5
    (b.) 4.5
    c. 45
14. 8.73 × 9
    a. 71.07
    (b.) 78.57
    c. 83.67
15. 20 × 5.1
    (a.) 102
    b. 94.2
    c. 98.2
16. 16 × 3.28
    (a.) 52.48
    b. 42.48
    c. 72.48
17. 33.51 × 2
    (a.) 67.02
    b. 47.14
    c. 105.2
18. 70 × 67.3
    a. 4,971.0
    b. 47,111
    (c.) 4,711.0

Chapter 9 • Lesson 13 429

## 3 Reflect

5

## Guided Discussion REASONING

Whole Group

1. Draw a rectangle on the board with width of 3.27 m and length of 4.18 m.
2. Ask questions such as the following:
   - **What are the boundaries for the area of this rectangle?** Possible boundaries are 12 and 20.
   - **Can you find the actual area using the procedures developed so far?** no
   - **What can we do to find the area?** Suggest changing both measurements to centimeters.
3. Convert 3.27 meters to 327 centimeters and 4.18 meters to 418 centimeters. Ask questions such as the following:
   - **What are the boundaries for the area of the rectangle now that we have converted meters to centimeters?** Possible boundaries are 120,000 and 200,000.
   - **What is the area of the rectangle in square centimeters?** 136,686 square centimeters

**Cumulative Review:** For review of parentheses, assign Problems 19–26 on student page 438.

**Family Involvement:** Assign the ***Practice, Reteach,*** or ***Enrichment*** activities depending on the needs of your students. Encourage students to play the **Decimal Roll a Problem Game** with a friend or relative.

**Concept/Question Board:** Have students attempt to answer any unanswered questions on the Concept/Question Board.

**Math Puzzler:** The net shown here represents an unfolded cube. If you fold it into a cube, which pair of opposite faces would have the greatest sum? 5.6 + 8.4 = 14.0 is greater than either 3.2 + 6.5 or 2.3 + 4.8.

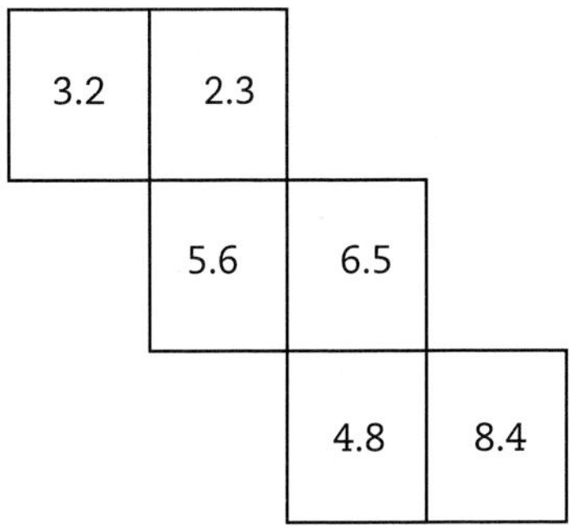

# 4 Assess and Differentiate

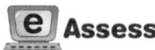

e Assess Use ***eAssess*** to record and analyze evidence of student understanding.

## A Gather Evidence

Use the Daily Class Assessment Records in ***Assessment*** or ***eAssess*** to record daily observations.

### Informal Assessment
**Mental Math**

Did the student COMPUTING
- ❑ respond accurately?
- ❑ respond quickly?
- ❑ respond with confidence?
- ❑ self-correct?

### Informal Assessment
**Guided Discussion**

Did the student REASONING
- ❑ provide a clear explanation?
- ❑ communicate reasons and strategies?
- ❑ choose appropriate strategies?
- ❑ argue logically?

## B Summarize Findings

Analyze and summarize assessment data for each student. Determine which Assessment Follow-Up is appropriate for each student. Use the Student Assessment Record in ***Assessment*** or ***eAssess*** to update assessment records.

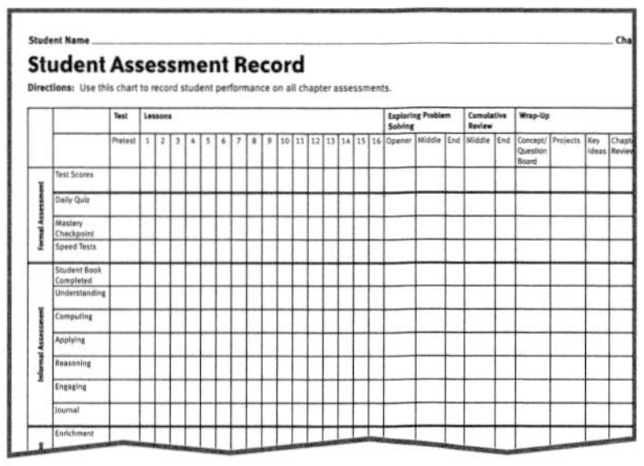


**Assessment Page T41**

## C Assessment Follow-Up • DIFFERENTIATE INSTRUCTION

Based on your observations, use these teaching strategies for assessment follow-up.

### INTERVENTION

Review student performance on ***Intervention*** Lesson 9.C to see if students have mastered prerequisite skills for this lesson.

### ENGLISH LEARNER

**Review**

Use Lesson 9.13 in ***English Learner Support Guide*** to preview lesson concepts and vocabulary.

### ENRICH

**If . . .** students are proficient in the lesson concepts,

**Then . . .** encourage them to work on the chapter projects or ***Enrichment*** Lesson 9.13.

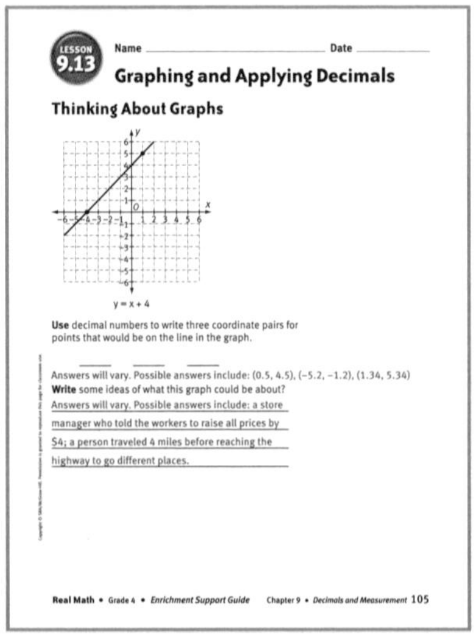

LESSON 9.13 Name ________ Date ________

**Graphing and Applying Decimals**

**Thinking About Graphs**

$y = x + 4$

**Use** decimal numbers to write three coordinate pairs for points that would be on the line in the graph.

Answers will vary. Possible answers include: (0.5, 4.5), (−5.2, −1.2), (1.34, 5.34)

**Write** some ideas of what this graph could be about?

Answers will vary. Possible answers include: a store manager who told the workers to raise all prices by $4; a person traveled 4 miles before reaching the highway to go different places.

Real Math • Grade 4 • *Enrichment Support Guide* Chapter 9 • *Decimals and Measurement* 105

Enrichment Lesson 9.13

### PRACTICE

**If . . .** students would benefit from additional practice,

**Then . . .** assign ***Practice*** Lesson 9.13.

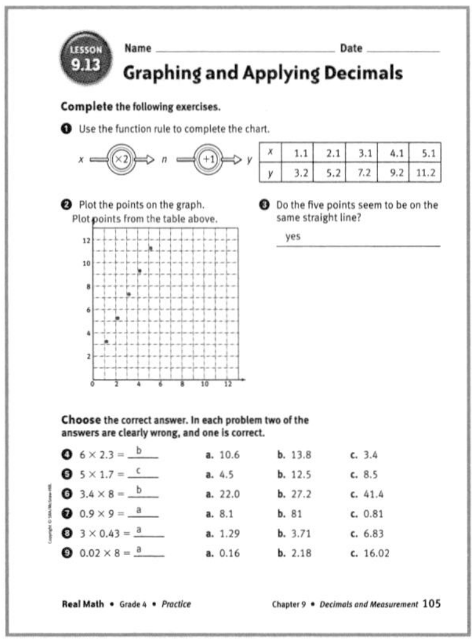

LESSON 9.13 Name ________ Date ________

**Graphing and Applying Decimals**

**Complete** the following exercises.

1. Use the function rule to complete the chart.

$x \rightarrow (\times 2) \rightarrow n \rightarrow (+1) \rightarrow y$

| x | 1.1 | 2.1 | 3.1 | 4.1 | 5.1 |
|---|---|---|---|---|---|
| y | 3.2 | 5.2 | 7.2 | 9.2 | 11.2 |

2. Plot the points on the graph. Plot points from the table above.
3. Do the five points seem to be on the same straight line? yes

**Choose** the correct answer. In each problem two of the answers are clearly wrong, and one is correct.

4. $6 \times 2.3 =$ b  a. 10.6  b. 13.8  c. 3.4
5. $5 \times 1.7 =$ c  a. 4.5  b. 12.5  c. 8.5
6. $3.4 \times 8 =$ b  a. 22.0  b. 27.2  c. 41.4
7. $0.9 \times 9 =$ a  a. 8.1  b. 81  c. 0.81
8. $3 \times 0.43 =$ a  a. 1.29  b. 3.71  c. 6.83
9. $0.02 \times 8 =$ a  a. 0.16  b. 2.18  c. 16.02

Real Math • Grade 4 • *Practice* Chapter 9 • *Decimals and Measurement* 105

Practice Lesson 9.13

### RETEACH

**If . . .** students have difficulty understanding graphing or computing decimals,

**Then . . .** have them use a large graph and mark some of the decimal points in between the grid lines.

## Lesson Planner

### OBJECTIVES
- To provide experience in measuring with metric units of weight and volume and practice in converting one metric unit to another
- To provide experience in plotting data and creating a line graph

### NCTM STANDARDS
**Data Analysis and Probability**
Formulate questions that can be addressed with data, and collect, organize, and display relevant data to answer them

**Measurement**
Apply appropriate techniques, tools, and formulas to determine measurements

### MATERIALS
- ***Response Wheels**
- Graph paper
- *Metric scale or balance and metric weights
- Liter containers
- Index cards (optional)
- ***Checkbook Game Mat** (optional)
- **Assessment** Page T74

### TECHNOLOGY
**ePresentation** Lesson 9.14
**eMathTools Metric and Customary Unit Tool**

### TEST PREP
**Cumulative Review**
Mental Math reviews multiplication and division by powers of 10 (Lesson 9.6).

*Manipulative Kit Item

# Metric Units of Weight and Volume

**Context of the Lesson** Measurement conversions in the metric system provide practice with multiplying by a decimal. This lesson is an extension of Lesson 9.8; however, the focus of this lesson should be more on the metric system's use of grams to represent weight and of liters to represent volume. This lesson will lead into the final lesson on the volume of a solid with cubic centimeters. This lesson includes a Mastery Checkpoint.

See page 382B for Math Background for teachers for this lesson.

## Planning for Learning • DIFFERENTIATE INSTRUCTION

### INTERVENTION

**If . . .** students lack the prerequisite skill of multiplying any two numbers,

**Then . . .** teach ***Intervention*** Lesson 9.C.

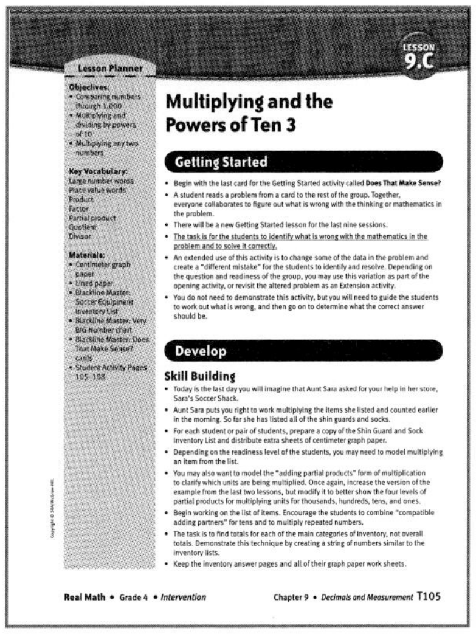

Lesson Planner

LESSON 9.C

Multiplying and the Powers of Ten 3

Getting Started

Develop

Skill Building

Intervention Lesson 9.C

### ENGLISH LEARNER

Preview

**If . . .** students need language support,

**Then . . .** use Lesson 9.14 in ***English Learner Support Guide*** to preview lesson concepts and vocabulary.

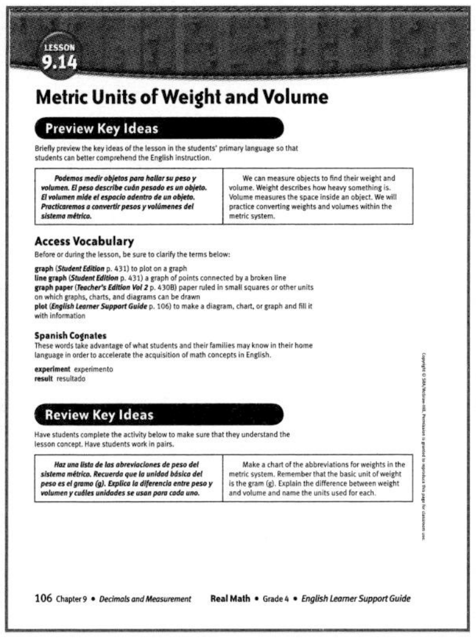

LESSON 9.14

Metric Units of Weight and Volume

Preview Key Ideas

Access Vocabulary

Spanish Cognates

Review Key Ideas

English Learner Lesson 9.14

### ENRICH

**If . . .** students are proficient in the lesson concepts,

**Then . . .** emphasize chapter projects.

### PRACTICE

**If . . .** students would benefit from additional practice,

**Then . . .** assign ***Practice*** Lesson 9.14.

### RETEACH

**If . . .** students have difficulty understanding metric units of weight and volume,

**Then . . .** extend Guided Discussion before assigning the student pages.

### Vocabulary
Review from Lesson 6.6:
**volume** **\vol´ ūm** ***n.*** the amount of space an object can hold

### Access Vocabulary
**plot** find the point on a graph where two coordinates intersect

### Spanish Cognates
**experiment** experimento
**result** resultado

## Mental Math 5

Review RESPONSE WHEEL Present exercises, such as the following, involving multiplication and division of decimals by powers of 10. Have students indicate the position of the decimal point on their ***Response Wheels*** with their index fingers.

**a.** 35 ÷ 10 = 3.5
**b.** 350 ÷ 1,000 = 0.35
**c.** 47 ÷ 100 = 0.47
**d.** 100 ÷ 1,000 = 0.1
**e.** 350 ÷ 100 = 3.5
**f.** 0.35 × 10 = 3.5
**g.** 0.47 × 1,000 = 470
**h.** 0.999 × 100 = 99.9

## 1 Develop 25

### Tell Students In Today's Lesson They Will

practice converting metric units of weights and volume.

## Guided Discussion

Whole Group

Remind students that they should be familiar with using metric units to measure length (millimeters, centimeters, meters, kilometers, and so on). The metric system rules also apply to the weight of an object. One unit of weight is a gram. Ask students questions such as the following:

- **If a kilometer is 1,000 meters, what do you think 1,000 grams would be?** 1 kilogram
- **If a millisecond is $\frac{1}{1,000}$ of a second, what part of a gram would you expect a milligram to be?** $\frac{1}{1,000}$

The same relationships are also true for volume, the amount of something that would fill an object. Ask students how many liters are equivalent to: 1 milliliter, 1 deciliter, 1 kiloliter, and so on. 0.001 liter, 0.1 liter, and 1,000 liters, respectively

Let students examine the gram and kilogram weights and handle the liter container. If the liter container has milliliter calibrations, point them out and show the difference between 1 milliliter of water and 1 liter of water. The ***eMathTools: Metric and Customary Unit Tool*** can also be used to demonstrate conversions.

## 2 Assign Student Pages 25

### Pages 430–431 APPLYING

Have students complete pages 430–431 in small groups. Complete the experiment from page 431, and graph as a whole class if there is only one balance. Have graph paper available.

### As Students Finish

Game **Checkbook Game** or **Harder Checkbook Game** (introduced in Lesson 9.11)

Student Page

## LESSON 9.14 Metric Units of Weight and Volume

### Key Ideas

You have measured objects to find their length. You can also measure objects to find their weight or volume.

**Weight describes how heavy something is. Volume measures the space inside an object.**

The gram and the kilogram are metric units of weight.

Two paper clips weigh about 1 gram (1 g).

A marble weighs about 5 grams (5 g).

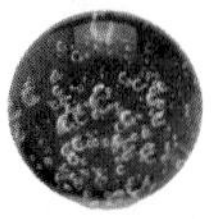

A man's shoe weighs about 500 grams (500 g).

1 kilogram is 1,000 grams. 1 kg = 1,000 g

1 gram is one-thousandth of a kilogram. 1 g = 0.001 kg

**Solve.**

1. 2 g = ▒ kg 0.002
2. 805 g = ▒ kg 0.805
3. 0.05 kg = ▒ g 50
4. 40 g = ▒ kg 0.04
5. 900 g = ▒ kg 0.900
6. 0.005 kg = ▒ g 5
7. 88 g = ▒ kg 0.088
8. 0.3 kg = ▒ g 300
9. 25 kg = ▒ g 25,000
10. 620 g = ▒ kg 0.620
11. 8 kg = ▒ g 8,000
12. 2.5 kg = ▒ g 2,500

The liter and milliliter are metric units of volume.

About how much is 1 liter?

Each of these containers holds about 1 liter (1 L).

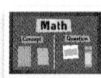

There are 1,000 milliliters in 1 liter. 1,000 mL = 1 L

1 milliliter is one-thousandth of a liter. 1 mL = 0.001 L

430 Textbook This lesson is available in the *eTextbook*.

Student Page

**Solve.**

13. 3 mL = ▒ L 0.003
14. 500 mL = ▒ L 0.500
15. 0.025 L = ▒ mL 25
16. 63 mL = ▒ L 0.063
17. 758 mL = ▒ L 0.758
18. 0.725 L = ▒ mL 725
19. 40 mL = ▒ L 0.040
20. 0.002 L = ▒ mL 2
21. 2.5 L = ▒ mL 2,500
22. 409 mL = ▒ L 0.409
23. 0.02 L = ▒ mL 20
24. 5 L = ▒ mL 5,000

**Work in groups with a set of containers and a balance. Measure the weights of various volumes of water in grams.**

Luisa made a chart to show the weight of each volume of water.

Make a chart to show your results, or copy and complete Luisa's chart.

25.

| Volume of Water in Container | Weight of Empty Container | Weight of Container with Water | Weight of Water |
|---|---|---|---|
| 0 milliliters | 8 grams | 8 grams | 0 grams |
| 10 | 8 | 18 | ▒ 10 |
| 20 | 8 | 27 | ▒ 19 |
| 40 | 8 | 47 | ▒ 39 |
| 50 | 8 | 57 | ▒ 49 |
| 0 | 10 | 10 | ▒ 0 |
| 60 | 10 | 71 | ▒ 61 |
| 80 | 10 | 91 | ▒ 81 |
| 100 | 10 | 110 | ▒ 100 |
| 0 | 21 | 21 | ▒ 0 |
| 120 | 21 | 141 | ▒ 120 |
| 140 | 21 | 163 | ▒ 142 |
| 160 | 21 | 185 | ▒ 164 |

Luisa made a line graph to show her results. Graph your results. If you haven't done the experiment, make a graph of Luisa's results.

Chapter 9 • Lesson 14 431

## 3 Reflect 5

### Guided Discussion REASONING

Whole Group

Have students explain the differen ce between weight and volume and which units are used for each. Ask for examples of things that are heavy but do not have great volume (gold, for example), and things that have a lot of volume but are not very heavy (a feather pillow, for example). You might want to explain that items in the first category are denser than items in the second category.

Use Mastery Checkpoint 21 found in ***Assessment*** to evaluate student mastery of measuring length, weight, and volume. By this time students should be able to correctly answer eighty percent of the Mastery Checkpoint items.

**Curriculum Connection:** Students may be interested in comparing the weights of various liquids.

**Cumulative Review:** For review of fractions and rational numbers, assign Problems 27–30 on student page 438.

**Family Involvement:** Assign the ***Practice, Reteach,*** or ***Enrichment*** activities depending on the needs of your students.

Encourage students to play the **Decimal Roll a Problem Game** with a friend or relative.

**Concept/Question Board:** Have students attempt to answer any unanswered questions on the Concept/Question Board.

**Math Puzzler:** Make a magic square out of the digits 2–10 so that the sum of each row and diagonal is 18. first row: 7, 8, 3; second row: 2, 6, 10; third row: 9, 4, 5

# 4 Assess and Differentiate

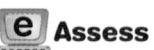

**eAssess** Use ***eAssess*** to record and analyze evidence of student understanding.

## A Gather Evidence

Use the Daily Class Assessment Records in ***Assessment*** or ***eAssess*** to record daily observations.

### Formal Assessment

**Mastery Checkpoint**

Did the student
- ❑ use correct procedures?
- ❑ respond with at least eighty-percent accuracy?

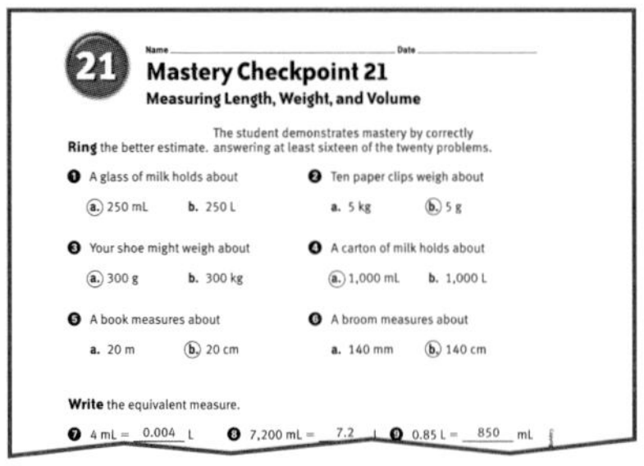
21 Name ______ Date ______
Mastery Checkpoint 21
Measuring Length, Weight, and Volume

**Ring** the better estimate. The student demonstrates mastery by correctly answering at least sixteen of the twenty problems.

1. A glass of milk holds about — (a.) 250 mL b. 250 L
2. Ten paper clips weigh about — a. 5 kg (b.) 5 g
3. Your shoe might weigh about — (a.) 300 g b. 300 kg
4. A carton of milk holds about — (a.) 1,000 mL b. 1,000 L
5. A book measures about — a. 20 m (b.) 20 cm
6. A broom measures about — a. 140 mm (b.) 140 cm

**Write** the equivalent measure.

7. 4 mL = 0.004 L 8. 7,200 mL = 7.2 L 9. 0.85 L = 850 mL

**Assessment Page T74**

## B Summarize Findings

Analyze and summarize assessment data for each student. Determine which Assessment Follow-Up is appropriate for each student. Use the Student Assessment Record in ***Assessment*** or ***eAssess*** to update assessment records.

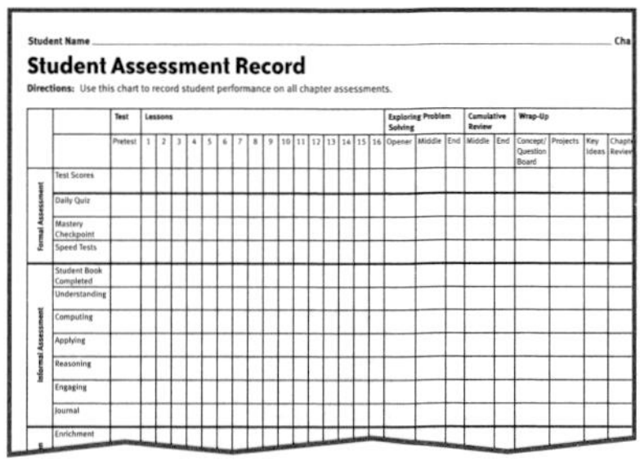


**Assessment Page T41**

## C Assessment Follow-Up • DIFFERENTIATE INSTRUCTION

Based on your observations, use these teaching strategies for assessment follow-up.

### INTERVENTION

Review student performance on ***Intervention*** Lesson 9.C to see if students have mastered prerequisite skills for this lesson.

### ENGLISH LEARNER

**Review**

Use Lesson 9.14 in ***English Learner Support Guide*** to review lesson concepts and vocabulary.

### ENRICH

**If . . .** students are proficient in the lesson concepts,

**Then . . .** encourage them to work on the chapter projects or ***Enrichment*** Lesson 9.14.

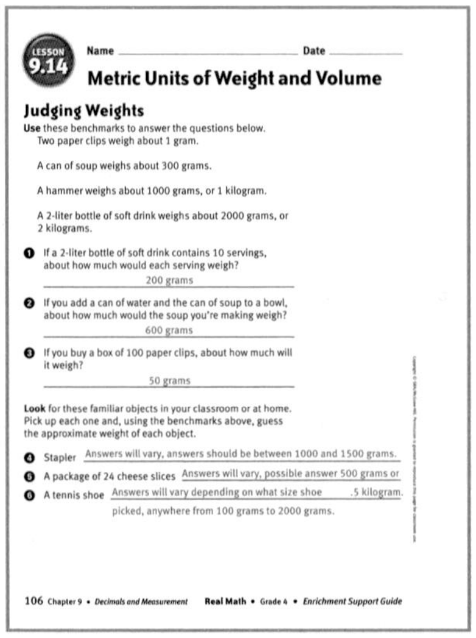
LESSON 9.14 Name ______ Date ______
Metric Units of Weight and Volume

**Judging Weights**

**Use** these benchmarks to answer the questions below.

Two paper clips weigh about 1 gram.

A can of soup weighs about 300 grams.

A hammer weighs about 1000 grams, or 1 kilogram.

A 2-liter bottle of soft drink weighs about 2000 grams, or 2 kilograms.

1. If a 2-liter bottle of soft drink contains 10 servings, about how much would each serving weigh? 200 grams
2. If you add a can of water and the can of soup to a bowl, about how much would the soup you're making weigh? 600 grams
3. If you buy a box of 100 paper clips, about how much will it weigh? 50 grams

**Look** for these familiar objects in your classroom or at home. Pick up each one and, using the benchmarks above, guess the approximate weight of each object.

4. Stapler Answers will vary, answers should be between 1000 and 1500 grams.
5. A package of 24 cheese slices Answers will vary, possible answer 500 grams or .5 kilogram.
6. A tennis shoe Answers will vary depending on what size shoe picked, anywhere from 100 grams to 2000 grams.

106 Chapter 9 • *Decimals and Measurement* **Real Math** • Grade 4 • *Enrichment Support Guide*

Reteaching Lesson 9.14

### PRACTICE

**If . . .** students would benefit from additional practice,

**Then . . .** assign ***Practice*** Lesson 9.14.

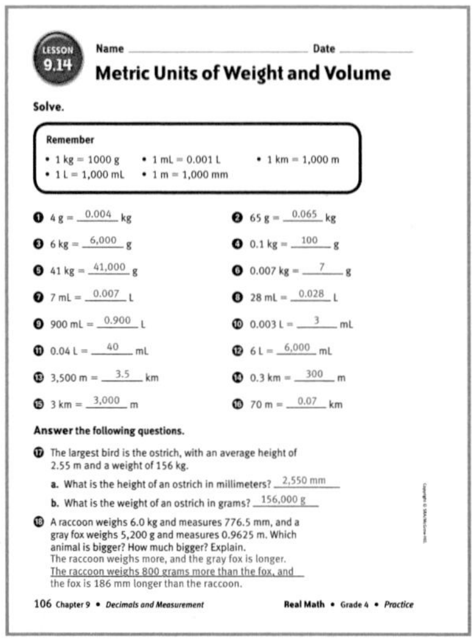
LESSON 9.14 Name ______ Date ______
Metric Units of Weight and Volume

**Solve.**

**Remember**
- 1 kg = 1000 g
- 1 mL = 0.001 L
- 1 km = 1,000 m
- 1 L = 1,000 mL
- 1 m = 1,000 mm

1. 4 g = 0.004 kg
2. 65 g = 0.065 kg
3. 6 kg = 6,000 g
4. 0.1 kg = 100 g
5. 41 kg = 41,000 g
6. 0.007 kg = 7 g
7. 7 mL = 0.007 L
8. 28 mL = 0.028 L
9. 900 mL = 0.900 L
10. 0.003 L = 3 mL
11. 0.04 L = 40 mL
12. 6 L = 6,000 mL
13. 3,500 m = 3.5 km
14. 0.3 km = 300 m
15. 3 km = 3,000 m
16. 70 m = 0.07 km

**Answer the following questions.**

17. The largest bird is the ostrich, with an average height of 2.55 m and a weight of 156 kg.
    a. What is the height of an ostrich in millimeters? 2,550 mm
    b. What is the weight of an ostrich in grams? 156,000 g
18. A raccoon weighs 6.0 kg and measures 776.5 mm, and a gray fox weighs 5,200 g and measures 0.9625 m. Which animal is bigger? How much bigger? Explain.
    The raccoon weighs more, and the gray fox is longer. The raccoon weighs 800 grams more than the fox, and the fox is 186 mm longer than the raccoon.

106 Chapter 9 • *Decimals and Measurement* **Real Math** • Grade 4 • *Practice*

Practice Lesson 9.14

### RETEACH

**If . . .** students are having difficulty understanding metric units of weight and volume,

**Then . . .** borrow a simple scale and metric weights so that students can discover what a gram feels like and what a kilogram feels like. To help students remember metric units, have them write common metric units on blank index cards: m, dm, cm, mm, kg, g, l, and ml. Then present measurements without the unit, saying, for example: "The classroom is 8 ____ long." Have students display the card that indicates the correct unit.

## Lesson Planner

**Objectives**
- To review volume as measured in cubic units
- To review the cubic centimeter as a standard unit of volume

**NCTM Standards**

**Measurement**
Apply appropriate techniques, tools, and formulas to determine measurements

**Problem Solving**
Build new mathematical knowledge through problem solving

**Materials**
- ***Response Wheels**
- *Measuring tools (optional)
- *Play money (optional)
- ***Number Cubes** (one 0–5)
- ***Metric Unit Game Mat**

**Technology**
**Presentation** Lesson 9.15
**MathTools** Base-Ten Blocks

**Test Prep**
**Cumulative Review**
Mental Math reviews parts of whole numbers (Lesson 9.1).

*Manipulative Kit Item

# Cubic Centimeters

**Context of the Lesson** This lesson extends the learning of volume from the previous lesson. Volume of liquids was the basis for Lesson 9.14. Here volume of solids is discussed. Students will be asked to calculate volume and calculate the volume of objects in cubic centimeters. The cubic centimeter was introduced in Grade 3.

See page 382B for Math Background for teachers for this lesson.

## Planning for Learning • DIFFERENTIATE INSTRUCTION

### INTERVENTION

**If . . .** students lack the prerequisite skill of multiplying any two numbers,

**Then . . .** teach ***Intervention*** Lesson 9.C.

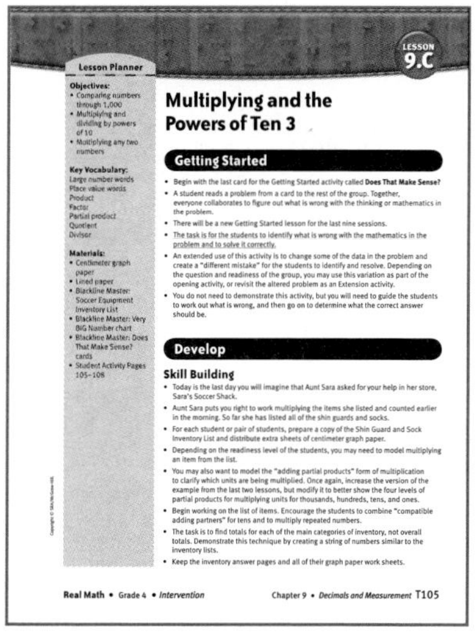
LESSON 9.C
Multiplying and the Powers of Ten 3
Getting Started
Develop
Skill Building

Intervention Lesson 9.C

### ENGLISH LEARNER

Preview

**If . . .** students need language support,

**Then . . .** use Lesson 9.15 in ***English Learner Support Guide*** to preview lesson concepts and vocabulary.

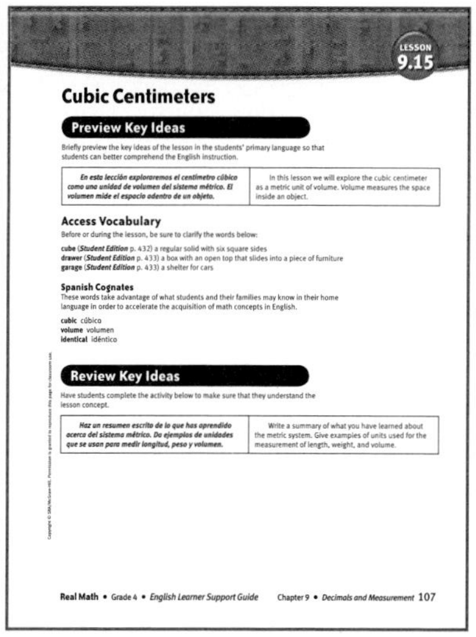
LESSON 9.15
Cubic Centimeters
Preview Key Ideas
Access Vocabulary
Spanish Cognates
Review Key Ideas

English Learner Lesson 9.15

### ENRICH

**If . . .** students are proficient in the lesson concepts,

**Then . . .** emphasize exploring ***eMathTools.***

### PRACTICE

**If . . .** students would benefit from additional practice,

**Then . . .** extend Guided Discussion before assigning the student pages.

### RETEACH

**If . . .** students have difficulty understanding volume,

**Then . . .** extend Guided Discussion before assigning the student pages.

**Vocabulary**
**cubic centimeter *n.*** a unit of volume equal to the volume of a cube 1 cm on each side

**Spanish Cognates**
**identical** idéntico
**volume** volumen

## Mental Math 5

Review | RESPONSE WHEEL Review fractions of whole numbers using exercises such as the following:

a. $\frac{1}{2}$ of 16 8
b. $\frac{1}{5}$ of 20 4
c. $\frac{1}{4}$ of 8 2
d. $\frac{3}{10}$ of 40 12
e. $\frac{2}{9}$ of 27 6
f. $\frac{4}{5}$ of 30 24
g. $\frac{1}{6}$ of 18 3
h. $\frac{5}{6}$ of 24 20
i. $\frac{3}{8}$ of 40 15
j. $\frac{3}{4}$ of 4 3

## 1 Develop 20

### Tell Students In Today's Lesson They Will

review volume and explore cubic centimeters as metric measures of volume.

### Guided Discussion UNDERSTANDING

Whole Group

In this lesson students find volume by counting the cubic centimeters in a picture of rectangular solids. Ask questions such as the following:

- **What is volume?** the amount of space an object can hold
- **When would we use volume?** Possible answers: filling a hole with dirt, gravel, or concrete; filling a container; filling a box

In previous lessons, students have worked with both metric and customary measurements. In this lesson, volume will be measured in metric units using cubic centimeters. The symbol for cubic centimeters is $cm^3$, but to avoid confusing students with superscripts, they are going to use the term *cubic centimeter*.

Hold up a base-ten block, or use ***eMathTools: Base-Ten Blocks*** or another similar representation of a cubic centimeter. Explain that this object is called a *cube*, and that it measures one centimeter on every side. The name for such a cube is one *cubic centimeter*. Create a box using ***eMathTools: Base-Ten Blocks*** that measures 2 cubes by 2 cubes by 2 cubes. Have a student come to the board and count how many cubic centimeters there are total. 8 cubic centimeters We would say the volume of this box is 8 cubic centimeters.

Stack cubes to make another box that measures 3 cubes by 4 cubes by 2 cubes. Have another student count how many cubic centimeters there are in the pile. 24 cubic centimeters Ask questions such as the following:

- **What is the volume of this box?** 24 cubic centimeters

Have a student create a box using cubic centimeters for another student to count. Check their answer.

Have students open their books to page 432. Go over the Key Ideas and the first problem on page 432.

### Strategy Building ENGAGING

Small Group

Game | eGames

**Metric Unit Game Mat**

Select two volunteers to demonstrate the ***Metric Unit Game Mat*** to the class. Have students play a few rounds to make sure they have an understanding of the objectives to the game. This game provides practice with determining metric units of weight and length.

## 2 Assign Student Pages 30

**Pages 432–433** APPLYING

Have students complete pages 432 and 433 independently. For Problem 8, allow the students to work with base-ten cubes or interlocking cubes if needed.

### As Students Finish

eGames | ***Metric Unit Game Mat***

Student Page

LESSON 9.15 **Cubic Centimeters**

**Key Ideas**

**Volume measures the space inside an object. The cubic centimeter is a metric unit of volume.**

This cube has a volume of 1 cubic centimeter, or 1 $cm^3$.

**Find** the volume of each object in cubic centimeters by figuring out how many cubes there are. (Assume all the cubes have a volume of 1 cubic centimeter.)

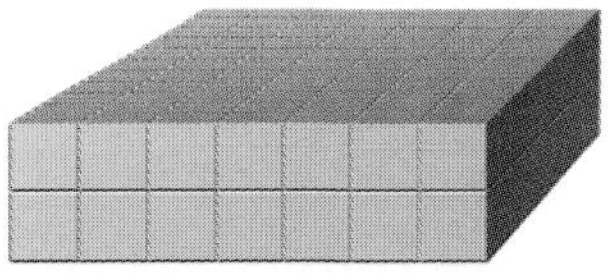

1. 154 $cm^3$

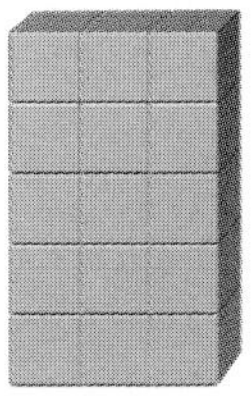

2. 30 $cm^3$

3. 216 $cm^3$

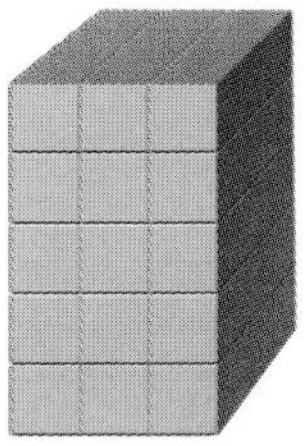

4. 105 $cm^3$

432

eTextbook This lesson is available in the ***eTextbook***.

Student Page

**Find** the volume of each object in cubic centimeters by figuring out how many cubes there are. (Assume all the cubes have a volume of 1 cubic centimeter.)

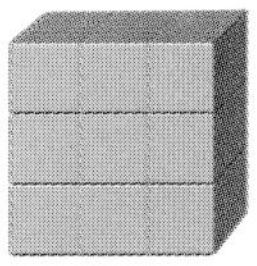

5. 27 $cm^3$

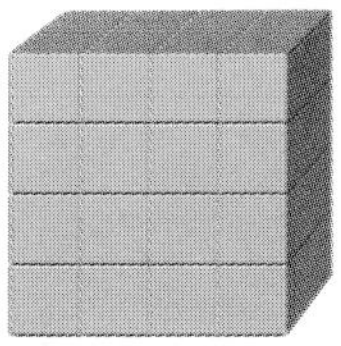

6. 64 $cm^3$

Marcia is trying to fit as many objects as possible in a drawer in her dad's garage. Each object looks like this:

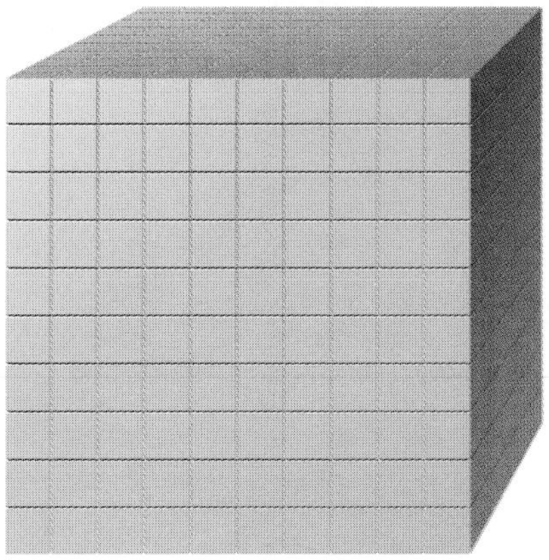

7. What is the volume in cubic centimeters for each object? 1,000 $cm^3$

8. Marcia was able to fit 50 objects in a drawer by making 2 layers of 25 objects. What is the volume, in cubic centimeters, of the drawer? 50,000 $cm^3$

Chapter 9 • Lesson 15 433

## 3 Reflect

5

### Guided Discussion REASONING

Whole Group

What if we changed the cubic centimeter to a cubic meter? How would a cubic meter differ from a cubic centimeter? Possible answers: it is larger; it would take up more volume; wouldn't be able to measure smaller items

How many cubic centimeters would fit into one cubic meter? Have the students demonstrate or draw a picture to show their answer. 1,000,000

**Cumulative Review:** For review of exponents, assign Problems 31–35 on student page 438.

**Family Involvement:** Assign the ***Practice, Reteach,*** or ***Enrichment*** activities depending on the needs of your students.

Encourage students to play the **Decimal Roll a Problem Game** with a friend or relative.

**Concept/Question Board:** Have students attempt to answer any unanswered questions on the Concept/Question Board.

**Math Puzzler:** Figure out how many 1-inch cubes are required to build a cube that is 1 foot long on each side. 1,728

# 4 Assess and Differentiate

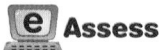

**e Assess** Use ***eAssess*** to record and analyze evidence of student understanding.

## A Gather Evidence

Use the Daily Class Assessment Records in ***Assessment*** or ***eAssess*** to record daily observations.

### Informal Assessment

**Guided Discussion**

Did the student UNDERSTANDING
- ❑ make important observations?
- ❑ extend or generalize learning?
- ❑ provide insightful answers?
- ❑ pose insightful questions?

### Performance Assessment

**Game**

Did the student ENGAGING
- ❑ pay attention to others' contributions?
- ❑ contribute information and ideas?
- ❑ improve on a strategy?
- ❑ reflect on and check the accuracy of his or her work?

## B Summarize Findings

Analyze and summarize assessment data for each student. Determine which Assessment Follow-Up is appropriate for each student. Use the Student Assessment Record in ***Assessment*** or ***eAssess*** to update assessment records.

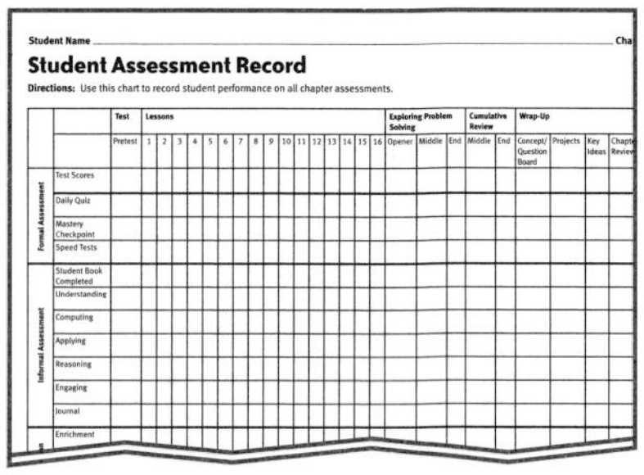


**Assessment Page T41**

## C Assessment Follow-Up • DIFFERENTIATE INSTRUCTION

Based on your observations, use these teaching strategies for assessment follow-up.

### INTERVENTION

Review student performance on ***Intervention*** Lesson 9.C to see if students have mastered prerequisite skills for this lesson.

### ENGLISH LEARNER

**Review**

Use Lesson 9.15 in ***English Learner Support Guide*** to review lesson concepts and vocabulary.

### ENRICH

**If . . .** students are proficient in the lesson concepts,

**Then . . .** encourage them to work on the chapter projects or ***Enrichment*** Lesson 9.15.

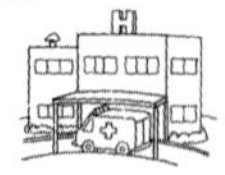

LESSON 9.15 Name ______ Date ______

**Cubic Centimeters**

**Health Care**

Health care workers often need to measure small amounts of liquid. They refer to cubic centimeters as "c.c."s rather than cm³.
**Find** answers to the medical questions below.

1. A lab technician drew 8 c.c. of blood from 7 different patients. How much blood did he take altogether? 56 c.c.
2. One medicine needs to be given at the rate of 0.02 c.c. per pound of body weight. If a patient weighs 92 pounds, how many c.c. does he or she need? 1.84 c.c.
3. The correct dose of a certain cough medicine for a child is 5 c.c. every 6 hours. How many c.c. could a child safely swallow in 24 hours? 20 c.c.
4. First, 7.4 c.c. of fluid was removed from an injured knee. Later, 6.7 c.c. of fluid was removed. How much fluid was removed altogether? 14.1 c.c.
5. One brand of liquid cold capsules has 1.6 c.c. of medicine per capsule. If a person takes 3 capsules a day, how much medicine are they taking? 4.8 c.c.

Real Math • Grade 4 • *Enrichment Support Guide* Chapter 9 • *Decimals and Measurement* 107

Enrichment Lesson 9.15

### PRACTICE

**If . . .** students would benefit from additional practice,

**Then . . .** assign ***Practice*** Lesson 9.15.

LESSON 9.15 Name ______ Date ______

**Cubic Centimeters**

**Find** the volume of each box in cubic centimeters by figuring out how many cubes there are (assume all the cubes are 1 cubic centimeter).

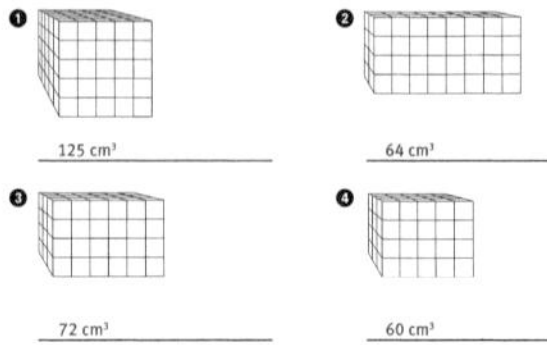

1. 125 cm³
2. 64 cm³
3. 72 cm³
4. 60 cm³

**Solve the following problems.**

5. Which is a better value—one 1.8-liter bottle of water for $2.16 or three 500-mL bottles of water for $0.89 each? one 1.8 liter bottle
6. Miyoko has an empty jar that weighs 150 grams. She fills the jar with 1000 pennies. The jar now weighs 2.65 kg.
   a. How much do the pennies in the jar weigh? 2500 grams
   b. On average, how much does each penny weigh? 2.5 grams

Real Math • Grade 4 • *Practice* Chapter 9 • *Decimals and Measurement* 107

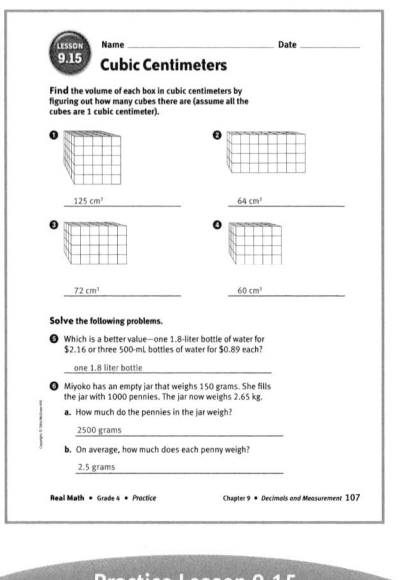

Practice Lesson 9.15

### RETEACH

**If . . .** students are having difficulty understanding volume,

**Then . . .** review how they measured the volume of liquids, and tell them you are now going to learn how to measure the volume of objects

# Exploring Problem Solving

**Objectives**

- To analyze television ratings data
- To use fractions, decimals, and proportional reasoning to calculate and interpret ratings
- To explore solving and presenting solutions to nonroutine problems
- To explore using decimals to express very large numbers

**Context of the Lesson** This lesson provides an opportunity for students to work with a common application of decimals—television ratings. It also builds on the theme established in earlier lessons in this chapter. You may want to have students conduct the survey described on student page 436 before you begin the lesson. Or you can use the survey results provided in the ***Teacher's Edition.***

## 1 Develop

5

### Tell Students In Today's Lesson They Will

- learn how the popularity of television shows is measured.
- figure out which television shows Americans watched on a Super Bowl Sunday.
- make their own ratings for some television shows and compare them to the national ratings.

## Guided Discussion

Recall previous discussions about television ratings in the Chapter Introduction. Then read the first two paragraphs of the news story on page 434 with the class. Ask questions such as the following:

- **What data is given in the first paragraph of the story?** About 86.1 million people watched this Super Bowl. A 30-second commercial costs $2.25 million to air.
- **Is $2.25 million how much it costs to make a Super Bowl commercial?** No, it is the price to show the commercial one time during the Super Bowl.
- **How else could you express 86.1 million?** 86,100,000 or eighty-six million one hundred thousand
- **What is $\frac{1}{10}$ of a million?** 100,000
- **How else could you express $2.25 million?** $2\frac{1}{4}$ million dollars; two million two hundred fifty thousand dollars; $2,250,000

Student Page

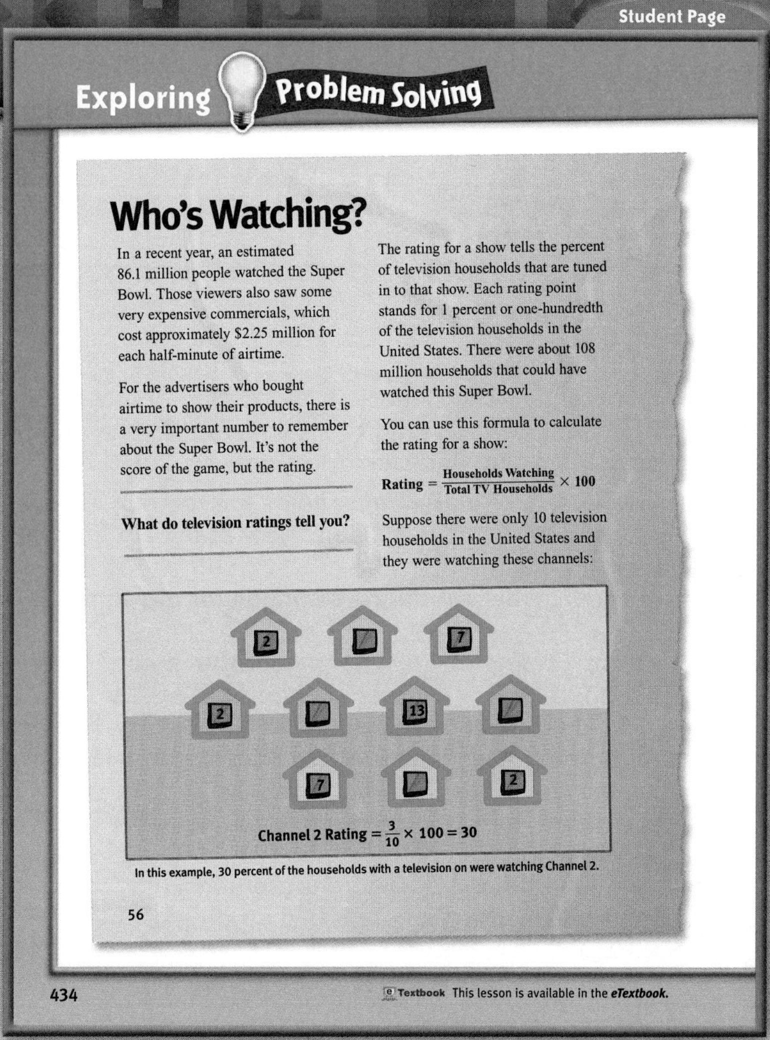

Exploring Problem Solving

### Who's Watching?

In a recent year, an estimated 86.1 million people watched the Super Bowl. Those viewers also saw some very expensive commercials, which cost approximately $2.25 million for each half-minute of airtime.

For the advertisers who bought airtime to show their products, there is a very important number to remember about the Super Bowl. It's not the score of the game, but the rating.

**What do television ratings tell you?**

The rating for a show tells the percent of television households that are tuned in to that show. Each rating point stands for 1 percent or one-hundredth of the television households in the United States. There were about 108 million households that could have watched this Super Bowl.

You can use this formula to calculate the rating for a show:

$$\text{Rating} = \frac{\text{Households Watching}}{\text{Total TV Households}} \times 100$$

Suppose there were only 10 television households in the United States and they were watching these channels:



In this example, 30 percent of the households with a television on were watching Channel 2.

56

434 Textbook This lesson is available in the *eTextbook.*

# 2 Exploring Problem Solving 30

## Using Student Pages

Go over the information about television ratings, recalling the data students discussed in the Chapter Introduction on page 383. To make sure students understand the definition of television ratings and how they are calculated, ask questions such as the following:

- **In the example, how many households are there in all?** 10
- **How many are watching television? How many are not watching television?** 6 are watching, 4 are not watching
- **In the example, what would the rating be for the show on Channel 7?** 20
- **If a show got a rating of 4.5, what would that mean?** Out of every 100 households, 4.5, or $4\frac{1}{2}$, were watching that show.
- **During the Super Bowl described in the news story, how many households were there in the United States with televisions?** 108 million
- **Were there more than 108 million televisions at the time?** Yes, because many households have more than one television.
- **If there are 108 million television households, how many households watched a show that had a rating of 1.0?** 10.8 million or 10,800,000
- **How many households watched a show that had a rating of 0.1?** 1.08 million or 1,080,000

Students may be interested to know these facts about television ratings:

- Ratings are based on a sample of only about 5,000 households, which are randomly selected to represent all the television households in the United States.
- The company that calculates the ratings for the networks uses people meters, which are electronic boxes that keep track of who is watching the television and to which station it is tuned.
- Because of statistical uncertainty and other factors, the ratings and related numbers are estimates.

Student Page

The circle graph shows the ratings for network shows between 7:30 and 8:00 P.M. on that Super Bowl Sunday.

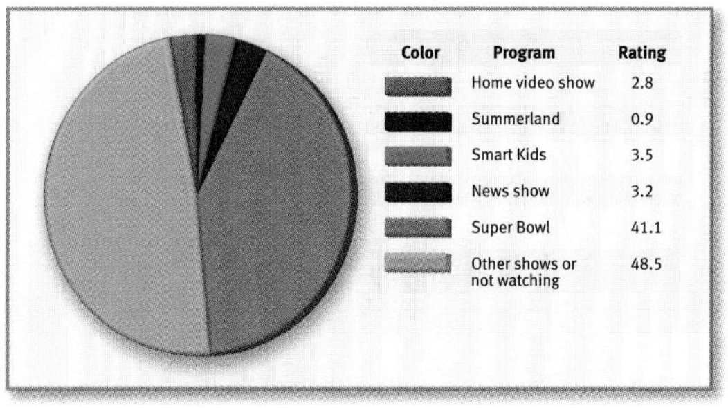


**Think** about and answer the following questions. Base your answers on the information in the news story on page 434 and on the circle graph.

1. How much higher was the rating for Smart Kids than for News show? 0.3
2. About how many more households watched Smart Kids than News show? How can you tell?
3. About how many households watched the Super Bowl? Explain.
4. Why is the number of households that watched the Super Bowl so much less than the number of viewers stated in the news article? There is more than one person per household.

❷ About $3\frac{1}{4}$ million households. Each rating point represents a hundredth of the 108 million households, or about 1.08 households. So, 3 rating points represent 3 × 1.08 million, or about 3.24 million. Students might also round 1.08 million to 1.1 million and get a result of 3.3 million.

❸ About 45 million. If each rating point represents about 1.1 million households, then 41 points represent about 41 × 1.1 million.

Chapter 9 435

Student Page

## Exploring Problem Solving

You can make your own measurements of television ratings. Here's how:

**A.** Pick one day and time when many students watch television.

**B.** Take a survey of all the students in your class or in your grade. Ask if they watched television at the time you chose. If they did, ask what show they watched.

**C.** Use this formula to calculate the rating for each show. Use a calculator when you need to.

$$\text{Rating of show} = \frac{\text{Number who watched the show}}{\text{Number of students surveyed}} \times 100$$

**D.** Copy and complete the chart below to show your results.

Include the following information with your chart:

- The date, day of the week, and time that the shows were on
- The total number of students who were surveyed

| Show | Number Who Watched It | Calculation | Rating |
|---|---|---|---|
| | | | |

**Work** in groups to discuss and solve these problems.

5. What fraction of the students you surveyed were watching television at the time the shows were on? Answers will depend on survey results.
6. What fraction of the students were not watching television at that time? Answers will depend on survey results.
7. Were the results of your survey and calculations what you expected? Explain.
8. Do you think the ratings formula is a fair way to judge how popular a show is? Why or why not?

436 eTextbook This lesson is available in the *eTextbook*.

Have students turn to page 435 and go over the graph with them. To make sure students understand the graph, ask questions such as the following:

- **What does the entire circle represent?** the total number of television households in the United States at the time—108 million
- **About what fraction of the television households in the United States were watching television during the Super Bowl?** about half

Give students time to read and work on Problems 1–4 individually or in small groups. Provide help as needed. Then go over the answers together as a class.

Have the students work in groups to answer Problems 5–8. If students do not conduct their own survey, have them skip Problem 8. Provide help as needed.

To answer the questions on page 436, students will need to conduct a survey, or they can use the information provided below.

| Show | Number Who Watched It | Calculation | Rating |
|---|---|---|---|
| A | 9 | 9/34 | 26.5 |
| B | 15 | 15/34 | 44.1 |
| Not Watching | 10 | 10/34 | 29.4 |

## 3 Reflect 15

**Knowledge Age Skills**

**Effective Communication** Discuss with the class their answers to Problems 5–8. Include the following points:

- Nationwide ratings that reflect all ages will probably differ quite a bit from students' ratings based on a sample of fourth graders.
- A sample of 25–100 students from the same school is not large enough or varied enough to give a very accurate picture of the percentage of all United States households that watched a particular show.
- Students may disagree on whether or not the rating formula is a good way to judge the popularity of a show. This might be a good time to talk about other numbers that the industry uses, such as *share,* which indicates how many of the households with their televisions turned on are watching a particular show. Share is calculated just like the rating, except that the denominator is the number of households watching television at that time instead of the total number of households with televisions.

## 4 Assess 10

When evaluating student work, focus not only on the correctness of the answer, but also on students' thinking and communication. Some questions to consider include the following:

- Did the student understand the circle graph, read data from it, and use that data in appropriate ways to solve the problems?
- Did the student understand large numbers written with decimals, such as 2.25 million?
- Did the student use proportional reasoning and estimation to solve the problems?

CHAPTER 9 Review

# Cumulative Review

## Assign Pages 437–438

Use this Cumulative Review as a review of concepts and skills that students have previously learned.

Here are different ways you can assign these problems to your students as they work through the chapter:

- For each lesson in the chapter, assign a set of Cumulative Review problems to be completed as practice or for homework.
  - Lesson 9.10—Problems 1–4
  - Lesson 9.11—Problems 5–10
  - Lesson 9.12—Problems 11–18
  - Lesson 9.13—Problems 19–26
  - Lesson 9.14—Problems 27–30
  - Lesson 9.15—Problems 31–35
- At any point during the chapter, assign part or all of the Cumulative Review problems to be completed as practice or for homework.

### Cumulative Review

**Problems 1–4** review length measurement and addition and subtraction of fractions, Lesson 8.12.

**Problems 5–10** review division with remainders, Lesson 3.11.

**Problems 11–18** review common multiples and common factors, Lesson 3.12.

**Problems 19–26** review parentheses, Lesson 3.13.

**Problems 27–30** review fractions and rational numbers, Lesson 8.3.

**Problems 31–35** review exponents, Lesson 5.11.

### Monitoring Student Progress

**If . . .** students miss more than one problem in a section, **Then . . .** refer to the indicated lesson for remediation suggestions.

Student Page

## Cumulative Review

**Measurement** Lesson 8.12

**Measure** the following lengths to the nearest $\frac{1}{4}$ of an inch.

1. ______________________ $3\frac{1}{4}$ in.
2. ____________________ $2\frac{2}{4}$ or $2\frac{1}{2}$

**Add** these fractions.

3. $3\frac{1}{2} + 6\frac{3}{4} = \square$ $9\frac{5}{4} = 10\frac{1}{4}$
4. $4\frac{2}{5} + 16\frac{3}{8} = \square$ $20\frac{31}{40}$

**Division with Remainders** Lesson 3.11

**Solve.**

5. $4\overline{)27}$ 6
6. $7\overline{)883}$ 126
7. $5\overline{)743}$

8. The Old Orchard School is buying 369 new books this year for the library. However, there is no more room left on the current shelves, so the school purchased 4 new bookcases.
   a. If they divide the books evenly between the bookcases, how many books will go in each case? 92
   b. Will there be any books left that do not fit on the shelves? Yes; 1
   c. What would be the best solution to this problem? A possible solution would be to buy another bookcase.
9. Sanjey is having a party. Balloons cost $7 a bunch. How many bunches can he buy with $75? 10 bunches
10. Eight half-hour piano lessons cost $160. What is the cost per lesson? $20



Student Page

## Cumulative Review

**Common Multiples and Common Factors** Lesson 3.12

**Find** two common multiples for each set of numbers.

11. 4 and 7 28, 56
12. 5 and 3 15, 30
13. 8 and 6 24, 48
14. 9 and 8 72, 144

**Find** the greatest common factor for each set of numbers.

15. 21 and 30 3
16. 24 and 15 3
17. 16 and 28 4
18. 36 and 27 9

**Parentheses** Lesson 3.13

**Solve** for $n$. Watch the parentheses and the signs.

19. $4 \times (3 + 6) = n$ 36
20. $(4 \times 3) + 6 = n$ 18
21. $(28 - 6) + 9 = n$ 31
22. $28 - (6 + 9) = n$ 13

**Insert** parentheses if needed to make the number sentence true.

23. $(10 - 3) \times 2 = 14$
24. $10 - (3 \times 2) = 4$
25. $(15 - 5) \div 2 = 5$
26. $55 = 15 + (10 \times 4)$

**Fractions and Rational Numbers** Lesson 8.3

**Answer** the following questions.

27. What is $\frac{1}{3}$ of 90? 30
28. What is $\frac{3}{4}$ of 100? 75
29. What is $\frac{1}{2}$ of $\frac{1}{3}$? $\frac{1}{6}$
30. What is $\frac{1}{4}$ of $\frac{5}{8}$? $\frac{5}{32}$

**Exponents** Lesson 5.11

**Solve** to make a true equation.

31. $5^2 = \square$ 25
32. $9^3 = \square$ 729
33. $2^9 = \square$ 512
34. $3^4 = \square$ 81
35. $10^5 = \square$ 100,000



eTextbook This lesson is available in the *eTextbook*.

# Wrap-Up

## 1 Discuss 5

### Concept/Question Board

Review the Concept/Question Board with students.

- Discuss students' contributions to the Concept side of the Board.
- Have students repose their questions, and lead a discussion to find satisfactory answers.

## Chapter Projects

Provide an opportunity for students who have worked on one or more of the chapter projects outlined on page 383C to share their work with the class. Allow each student or student group five minutes to present or discuss their projects. For formal assessment, use the rubrics found in ***Across the Curriculum Math Connections;*** the rubric for **Design a Set Using Metric Units** is on page 95, and the rubric for **Research Television Ratings** is on page 101. For informal assessment, use the following rubric and questions.

| | Exceeds Expectations | Meets Expectations | Minimally Meets Expectations |
|---|---|---|---|
| Applies mathematics in real-world situations: | ❑ | ❑ | ❑ |
| Demonstrates strong engagement in the activity: | ❑ | ❑ | ❑ |

### Design a Set Using Metric Units

ART

- Describe your set. Is it realistic or abstract?
- Does your set show the time, place, or mood of the play?
- What scale did you use for your set and your model?
- Which design did you use for your model?
- Did learning how to draw in one-point perspective help you build your model? How?
- If you had to use another design for your set, which one would you use? Why?

### Research Television Ratings

SOCIAL STUDIES WebQuest

- What product did you advertise? Which age group did you choose? Why?
- How did you calculate your target audience?
- How do rating points and demographics help advertisers?
- What other information did you use while creating your television commercial?
- If you had to choose another age group, would you? Why or why not?
- Did the demographics information help you effectively advertise your product?
- Do you think an advertiser can accurately anticipate the target audience for a product? How?

## 2 Assign Student Pages 25

### Key Ideas Review UNDERSTANDING

Have students complete the Review questions independently or in small groups. Then discuss each question as a class.

#### Possible Answers

**Problem 1** Problems 1–4 involve addition, subtraction, division, and multiplication of decimals. The answer is 3.29. Students should remember to align the decimal points for Problems 1 and 2.

**Problem 2** The answer is 57.34.

**Problem 3** Students should recognize where the decimal point goes in the final product. The answer is 64.48.

**Problem 4** Students should use their knowledge of dividing by powers of 10 from Lesson 9.6. The answer is 2.936.

**Problem 5** Problems 5–7 involve creating decimals and deciphering where the halfway mark is between those decimals. The halfway mark for this problem is 6.5. Some possible decimals include the following:

- 6.3
- 6.8
- 6.4

**Problem 6** The halfway mark for this problem is 18. Some possible decimals include the following:

- 17.9
- 18.2
- 17.65

**Problem 7** The halfway mark for this problem is 23.7. Some possible decimals include the following:

- 23.9
- 24
- 23.25

**Problem 8** The halfway mark for this problem is 1.3. Some possible decimals include the following:

- 0.9
- 1.4
- 1

Extended Response

**Problem 9** The purpose of this exercise is to see if students can bridge the gap between decimals and fractions. Students may say an equivalent fraction of $\frac{2}{5}$ is $\frac{4}{10}$; $\frac{4}{10}$ as a decimal is 0.4.

Extended Response

**Problem 10** Possible answers: When converting from centigrams to milligrams, the number of centigrams is multiplied by 10. When converting from centigrams to grams, the number of centigrams is divided by 100.

CHAPTER 9

### Key Ideas Review

**In this chapter you discovered various features of decimals.**

You learned how to add, subtract, multiply, and divide decimals.

You learned how decimals represent parts of wholes.

**Solve** each problem.

1. 3.09 + 0.2 = ▒ 3.29
2. 62.37 − 5.03 = ▒ 57.34
3. 16.12 × 4 = ▒ 64.48
4. 29.36 ÷ 10 = ▒ 2.936

**Find** three numbers that fall between the two decimals listed. One of the numbers must be halfway between the two decimals.

5. 6 and 7 6.5 is halfway. Other possibilities are 6.3 and 6.8.
6. 17.5 and 18.5 18 is halfway. Other possibilities are 17.9 and 18.2.
7. 23.2 and 24.2 23.7 is halfway. Other possibilities are 23.9 and 24.
8. 0.8 and 1.8 1.3 is halfway. Other possibilities are 0.9 and 1.4.

**Solve** each exercise.

9. Extended Response Explain how $\frac{2}{5} = 0.4$.
10. Extended Response Explain how 1 centigram = 10 milligrams = 0.01 gram.

439

## Chapter Review

Use this Chapter 9 Review as a preliminary chapter test to identify areas in which each student is having difficulty or in which the class may need help. If students do well on the Chapter 9 Review, you may wish to skip directly to the next chapter. If not, you may want to spend time helping students overcome their individual difficulties before they take the Chapter Test.

Each set of problems reviews concepts from one or more lessons in the chapter. Students can refer to a specific lesson for additional instruction if they need help. You can also use this information to assign additional practice based on the previous lesson concepts.

Have students complete pages 440–441 on their own. For review purposes, you may want to do some of the word problems on page 441 as a class.

### Monitoring Student Progress

**Problems 1–4 Lesson 9.1**

**If . . .** students miss more than one of these parts-of-a-whole problems,

**Then . . .** provide more practice and encourage students to say decimals out loud as they work.

**Problems 5–8 Lesson 9.2**

**If . . .** students miss more than one of these problems,

**Then . . .** allow more practice time and encourage students to verbalize their understanding of the relationship between decimals, fractions, and percentages.

**Problems 9–12 Lesson 9.3**

**If . . .** students miss more than one of these comparing decimals problems,

**Then . . .** show students how zeros can be written to the right of a decimal number without changing its value.

**Problems 13–16 Lesson 9.5**

**If . . .** students miss two or more of these rounding problems,

**Then . . .** explain that rounding decimals is much like rounding whole numbers. At times you round up, and others you round down.

**Problems 17–20 Lesson 9.6 and 9.12**

**If . . .** students miss more than one of these problems involving multiplying with decimals,

**Then . . .** assess to determine if the trouble is with moving the decimal point in the wrong direction, or if the trouble is moving the decimal point the wrong number of places.

### Monitoring Student Progress

**Problems 21–25 Lessons 9.7–9.8**

**If . . .** students miss more than one of these problems on metric measurements,

**Then . . .** pair them with students who are having less difficulty. Have them measure objects in the room. The students who need help should do the measuring while the other students record the results and check to see that the work is being done correctly.

**Problems 26–33 Lessons 9.9–9.11**

**If . . .** students miss more than one of the problems involving adding and subtracting with decimals,

**Then . . .** check to determine the difficulty. Reteach the concept as necessary, pointing out the similarity to whole number addition and subtraction. Emphasize the importance of lining up decimals correctly. Take care in assessing the Extended Response problem, which is a multistep problem. Look for difficulty in understanding the question, in how to set up a solution, and in doing the arithmetic. Watch for students who only do the first step. Intervene, and explain the necessity of following through with each step for a complete answer.

**Problems 34–36 Lessons 9.14–9.15**

**If . . .** students miss more than one of these metric unit problems on weight and volume,

**Then . . .** students may need concrete experiences. Give students centimeter cubes that they can use to build and manipulate figures and to check their answers.

Student Page

# Chapter 9 Chapter Review

Lesson 9.1 **Write** in standard form.

1. 9 tens, 5 ones, 9 tenths, 2 hundredths 95.92
2. 9 + 0.9 + 0.09 9.99
3. 2 hundreds, 9 tens, 5 ones, 2 tenths 295.2
4. 30 + 6 + 0.3 + 0.03 36.33

Lesson 9.2 **Write** each decimal as a fraction or a mixed number.

5. 0.6 $\frac{6}{10}$
6. 0.06 $\frac{6}{100}$
7. 0.99 $\frac{99}{100}$
8. 6.005 $6\frac{5}{1000}$

Lesson 9.3 **Replace** each ■ with <, >, or =.

9. 0.7 ■ 0.07 >
10. 0.2 ■ 0.09 >
11. 0.14 ■ 0.32 <
12. 0.325 ■ 0.096 >

Lesson 9.5 **Round** each number to the nearest tenth, hundredth, and thousandth.

13. 9.6803 9.7, 9.68, 9.680
14. 12.2864 12.3, 12.29, 12.286
15. 4.7267 4.7, 4.73, 4.727
16. 37.1449 37.1, 37.14, 37.145

Lessons 9.6 and 9.12 **Find** each product.

17. 52.3 × 14 = 732.2
18. 2.7 × 34 = 91.8
19. 8.5 × 100 = 850
20. 3.654 × 22 = 80.388

Lessons 9.7 and 9.8 **Solve.**

21. 3 dm = ■ m 0.3
22. 100 cm = ■ m 1
23. ■ mm = 0.650 m 650
24. 82 mL = ■ L 0.082

**Find** the volume in cubic centimeters. Each small cube is 1 centimeter long.

25. 60 $cm^3$

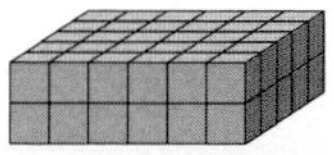



eTextbook This lesson is available in the *eTextbook*.

Student Page

Lesson 9.8

**Give** the length of each object to the nearest centimeter.

26. ■ cm 11

27. ■ cm 14

Lessons 9.9–9.11

**Add** or subtract.

28. 3.6 + 1.5 5.1
29. 15.17 − 13.29 1.88
30. 90.528 − 18.016 72.512
31. \$12.20 − \$8.90 \$3.30
32. \$20. 13 + \$9.18 \$29.31
33. 3.11 + 20.26 23.37

**Solve** each problem.

34. If 1 milliliter (or 1 cubic centimeter) of water weighs 1 gram, how much does 1 liter of water weigh? 1,000 g or 1 kg
35. An empty aquarium weighs 7.5kg. When it is filled with water, the aquarium weighs 33.5 kg. How much does the water in the aquarium weigh? 26 kg
36. **Extended Response** Clarissa grew 6 centimeters during the summer break. Maurice grew twice as much as Janice, who grew 50 millimeters. How much more did Maurice grow than Clarissa? Use words and number sentences to explain how you found your answer.
    50 millimeters = 5 centimeters; 5 × 2 = 10 centimeters (the amount Maurice grew); 10 − 6 = 4; Maurice outgrew Clarissa by 4 centimeters.

CHAPTER 9

# Assessment

## 3 Chapter Tests

40

### Practice Test

#### Student Pages 442–445

- The Chapter 9 Practice Test on ***Student Edition*** pages 442–445 provides an opportunity to formally evaluate students' proficiency with concepts developed in this chapter.
- The content is similar to the Chapter 9 Review in standardized format.

**Problem 25** Extended Response

Students can solve Problem 25 by creating a mini-ledger showing debits and credits. This can help students sort the items into the appropriate category (credit or debit). Students might want to use different colors for debits and credits to make it easier for them to differentiate between the two. Once students have correctly sorted the items, the rest of the problem requires careful computation.

Student Page

CHAPTER 9 **Practice Test**

**Solve** the following. Write the letter for the correct answer.

1. Put these numbers in order from greatest to least.
   0.92, 0.29, 0.902, 0.092
   Ⓐ 0.092, 0.92, 0.902, 0.29
   ● 0.92, 0.902, 0.29, 0.092
   Ⓒ 0.092, 0.29, 0.902, 0.92
   Ⓓ 0.92, 0.29, 0.902, 0.092
2. How many centimeters are in 250 millimeters?
   Ⓐ 2.5 centimeters
   Ⓑ 0.25 centimeters
   ● 25 centimeters
   Ⓓ 2,500 centimeters
3. How many meters are in 8 kilometers?
   ● 8,000 meters
   Ⓑ 800 meters
   Ⓒ 80 meters
   Ⓓ 0.8 meters
4. Each side of a cube is 5 centimeters. What is the volume of the cube in cubic centimeters?
   Ⓐ 25 ● 125
   Ⓒ 250 Ⓓ 12.5
5. Tim is going to the movies. The movie ticket costs $8.75. He also wants to buy popcorn that costs $4.00 and a soda that costs $3.25. How much money will Tim need?
   Ⓐ $17.00 Ⓑ $20.00
   Ⓒ $12.00 ● $16.00
6. Celia plays on the school softball team. Her batting average for the season is 0.23386. What is her average rounded to the nearest thousandths?
   ● 0.234 Ⓑ 0.23
   Ⓒ 0.233 Ⓓ 0.2338
7. Jorge is buying notebooks for school. He can buy five 100-page notebooks or three 200-page notebooks. The 100-page notebook costs $1.79 and the 200-page notebook costs $2.59. Which will cost him more: five 100-page notebooks or three 200-page notebooks? By how much?
   Ⓐ five 100-page notebooks cost $1.20 more
   Ⓑ three 200-page notebooks cost $1.20 more
   ● five 100-page notebooks cost $1.18 more
   Ⓓ three 200-page notebooks cost $1.18 more

 Textbook This lesson is available in the *eTextbook*.

Student Page

**Write** the correct answer.

8. What is the lowest place value represented in 2,652.1?
   Ⓐ tens
   ● tenths
   Ⓒ hundredths
   Ⓓ thousandths
9. Which symbol makes this statement correct?
   0.14 ___ 0.04
   Ⓐ = ● >
   Ⓒ <
10. Which of the following show the numbers in order from greatest to least?
    Ⓐ 1.678, 1.2, 1.65, 1.73
    Ⓑ 1.2, 1.65, 1.678, 1.73
    Ⓒ 1.73, 1.2, 1.65, 1.678
    ● 1.73, 1.678, 1.65, 1.2
11. Round 39,172.69 to the nearest tenth.
    Ⓐ 39,18 Ⓑ 39,173
    Ⓒ 39,172.60 ● 39,172.7
12. Round 141.8426 to the nearest hundredth.
    Ⓐ 200 ● 141.84
    Ⓒ 140.84 Ⓓ 100.00
13. 3 meters = ___ centimeters
    Ⓐ 0.3 Ⓑ 30
    ● 300 Ⓓ 3,000
14. Kyle swims 1 kilometer in 9 minutes. How long will it take him to swim 2,000 meters?
    Ⓐ 36 minutes
    Ⓑ 34 minutes
    Ⓒ 27 minutes
    ● 18 minutes
15. $\begin{array}{r} 7.32 \\ +\ 2.40 \\ \hline \end{array}$
    Ⓐ 10.122 ● 9.72
    Ⓒ 8.72 Ⓓ 8.122
16. Amanda rides 14 kilometers on the bus. The bus stops after 3.2 kilometers. How many more kilometers does Amanda have left?
    Ⓐ 17.2 Ⓑ 11.4
    ● 10.8 Ⓓ 9.8
17. Maggie wants to buy 10 new books. Each book costs $12.55. How much will Maggie spend?
    Ⓐ $1,250.50
    ● $125.50
    Ⓒ $125.55
    Ⓓ $120.50

## CHAPTER 9 Practice Test

18. Jenna's backpack weighs 5.7 kilograms. How much less is this than a 10-kilogram backpack?
    - Ⓐ 4.3 kilograms (marked)
    - Ⓑ 3.3 kilograms
    - Ⓒ 5.1 kilograms
    - Ⓓ 15.7 kilograms

19. What is $\frac{1}{4}$ of $\frac{3}{8}$?
    - Ⓐ $\frac{3}{8}$
    - Ⓑ $\frac{4}{12}$
    - Ⓒ $\frac{3}{12}$
    - Ⓓ $\frac{3}{32}$ (marked)

20. Find the value of y.

    9 → (+6) → n → (÷3) → y

    - Ⓐ 12
    - Ⓑ 5 (marked)
    - Ⓒ 1
    - Ⓓ 18

21. $2 \times (5.2 + 2.5) =$
    - Ⓐ 5.4
    - Ⓑ 14.7
    - Ⓒ 15.4 (marked)
    - Ⓓ 24.5

22. What is the probability that the pointer will stop on green?

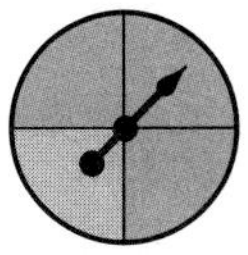

    - Ⓐ $\frac{1}{4}$
    - Ⓑ $\frac{3}{5}$
    - Ⓒ $\frac{2}{4}$
    - Ⓓ $\frac{3}{4}$ (marked)

23. Which ordered pair matches the function below?

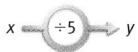

    x → (÷5) → y

    - Ⓐ (10, 50)
    - Ⓑ (2, 10)
    - Ⓒ (25, 5) (marked)
    - Ⓓ (20, 15)

24. Tony had $40. He spent $8 at the skating rink. What fraction of his money did he spend?
    - Ⓐ $\frac{1}{10}$
    - Ⓑ $\frac{2}{10}$ (marked)
    - Ⓒ $\frac{4}{10}$
    - Ⓓ $\frac{8}{10}$



eTextbook This lesson is available in the *eTextbook*.

Student Page

**Extended Response** **Use the following information to answer Question 25. Show your work.**

At the beginning of the month, Mrs. Fielding had $1,972.25 in her checking account. She wrote a check for $400 to pay her rent. Then she bought groceries for $110.05. On payday her company deposited $1,275.50 into her account. She paid her electricity bill with a check for $89.73 and her gas bill with a check for $59.07.

25. During the month there are five transactions into Mrs. Fielding's account.
    - **a.** How many of the transactions are credits? Explain.
    - **b.** How many of the transactions are debits? Explain how you know.
    - **c.** How much did Mrs. Fielding spend during the month? Explain how to determine this amount.
    - **d.** How much more money did Mrs. Fielding deposit into her account than she spent during the month? Explain how you figured this out.
    - **e.** How much does Mrs. Fielding have in her account at the end of the month? Explain how you determined the total.

a. 1; Her deposit is the only time she added money to her account.
b. 4; She wrote checks for purchases or bills.
c. $658.85; You need to add all the debits for the month.
d. $616.65; You need to subtract the total of the debits from the amount of the paycheck.
e. $2,588.90; You need to add the amount she started with in her account and the final total left from her deposit.

Real Math • Chapter 9 445

## Chapter Test COMPUTING

- For further evaluation instead of or in addition to this test, you may wish to have students take the Chapter 9 Test provided in ***Assessment.***

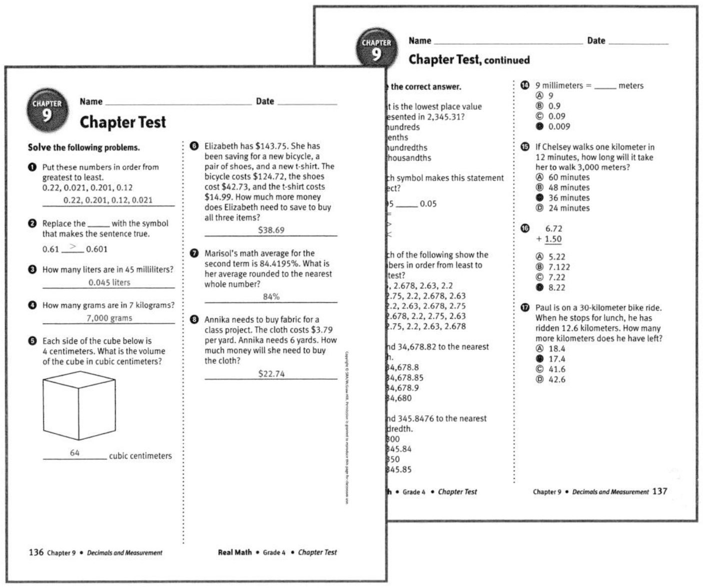

**Assessment, pages 136–137**

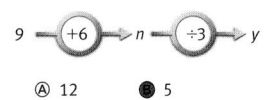

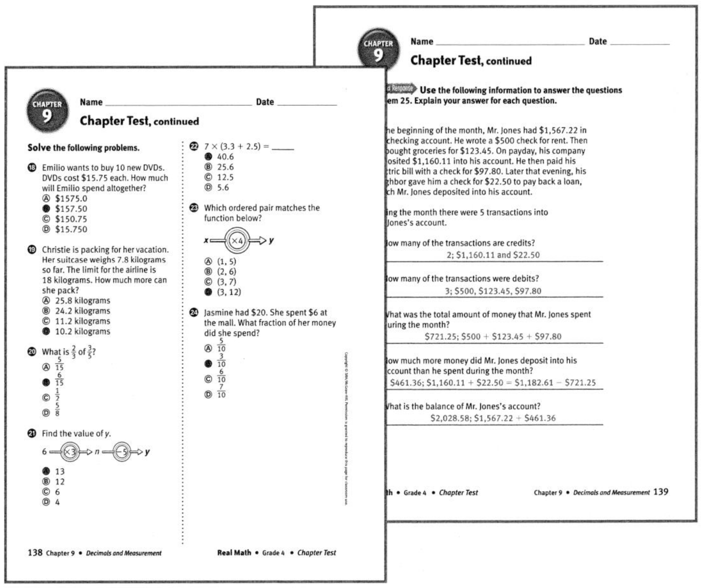

**Assessment, pages 138–139**

# CHAPTER 9 Assessment

## 4 Assess and Differentiate

**eAssess** Use ***eAssess*** to record and analyze evidence of student understanding.

## A Gather Evidence

Use the Daily Class Assessment Records in ***Assessment*** or ***eAssess*** to record Informal and Formal Assessments.

### Informal Assessment

**Key Ideas Review** UNDERSTANDING

Did the student
- ❑ answer questions?
- ❑ pose new questions?
- ❑ extend the discussion?
- ❑ provide insight?

### Informal Assessment

**Project** APPLYING

Did the student
- ❑ meet the project objectives?
- ❑ communicate clearly?
- ❑ complete the project accurately?
- ❑ connect mathematics to real-world situations?

### Formal Assessment

**Chapter Test** COMPUTING

Score the test, and record the results.

## B Summarize Findings

Analyze and summarize assessment data for each student. Determine which Chapter Follow-Up is appropriate for each student. Use the Student Assessment Record in ***Assessment*** or ***eAssess*** to update assessment records.

## C Chapter Follow-Up • DIFFERENTIATE INSTRUCTION

Based on your observations, use these teaching strategies for chapter follow-up.

| ENRICH | PRACTICE | RETEACH | INTERVENTION |
|---|---|---|---|
| **If . . .** students demonstrate **secure understanding** of chapter concepts,<br>**Then . . .** have them move on to the next chapter. | **If . . .** students exhibit **competent understanding** of chapter concepts,<br>**Then . . .** have them move on to the next chapter. | **If . . .** students demonstrate **emerging understanding** of chapter concepts,<br>**Then . . .** move on to the next chapter, but continue to provide cumulative review. | **If . . .** students demonstrate **minimal understanding** of chapter concepts,<br>**Then . . .** intensive intervention is needed before they start the next chapter. |

CHAPTER 9

# Teacher Reflection

## Lesson Study

Reflect on each of the lessons you taught in this chapter. Rate each one on the following scale, then consider ways to maintain or improve positive teaching experiences in the future.

| Lessons | Very Effective | Effective | Less Effective | What Worked | Ways to Improve |
|---|---|---|---|---|---|
| 9.1 Parts of a Whole | | | | | |
| 9.2 Decimals and Fractions | | | | | |
| 9.3 Comparing Decimals | | | | | |
| 9.4 Ordering Decimals | | | | | |
| 9.5 Rounding Decimals | | | | | |
| 9.6 Multiplying and Dividing by Powers of 10 | | | | | |
| 9.7 Metric Units | | | | | |
| 9.8 Metric Measurements of Length | | | | | |
| 9.9 Adding and Subtracting Decimals | | | | | |
| 9.10 Using Decimals | | | | | |
| 9.11 Balancing a Checkbook | | | | | |
| 9.12 Multiplying by a Whole Number | | | | | |
| 9.13 Graphing and Applying Decimals | | | | | |
| 9.14 Metric Units of Weight and Volume | | | | | |
| 9.15 Cubic Centimeters | | | | | |

# Geometry



## Teaching for Understanding

***This chapter provides a comprehensive look at geometry by extending geometrical basics (lines, points, rays, and so on) to a more complex understanding of figures and the relationships between those figures.*** Students informally explore traits of both plane and space figures as they find and describe patterns.

## Prerequisite Skills and Concepts

- Classifying Figures
- Recognizing Right Angles
- Drawing and Recognizing Polygons

## Geometry Skills Trace

| Before Grade 4 | Grade 4 | After Grade 4 |
|---|---|---|
| **Grades K**<br>Formally taught basic shapes and patterns<br>**Grade 1**<br>Formally introduced to polygons, symmetry, and space figures<br>**Grade 2**<br>Formally studied the parts of plane figures and introduced to angles<br>**Grade 3**<br>Formal use of figures to explore congruency and symmetry and to introduce circles, surface area, and volume | **Chapter 1** studied the perimeter of various figures.<br>**Chapter 4** introduced students to the Pythagorean Theorem.<br>**Chapter 6** developed strategies in finding area and perimeter for figures.<br>**This chapter** reviews plane figures, the classification of plane figures, and parts of plane figures, as well as space figures and their composition. Polyhedra, pyramids, and prisms are formally introduced. | Review and mastery of plane and space figures, angles, and composition of figures<br>Computation of area in various regular and irregular shapes and circumference will be formally introduced. |

## Problem Solving

Problem solving is in every lesson. This chapter includes the following:

**CHAPTER INTRODUCTION** Students solve a problem that uses geometry and words to create complex objects (pp. 446I–447C).

**EXPLORING PROBLEM SOLVING** The first lesson provides a specific focus on using arrangements to create geometric patterns (pp. 462–463A). The second lesson explores transformations in the context of the Braille system (pp. 490–492A).

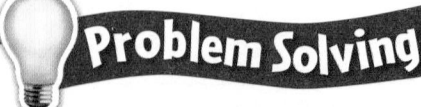

# Math Background

## Geometry

### The Value of Geometry

*Geometry can be used to understand and to represent the objects, directions, and locations in our world, and the relationships between them. Geometric shapes can be described, analyzed, transformed and composed and decomposed into other shapes.*

Clements, Douglas, and Sarama, J. eds. *Engaging Young Children in Mathematics: Standards for Early Childhood Mathematics Education*. Mahwah, New Jersey: Lawrence Erlbaum Associates, Publishers, 2004. p39.

Geometry is a branch of mathematics that includes properties and relationships of points, lines, angles, surfaces, and solid figures. The importance of geometry is not in the vocabulary of names of figures and other geometric terms. Rather, geometry is important because we live in a world of objects and need some spatial sense to interact with our world. Geometry also provides an opportunity to notice patterns and form conjectures in a more concrete way than in other mathematical strands.

### Plane and Space Figures

- A *plane* is a geometric concept that cannot be created in our three-dimensional world. In geometry a plane is a flat surface that extends indefinitely in every direction. A plane has no thickness, nor do geometric figures that lie in a plane.
- People often use the word *solid* to refer to figures in space, such as a cube or sphere. However, in mathematics we generally think of such figures as only the empty shell. Therefore, in ***Real Math*** we refer to figures in a plane as plane figures and those that can not be placed in a plane as space figures.
- Note also that a square and a circle are one-dimensional objects in a plane (because they are composed of line segments, which have only the dimension of length), and a cube and sphere are two-dimensional objects in space (because their surfaces have length and width but not depth).

### Polygons

- A closed figure separates the plane into two nonconnected parts.
  - This is a closed figure: 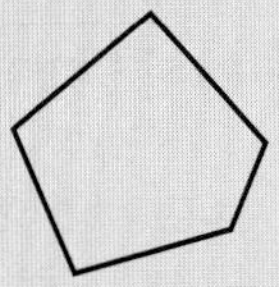
  - This is not a closed figure: 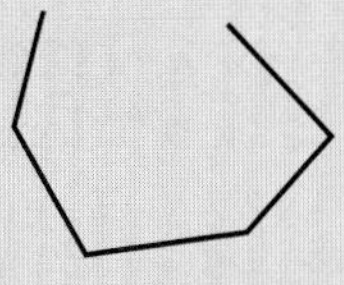
- A *polygon* is a closed figure with straight (not curved) sides.
- A regular polygon has sides that are all the same length and angles that all have the same measure. A regular polygon may have any number of sides.

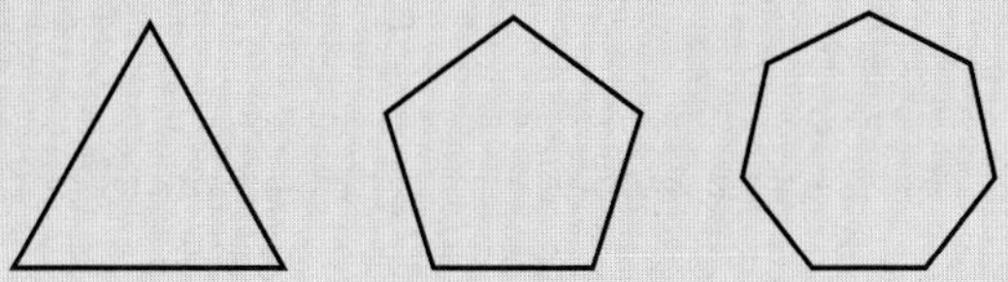

### Polyhedra

- A *polyhedron* (the plural is *polyhedra*) is a space figure whose faces are polygons.
- Every polyhedron (that does not have any "holes") has the same relationship between its faces, edges, and vertices. This relationship can be expressed as $E + 2 = V + F$, where $E$ is the number of edges, $V$ is the number of vertices, and $F$ is the number of faces. For example, a cube has 6 faces, 12 edges, and 8 vertices, and $12 + 2 = 6 + 8$.
- A regular polyhedron is a polyhedron which has faces that are all congruent polygons and which has the same number of faces meeting at each vertex (corner).
- There are only five regular polyhedra, which are sometimes called Platonic Solids after the Greek philosopher Plato. These are introduced in Lesson 10.11.

# What Research Says

## About Geometry

### How Children Learn to Work with Geometric Figures

Work in geometry requires thinking *and* doing for fourth-grade students to develop the ability to reason and to visualize geometric relationships. They will need opportunities to use common language and geometric vocabulary while they make, test, explain, and justify their thinking about these relationships.

(Based upon the geometry section from National Council of Teachers of Mathematics. *Principles and Standards for School Mathematics*. Reston, VA: NCTM, 2000)

### Learning Trajectories for Geometry

Geometric shapes can be used to represent and understand objects. Analyzing, comparing, and classifying shapes help create new knowledge of shapes and their relationships. Shapes can be decomposed or composed into other shapes. Through their everyday activity, children build both intuitive and explicit knowledge of geometric figures.

Key steps in the learning trajectory for geometry from the fourth-grade range are described below. For the complete trajectory, see Appendix B.

| Level | Description |
|---|---|
| Constructor of Shapes from Parts 2 | A child can represent a shape with completely correct construction, based on knowledge of components and relationships. For example, asked to make a triangle with sticks, creates the following: $\triangle$. |
| Shape Class Identifier | They begin to use class membership (for example, to sort) not explicitly based on properties. For example, a child at this level may say, "I put the triangles over here, and the quadrilaterals there." |
| Shape Property Identifier | A child can use properties explicitly. For example, a child may say, "I put those with four sides but not both pairs of sides parallel over here." |
| Angle Size Comparer | A child can separate and compare angle sizes. For example, the child may say, "I put all the shapes that have right angles here, and all the shapes that have bigger or smaller angles over there." |
| Angle Measurer | A child can use a protractor to measure angles. |

(Clements, Douglas and Sarama, J. eds. *Engaging Young Children in Mathematics: Standards for Early Childhood Mathematics Education*. Mahwah, New Jersey: Lawrence Erlbaum Associates, Publishers, 2004.)

### Research-Based Teaching Strategies

Explorations for fourth-grade students in geometry require opportunities for students to sort, draw, model, trace, measure, and build figures. The abilities of students to recognize geometric relationships strengthen as the children have more opportunities to make, test, reason, and justify their thoughts about these geometric relationships. This exploration can be with the use of graph paper, rulers, pattern blocks, geoboards, and geometric solids.

Fourth-grade students need a variety of opportunities to nurture their use of geometric language and symbolism, their growth in understanding of geometric concepts, and their recognition of geometric figures. This will contribute to the child's development of spatial sense and geometric thinking.

### RESEARCH IN ACTION

**Geometric Figures** Chapter 10 provides students with opportunities to explore, compare, describe, and classify geometric shapes and figures that include points, lines, angles, circles, triangles, polygons, and platonic solids.

**Attributes** In Chapter 10 the students will work with various shapes and figures in order to classify, compare, and describe the attributes of those figures.

**Language Development** In Chapter 10 students will gain greater fluency and awareness of the language of geometry. Students will use the language of geometry to compare, classify, and describe geometric figures.

## Vocabulary

**acute angle** (Lesson 10.2) an angle which measures between 0° and 90°

**area** (Lesson 3.4) the measure of the interior, or inside, of a figure

**congruent** (Lesson 10.7) figures that are the same size and same shape; that is, they fit perfectly when placed on top of one another

**diameter** (Lesson 10.6) a straight line passing through the center of a circle or sphere, from one side to the other

**face** (Lesson 10.12) a plane figure that serves as one side of a space figure

**isosceles** (Lesson 10.5) having two equal sides

**line of symmetry** (Lesson 10.9) a line on which a figure can be folded into two or more congruent parts

**line segment** (Lesson 10.1) a part of a line that has two endpoints

**net** (Lesson 10.10) a pattern used to create a three-dimensional shape

**obtuse angle** (Lesson 10.2) an angle that is greater than 90°

**parallel** (Lesson 10.3) lines that are the same distance apart, go in the same direction, and never meet

**perimeter** (Lesson 1.8) the distance around a closed plane figure

**perpendicular** (Lesson 10.3) lines that intersect at right angles

**plane** (Lesson 10.1) a flat surface wholly containing every line that connects any two points on it

**plane figure** (Lesson 10.4) a figure having only height and width

**polygon** (Lesson 10.4) a closed plane figure with three or more line segments as sides

**polyhedron** (Lesson 10.11) a space figure that has only flat faces, which are polygons

**radius** (Lesson 10.6) a line segment going from the center to the outside of a circle or sphere

**ray** (Lesson 10.1) a line that has one endpoint and extends forever in one direction

**reflection** (Lesson 10.8) a change in location of a figure when it is flipped over a line

**regular polygon** (Lesson 10.11) a polygon with sides of equal length

**right angle** (Lesson 10.2) an angle which measures exactly 90°

**rotation** (Lesson 10.8) a change in the location of a figure when it is turned in a circle around a point

**similar** (Lesson 10.7) figures that have the same shape but differ in size

**translation** (Lesson 10.8) a change in the location of a figure in which it slides without being turned

**vertex** (Lessons 10.2) the point where two rays meet; the point of intersection of two sides of a polygon; the point of intersection of three edges of a space figure

## English Learner

### Cognates

For English learners, a quick way to acquire new English vocabulary words is to build on what is known in the primary language.

| English | Spanish |
|---|---|
| angle | ángulo |
| geometry | geometría |
| parallel | paralelo |
| vertex | vértice |

### Access Vocabulary

English learners may understand words in different contexts or not understand idioms. Review chapter vocabulary for this concern. For example:

| | |
|---|---|
| point | exact location in space |
| degree | a unit of measurement used for temperature and size of angles |
| equidistant | equal distance |

# Chapter Planner

| Lessons | Objectives | NCTM Standards | State Standards |
| --- | --- | --- | --- |
| 10.1 **Lines** pages 448A–449A 60 minutes | **Explore relationships** by creating, manipulating, and postulating about lines, points, and angles | Geometry<br>Reasoning and Proof | |
| 10.2 **Angles** pages 450A–453B 60 minutes | **Begin to develop concepts of angles** by measuring and describing right, obtuse, and acute angles | Measurement<br>Geometry | |
| 10.3 **Parallel, Perpendicular, and Intersecting Lines** pages 454A–455A 60 minutes | **Explore parallel, perpendicular, and intersecting lines** by extending the knowledge of lines learned in Lessons 10.1 and 10.2 | Geometry | |
| 10.4 **Quadrilaterals and Other Polygons** pages 1456A–457A 60 minutes | **Explore polygon classification** by identifying, comparing, and analyzing attributes of two-dimensional shapes | Geometry | |
| 10.5 **Triangles** pages 458A–459A 60 minutes | **Begin to develop concepts of triangle classification** by identifying, comparing, and analyzing attributes of two-dimensional shapes | Geometry | |
| 10.6 **Circles** pages 460A–461A 60 minutes | **Explore properties of circles** by using terms such as radius, diameter, and circumference | Geometry | |
| 10.7 **Congruence and Similarity** pages 466A–467A 60 minutes | **Explore geometric concepts of congruence and similarity** by finding real-world examples of shapes and learning about the difference between congruence and similarity | Geometry | |
| 10.8 **Rotation, Translation, and Reflection** pages 468A–469A 60 minutes | **Develop concepts of congruency** by describing the motion of figures as they are rotated, translated, and reflected | Geometry | |
| 10.9 **Lines of Symmetry** pages 470A–473B 60 minutes | **Discover lines of symmetry of common polygons** to explore the relationship between geometry and fractions | Geometry | |
| 10.10 **Space Figures** pages 474A–477B 60 minutes | **Begin to develop concepts of space figures** by creating and identifying nets that fold into space figures | Geometry | |
| 10.11 **The Five Regular Polyhedra (Platonic Solids)** pages 478A–481B 60 minutes | **Introduce concepts and characteristics of regular polyhedra** by identifying them by their number of vertices, edges, and faces | Geometry | |
| 10.12 **Pyramids and Prisms** pages 482A–485B 60 minutes | **Explore traits of pyramids and prisms** by computing or counting their vertices, edges, and faces | Geometry | |
| 10.13 **Calculating Area** pages 486B–487A 60 minutes | **Explore strategies for calculating and estimating the areas of compound figures** by using a grid | Measurement | |
| 10.14 **Measuring and Calculating Perimeter** pages 488A–489A 60 minutes | **Develop strategies to find the perimeter of a figure** by using a grid | Measurement | |

| Vocabulary | Manipulatives and Materials | Games to reinforce skills and concepts |
|---|---|---|
| ray<br>plane<br>line segment | • Response Wheels<br>• Ruler or straightedge<br>• Flashlight | |
| acute, right, and obtuse angles<br>vertex | • Response Wheels<br>• Protractors | |
| parallel<br>perpendicular | • Response Wheels<br>• Rulers or straightedges<br>• Paper | |
| plane figure<br>polygon | • Response Wheels<br>• Rulers or straightedges<br>• Rubber bands<br>• Geoboards and overhead geoboard<br>• Polygons and quadrilaterals | |
| isosceles | • Geoboards<br>• Rubber bands | |
| diameter<br>radius | • Response Wheels<br>• Pencils<br>• String<br>• Paper | |
| congruent<br>similar | • Response Wheels<br>• Paper for tracing<br>• Attribute blocks | |
| translation<br>rotation<br>reflection | • Response Wheels<br>• Paper for tracing<br>• Transparencies showing congruent shapes<br>• Polygon models | |
| line of symmetry | • Rectangular paper<br>• Paper for tracing<br>• Scissors<br>• Metric ruler<br>• Mirrors (optional) | |
| plane<br>net | • Response Wheels<br>• Everyday objects<br>• Space figures (from nets)<br>• Cardboard (foldable) boxes<br>• Scissors<br>• Tape | |
| polyhedron<br>regular polygon | • Response Wheels<br>• Space figures<br>• Poster of polyhedra models<br>• Copies of ***Practice*** page 143 (optional) | |
| face | • Response Wheels<br>• Models of Polyhedra<br>• Light-colored paper or tagboard | |
| area | • Response Wheels<br>• Graph paper | |
| perimeter<br>area | • Response Wheels<br>• Graph paper | |

# Additional Resources

## Differentiated Instruction

*Intervention Support Guide* provides instruction for the following prerequisite skills:

- Lesson 10.A Classifying Figures
- Lesson 10.B Recognizing Right Angles
- Lesson 10.C Drawing and Recognizing Polygons

*Enrichment Support Guide*

*Practice*

*Reteach Support Guide*

*English Learner Support Guide*

## Technology

The following electronic resources are available:

**ePlanner** Lessons 10.1–10.14

**ePresentation** Lessons 10.1–10.14

**eTextbook** Lessons 10.1–10.14

**eAssess** Lessons 10.1–10.14

**eMathTools** **Geometry Sketch Tool** Lessons 10.1–10.7, 10.9, 10.13; **Shape Tool** Lesson 10.4; **Net Tool** Lessons 10.4, 10.10–10.12; **Tessellations Tool** Lesson 10.8

# Chapter Planner, continued

| Problem Solving | When to Use | Objectives | NCTM Standards | Skills Covered |
|---|---|---|---|---|
| **Chapter Introduction** pages 446I–447C 15–30 minutes | Use after the Chapter 10 Pretest | Introduce chapter concepts in a problem-solving setting | Geometry<br>Communication | Creating Geometric Figures |
| **Exploring Problem Solving** pages 462–463A 30–45 minutes | Use any time during the chapter | Explore methods of solving nonroutine problems | Geometry<br>Representations | Geometric Patterns<br>Problem Solving |
| **Exploring Problem Solving** pages 490–492A 45–60 minutes | Use any time after the first Exploring Problem Solving | Develop logical reasoning while integrating reading skills with mathematics | Geometry<br>Connections | Geometric Patterns |

| Review | When to Use | Objectives | NCTM Standards | Skills Covered |
|---|---|---|---|---|
| **Cumulative Review** pages 464–465 15–30 minutes | Use any time after Lesson 10.6 | Review concepts and skills taught earlier in the year | Number and Operations<br>Algebra | Multiplication and Division<br>Missing Digit Problems<br>Ordering Decimals |
| **Cumulative Review** pages 493–494 15–30 minutes | Use any time after Lesson 10.14 | Review concepts and skills taught earlier in the year | Algebra<br>Measurement<br>Problem Solving | Converting Customary Measurements<br>Algebraic Problems<br>Fractions |
| **Chapter 10 Review** pages 496A–497 30–45 minutes | Use after Lesson 10.14 | Review concepts and skills taught in the chapter | Geometry<br>Measurement<br>Representation | Chart Reading<br>Geometry<br>Measuring Angles |

| Assessment | When to Use | Objectives | NCTM Standards | Skills Covered |
|---|---|---|---|---|
| **Informal Assessment** (pp. 449A–489A) Rubrics | Use at the end of the lesson | Provide daily evaluation of math proficiency | Problem Solving<br>Reasoning and Proof<br>Communication | Computing, Understanding, Reasoning, Applying, Engaging |
| **Pretest** (*Assessment* p. 141) 15–30 minutes | Use after or in place of the Chapter 9 Review | Provide assessment or additional practice of the chapter concepts | Number and Operations<br>Geometry | Geometry<br>Multiplication |
| **Individual Oral Assessment** (p. 465A) 5 minutes per student | Begin after Lesson 10.6 | Provide alternate means of assessing students' progress | Geometry | Geometry |
| **Chapter 10 Practice Test** (pp. 498A–501A) 30–45 minutes | Use after or in place of the Chapter 10 Review | Provide assessment or additional practice of the chapter concepts | Geometry<br>Representation | Geometry<br>Chart Reading |
| **Chapter 10 Test** (*Assessment* pp. 150–153) 30–45 minutes | Use after or in place of the Chapter 10 Review | Provide assessment or additional practice of the chapter concepts | Geometry<br>Number and Operations | Geometry<br>Multiplication |

# Technology Resources and Support

Visit SRAonline.com for online versions of the ***Real Math eSuite.***

## Technology for Teachers

| | |
|---|---|
| **Presentation** | Lessons 10.1–10.14 Use the ***ePresentation*** to interactively present chapter content. |
| **Planner** | Use the Chapter and Lesson Planners to outline activities and time frames for Chapter 10. |
| **Assess** | Students can take the following assessment in ***eAssess:***<br>• Chapter Pretest<br>• Chapter Test<br>Teachers can record results and print reports for all assessments in this chapter. |
| **MathTools** | **Geometry Sketch Tool** Lessons 10.1–10.7, 10.9, 10.13<br>**Shape Tool** Lessons 10.4<br>**Net Tool** Lessons 10.4, 10.10–10.12<br>**Tessellations Tool** Lesson 10.8 |

## Technology for Students

| | |
|---|---|
| **Textbook** | An electronic, interactive version of the ***Student Edition*** is available for all lessons in Chapter 10. |
| **MathTools** | **Geometry Sketch Tool** Lessons 10.1–10.7, 10.9, 10.13<br>**Shape Tool** Lesson 10.4<br>**Net Tool** Lessons 10.4, 10.10–10.12<br>**Tessellations Tool** Lesson 10.8 |
| TECH KNOWLEDGE | ***TechKnowledge*** Level 4 provides lessons that specifically teach the Unit 10 Internet and Unit 4 Drawing and Graphics applications that students can use while working on this chapter's projects. |

# Geometry

## 1 Introduce Chapter 10 5

### Chapter Objectives

Explain to students that in this chapter they will build on what they already know about geometry. They will

- learn about lines, angles, polygons, and circles.
- explore congruence, similarity, and symmetry.
- create models of space figures.

### Pretest COMPUTING

Administer the Pretest in ***Assessment.***

The Pretest for Chapter 10 covers the following prerequisite skills:

- Perimeter and area (Problems 1–3)
- Multidigit multiplication (Problems 4–9)
- Exponents (Problems 10–11)

The Pretest also covers the following topics from this chapter:

- Angles (Problems 12–14)
- Lines (Problems 15–16)
- Quadrilaterals (Problem 17)
- Triangles (Problem 18)

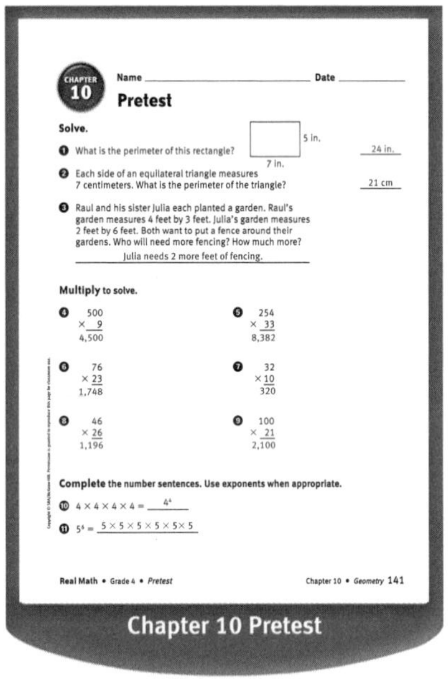
CHAPTER 10 Name ______ Date ______

**Pretest**

**Solve.**

1. What is the perimeter of this rectangle? (5 in., 7 in.) 24 in.
2. Each side of an equilateral triangle measures 7 centimeters. What is the perimeter of the triangle? 21 cm
3. Raul and his sister Julia each planted a garden. Raul's garden measures 4 feet by 3 feet. Julia's garden measures 2 feet by 6 feet. Both want to put a fence around their gardens. Who will need more fencing? How much more? Julia needs 2 more feet of fencing.

**Multiply** to solve.

4. 500 × 9 = 4,500
5. 254 × 33 = 8,382
6. 76 × 23 = 1,748
7. 32 × 10 = 320
8. 46 × 26 = 1,196
9. 100 × 21 = 2,100

**Complete** the number sentences. Use exponents when appropriate.

10. $4 \times 4 \times 4 \times 4 = 4^4$
11. $5^6 = 5 \times 5 \times 5 \times 5 \times 5 \times 5$

Real Math • Grade 4 • *Pretest* Chapter 10 • *Geometry* 141

Chapter 10 Pretest

### Access Prior Knowledge UNDERSTANDING

Have students talk about what it would be like to be blind. Discuss how people, many of them famous, have overcome enormous challenges such as the absence of sight or hearing.

## 2 Exploring Problem Solving 20

**Tell Students In Today's Lesson They Will**

feel an object and tell someone how to build it, even though they cannot see it.

**Materials**

- About 20 interlocking cubes for each group of 3 students
- Graph paper

### Using Student Pages

Have three volunteers demonstrate the activity described on student page 447. Make sure students understand the following points:

- Players 2 and 3 must not look at the mystery model until Player 3 has finished building the copy of it.
- They should play three times so that each player gets a turn being Player 1, Player 2, and Player 3.
- After each round, students should try to agree on the meaning of certain words. They should use those words during the next round of play.

Have students work in groups of three to play Mystery Model Match and to answer Problems 1 and 2. If some groups have only two players, the teacher or another group can make the mystery model for them. Provide help as needed. If students are using cubes that do not snap together, tell Player 2 to be careful not to disturb the arrangement of the cubes. If the arrangement is disturbed, Player 1 can put it back together.

### CyberSolver

To extend problem solving, have students use the Internet to find the answers to the following questions:

- **Who invented the reading system that visually-impaired people use?**
- **How long did it take to invent?**
- **How does the system work?**

Students can search for information about visually-impaired people by using a key phrase, such as *history of reading for the blind.* If they are familiar with the term *braille,* they can use that as a search word to find many sites with information about Louis Braille and his alphabet.

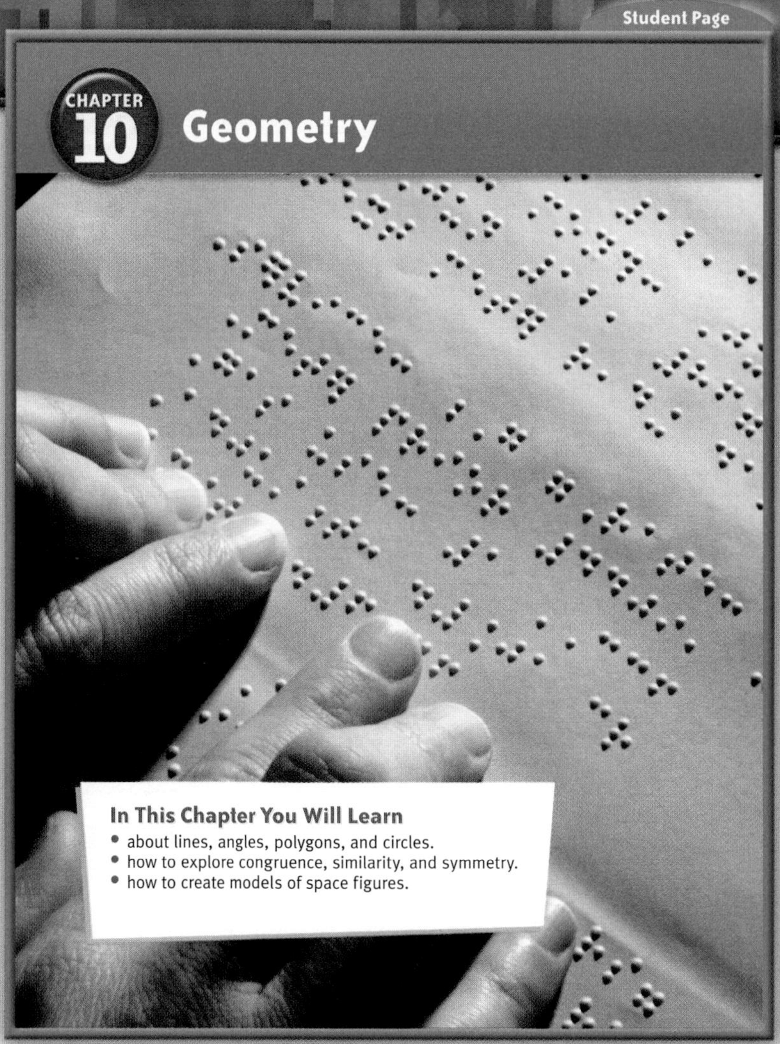

Student Page

CHAPTER 10 Geometry

**In This Chapter You Will Learn**
- about lines, angles, polygons, and circles.
- how to explore congruence, similarity, and symmetry.
- how to create models of space figures.

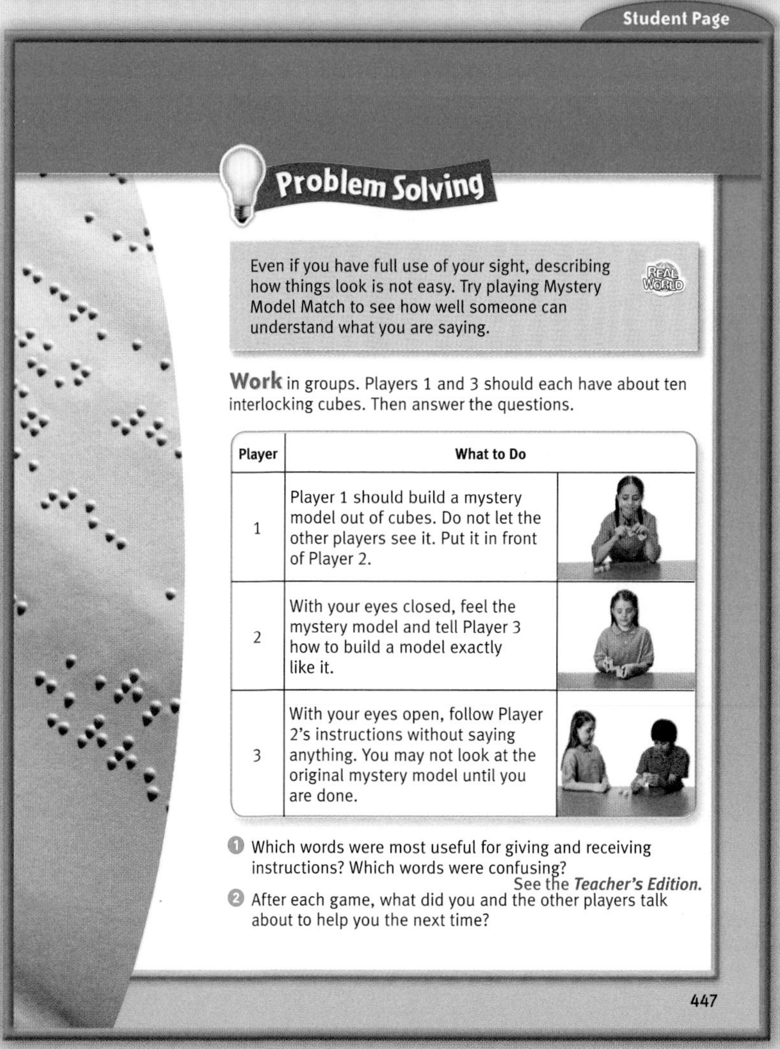

Student Page

**Problem Solving**

Even if you have full use of your sight, describing how things look is not easy. Try playing Mystery Model Match to see how well someone can understand what you are saying.

**Work** in groups. Players 1 and 3 should each have about ten interlocking cubes. Then answer the questions.

| Player | What to Do |
|---|---|
| 1 | Player 1 should build a mystery model out of cubes. Do not let the other players see it. Put it in front of Player 2. |
| 2 | With your eyes closed, feel the mystery model and tell Player 3 how to build a model exactly like it. |
| 3 | With your eyes open, follow Player 2's instructions without saying anything. You may not look at the original mystery model until you are done. |

1. Which words were most useful for giving and receiving instructions? Which words were confusing? See the *Teacher's Edition.*
2. After each game, what did you and the other players talk about to help you the next time?

447

## Concept/Question Board

APPLYING

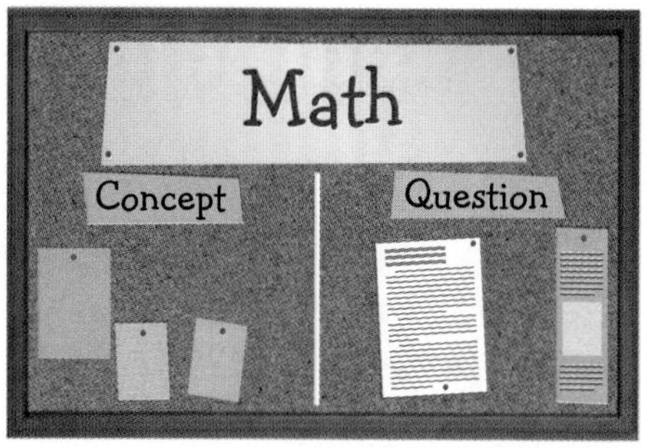


### Questions

Have students write three questions they have about geometry and how it can be used. Then have them select one question to post on the Question side of the Board.

### Concepts

As students work through the chapter, have them collect examples of how geometry is used in everyday situations. For each example, have students write problems that relate to the item(s). Have them display their examples on the Concept side of the Board.

Suggest the following:

- the floorplan of a house
- a photograph of a totem pole
- a blank compact disc

### Answers

Throughout the chapter, have students post answers to the questions and solutions to the problems on the Board.

# CHAPTER 10 Introduction

## 3 Reflect

5

### Knowledge Age Skills

**Effective Communication** Have groups share their experiences playing Mystery Model Match. Ask them whether they think they got better the more they played. Review Problems 1 and 2.

- For Problem 1 students may use phrases such as *to the right of* and *to the left of.* Students may say that a phrase like *next to* was not clear enough when they wanted someone to place a cube in a particular position.
- Use Problem 2 to help students see the usefulness of precise language. This will help them see why subsequent lessons pay so much attention to the definitions of geometric terms.

## Home Connection

At this time, you may want to send home the letter on pages 38–41 of ***Home Connection.*** This letter describes what students will be learning and what activities they can do at home to support their work in school.

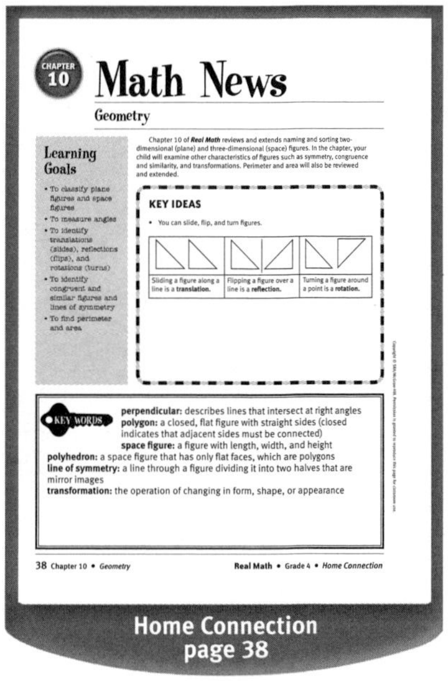
CHAPTER 10 Math News

Geometry

Learning Goals

- To classify plane figures and space figures
- To measure angles
- To identify translations (slides), reflections (flips), and rotations (turns)
- To identify congruent and similar figures and lines of symmetry
- To find perimeter and area

Chapter 10 of ***Real Math*** reviews and extends naming and sorting two-dimensional (plane) and three-dimensional (space) figures. In the chapter, your child will examine other characteristics of figures such as symmetry, congruence and similarity, and transformations. Perimeter and area will also be reviewed and extended.

KEY IDEAS

- You can slide, flip, and turn figures.

| | | |
|---|---|---|
| Sliding a figure along a line is a **translation.** | Flipping a figure over a line is a **reflection.** | Turning a figure around a point is a **rotation.** |

KEY WORDS

**perpendicular:** describes lines that intersect at right angles
**polygon:** a closed, flat figure with straight sides (closed indicates that adjacent sides must be connected)
**space figure:** a figure with length, width, and height
**polyhedron:** a space figure that has only flat faces, which are polygons
**line of symmetry:** a line through a figure dividing it into two halves that are mirror images
**transformation:** the operation of changing in form, shape, or appearance

38 Chapter 10 • *Geometry* **Real Math** • Grade 4 • *Home Connection*

Home Connection page 38

# 4 Assess and Differentiate

eAssess Use ***eAssess*** to record and analyze evidence of student understanding.

## A Gather Evidence

Use the Daily Class Assessment Records in ***Assessment*** or ***eAssess*** to record daily observations.

### Informal Assessment

**Access Prior Knowledge**

Did the student UNDERSTANDING

- ❑ make important observations?
- ❑ extend or generalize learning?
- ❑ provide insightful answers?
- ❑ pose insightful questions?

### Informal Assessment

**Concept/Question Board**

Did the student APPLYING

- ❑ apply learning in new situations?
- ❑ contribute concepts?
- ❑ contribute answers?
- ❑ connect mathematics to real-world situations?

### Formal Assessment

**Pretest** COMPUTING

Review student answers in each problem set.

- ❑ Perimeter and area (Problems 1–3)
- ❑ Multidigit multiplication (Problems 4–9)
- ❑ Exponents (Problems 10–11)
- ❑ Angles (Problems 12–14)
- ❑ Lines (Problems 15–16)
- ❑ Quadrilaterals (Problem 17)
- ❑ Triangles (Problem 18)

## B Summarize Findings

Analyze and summarize assessment data for each student. Determine which Assessment Follow-Up is appropriate for each student. Use the Student Assessment Record in ***Assessment*** or ***eAssess*** to update assessment records.

## C Assessment Follow-Up • DIFFERENTIATE INSTRUCTION

| ENRICH | PRACTICE | RETEACH | INTERVENTION | ENGLISH LEARNER |
|---|---|---|---|---|
| **If . . .** students demonstrate a secure understanding of chapter concepts,<br>**Then . . .** move quickly through the chapter or use ***Enrichment*** Lessons 10.1–10.14 as assessment follow-up to extend and apply understanding. | **If . . .** students grasp chapter concepts with competent understanding,<br>**Then . . .** use ***Practice*** Lessons 10.1–10.14 as lesson follow-up to develop fluency. | **If . . .** students have prerequisite understanding but demonstrate emerging understanding of chapter concepts,<br>**Then . . .** use ***Reteach*** Lesson 10.7 to reteach lesson concepts. | **If . . .** students are not competent with prerequisite skills,<br>**Then . . .** use ***Intervention*** Lessons 10.A–10.C before each lesson to develop fluency with prerequisite skills. | Use ***English Learner Support Guide*** Lessons 10.1–10.14 for strategies to preteach lesson vocabulary and concepts. |

# Math Across the Curriculum

Preview the chapter projects with students. Assign or have students choose from the projects to extend and enrich concepts in this chapter.

## Write a Shape Poem in Uncontracted Braille

LANGUAGE ARTS

2–3 weeks

**MATH OBJECTIVE**
To reinforce studies of shape by choosing and drawing a shape for a shape poem

**LANGUAGE ARTS OBJECTIVE**
To reinforce studies of rhyme by writing a shape poem with rhyming words

**TECHNOLOGY OBJECTIVE**
To use keyboarding skills to write a poem

Have students use mathematics to write a shape poem in uncontracted Braille. To broaden the language arts concept, have students write poems using types of figurative language you are currently studying.

As part of the project, students should consider the following issues:

- the shape of objects
- the mathematical properties of shapes
- how to write a shape poem
- how to create a shape poem in a word processing program
- the use of rhyme
- the uncontracted Braille alphabet

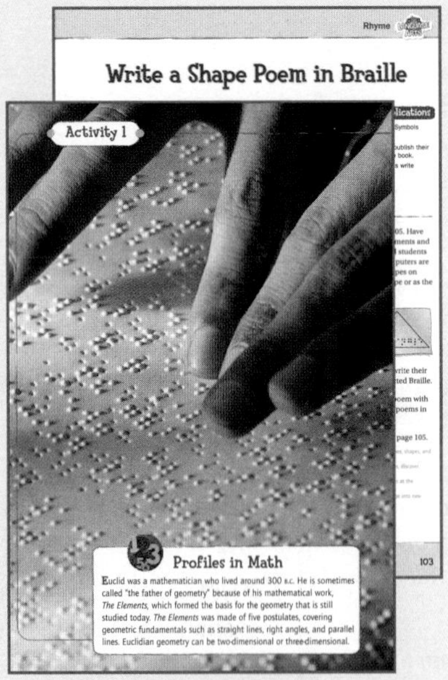


For specific step-by-step instructions for this project, see ***Across the Curriculum Math Connections*** pages 102–105.

### Knowledge Age Skills

**Problem Formulation, Planning, and Strategizing** Students plan and strategize to write a rhyming poem within a shape, in both standard English and uncontracted Braille.

**Creative Work with Ideas** Students explore the information within the task of writing a shape poem in uncontracted Braille.

## Design a New Writing System

SCIENCE WebQuest

1–2 weeks

**MATH OBJECTIVE**
To reinforce studies of math by using geometry to create a new written language

**SCIENCE OBJECTIVE**
To reinforce studies of the concepts of rotation, reflection, and translation

**TECHNOLOGY OBJECTIVE**
To use a drawing and graphics program to design a new written language

Have students use technology to research ancient written languages and create a geometry-based written language.

- Have students use the Internet to view ancient written languages.
- Have students use a drawing and graphics program to design their geometry-based written languages.

For this project, students use the Internet to investigate the following types of information:

- rotation, reflection, and translation of geometric shapes
- ancient written languages
- international symbols

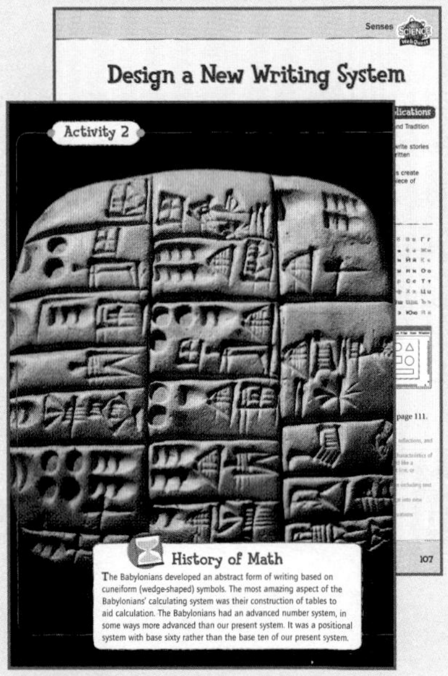


For specific step-by-step instructions for this project, see ***Across the Curriculum Math Connections*** pages 106–111.

### Knowledge Age Skills

**Effective Communication** Students create a written language they use to communicate information to a classmate.

**Creative Work with Ideas** Students use ancient written languages to think creatively about human communication and to design a written system that uses the conventions of geometry.

***TechKnowledge*** Level 4 provides lessons that specifically teach the Unit 10 Internet and Unit 4 Drawing and Graphics applications that students can use in this project.

## Lesson Planner

**OBJECTIVES**
- To introduce the terms *line segment, ray,* and *vertex*
- To allow students to explore relationships among lines, points, and angles

**NCTM STANDARDS**

**Geometry**
- Develop vocabulary to describe the attributes of two- and three-dimensional shapes
- Draw geometric objects

**Reasoning and Proof**
Investigate mathematical conjectures

**MATERIALS**
- *Response Wheels
- *Ruler or straightedge
- Flashlight

**TECHNOLOGY**
- **Presentation** Lesson 10.1
- **MathTools** Geometry Tool
- **MathTools** Net Tool
- **Games** Don't Go Over 1,000 Game

**TEST PREP**

**Cumulative Review**
Mental Math reviews multiplying by multiples of 10.

**Extended Response**
Problems 1b, 7, and 12

### Looking Ahead

For Lesson 10.2, you will need a clock with moveable hands and an overhead projector. You will also have to prepare an overhead projector transparency showing two angles (40° and 140°).

*Manipulative Kit Item

# Lines

**Context of the Lesson** This lesson begins a series of fourteen lessons in which students explore topics in geometry by creating, manipulating, and postulating about figures, lines, and points. This informal approach of allowing students to explore geometric concepts is more appropriate in Grade 4 than taking a more formal approach. This is the first of three lessons devoted to points, lines, and angles.

See page 446B for Math Background for teachers for this lesson.

## Planning for Learning • DIFFERENTIATE INSTRUCTION

### INTERVENTION

**If . . .** students lack the prerequisite skill of classifying figures,

**Then . . .** teach ***Intervention*** Lesson 10.A.

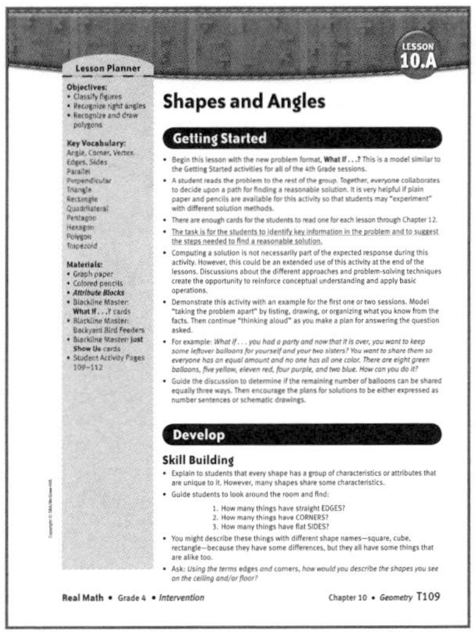


Intervention Lesson 10.A

### ENGLISH LEARNER

Preview

**If . . .** students need language support,

**Then . . .** use Lesson 10.1 in ***English Learner Support Guide*** to preview lesson concepts and vocabulary.

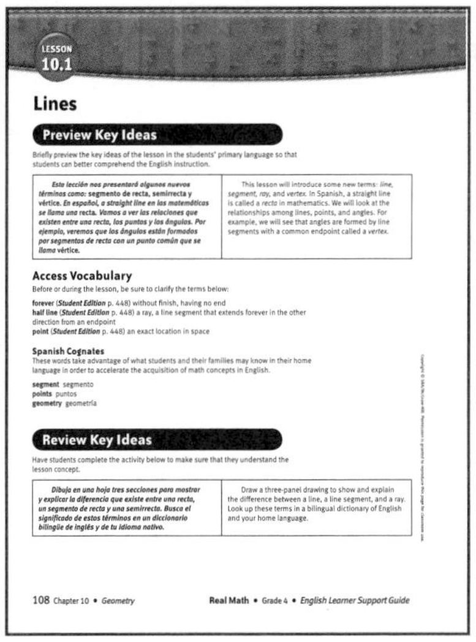


English Learner Lesson 10.1

### ENRICH

**If . . .** students are proficient in the lesson concepts,

**Then . . .** have them explore the ***eMathTools: Geometry Tool*** to create an activity involving lines.

### PRACTICE

**If . . .** students would benefit from additional practice,

**Then . . .** extend Guided Discussion before assigning the student pages.

### RETEACH

**If . . .** students have difficulty identifying lines, line segments, and rays,

**Then . . .** extend Guided Discussion before assigning the student pages.

**Vocabulary**

**ray** \rā\ ***n.*** a part of a line that has one endpoint and extends indefinitely in one direction

**line segment *n.*** a connected part of a line with two endpoints

**Access Vocabulary**

**point** an exact location in space

**Spanish Cognates**

**segment** segmento
**points** puntos
**geometry** geometría

## Mental Math

5

RESPONSE WHEEL Provide practice in multiplying by multiples of 10 and 100, using problems such as the following:

**a.** $2 \times 10 = 20$ **b.** $7 \times 60 = 420$
**c.** $8 \times 50 = 400$ **d.** $2 \times 20 = 40$
**e.** $70 \times 6 = 420$ **f.** $8 \times 500 = 4{,}000$
**g.** $2 \times 40 = 80$ **h.** $7 \times 600 = 4{,}200$

## 1 Develop

25

**Tell Students In Today's Lesson They Will**
learn the difference and relation between a point, a line, a line segment, and a ray.

### Guided Discussion

UNDERSTANDING **e MathTools**

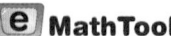

Discuss the meanings of the words *point, line,* and *angle,* and have students come to the board to draw examples of each.

1. Draw an example of a ray on the board or use the ***eMathTools: Geometry Tool.*** Ask questions such as the following:
   - **This is an example of a ray. Does a ray look different from a line?** yes
   - **How is a ray different from a line?** A ray continues in only one direction.
2. Then draw the angle *ABC* on the board. Ask questions such as the following:

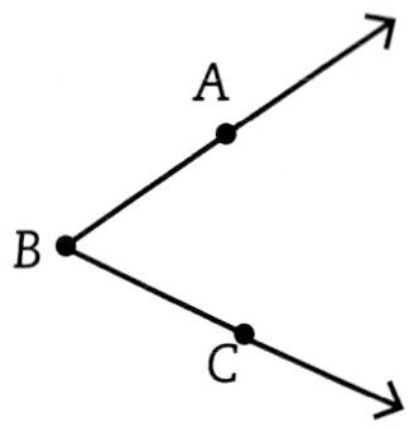


   - **Examine this angle closely. What does it look like?** It looks like two rays joined together at a common endpoint.
   - **What would you name this angle?** angle *ABC*

   Point out that the common endpoint of an angle is called the vertex, and angles can be named by using only the vertex, if there is only one angle with that vertex.
   - **What is another name for this angle?** angle *B*
3. Next draw an example of a line segment on the board. Ask questions such as the following:
   - **This is an example of a line segment. How is it different from a ray?** It has two endpoints, not one.
   - **What is the difference between a line and a line segment?** A line segment is part of a line and has two endpoints. A line does not have endpoints.

## 2 Assign Student Pages

20

**Pages 448–449** APPLYING

Small Group

Have students complete page 449 in pairs or small groups. Encourage students to draw enough examples to ensure they have adequately resolved each problem. Bring the pairs or groups together to discuss their answers as a class.

**Monitoring Student Progress**

| If . . . | Then . . . |
|---|---|
| **If . . .** students need a concrete example of a ray or a line segment, | **Then . . .** use a flashlight to demonstrate a ray, and a piece of string with knots tied at the ends to demonstrate a line segment. |

### As Students Finish

**Game** **Don't Go Over 1,000 Game**

**e Games** ***Don't Go Over 1,000 Game*** (reviews addition)

**e MathTools** In preparation for later lessons, have students use the ***eMathTools: Net Tool*** to make space figures. They can also use the polygon patterns provided in ***Practice.***

Student Page

LESSON 10.1 Lines

## Key Ideas

**Words like *line, point, ray, angle,* and *vertex* are used to describe geometric figures.**

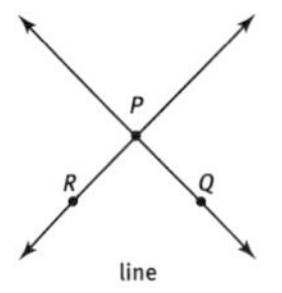


A point is an exact location in the plane or in space. Two points determine a straight line (which will be called a line from now on). If two lines intersect, they intersect at a point. We draw arrows on the end of lines to indicate that the line goes on forever in both directions.

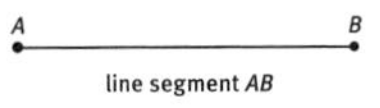


Sometimes you will need to refer to just a part of a line. If the part has two endpoints, it is called a line segment (see line segment *AB* in the picture below).

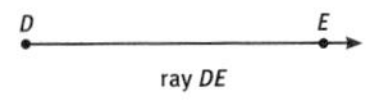


If the part has only one endpoint and goes on forever in the other direction, it is called a ray, or sometimes a half-line (see ray *DE*). The first letter in the name of the ray is its endpoint.

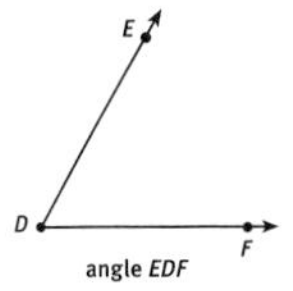


An angle is made from two rays with the same endpoint, also called the vertex. Angles are named using a point on one ray, the vertex, and a point on the other ray. Sometimes angles are named simply by their vertex. For example, the angle to the left is named angle *EDF*, angle *FDE*, or angle *D*.



eTextbook This lesson is available in the ***eTextbook***.

Student Page

**Answer** the following questions.

1. Suppose two distinct lines meet at point *P*.
   - **a.** Could they also meet at some other point? At point *T*? no
   - **b.** Extended Response Explain why you think this. See Reflect in the ***Teacher's Edition.***
2. Suppose there are two points. How many lines do you think you could draw that go through both points? one
3. On your paper, draw two lines that meet at as many points as possible. At how many points do they meet? one
4. On your paper mark two points.
   - **a.** Draw as many different lines through the two points as you can.
   - **b.** How many lines is that? one
5. Look at angle *EDF* in the picture on page 448.
   - **a.** Is it made up of two rays? yes
   - **b.** What is the endpoint of each ray? point *D*
6. Can you tell which angle is angle *D* on page 448? yes
7. Extended Response On page 448, can you tell which angle is angle *P*? Explain. See Reflect in the ***Teacher's Edition.***

**Name** the following in two ways. Remember to use only two letters for lines, line segments, and rays.

8. 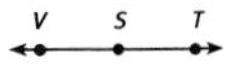

For example, line *VS*, line *ST*, or line *VT*
9. 

ray *XY*, ray *XZ*
10. 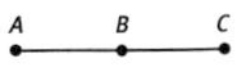

line segment *AC*, line segment *CA*
11. Draw a line, a ray, and a line segment.
12. Extended Response Which is longer, a line segment or a line? Explain. See Reflect in the ***Teacher's Edition.***



# 3 Reflect

10

## Guided Discussion REASONING

Whole Group

1. Show students a globe and ask questions such as the following:
   - **What are the lines going through the North and South Poles called?** longitude lines
   - **Are these lines like the ones we have been studying?** Students will probably say no.
2. Explain to the students that the lines of longitude can only be considered straight lines, like they have been studying, if they look at a small portion of Earth as a plane.

## Extended Response

**Problem 1b** Look for insightful remarks about how straight lines cannot bend back to cross each other a second time. Someone might argue that if the two lines were on top of each other, there would be a lot of common points. All the points would be on both lines, and therefore they would not be distinct lines.

**Problem 7** Students should respond that they do not know which angle is angle *P* because it could be one of four angles or one of two straight angles.

**Problem 12** Students should indicate that a line is longer than a line segment because its arrows dictate that it goes on forever in both directions, whereas a line segment contains two endpoints.

**Cumulative Review:** For review of multidigit addition and subtraction, assign Problems 1–2 on student page 464.

**Family Involvement:** Assign the ***Practice, Reteach,*** or ***Enrichment*** activities depending on the needs of your students.

**Concept/Question Board:** Have students think of additional examples of lines and post them on the Concept/Question Board.

**Math Puzzler:** Between 8:00 A.M. and 4:00 P.M. about what times do the clock hands form straight line segments? 8:10 A.M., 9:15 A.M., 10:20 A.M., 11:25 A.M., 12:30 P.M., 1:40 P.M., 2:45 P.M., and 3:50 P.M.

# 4 Assess and Differentiate

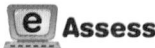

e Assess Use ***eAssess*** to record and analyze evidence of student understanding.

## A Gather Evidence

Use the Daily Class Assessment Records in ***Assessment*** or ***eAssess*** to record daily observations.

### Informal Assessment

**✓ Mental Math**

Did the student COMPUTING

- ❑ respond accurately?
- ❑ respond quickly?
- ❑ respond with confidence?
- ❑ self-correct?

### Formal Assessment

**✓ Extended Response**

Did the student REASONING

- ❑ provide a clear explanation?
- ❑ communicate reasons and strategies?
- ❑ choose appropriate strategies?
- ❑ argue logically?

## B Summarize Findings

Analyze and summarize assessment data for each student. Determine which Assessment Follow-Up is appropriate for each student. Use the Student Assessment Record in ***Assessment*** or ***eAssess*** to update assessment records.

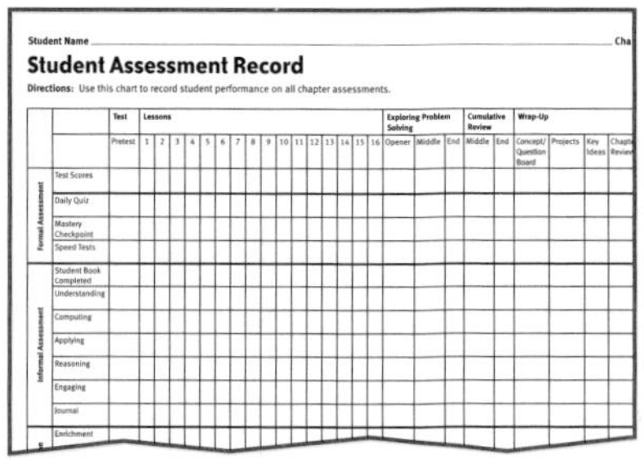

Student Assessment Record

Assessment Page T41

## C Assessment Follow-Up • DIFFERENTIATE INSTRUCTION

Based on your observations, use these teaching strategies for assessment follow-up.

### INTERVENTION

Review student performance on ***Intervention*** Lesson 10.A to see if students have mastered prerequisite skills for this lesson.

### ENGLISH LEARNER

**Review**

Use Lesson 10.1 in ***English Learner Support Guide*** to review lesson concepts and vocabulary.

### ENRICH

**If . . .** students are proficient in the lesson concepts,

**Then . . .** encourage them to work on the chapter projects or ***Enrichment*** Lesson 10.1.

LESSON 10.1 Name ______ Date ______

**Lines**

**Sea Shells**

A scientist did five shells find
While nothing much was on his mind.
He made two lines—three shells in each—
While he relaxed on the sunny beach.

One vertical line of shells appeared,
And then, just as you may have feared,
A horizontal line he made,
And then he drank some lemonade!

**Draw** how the scientist made two lines of three shells using only five shells.

Answers vary. An example is shown.

108 Chapter 10 • *Geometry* **Real Math** • Grade 4 • *Enrichment Support Guide*

Enrichment Lesson 10.1

### PRACTICE

**If . . .** students would benefit from additional practice,

**Then . . .** assign ***Practice*** Lesson 10.1.

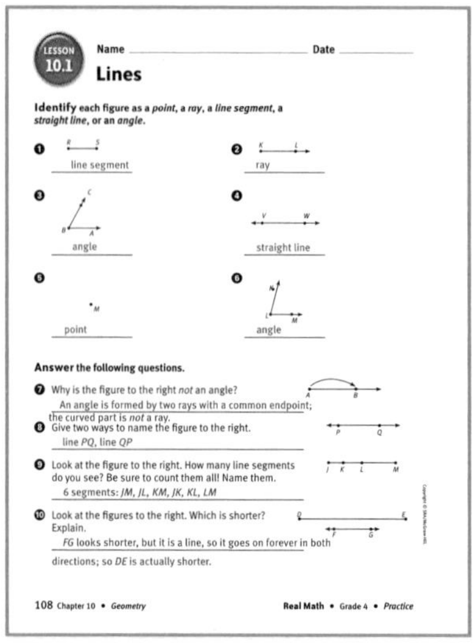

LESSON 10.1 Name ______ Date ______

**Lines**

**Identify** each figure as a *point*, a *ray*, a *line segment*, a *straight line*, or an *angle*.

1. line segment
2. ray
3. angle
4. straight line
5. point
6. angle

**Answer the following questions.**

7. Why is the figure to the right *not* an angle? An angle is formed by two rays with a common endpoint; the curved part is *not* a ray.
8. Give two ways to name the figure to the right. line *PQ*, line *QP*
9. Look at the figure to the right. How many line segments do you see? Be sure to count them all! Name them. 6 segments: *JM, JL, KM, JK, KL, LM*
10. Look at the figures to the right. Which is shorter? Explain. *FG* looks shorter, but it is a line, so it goes on forever in both directions; so *DE* is actually shorter.

108 Chapter 10 • *Geometry* **Real Math** • Grade 4 • *Practice*

Practice Lesson 10.1

### RETEACH

**If . . .** students have difficulty identifying lines, line segments, and rays,

**Then . . .** have them find examples of each around the classroom. Have students write down each of the words introduced in this lesson. Then have them draw an example of what that word means. Have students share their examples on the board. Discuss ways that their examples are similar and different.

## Lesson Planner

**OBJECTIVES**
- To demonstrate that an angle can be thought of as a rotation
- To define *right, acute,* and *obtuse* angles
- To help students develop the concept of the measurement of angles as fractions of a complete rotation
- To define the rotational directions *clockwise* and *counterclockwise*

**NCTM STANDARDS**

**Measurement**
Measure angles

**Geometry**
Recognize angles as right, acute, and obtuse

**MATERIALS**
- *Response Wheels
- *Protractors
- Overhead projector and prepared transparency

**TECHNOLOGY**

**e Presentation** Lesson 10.2
**e MathTools** Geometry Tool and Net Tool
**e Games** Roll a 15 Game

**TEST PREP**

**Cumulative Review**
Mental Math reviews multidigit operational exercises (Lessons 2.3 and 5.4).

**Extended Response**
Problems 2, 3, and 10

**Writing + Math**
Journal

*Manipulative Kit Item

# Angles

**Context of the Lesson** This is the second of three lessons on lines, points, and angles. In this lesson, students will be introduced to the terms *obtuse* and *acute* to describe angles. Students will also be asked to measure angles with a protractor and recognize that angles are related to fractional turns of rays. In Lesson 10.5 students will be asked to use the terms *right*, *acute*, and *obtuse* to classify triangles.

See page 446B for Math Background for teachers for this lesson.

## Planning for Learning • DIFFERENTIATE INSTRUCTION

### INTERVENTION

**If . . .** students lack the prerequisite skill of recognizing right angles,

**Then . . .** teach ***Intervention*** Lesson 10.B.

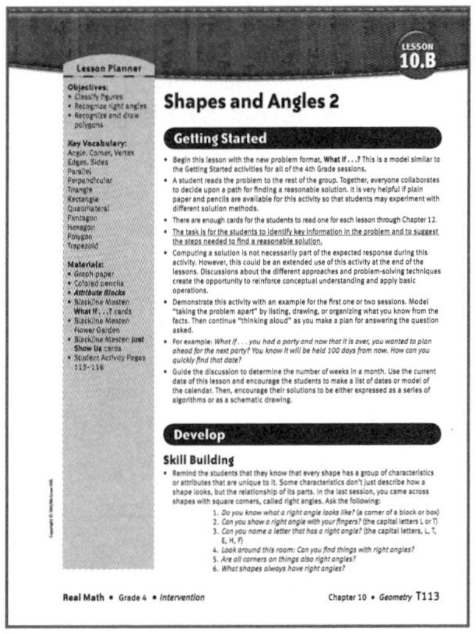
LESSON 10.B
Lesson Planner
Shapes and Angles 2
Getting Started
Develop
Skill Building
Real Math • Grade 4 • Intervention Chapter 10 • Geometry T113

Intervention Lesson 10.B

### ENGLISH LEARNER

Preview

**If . . .** students need language support,

**Then . . .** use Lesson 10.2 in ***English Learner Support Guide*** to preview lesson concepts and vocabulary.

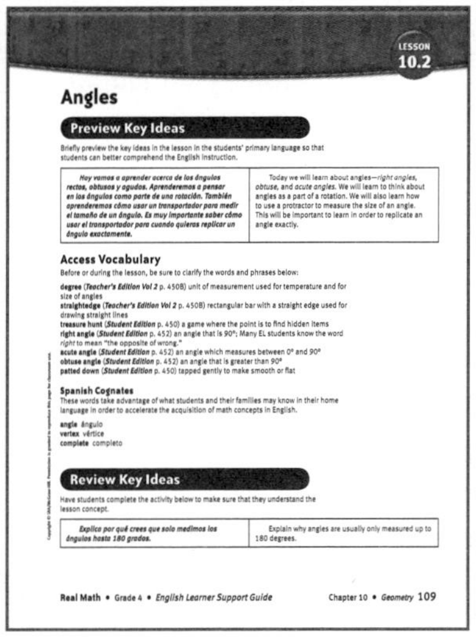
LESSON 10.2
Angles
Preview Key Ideas
Access Vocabulary
Spanish Cognates
Review Key Ideas
Real Math • Grade 4 • English Learner Support Guide Chapter 10 • Geometry 109

English Learner Lesson 10.2

### ENRICH

**If . . .** students are proficient in the lesson concepts,

**Then . . .** have them explore the ***eMathTools: Geometry Tool*** to create an activity involving angles.

### PRACTICE

**If . . .** students would benefit from additional practice,

**Then . . .** extend Skill Building before assigning the student pages.

### RETEACH

**If . . .** students have difficulty measuring angles correctly,

**Then . . .** extend Skill Building before assigning the student pages.

### Vocabulary

**vertex \ver′ teks\ *n.*** 1. the point on an angle where two rays meet 2. the point of intersection of two adjacent sides of a polygon 3. the point of intersection of three or more edges of a space figure

### Access Vocabulary

**degree** a unit of measurement used for temperature and for size of angles
**straightedge** a rectangular bar with a straight edge used for drawing straight lines

**Spanish Cognates**
**angle** ángulo
**vertex** vértice

## Mental Math 5

Review  RESPONSE WHEEL  Give the students exercises with multidigit numbers such as the following:

| | |
|---|---|
| **a.** 25 + 37 = 62 | **b.** 358 + 30 = 388 |
| **c.** 68 − 29 = 39 | **d.** 322 − 97 = 225 |
| **e.** 3 × 40 = 120 | **f.** 30 × 40 = 1,200 |
| **g.** 120 × 4 = 480 | **h.** 12 × 40 = 480 |

## 1 Develop 30

**Tell Students In Today's Lesson They Will**
learn about right, acute, and obtuse angles and how to measure them.

Whole Group

### Using Student Pages UNDERSTANDING eMathTools

Introduce the concept of angles with a story such as the one on student page 450, pointing out the need for a way to measure angles.

1. Begin the activity with questions such as the following:
   - **What does *clockwise* mean?** the direction in which the hands of a clock move
   - **What does *counterclockwise* means?** Explain that *counter* means "opposite or reverse," so the counterclockwise direction is opposite to that of a clock hand's rotation.
   - **What is a treasure hunt?** Make sure students understand how a treasure hunt works.
2. Read and discuss the story, which starts on page 450 and continues through page 451, with the class. As you are reading the story, pause for the discussion questions. Be sure students understand why Ahmal's eventual solution, including both distance (7 meters) and direction ($\frac{1}{6}$ of a turn clockwise), provides sufficient information.

   To make sure students understand how to describe the measures of angles by fractions of a turn, draw a few examples on the board or overhead projector, and ask for volunteers to demonstrate the corresponding rotation by turning their bodies. You can also use the ***eMathTools: Geometry Tool*** to draw the angles.

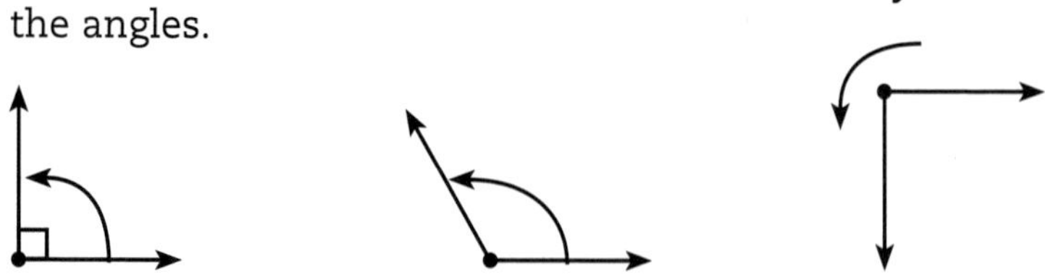

$\frac{1}{4}$ turn  $\frac{1}{3}$ turn  $\frac{3}{4}$ turn

3. Read page 452 with students. Ask them to draw examples on the board of acute, right and obtuse angles.

### Skill Building UNDERSTANDING

Make sure each student has a protractor. Explain that a protractor is the tool used to measure angles in degrees. Using an overhead projector, show students how to measure an angle.

1. Draw any angle and show them how to place the protractor so that the little hole is on the vertex of the angle and the line of the protractor is on one side of the angle. Explain that the other side of the angle goes through a number that tells you how many degrees are in the angle. Explain that if students have a difficult time reading the measurement, they can use a straightedge to extend the length of the ray.
2. On a transparency prepared ahead of time, show two angles, P and Q, that might appear to have similar measurements, such as 40°and 140°.

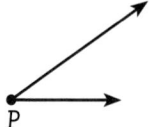

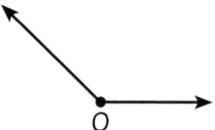

   Place a protractor on angle P (40°) and ask questions such as the following:
   - **Is angle P an acute or an obtuse angle?** acute
   - **Since the angle is acute, what do you know about its size?** Its measure must be less than 90°.
   - **Use the protractor to find the measurement of angle P.** The measure of angle P must be 40°.

   Place the protractor on angle Q (140°). Ask students questions such as the following:
   - **Is angle Q an acute or an obtuse angle?** obtuse
   - **Since the angle is obtuse, what do you know about its size?** Its measure must be greater than 90° and less than 180°.
   - **If you use a protractor to find the size of angle Q, what do you notice?** One side of angle Q goes through the same numbers that the side of angle P went through.
   - **Does this mean that the angles P and Q are the same size?** No, they cannot be the same size because angle P is acute and angle Q is obtuse.
3. Show students that there are two scales on a protractor. Ask them questions such as the following:
   - **Why do you think there are two scales?** So you do not have to flip the protractor over. One scale measures the angle to the right and one measures the angle to the left.
   - **What is the measurement of angle Q?** 140°

   Have students use a straightedge to draw some angles on a piece of paper. Have them practice measuring the angles using a protractor. Walk around the room to check students' progress and assist students who are having difficulty using a protractor.

# 2 Assign Student Pages

20

### Page 451

The questions on page 451 may be answered as a class or individually. These questions correspond with the story that began on page 450. These pages show students how angles can be seen in relation to objects turning. You may wish to provide more practice for this idea by having students move their bodies a certain fraction of a circle to demonstrate different angles.

#### RESEARCH IN ACTION

"Overall research indicates that all types of geometric ideas appear to develop over time, becoming increasingly integrated and synthesized. . . . Children's ideas about shapes do not come from passive looking. Instead, they come as children's bodies, hand, eyes, and minds engage in active construction. In addition, children need to explore shapes extensively to fully understand them; merely seeing and naming pictures is insufficient. Finally, they have to explore the parts and attributes of shapes."

Clements, Douglas H. "Teaching and Learning Geometry" in Kilpatrick, Jeremy, Martin, W. Gary, and Schifter, Deborah, eds. *A Research Companion to Principles and Standards for School Mathematics.* Reston, VA: National Council of Teachers of Mathematics, Inc. 2003. p. 152.

Student Page

LESSON 10.2

## Angles

**Key Ideas**

**Angles are just as important as distance when giving directions, and, just like distances, angles can be measured.**

**Which Way to the Prize?** READING

"Everyone at our party is going to enjoy the treasure hunt," said Ahmal. He and Hadley were burying the treasure, a new calculator, in their backyard.

"And whoever finds the prize will enjoy the hunt most of all," said Hadley.

Ahmal and Hadley filled in the hole, patted down the dirt, and then made up clues that would lead people to the treasure map.

"The directions we make should tell where the prize is so that whoever finds the map can find the buried calculator without any more guessing," said Hadley.

Ahmal wrote directions saying that the prize was buried seven meters from the big rock.

But Hadley didn't think the directions were complete. "Whoever reads these directions still won't know where the prize is," he said.

Why not? Ahmal's directions tell how far the treasure is from the rock, but they do not show the direction.

"Well," said Ahmal, "I'll write these words: 'Stand at the rock, look at the tree, and walk seven meters to the right'."

"But the person still won't know where to dig," said Hadley.

1. Why isn't Ahmal's idea good enough? There may be more than one tree and more than one way to go "to the right."

450 Textbook This lesson is available in the *eTextbook.*

Student Page

"I've got another idea," said Ahmal, as he drew a line on the map from the tree to the rock. "All I have to do is write down how big this angle is," he said. "Then whoever reads the directions can stand at the rock, look at the tree, turn the correct amount to the right, walk seven meters, and dig."

How can Ahmal write down how big the angle is?

Ahmal thought about how to describe the size of the angle. "If I stand on the rock, face the tree, and then turn completely around, I will be facing the tree again. If I turn one-half of the way around, I will be facing directly away from the tree. If I turn one-quarter of the way around, I still will have passed the point where I would be facing the treasure. I think I would be facing the treasure if I just turned about one-sixth of the way around."

Ahmal wrote,

"Stand on the big rock. Look at the closest tree. Turn to your right (or clockwise) until you have made $\frac{1}{6}$ of a complete turn. Walk 7 meters. Dig."

2. Extended Response Is this enough information? Explain. See Reflect in the *Teacher's Edition.*

Chapter 10 • Lesson 2 451

# Assign Student Pages, continued

### Pages 452–453

Small Group

Have students begin work on the problems on pages 452–453 with partners. Encourage students to double check each other's work and help each other with measuring angles.

## Monitoring Student Progress

| | |
|---|---|
| **If . . .** students are confused between the size of an angle and the length of its sides, | **Then . . .** it may help to show how extending the sides of the angle does not change the "measure" of the angle. It may also help to define *acute, right,* and *obtuse* angles in terms of fractions of a turn. |
| **If . . .** students have difficulty classifying the angle when it does not have a horizontal side, | **Then . . .** have students use a moveable right angle, such as the corner of an index card. They can place the right angle at the vertex of any angle. It should be easy to see whether the angle is less than a right angle, equal to a right angle, or greater than a right angle. |

## As Students Finish

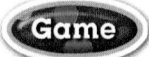

**Game** **Roll a 15 Game** (reviews addition and subtraction)

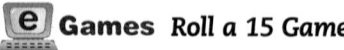

**eGames** ***Roll a 15 Game***

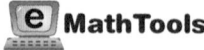

**eMathTools** In preparation for later lessons, have students use the ***eMathTools***: ***Net Tool*** to make space figures. They can also use the polygon patterns provided in ***Practice.***



---

Student Page



An angle that is "one-fourth of a complete turn" is called a right angle. These are right angles:

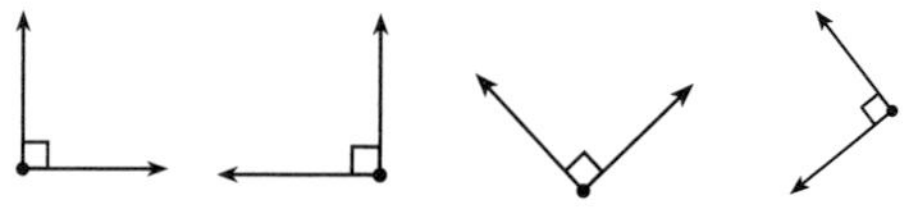

An angle that is less than a right angle is called an acute angle. These are acute angles:

An angle that is more than a right angle (but less than half of a complete turn) is called an obtuse angle. These are obtuse angles:

3 **Extended Response** What kind of an angle is $\frac{1}{6}$ of a complete turn? Explain your answer. See Reflect in the *Teacher's Edition.*



**eTextbook** This lesson is available in the ***eTextbook.***

---

Student Page

Each angle below is labeled with a letter at the corner of the angle.

The corner of the angle is called the vertex. The two intersecting lines, rays, or line segments that make the angle are called the *sides of the angle.*

Tell whether each angle is an acute angle, a right angle, or an obtuse angle.

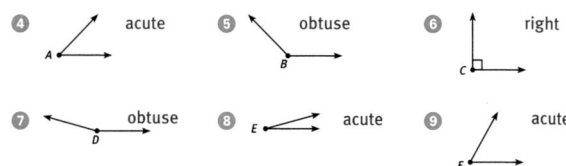

4 A acute

5 B obtuse

6 C right

7 D obtuse

8 E acute

9 F acute

10 **Extended Response** Explain an easy way to describe the difference between acute, obtuse and right angles to another student. See Reflect in the *Teacher's Edition.*

**Use** **your protractor to measure these angles.**

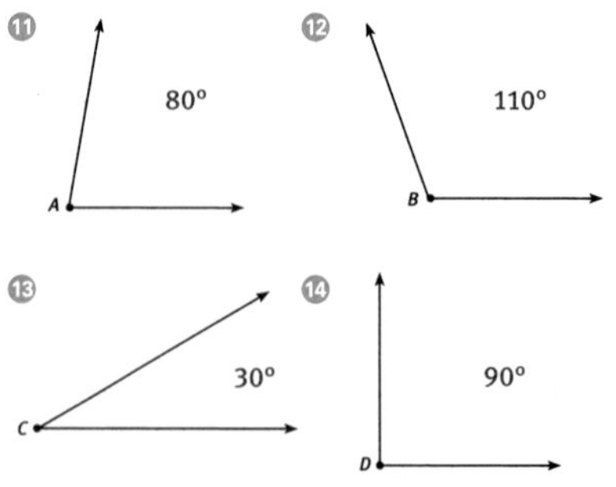


**Writing + Math**

**Journal**

Explain how fractional turns are related to angles, and provide two examples of fractional turns as angles.

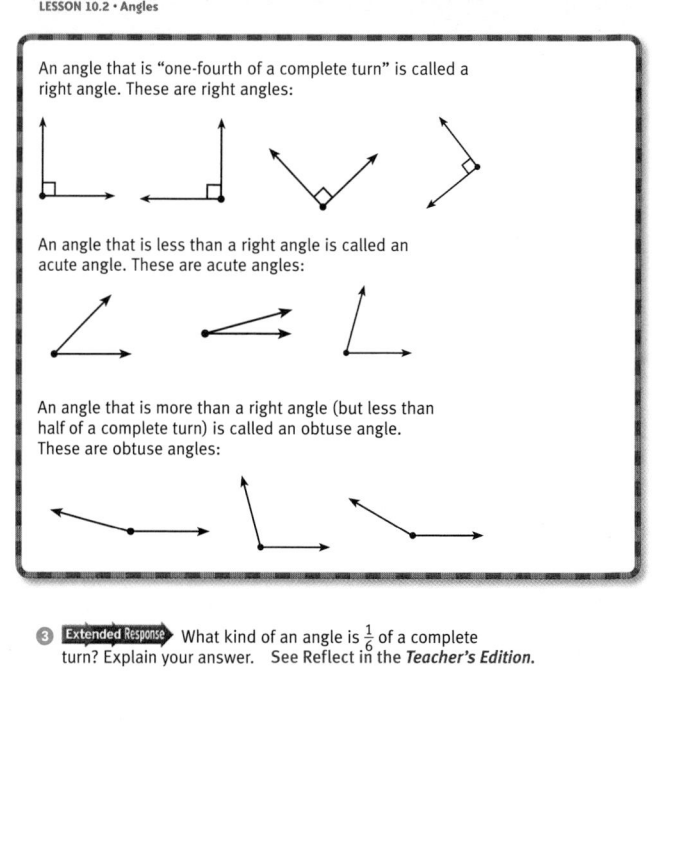

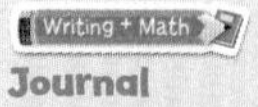

# 3 Reflect

5

## Guided Discussion REASONING

Whole Group

Prompt students to explain how they decide whether an angle is acute, right, or obtuse. Ask questions such as the following:

- **Did you use any tools or rules of thumb to tell the difference between the types of angles?**
- **Can you think of a memory tool to help you remember how to tell the difference between the types of angles?** Possible answers: An acute angle is "a cute little angle," or an obtuse angle is more "open" than a right angle (because both start with the letter *o*).

### Applications APPLYING

Present the following problem to the class: Eleanor wants a house with no right angles. Draw an example for her. Remember, even doors and windows cannot have right angles.

## Extended Response

**Problem 2** The reader is provided enough information to travel to the right place.

**Problem 3** Students may notice that $\frac{1}{6}$ is a smaller fraction than $\frac{1}{4}$; therefore a $\frac{1}{6}$ rotation is less than a rotation through 90°.

**Problem 10** Students should define the various angles. One possibility: Right angles are similar to a corner of a sheet of paper, while an obtuse angle is larger than a corner, and an acute angle is smaller than a corner.

Writing + Math Journal

Students will need to mention how the movement of an object in a clockwise or counterclockwise motion can be measured as a specific angle from the objects' origin. Common examples: a $\frac{1}{4}$ turn is equal to a 90° angle, and a $\frac{1}{2}$ turn is equal to a 180° angle.

**Curriculum Connection:** Students interested in treasures and treasure maps may enjoy reading Robert Louis Stevenson's classic novel *Treasure Island,* or *Holes* by Louis Sachar. Both books should be available at your library.

**Cumulative Review:** For review of addition and subtraction with hidden digits, assign Problems 3–5 on student page 464.

**Family Involvement:** Assign the ***Practice, Reteach,*** or ***Enrichment*** activities depending on the needs of your students.

**Concept/Question Board:** Have students think of additional examples of angles and post them on the Concept/Question Board.

**Math Puzzler:** Look at the clock and determine which times will create acute, right, and obtuse angles using the hands of the clock. Some possibilities: acute angles: 1:10, 2:05, 10:50, and 11:00; obtuse angles: 4:00, 5:45, 7:10, and 8:00; and right angles: 3:00 and 9:00.

# 4 Assess and Differentiate

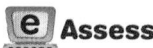

**e Assess** Use ***eAssess*** to record and analyze evidence of student understanding.

## A Gather Evidence

Use the Daily Class Assessment Records in ***Assessment*** or ***eAssess*** to record daily observations.

### Portfolio Assessment

**Journal**

ENGAGING

Did the student

- ❑ pay attention to others' contributions?
- ❑ contribute information and ideas?
- ❑ improve on a strategy?
- ❑ reflect on and check the accuracy of his or her work?

### Informal Assessment

**Skill Building**

UNDERSTANDING

Did the student

- ❑ make important observations?
- ❑ extend or generalize learning?
- ❑ provide insightful answers?
- ❑ pose insightful questions?

## B Summarize Findings

Analyze and summarize assessment data for each student. Determine which Assessment Follow-Up is appropriate for each student. Use the Student Assessment Record in ***Assessment*** or ***eAssess*** to update assessment records.

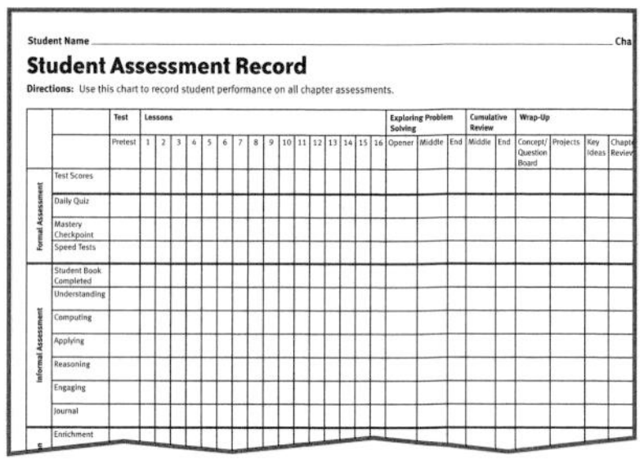


Assessment Page T41

## C Assessment Follow-Up • DIFFERENTIATE INSTRUCTION

Based on your observations, use these teaching strategies for assessment follow-up.

### INTERVENTION

Review student performance on ***Intervention*** Lesson 10.B to see if students have mastered prerequisite skills for this lesson.

### ENGLISH LEARNER

**Review**

Use Lesson 10.2 in ***English Learner Support Guide*** to review lesson concepts and vocabulary.

### ENRICH

**If . . .** students are proficient in the lesson concepts,

**Then . . .** encourage them to work on the chapter projects or ***Enrichment*** Lesson 10.2.

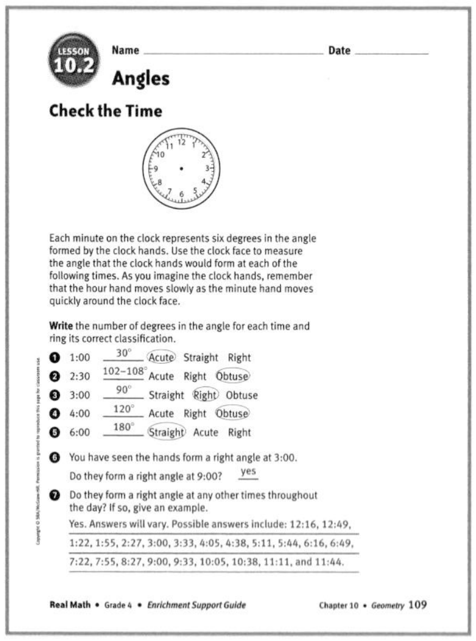

LESSON 10.2 Name ______ Date ______

**Angles**

**Check the Time**

Each minute on the clock represents six degrees in the angle formed by the clock hands. Use the clock face to measure the angle that the clock hands would form at each of the following times. As you imagine the clock hands, remember that the hour hand moves slowly as the minute hand moves quickly around the clock face.

**Write** the number of degrees in the angle for each time and ring its correct classification.

1. 1:00 30° (Acute) Straight Right
2. 2:30 102–108° Acute Right (Obtuse)
3. 3:00 90° Straight (Right) Obtuse
4. 4:00 120° Acute Right (Obtuse)
5. 6:00 180° (Straight) Acute Right
6. You have seen the hands form a right angle at 3:00. Do they form a right angle at 9:00? yes
7. Do they form a right angle at any other times throughout the day? If so, give an example. Yes. Answers will vary. Possible answers include: 12:16, 12:49, 1:22, 1:55, 2:27, 3:00, 3:33, 4:05, 4:38, 5:11, 5:44, 6:16, 6:49, 7:22, 7:55, 8:27, 9:00, 9:33, 10:05, 10:38, 11:11, and 11:44.

Real Math • Grade 4 • *Enrichment Support Guide* Chapter 10 • *Geometry* 109

Enrichment Lesson 10.2

### PRACTICE

**If . . .** students would benefit from additional practice,

**Then . . .** assign ***Practice*** Lesson 10.2.

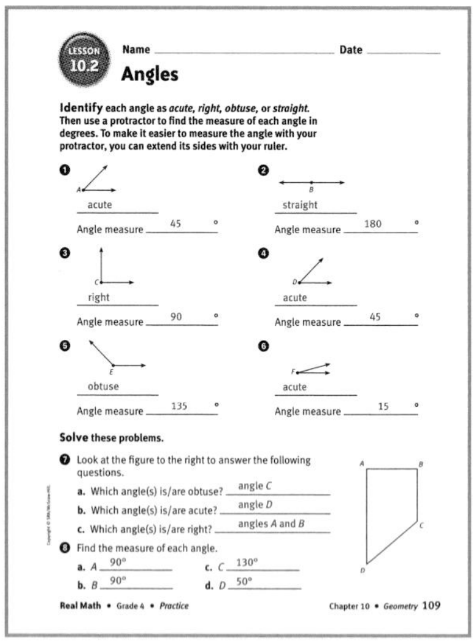

LESSON 10.2 Name ______ Date ______

**Angles**

**Identify** each angle as *acute, right, obtuse,* or *straight.* Then use a protractor to find the measure of each angle in degrees. To make it easier to measure the angle with your protractor, you can extend its sides with your ruler.

1. acute — Angle measure 45°
2. straight — Angle measure 180°
3. right — Angle measure 90°
4. acute — Angle measure 45°
5. obtuse — Angle measure 135°
6. acute — Angle measure 15°

**Solve** these problems.

7. Look at the figure to the right to answer the following questions.
   a. Which angle(s) is/are obtuse? angle *C*
   b. Which angle(s) is/are acute? angle *D*
   c. Which angle(s) is/are right? angles *A* and *B*
8. Find the measure of each angle.
   a. *A* 90°  c. *C* 130°
   b. *B* 90°  d. *D* 50°

Real Math • Grade 4 • *Practice* Chapter 10 • *Geometry* 109

Practice Lesson 10.2

### RETEACH

**If . . .** students have difficulty measuring angles correctly,

**Then . . .** have them practice correctly placing the protractor on angles. Students who have difficulty naming angles may benefit from a simple mnemonic trick. Have them trace over an angle in one continuous motion with their fingers. They must give the letters that name the angle in the same order that their fingers moved. So, the letter at the vertex must be the middle of the three letters, just as the vertex is in the middle position of the angle as it is traced.

# Parallel, Perpendicular, and Intersecting Lines

**Context of the Lesson** This is the third of fourteen lessons on topics in geometry. Lines were covered in Grade 3. From now on, students will use the terms *parallel*, *perpendicular*, and *intersecting* to describe and identify lines of various figures.

See page 446B for Math Background for teachers for this lesson.

### Objectives

To teach or review the recognition of parallel, perpendicular, and intersecting lines

### NCTM Standards

**Geometry**

Develop vocabulary to describe and recognize the organization of lines in the plane

### Materials

- *Response Wheels
- *Rulers or straightedges
- Paper

### Technology

**Presentation** Lesson 10.3

**MathTools** Geometry Tool and Net Tool

**Games** Harder Roll a Problem Game

### Test Prep

**Cumulative Review**

Mental Math reviews multidigit multiplication of a two-digit or three-digit number by a one-digit number (Lessons 5.8–5.9).

### Looking Ahead

For Lesson 10.4, you will need geoboards and rubberbands. You will also need polygons and quadrilaterals from the *Attribute Blocks Set* for the overhead projector. You may also want to use the overhead geoboard from the manipulative kit.

## Planning for Learning • DIFFERENTIATE INSTRUCTION

### INTERVENTION

**If . . .** students lack the prerequisite skill of classifying figures,

**Then . . .** teach ***Intervention*** Lesson 10.A.

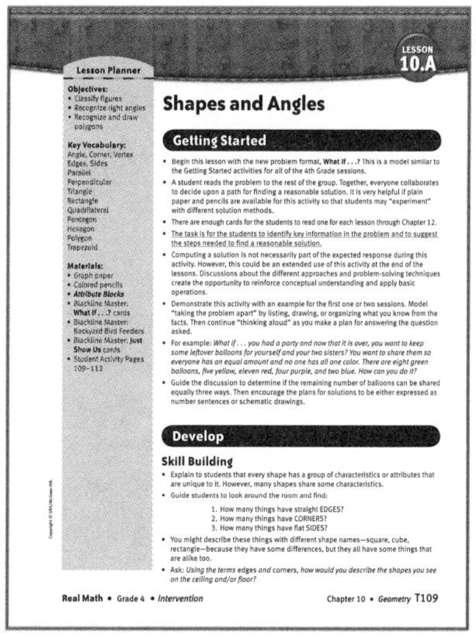
LESSON 10.A
Lesson Planner
Shapes and Angles
Getting Started
Develop
Skill Building

Intervention Lesson 10.A

### ENGLISH LEARNER

Preview

**If . . .** students need language support,

**Then . . .** use Lesson 10.3 in ***English Learner Support Guide*** to preview lesson concepts and vocabulary.

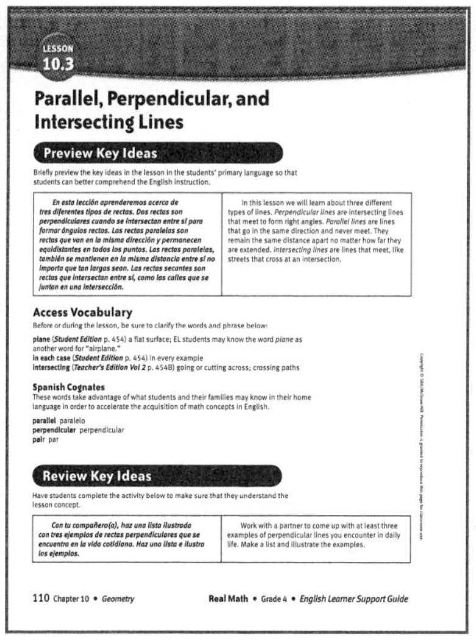
LESSON 10.3
Parallel, Perpendicular, and Intersecting Lines
Preview Key Ideas
Access Vocabulary
Spanish Cognates
Review Key Ideas

English Learner Lesson 10.3

### ENRICH

**If . . .** students are proficient in the lesson concepts,

**Then . . .** have them use the ***eMathTools: Geometry Tool*** to show the difference among parallel, perpendicular, and intersecting lines.

### PRACTICE

**If . . .** students would benefit from additional practice,

**Then . . .** extend Skill Practice before assigning the student pages.

### RETEACH

**If . . .** students have difficulty understanding parallel, intersecting, or perpendicular lines,

**Then . . .** extend Guided Discussion before assigning the student pages.

### Vocabulary

**perpendicular \pər´ pən di´ kyə lər\ *adj.*** lines that intersect at right angles

**parallel \par´ ə lel\ *adj.*** lines that remain the same distance apart, go in the same direction, and never meet

### Access Vocabulary

**right angle** Many students know the word *right* as the opposite of wrong. Here, right angle means straight.

### Spanish Cognates

**intersection** intersección
**parallel** paralelo
**perpendicular** perpendicular

*Manipulative Kit Item

# Teaching Lesson 10.3

## Mental Math 5

Review RESPONSE WHEEL Provide practice in multiplying greater numbers, using problems such as the following:

| | | |
|---|---|---|
| **a.** $3 \times 10 = 30$ | $3 \times 30 = 90$ | $3 \times 29 = 87$ |
| **b.** $4 \times 10 = 40$ | $2 \times 40 = 80$ | $2 \times 41 = 82$ |
| **c.** $4 \times 100 = 400$ | $5 \times 100 = 500$ | $5 \times 99 = 495$ |
| **d.** $5 \times 20 = 100$ | $6 \times 20 = 120$ | $6 \times 19 = 114$ |

## 1 Develop 25

**Tell Students In Today's Lesson They Will**
learn about and identify parallel, perpendicular, and intersecting lines.

Whole Group

### Guided Discussion UNDERSTANDING eMathTools

Review the definitions for parallel, perpendicular, and intersecting lines, and draw examples on the board. Explain that any two lines in a plane that are not parallel will be intersecting, but may or may not be perpendicular. Then ask questions such as the following:

- **Where do you see parallel lines every day?** Possible answers: railroad tracks, the double-yellow line in the center of a road, strings on a guitar or violin, crosswalk lines on a street, lines on notebook paper
- **Where do you see perpendicular lines every day?** Possible answers: window panes, a net, strings on a tennis racquet, railroad crossing symbol
- **Can you give examples of intersecting lines that are not perpendicular?** Possible answers: some street intersections, tree branches

Have students look at the parallel lines you drew on the board. Ask questions such as the following:

- **Do the two lines look as though they will ever meet each other?** no
- **Do the lines look as though they stay the same distance apart?** yes

Draw two lines on the board that are not parallel but look like they will intersect eventually. You can also use the ***eMathTools: Geometry Tool*** to draw these lines.

- **Are these parallel lines? Why or why not?** No; they are not the same distance apart.
- **What would happen if the lines were extended?** They would intersect.

### Skill Practice ENGAGING

On a sheet of paper, have students write the words *parallel, perpendicular*, and *intersecting but not perpendicular* in three different columns. Then have them look around the room for parallel, perpendicular, and intersecting nonperpendicular lines and record their findings. After about five minutes, stop the students and ask them to share what they found. Have them physically show you the various relationships between the lines they found by walking over to the item, if necessary, and pointing out the lines.

## 2 Assign Student Pages 20

**Pages 454–455** APPLYING
Have students work independently on pages 454–455.

**Monitoring Student Progress**

| | |
|---|---|
| **If . . .** students have a solid understanding of parallel and perpendicular lines, | **Then . . .** introduce the mathematical symbols used to indicate parallel $\|$ and perpendicular $\perp$ lines, and explain how to use these symbols to write geometric statements. |

**As Students Finish**

eGames ***Harder Roll a Decimal Game*** (reviews place value and subtracting decimals).

eMathTools In preparation for later lessons, have students use the ***eMathTools: Net Tool*** to make space figures. They can also use the polygon patterns provided in ***Practice.***

Student Page

LESSON 10.3 **Parallel, Perpendicular, and Intersecting Lines**

## Key Ideas

**Two lines in the same plane are either parallel or intersecting. Some intersecting lines are perpendicular.**

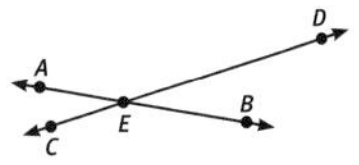


Intersecting lines are lines that meet. In this figure, lines *AB* and *CD* intersect at point *E*.

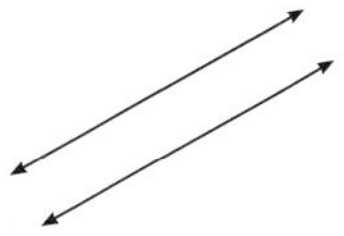

Parallel lines are lines that go in the same direction. The lines in this figure are parallel lines. Parallel lines never meet. They remain the same distance apart no matter how far they are extended.

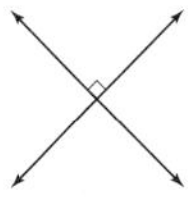

Two lines are perpendicular if they meet to form right angles.

These lines are perpendicular.

**Answer** the following questions.

1. Try to draw two lines that meet to form one right angle and three other angles that are not right angles. The two lines must be straight and must continue through the point where they meet. Can you do it? **no**
2. If two lines meet so that one angle formed is a right angle, what kind of angles will the other three angles be? **right angles**
3. Draw two capital letters from the alphabet that demonstrate intersecting line segments. **Possible answers: A, K, M, N, V, W, X, Y, Z**



eTextbook This lesson is available in the *eTextbook*.

Student Page

**In** each case, tell whether the two lines are perpendicular or not perpendicular.

4. 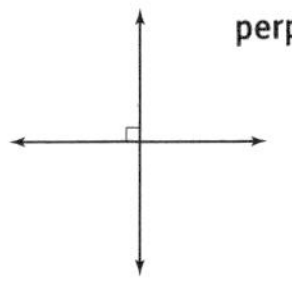 **perpendicular**
5. 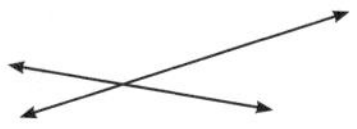 **not perpendicular**
6. 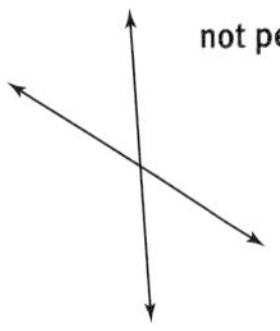 **not perpendicular**
7. 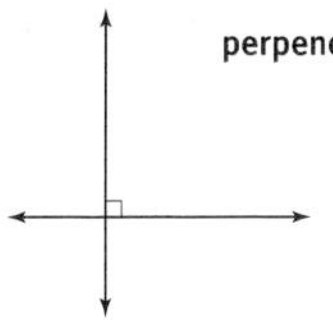 **perpendicular**

**In** each case, tell whether the two lines are parallel, perpendicular, or neither.

8. 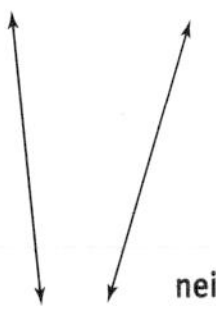 **neither**
9.  **neither**
10. 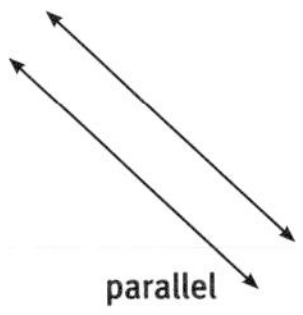 **parallel**
11. 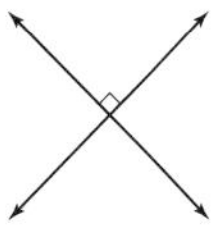 **perpendicular**
12. 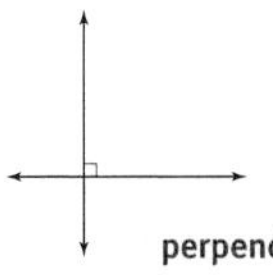 **perpendicular**
13. 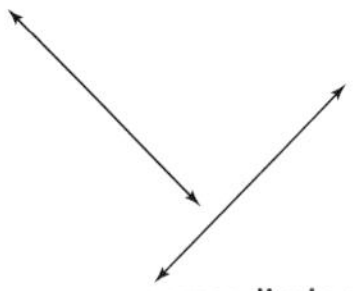 **perpendicular**
14. Draw a line. Now draw two more lines, each perpendicular to the first. What do you think is true of these last two lines? **They are parallel.**



# 3 Reflect

5

## Guided Discussion REASONING

Whole Group

Have students look around the room. Then ask questions such as the following:

- **Can you find parts of two lines that are not parallel but will never meet, no matter how far you extend them?** One possible example is the line that is formed by the ceiling and front wall of the room and the line that is formed by the floor and side wall of the room.
- **Are these lines always the same distance apart?** no
- **Is there a plane that contains both lines?** no

**Cumulative Review**: For review of multiplication, assign Problems 6–9 on student page 464.

**Family Involvement:** Assign the ***Practice, Reteach,*** or ***Enrichment*** activities depending on the needs of your students.

**Concept/Question Board:** Have students think of additional examples of perpendicular, parallel, and intersecting lines and post them on the Concept/Question Board.

**Math Puzzler:** Glenn bought 6 pairs of socks and 3 ties for $66. Rick bought 1 tie and 1 pair of socks for $16. What is the cost of a pair of socks? $6

# 4 Assess and Differentiate

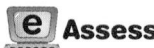

eAssess Use ***eAssess*** to record and analyze evidence of student understanding.

## A Gather Evidence

Use the Daily Class Assessment Records in ***Assessment*** or ***eAssess*** to record daily observations.

### Informal Assessment
**Guided Discussion**

Did the student UNDERSTANDING
- ❑ make important observations?
- ❑ extend or generalize learning?
- ❑ provide insightful answers?
- ❑ pose insightful questions?

### Informal Assessment
**Skill Practice**

Did the student ENGAGING
- ❑ pay attention to others' contributions?
- ❑ contribute information and ideas?
- ❑ improve on a strategy?
- ❑ reflect on and check the accuracy of his or her work?

## B Summarize Findings

Analyze and summarize assessment data for each student. Determine which Assessment Follow-Up is appropriate for each student. Use the Student Assessment Record in ***Assessment*** or ***eAssess*** to update Assessment Records.

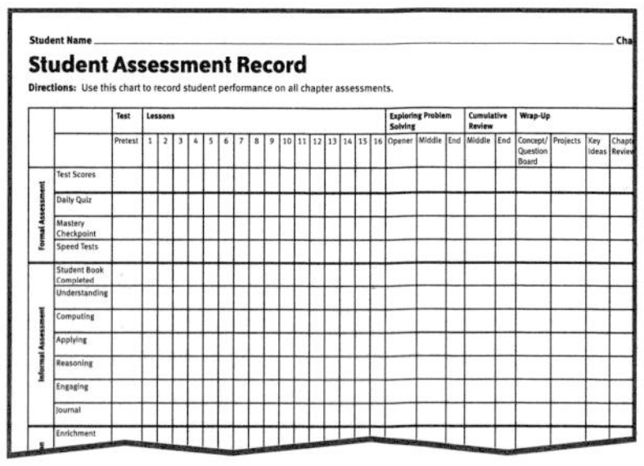


**Assessment Page T41**

## C Assessment Follow-Up • DIFFERENTIATE INSTRUCTION

Based on your observations, use these teaching strategies for assessment follow-up.

### INTERVENTION

Review student performance on ***Intervention*** Lesson 10.A to see if students have mastered prerequisite skills for this lesson.

### ENGLISH LEARNER

**Review**

Use Lesson 10.3 in ***English Learner Support Guide*** to review lesson concepts and vocabulary.

### ENRICH

**If . . .** students are proficient in the lesson concepts,

**Then . . .** encourage them to work on the chapter projects or ***Enrichment*** Lesson 10.3.

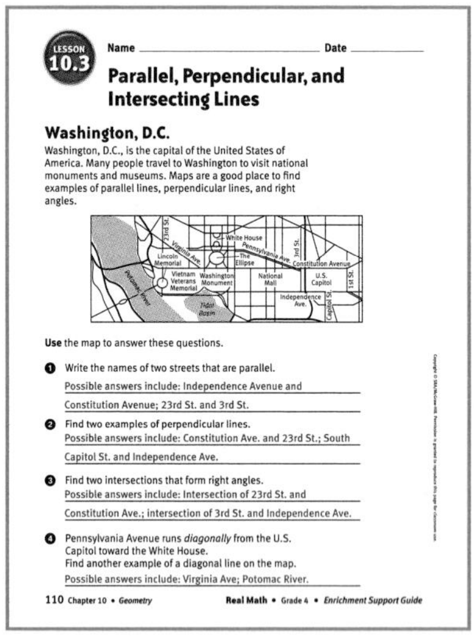
LESSON 10.3 Name ______ Date ______

**Parallel, Perpendicular, and Intersecting Lines**

**Washington, D.C.**

Washington, D.C., is the capital of the United States of America. Many people travel to Washington to visit national monuments and museums. Maps are a good place to find examples of parallel lines, perpendicular lines, and right angles.



**Use** the map to answer these questions.

1. Write the names of two streets that are parallel.
Possible answers include: Independence Avenue and Constitution Avenue; 23rd St. and 3rd St.
2. Find two examples of perpendicular lines.
Possible answers include: Constitution Ave. and 23rd St.; South Capitol St. and Independence Ave.
3. Find two intersections that form right angles.
Possible answers include: Intersection of 23rd St. and Constitution Ave.; intersection of 3rd St. and Independence Ave.
4. Pennsylvania Avenue runs *diagonally* from the U.S. Capitol toward the White House. Find another example of a diagonal line on the map.
Possible answers include: Virginia Ave; Potomac River.

110 Chapter 10 • *Geometry* **Real Math** • Grade 4 • *Enrichment Support Guide*

Enrichment Lesson 10.3

### PRACTICE

**If . . .** students would benefit from additional practice,

**Then . . .** assign ***Practice*** Lesson 10.3.

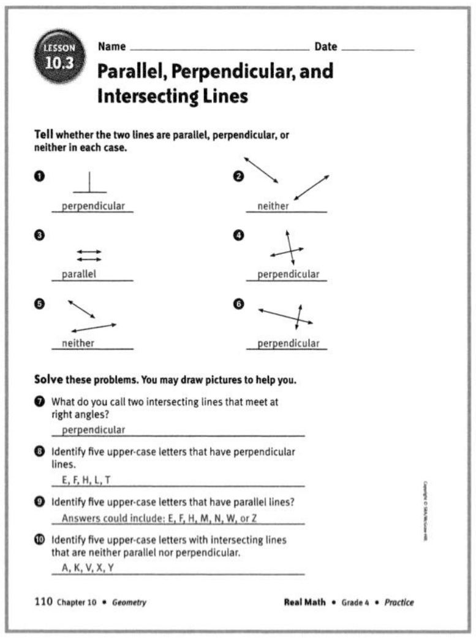
LESSON 10.3 Name ______ Date ______

**Parallel, Perpendicular, and Intersecting Lines**

**Tell whether the two lines are parallel, perpendicular, or neither in each case.**

1. perpendicular
2. neither
3. parallel
4. perpendicular
5. neither
6. perpendicular

**Solve these problems. You may draw pictures to help you.**

7. What do you call two intersecting lines that meet at right angles?
perpendicular
8. Identify five upper-case letters that have perpendicular lines.
E, F, H, L, T
9. Identify five upper-case letters that have parallel lines?
Answers could include: E, F, H, M, N, W, or Z
10. Identify five upper-case letters with intersecting lines that are neither parallel nor perpendicular.
A, K, V, X, Y

110 Chapter 10 • *Geometry* **Real Math** • Grade 4 • *Practice*

Practice Lesson 10.3

### RETEACH

**If . . .** students have difficulty understanding parallel, intersecting, or perpendicular lines,

**Then . . .** have them take two pieces of paper and extend the lines with the edges of the paper. If the papers touch, the lines are not parallel. Have students make a right angle symbol whenever they draw perpendicular lines. This way they never have to question if the lines are perpendicular. You could also have students line up to create parallel, perpendicular, and other intersecting lines.

Lesson Planner

**OBJECTIVES**
To help students explore the classification of polygons, especially quadrilaterals

**NCTM STANDARDS**
**Geometry**
- Identify, compare, and analyze attributes of plane figures
- Classify plane figures according to their properties
- Draw geometric objects

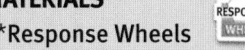

**MATERIALS**
- *Response Wheels
- *Rulers or straightedges
- *Rubber bands
- *Geoboards and Overhead Geoboard
- *Polygons and quadrilaterals from the **Attribute Block Set**

**TECHNOLOGY**
**e Presentation** Lesson 10.4
**e MathTools** Shape Tool and Net Tool
**e Games** Baseball Game

**TEST PREP**
**Cumulative Review**
- Mental Math reviews ×12 facts (Lesson 3.7).
- Problems 4–8 review the term *parallel* (Lesson 10.3).

**Extended Response**
Problems 9–10

**Writing + Math**
Journal

**Looking Ahead**
For Lesson 10.5, you will need geoboards and rubber bands.

# Quadrilaterals and Other Polygons

**Context of the Lesson** This is the first of six lessons on plane figures. This lesson introduces polygons with various numbers of sides and the names of those shapes. Students will gain valuable information from this lesson, which will be used again as the chapter progresses.
See page 446B for Math Background for teachers for this lesson.

## Planning for Learning • DIFFERENTIATE INSTRUCTION

### INTERVENTION

**If . . .** students lack the prerequisite skill of recognizing right angles,

**Then . . .** teach ***Intervention*** Lesson 10.B.

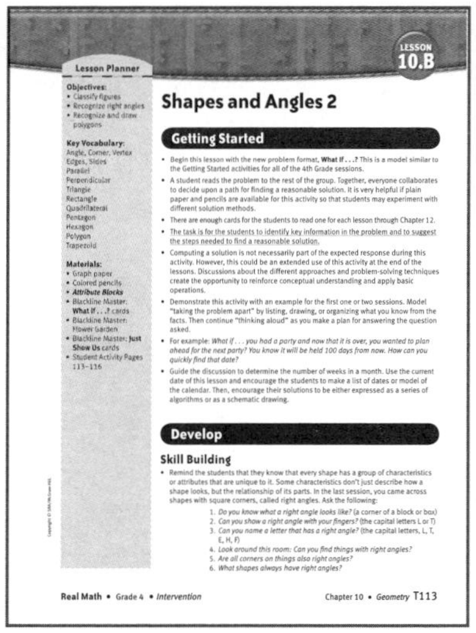
Lesson Planner
LESSON 10.B
Shapes and Angles 2
Getting Started
Develop
Skill Building

Intervention Lesson 10.B

### ENGLISH LEARNER

**Preview**

**If . . .** students need language support,

**Then . . .** use Lesson 10.4 in ***English Learner Support Guide*** to preview lesson concepts and vocabulary.

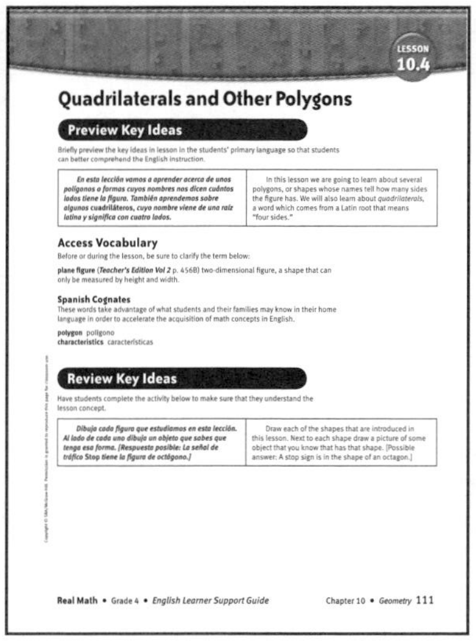
LESSON 10.4
Quadrilaterals and Other Polygons
Preview Key Ideas
Access Vocabulary
Spanish Cognates
Review Key Ideas

English Learner Lesson 10.4

### ENRICH

**If . . .** students are proficient in the lesson concepts,

**Then . . .** have them explore the ***eMathTools: Shape Tool*** to create an activity involving polygons.

### PRACTICE

**If . . .** students would benefit from additional practice,

**Then . . .** extend Skill Practice before assigning the student pages.

### RETEACH

**If . . .** students have difficulty understanding polygons,

**Then . . .** extend Guided Discussion before assigning the student pages.

**Vocabulary**
**plane figure *n.*** a figure that can be drawn entirely in one plane

**Access Vocabulary**
**plane figure** Here, the word *plane* means two-dimensional, a shape that can only be measured by height and width.

**Spanish Cognates**
**polygon** polígono
**characteristics** características

*Manipulative Kit Item

# Teaching Lesson 10.4

## Mental Math 5

RESPONSE WHEEL Have students practice ×12 facts. Present problems such as the following:

**a.** $2 \times 12 = 24$ **b.** $8 \times 12 = 96$
**c.** $4 \times 12 = 48$ **d.** $12 \times 12 = 144$
**e.** $3 \times 12 = 36$ **f.** $10 \times 12 = 120$
**g.** $9 \times 12 = 108$ **h.** $5 \times 12 = 60$

## 1 Develop 25

**Tell Students In Today's Lesson They Will**
learn about and identify polygons, including special quadrilaterals.

Whole Group

### Guided Discussion UNDERSTANDING eMathTools

Explain the terms *plane figure* and *polygon.* Write these terms on the board. Ask questions such as the following:

- **What is a plane figure?** It is a figure that can be drawn entirely in one plane.

Students might have trouble with the concept of plane figures. Show examples of plane figures and those that are not. For example, a rectangle that is drawn on the board is a plane figure, but a tissue box is not.

- **What is a polygon?** A polygon is a closed plane figure with three or more line segments as sides. In a polygon, every corner (or vertex) belongs to two sides.

Tell students to think of a polygon as a fence with straight sides and no break in it. (Somebody inside would not be able to get out without climbing the fence.)

Using the Attribute Blocks from the manipulative kit, show various polygons and quadrilaterals. Begin with a pentagon, a hexagon, and an octagon. Place each one on the overhead projector and explain its attributes.

Tell the class that a four-sided polygon is called a quadrilateral. Show an example of a quadrilateral on the overhead projector, or use the ***eMathTools: Shape Tool,*** and explain that some quadrilaterals have special names. Ask questions such as the following:

- **Now that you know a quadrilateral has four sides and that some quadrilaterals have special names, what figures do you think are special quadrilaterals?** Possible answers: square or rectangle

Place a square and a rectangle on the overhead projector. Then add a trapezoid, a parallelogram, and a rhombus, and have the students explain how these other special quadrilaterals are different from a square and a rectangle. Have them focus on the angles and the lines.

### Skill Practice ENGAGING

Small Group

1. Divide the class into pairs, giving each pair a geoboard and some rubber bands.
2. Write the following names on the board: *pentagon, octagon, hexagon, quadrilateral, square, rectangle, trapezoid, parallelogram,* and *rhombus.* Have students create these figures on their geoboards, using the square side. Students should be able to fit all nine figures on the geoboard. Walk around the room to assist students.
3. When the pairs have finished creating the nine figures, have volunteers show their creations to the class. Have students explain how some of the quadrilaterals they created are different from others.

## 2 Assign Student Pages 20

**Page 457** APPLYING

Have students work independently on page 457.

**As Students Finish**

Game **Baseball Game Mat** (reviews coordinates on a graph)

eGames ***Baseball Game***

eMathTools In preparation for later lessons, have students use the ***eMathTools: Net Tool*** to make space figures. They can also use the polygon patterns provided in ***Practice.***

LESSON 10.4 **Quadrilaterals and Other Polygons**

## Key Ideas

**A polygonal region includes the inside of a plane figure. A polygon is the line segments that form the polygonal region.**

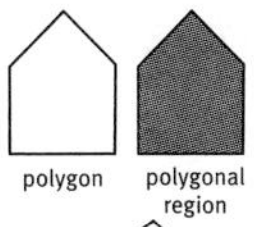


All the figures shown are called polygons. A polygon is a figure in a plane with three or more line segments as sides (*poly-* in Greek means "many").

A polygon with five sides is called a pentagon (*penta-* in Greek means "five"). A polygon with six sides is a hexagon (*hexa-* in Greek means "six"). A polygon with eight sides is an octagon (*octa-* in Greek means "eight").

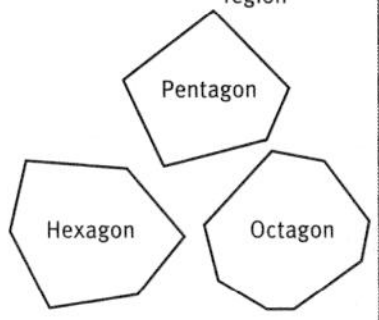


Four-sided polygons are called quadrilaterals (which in Latin means "four sides"). Some quadrilaterals have special names. A square, a rectangle, a trapezoid, a parallelogram, and a rhombus are all special quadrilaterals.

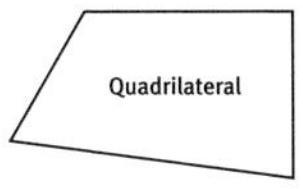


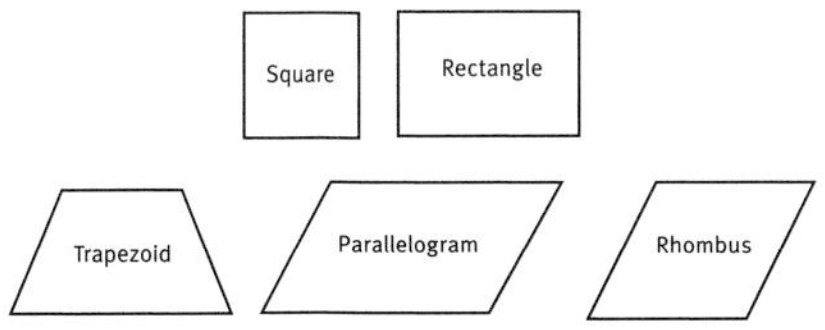


 eTextbook This lesson is available in the *eTextbook*.



**Draw** the following. Polygons need not be regular.

1. Draw an octagon. 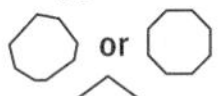
2. Draw a pentagon. 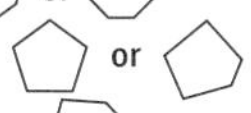
3. Draw a hexagon. 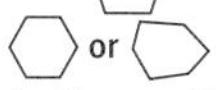
4. Draw a quadrilateral with two of its sides parallel but the other two sides not parallel. 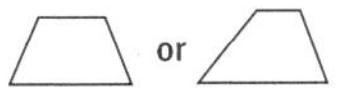
5. Draw a quadrilateral with two pairs of parallel sides. 
6. Draw a quadrilateral with two pairs of parallel sides and all sides of the same length. 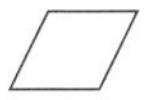
7. Draw a quadrilateral with two pairs of parallel sides and all angles of the same size. 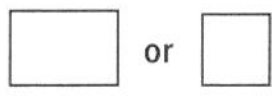
8. Draw a quadrilateral with two pairs of parallel sides and all sides and angles of the same size. 
9. **Extended Response** What is the difference between the parallelogram and the rectangle on page 456? See Reflect in the *Teacher's Edition.*
10. **Extended Response** What is the difference between the square and the rhombus on page 456? See Reflect in the *Teacher's Edition.*

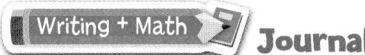

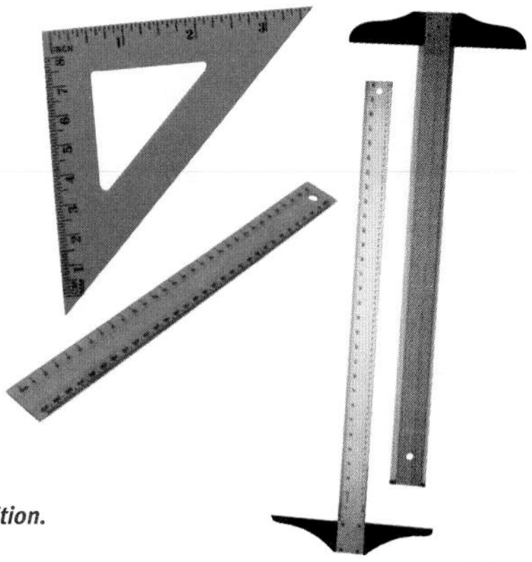

Writing + Math
**Journal**
Create a shape containing only three pairs of parallel sides. Explain how you found your answer.

See Reflect in the *Teacher's Edition.*





# 3 Reflect

10

## Guided Discussion REASONING

Whole Group

Have students explain what they learned about polygons. Ask questions such as the following:

- **Is it true that all quadrilaterals are polygons, but not all polygons are quadrilaterals?** yes
- **What is true about all quadrilaterals?** All quadrilaterals have four sides.
- **What is the difference between a regular polygon and an irregular polygon?** The sides of a regular polygon are the same length. The sides of an irregular polygon are not all the same.
- **Can you give an example of a figure that is not a polygon?** a circle

## Extended Response

**Problem 9** Students should notice that the rectangle has all right angles while a parallelogram usually does not.

**Problem 10** Students should notice that the square has all right angles while a rhombus usually does not.

Writing + Math **Journal**

Students may have noticed that a regular hexagon fits the description. If they focus on the idea that the figure has three pairs of parallel lines, then students will realize that there would have to be at least six lines in the figure.

Review **Cumulative Review:** For review of division, assign Problems 10–13 on student page 464.

**Family Involvement:** Assign the ***Practice, Reteach,*** or ***Enrichment*** activities depending on the needs of your students.

**Concept/Question Board:** Have students think of additional examples of polygons and post them on the Concept/Question Board.

**Math Puzzler:** Which two polygons make up the pattern on a soccer ball? pentagon and hexagon

# 4 Assess and Differentiate

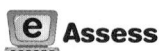

e Assess Use ***eAssess*** to record and analyze evidence of student understanding.

## A Gather Evidence

Use the Daily Class Assessment Records in ***Assessment*** or ***eAssess*** to record daily observations.

### Informal Assessment
**Mental Math**

Did the student COMPUTING
- ❑ respond accurately?
- ❑ respond quickly?
- ❑ respond with confidence?
- ❑ self-correct?

### Informal Assessment
**Concept/Question Board**

Did the student APPLYING
- ❑ apply learning in new situations?
- ❑ contribute concepts?
- ❑ contribute answers?
- ❑ connect mathematics to real-world situations?

## B Summarize Findings

Analyze and summarize assessment data for each student. Determine which Assessment Follow-Up is appropriate for each student. Use the Student Assessment Record in ***Assessment*** or ***eAssess*** to update assessment records.

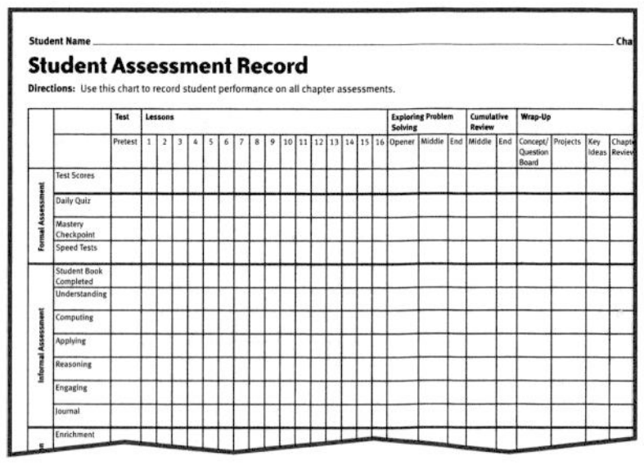
Student Name
Student Assessment Record
Directions: Use this chart to record student performance on all chapter assessments.

**Assessment Page T41**

## C Assessment Follow-Up • DIFFERENTIATE INSTRUCTION

Based on your observations, use these teaching strategies for assessment follow-up.

### INTERVENTION

Review student performance on ***Intervention*** Lesson 10.B to see if students have mastered prerequisite skills for this lesson.

### ENGLISH LEARNER

**Review**

Use Lesson 10.4 in ***English Learner Support Guide*** to review lesson concepts and vocabulary.

### ENRICH

**If . . .** students are proficient in the lesson concepts,

**Then . . .** encourage them to work on the chapter projects or ***Enrichment*** Lesson 10.4.

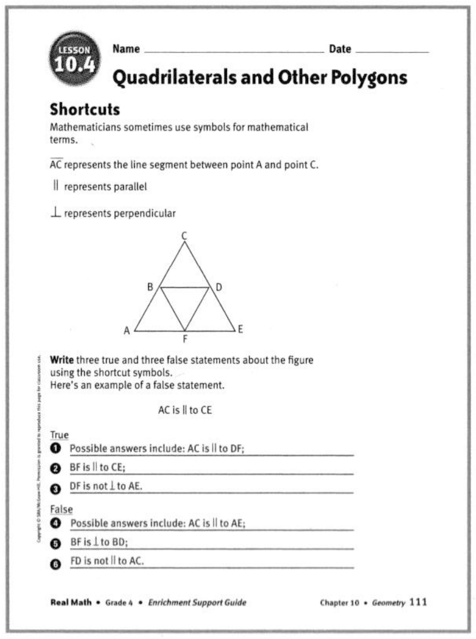
LESSON 10.4 Name ______ Date ______

Quadrilaterals and Other Polygons

**Shortcuts**

Mathematicians sometimes use symbols for mathematical terms.

$\overline{AC}$ represents the line segment between point A and point C.

∥ represents parallel

⊥ represents perpendicular



**Write** three true and three false statements about the figure using the shortcut symbols.
Here's an example of a false statement.

AC is ∥ to CE

True
1. Possible answers include: AC is ∥ to DF;
2. BF is ∥ to CE;
3. DF is not ⊥ to AE.

False
4. Possible answers include: AC is ∥ to AE;
5. BF is ⊥ to BD;
6. FD is not ∥ to AC.

Real Math • Grade 4 • *Enrichment Support Guide* Chapter 10 • *Geometry* 111

Enrichment Lesson 10.4

### PRACTICE

**If . . .** students would benefit from additional practice,

**Then . . .** assign ***Practice*** Lesson 10.4.

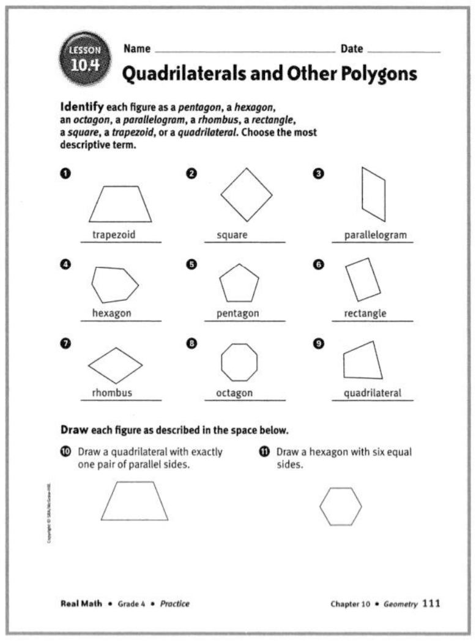
LESSON 10.4 Name ______ Date ______

Quadrilaterals and Other Polygons

**Identify** each figure as a *pentagon*, a *hexagon*, an *octagon*, a *parallelogram*, a *rhombus*, a *rectangle*, a *square*, a *trapezoid*, or a *quadrilateral*. Choose the most descriptive term.

1. trapezoid
2. square
3. parallelogram
4. hexagon
5. pentagon
6. rectangle
7. rhombus
8. octagon
9. quadrilateral

**Draw each figure as described in the space below.**

10. Draw a quadrilateral with exactly one pair of parallel sides.
11. Draw a hexagon with six equal sides.

Real Math • Grade 4 • *Practice* Chapter 10 • *Geometry* 111

Practice Lesson 10.4

### RETEACH

**If . . .** students have difficulty understanding polygons,

**Then . . .** have them make flash cards of the prefix and the number of sides that the shape has. Give teams of students toothpicks and clay. Have them make the shapes introduced in the lesson, using the toothpicks as the sides and the clay to join the corners. Discuss whether the length of each side matters. Students can break the toothpicks to change the lengths of the sides. Students can also use these to model their answers for the exercises.

## Lesson Planner

**Objectives**
- To identify different types of triangles
- To practice measuring angles

**NCTM Standards**

**Geometry**
- Identify, compare, and analyze attributes of plane figures
- Classify plane figures according to their properties
- Draw geometric objects

**Materials**
- *Geoboards
- *Rubber bands

**Technology**

**Presentation** Lesson 10.5
**MathTools Geometry Shape Tool** and **Net Tool**
Building Blocks **Shape Parts 7**

**Test Prep**

**Cumulative Review**
Mental Math reviews the identification of angles as acute or obtuse (Lesson 10.2).

### Looking Ahead

For Lesson 10.6, you will need four inches of string for each student.

*Manipulative Kit Item

# Triangles

**Context of the Lesson** This is the second of six lessons on plane figures. This lesson reviews the properties of triangles and compares the triangles to each other and to real-world objects. Students will use vocabulary they have gathered from earlier in the chapter to create and classify the characteristics of triangles.

See page 446B for Math Background for teachers for this lesson.

## Planning for Learning • DIFFERENTIATE INSTRUCTION

### INTERVENTION

**If . . .** students lack the prerequisite skill of classifying figures,

**Then . . .** teach ***Intervention*** Lesson 10.A

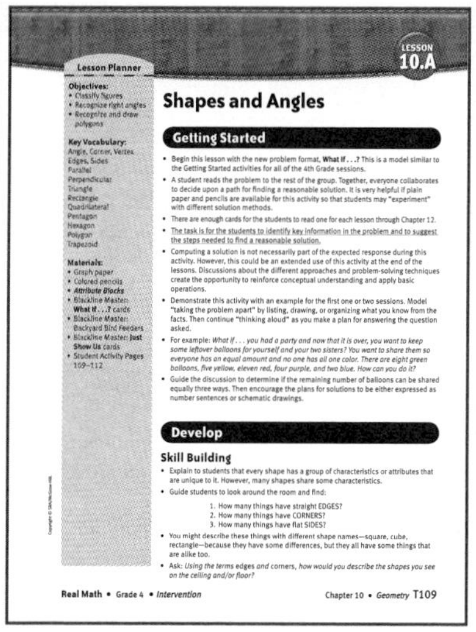
Lesson 10.A
Shapes and Angles
Getting Started
Develop

Intervention Lesson 10.A

### ENGLISH LEARNER

**Preview**

**If . . .** students need language support,

**Then . . .** use Lesson 10.5 in ***English Learner Support Guide*** to preview lesson concepts and vocabulary.

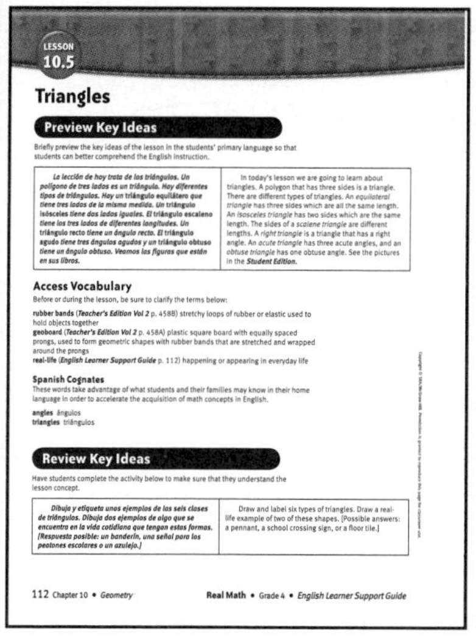
Lesson 10.5
Triangles
Preview Key Ideas
Access Vocabulary
Spanish Cognates
Review Key Ideas

English Learner Lesson 10.5

### ENRICH

**If . . .** students are proficient in the lesson concepts,

**Then . . .** have them explore the ***eMathTools: Shape Tool*** to create an activity involving triangles.

### PRACTICE

**If . . .** students would benefit from additional practice,

**Then . . .** extend Skill Practice before assigning the student pages.

### RETEACH

**If . . .** students have difficulty understanding triangles,

**Then . . .** extend Guided Discussion before assigning the student pages.

**Vocabulary**
**isosceles** \ī sä´ sə lēz\ *adj.* having exactly two equal sides

**Access Vocabulary**
**geoboard** a plastic square board with equally spaced prongs on which to stretch elastic bands to form geometric shapes

**Spanish Cognates**
**angles** ángulos
**triangles** triángulos

# Teaching Lesson 10.5

## Mental Math

5

Review THUMBS UP

Have students identify angles, such as the following, as obtuse or acute. Have them show thumbs-up if the angle is obtuse, or thumbs-down if it is acute.

| | | |
|---|---|---|
| **a.** 120° up | **b.** 56° down | **c.** 87° down |
| **d.** 104° up | **e.** 99° up | **f.** 20° down |
| **g.** 8° down | **h.** 175° up | **i.** 91° up |

## 1 Develop

25

**Tell Students In Today's Lesson They Will**
learn names for some different types of triangles.

Whole Group

### Guided Discussion

UNDERSTANDING eMathTools

Review the term *polygon*. Ask questions such as the following:

- **What is the name for a four-sided polygon?** quadrilateral
- **What are some examples of a quadrilateral?** square, rectangle, rhombus, trapezoid, parallelogram
- **Can anyone draw an example of what a three-sided polygon looks like?**

Have volunteers come to the board to draw examples. Then ask questions such as the following:

- **What is the common name for a three-sided polygon?** a triangle

Tell the class there are different types of triangles. Identify equilateral, isosceles, scalene, obtuse, acute, and right triangles, using the triangles the students drew on the board. Add any types that are missing.

Explain to the class that they can measure the angles in a triangle using a protractor. Ask questions such as the following:

- **How many angles are there in a triangle? The word *triangle* gives you a clue.** three

Draw a triangle named *ABC* on an overhead projector transparency, or use the ***eMathTools: Shape Tool.***

- **How would you measure angle *A* in this triangle?** Make sure students can correctly place the protractor to measure angle *A*.

### Skill Practice

ENGAGING

Small Group

1. Divide the class into pairs, giving each pair a geoboard and some rubber bands.
2. Call out a type of triangle and have each pair create that kind of triangle on the triangle side of their geoboard. When the students are done, have them hold up their geoboards so you can see them.
3. Continue this activity until the students have created at least one equilateral, isosceles, scalene, acute, right, and obtuse triangle.

## 2 Assign Student Pages

25

**Page 459**
Have students work independently on page 459.

**As Students Finish**

Building Blocks *Shape Parts 7*

eMathTools In preparation for later lessons, have students use the ***eMathTools: Net Tool*** to make space figures. They can also use the polygon patterns provided in ***Practice.***

Student Page

LESSON 10.5 **Triangles**

## Key Ideas

**A polygon that has three sides is called a *triangle*. There are different types of triangles.**

**equilateral triangle**—all three sides are equal in length

**isosceles triangle**—two sides are equal in length

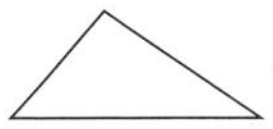

**scalene triangle**—all the sides have a different length

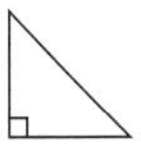

**right triangle**—a triangle with a right angle

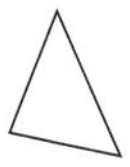

**acute triangle**—a triangle with three acute angles

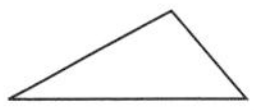

**obtuse triangle**—a triangle with one obtuse angle

458 Textbook This lesson is available in the *eTextbook*.

Student Page

**Identify** each type of triangle according to its sides and angles. Some images might have more than one type.

1.  right, scalene
2. 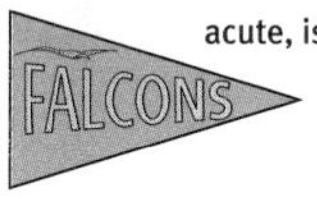

acute, isosceles
3. 

acute, equilateral
4. 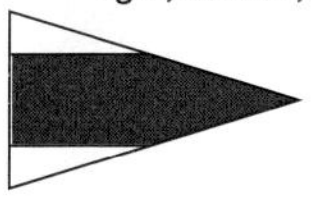 right, scalene, acute, isosceles
5.  acute, isosceles
6. 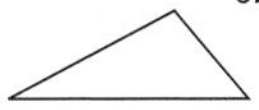 obtuse, scalene
7. 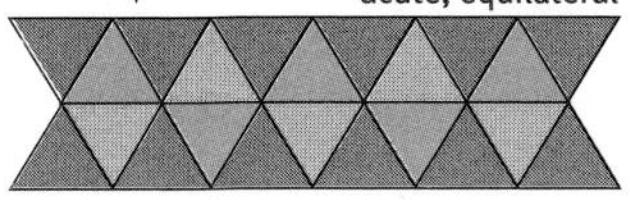 acute, equilateral

**Measure** the angles in the triangle and name each.

8. 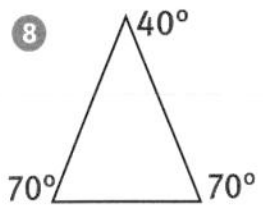

isosceles, acute
9. 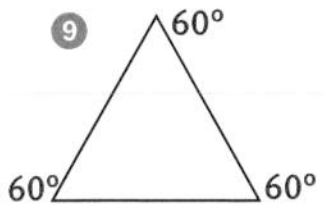

equilateral, acute
10. 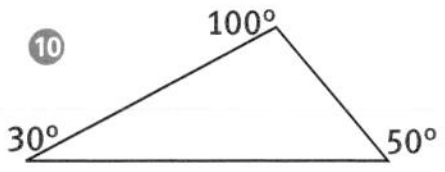

scalene, obtuse

11. Draw a triangle with two sides that are 3 cm long and one side that is 2 cm long. What kind of triangle did you make? acute, isosceles
12. Draw a triangle with one right angle and sides that measure 3 cm, 4 cm, and 5 cm. What kind of triangle did you make? right, scalene

Chapter 10 • Lesson 5 459

# 3 Reflect 5

## Guided Discussion APPLYING

Have students apply their knowledge of triangles and angles. Ask a question such as the following:

- **Can you create an isosceles right triangle?** yes

Have the class draw an isosceles right triangle. A possible answer, where x = y, might look like:

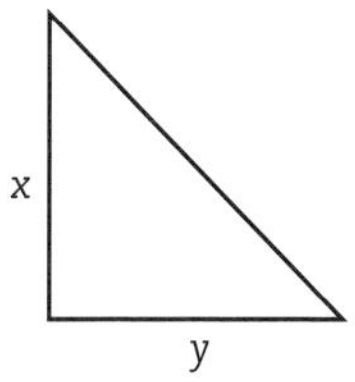


**RESEARCH IN ACTION**

"Geometry can be used to understand and to represent the objects, directions, and locations in our world, and the relationships between them. Geometric shapes can be described, analyzed, transformed, and composed and decomposed into other shapes."

Clements, Douglas and Sarama, J. eds. *Engaging Young Children in Mathematics: Standards for Early Childhood Mathematics Education.* Mahwah, New Jersey: Lawrence Erlbaum Associates, Publishers, 2004. p. 39.

**Cumulative Review:** For review of multidigit multiplication, assign Problems 14–20 on student page 465.

**Family Involvement:** Assign the ***Practice, Reteach,*** or ***Enrichment*** activities depending on the needs of your students.

**Concept/Question Board:** Have students think of additional examples of triangles and post them on the Concept/Question Board.

**Math Puzzler:** A 6-foot tall pillar casts a 3-foot long shadow on the ground. If the pillar was 10 feet tall, how many feet in length would the shadow be? 5

# 4 Assess and Differentiate

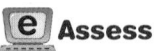

**e Assess** Use ***eAssess*** to record and analyze evidence of student understanding.

## A Gather Evidence

Use the Daily Class Assessment Records in ***Assessment*** or ***eAssess*** to record daily observations.

### Informal Assessment
**Guided Discussion**

Did the student APPLYING
- ❑ apply learning in new situations?
- ❑ contribute concepts?
- ❑ contribute answers?
- ❑ connect mathematics to real-world situations?

### Informal Assessment
**Skill Practice**

Did the student ENGAGING
- ❑ pay attention to others' contributions?
- ❑ contribute information and ideas?
- ❑ improve on a strategy?
- ❑ reflect on and check the accuracy of his or her work?

## B Summarize Findings

Analyze and summarize assessment data for each student. Determine which Assessment Follow-Up is appropriate for each student. Use the Student Assessment Record in ***Assessment*** or ***eAssess*** to update assessment records.

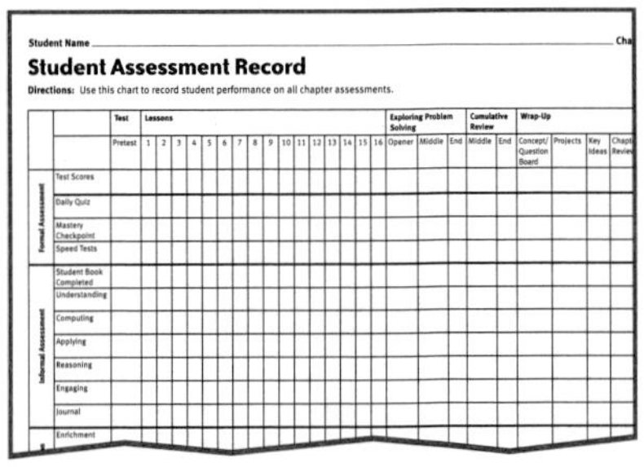


**Assessment Page T41**

## C Assessment Follow-Up • DIFFERENTIATE INSTRUCTION

Based on your observations, use these teaching strategies for assessment follow-up.

### INTERVENTION

Review student performance on ***Intervention*** Lesson 10.A to see if students have mastered prerequisite skills for this lesson.

### ENGLISH LEARNER

**Review**

Use Lesson 10.5 in ***English Learner Support Guide*** to review lesson concepts and vocabulary.

### ENRICH

**If . . .** students are proficient in the lesson concepts,

**Then . . .** encourage them to work on the chapter projects or ***Enrichment*** Lesson 10.5.

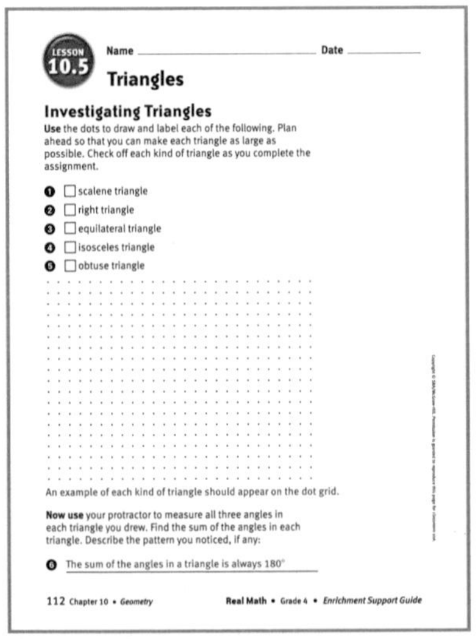

LESSON 10.5 Name ________ Date ________

**Triangles**

**Investigating Triangles**

**Use** the dots to draw and label each of the following. Plan ahead so that you can make each triangle as large as possible. Check off each kind of triangle as you complete the assignment.

1. ☐ scalene triangle
2. ☐ right triangle
3. ☐ equilateral triangle
4. ☐ isosceles triangle
5. ☐ obtuse triangle

An example of each kind of triangle should appear on the dot grid.

**Now use** your protractor to measure all three angles in each triangle you drew. Find the sum of the angles in each triangle. Describe the pattern you noticed, if any:

6. The sum of the angles in a triangle is always 180°

112 Chapter 10 • *Geometry* **Real Math** • Grade 4 • *Enrichment Support Guide*

Enrichment Lesson 10.5

### PRACTICE

**If . . .** students would benefit from additional practice,

**Then . . .** assign ***Practice*** Lesson 10.5.

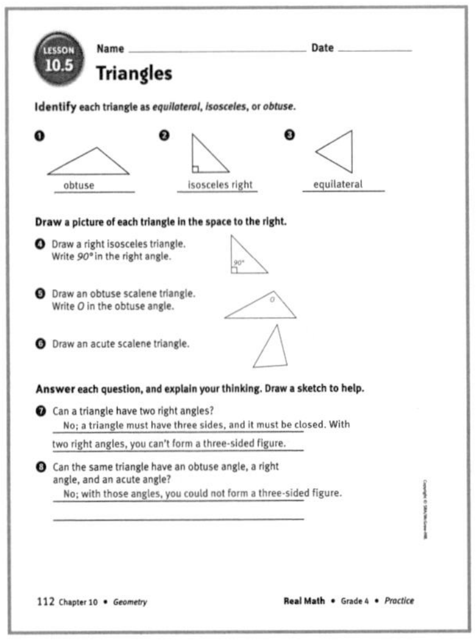

LESSON 10.5 Name ________ Date ________

**Triangles**

**Identify** each triangle as *equilateral*, *isosceles*, or *obtuse*.

1. obtuse
2. isosceles right
3. equilateral

**Draw a picture of each triangle in the space to the right.**

4. Draw a right isosceles triangle. Write *90°* in the right angle.
5. Draw an obtuse scalene triangle. Write *O* in the obtuse angle.
6. Draw an acute scalene triangle.

**Answer each question, and explain your thinking. Draw a sketch to help.**

7. Can a triangle have two right angles?
   No; a triangle must have three sides, and it must be closed. With two right angles, you can't form a three-sided figure.
8. Can the same triangle have an obtuse angle, a right angle, and an acute angle?
   No; with those angles, you could not form a three-sided figure.

112 Chapter 10 • *Geometry* **Real Math** • Grade 4 • *Practice*

Practice Lesson 10.5

### RETEACH

**If . . .** students have difficulty understanding triangles,

**Then . . .** remind them that they do not have to worry about exact measurements of angles. They are only looking for less than, greater than, or equal to 90 degrees. Give teams of students toothpicks and clay. Have them make the types of triangles introduced in the lesson, using the toothpicks as the sides and the clay to join the corners. Students can break the toothpicks to change the lengths of the sides. Have students lay the triangles on grid paper to help them form right triangles. Students can also use these tools to model their answers for the exercises.

## Lesson Planner

**OBJECTIVES**
To learn more about circles

**NCTM STANDARDS**
**Geometry**
Classify plane figures according to their properties

**MATERIALS**
- *Response Wheels
- Pencils
- String
- Paper

**TECHNOLOGY**
**Presentation** Lesson 10.6
**MathTools** **Geometry Shape Tool** and **Net Tool**

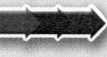

**TEST PREP**
**Cumulative Review**
Mental Math reviews multistep computational problems (Lesson 3.13).
**Extended Response**
Problems 7–8

**Looking Ahead**
For Lesson 10.7, you will need a map of the United States or the state in which you live.

*Manipulative Kit Item

# Circles

**Context of the Lesson** This is the third of six lessons on plane figures. Throughout this lesson, students will learn information regarding the parts of a circle, which will be the cornerstone of future math courses dealing with circles. This lesson defines the terms *radius*, *diameter*, and *circumference,* and offers students opportunities to create examples of these terms.

See page 446B for Math Background for teachers for this lesson.

## Planning for Learning • DIFFERENTIATE INSTRUCTION

### INTERVENTION

**If . . .** students lack the prerequisite skill of classifying figures,

**Then . . .** teach ***Intervention*** Lesson 10.A.

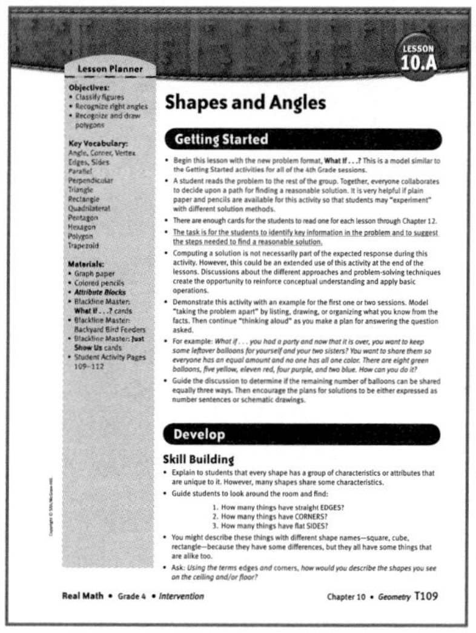
LESSON 10.A
Lesson Planner
Shapes and Angles
Getting Started
Develop
Skill Building

Intervention Lesson 10.A

### ENGLISH LEARNER

**Preview**

**If . . .** students need language support,

**Then . . .** use Lesson 10.6 in ***English Learner Support Guide*** to preview lesson concepts and vocabulary.

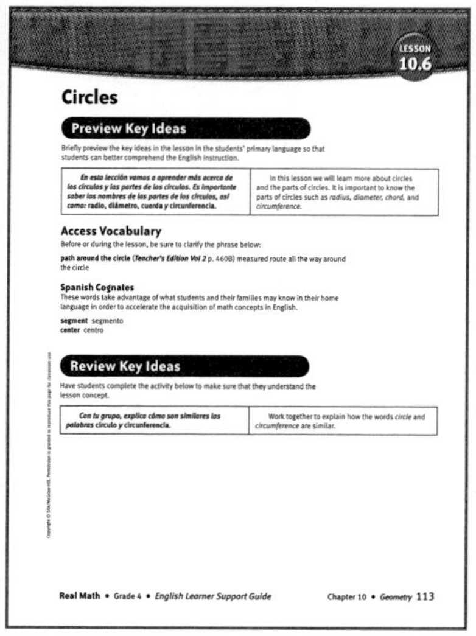
LESSON 10.6
Circles
Preview Key Ideas
Access Vocabulary
Spanish Cognates
Review Key Ideas

English Learner Lesson 10.6

### ENRICH

**If . . .** students are proficient in the lesson concepts,

**Then . . .** have them explore the ***eMathTools: Shape Tool*** to create an activity involving circles.

### PRACTICE

**If . . .** students would benefit from additional practice,

**Then . . .** extend Skill Practice before assigning the student pages.

### RETEACH

**If . . .** students are having difficulty drawing a circle,

**Then . . .** extend Guided Discussion before assigning the student pages.

**Vocabulary**
**diameter** \dī am' i tər\ *n.* a straight line passing through the center of a circle (or sphere) from one point on the circumference (or surface) to another; also used for the length of a diameter

**Access Vocabulary**
**path around the circle** a measured route all the way around the circle

**Spanish Cognates**
**segment** segmento
**center** centro

## Mental Math

5

Review RESPONSE WHEEL

Present mixed computation problems, such as the following. Have students do the operations in the sequence presented.

a. $5 + 6 + 7 = 18$
b. $35 \div 5 \times 5 = 35$
c. $3 \times 3 + 10 = 19$
d. $49 - 49 \times 5 = 0$
e. $45 - 40 \times 10 = 50$
f. $8 \times 8 \div 8 = 8$

## 1 Develop

25

### Tell Students In Today's Lesson They Will

learn about the different parts of a circle.

Whole Group

### Guided Discussion UNDERSTANDING eMathTools

Have students think about a circle. Ask questions such as the following:

- **Is a circle a polygon? Why or why not?** No, because it does not have straight sides.
- **Can the shape of a circle vary?** The shape of a circle is always the same, but the size can vary.

Based on the definition of a circle, explain that all the points on the outside of a circle are the same distance from a single point called the center.

- **Where do you think this point is located?** in the middle

Draw a point in the middle of a circle and label it P. Write the following next to the circle: *Point P is the center.* You may wish to use the ***eMathTools: Shape Tool*** to draw the circle.

Draw a line from the center to a point on the circle. Label the point Q. Write the following on the board: *PQ is a radius.* Ask questions such as the following:

- **What does PQ look like?** a line segment
- **What do you think the definition of a *radius* is?** a line segment that goes from the center of a circle to a point on the circle

Explain that there are line segments that go through the center of the circle called the diameters. Draw a diameter on the circle and name the endpoints R and S.

- **Based on the drawing, what is the relationship between the radius and the diameter of a circle?** The radius is half the diameter.

Explain that the *circumference* is the length of the path around the circle.

Draw a chord with endpoints *TU*. Write the following on the board: *TU is a chord.* Ask questions such as the following:

- **What does *TU* look like?** a line segment
- **What do you think is the definition of a chord?** a line segment that has endpoints on a circle

### Skill Practice ENGAGING

Small Group

1. Have students work in pairs using two pencils and a four-inch piece of string to explore the circumference of a circle. Have them attach the string to the pencils.
2. Explain that the string represents the radius of a circle. Have one student keep a pencil still, while the other student extends the string as far as he or she can. Have the student move the outer pencil to draw a circle. Explain that the full turn they created is the circumference, and that the pencil that did not move was the center point of the circle. Tell students that the circumference is the path running around the boundary of a circle.
3. Have students label the radius, the diameter, and a chord on their drawings.

   Students may want to do this several times to create a quality circle to label.

## 2 Assign Student Pages

20

### Page 461 APPLYING

Have students work independently on page 461.

#### Monitoring Student Progress

| If . . . | Then . . . |
|---|---|
| **If . . .** students have a hard time drawing circles, | **Then . . .** allow them to use a larger sheet of paper. Instead of pencils, they could also use chalk and a board, or one student could hold string with his or her thumb in the center of a circle as another student moves around him or her. |

### As Students Finish

Game **Inequality Game** (reviews true and false inequality statements)

eMathTools In preparation for later lessons, have students use the ***eMathTools: Net Tool*** to make space figures. They can also use the polygon patterns provided in ***Practice.***

Student Page

LESSON 10.6 **Circles**

## Key Ideas

**A circle is a figure in which all points are the same distance from a point called the *center*. A radius is a line segment that goes from the center of a circle to a point on the circumference.**

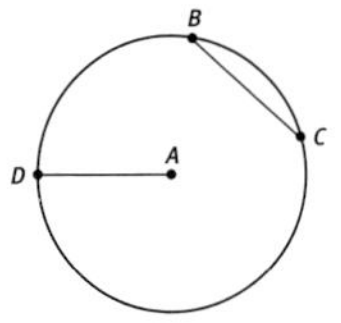


In the circle below, point *A* is the center and *AD* is a radius.

A *chord* is a line segment that has its endpoints on the circle. *BC* is an example of a chord in the circle with center *A*.

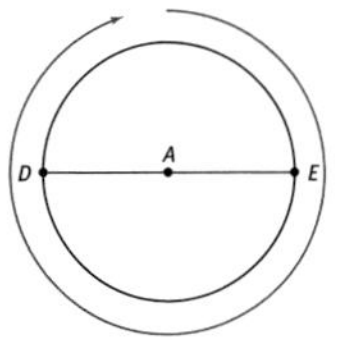


The diameter is a line segment that goes through the center of a circle with its endpoints on the circle. *DE* is the diameter of the circle with center *A*. The *circumference* of a circle is the length of the path around the circle. The arrow shows the circumference around the circle with center *A*. The word circumference is also used for the path itself.



eTextbook This lesson is available in the ***eTextbook***.

Student Page

**Identify** the following parts of the circle with center *J*.

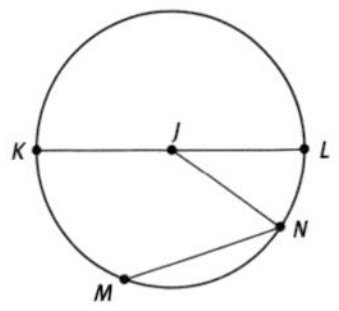


1. line segment *JK* radius
2. line segment *JN* radius
3. line segment *MN* chord
4. line segment *KL* diameter
5. What is the center of the circle? point *J*

**Answer** the following questions.

6. How is the length of a radius related to the length of the diameter of a circle? The length of a radius is half the length of the diameter.
7. **Extended Response** Is the diameter of a circle a chord? Why or why not? See Reflect in the ***Teacher's Edition***.
8. **Extended Response** Which is longer, the diameter of a circle or the circumference of a circle? See Reflect in the ***Teacher's Edition***.

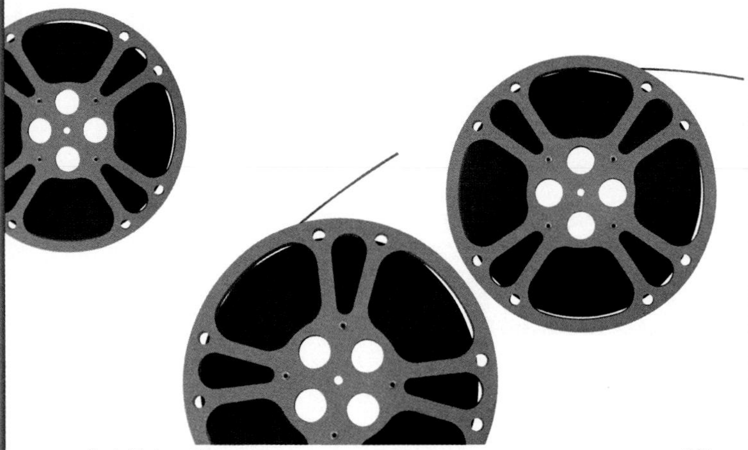



LESSON 10.6

# 3 Reflect

10

## Guided Discussion

APPLYING

Whole Group

Have students apply their knowledge of circles to a clock face. Remind them that a clock face is usually circular in shape. Ask questions such as the following.

- **It is twelve o'clock. Are the hands of the clock forming a radius, a diameter, or a chord?** radius
- **It is six o'clock. Are the hands of the clock forming a radius, a diameter, or a chord?** The hands form a diameter, which can also be considered a chord.

## Extended Response

**Problem 7** Students should see that a diameter meets the requirements to be a chord. It is simply a chord passing through the center.

**Problem 8** Students should say something about a diameter going across a circle, while the circumference goes around the circle. They should also notice that the circumference is not straight and is longer than a diameter.

**Cumulative Review:** For review of ordering decimals, assign Problems 21–25 on student page 465.

**Family Involvement:** Assign the ***Practice, Reteach,*** or ***Enrichment*** activities depending on the needs of your students.

**Concept/Question Board:** Encourage students to continue to post questions, answers, and examples on the Concept/Question Board.

**Math Puzzler:** A number of children are standing in a circle. They are evenly spaced, and the eighth child is directly opposite the sixteenth child. How many children are there altogether? 16

# 4 Assess and Differentiate

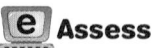

**e Assess** Use ***eAssess*** to record and analyze evidence of student understanding.

## A Gather Evidence

Use the Daily Class Assessment Records in ***Assessment*** or ***eAssess*** to record daily observations.

### Informal Assessment
**✓ Extended Response**

Did the student **REASONING**
- ❑ provide a clear explanation?
- ❑ communicate reasons and strategies?
- ❑ choose appropriate strategies?
- ❑ argue logically?

### Informal Assessment
**✓ Guided Discussion**

Did the student **APPLYING**
- ❑ apply learning in new situations?
- ❑ contribute concepts?
- ❑ contribute answers?
- ❑ connect mathematics to real-world situations?

## B Summarize Findings

Analyze and summarize assessment data for each student. Determine which Assessment Follow-Up is appropriate for each student. Use the Student Assessment Record in ***Assessment*** or ***eAssess*** to update assessment records.

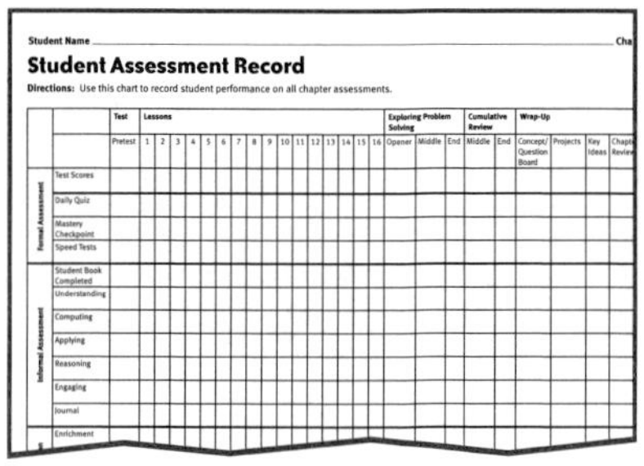
Student Name

Student Assessment Record

Directions: Use this chart to record student performance on all chapter assessments.

**Assessment Page T41**

## C Assessment Follow-Up • DIFFERENTIATE INSTRUCTION

Based on your observations, use these teaching strategies for assessment follow-up.

### INTERVENTION

Review student performance on ***Intervention*** Lesson 10.A to see if students have mastered prerequisite skills for this lesson.

### ENGLISH LEARNER

**Review**

Use Lesson 10.6 in ***English Learner Support Guide*** to review lesson concepts and vocabulary.

### ENRICH

**If . . .** students are proficient in the lesson concepts,

**Then . . .** encourage them to work on the chapter projects or ***Enrichment*** Lesson 10.6.

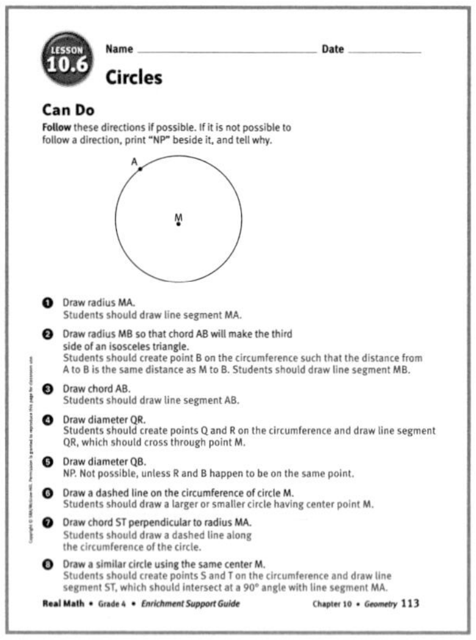
LESSON 10.6 Name ____ Date ____

Circles

Can Do

Follow these directions if possible. If it is not possible to follow a direction, print "NP" beside it, and tell why.

1. Draw radius MA. Students should draw line segment MA.
2. Draw radius MB so that chord AB will make the third side of an isosceles triangle. Students should create point B on the circumference such that the distance from A to B is the same distance as M to B. Students should draw line segment MB.
3. Draw chord AB. Students should draw line segment AB.
4. Draw diameter QR. Students should create points Q and R on the circumference and draw line segment QR, which should cross through point M.
5. Draw diameter QB. NP. Not possible, unless R and B happen to be on the same point.
6. Draw a dashed line on the circumference of circle M. Students should draw a larger or smaller circle having center point M.
7. Draw chord ST perpendicular to radius MA. Students should draw a dashed line along the circumference of the circle.
8. Draw a similar circle using the same center M. Students should create points S and T on the circumference and draw line segment ST, which should intersect at a 90° angle with line segment MA.

Real Math • Grade 4 • Enrichment Support Guide  Chapter 10 • Geometry 113

Enrichment Lesson 10.6

### PRACTICE

**If . . .** students would benefit from additional practice,

**Then . . .** assign ***Practice*** Lesson 10.6.

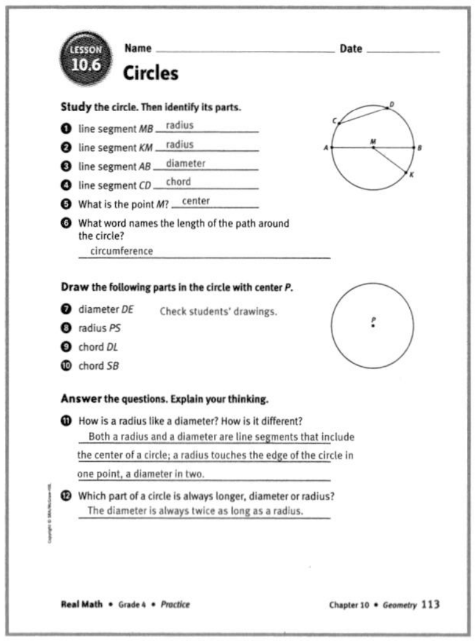
LESSON 10.6 Name ____ Date ____

Circles

Study the circle. Then identify its parts.
1. line segment MB radius
2. line segment KM radius
3. line segment AB diameter
4. line segment CD chord
5. What is the point M? center
6. What word names the length of the path around the circle? circumference

Draw the following parts in the circle with center P.
7. diameter DE  Check students' drawings.
8. radius PS
9. chord DL
10. chord SB

Answer the questions. Explain your thinking.
11. How is a radius like a diameter? How is it different? Both a radius and a diameter are line segments that include the center of a circle; a radius touches the edge of the circle in one point, a diameter in two.
12. Which part of a circle is always longer, diameter or radius? The diameter is always twice as long as a radius.

Real Math • Grade 4 • Practice  Chapter 10 • Geometry 113

Practice Lesson 10.6

### RETEACH

**If . . .** students have difficulty drawing a circle,

**Then . . .** have them tape their paper to a piece of cardboard. Anchor the string with a tack or straight pin. Then attach the pencil to the other end of the string and draw a circle. Have students practice finding circles in the classroom. Common items with circles can include cans, chalk, clocks, pencil erasers, light fixtures, and chair legs. Have them trace the circles (as closely as possible), and identify the radius of each circle.

# Exploring Problem Solving

**Objectives**
- To explore how to use transformations to create geometric patterns
- To decide whether two arrangements that look different should be considered the same
- To explore the Say the Problem in a Different Way Strategy

**Materials**
- Graph paper
- Crayons or markers

**Context of the Lesson** In this lesson, students use what they have been learning about transformations to analyze geometric patterns. The 2-square × 3-square grid in this lesson also appears again in the second Problem Solving Lesson in Chapter 10 where students solve problems relating to the braille alphabet.

## 1 Develop

5

### Tell Students In Today's Lesson They Will
- look at some geometric patterns used by different cultures.
- try to match a pattern to the basic design used to create it.
- compare two problem-solving strategies, and then use one of them or their own to solve challenging problems.

## Guided Discussion

Have students describe the patterns they see in the photo on page 462. Ask questions such as the following:

- **How is repetition used to create a geometric design?**
- **What basic design do you see repeated in the photo?**
- **Do you think the pattern in the cloth has meaning?**

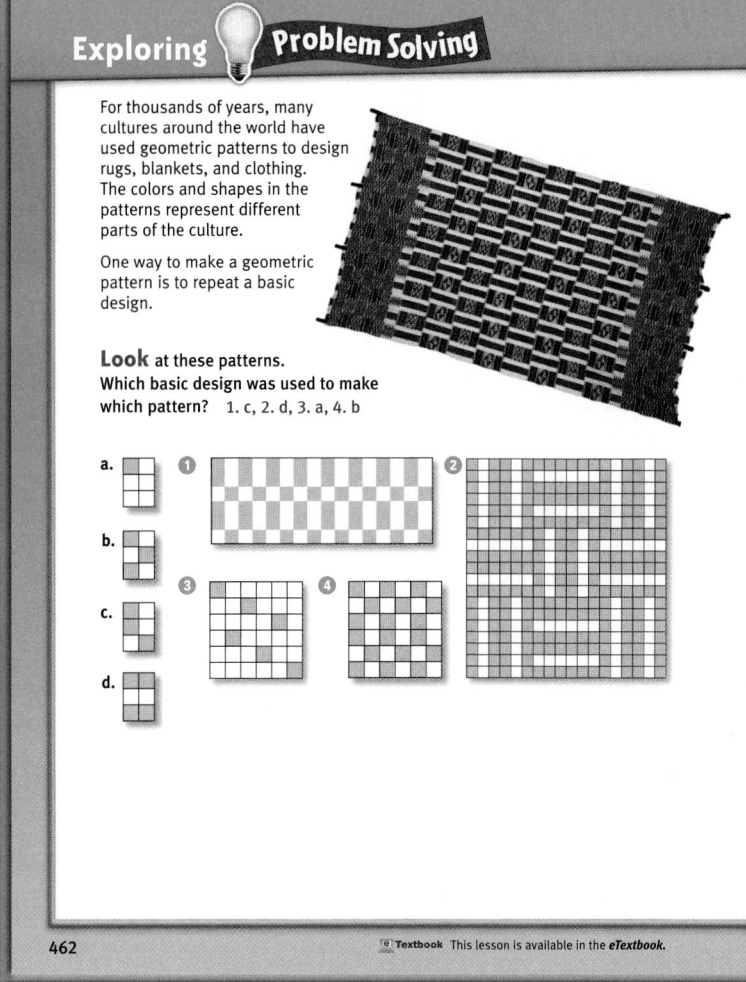

Student Page

**Exploring Problem Solving**

For thousands of years, many cultures around the world have used geometric patterns to design rugs, blankets, and clothing. The colors and shapes in the patterns represent different parts of the culture.

One way to make a geometric pattern is to repeat a basic design.

**Look** at these patterns.
Which basic design was used to make which pattern? 1. c, 2. d, 3. a, 4. b

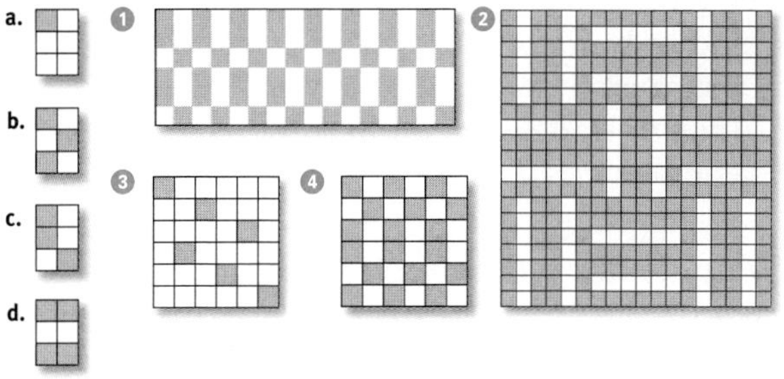


462

Textbook This lesson is available in the *eTextbook*.

Student Page

Each basic design on page 462 uses a 2-square × 3-square grid. By coloring different squares red, you can make other basic designs on this grid. How many different basic designs can you make by coloring 5 of the 6 squares in the grid red?

**Ramon and Elli solved the problem in different ways:**

Ramon Made a Diagram to begin to solve the problem.

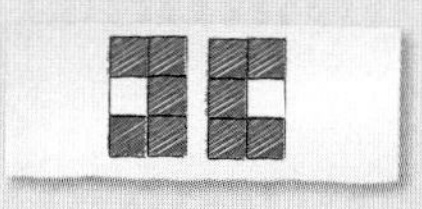

Elli decided to Say the Problem Another Way.

Each time I shade 5 squares, I leave 1 square blank. So, I can say the problem in this way:

How many ways can I leave 1 square blank?

**Answer** these questions.

5. Do you think the two designs that Ramon drew are different? Why or why not? See the *Teacher's Edition*.
6. If you use Elli's strategy, what answer will you get? Why? 6; there are 6 different squares that can be left blank.
7. What do you think of these two strategies?

**Solve** these problems. Use Ramon's strategy, Elli's strategy, or a strategy of your own.

8. How many different designs can you make by shading 15 squares on a 4-by-4 grid? If designs that can be transformed into each other are considered the same, then there are 4; otherwise there are 16.
9. A pizza place offers 6 different toppings. How many different kinds of 5-topping pizzas can you make? 6
10. Which is more like the problem Ramon and Elli solved, Problem 8 or Problem 9? Why?

Chapter 10 463

## 2 Exploring Problem Solving 20

### Using Student Pages

Have students look at Patterns 1–4 illustrated below the photograph, and ask what similarities they see between those patterns and the patterns in the photograph. Have the class complete the matching exercise described on the page. Then ask questions such as the following:

- **What kind of transformation was used to create Pattern 1 from Basic Design c?** translation
- **What kinds of transformations were used to create Pattern 4 from Basic Design b?** translation and rotation

Read the problem at the top of page 463 with the students. Make sure they understand the problem by asking questions such as the following:

- **What is the problem asking? How many different ways are there to color 5 of the 6 squares in a 2 × 3 grid?**
- **How might you solve the problem?** Allow students to suggest strategies.

Discuss Ramon's strategy. Ask questions such as the following:

- **What do you think Ramon will draw next?** another 2 × 3 grid with 5 different squares colored
- **Do you think Ramon's strategy will work?** It can work if he is careful not to use duplicates or to leave out any options.
- **How might you improve on Ramon's strategy?** Possible answer: Use a pattern to organize the possibilities. For example, start by leaving the upper left square blank, then leave the one below that blank, and so on.

Discuss Elli's strategy. Ask questions such as the following:

- **Is it okay for Elli to change the problem?** as long as she can show that the new problem has the same answer as the original problem
- **Do you think the new problem is the same as the original one?** These are simply two ways of stating the same mathematical problem. Every different group of five squares on the grid can also be looked at as a different blank square.

Give students time to think about Problems 5–7. Then discuss them.

### Answer

#### Problem 5

A good case can be made either way. Some students might say the designs are the same because if you rotate one a half turn it becomes the other. Other students may say the two designs are different because they look different unless you do something to them. Both arguments have merit because the problem is not clear and does not say how the designs will be used.

Have students work individually or in small groups to solve Problems 8–10.

## 3 Reflect 10

**Knowledge Age Skills**

**Effective Communication** Call on groups to show and explain their solutions and strategies. After each method is presented, ask questions such as the following:

- **How did the presenters make sure they counted all possibilities and didn't have any duplicates?**
- **What did you like about the method or the way it was presented?**

Discuss the following points:

- Arrangements or designs that look different may be the same if they can be rotated or reflected.
- Sometimes the situation in a problem tells you how to count different possibilities. For example, in Problem 9, since each topping is different, none of the six possible combinations can be considered duplicates.
- Saying the Problem in a Different Way can be a powerful strategy that can turn a very complicated problem into a very easy one.
- Problems that look very different can be mathematically similar and can thus be solved in the same way.
- When they use the Say the Problem in a Different Way Strategy, students should be sure that the new problem has the same answer as the original one. If not, they should adjust their solution accordingly or use a different strategy.

### Sample Solutions Strategies

In addition to the strategies presented on page 463, students might use the following strategies:

#### Make a Model

Students might find it easier to identify congruent designs if they make cutouts that they can turn and flip.

#### Make an Organized List

Students might solve Problem 9 by assigning letters, names, or numbers to the toppings, and then using a pattern to list the possible combinations.

## 4 Assess 10

When evaluating student work, focus not only on the correctness of the answer but also on whether students thought rationally about the problem and the various solutions presented. Some questions to consider include the following:

- Did the student understand the problem?
- Did the student use transformations to find arrangements that could be considered equivalent?
- Could the student articulate what was and wasn't useful about a particular strategy?
- Did the student look back to see if the reasoning and the answer made sense?

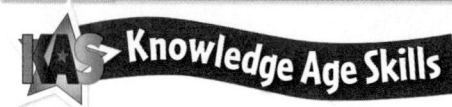

# CHAPTER 10 Review

# Cumulative Review

Review

## Assign Pages 464–465

Use this Cumulative Review as a review of concepts and skills that students have previously learned.

Here are different ways you can assign these problems to your students as they work through the chapter:

- For each lesson in the chapter, assign a set of Cumulative Review problems to be completed as practice or for homework.
  - Lesson 10.1—Problems 1–2
  - Lesson 10.2—Problems 3–5
  - Lesson 10.3—Problems 6–9
  - Lesson 10.4—Problems 10–13
  - Lesson 10.5—Problems 14–20
  - Lesson 10.6—Problems 21–25
- At any point during the chapter, assign part or all of the Cumulative Review problems to be completed as practice or for homework.

### Cumulative Review

**Problems 1–2** review multidigit addition and subtraction, Lesson 2.3.

**Problems 3–5** review addition and subtraction with hidden digits, Lesson 2.5.

**Problems 6–9** review multiplication, Lessons 3.1–3.5.

**Problems 10–13** review division, Lesson 3.10.

**Problems 14–20** review multidigit multiplication, Lessons 6.2 and 6.5.

**Problems 21–25** review ordering decimals, Lesson 9.4.

### Monitoring Student Progress

**If . . .** students miss more than one problem in a section, **Then . . .** refer to the indicated lesson for remediation suggestions.

Student Page

## Cumulative Review

Multidigit Addition and Subtraction Lesson 2.3

**Solve** each problem.

1. 526 + 1678 + 381 = ■ 2,585
2. 9000 − 165 = ■ 8,835

Addition and Subtraction with Hidden Digits Lesson 2.5

**Find** the hidden digits.

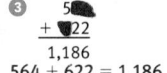

3. 5■ + ■22 = 1,186   564 + 622 = 1,186
4. ■24 + 3■ = 1,075   724 + 351 = 1,075
5. ■27 + 5■ = 925   327 + 598 = 925

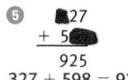

Multiplying Lesson 3.1–3.5

**Solve.**

6. 3 × 6 = ■ 18
7. 6 × 6 = ■ 36
8. 5 × 4 = ■ 20
9. 11 × 10 = ■ 110

Division Lesson 3.10

**Solve.**

10. 24 ÷ 3 = ■ 8
11. 56 ÷ 8 = ■ 7
12. 42 ÷ 7 = ■ 6
13. 100 ÷ 1 = ■ 100



Textbook This lesson is available in the *eTextbook*.

Student Page

Multidigit Multiplication Lessons 6.2 and 6.5

**Multiply.**

14. 48 × 26 = ■ 1,248
15. 73 × 64 = ■ 4,672
16. 80 × 35 = ■ 2,800
17. 650 × 700 = ■ 455,000
18. 965 × 351 = ■ 338,715
19. 600 × 90 = ■ 54,000
20. 6291 × 103 = ■ 647,973

Ordering Decimals Lesson 9.4

**Order** the following decimals from least to greatest.

21. 1.05, 1.5, 1.45, 1.04, 2, and 1.03   1.03, 1.04, 1.05, 1.45, 1.5, and 2
22. 5, 4.6, 4.06, 3.95, 3.30, and 4.5   3.30, 3.95, 4.06, 4.5, 4.6, and 5

**Order** the following decimals from greatest to least.

23. 8.6, 9, 8.07, 8.70, and 8.31   9, 8.70, 8.6, 8.31, and 8.07
24. 12.35, 123.5, 1.235, 0.1235, and 1,235   1,235, 123.5, 12.35, 1.235, and 0.1235
25. 0.598, 59.8, 0.0598, 50.9, 0.509   59.8, 50.9, 0.598, 0.509, and 0.0598

## Mid-Test

# Individual Oral Assessment

## Purpose of the Test

The Individual Oral Assessment is designed to measure students' growing knowledge of chapter concepts. It is administered to each student individually, and it requires oral responses from each student. The test takes about five minutes to complete.

See ***Assessment*** for detailed instructions for administering and interpreting the test, and record students' answers on the Student Assessment Recording Sheet.

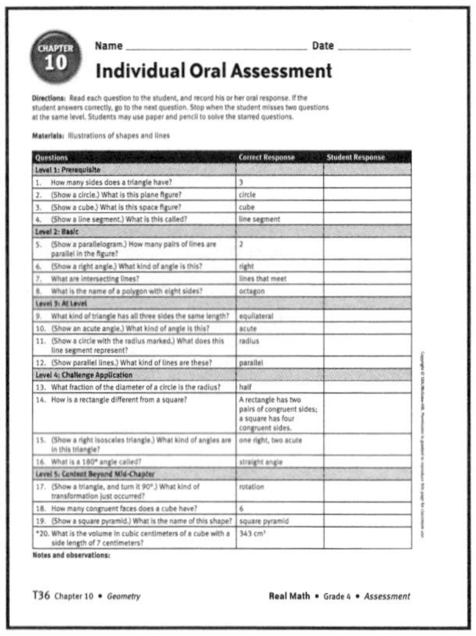

CHAPTER 10 Name ______ Date ______

**Individual Oral Assessment**

**Directions:** Read each question to the student, and record his or her oral response. If the student answers correctly, go to the next question. Stop when the student misses two questions at the same level. Students may use paper and pencil to solve the starred questions.

**Materials:** Illustrations of shapes and lines

| Questions | Correct Response | Student Response |
|---|---|---|
| **Level 1: Prerequisite** | | |
| 1. How many sides does a triangle have? | 3 | |
| 2. (Show a circle.) What is this plane figure? | circle | |
| 3. (Show a cube.) What is this space figure? | cube | |
| 4. (Show a line segment.) What is this called? | line segment | |
| **Level 2: Basic** | | |
| 5. (Show a parallelogram.) How many pairs of lines are parallel in the figure? | 2 | |
| 6. (Show a right angle.) What kind of angle is this? | right | |
| 7. What are intersecting lines? | lines that meet | |
| 8. What is the name of a polygon with eight sides? | octagon | |
| **Level 3: At Level** | | |
| 9. What kind of triangle has all three sides the same length? | equilateral | |
| 10. (Show an acute angle.) What kind of angle is this? | acute | |
| 11. (Show a circle with the radius marked.) What does this line segment represent? | radius | |
| 12. (Show parallel lines.) What kind of lines are these? | parallel | |
| **Level 4: Challenge Application** | | |
| 13. What fraction of the diameter of a circle is the radius? | half | |
| 14. How is a rectangle different from a square? | A rectangle has two pairs of congruent sides; a square has four congruent sides. | |
| 15. (Show a right isosceles triangle.) What kind of angles are in this triangle? | one right, two acute | |
| 16. What is a 180° angle called? | straight angle | |
| **Level 5: Content Beyond Mid-Chapter** | | |
| 17. (Show a triangle, and turn it 90°.) What kind of transformation just occurred? | rotation | |
| 18. How many congruent faces does a cube have? | 6 | |
| 19. (Show a square pyramid.) What is the name of this shape? | square pyramid | |
| *20. What is the volume in cubic centimeters of a cube with a side length of 7 centimeters? | 343 cm³ | |

**Notes and observations:**

T36 Chapter 10 • *Geometry* — **Real Math** • Grade 4 • *Assessment*

**Assessment Page T36**

### Directions

Read each question to the student, and record his or her oral response. If the student answers correctly, go to the next question. Stop when the student misses two questions at the same level. Students may use paper and pencil to solve the starred questions.

**Materials:** Illustrations of shapes and lines

## Questions

### Level 1: Prerequisite

1. How many sides does a triangle have? 3
2. (Show a circle.) What is this plane figure? circle
3. (Show a cube.) What is this space figure? cube
4. (Show a line segment.) What is this called? line segment

### Level 2: Basic

5. (Show a parallelogram.) How many pairs of lines are parallel in the figure? 2
6. (Show a right angle.) What kind of angle is this? right
7. What are intersecting lines? lines that meet
8. What is the name of a polygon with eight sides? octagon

### Level 3: At Level

9. What kind of triangle has all three sides the same length? equilateral
10. (Show an acute angle.) What kind of angle is this? acute
11. (Show a circle with the radius marked.) What does this line segment represent? radius
12. (Show parallel lines.) What kind of lines are these? parallel

### Level 4: Challenge Application

13. What fraction of the diameter of a circle is the radius? half
14. How is a rectangle different from a square? A rectangle has two pairs of congruent sides; a square has four congruent sides.
15. (Show a right isosceles triangle.) What kind of angles are in this triangle? one right, two acute
16. What is a 180° angle called? straight angle

### Level 5: Content Beyond Mid-Chapter

17. (Show a triangle, and turn it 90°.) What kind of transformation just occurred? rotation
18. How many congruent faces does a cube have? 6
19. (Show a square pyramid.) What is the name of this shape? square pyramid

*20. What is the volume in cubic centimeters of a cube with a side length of 7 centimeters? 343 $cm^3$

## Lesson Planner

**OBJECTIVES**
To introduce the geometric concepts of congruence and similarity

**NCTM STANDARDS**
**Geometry**
- Explore congruence and similarity
- Make and test conjectures about geometric properties and relationships

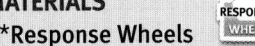

**MATERIALS**
- ***Response Wheels**
- Paper for tracing
- Map of the United States or the state in which you live

**TECHNOLOGY**
**Presentation** Lesson 10.7
**MathTools Tesselations Tool** and **Net Tool**
**Games** Multigo Game

**TEST PREP**
**Cumulative Review**
Mental Math reviews the number of sides of polygons (Lesson 10.4).
**Extended Response**
Problems 7 and 9

*Manipulative Kit Item

# Congruence and Similarity

**Context of the Lesson** This is the fourth of six lessons on plane figures. As with previous and subsequent lessons in this sequence, our informal approach to the development of geometric concepts allows for much exploration. Formal proofs for congruence and similarity are introduced in later grades.

See page 446B for Math Background for teachers for this lesson.

## Planning for Learning • DIFFERENTIATE INSTRUCTION

### INTERVENTION

**If . . .** students lack the prerequisite skill of classifying figures,

**Then . . .** teach ***Intervention*** Lesson 10.A.

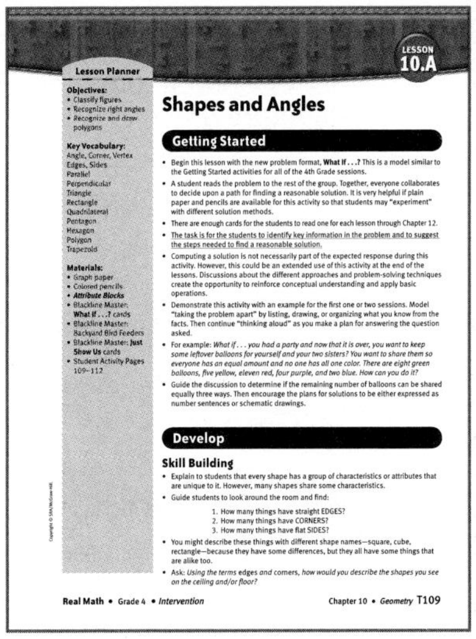
LESSON 10.A
Lesson Planner
Shapes and Angles
Getting Started
Develop
Skill Building
Real Math • Grade 4 • Intervention    Chapter 10 • Geometry T109

Intervention Lesson 10.A

### ENGLISH LEARNER

Preview

**If . . .** students need language support,

**Then . . .** use Lesson 10.7 in ***English Learner Support Guide*** to preview lesson concepts and vocabulary.

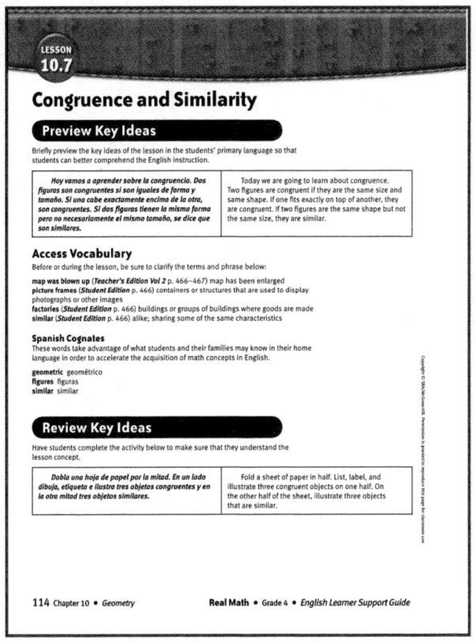
LESSON 10.7
Congruence and Similarity
Preview Key Ideas
Access Vocabulary
Spanish Cognates
Review Key Ideas
114 Chapter 10 • Geometry    Real Math • Grade 4 • English Learner Support Guide

English Learner Lesson 10.7

### ENRICH

**If . . .** students are proficient in the lesson concepts,

**Then . . .** have them explore the ***eMathTools: Tesselations*** to create an activity involving congruence and similarity.

### PRACTICE

**If . . .** students would benefit from additional practice,

**Then . . .** extend Guided Discussion before assigning the student pages.

### RETEACH

**If . . .** students have difficulty understanding congruence and similarity,

**Then . . .** extend Strategy Building before assigning the student pages.

### Vocabulary

**congruent** \kən grü' ənt\ *adj.* figures that are the same size and same shape; that is, they fit perfectly when placed on top of one another

### Access Vocabulary

**pattern** a design that is repeated in some recognizable fashion

**Spanish Cognates**
**figures** figures
**similar** similar

## Mental Math 5

Review | Response Wheel

Review the number of sides in different polygons. Name polygons such as the following, and have students show how many sides each polygon has.

**a.** triangle 3 **b.** hexagon 6
**c.** octagon 8 **d.** quadrilateral 4
**e.** pentagon 5 **f.** parallelogram 4
**g.** rectangle 4 **h.** rhombus 4

## 2 Develop 25

### Tell Students In Today's Lesson They Will

learn about congruence and similarity.

### Strategy Building — UNDERSTANDING — Small Group

Go over the definitions and pronunciations for the words *congruent*, *congruence*, and *similar*. Strictly speaking, all congruent figures are similar, but similar figures are not necessarily congruent. Students will explore these concepts in more depth in higher levels of mathematics. Show students some shapes that are similar and some that are congruent.

Split the class into several groups and assign each group one of the following shapes: rectangle, square, or circle. Have each group look around the room to find congruent and similar shapes. After a few minutes, have each group report their findings. Ask questions such as the following:

- **Which objects in the room are similar?**
- **Which objects in the room are congruent?**

Have students explain why they think their objects are either congruent or similar. Repeat this activity with other shapes that are not geometric. For example, the chairs in the room or students' eyeglass lenses could be congruent. Backpacks and school supplies could be similar.

### Guided Discussion — REASONING — Whole Group

Review the definitions for area and perimeter. Have students think about the area and perimeter of similar and congruent shapes. Ask questions such as the following:

- **If two shapes are congruent, what can be said about the area and perimeter of each shape?** Both shapes will have the same area and perimeter.
- **If you have two similar shapes, and one is larger than the other what can be said about the area and perimeter of each shape?** The larger of the two shapes will have a larger perimeter and a larger area.
- **Is it possible for two right triangles to be put together in such a way as to be congruent to a square? If so, describe what it would look like.** Yes. For example, two right triangles with two equal sides of 5 units could be placed together to form a square with sides of 5 units.

## 2 Assign Student Pages 20

### Pages 466–467 — APPLYING

Have students work independently on pages 466–467. You may wish to provide tracing paper for them to use to check for congruence and graph paper to help them complete Problem 10.

#### Monitoring Student Progress

**If . . .** students do not see figures *H* and *J* as congruent to figure *B*,

**Then . . .** explain that the figures can be flipped over in space to resemble figure *B*, so we still say they are congruent.

### As Students Finish

**Game** — **Multigo Game** (reviews missing factors and multiplication)

**eGames** — ***Multigo Game***

**eMathTools** — In preparation for later lessons, have students use the ***eMathTools: Net Tool*** to make space figures. They can also use the polygon patterns provided in ***Practice.***

Student Page

LESSON 10.7 Congruence and Similarity

**Key Ideas**

**Two figures are congruent if they are the same size and same shape.**

If one figure fits exactly on top of another, they are congruent. If two figures are the same shape but not necessarily the same size, they are similar.

**Use** the figures shown to answer the following questions.

1. List all the figures below that look congruent to figure *A*. *E, G, I*
2. List all the figures below that look similar to figure *A* but not congruent to it. *D, K*
3. List all the figures below that look congruent to figure *B*. *H, J*
4. List all the figures below that look similar to figure *B* but not congruent to it. *C, F, L, M*

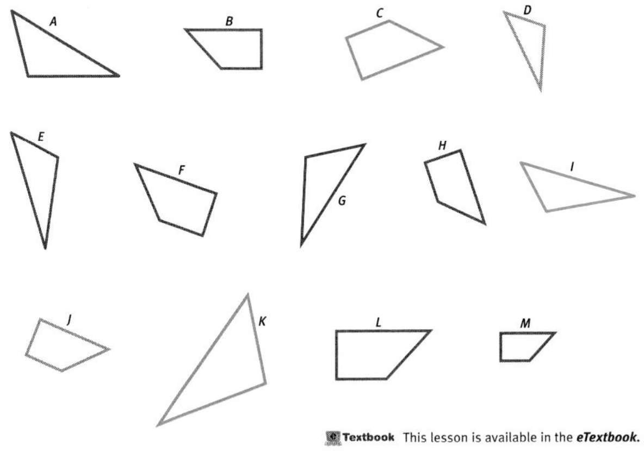




eTextbook This lesson is available in the *eTextbook*.

Student Page

5. List five examples of congruent objects, such as tires on a car.
6. List five examples of similar objects, such as picture frames.
7. Extended Response Before factories began producing items, do you think there were as many good examples of congruent objects as there are today? Why or why not? See Reflect in the *Teacher's Edition*.

5. Possible answers: windows in the classroom, checkers in a game set

6. Possible answers: different sizes of the same item of clothing; a small plate and a large plate

**Consider** three similar squares.
The first one is 1 cm on each side.
The second is 2 cm on each side.
The third is 3 cm on each side.

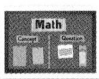

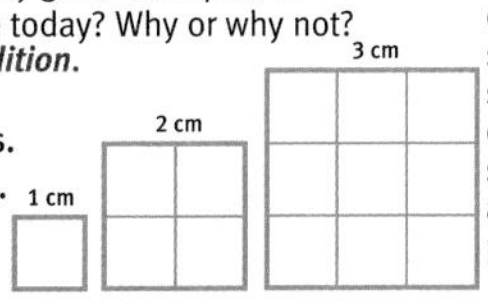


8. Complete the chart about each square.

| Length of side | Perimeter | Area |
|---|---|---|
| 1 cm | 4 cm | 1 cm² |
| 2 cm | 8 cm | 4 cm² |
| 3 cm | 12 cm | 9 cm² |
| 4 cm | 16 cm | 16 cm² |
| 5 cm | 20 cm | 25 cm² |
| 6 cm | 24 cm | 36 cm² |
| 7 cm | 28 cm | 49 cm² |
| 8 cm | 32 cm | 64 cm² |
| 9 cm | 36 cm | 81 cm² |
| 10 cm | 40 cm | 100 cm² |

9. Extended Response What happens to the perimeter and area of each square as the side lengths are doubled? See Reflect in the *Teacher's Edition*.
10. How many squares, with sides of 10 meters, could be enclosed by a fence surrounding a 20-meter-square garden? 4 squares





# 3 Reflect

10

## Guided Discussion REASONING

Whole Group

Have students give examples of congruent objects outside of school and explain why these things are made to match. Students might select any number of manufactured items, such as parts of cars, light bulbs, and so on. These things are made to be congruent so they can be replaced with ease and so machines can make them easily.

### Applications APPLYING

Show students a map of the United States or of the state in which you live, and ask questions such as the following:

- **Is this map congruent to the land that it represents?** no
- **How do you know the map is not congruent?** Students should mention that the map is a representation of the land, not an exact copy of it, and it is much smaller.

Point out the scale shown on the map, and explain that the scale on the map shows the difference between the size of the map and the actual size of the land that it represents. If the map was blown up large enough, it would, in theory, show the exact distance between places in the real world. Go on to explain that maps can be made larger or smaller, and the scale can increase or decrease proportionately. Ask questions about the scale on the map.

- **If 1 inch on the map is equal to 100 miles in the real world, how many inches would it take to represent 300 miles?** 3
- **If 1 inch is equal to 100 miles, how many miles would 4 inches represent?** 400

## Extended Response

**Problem 7** The examples of congruent objects are better today because more products are produced by machines, which eliminate possible human errors.

**Problem 9** Students should see that the area quadruples and the perimeter doubles when the sides double.

**Cumulative Review:** For review of converting customary units, assign Problems 1–8 on student page 493.

**Family Involvement:** Assign the ***Practice, Reteach,*** or ***Enrichment*** activities depending on the needs of your students.

**Concept/Question Board:** Encourage students to continue to post questions, answers, and examples on the Concept/Question Board.

**Math Puzzler:** If you want to divide a line segment into nine equal parts, how many parallel lines will you need? 8

# 4 Assess and Differentiate

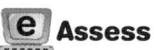

**e Assess** Use ***eAssess*** to record and analyze evidence of student understanding.

## A Gather Evidence

Use the Daily Class Assessment Records in ***Assessment*** or ***eAssess*** to record daily observations.

### Informal Assessment

**☑ Strategy Building** UNDERSTANDING

Did the student

- ❑ make important observations?
- ❑ extend or generalize learning?
- ❑ provide insightful answers?
- ❑ pose insightful questions?

### Informal Assessment

**☑ Guided Discussion** REASONING

Did the student

- ❑ provide a clear explanation?
- ❑ communicate reasons and strategies?
- ❑ choose appropriate strategies?
- ❑ argue logically?

## B Summarize Findings

Analyze and summarize assessment data for each student. Determine which Assessment Follow-Up is appropriate for each student. Use the Student Assessment Record in ***Assessment*** or ***eAssess*** to update assessment records.

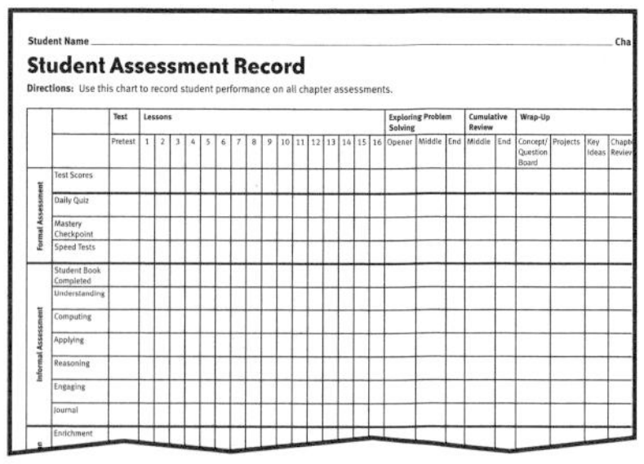
Student Name
Student Assessment Record
Directions: Use this chart to record student performance on all chapter assessments.

**Assessment Page T41**

## C Assessment Follow-Up • DIFFERENTIATE INSTRUCTION

Based on your observations, use these teaching strategies for assessment follow-up.

### INTERVENTION

Review student performance on ***Intervention*** Lesson 10.A to see if students have mastered prerequisite skills for this lesson.

### ENGLISH LEARNER

**Review**

Use Lesson 10.7 in ***English Learner Support Guide*** to review lesson concepts and vocabulary.

### ENRICH

**If . . .** students are proficient in the lesson concepts,

**Then . . .** encourage them to work on chapter projects or ***Enrichment*** Lesson 10.7.

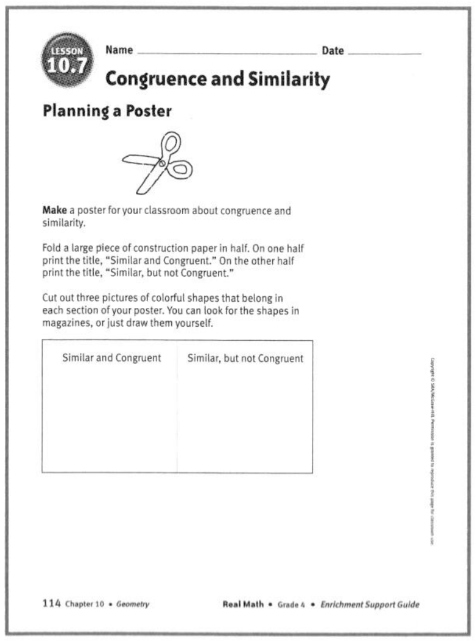
LESSON 10.7 Name Date
Congruence and Similarity
Planning a Poster
Make a poster for your classroom about congruence and similarity.
Fold a large piece of construction paper in half. On one half print the title, "Similar and Congruent." On the other half print the title, "Similar, but not Congruent."
Cut out three pictures of colorful shapes that belong in each section of your poster. You can look for the shapes in magazines, or just draw them yourself.

| Similar and Congruent | Similar, but not Congruent |
| --- | --- |
| | |

114 Chapter 10 • Geometry Real Math • Grade 4 • Enrichment Support Guide

Enrichment Lesson 10.7

### PRACTICE

**If . . .** students would benefit from additional practice,

**Then . . .** assign ***Practice*** Lesson 10.7.

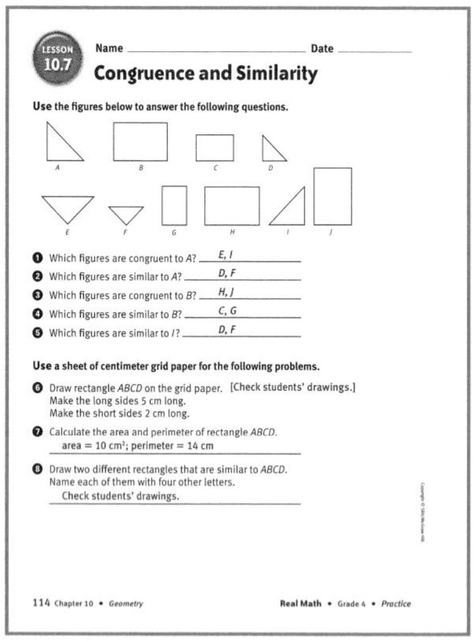
LESSON 10.7 Name Date
Congruence and Similarity
Use the figures below to answer the following questions.
1. Which figures are congruent to A? E, I
2. Which figures are similar to A? D, F
3. Which figures are congruent to B? H, J
4. Which figures are similar to B? C, G
5. Which figures are similar to I? D, F
Use a sheet of centimeter grid paper for the following problems.
6. Draw rectangle ABCD on the grid paper. Make the long sides 5 cm long. Make the short sides 2 cm long. [Check students' drawings.]
7. Calculate the area and perimeter of rectangle ABCD. area = 10 cm²; perimeter = 14 cm
8. Draw two different rectangles that are similar to ABCD. Name each of them with four other letters. Check students' drawings.
114 Chapter 10 • Geometry Real Math • Grade 4 • Practice

Practice Lesson 10.7

### RETEACH

**If . . .** students have difficulty understanding congruence and similarity,

**Then . . .** reteach the concept using ***Reteach*** Lesson 10.7.

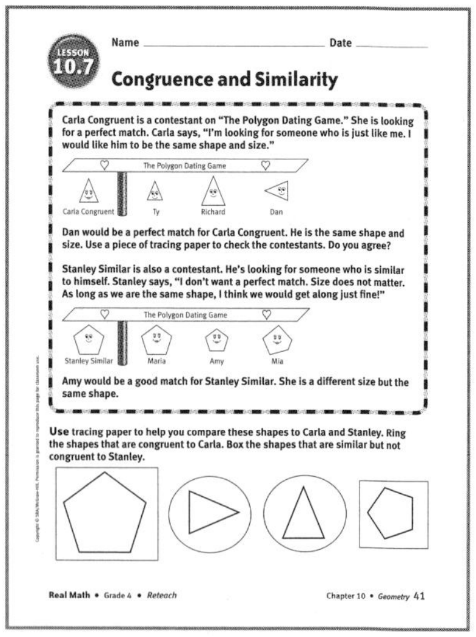
LESSON 10.7 Name Date
Congruence and Similarity
Carla Congruent is a contestant on "The Polygon Dating Game." She is looking for a perfect match. Carla says, "I'm looking for someone who is just like me. I would like him to be the same shape and size."
The Polygon Dating Game
Carla Congruent Ty Richard Dan
Dan would be a perfect match for Carla Congruent. He is the same shape and size. Use a piece of tracing paper to check the contestants. Do you agree?
Stanley Similar is also a contestant. He's looking for someone who is similar to himself. Stanley says, "I don't want a perfect match. Size does not matter. As long as we are the same shape, I think we would get along just fine!"
The Polygon Dating Game
Stanley Similar Maria Amy Mia
Amy would be a good match for Stanley Similar. She is a different size but the same shape.
Use tracing paper to help you compare these shapes to Carla and Stanley. Ring the shapes that are congruent to Carla. Box the shapes that are similar but not congruent to Stanley.
Real Math • Grade 4 • Reteach Chapter 10 • Geometry 41

Reteach Lesson 10.7

# Rotation, Translation, and Reflection

**Context of the Lesson** This is the fifth of six lessons on plane figures. This lesson extends the idea of congruence that was introduced in Lesson 10.7. Students will see that the movement of shapes on a plane can show that two objects are congruent. The terms from this lesson will also be applied to lessons involving space figures and polyhedra.

See page 446B for Math Background for teachers for this lesson.

### Objectives
To have students explore congruence by translation, rotation, and reflection

### NCTM Standards
**Geometry**
- Predict and describe the results of sliding, flipping, and turning plane figures
- Describe a motion or a series of motions that will show that two figures are congruent

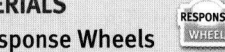

### Materials
- *Response Wheels
- Paper for tracing
- Polygon models that students previously created
- Overhead projector and Pattern Blocks

### Technology
- **ePresentation** Lesson 10.8
- **eMathTools** Shape Tool and Net Tool
- Building Blocks Geometry Snapshots 7

### Test Prep
**Cumulative Review**
Mental Math reviews basic facts (Lesson 3.10).

**Extended Response**
Problem 4c

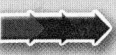

## Planning for Learning • DIFFERENTIATE INSTRUCTION

### INTERVENTION

**If . . .** students lack the prerequisite skill of classifying figures,

**Then . . .** teach ***Intervention*** Lesson 10.A.

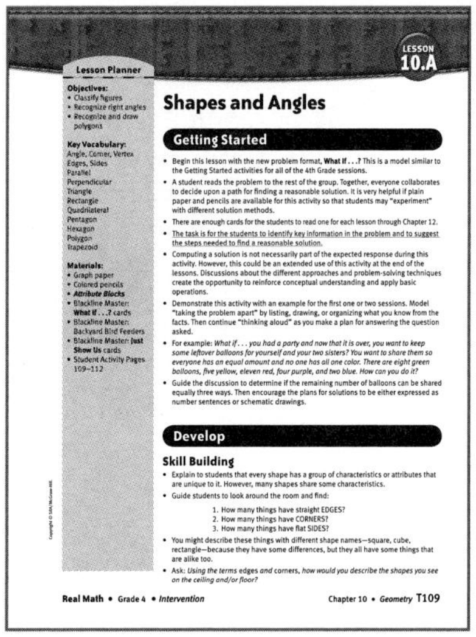
LESSON 10.A

Shapes and Angles

Getting Started

Develop

Intervention Lesson 10.A

### ENGLISH LEARNER

Preview

**If . . .** students need language support,

**Then . . .** use Lesson 10.8 in ***English Learner Support Guide*** to preview lesson concepts and vocabulary.

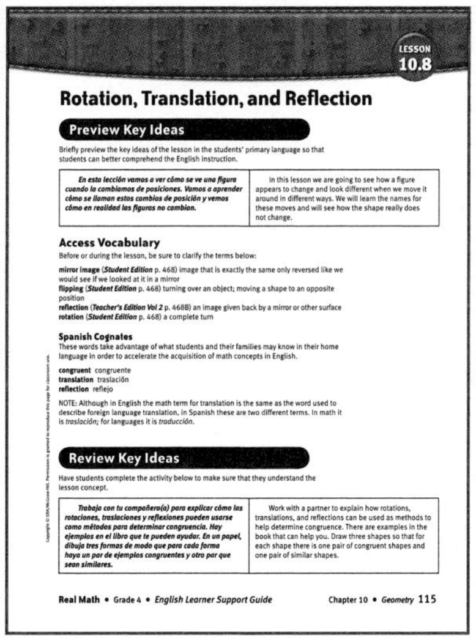
LESSON 10.8

Rotation, Translation, and Reflection

Preview Key Ideas

Access Vocabulary

Spanish Cognates

Review Key Ideas

English Learner Lesson 10.8

### ENRICH

**If . . .** students are proficient in the lesson concepts,

**Then . . .** have them use the ***eMathTools: Shape Tool*** to create a game involving rotation, translation, and reflection.

### PRACTICE

**If . . .** students would benefit from additional practice,

**Then . . .** extend Guided Discussion before assigning the student pages.

### RETEACH

**If . . .** students have difficulty understanding rotation, translation, and reflection,

**Then . . .** extend the Guided Discussion before assigning the student pages.

### Vocabulary
**translation \tranz la' shən\ *n.*** a change in the location of a figure in which it slides without being turned

### Access Vocabulary
**translation** a figure that does not change; it moves to a new location

### Spanish Cognates
**congruent** congruente
**translation** traslación

*Manipulative Kit Item

## Mental Math
5

RESPONSE WHEEL

Provide practice for basic addition, subtraction, multiplication, and division facts, using exercises such as the following:

| | | |
|---|---|---|
| **a.** 7 + 6 = 13 | **b.** 11 − 3 = 8 | **c.** 4 × 8 = 32 |
| **d.** 72 ÷ 8 = 9 | **e.** 9 + 7 = 16 | **f.** 6 × 7 = 42 |
| **g.** 10 − 9 = 1 | **h.** 27 ÷ 3 = 9 | **i.** 6 + 3 = 9 |

## 1 Develop
25

**Tell Students In Today's Lesson They Will**
learn about sliding, flipping, and turning shapes.

Whole Group

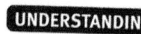

### Guided Discussion
UNDERSTANDING eMathTools

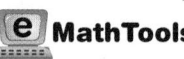

Review congruence and similarity with the class. Ask questions such as the following:

- **Can you think of an example of two congruent shapes? Draw some examples on the board.** Possible answer: two squares of the same size
- **Can you think of an example of two similar shapes? Draw some examples on the board.** Possible answer: two squares, one is larger than the other

Model a translation, a rotation, and a reflection, using an overhead projector and Pattern Blocks or the ***eMathTools: Shape Tool.*** Ask questions such as the following:

- **Watch as I make a translation. What word would you use to describe the motion?** slide

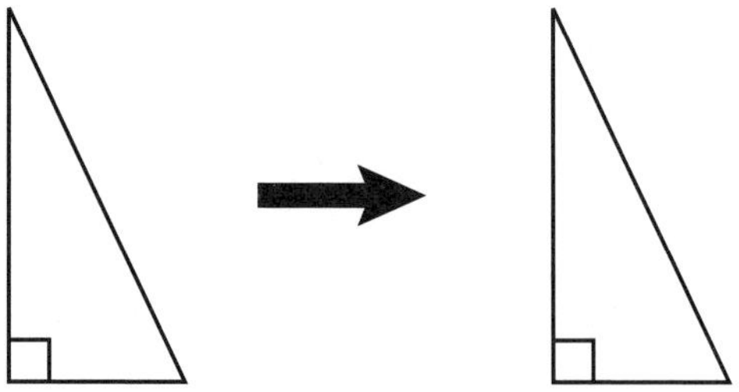

- **Watch as I make a rotation. What word would you use to describe the motion?** turn

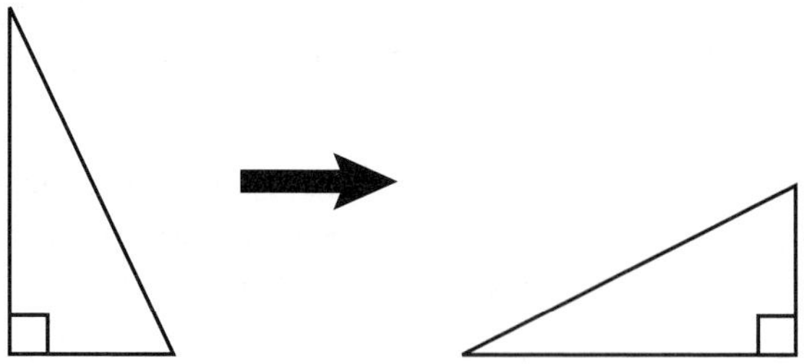

- **Watch as I make a reflection. What word would you use to describe the motion?** flip

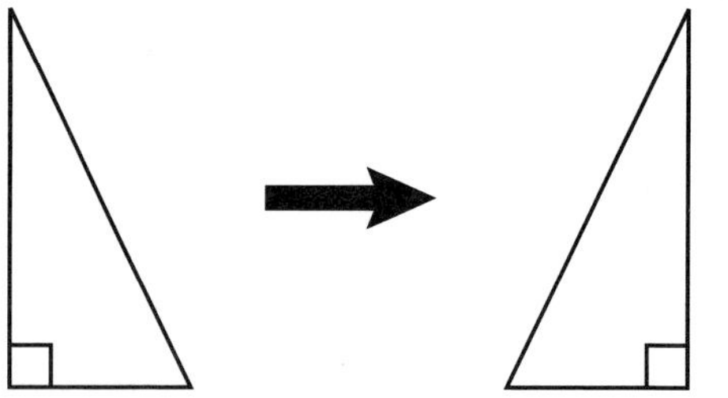

Using an overhead projector and Pattern Blocks or the ***eMathTools: Shape Tool,*** demonstrate several examples of translations, rotations, and reflections. Include at least one example of a translation, a rotation, and a reflection that demonstrates congruence. Also include one or two examples of figures that are not congruent. Have volunteers come to the overhead projector or computer to translate, rotate, and reflect the shapes to cause them to become congruent. Point out that none of these motions will cause the shapes to become congruent.

## 2 Assign Student Pages
20

**Pages 468–469**
APPLYING

Have students work independently on pages 468–469. Provide paper for tracing. Students may use the polygon models they made to demonstrate rotations and reflections.

### Monitoring Student Progress

| | |
|---|---|
| **If . . .** students have difficulty with the ideas of translation, rotation, and reflection of an object, | **Then . . .** have students use objects such as books or regular polygons they have cut out to demonstrate ideas in a more interactive way. |

**As Students Finish**

Building Blocks *Geometry Snapshots 7*

eMathTools In preparation for later lessons, have students use the ***eMathTools: Net Tool*** to make space figures. They can also use the polygon patterns provided in ***Practice.***

Student Page

## LESSON 10.8 Rotation, Translation, and Reflection

### Key Ideas

**The movement of figures can be described in various ways.**

When you slide a piece of paper in a straight line without turning it, you make a translation. If you turn the paper around a point, that move is called a *rotation*.

Flipping the figure over makes it into a mirror image of itself. This is called a *reflection*. You get the same effect by holding a mirror beside the figure and looking only at the mirror image rather than at the figure itself.

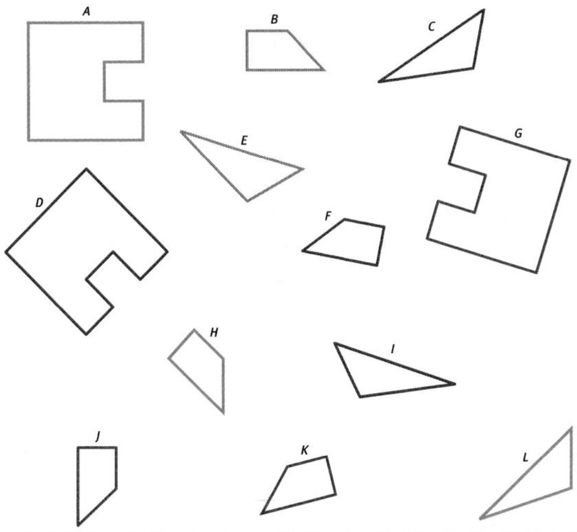






Student Page

**Use tracing paper or waxed paper to complete the following activities. Then answer the questions about the figures from the previous page.**

1. Trace figures *A*, *B*, and *C* on your paper.
2. List the figures that you think are congruent to figure *A*. *D, G*
3. Slide your paper so your copy of figure *A* is directly over each figure that you thought was congruent to figure *A*. Does your figure fit on top of each of them? yes
4. Look at figure *B*.
   - **a.** List the figures that you think are congruent to figure *B*. *F, H, J, K*
   - **b.** Slide your paper (translating and rotating) to see if your tracing fits on top of each figure that you thought was congruent to figure *B*.
   - **c.** Extended Response Can you make your tracing fit on each figure using only translations and rotations? Why or why not? See Reflect in the *Teacher's Edition*.
   - **d.** Can you think of something to do with the tracing to make your copy of figure *B* fit on the figures that appear to be congruent to it? Turn the tracing paper over.
5. Look at figure *C*.
   - **a.** List the figures you think are congruent to figure *C*. *E, I, L*
   - **b.** Can you make your tracing of figure *C* fit on each of them if flipping is allowed? yes
   - **c.** Did you have to turn the paper over for some of those figures? yes
6. Why didn't you have to turn the tracing over to check for congruency with figure *A*? The mirror image of figure *A* is the same as figure *A*.





# 3 Reflect

10

## Guided Discussion REASONING

Whole Group

Have students use an object from the classroom to demonstrate translation, reflection, and rotation to determine congruence. Ask questions such as the following:

- **Is a right shoe usually congruent to a left shoe (for the same individual)?** yes
- **Which move would show this?** reflection
- **Can you "flip" one shoe so it would fit the other?** No, not unless you can flip it in a fourth dimension.

Explain to students that to "flip" a plane figure, we need space. To "flip" a space figure, we need hyperspace.

## Extended Response

**Problem 4** Students should see that their tracings will not fit on all the images because the tracing needs to be reflected in order to fit on *F* and *K*. For part d, students should realize that *B* will fit on *F* and *K* when the tracing paper is reflected.

**Curriculum Connection:** Students interested in the study of architecture can research this topic online or at the library.

**Cumulative Review:** For review of ordering decimals, assign Problems 9–10 on student page 493.

**Family Involvement:** Assign the ***Practice, Reteach,*** or ***Enrichment*** activities depending on the needs of your students.

**Concept/Question Board:** Encourage students to continue to post questions, answers, and examples on the Concept/Question Board.

**Math Puzzler:** Find the pattern in the following sequence, then give the next three numbers: 1, 2, 3, 5, 8, 13 . . .. The numbers in the pattern, starting with 3, are the sum of the two previous numbers. The next three numbers are 21, 34, and 55.

# 4 Assess and Differentiate

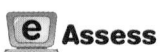

e Assess Use ***eAssess*** to record and analyze evidence of student understanding.

## A Gather Evidence

Use the Daily Class Assessment Records in ***Assessment*** or ***eAssess*** to record daily observations.

### Informal Assessment

**Mental Math**

Did the student COMPUTING

- ❑ respond accurately?
- ❑ respond quickly?
- ❑ respond with confidence?
- ❑ self-correct?

### Informal Assessment

**Guided Discussion**

Did the student UNDERSTANDING

- ❑ make important observations?
- ❑ extend or generalize learning?
- ❑ provide insightful answers?
- ❑ pose insightful questions?

## B Summarize Findings

Analyze and summarize assessment data for each student. Determine which Assessment Follow-Up is appropriate for each student. Use the Student Assessment Record in ***Assessment*** or ***eAssess*** to update assessment records.

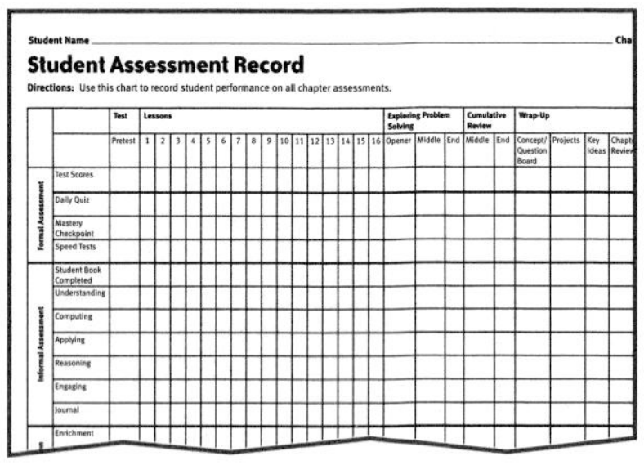
Student Assessment Record

Assessment Page T41

## C Assessment Follow-Up • DIFFERENTIATE INSTRUCTION

Based on your observations, use these teaching strategies for assessment follow-up.

### INTERVENTION

Review student performance on ***Intervention*** Lesson 10.A to see if students have mastered prerequisite skills for this lesson.

### ENGLISH LEARNER

**Review**

Use Lesson 10.8 in ***English Learner Support Guide*** to review lesson concepts and vocabulary.

### ENRICH

**If . . .** students are proficient in the lesson concepts,

**Then . . .** encourage them to work on the chapter projects or ***Enrichment*** Lesson 10.8.

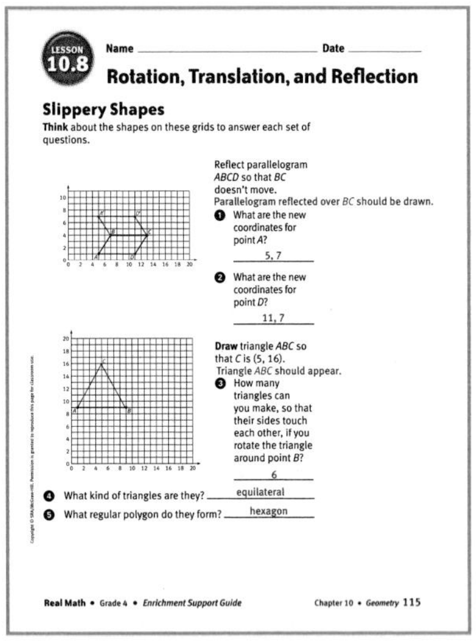
LESSON 10.8 Name ______ Date ______

Rotation, Translation, and Reflection

Slippery Shapes

Think about the shapes on these grids to answer each set of questions.

Reflect parallelogram ABCD so that BC doesn't move. Parallelogram reflected over BC should be drawn.

1. What are the new coordinates for point A? 5, 7
2. What are the new coordinates for point D? 11, 7

Draw triangle ABC so that C is (5, 16). Triangle ABC should appear.

3. How many triangles can you make, so that their sides touch each other, if you rotate the triangle around point B? 6
4. What kind of triangles are they? equilateral
5. What regular polygon do they form? hexagon

Real Math • Grade 4 • Enrichment Support Guide    Chapter 10 • Geometry 115

Enrichment Lesson 10.8

### PRACTICE

**If . . .** students would benefit from additional practice,

**Then . . .** assign ***Practice*** Lesson 10.8.

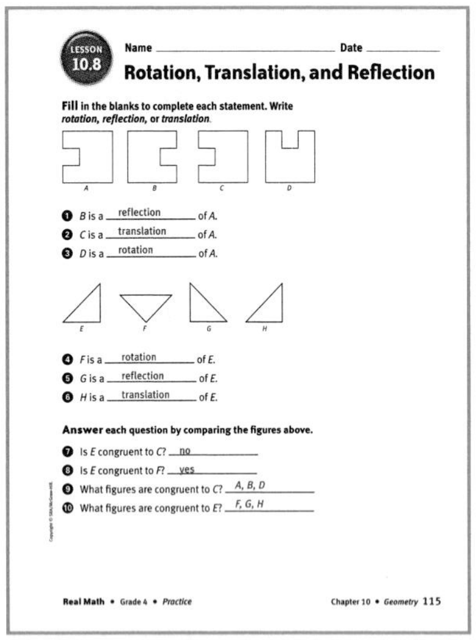
LESSON 10.8 Name ______ Date ______

Rotation, Translation, and Reflection

Fill in the blanks to complete each statement. Write *rotation, reflection,* or *translation.*

1. B is a reflection of A.
2. C is a translation of A.
3. D is a rotation of A.
4. F is a rotation of E.
5. G is a reflection of E.
6. H is a translation of E.

Answer each question by comparing the figures above.

7. Is E congruent to C? no
8. Is E congruent to F? yes
9. What figures are congruent to C? A, B, D
10. What figures are congruent to E? F, G, H

Real Math • Grade 4 • Practice    Chapter 10 • Geometry 115

Practice Lesson 10.8

### RETEACH

**If . . .** students have difficulty understanding rotation, translation, and reflection,

**Then . . .** have students model them using blocks of different shapes. Students can trace the block, perform a change, then trace the result. Defining the terms in a more general sense may help some students: A translation slides all the points in the plane the same distance in the same direction. A rotation turns all the points in the plane around one point, which is called the *center of rotation.* A reflection flips all the points in the plane over a line, which is called the *mirror.*

**Objectives**
- To provide experience in finding lines of symmetry
- To teach or review the names and properties of common polygons
- To demonstrate the relationship between geometry and fractions

**NCTM Standards**
**Geometry**
Identify and describe lines of symmetry in two-dimensional shapes

**Materials**
- Rectangular paper (such as copier or construction paper)
- Paper for tracing
- Scissors
- *Rulers (with metric units)
- Mirrors (optional)

**Technology**
e **Presentation** Lesson 10.9
e **MathTools** Geometry Tool and Net Tool
e **Games** More or Less Game

**Test Prep**
**Cumulative Review** (Review)
Mental Math reviews the approximation of answers across different operations (Lessons 2.6, 3.10, and 6.10).

**Writing + Math**
Journal

## Looking Ahead

For Lesson 10.10, you will need models of space figures, everyday objects that look like space figures, and cardboard (foldable) boxes.

# Lines of Symmetry

**Context of the Lesson** This is the sixth and final lesson on plane figures. Symmetry was introduced in the Kindergarten level of ***Real Math***. This lesson provides students with the opportunity to find lines of symmetry among shapes they recognize. Students will also apply their knowledge of the properties of half an object by dividing figures into two.

See page 446B for Math Background for teachers for this lesson.

## Planning for Learning • DIFFERENTIATE INSTRUCTION

### INTERVENTION

**If . . .** students lack the prerequisite skill of classifying figures,

**Then . . .** teach ***Intervention*** Lesson 10.A.

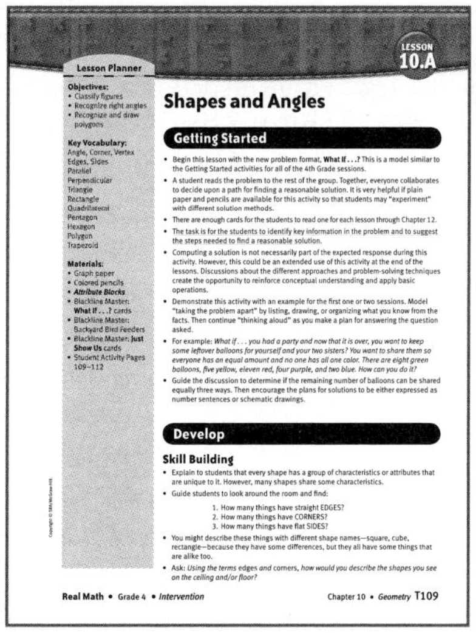
Lesson Planner

LESSON 10.A

Shapes and Angles

Getting Started

Develop

Skill Building

Intervention Lesson 10.A

### ENGLISH LEARNER

Preview

**If . . .** students need language support,

**Then . . .** use Lesson 10.9 in ***English Learner Support Guide*** to preview lesson concepts and vocabulary.

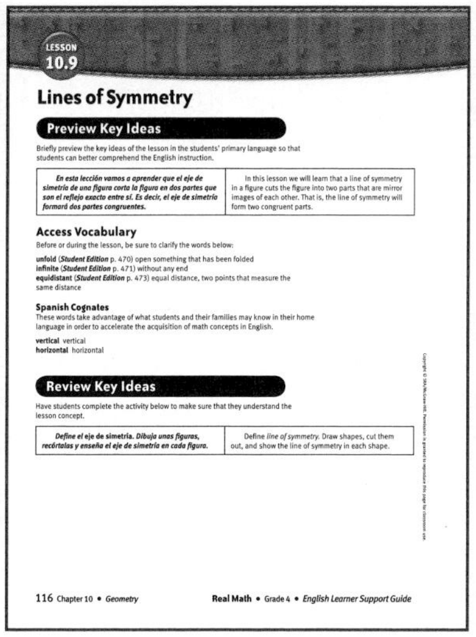
LESSON 10.9

Lines of Symmetry

Preview Key Ideas

Access Vocabulary

Spanish Cognates

Review Key Ideas

English Learner Lesson 10.9

### ENRICH

**If . . .** students are proficient in the lesson concepts,

**Then . . .** have them use the ***eMathTools: Geometry Tool*** to show figures and their lines of symmetry.

### PRACTICE

**If . . .** students would benefit from additional practice,

**Then . . .** extend Guided Discussion before assigning the student pages.

### RETEACH

**If . . .** students have difficulty finding lines of symmetry,

**Then . . .** extend Skill Building before assigning the student pages.

**Vocabulary**
**line of symmetry *n.*** a line on which a figure can be folded into two congruent parts

**Access Vocabulary**
**infinite** without any end
**equidistant** equal distance; two points that measure the same distance

**Spanish Cognates**
**vertical** vertical
**horizontal** horizontal

*Manipulative Kit Item

# Teaching Lesson 10.9

## Mental Math 5

Review THUMBS UP Provide practice with approximation problems, using a number range from 500 to 1,000. Have students show thumbs-up if the answer is more than 1,000 and thumbs-down if the answer is less than 1,000. Students should stand up if the answer is equal to 1,000.

**a.** 50 × 200 up
**b.** 8,300 − 8,000 down
**c.** 60 × 80 up
**d.** 6,000 ÷ 5 up
**e.** 60 × 5 down
**f.** 780 + 25 down
**g.** 50 × 20 stand up
**h.** 540 + 450 down
**i.** 980 + 90 up
**j.** 900 − 90 down

## 1 Develop 25

**Tell Students In Today's Lesson They Will**
find lines of symmetry and explore the relationship between geometry and fractions.

### Guided Discussion UNDERSTANDING

Whole Group

1. Give each student a rectangular sheet of paper. Have students fold the paper diagonally, matching the edge of the short side to the edge of the long side. Have them tear off or cut the smaller portion from the rest of the paper, leaving a square piece.
2. Demonstrate how to fold the square horizontally, then have the students fold their squares.
3. Once everyone has finished and has opened his or her square, tell the students that the fold represents a line of symmetry. Explain that a line of symmetry cuts objects into congruent parts.
4. Display the following on an overhead projector or on the board:

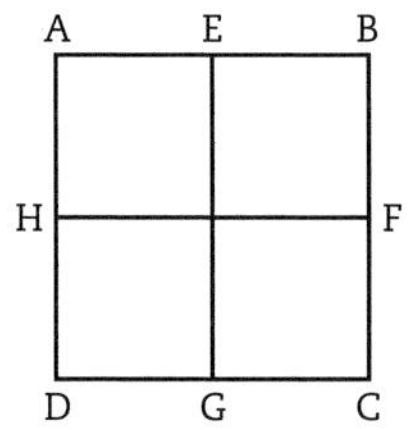


5. Explain that when something is folded so its two halves match exactly, the crease is a line of symmetry. Have students examine the figure on the overhead projector or on the board as you ask them questions such as the following:

- **HF is a line of symmetry. Fold your square along a line like HF. Do the two sides fall exactly on top of each other?** yes
- **Find another line of symmetry in your square. Is there a line already drawn like it in the square?** For those students who find a line of symmetry like EG, the answer is yes; for those who choose a diagonal, the answer is no.
- **Try to find two more lines of symmetry in the square. Fold to make sure they are lines of symmetry.** The four lines of symmetry in the square are HF, EG, AC, and BD.
- **Are there any more lines of symmetry in the square? Check any line you think might be a line of symmetry by folding along it.** no
- **How many lines of symmetry are there in the square?** 4
- **How many lines of symmetry do you think there are in other squares?** 4

6. Next, tell the students that a square has four lines of symmetry. Ask them to find a line of symmetry other than the horizontal line. Ask volunteers to share their answers. When students have explained the fold they made, have everyone fold his or her square that way to explore the various lines of symmetry an object can have.
7. Now have students create an equilateral triangle that is five centimeters in length on all three sides. Show the class one of the three possible lines of symmetry and then have the class find the other two lines of symmetry.

### Skill Building ENGAGING

Small Group

1. Have students draw a large plane figure of their choice on a piece of paper. Students may draw geometric figures, such as polygons, but it is not necessary. Tell them to keep their drawings limited to the outline of a figure.
2. Have students trade their drawings with a partner. Students should find the total number of lines of symmetry in the figure they are given. Remind them that not all figures have a line of symmetry. When students have finished, ask questions such as the following. Students only need to raise their hands to respond to your questions.
   - **Does anyone have a figure that has zero lines of symmetry?**
   - **Does anyone have a figure that has one line of symmetry?**
   - **Does anyone have a figure that has two lines of symmetry?**
   - **Does anyone have a figure that has three or more lines of symmetry?**

When students raise their hands, collect the drawings. Show at least two of the drawings to the class, if possible, and have them determine if the correct number of lines of symmetry have been indicated.

# 2 Assign Student Pages

25

**Page 471** APPLYING

Have students complete page 471 on their own.

## Monitoring Student Progress

**If . . .** students still do not understand the concept of lines of symmetry,

**Then . . .** use a rectangular piece of paper as another example. A rectangle has two lines of symmetry that the student can discover.

Student Page

LESSON 10.9 **Lines of Symmetry**

### Key Ideas

**A line of symmetry in a figure cuts the figure into two parts that are mirror images of one another. That is, the line of symmetry will divide the figure into two congruent parts.**

You can easily make a square out of a rectangular piece of paper. Just fold it diagonally, matching the edge of the short side to the edge of the long side, and cut off the leftover part. Unfold the paper, and you have a square. The fold in the square is a line of symmetry.

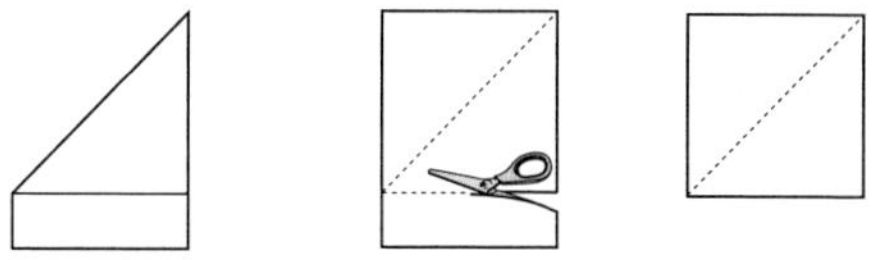

If you fold a figure on a line of symmetry, the two parts will fit exactly on top of one another.

The dashed line in the heart-shaped figure is a line of symmetry.

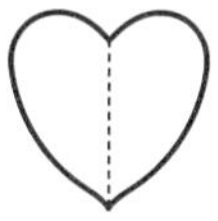

Look at the rectangle. Where is the line of symmetry? Actually, there are two possible lines of symmetry: one is up-and-down, and the other one goes from side to side.



Textbook This lesson is available in the *eTextbook*.

Student Page

**Trace** or copy the figures. Then figure out how many lines of symmetry there are in each.

1. 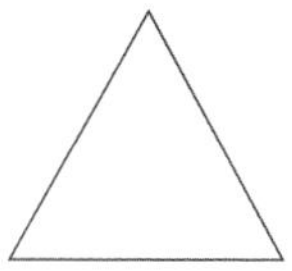 3

2.  4

3. 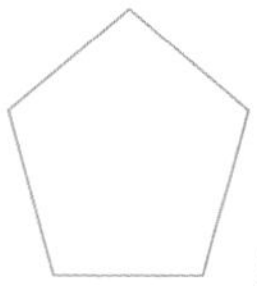 5

4. 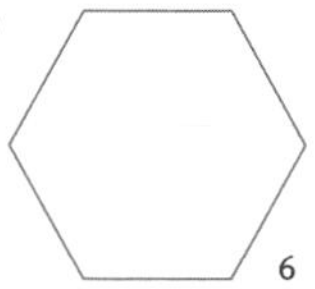 6

5. 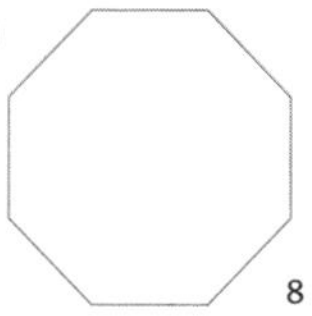 8

6.  an infinite number

7. 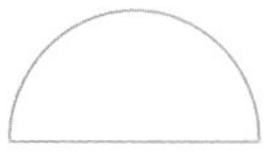 1

8. 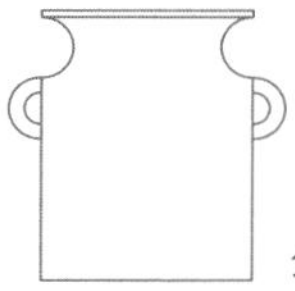 1

9.  1

10.  5

# Assign Student Pages, continued

## Pages 472–473 APPLYING

Discuss the directions on page 473, making sure students place the line segment correctly across the seven parallel lines. Then have students work independently on pages 472–473. The answers in the ***Student Edition*** are examples only; check students' work to see if half of the figure has been shaded.

### Monitoring Student Progress

**If . . .** students have difficulty finding a line of symmetry of a figure,

**Then . . .** have them fold the figure along the line being checked, or have them place a mirror on the line and consider the reflection. If one part matches the other part, then the line is a line of symmetry.

### As Students Finish

**Game** **More or Less Game** (reviews multidigit multiplication and inequalities)

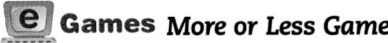

**e Games** ***More or Less Game***

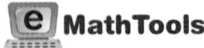

**e MathTools** In preparation for later lessons, have students use the ***eMathTools: Net Tool*** to make space figures. They can also use the polygon patterns provided in ***Practice***.

Student Page

LESSON 10.9 • Lines of Symmetry

**Trace** the figures. Divide each figure into halves, using a line of symmetry. Shade $\frac{1}{2}$ of each figure.

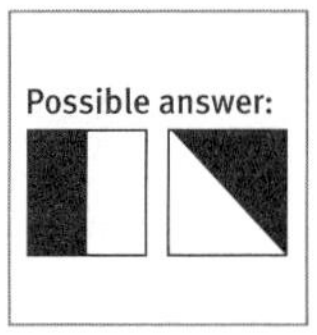


11 Square

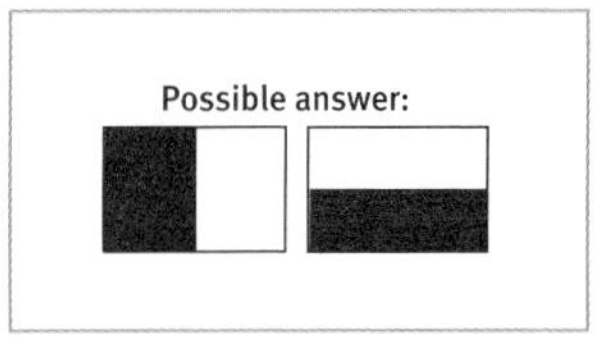


12 Rectangle

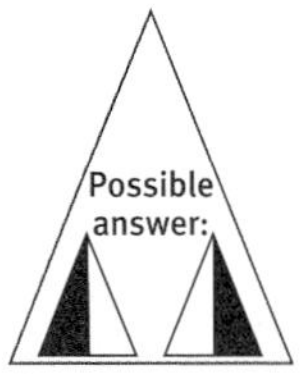


13 Isosceles triangle
Two equal sides
Two equal angles

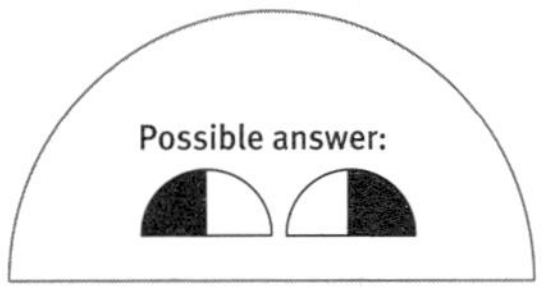


14 Semicircle

15 Trace each figure again. Try to shade $\frac{1}{2}$ the area of each figure in such a way that there is *not* a line of symmetry between the shaded and unshaded parts. (This is difficult for the figures in Problems 13 and 14. Do the best you can.) Answers will vary. See possible answers in Reflect in the *Teacher's Edition*.



Textbook This lesson is available in the ***eTextbook***.

Student Page

Parallel lines can be used to divide line segments into equal parts.

The seven lines above are parallel, and the distances between them are the same.

Copy the line segment below on a sheet of paper.

Place your paper with the line segment over the seven parallel lines at the top of this page. Move the paper so that one end of the line segment just touches the top line and the other just touches the bottom line.

Mark the points where the line segment crosses each of the parallel lines.

**Answer** the following questions.

16 Into how many parts has your line segment been divided? 6

17 Do the parts seem about equal in length? yes

18 Is each part $\frac{1}{6}$ the length of the segment? yes

19 How many centimeters long is the segment? 12 cm

20 How many centimeters long is each small part of the segment? 2 cm

21 What is $\frac{1}{6}$ of 12? 2

**Copy** the line segment again. Place it across five of the parallel lines. Mark the points where the line segment crosses each parallel line.

22 Into how many parts has your line segment been divided? 4

23 Measure to find how many centimeters there are in $\frac{1}{4}$ of the segment. 3 cm

24 What is $\frac{1}{4}$ of 12? 3

Writing + Math **Journal**
Explain how a circle could have an unlimited number of lines of symmetry.

See Reflect in the *Teacher's Edition*.

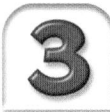

## 3 Reflect 5

### Guided Discussion REASONING

Whole Group

1. Have students define *line of symmetry*. Ask questions such as the following:
   - **How many equal sides does an equilateral triangle have? A square? A regular octagon?** 3; 4; 8
   - **How many lines of symmetry does an equilateral triangle have? A square? A regular octagon?** 3; 4; 8
   - **Is there a relationship between the number of equal sides of a figure and the number of lines of symmetry it contains?** Yes, they are the same.
2. Explain to students that this works only for regular polygons.
3. Discuss students' answers to Problem 15 on page 472. Possible answers for Figures 13 and 14 might look like this:

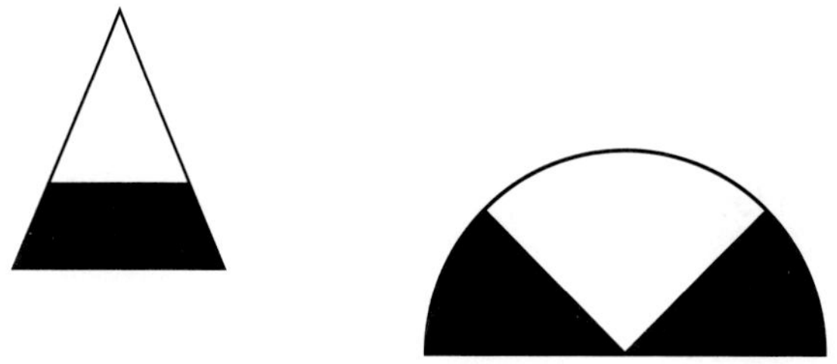

### Writing + Math Journal

Look for students to say that the distance from the center to the outside should be equal in all locations. If it is, then any time the circle is folded across the center, a line of symmetry is created.

**Cumulative Review:** For review of relation signs, assign Problems 11–14 on student page 493.

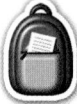

**Family Involvement:** Assign the ***Practice, Reteach,*** or ***Enrichment*** activities depending on the needs of your students.

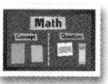

**Concept/Question Board:** Encourage students to continue to post questions, answers, and examples on the Concept/Question Board.

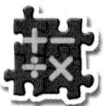

**Math Puzzler:** Think of a word that has a vertical line of symmetry when printed in uppercase letters; for example, MOM. Think of a word that has a horizontal line of symmetry when printed in uppercase letters; for example, DID. Possible answers: HOOK, DID, BOB; WOW, TOT, MOM

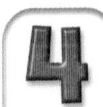

# 4 Assess and Differentiate

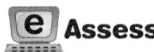

e Assess Use *eAssess* to record and analyze evidence of student understanding.

## A Gather Evidence

Use the Daily Class Assessment Records in ***Assessment*** or ***eAssess*** to record daily observations.

### Informal Assessment
**Skill Building** ENGAGING

Did the student
- ❑ pay attention to others' contributions?
- ❑ contribute information and ideas?
- ❑ improve on a strategy?
- ❑ reflect on and check the accuracy of his or her work?

### Informal Assessment
**Guided Discussion** UNDERSTANDING

Did the student
- ❑ make important observations?
- ❑ extend or generalize learning?
- ❑ provide insightful answers?
- ❑ pose insightful questions?

## B Summarize Findings

Analyze and summarize assessment data for each student. Determine which Assessment Follow-Up is appropriate for each student. Use the Student Assessment Record in ***Assessment*** or ***eAssess*** to update assessment records.

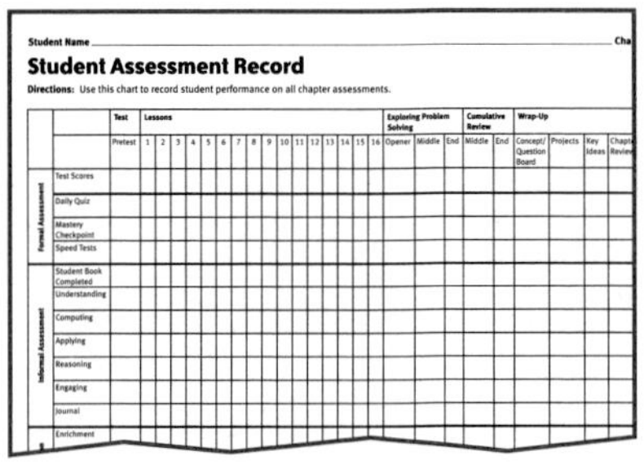
Student Assessment Record
Directions: Use this chart to record student performance on all chapter assessments.

Assessment Page T41

## C Assessment Follow-Up • DIFFERENTIATE INSTRUCTION

Based on your observations, use these teaching strategies for assessment follow-up.

### INTERVENTION

Review student performance on ***Intervention*** Lesson 10.A to see if students have mastered prerequisite skills for this lesson.

### ENGLISH LEARNER

**Review**

Use Lesson 10.9 in ***English Learner Support Guide*** to review lesson concepts and vocabulary.

### ENRICH

**If . . .** students are proficient in the lesson concepts,

**Then . . .** encourage them to work on the chapter projects or ***Enrichment*** Lesson 10.9.

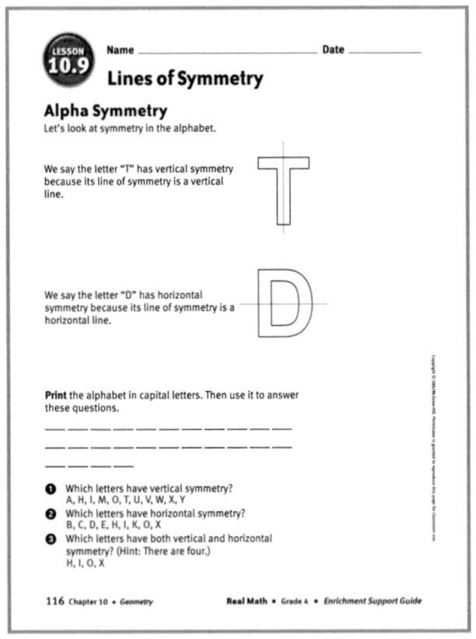
LESSON 10.9 Name Date

Lines of Symmetry

Alpha Symmetry

Let's look at symmetry in the alphabet.

We say the letter "T" has vertical symmetry because its line of symmetry is a vertical line.

We say the letter "D" has horizontal symmetry because its line of symmetry is a horizontal line.

Print the alphabet in capital letters. Then use it to answer these questions.

1. Which letters have vertical symmetry? A, H, I, M, O, T, U, V, W, X, Y
2. Which letters have horizontal symmetry? B, C, D, E, H, I, K, O, X
3. Which letters have both vertical and horizontal symmetry? (Hint: There are four.) H, I, O, X

116 Chapter 10 • Geometry Real Math • Grade 4 • Enrichment Support Guide

Enrichment Lesson 10.9

### PRACTICE

**If . . .** students would benefit from additional practice,

**Then . . .** assign ***Practice*** Lesson 10.9.

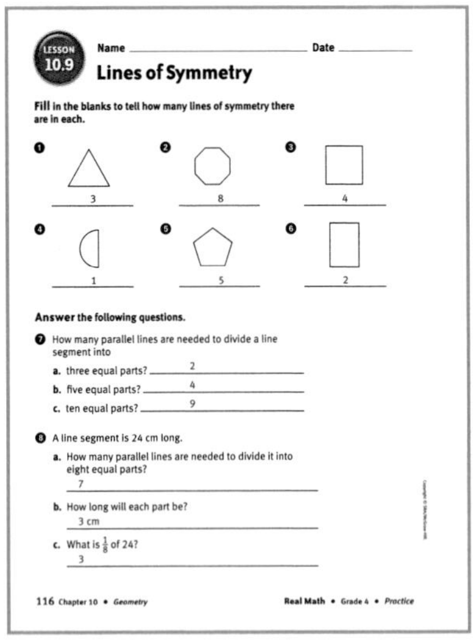
LESSON 10.9 Name Date

Lines of Symmetry

Fill in the blanks to tell how many lines of symmetry there are in each.

1. 3
2. 8
3. 4
4. 1
5. 5
6. 2

Answer the following questions.

7. How many parallel lines are needed to divide a line segment into
   a. three equal parts? 2
   b. five equal parts? 4
   c. ten equal parts? 9
8. A line segment is 24 cm long.
   a. How many parallel lines are needed to divide it into eight equal parts? 7
   b. How long will each part be? 3 cm
   c. What is $\frac{1}{8}$ of 24? 3

116 Chapter 10 • Geometry Real Math • Grade 4 • Practice

Practice Lesson 10.9

### RETEACH

**If . . .** students have difficulty finding lines of symmetry,

**Then . . .** have them look through magazines or architecture books with a mirror in hand. Have them find examples of symmetry in nature, advertising, and construction.

## Lesson Planner

### Objectives
- To introduce the names and properties of space figures
- To create and identify nets that fold into three-dimensional figures

### NCTM Standards
**Geometry**
- Identify, compare, and analyze attributes of three-dimensional shapes
- Classify three-dimensional shapes according to their properties

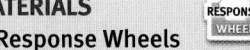

### Materials
RESPONSE WHEEL
- ***Response Wheels**
- Everyday objects that look like space figures
- *Space figures (from nets)
- Cardboard (foldable) boxes
- Scissors
- Tape

### Technology
**e Presentation** Lesson 10.10
**e MathTools Net Tool**
Building Blocks Geometry Snapshots 8

### Test Prep
**Cumulative Review** Review
Mental Math reviews multiplication facts (Lesson 3.10).

### Looking Ahead
For Lesson 10.11, you will need models of space figures including regular polyhedra (Platonic Solids).

*Manipulative Kit Item

# Space Figures

**Context of the Lesson** This is the first of three lessons on space figures. This lesson differs from the previous seven lessons in that objects in this lesson can not be contained in a plane, whereas the objects in the previous lessons lie in a plane. The goal of this lesson is for the students to identify which plane figures are needed to create specific space figures, through the use of nets.

See page 446B for Math Background for teachers for this lesson.

## Planning for Learning • DIFFERENTIATE INSTRUCTION

### INTERVENTION

**If . . .** students lack the prerequisite skill of drawing and recognizing polygons,

**Then . . .** teach ***Intervention*** Lesson 10.C.

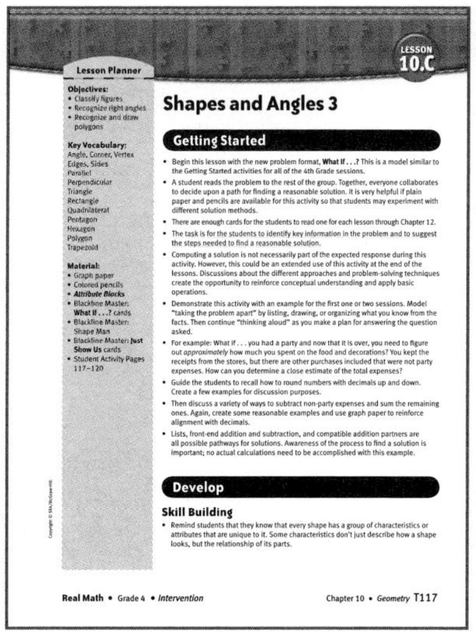
LESSON 10.C

Lesson Planner

Objectives:
- Classify figures
- Recognize right angles
- Recognize and draw polygons

Key Vocabulary:
Angle, Corner, Vertex
Edges, Sides
Parallel
Perpendicular
Triangle
Rectangle
Quadrilateral
Pentagon
Hexagon
Polygon
Trapezoid

Material:
- Graph paper
- Colored pencils
- *Attribute Blocks*
- Blackline Master: **What If . . . ?** cards
- Blackline Master: Shape Man
- Blackline Master: **Just Show Us** cards
- Student Activity Pages 117–120

Shapes and Angles 3

Getting Started

- Begin this lesson with the new problem format, **What If . . . ?** This is a model similar to the Getting Started activities for all of the 4th Grade sessions.
- A student reads the problem to the rest of the group. Together, everyone collaborates to decide upon a path for finding a reasonable solution. It is very helpful if plain paper and pencils are available for this activity so that students may experiment with different solution methods.
- There are enough cards for the students to read one for each lesson through Chapter 12.
- The task is for the students to identify key information in the problem and to suggest the steps needed to find a reasonable solution.
- Computing a solution is not necessarily part of the expected response during this activity. However, this could be an extended use of this activity at the end of the lessons. Discussions about the different approaches and problem-solving techniques create the opportunity to reinforce conceptual understanding and apply basic operations.
- Demonstrate this activity with an example for the first one or two sessions. Model "taking the problem apart" by listing, drawing, or organizing what you know from the facts. Then continue "thinking aloud" as you make a plan for answering the question asked.
- For example: What if . . . you had a party and now that it is over, you need to figure out *approximately* how much you spent on the food and decorations? You kept the receipts from the stores, but there are other purchases included that were not party expenses. How can you determine a close estimate of the total expenses?
- Guide the students to recall how to round numbers with decimals up and down. Create a few examples for discussion purposes.
- Then discuss a variety of ways to subtract non-party expenses and sum the remaining ones. Again, create some reasonable examples and use graph paper to reinforce alignment with decimals.
- Lists, front-end addition and subtraction, and compatible addition partners are all possible pathways for solutions. Awareness of the process to find a solution is important; no actual calculations need to be accomplished with this example.

Develop

Skill Building

- Remind students that they know that every shape has a group of characteristics or attributes that are unique to it. Some characteristics don't just describe how a shape looks, but the relationship of its parts.

Real Math • Grade 4 • *Intervention* Chapter 10 • *Geometry* T117

Intervention Lesson 10.C

### ENGLISH LEARNER

Preview

**If . . .** students need language support,

**Then . . .** use Lesson 10.10 in ***English Learner Support Guide*** to preview lesson concepts and vocabulary.

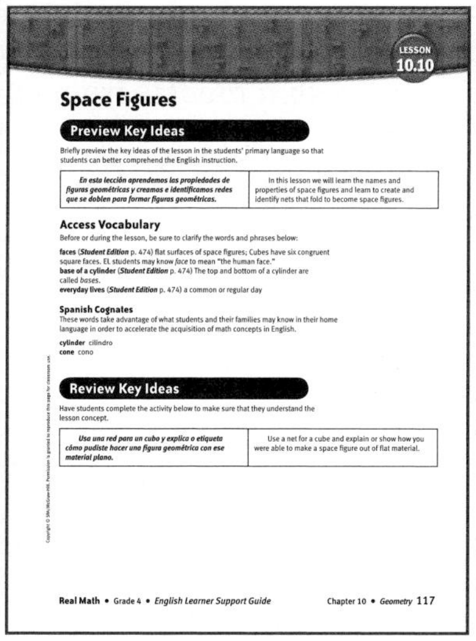
LESSON 10.10

Space Figures

Preview Key Ideas

Briefly preview the key ideas of the lesson in the students' primary language so that students can better comprehend the English instruction.

| | |
|---|---|
| *En esta lección aprendemos las propiedades de figuras geométricas y creamos e identificamos redes que se doblen para formar figuras geométricas.* | In this lesson we will learn the names and properties of space figures and learn to create and identify nets that fold to become space figures. |

Access Vocabulary

Before or during the lesson, be sure to clarify the words and phrases below:

**faces** (***Student Edition*** p. 474) flat surfaces of space figures; Cubes have six congruent square faces. EL students may know *face* to mean "the human face."
**base of a cylinder** (***Student Edition*** p. 474) The top and bottom of a cylinder are called *bases*.
**everyday lives** (***Student Edition*** p. 474) a common or regular day

Spanish Cognates

These words take advantage of what students and their families may know in their home language in order to accelerate the acquisition of math concepts in English.

**cylinder** cilindro
**cone** cono

Review Key Ideas

Have students complete the activity below to make sure that they understand the lesson concept.

| | |
|---|---|
| *Usa una red para un cubo y explica o etiqueta cómo pudiste hacer una figura geométrica con ese material plano.* | Use a net for a cube and explain or show how you were able to make a space figure out of flat material. |

Real Math • Grade 4 • *English Learner Support Guide* Chapter 10 • *Geometry* 117

English Learner Lesson 10.10

### ENRICH

**If . . .** students are proficient in the lesson concepts,

**Then . . .** have them explore the ***eMathTools: Net Tool*** to create space figures.

### PRACTICE

**If . . .** students would benefit from additional practice,

**Then . . .** extend Skill Practice before assigning the students pages.

### RETEACH

**If . . .** students have difficulty understanding space figures,

**Then . . .** extend Guided Discussion before assigning the students pages.

### Vocabulary
**net** **\net** ***n.*** a pattern used to create a space figure

### Access Vocabulary
**plane** flat surface; not referring to an airplane
**base of a cylinder** the top and bottom of a cylinder are called bases.

### Spanish Cognates
**cylinder** cilindro
**cone** cono

# Teaching Lesson 10.10

## Mental Math

5

Review RESPONSE WHEEL Review multiplication facts using problems such as the following:

| | |
|---|---|
| **a.** $6 \times 8 = 48$ | **b.** $4 \times 7 = 28$ |
| **c.** $2 \times 9 = 18$ | **d.** $1 \times 7 = 7$ |
| **e.** $9 \times 8 = 72$ | **f.** $5 \times 7 = 35$ |
| **g.** $7 \times 5 = 35$ | **h.** $3 \times 6 = 18$ |
| **i.** $8 \times 2 = 16$ | **j.** $0 \times 7 = 0$ |

## 1 Develop

25

**Tell Students In Today's Lesson They Will**
learn the names and properties of space figures by creating and identifying nets that fold into space figures.

### Skill Practice UNDERSTANDING

Whole Group

1. Display an assortment of geometric space figures. Have students find ways to sort the objects and describe the characteristics they use to do so. For instance, students might group spheres together because they look like balls, or they might group spheres, cones, and cylinders together because they do not have polygonal faces. Although pyramid-shaped objects are not common, you might obtain models from an upper-grade math or science teacher.
2. List students' groups on the board. Then introduce the terms *sphere, cylinder, pyramid, prism, cone,* and *cube* by drawing or showing an example of each space figure and labeling it. Tell students the following about these space figures:
   - The points on the surface of a sphere are all exactly the same distance from a point in the center of the sphere.
   - A cylinder is a space figure with two congruent curved bases. We usually think of cylinders as having circles for their bases.
   - A pyramid has only one base that is a polygon. The sides of a pyramid are triangles, all of which meet in a point.
   - A prism is a space figure with two congruent bases. The sides of a prism are parallelograms.
   - A cone is made by connecting every point of a circle to a point not in the plane of the circle.
   - A cube has six congruent square faces.

   Have each group explain their reasoning for sorting space figures the way they did. Students may have various reasons for classifications, and figures may need to be resorted.

### Guided Discussion UNDERSTANDING

Whole Group

Discuss with students that many everyday objects are manufactured as two-dimensional flat figures designed to be folded into space figures. Show students some examples, such as gift boxes, shipping boxes, or party decorations. Ask questions such as the following:

- **Does a regular cardboard box have two congruent bases?** yes
- **Are the sides of a box parallelograms? Remember that a rectangle is a special kind of parallelogram.** yes
- **Is a box a prism?** yes
- **Look at the room you are in. Is it a prism?** probably

### Skill Practice ENGAGING

Small Group

Provide various flat cardboard boxes and have pairs of students fold and form them. You can also have students deconstruct assorted boxes to see their flat net shapes.

Have students turn to student page 475. Working in pairs, have one student trace the net of the cube and the other student trace the net of the prism. Then have them cut, fold, and tape the nets. Make sure that students construct the cube and the prism so that the faces are in proper position and edges are aligned.

# 2 Assign Student Pages

25

## Pages 474–475

Review pages 474–475 with the class, pointing out the various types of space figures that students may encounter and two more examples of nets.

### RESEARCH IN ACTION

As with 2-D figures, children need more and richer experiences with solids. Research indicates that construction activities involving nets (foldout shapes of solids) may help students learn to discriminate between 2-D and 3-D figures.

Clements, Douglas and Sarama, J., eds. *Engaging Young Children in Mathematics: Standards for Early Childhood Mathematics Education*. Mahwah, New Jersey: Lawrence Erlbaum Associates, Publishers, 2004. p. 289.

Student Page

LESSON 10.10 **Space Figures**

## Key Ideas

**There are mathematical names for many of the objects we see and use in our everyday lives. We will refer to those that do not fit in a plane as space figures.**

The points on the surface of a sphere are all exactly the same distance from a point called the *center* of the sphere.

A **cylinder** is an object with two congruent curved bases. We usually think of cylinders as having circles for their bases.

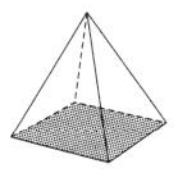

A **pyramid** has only one base that is a polygon. The sides of a pyramid are triangles, all of which meet at the same point.

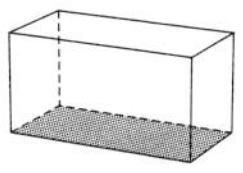

A **prism** has two congruent bases. The sides of a prism are parallelograms.

A **cone** is made by connecting every point of a circle to a point not in the plane of the circle.

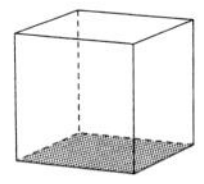

A **cube** has six congruent square faces.



eTextbook This lesson is available in the *eTextbook*.

Student Page

You can make some space figures out of flat material. Draw a pattern for the figure on flat, foldable material, such as cardboard. Then cut, fold, and tape the pattern together to make the space figure. The pattern is sometimes called a net.

Look at the following nets. The first net makes a cube, and the other makes a hexagonal prism. Trace, cut, and fold each net to see what it looks like.

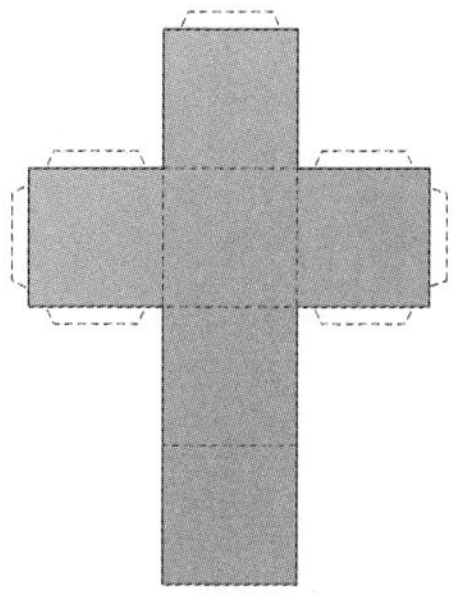

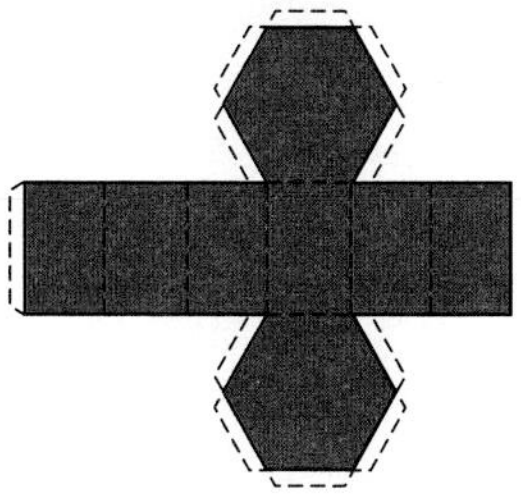

# Assign Student Pages, continued

## Pages 476–477

Have students complete pages 476–477 independently. Provide paper, scissors, and tape so students can trace, cut, fold, and fasten the net to see what figure it forms. You may want to trace the figures from the student page onto a piece of acetate and enlarge them for use on an overhead projector. Set aside extra time so students can explore and experiment more extensively with an assortment of figures.

### Monitoring Student Progress

**If . . .** students have difficulty visualizing the correlations between two-dimensional nets and the space figures they form,

**Then . . .** provide adequate time for hands-on manipulation. If possible, provide sturdy cardboard boxes that students can fold and unfold until they become more familiar with the characteristics of the patterns.

### As Students Finish

Building Blocks *Geometry Snapshots 8*

eMathTools In preparation for later lessons, have students use the ***eMathTools: Net Tool*** to make figures. They can also use the polygon patterns provided in ***Practice.***

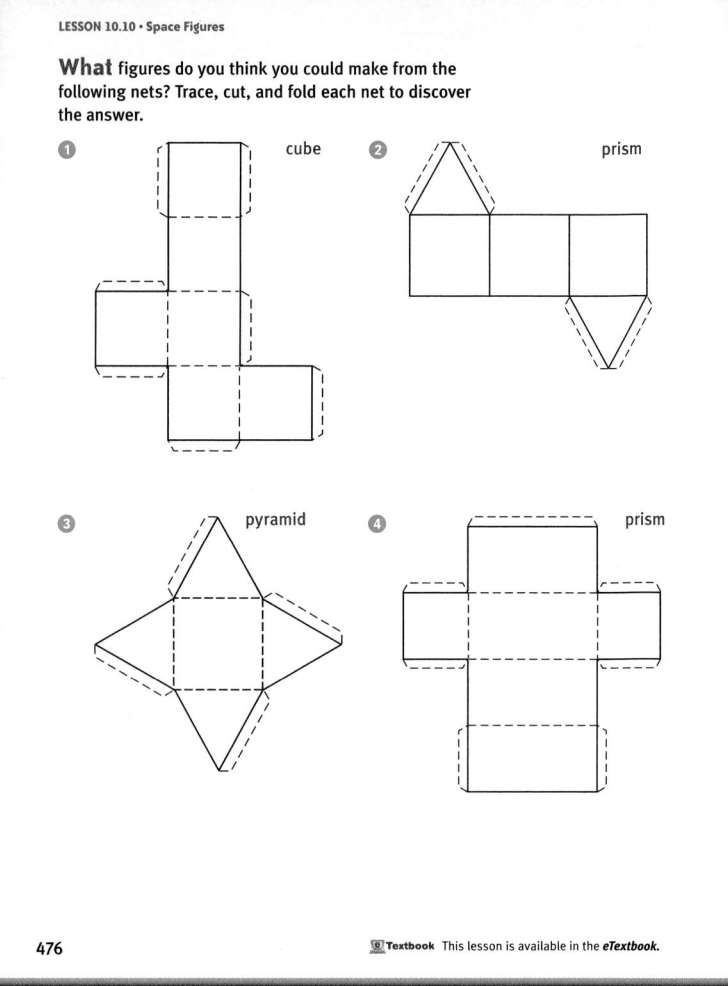

Student Page

LESSON 10.10 • Space Figures

**What** figures do you think you could make from the following nets? Trace, cut, and fold each net to discover the answer.

1 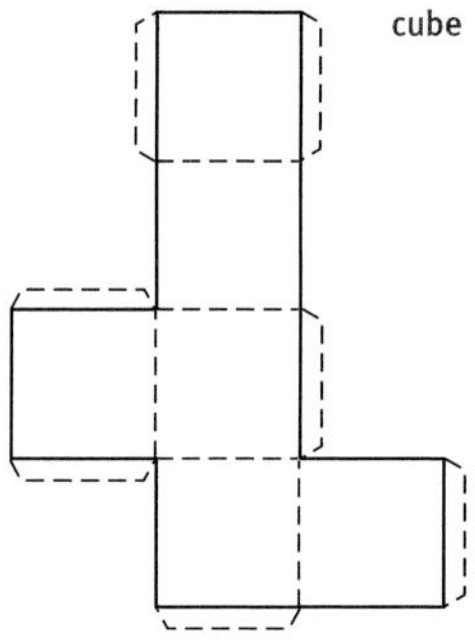
cube

2 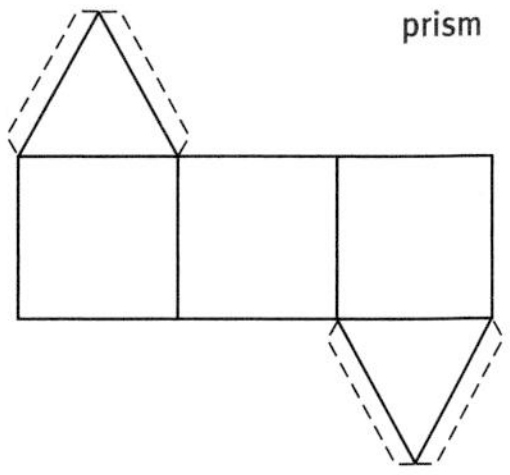
prism

3 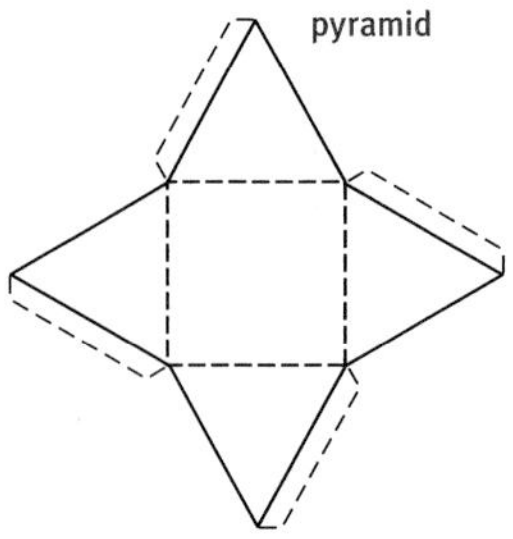
pyramid

4 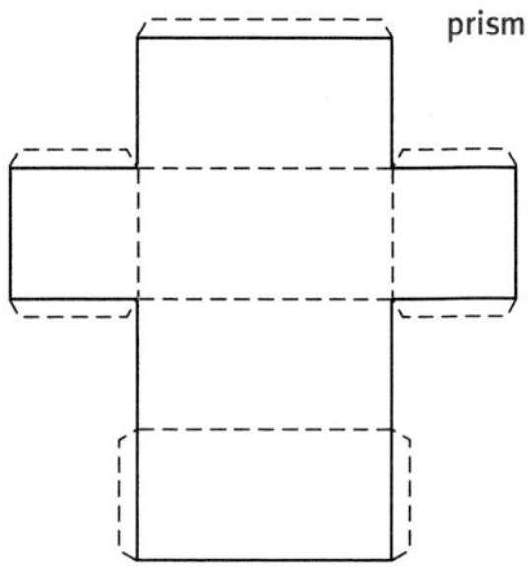
prism

476

eTextbook This lesson is available in the ***eTextbook***.

Student Page

**Decide** whether each net would make a cube. Compare your answers with those of your classmates. If you disagree, the person who thinks it is possible should show that it will make a cube.

5 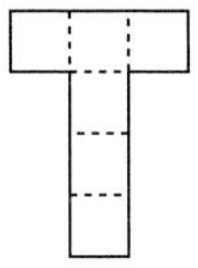
yes

6 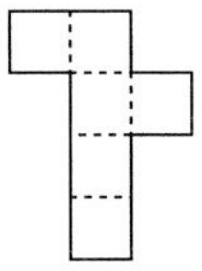
yes

7 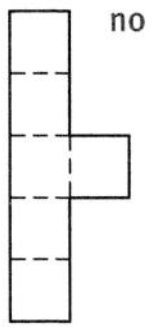
no

8 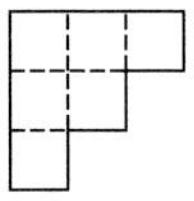
no

9 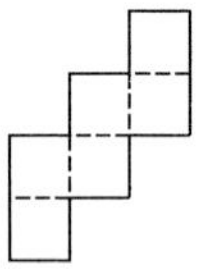
yes

10 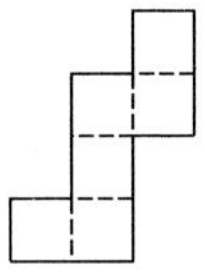
yes

11 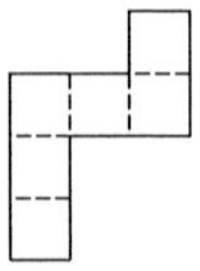
no

12 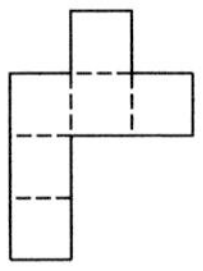
no

Chapter 10 • Lesson 10

477

## 3 Reflect 5

### Guided Discussion REASONING

Whole Group

Have students identify the properties of a sphere, cylinder, pyramid, cube, cone, and prism and give examples of each. Ask questions such as the following:

- **Imagine drawing all possible lines between the midpoints of the faces of a pyramid. What would the new figure be?** a pyramid similar to the original, but upside down inside the original

Have students explain how they visualize a two-dimensional net to figure out what three-dimensional shape it folds into. Encourage them to describe any clues or techniques they use.

**Curriculum Connection:** Students may be interested in researching real-world space figures similar to those discussed in today's lesson. Students may find pictures or information online or at the library.

**Cumulative Review:** For review of percents, assign Problems 15–18 on student page 493.

**Family Involvement:** Assign the ***Practice, Reteach,*** or ***Enrichment*** activities depending on the needs of your students.

**Concept/Question Board:** Encourage students to continue to post questions, answers, and examples on the Concept/Question Board.

**Math Puzzler:** Which figure does not belong in this group: square, rhombus, pentagon, or parallelogram? Pentagon; the others are quadrilaterals.

# 4 Assess and Differentiate

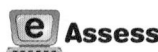

**e Assess** Use ***eAssess*** to record and analyze evidence of student understanding.

## A Gather Evidence

Use the Daily Class Assessment Records in ***Assessment*** or ***eAssess*** to record daily observations.

### Informal Assessment
**Guided Discussion**

Did the student REASONING
- ❑ provide a clear explanation?
- ❑ communicate reasons and strategies?
- ❑ choose appropriate strategies?
- ❑ argue logically?

### Informal Assessment
**Skill Practice**

Did the student UNDERSTANDING
- ❑ make important observations?
- ❑ extend or generalize learning?
- ❑ provide insightful answers?
- ❑ pose insightful questions?

## B Summarize Findings

Analyze and summarize assessment data for each student. Determine which Assessment Follow-Up is appropriate for each student. Use the Student Assessment Record in ***Assessment*** or ***eAssess*** to update assessment records.

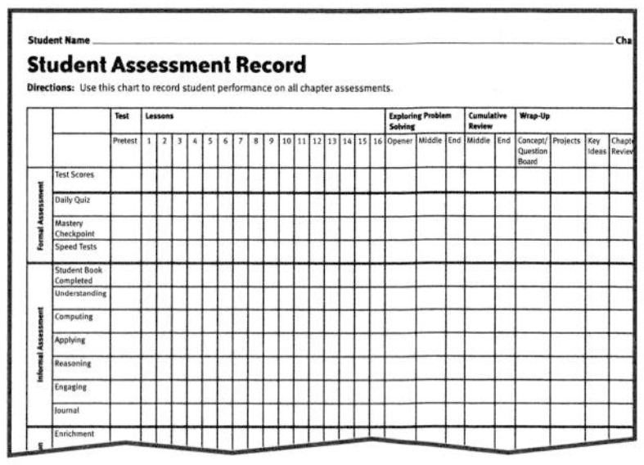
Student Assessment Record

Assessment Page T41

## C Assessment Follow-Up • DIFFERENTIATE INSTRUCTION

Based on your observations, use these teaching strategies for assessment follow-up.

### INTERVENTION

Review student performance on ***Intervention*** Lesson 10.C to see if students have mastered prerequisite skills for this lesson.

### ENGLISH LEARNER

**Review**

Use Lesson 10.10 in ***English Learner Support Guide*** to review lesson concepts and vocabulary.

### ENRICH

**If . . .** students are proficient in the lesson concepts,

**Then . . .** encourage them to work on chapter projects or ***Enrichment*** Lesson 10.10.

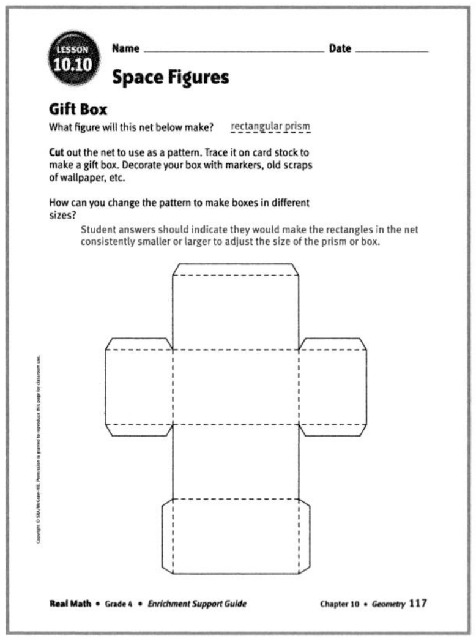
LESSON 10.10 Name Date

Space Figures

Gift Box

What figure will this net below make? rectangular prism

Cut out the net to use as a pattern. Trace it on card stock to make a gift box. Decorate your box with markers, old scraps of wallpaper, etc.

How can you change the pattern to make boxes in different sizes?

Student answers should indicate they would make the rectangles in the net consistently smaller or larger to adjust the size of the prism or box.

Real Math • Grade 4 • Enrichment Support Guide Chapter 10 • Geometry 117

Enrichment Lesson 10.10

### PRACTICE

**If . . .** students would benefit from additional practice,

**Then . . .** assign ***Practice*** Lesson 10.10.

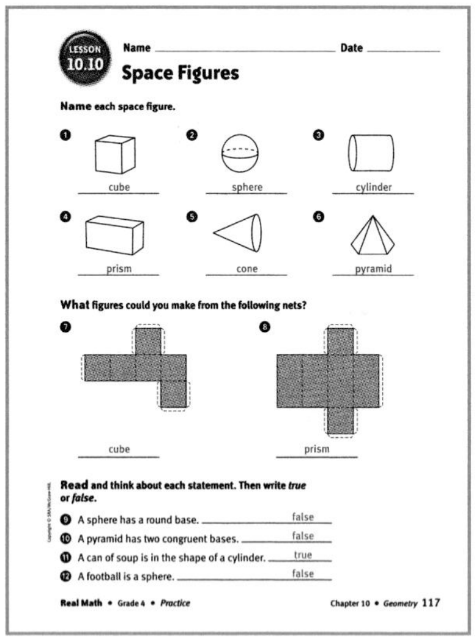
LESSON 10.10 Name Date

Space Figures

Name each space figure.

1 cube 2 sphere 3 cylinder

4 prism 5 cone 6 pyramid

What figures could you make from the following nets?

7 cube 8 prism

Read and think about each statement. Then write *true* or *false*.

9 A sphere has a round base. false

10 A pyramid has two congruent bases. false

11 A can of soup is in the shape of a cylinder. true

12 A football is a sphere. false

Real Math • Grade 4 • Practice Chapter 10 • Geometry 117

Practice Lesson 10.10

### RETEACH

**If . . .** students have difficulty understanding space figures,

**Then . . .** have them think about a cross-section of the three-dimensional figure and identify a two-dimensional shape that has that cross-section. Have students wrap solid figures with paper, then unfold the paper so that the nets can be seen. Have them trace the fold lines and cut the nets out.

## Lesson Planner

**Objectives**
- To introduce the concept of regular polyhedra and to begin to identify them
- To compute, or count, the vertices, edges, and faces for the Platonic Solids and to look for patterns among these values

**NCTM Standards**
**Geometry**
- Classify three-dimensional shapes according to their properties and develop definitions of classes of shapes
- Build and draw geometric objects

**Materials**
- *Response Wheels
- Space figures, including each of the polyhedra shown on page 479
- *Poster of polyhedra models

**Technology**
**e Presentation** Lesson 10.11
**e MathTools** Net Tool
**e Games** Cube Game

**Test Prep**
**Cumulative Review**
Mental Math reviews computational number sequences (Lessons 2.3 and 3.10).
**Extended Response**
Problem 8b

**Looking Ahead**
Lesson 10.12 involves prisms and pyramids. Have models of these space figures ready for Guided Discussion.

*Manipulative Kit Item

# The Five Regular Polyhedra

**Context of the Lesson** This is the second of three lessons on space figures. This lesson introduces more advanced objects for students to decompose in order to recognize the plane figures involved in the creation of these three-dimensional figures. Even though "Platonic Solids" are not actually solid, we will be referring to them as such because it is the traditional way to describe them.

See page 446B for Math Background for teachers for this lesson.

## Planning for Learning • DIFFERENTIATE INSTRUCTION

### INTERVENTION

**If . . .** students lack the prerequisite skill of drawing and recognizing polygons,

**Then . . .** teach ***Intervention*** Lesson 10.C.

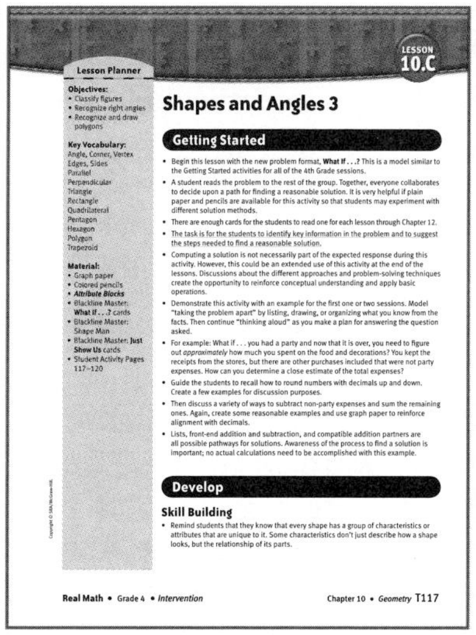
Lesson Planner
LESSON 10.C
Shapes and Angles 3
Getting Started
Develop
Skill Building
Real Math • Grade 4 • Intervention    Chapter 10 • Geometry T117

Intervention Lesson 10.C

### ENGLISH LEARNER

**Preview**

**If . . .** students need language support,

**Then . . .** use Lesson 10.11 in ***English Learner Support Guide*** to preview lesson concepts and vocabulary.

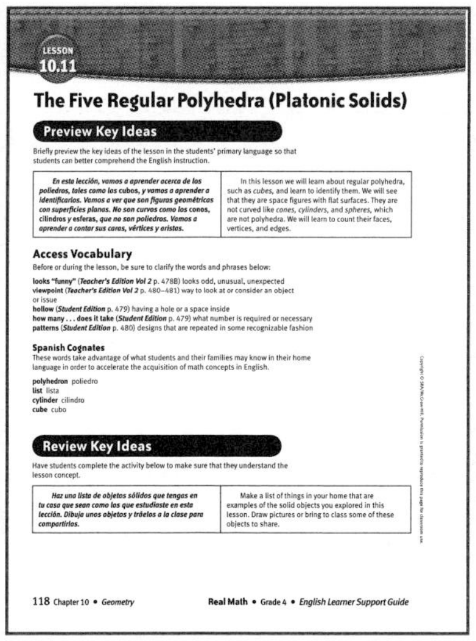
LESSON 10.11
The Five Regular Polyhedra (Platonic Solids)
Preview Key Ideas
Access Vocabulary
Spanish Cognates
polyhedron poliedro
list lista
cylinder cilindro
cube cubo
Review Key Ideas
118 Chapter 10 • Geometry    Real Math • Grade 4 • English Learner Support Guide

English Learner Lesson 10.11

### ENRICH

**If . . .** students are proficient in the lesson concepts,

**Then . . .** have them explore the ***eMathTools: Net Tool*** to create regular polyhedra.

### PRACTICE

**If . . .** students would benefit from additional practice,

**Then . . .** extend Skill Practice before assigning the student pages.

### RETEACH

**If . . .** students have difficulty understanding regular polyhedra,

**Then . . .** extend Strategy Building before assigning the student pages.

**Vocabulary**
**polyhedron** \pä´ lē´ hē´ drən\ ***n.*** a space figure that has only flat faces, which are polygons
**regular polygon *n.*** a polygon with sides of equal length and equal angles

**Access Vocabulary**
**faces** flat surfaces of space figures
**viewpoint** a way to look at or consider an object or issue

**Spanish Cognates**
**polyhedron** poliedro

## Mental Math

5

Review RESPONSE WHEEL Present related number sequences such as the following:

**a.** $3 \times 9 = 27, 27 \div 3 = 9, n \times 9 = 27$ $n = 3$
**b.** $5 \times 4 = 20, 20 \div 4 = 5, n \times 5 = 20$ $n = 4$
**c.** $60 + 40 = 100, 100 - 60 = 40, n + 40 = 100$ $n = 60$
**d.** $40 - 20 = 20, 20 + 20 = 40, n - 20 = 20$ $n = 40$

## 1 Develop

25

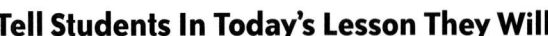

### Tell Students In Today's Lesson They Will

learn about regular polyhedra and identify them by their number of vertices, edges, and faces.

### Strategy Building ENGAGING

Small Group

1. Begin by showing students a collection of models that are space figures (polyhedra like those on student page 479 and some cones, cylinders and spheres). Explain that all of these are called *space figures*, but the ones that have flat faces that are polygons are a special set of space figures called *polyhedra*. Tell students only some of the space figures are called polyhedra. Contrast the polyhedra with other space figures that have curved surfaces (cones, cylinders, spheres). The space figures with curved surfaces are not called polyhedra.
2. Separate the class into small groups and give each group a variety of space figures. Have students identify and put aside all of the models that are *not* polyhedra. Then ask the class questions such as the following:
   - **Which of these polyhedra do you think should be called regular? Look at them from different points of view, or close your eyes and feel the models to see if that helps you to decide which ones should be called regular. (At this time students should not be told what regular means. They should examine the models and come to their own conclusions.)**

   Put the models that they decide should be regular in one spot and put the others aside. Ask students questions such as the following:
   - **Why did you decide that some of these polyhedra are not regular?** Good reasons for rejecting a model would be that not all the faces are the same, it looks "funny" from one direction, and not all the vertices have the same number of polygons meeting there.

   Students' responses will probably not be precise, but listen to what they have to say because it will give you insight into their thinking processes.
3. Tell the class that mathematicians have agreed that a regular polyhedron should have the same regular polygon as all of its faces, and that the same number of polygons should meet at each vertex. This means, on a regular polyhedron, if students
   - look straight at any face, it should look the same.
   - look straight at any vertex, it should look the same.
   - look straight at any edge, it should look the same.

   Have students check to make sure the models they called *regular* satisfy these requirements and the visual consequences.
4. Show students the poster containing models of the five regular polyhedra and introduce their names: tetrahedron, cube or hexahedron, octahedron, dodecahedron, and icosahedron.

### Skill Practice UNDERSTANDING

Whole Group

1. Show students a dodecahedron. Ask questions such as the following:
   - **How many pentagons make up the dodecahedron?** 12
   - **How many corners do these twelve pentagons have altogether?** $12 \times 5 = 60$

   Write on the board: 60 = *number of corners.*
   - **How many sides do these twelve pentagons have altogether?** 60; the same as the number of corners

   Write on the board: 60 = *number of sides.*
2. Remind students that they used two sides to make each edge. Then ask questions such as the following:
   - **Can you think of an easy way to find the number of edges on the dodecahedron?** $60 \div 2 = 30$
   - **How many corners meet at every vertex?** 3
   - **Can you think of an easy way to find the number of vertices on the dodecahedron?** $60 \div 3 = 20$
3. Each student should have his or her own icosahedron (from the Strategy Building activity in this lesson), if possible. Have them set an icosahedron on a flat surface and look straight down at it. Show students they can rotate it $\frac{1}{3}$ of a turn and it looks the same. Also point out they can rotate it $\frac{2}{3}$ of a turn and it looks the same. They can also rotate it $\frac{3}{3}$ of a turn, which is one complete turn.
4. Have students practice rotating the icosahedron and tell them to draw what they see. Suggest that they look at the boundary and the center polygons first, and then begin sketching. You might want to put a step-by-step procedure like this on the board to show them one way to proceed.

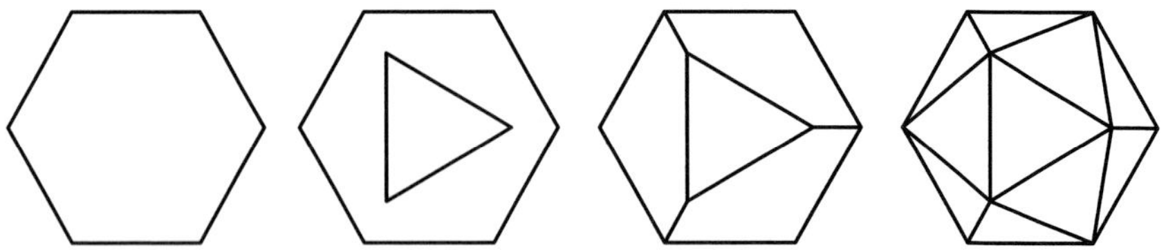

# 2 Assign Student Pages 20

**Pages 478–479** APPLYING Small Group

Have students review page 478. You may want to have the students work in groups to complete page 479. You may also wish to review the meanings of the terms *side, vertex, corner, face, edge,* and *polygon*.

Student Page

LESSON 10.11 **The Five Regular Polyhedra**

## Key Ideas

**Every polyhedron is made up of polygons joined together to form a closed surface.**

For example, a cube is made from six squares, each with four corners and four sides. This figure shows how we will refer to the parts of the polygons in the plane and to the parts of the polyhedra in space.

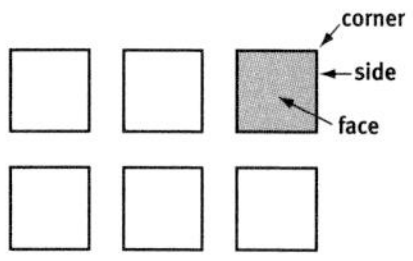


When the six faces are put together to make a cube, the places where two sides meet are called *edges*. The place where the corners meet is called a *vertex* (the plural of vertex is vertices). The polygons themselves are called *faces*. The cube is actually hollow.

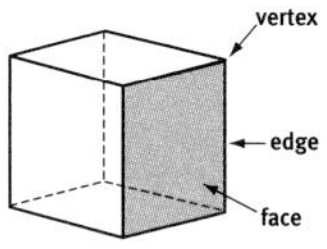


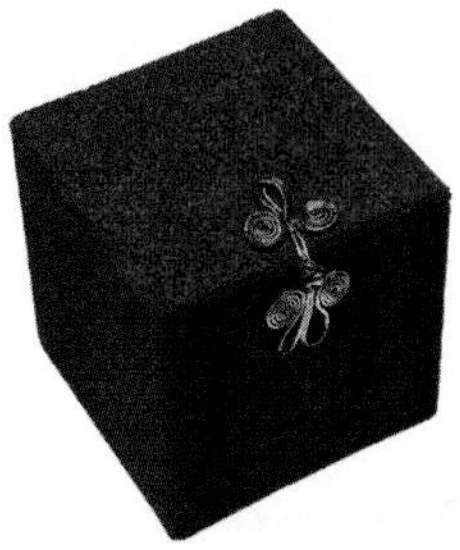



Textbook This lesson is available in the ***eTextbook***.

Student Page

There are only five regular polyhedra. These regular polyhedra are also known as platonic solids, although they are actually hollow. In a regular polyhedron, all the faces are regular polygons, and the same number of polygons meet at each vertex. For example, the dodecahedron is made up of twelve regular pentagons, and three pentagons meet at each vertex. The icosahedron is made up of twenty equilateral triangles, and five triangles meet at each vertex.

**The Platonic Solids**

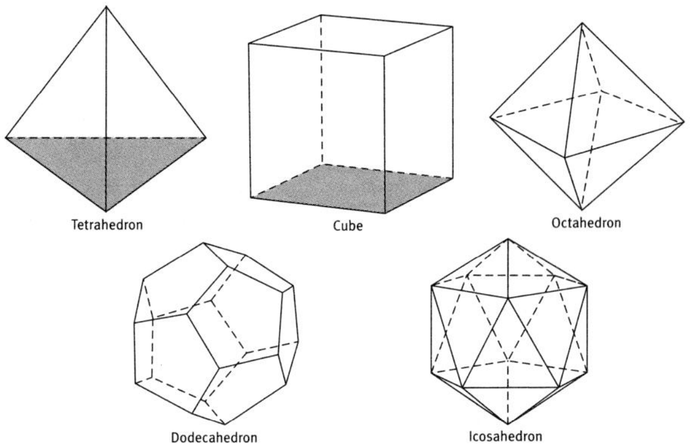


**Answer** these questions.

1. How many triangles does it take to make a tetrahedron? 4
2. How many triangles meet at each vertex of a tetrahedron? 3
3. How many squares does it take to make a cube? 6
4. How many squares meet at each vertex of a cube? 3
5. How many triangles does it take to make an octahedron? 8
6. How many triangles meet at each vertex of an octahedron? 4

# Teaching Lesson 10.11

## Assign Student Pages, continued

### Pages 480–481

Have students complete the student pages 480–481 independently. Tell them they can use the figures on page 479 or models to help them answer the questions in the lesson.

### Monitoring Student Progress

**If . . .** students thought a polyhedron should be called regular, but it is actually not regular,

**Then . . .** have them look directly at the top and bottom vertices, then look directly at a vertex around the equator. They should see that this model does not look the same from those two viewpoints, so it does not qualify to be called regular.

### As Students Finish

**Game** **Cubo Game** (reviews mental arithmetic)

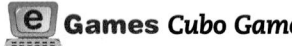

**e Games** ***Cubo Game***

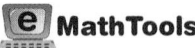

**e MathTools** Have students explore the ***eMathTools: Net Tool*** to make other polyhedra.

Student Page



**Use** **models of regular polyhedra to complete the table and the questions that follow it. Look for patterns.**

$V$ = number of vertices $E$ = number of edges $F$ = number of faces

7

| Name of Polyhedron | Illustration of Model | $V$ | $E$ | $F$ |
|---|---|---|---|---|
| Tetrahedron | 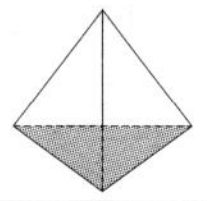 | 4 | 6 | 4 |
| Cube | 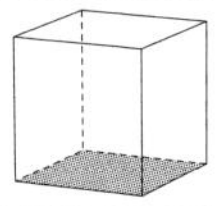 | 8 | 12 | 6 |
| Octahedron | 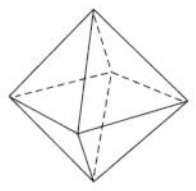 | 6 | 12 | 8 |
| Dodecahedron | 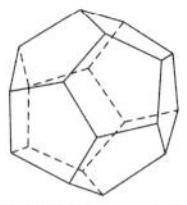 | 20 | 30 | 12 |
| Icosahedron | 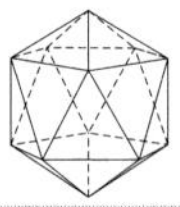 | 12 | 30 | 20 |

8 Look at your completed table.

**a.** What do you notice about the entries for $V$, $E$, and $F$ for the entire table? Express this as an equation. $V + F = E + 2$

**b.** Extended Response What do you notice about the entries for $V$, $E$, and $F$ for both the dodecahedron and the icosahedron? For both the cube and octahedron?

See Reflect in the *Teacher's Edition.*



Textbook This lesson is available in the ***eTextbook***.

Student Page

Put a regular tetrahedron on the desk and look straight down at a vertex. It should look like this:

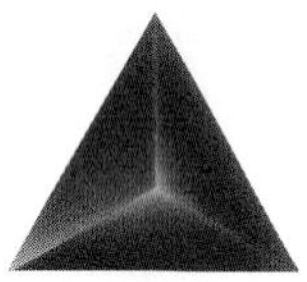

This means you can rotate a regular tetrahedron $\frac{1}{3}$ of a turn and it will look the same as before you rotated it. You could also rotate it $\frac{2}{3}$ of a turn.

**Complete** **the following.**

9 Set a cube on a table and draw what you see when you look straight down at it. $\frac{1}{4}$ of a turn and $\frac{2}{4}$ and $\frac{3}{4}$ of a turn

10 How much can you rotate the cube so that it still looks the same as before you rotated it?

11 Set a decahedron on a table and draw what you see if you look straight down at it. $\frac{1}{5}$ of a turn and $\frac{2}{5}$, $\frac{3}{5}$, and $\frac{4}{5}$ of a turn

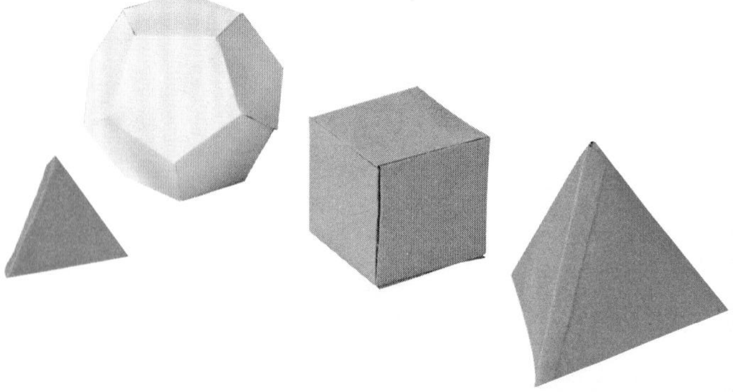

## 3 Reflect 10

### Guided Discussion REASONING

Whole Group

1. Discuss the patterns students found in the table of values on page 480. Put special emphasis on the fact that in all cases $V + F = E + 2$. Ask students questions such as the following:
   - **Do you think this will be generally true?**

   Take a vote to see how many students think it will always be true and how many think it won't always be true. They will not know now, but try to make them curious to investigate to find an answer. Tell students they will look at other polyhedra in the next lesson and that they should see if this formula always holds true.
2. Have students who drew particularly good diagrams of the dodecahedron explain to the other students how they went about it. Discuss how they might be able to position the polyhedra so that they can draw them as they appear when looking directly at a vertex or an edge instead of at a face. Suggestions here might include building some sort of base to sit the polyhedron on, or having a friend hold it for you.

### Extended Response

**Problem 8b** Students should see that the number of edges in the cube and octahedron are the same, and the number of vertices and faces are exchanged. The same is true for the dodecahedron and the icosahedron.

**Cumulative Review:** For review of equivalent fractions, assign Problems 19–22 on student page 494.

**Family Involvement:** Assign the ***Practice, Reteach,*** or ***Enrichment*** activities depending on the needs of your students.

**Concept/Question Board:** Have students attempt to answer any unanswered questions on the Concept/Question Board.

**Math Puzzler:** Margo is 4 years older than Barrett and 16 years younger than Rosa. Rosa is 3 times as old as Margo. What are their ages? Margo is 8; Barrett is 4; and Rosa is 24.

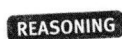

# 4 Assess and Differentiate

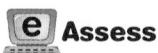

**eAssess** Use ***eAssess*** to record and analyze evidence of student understanding.

## A Gather Evidence

Use the Daily Class Assessment Records in ***Assessment*** or ***eAssess*** to record daily observations.

### Informal Assessment
**Guided Discussion**

Did the student REASONING
- provide a clear explanation?
- communicate reasons and strategies?
- choose appropriate strategies?
- argue logically?

### Informal Assessment
**Strategy Building**

Did the student ENGAGING
- pay attention to others' contributions?
- contribute information and ideas?
- improve on a strategy?
- reflect on and check the accuracy of his or her work?

## B Summarize Findings

Analyze and summarize assessment data for each student. Determine which Assessment Follow-Up is appropriate for each student. Use the Student Assessment Record in ***Assessment*** or ***eAssess*** to update assessment records.

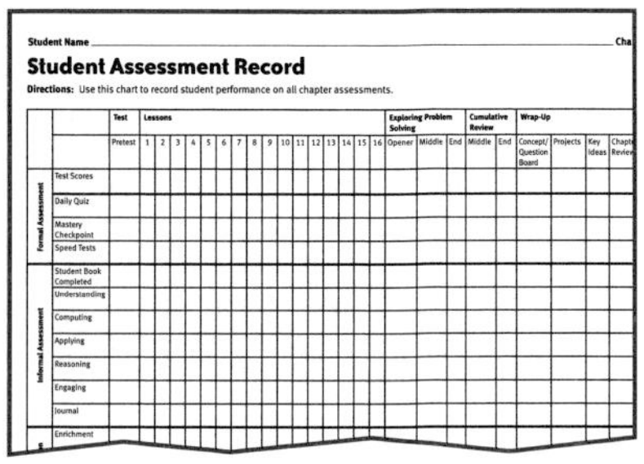


**Assessment T41**

## C Assessment Follow-Up • DIFFERENTIATE INSTRUCTION

Based on your observations, use these teaching strategies for assessment follow-up.

### INTERVENTION

Review student performance on ***Intervention*** Lesson 10.C to see if students have mastered prerequisite skills for this lesson.

### ENGLISH LEARNER

**Review**

Use Lesson 10.11 in ***English Learner Support Guide*** to review lesson concepts and vocabulary.

### ENRICH

**If . . .** students are proficient in the lesson concepts,

**Then . . .** encourage them to work on chapter projects or ***Enrichment*** Lesson 10.11.

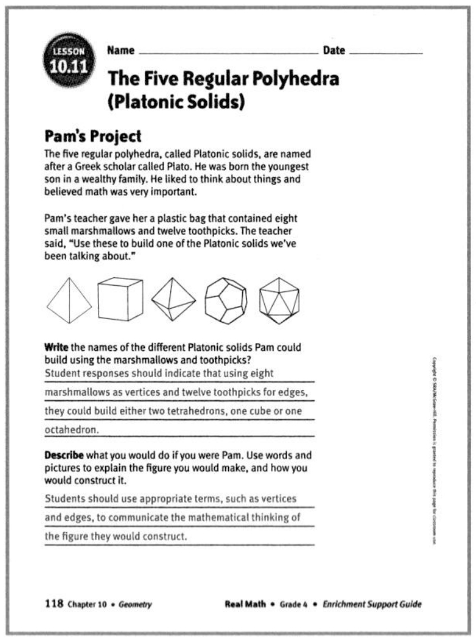

LESSON 10.11 Name ______ Date ______

**The Five Regular Polyhedra (Platonic Solids)**

**Pam's Project**

The five regular polyhedra, called Platonic solids, are named after a Greek scholar called Plato. He was born the youngest son in a wealthy family. He liked to think about things and believed math was very important.

Pam's teacher gave her a plastic bag that contained eight small marshmallows and twelve toothpicks. The teacher said, "Use these to build one of the Platonic solids we've been talking about."

**Write** the names of the different Platonic solids Pam could build using the marshmallows and toothpicks?

Student responses should indicate that using eight marshmallows as vertices and twelve toothpicks for edges, they could build either two tetrahedrons, one cube or one octahedron.

**Describe** what you would do if you were Pam. Use words and pictures to explain the figure you would make, and how you would construct it.

Students should use appropriate terms, such as vertices and edges, to communicate the mathematical thinking of the figure they would construct.

118 Chapter 10 • *Geometry* **Real Math** • Grade 4 • *Enrichment Support Guide*

Enrichment Lesson 10.11

### PRACTICE

**If . . .** students would benefit from additional practice,

**Then . . .** assign ***Practice*** Lesson 10.11.

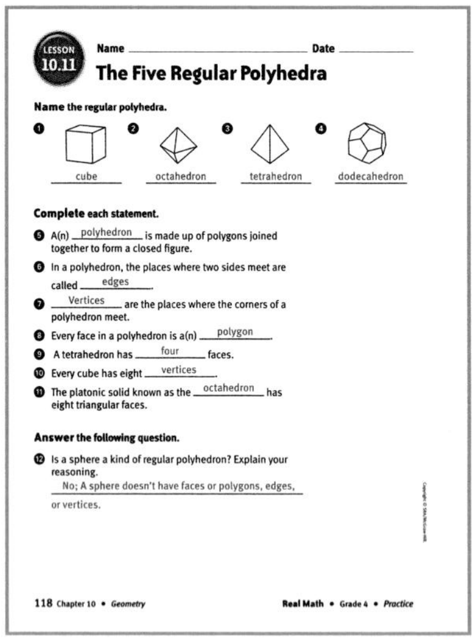

LESSON 10.11 Name ______ Date ______

**The Five Regular Polyhedra**

**Name the regular polyhedra.**

1. cube
2. octahedron
3. tetrahedron
4. dodecahedron

**Complete each statement.**

5. A(n) polyhedron is made up of polygons joined together to form a closed figure.
6. In a polyhedron, the places where two sides meet are called edges.
7. Vertices are the places where the corners of a polyhedron meet.
8. Every face in a polyhedron is a(n) polygon.
9. A tetrahedron has four faces.
10. Every cube has eight vertices.
11. The platonic solid known as the octahedron has eight triangular faces.

**Answer the following question.**

12. Is a sphere a kind of regular polyhedron? Explain your reasoning.
No; A sphere doesn't have faces or polygons, edges, or vertices.

118 Chapter 10 • *Geometry* **Real Math** • Grade 4 • *Practice*

Practice Lesson 10.11

### RETEACH

**If . . .** students have difficulty understanding regular polyhedra,

**Then . . .** have students make models of each of the regular polyhedra introduced in this lesson. Have them cut enough of each polygon to make the shape. They can then use strips of paper as connectors as they build.

# Pyramids and Prisms

**Context of the Lesson** This is the final lesson on space geometry. This lesson builds upon the use of polygons from Lesson 10.4. Here, the polygons are the base of different pyramids and prisms. Students will be decomposing these figures to describe their faces, edges, and vertices.

See page 446B for Math Background for teachers for this lesson.

### Objectives
- To use pyramids and prisms to give students experience looking for patterns
- To calculate, or count, the vertices, edges, and faces of the pyramids and prisms

### NCTM Standards
**Geometry**
- Classify space figures according to their properties and develop definitions of classes of shapes
- Build and draw geometric objects

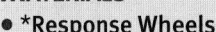

### Technology
- **Presentation** Lesson 10.12
- **MathTools** Net Tool
- **Games** Get the Point Game

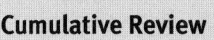

### Materials
- *Response Wheels
- *Models of polyhedra: a cube, the pyramids shown on page 482, and the prisms on page 483
- Light-colored paper or tagboard (1 sheet per student)

### Test Prep
**Cumulative Review**
- Mental Math reviews division with remainders (Lesson 3.11).
- Problems 2–25 review the terms *edges, vertices, faces,* and *sides* (Lesson 10.2).

*Manipulative Kit Item

## Planning for Learning • DIFFERENTIATE INSTRUCTION

### INTERVENTION

**If . . .** students lack the prerequisite skill of drawing and recognizing polygons,

**Then . . .** teach ***Intervention*** Lesson 10.C.

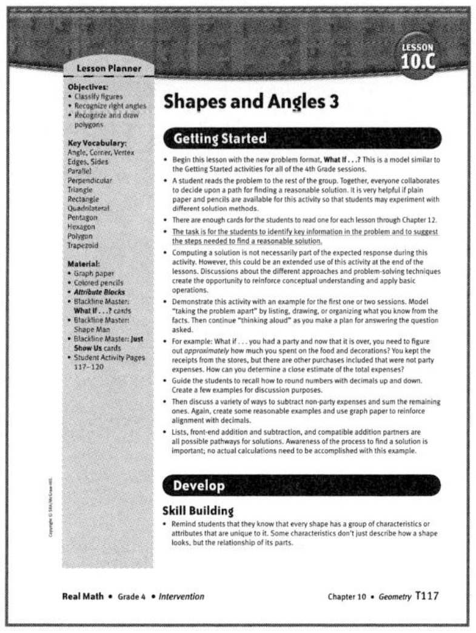
LESSON 10.C

Lesson Planner

Shapes and Angles 3

Getting Started

Develop

Skill Building

Intervention Lesson 10.C

### ENGLISH LEARNER

**Preview**

**If . . .** students need language support,

**Then . . .** use Lesson 10.12 in ***English Learner Support Guide*** to preview lesson concepts and vocabulary.

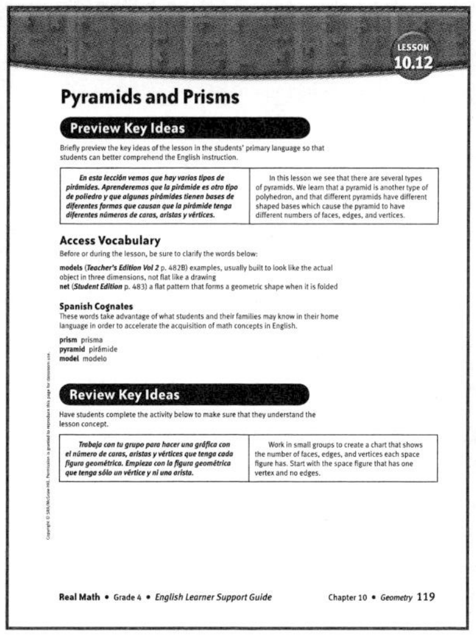
LESSON 10.12

Pyramids and Prisms

Preview Key Ideas

Access Vocabulary

Spanish Cognates

Review Key Ideas

English Learner Lesson 10.12

### ENRICH

**If . . .** students are proficient in the lesson concepts,

**Then . . .** have them explore the ***eMathTools: Net Tool*** to create an activity involving pyramids and prisms.

### PRACTICE

**If . . .** students would benefit from additional practice,

**Then . . .** extend Skill Practice before assigning the student pages.

### RETEACH

**If . . .** students are having difficulty understanding pyramids and prisms,

**Then . . .** extend Guided Discussion before assigning the student pages.

### Access Vocabulary
**models** examples that are usually built to look like the actual object
**net** in geometry, a net is a flat pattern that forms a geometric shape when it is folded

**Spanish Cognates**
**prism** prisma
**pyramid** pirámide

## Mental Math

5

THUMBS UP Ask students to show thumbs-up if there is a remainder or thumbs-down if there is no remainder, for problems such as the following:

**a.** 25 ÷ 8 = up
**b.** 14 ÷ 7 = down
**c.** 35 ÷ 5 = down
**d.** 100 ÷ 25 = down
**e.** 66 ÷ 3 = down
**f.** 25 ÷ 2 = up
**g.** 325 ÷ 5 = down
**h.** 80 ÷ 9 = up
**i.** 19 ÷ 9 = up

## 1 Develop

25

### Tell Students In Today's Lesson They Will

look for patterns in numbers of vertices, edges, and faces of pyramids and prisms, and create pyramids and prisms.

### Guided Discussion

APPLYING

Whole Group

**1.** Show students a regular triangular pyramid (tetrahedron) and ask questions such as the following:

- **How many and what kind of polygons would it take to make this model?** 4 equilateral triangles

Draw four triangles like these on the board:

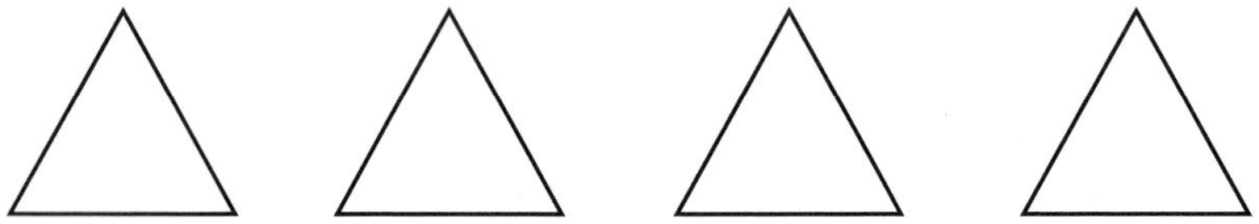

- **How many faces does this model have?** 4
- **How many sides are on these polygons altogether?** 12
- **How did you know how many sides are on the polygons?** Possible answers: by counting; by noticing there are 4 triangles and each has 3 sides so the answer is 3 + 3 + 3 + 3 = 12 or 4 × 3 = 12.

Discuss the methods students used and point out that some of them are faster and easier than others. Encourage students to use the most efficient method they can.

**2.** Show students the triangular pyramid model again and remind them that two sides meet on each edge. Then hide the model and ask questions such as the following:

- **Can you use what you know about the total number of sides to tell you how many edges there are *without counting?*** They should notice that the number of edges can be found by taking the total number of sides and dividing by 2. Thus 12 ÷ 2 = 6. You can check this on the model.
- **Look at the four triangles. How many corners are there altogether? Is there an easy way to find this?** There are 12 corners. An easy way to get this is to notice that every polygon has the same number of sides as corners. So if you have found the total number of sides, then you know the total number of corners will be the same. Another option is to multiply 4 × 3.

**3.** Show students the model again and ask questions such as the following:

- **How many corners come together at each vertex?** 3
- **Can you use what you know about the corners to calculate the number of vertices?** Since every vertex "uses up" 3 of the 12 corners, there must be 12 ÷ 3 = 4 vertices. You can check this on the model.

**4.** Show the class a triangular pyramid, a square pyramid, and a pentagonal pyramid. Ask questions such as the following:

- **What kinds of space figures are these models?** pyramids
- **How are each of these pyramids different?** They each have a different polygon for a base.
- **What do you think the names are for each pyramid?** triangular pyramid, square pyramid, and pentagonal pyramid

### Skill Practice

ENGAGING eMathTools

Whole Group

Hold up a square prism, a triangular prism, and a pentagonal prism. Ask questions such as the following:

- **What kind of space figures are these?** prisms
- **What makes each prism different?** The two parallel congruent faces are different for each model.

Draw the following net on the board or print one using the ***eMathTools: Net Tool.*** Have students draw the net on paper or tagboard and then cut and fold it to create a triangular prism.

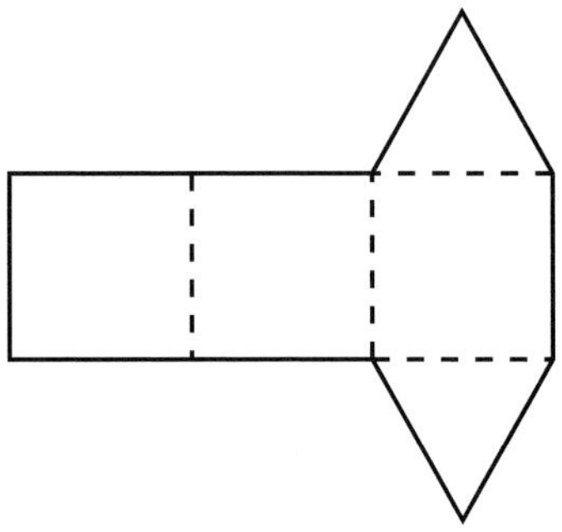

When students finish, ask questions such as the following:

- **What kind of triangles did you create?** equilateral
- **Could you make a net for a triangular prism using a right or isosceles triangle?** yes
- **Would you have to make changes to the net you just designed in order to use the other triangles?** Yes, some of the squares would have to be rectangles.

If time permits, have students try to draw a net using a right or isosceles triangle.

# 2 Assign Student Pages 25

## Pages 482–483 APPLYING

Have students complete pages 482–483 independently. Tell them they should try to use only the figures on the student pages to answer the questions. However, if they need to, students can look at the real models.

Student Page

## LESSON 10.12 Pyramids and Prisms

### Key Ideas

**Pyramids and prisms can have any polygon as their base.**

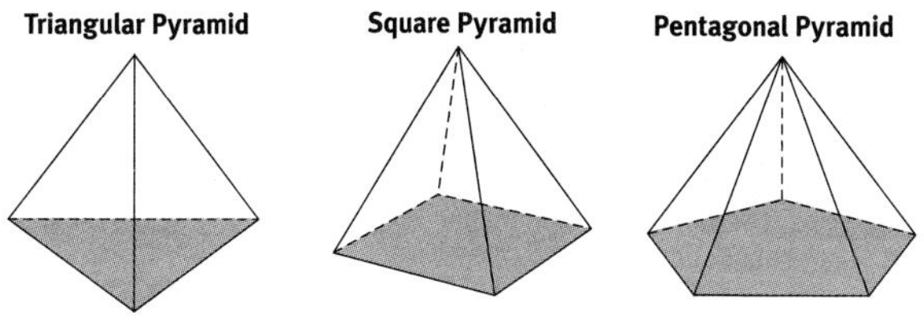


If you were going to make a square pyramid, you would need the following polygons:

How many faces, edges, and vertices does a square pyramid have? It has five faces, eight edges, and five vertices. How many sides are there in all the polygons that make up a square pyramid? There are sixteen sides.

**Answer** the following questions.

1. Draw the polygons you would need to construct a pentagonal pyramid.

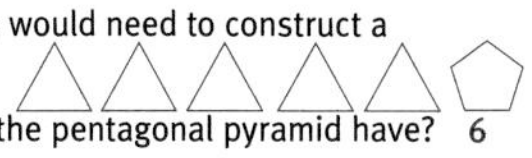

2. How many faces does the pentagonal pyramid have? 6
3. How many sides are there in all these polygons? $5 \times 3 + 5 = 20$
4. How many edges does the pentagonal pyramid have? $20 \div 2 = 10$
5. How many vertices does the pentagonal pyramid have? 6



eTextbook This lesson is available in the *eTextbook*.

Student Page

A *prism* is a space figure with two parallel, congruent bases. Here are some net diagrams that produce prisms.

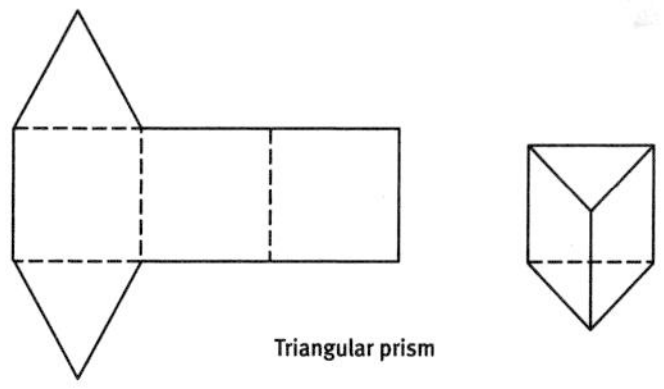

Triangular prism

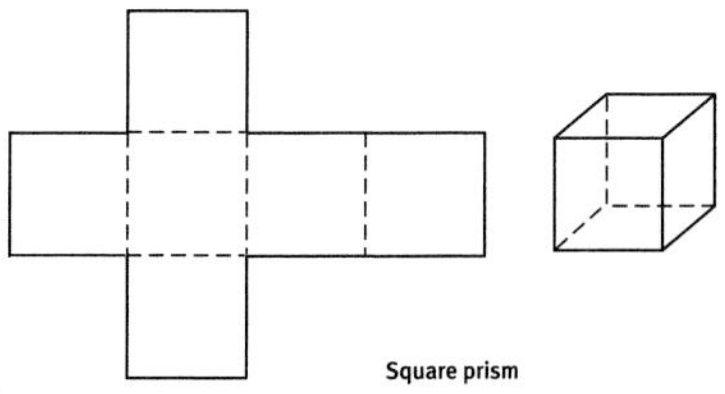

Square prism

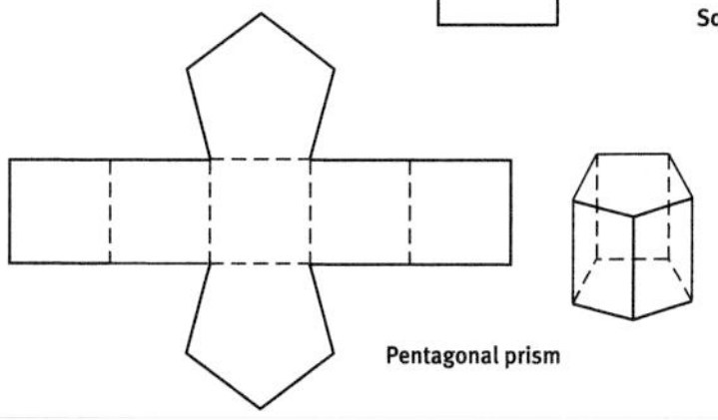

Pentagonal prism

**Examine** a triangular prism.

6. How many faces does the triangular prism have? 5
7. How many sides are there altogether in these polygons? $(3 \times 4) + (2 \times 3) = 18$
8. How many edges does the triangular prism have? $18 \div 2 = 9$
9. How many corners do these polygons have altogether? $(3 \times 4) + (2 \times 3) = 18$
10. How many vertices does the triangular prism have? $18 \div 3 = 6$

# Assign Student Pages, continued

## Pages 484–485

Have students complete pages 484–485 independently. Tell students they may use real models and the patterns within the table to check their work. If one of the numbers seems to be out of order, then perhaps they made a mistake. Remind students they are also checking to see if the formula $V + F = E + 2$ seems to be true for these polyhedra.

### Monitoring Student Progress

**If . . .** students who are typically fast at mathematical thinking are having a hard time with manual tasks, such as cutting and folding,

**Then . . .** be sure not to assume that a student who is good at one thing will be equally good at other things. Conversely, be aware that there may be students who will excel at this particular task who have had difficulties doing other sorts of mathematics.

### As Students Finish

**Game** **Get the Point Game** (reviews coordinate grids)

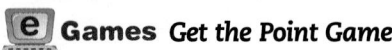

**e Games** ***Get the Point Game***

**e MathTools** Have students explore the ***eMathTools: Net Tool*** to make other pyramids and prisms.

Student Page

LESSON 10.12 • Pyramids and Prisms

**Answer** the following questions.

11. How many faces does the pentagonal prism have? 7
12. How many sides are there altogether in the polygons that form the pentagonal prism? $(5 \times 4) + (2 \times 5) = 30$
13. How many edges does the pentagonal prism have? $30 \div 2 = 15$
14. How many corners do the polygons that form the pentagonal prism have altogether? $(5 \times 4) + (2 \times 5) = 30$
15. How many vertices does the pentagonal prism have? $30 \div 3 = 10$

**Use** models to fill in the tables below and answer the questions. Look for patterns. Remember that $V$ = number of vertices, $E$ = number of edges, and $F$ = number of faces.

16.

| Name of Polyhedron | Illustration of Model | V | E | F |
|---|---|---|---|---|
| Triangular Pyramid | 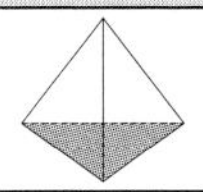 | 4 | 6 | 4 |
| Square Pyramid | 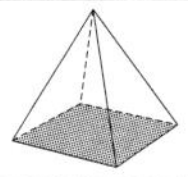 | 5 | 8 | 5 |
| Pentagonal Pyramid | 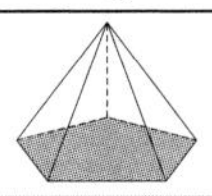 | 6 | 10 | 6 |

17. If you continue to increase the number of sides of the bases by one, what would you expect the values of $V$, $E$, and $F$ to be? $V = 7$, $E = 12$, $F = 7$
18. What is another name for a triangular pyramid? a tetrahedron



eTextbook This lesson is available in the *eTextbook*.

Student Page

**Fill** in the table, and answer the questions below. Look for patterns.

19.

| Name of Polyhedron | Illustration of Model | V | E | F |
|---|---|---|---|---|
| Triangular Prism | 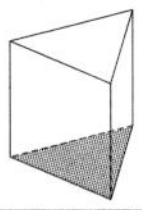 | 6 | 9 | 5 |
| Square Prism | 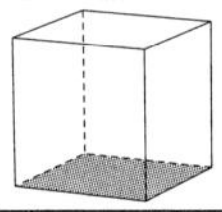 | 8 | 12 | 6 |
| Pentagonal Prism | 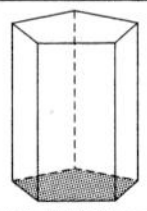 | 10 | 15 | 7 |

20. If you continue to increase the number of sides of the bases by one, what would you expect the next number to be for $V$? For $E$? For $F$? $V = 12$, $E = 18$, $F = 8$
21. If you continue to increase the number of sides of the bases, what will a prism "look" like? a cylinder

**Answer** these questions.

22. What is the relationship between the vertices, edges, and faces of a pyramid or prism? $V + F = E + 2$
23. Which models can be rotated $\frac{1}{3}$ of a turn and still look the same?
24. Which models can be rotated $\frac{1}{4}$ of a turn and still look the same?
25. Which models can be rotated $\frac{1}{5}$ of a turn and still look the same? the pentagonal pyramid and the pentagonal prism

23. The regular triangular pyramid and the regular triangular prism can be rotated. Note that the regular triangular pyramid, or tetrahedron, has four such axes.

24. The square pyramid and the square prism can be rotated. Note that the cube has three such axes.

Chapter 10 • Lesson 12 485

# 3 Reflect

5

## Guided Discussion REASONING

Whole Group

1. Ask students questions such as the following:
   - **Are any of the pyramids or prisms regular polyhedra?** The triangular pyramid can be a regular polyhedron if all of its faces, including the base, are equilateral triangles. The rectangular prism can be a cube if all of its faces are squares.
   - **Is a triangular pyramid always a regular polyhedron?** No, if not all the faces are congruent equilateral triangles, then the triangular pyramid is not a regular polyhedron.
   - **Is a square prism always a regular polyhedron?** No, if the faces that join the bases are not squares, then the square prism formed is not a regular polyhedron. In this case it is called either a square prism, or a rectangular box.
   - **What happens if you increase the number of sides of the regular base of a pyramid?** It begins to look like a cone.
   - **What happens if you increase the number of sides of the regular polygons forming the bases of a prism?** It begins to look like a cylinder.
2. Have students experiment with the models. If you have small plastic polyhedra, place them on the overhead projector one at a time. Shield the model with your hand or another object to prevent students from seeing it. They should only be seeing the shadow the model is casting. Then ask students to guess which model it is. The octahedron, the icosahedron, the hexagonal pyramid, and the hexagonal prism will cast the same shadow (a hexagon).

   Holding a model on the overhead projector with its edge or vertex straight down is harder, but interesting. Students can get the same effect by holding up the models in various positions next to a lamp and observing what kinds of shadows they make. Ask students, for example, which model they can hold up so its shadow is a triangle, a square, or a hexagon.

**Cumulative Review:** For review of function rules and ordered pairs, assign Problems 23–25 on student page 494.

**Family Involvement:** Assign the ***Practice, Reteach,*** or ***Enrichment*** activities depending on the needs of your students.

**Concept/Question Board:** Have students attempt to answer any unanswered questions on the Concept/Question Board.

**Math Puzzler:** Which space figure has one vertex and no edges? cone

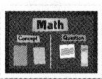

# 4 Assess and Differentiate

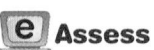

e Assess — Use ***eAssess*** to record and analyze evidence of student understanding.

## A Gather Evidence

Use the Daily Class Assessment Records in ***Assessment*** or ***eAssess*** to record daily observations.

### Informal Assessment

**Mental Math**

Did the student COMPUTING

- ❑ respond accurately?
- ❑ respond quickly?
- ❑ respond with confidence?
- ❑ self-correct?

### Informal Assessment

**Guided Discussion**

Did the student APPLYING

- ❑ apply learning in new situations?
- ❑ contribute concepts?
- ❑ contribute answers?
- ❑ connect mathematics to real-world situations?

## B Summarize Findings

Analyze and summarize assessment data for each student. Determine which Assessment Follow-Up is appropriate for each student. Use the Student Assessment Record in ***Assessment*** or ***eAssess*** to update assessment records.

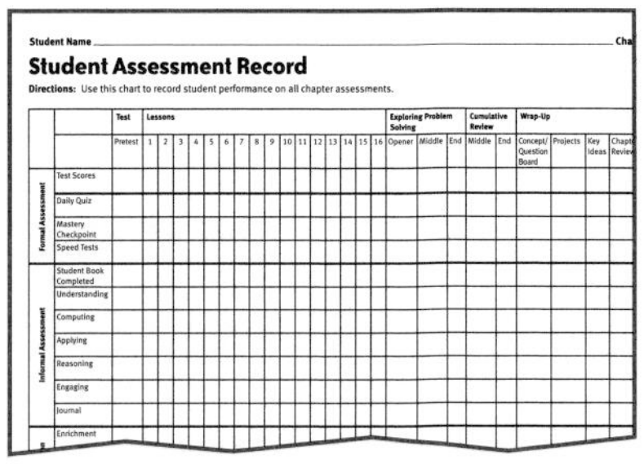


Assessment Page T41

## C Assessment Follow-Up • DIFFERENTIATE INSTRUCTION

Based on your observations, use these teaching strategies for assessment follow-up.

### INTERVENTION

Review student performance on ***Intervention*** Lesson 10.C to see if students have mastered prerequisite skills for this lesson.

### ENGLISH LEARNER

**Review**

Use Lesson 10.12 in ***English Learner Support Guide*** to review lesson concepts and vocabulary.

### ENRICH

**If . . .** students are proficient in the lesson concepts,

**Then . . .** encourage them to work on the chapter projects or ***Enrichment*** Lesson 10.12.

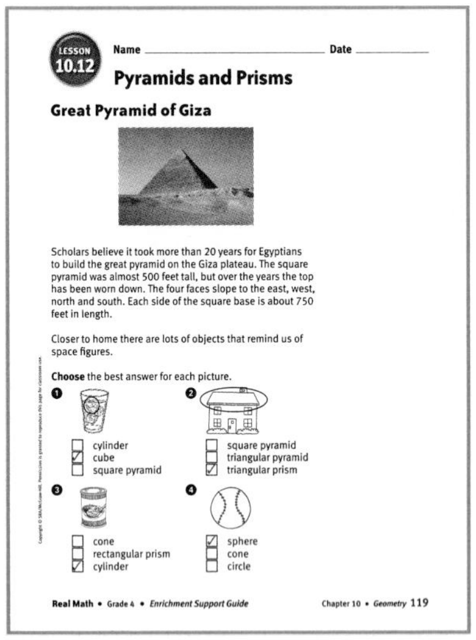

LESSON 10.12 Name ____ Date ____

**Pyramids and Prisms**

**Great Pyramid of Giza**

Scholars believe it took more than 20 years for Egyptians to build the great pyramid on the Giza plateau. The square pyramid was almost 500 feet tall, but over the years the top has been worn down. The four faces slope to the east, west, north and south. Each side of the square base is about 750 feet in length.

Closer to home there are lots of objects that remind us of space figures.

**Choose** the best answer for each picture.

1. ☐ cylinder ☑ cube ☐ square pyramid
2. ☐ square pyramid ☐ triangular pyramid ☑ triangular prism
3. ☐ cone ☐ rectangular prism ☑ cylinder
4. ☑ sphere ☐ cone ☐ circle

Real Math • Grade 4 • *Enrichment Support Guide* Chapter 10 • *Geometry* 119

Enrichment Lesson 10.12

### PRACTICE

**If . . .** students would benefit from additional practice,

**Then . . .** assign ***Practice*** Lesson 10.12.

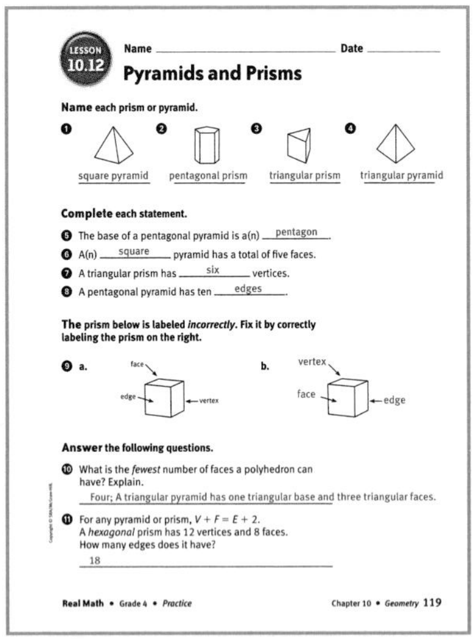

LESSON 10.12 Name ____ Date ____

**Pyramids and Prisms**

**Name** each prism or pyramid.

1. square pyramid
2. pentagonal prism
3. triangular prism
4. triangular pyramid

**Complete** each statement.

5. The base of a pentagonal pyramid is a(n) pentagon.
6. A(n) square pyramid has a total of five faces.
7. A triangular prism has six vertices.
8. A pentagonal pyramid has ten edges.

**The prism below is labeled *incorrectly*. Fix it by correctly labeling the prism on the right.**

9. a. face, edge, vertex  b. vertex, face, edge

**Answer** the following questions.

10. What is the *fewest* number of faces a polyhedron can have? Explain.
Four; A triangular pyramid has one triangular base and three triangular faces.
11. For any pyramid or prism, $V + F = E + 2$.
A *hexagonal* prism has 12 vertices and 8 faces.
How many edges does it have?
18

Real Math • Grade 4 • *Practice* Chapter 10 • *Geometry* 119

Practice Lesson 10.12

### RETEACH

**If . . .** students have difficulty understanding pyramids and prisms,

**Then . . .** have students make models of each of the shapes introduced in this lesson. They can use paper or clay or straws and clay. Have them experiment with bases of different sizes and shapes. Have them label their model and share it with the class.

## Objectives
- To calculate and estimate the area of a figure using a grid
- To find the area of compound figures
- To review finding the areas of a square and of a rectangle

## NCTM Standards
**Measurement**
- Understand area and select the appropriate unit for measuring it
- Develop strategies for estimating area
- Understand and use formulas to find areas of rectangles and related triangles and parallelograms

## Materials
- ***Response Wheels**
- Graph paper

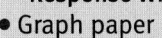

## Technology
**Presentation** Lesson 10.13
**MathTool** Geometry Tool

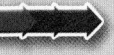

## Test Prep
**Cumulative Review**
- Mental Math reviews multiplication facts (Lesson 3.1).
- Problems 1–8 review area (Lesson 6.1).

**Extended Response**
Problem 8

*Manipulative Kit Item

# Calculating Area

**Context of the Lesson** This is the first of two lessons on measuring within geometry. Students reviewed how to find area in Lesson 6.1. This lesson asks students to find area by counting grid spaces and to estimate area by looking at figures composed of basic shapes.

See pages 446B for Math Background for teachers for this lesson.

## Planning for Learning • DIFFERENTIATE INSTRUCTION

### INTERVENTION

**If . . .** students lack the prerequisite skill of recognizing right angles,

**Then . . .** teach ***Intervention*** Lesson 10.B.

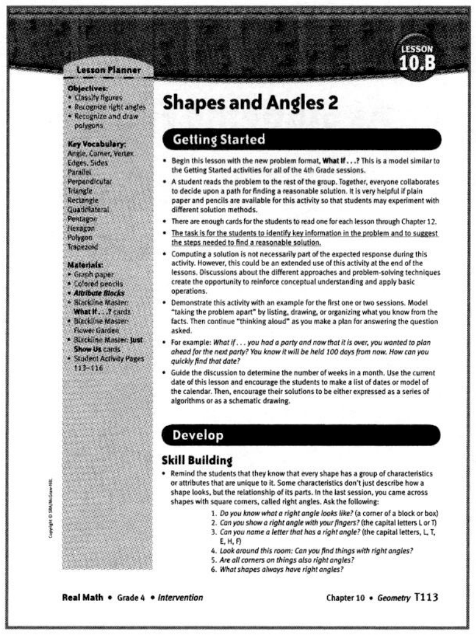
LESSON 10.B
Shapes and Angles 2
Getting Started
Develop
Skill Building
Real Math • Grade 4 • Intervention Chapter 10 • Geometry T113

Intervention Lesson 10.B

### ENGLISH LEARNER

Preview

**If . . .** students need language support,

**Then . . .** use Lesson 10.13 in ***English Learner Support Guide*** to preview lesson concepts and vocabulary.

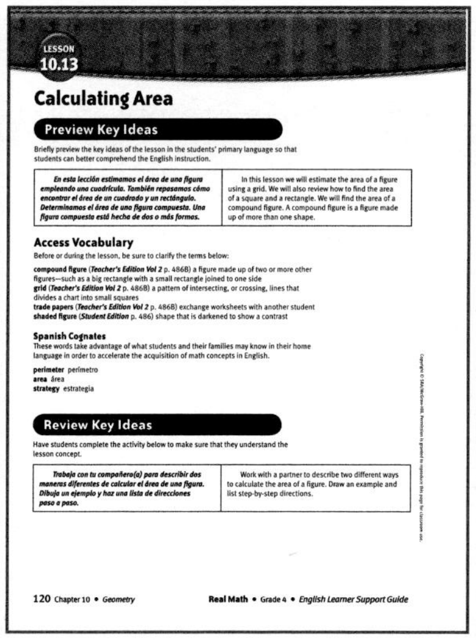
LESSON 10.13
Calculating Area
Preview Key Ideas
Access Vocabulary
Spanish Cognates
Review Key Ideas
120 Chapter 10 • Geometry Real Math • Grade 4 • English Learner Support Guide

English Learner Lesson 10.13

### ENRICH

**If . . .** students are proficient in the lesson concepts,

**Then . . .** have them explore the ***eMathTools: Geometry Tool*** to calculate area.

### PRACTICE

**If . . .** students would benefit from additional practice,

**Then . . .** extend Skill Practice before assigning the student pages.

### RETEACH

**If . . .** students have difficulty calculating area,

**Then . . .** extend Guided Discussion before assigning the student pages.

**Vocabulary**
Review from Lesson 6.1: **area**

**Access Vocabulary**
**shaded figure** a shape that is darkened to show a contrast

**Spanish Cognates**
**area** área

# Teaching Lesson 10.13

## Mental Math
5

Review RESPONSE WHEEL Provide practice for multiplication facts using exercises such as the following:

| | | |
|---|---|---|
| **a.** $4 \times 4 = 16$ | **b.** $7 \times 9 = 63$ | **c.** $8 \times 8 = 64$ |
| **d.** $9 \times 4 = 36$ | **e.** $8 \times 7 = 56$ | **f.** $6 \times 8 = 48$ |
| **g.** $6 \times 6 = 36$ | **h.** $4 \times 6 = 24$ | **i.** $7 \times 7 = 49$ |

## 1 Develop
25

**Tell Students In Today's Lesson They Will**
estimate the area of a figure using a grid, and find the area of compound figures.

Whole Group

### Guided Discussion
UNDERSTANDING eMathTools

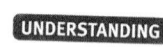

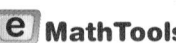

1. Review finding the area of a square and a rectangle with the class. Ask questions such as the following:
   - **How can you find the area of a rectangle?** Multiply the length by the width.
   - **How can you find the area of a square?** Multiply the length of a side by itself.
2. Using a grid, draw a compound shape that is comprised of a square and rectangle. For example:

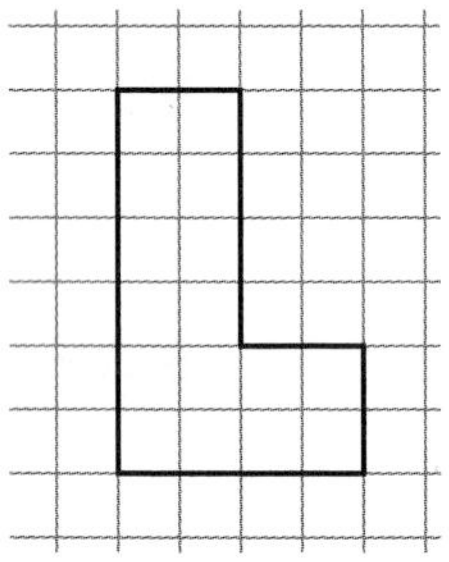

3. Draw another compound shape without the help of a grid. You may wish to use the ***eMathTools: Geometry Tool*** to draw. Show students how they can break the compound shape into smaller shapes to determine the area. For example:

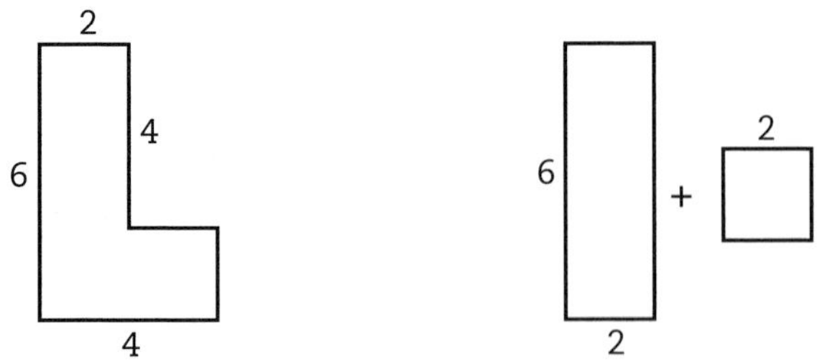


4. Show that a parallelogram has the same area as a rectangle with the same base and height. Then show that by drawing an approximate triangle in the right plane, you can form a parallelogram with the same base and height as the triangle. Since the two triangles have the same area, then the area of the triangle is $\frac{1}{2}bh$.

### Skill Practice
ENGAGING

Small Group

Have students draw three compound figures on graph paper. Then have them trade their papers with a partner. Have students find the areas of the figures their partners drew. Trade a third time and have students check the answers.

## 2 Assign Student Pages
20

**Page 487**
Have students work independently on page 487.

**Monitoring Student Progress**

| | |
|---|---|
| **If . . .** students' estimates from plane figures on grids differ slightly from the true answers, | **Then . . .** accept answers that are close. |

**As Students Finish**

Game **Snake Game Mat** (reviews missing term problems and mental arithmetic)

eMathTools Have students explore the ***eMathTools: Geometry Tool*** to help them solve problems involving area.

Student Page

## LESSON 10.13 Calculating Area

### Key Ideas

**You can calculate the area of a figure by counting squares and parts of squares on a grid.**

Each square has an area of 1 square centimeter. The area of the shaded rectangle is 21 square centimeters.

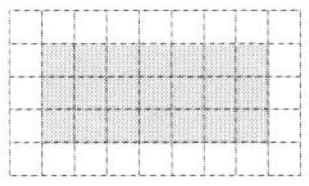

You can also calculate the area of the rectangle by multiplying the length by the width. The length is 7 centimeters and the width is 3 centimeters. So the area is 21 square centimeters.

Look at the figure below.

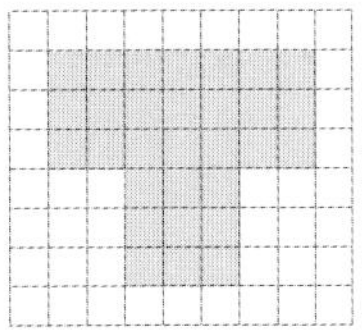

Calculate the area of this shaded shape by counting the number of squares. Did you count 30 squares?

What would you do if you could not count squares? You do not know how to find the area of such a figure. But, you do know how to find the area of a rectangle and of a square. Try breaking the figure into smaller parts.

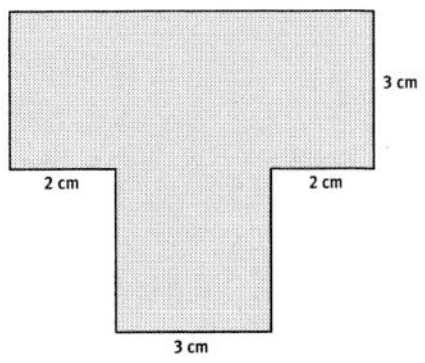


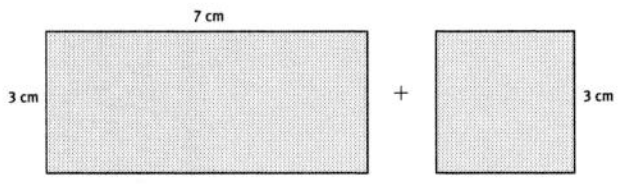


**Rectangle**
$A$ = length × width
$A$ = 7 cm × 3 cm
$A$ = 21 square cm

**Square**
$A$ = side × side
$A$ = 3 cm × 3 cm
$A$ = 9 square cm

Area of the shaded figure = 21 square cm + 9 square cm = 30 square cm



eTextbook This lesson is available in the ***eTextbook***.

Student Page

**Find** the area of each figure.

1. 12 square units

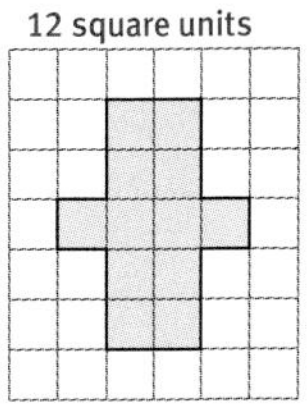

2. 28 square units

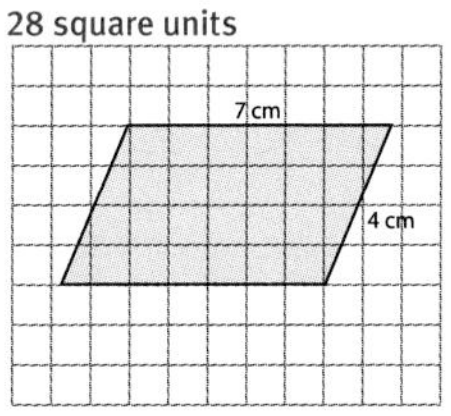


**Estimate** the area of the figures.

3.

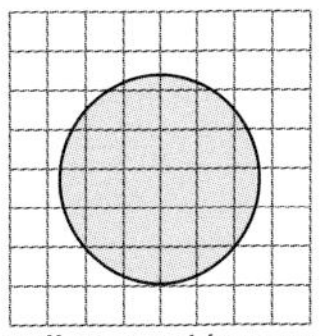

Accept all reasonable answers, but should be about 20 square units.

4. Accept all reasonable answers, but should be about 35 square units.

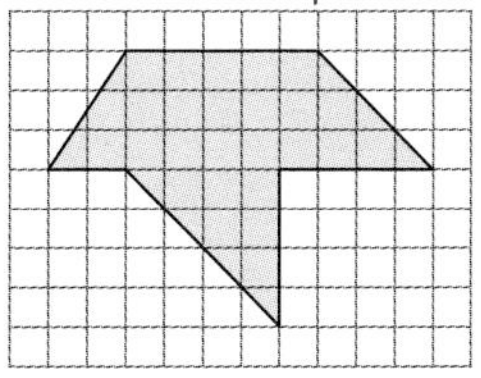

**Find** the area. Assume that if a figure looks like a square or a rectangle, then it is.

5.

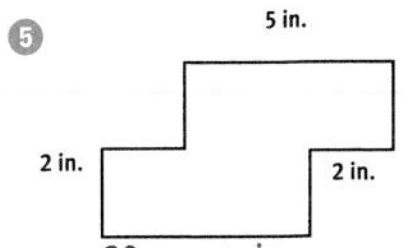


20 square in.

6.

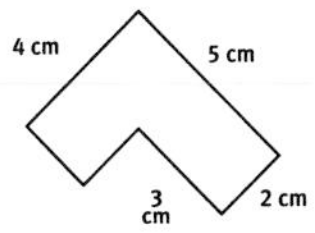


14 square cm

7.

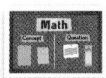

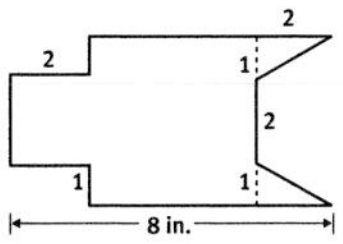


22 square in.

8. **Extended Response** In Problem 4, can you divide the large figure into smaller figures? Explain why or why not. If it is possible, estimate the area of each of the smaller figures using the grid. Yes, the shape can be divided into three triangles and a rectangle.



# 3 Reflect

10

## Guided Discussion REASONING

Whole Group

Have students explain the strategies they used to find the area of the figures on page 487. Ask questions such as the following:

- **What smaller figures make up Figure 1? Give the dimensions.** Possible answer: two 2 × 2 squares and one 1 × 5 rectangle
- **What smaller figures form Figure 4?** Possible answer: three triangles and one rectangle
- **Look closely at Figure 2. What happens if you put the two triangles together?** They form a rectangle.

## Extended Response

**Problem 8** Students should describe how to divide the figure into smaller pieces and find the area by counting square units.

**Cumulative Review:** For review of perimeter and area, assign Problems 26–27 on student page 494.

**Family Involvement:** Assign the ***Practice, Reteach,*** or ***Enrichment*** activities depending on the needs of your students.

**Concept/Question Board:** Have students attempt to answer any unanswered questions on the Concept/Question Board.

**Math Puzzler:** The floor of a tree house is shaped like a regular pentagon. If the perimeter of the floor is 35 feet long, how long is each side of the floor? 7 feet

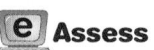

# 4 Assess and Differentiate

**eAssess** Use ***eAssess*** to record and analyze evidence of student understanding.

## A Gather Evidence

Use the Daily Class Assessment Records in ***Assessment*** or ***eAssess*** to record daily observations.

### Formal Assessment

**✓ Extended Response**

Did the student REASONING

- ❑ provide a clear explanation?
- ❑ communicate reasons and strategies?
- ❑ choose appropriate strategies?
- ❑ argue logically?

### Informal Assessment

**✓ Guided Discussion**

Did the student UNDERSTANDING

- ❑ make important observations?
- ❑ extend or generalize learning?
- ❑ provide insightful answers?
- ❑ pose insightful questions?

## B Summarize Findings

Analyze and summarize assessment data for each student. Determine which Assessment Follow-Up is appropriate for each student. Use the Student Assessment Record in ***Assessment*** or ***eAssess*** to update assessment records

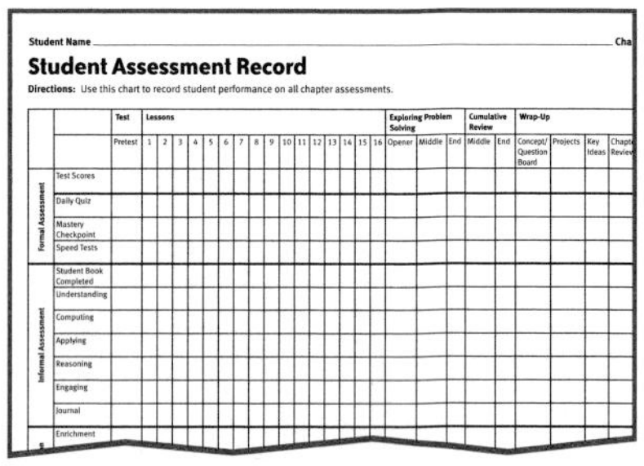
Student Name
Student Assessment Record
Directions: Use this chart to record student performance on all chapter assessments.

**Assessment Page T41**

## C Assessment Follow-Up • DIFFERENTIATE INSTRUCTION

Based on your observations, use these teaching strategies for assessment follow-up.

### INTERVENTION

Review student performance on ***Intervention*** Lesson 10.B to see if students have mastered prerequisite skills for this lesson.

### ENGLISH LEARNER

**Review**

Use Lesson 10.13 in ***English Learner Support Guide*** to review lesson concepts and vocabulary.

### ENRICH

**If . . .** students are proficient in the lesson concepts,

**Then . . .** encourage them to work on the chapter projects or ***Enrichment*** Lesson 10.13.

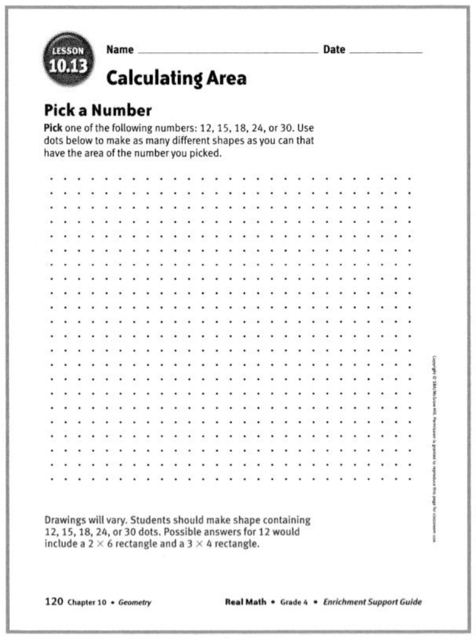
LESSON 10.13 Name ______ Date ______
Calculating Area
Pick a Number
Pick one of the following numbers: 12, 15, 18, 24, or 30. Use dots below to make as many different shapes as you can that have the area of the number you picked.
Drawings will vary. Students should make shape containing 12, 15, 18, 24, or 30 dots. Possible answers for 12 would include a 2 × 6 rectangle and a 3 × 4 rectangle.
120 Chapter 10 • Geometry    Real Math • Grade 4 • Enrichment Support Guide

Enrichment Lesson 10.13

### PRACTICE

**If . . .** students would benefit from additional practice,

**Then . . .** assign ***Practice*** Lesson 10.13.

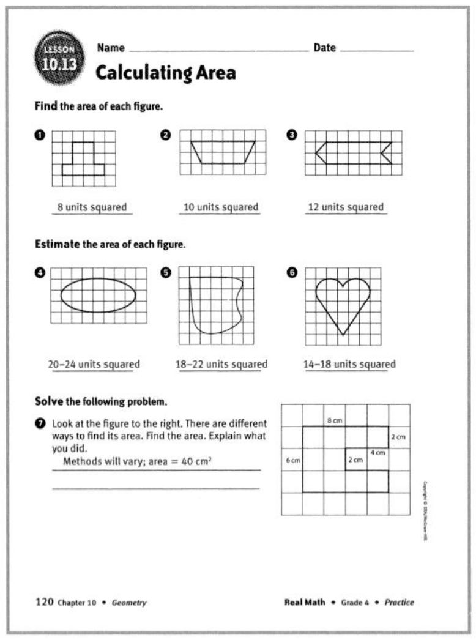
LESSON 10.13 Name ______ Date ______
Calculating Area
Find the area of each figure.
1. 8 units squared
2. 10 units squared
3. 12 units squared
Estimate the area of each figure.
4. 20–24 units squared
5. 18–22 units squared
6. 14–18 units squared
Solve the following problem.
7. Look at the figure to the right. There are different ways to find its area. Find the area. Explain what you did.
Methods will vary; area = 40 cm²
120 Chapter 10 • Geometry    Real Math • Grade 4 • Practice

Practice Lesson 10.13

### RETEACH

**If . . .** students have difficulty calculating area,

**Then . . .** have them create word problems in which area is to be measured.

**Objectives**
- To find the perimeter of a figure using a grid
- To explore how perimeter and area are related

**NCTM Standards**

**Measurement**
- Understand perimeter and select the appropriate unit for measuring it
- Develop strategies for estimating the perimeter of irregular shapes

**Materials**
- *Response Wheels
- Graph paper

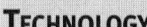

**Technology**

**e Presentation** Lesson 10.14

**e MathTools** Geometry Tool

**Test Prep**

**Cumulative Review**

Mental Math reviews quadrilaterals (Lesson 10.4).

**Writing + Math**

Journal

*Manipulative Kit Item

# Measuring and Calculating Perimeter

**Context of the Lesson** This is the second lesson on measuring in geometry. This lesson deals with the perimeter of shapes that lie on a grid.

See page 446B for Math Background for teachers for this lesson.

## Planning for Learning • DIFFERENTIATE INSTRUCTION

### INTERVENTION

**If . . .** students lack the prerequisite skill of recognizing right angles,

**Then . . .** teach ***Intervention*** Lesson 10.B.

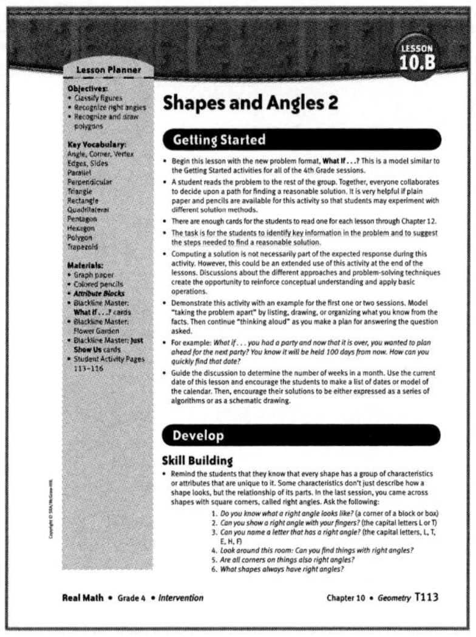

Lesson Planner

LESSON 10.B

Shapes and Angles 2

Getting Started

Develop

Skill Building

Intervention Lesson 10.B

### ENGLISH LEARNER

Preview

**If . . .** students need language support,

**Then . . .** use Lesson 10.14 in ***English Learner Support Guide*** to preview lesson concepts and vocabulary.

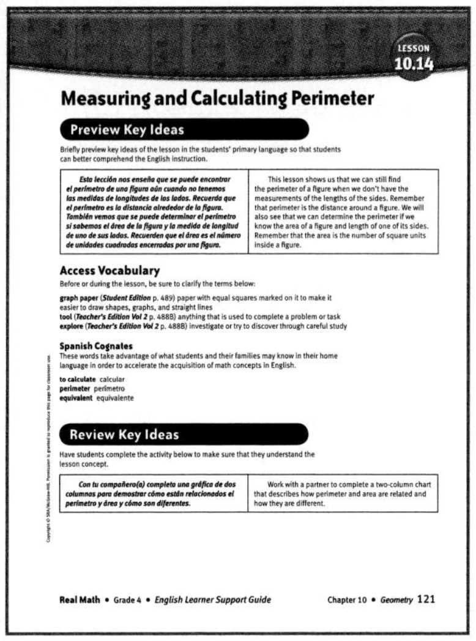

LESSON 10.14

Measuring and Calculating Perimeter

Preview Key Ideas

Access Vocabulary

Spanish Cognates

Review Key Ideas

English Learner Lesson 10.14

### ENRICH

**If . . .** students are proficient in the lesson concepts,

**Then . . .** have them explore the ***eMathTools: Geometry Tool*** to show the relationship between perimeter and area.

### PRACTICE

**If . . .** students would benefit from additional practice,

**Then . . .** extend Guided Discussion before assigning the student pages.

### RETEACH

**If . . .** students have difficulty finding perimeter when given the area,

**Then . . .** extend Guided Discussion before assigning the student pages.

**Access Vocabulary**

**graph paper** paper that has equal squares marked on it to make it easier to draw shapes, graphs, and straight lines

**Spanish Cognates**

**calculate** calcular

**perimeter** perímetro

## Mental Math
5

Review THUMBS UP Provide practice in identifying quadrilaterals. Say the following figures and have students show thumbs-up if the figure is a quadrilateral and thumbs-down if the figure is not a quadrilateral.

**a.** square up
**b.** triangle down
**c.** octagon down
**d.** trapezoid up
**e.** rectangle up
**f.** hexagon down
**g.** rhombus up
**h.** parallelogram up

## 1 Develop
25

### Tell Students In Today's Lesson They Will
find the perimeter of a figure using a grid, and explore how perimeter and area are related.

### Guided Discussion
UNDERSTANDING — Whole Group

1. Review how to find the perimeter of a figure with the class. Ask questions such as the following:
   - **How can you find the perimeter of a rectangle?** add the lengths of the sides
   - **Is finding the perimeter of a triangle or a hexagon different from finding the perimeter of a rectangle?** No, you add the lengths of the sides for both.
2. Using a grid, draw a compound shape (similar to the one below).

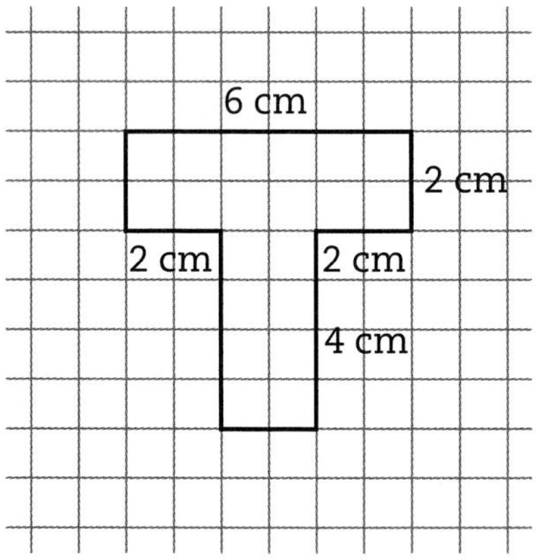


Ask questions such as the following:
   - **Each square on this grid is equivalent to one square centimeter. What is the length of each side?** 1 cm
   - **Since no measurements are given, how can you find the perimeter of this figure?** Most students will say you can use the grid and count the number of squares that make up each side of the figure. The perimeter is 24 centimeters.
   - **Can anyone create another figure that looks different but has the same perimeter?** Possible answer: 6 × 6 unit square.

### Strategy Building
ENGAGING — Small Group

1. Divide the class into small groups.
2. Draw a square on the board. Tell the class that the area of the square is 81 square inches and ask them questions such as the following:
   - **If you know the area of this square is 81 square inches, can you find its perimeter? Have each group explain how they arrived at their answers. Students should conclude that 9 × 9 equals 81, and the area of a square is side × side. Therefore, the sides of the square are 9 inches long, and the perimeter of the square is 36 inches.**
   - **Is this true for a rectangle? Can you find its perimeter if you know only its area?** No, but you could find it if you know the area and length of one side.

## 2 Assign Student Pages
20

### Page 489
Have students work independently on page 489.

### As Students Finish
Game **Function Game**

eMathTools Have students explore the ***eMathTool: Geometry Tool*** to solve problems involving perimeter.

Student Page

LESSON 10.14 Measuring and Calculating Perimeter

## Key Ideas

**A grid can be a useful tool for finding the perimeter of an object.**

Remember that *perimeter* is the distance around a figure. Look at the figure below. What is the perimeter?

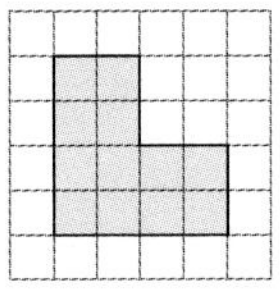

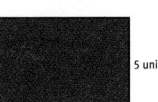

Count the sides of the squares that make the boundary of the figure. Since you are solving for perimeter, you count *around* the figure.

The perimeter of this figure is 16 units.

You can also find the perimeter of a rectangle if you know its area and the length of one of its sides.

5 units

For example, the area of this rectangle is 35 square centimeters, and the length of one side is 5 centimeters. What number multiplied by 5 equals 35? The length of the other side is 7 centimeters. Now that you know the length of the sides of the rectangle, you can find the perimeter.

$P = 7 + 5 + 7 + 5 = 24$ units



eTextbook This lesson is available in the *eTextbook.*

Student Page

**Find** the perimeter of each figure. Each square on the graph paper represents one centimeter on each side.

1. 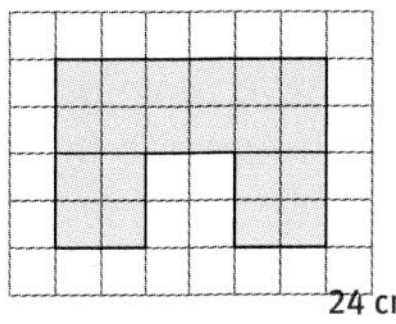
24 cm

2. 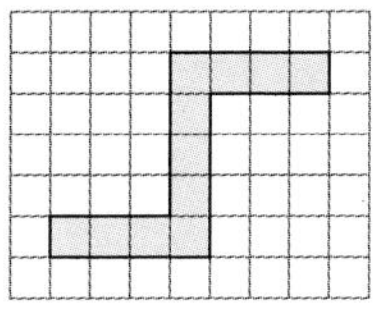
24 cm

3. 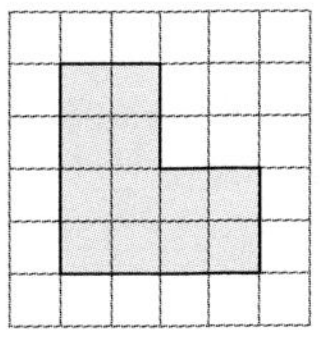
16 cm

4. 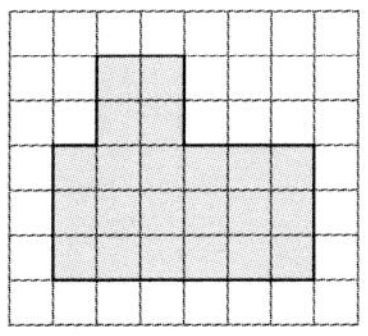
22 cm

5. 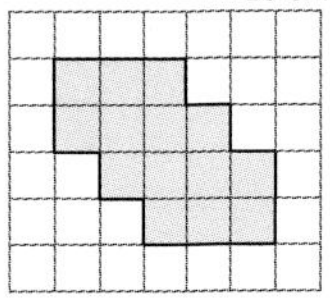
18 cm

6. 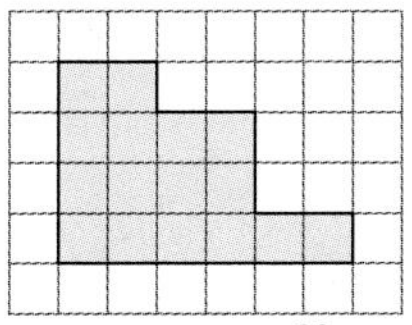
20 cm

7. If a square has an area of 49 square meters, what is its perimeter? 28 m
8. If you know one of the sides of a rectangle is 9 centimeters, and its area is 27 square centimeters, what is its perimeter? 24 cm
9. Can rectangles that have the same area have different perimeters? yes
10. Can rectangles that have the same perimeter have different areas? yes

Writing + Math Journal
How many different rectangles have a perimeter of 24 units and side lengths that are whole units? Which has the greatest area?
See Reflect in the *Teacher's Edition*.





# 3 Reflect

10

## Guided Discussion REASONING

Whole Group

The perimeter of a specific rectangle is 16 cm. Find several possible areas the rectangle may have. For which shape is the area the greatest? Possible answers: a 5 × 3 rectangle with an area of 15; a 6 × 2 rectangle with an area of 12; or a 7 × 1 rectangle with an area of 7. The 4 × 4 rectangle which has an area of 16.

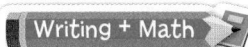

### Writing + Math Journal

There are 6 different rectangles with perimeters of 24 units each and sides that are a whole number of units long. The largest area among these rectangles is created by a 6 × 6 rectangle. (A 6 × 6 square can be considered a rectangle because a square is a special type of rectangle.) This problem requires students to use the knowledge they have developed about perimeter to think about the various pairs of whole numbers that add to 12.

**Cumulative Review:** For review of finding missing factors, assign Problems 28–30 on student page 494.

**Family Involvement:** Assign the ***Practice, Reteach,*** or ***Enrichment*** activities depending on the needs of your students.

**Concept/Question Board:** Have students attempt to answer any unanswered questions on the Concept/Question Board.

**Math Puzzler:** As you triple the length of the sides of a rectangle, what happens to its perimeter? It triples.

# 4 Assess and Differentiate

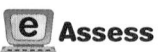

e Assess Use ***eAssess*** to record and analyze evidence of student understanding.

## A Gather Evidence

Use the Daily Class Assessment Records in ***Assessment*** or ***eAssess*** to record daily observations

### Portfolio Assessment

**✓ Journal**

Did the student REASONING

- ❑ provide a clear explanation?
- ❑ communicate reasons and strategies?
- ❑ choose appropriate strategies?
- ❑ argue logically?

### Informal Assessment

**✓ Strategy Building**

Did the student ENGAGING

- ❑ pay attention to others' contributions?
- ❑ contribute information and ideas?
- ❑ improve on a strategy?
- ❑ reflect on and check the accuracy of his or her work?

## B Summarize Findings

Analyze and summarize assessment data for each student. Determine which Assessment Follow-Up is appropriate for each student. Use the Student Assessment Record in ***Assessment*** or ***eAssess*** to update assessment records.

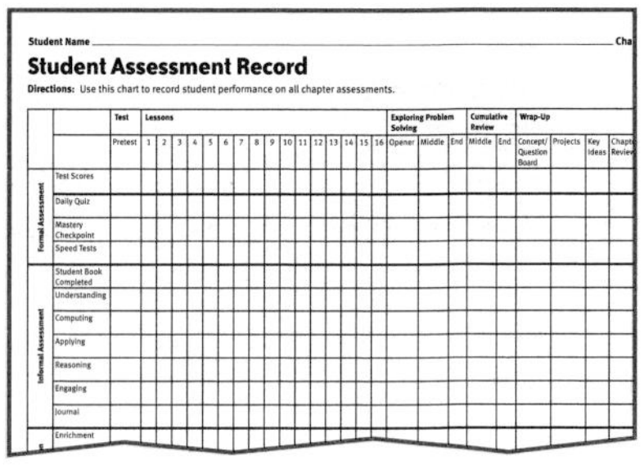


**Assessment Page T41**

## C Assessment Follow-Up • DIFFERENTIATE INSTRUCTION

Based on your observations, use these teaching strategies for assessment follow-up.

### INTERVENTION

Review student performance on ***Intervention*** Lesson 10.B to see if students have mastered prerequisite skills for this lesson.

### ENGLISH LEARNER

**Review**

Use Lesson 10.14 in ***English Learner Support Guide*** to review lesson concepts and vocabulary.

### ENRICH

**If . . .** students are proficient in the lesson concepts,

**Then . . .** encourage them to work on the chapter projects or ***Enrichment*** Lesson 10.14.

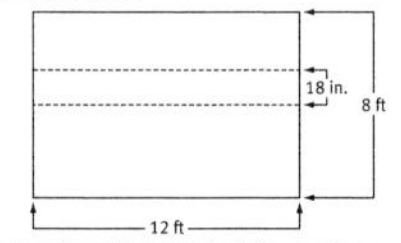

LESSON 10.14 Name ______ Date ______

**Measuring and Calculating Perimeter**

**Earthworms**



Homero raises earthworms and sells the worms to earn money. His earthworm bed is 8 feet by 12 feet. He wants to put a concrete path down the middle to make it easier to collect worms. He knows he needs at least 75 square feet of good soil to maintain his earthworms.

**Answer** these questions.

1. Homero wants to make the path 18 inches wide. Can he? Tell why you think so.
   Yes. The worm bed is 96 sq. feet.The path would be 18 sq. feet. He would still have 78 square feet of good soil left.
2. Homero is also thinking about fencing the worm bed so that other animals don't get into it. He would need two 18-inch gates; one at either end of the path. How many feet of fencing would he need for the rest of the perimeter?
   The perimeter is 40 ft – 3 feet for the gates = 37 ft of fencing.

Real Math • Grade 4 • *Enrichment Support Guide* Chapter 10 • *Geometry* 121

Enrichment Lesson 10.14

### PRACTICE

**If . . .** students would benefit from additional practice,

**Then . . .** assign ***Practice*** Lesson 10.14

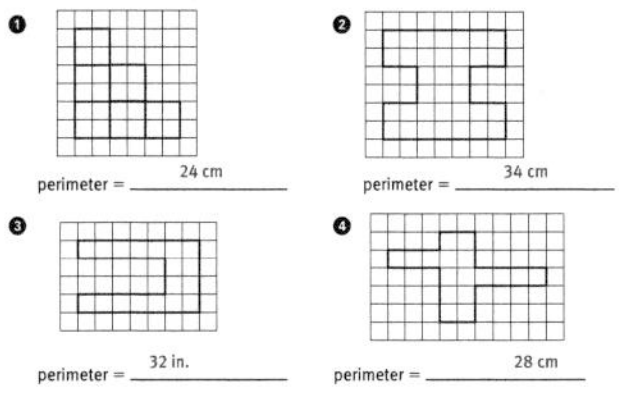

LESSON 10.14 Name ______ Date ______

**Measuring and Calculating Perimeter**

**Find** the perimeter of each figure. Each square on the graph paper is one centimeter on a side.

1. perimeter = 24 cm
2. perimeter = 34 cm
3. perimeter = 32 in.
4. perimeter = 28 cm

**Solve** the following problems.

5. A square has an area of 64 square inches. What is its perimeter? 32 inches
6. One side of a rectangle is 7 meters. Its area is 21 square meters. What is its perimeter? 20 inches
7. A rectangular rug has an area of 16 square meters. It has a perimeter of 20 meters. What is its length? What is its width? L = 8 meters; W = 2 meters
8. How many other rectangles can you draw that have a perimeter of 22 centimeters? Give the dimensions of each one. 4 other possibilities: $10 \times 1$, $9 \times 2$, $7 \times 4$, $6 \times 5$

Real Math • Grade 4 • *Practice* Chapter 10 • *Geometry* 121

Practice Lesson 10.14

### RETEACH

**If . . .** students have difficulty finding perimeter when given the area,

**Then . . .** have them draw a model of the figure and label the sides. Have students use an area of floor that has square tiles on it, like a grid. Then have them use tape to make a shape on the grid. Have each student walk the outline of the grid, counting tiles as they go. This will give them the perimeter of the shape.

# Exploring Problem Solving

**Objectives**
- To use transformations to analyze letters in the braille alphabet and in the standard alphabet
- To explore solving and presenting solutions to nonroutine problems that involve geometric patterns

**Context of the Lesson** This lesson builds on what the students learned about transformations in Lesson 10.8. It also builds on the discussions in the first Problem Solving Lesson about congruent arrangements in a 2 × 3 array.

## 1 Develop

5

**Tell Students In Today's Lesson They Will**
- read about the boy who invented a way for blind people to read quickly.
- make letters and words that can be read without seeing them.
- figure out what happens to letters in the standard alphabet and in the braille alphabet when they are reflected.

## Guided Discussion

Have students discuss different items that assist people with disabilities. Ask questions such as the following:

- **What inventions have been created to help people who have impaired hearing?** Possible answer: hearing aids
- **What are some things that help people who are visually impaired?** Possible answers: seeing-eye dogs or books on tape

Student Page

Exploring Problem Solving

### *Not* Seeing Is Believing

In 1820, there was only one way for people who are blind to read. Each letter of the alphabet was raised from the page so it could be felt with the fingers. This might sound simple, but it was not. The Qs felt like Os. The Os felt like Cs. The Is turned out to be Ts, and the Rs were really Bs.

Louis Braille, who was blind, was one of the brightest boys in his school. But often even he forgot the beginning of a sentence before he got to the end of it. It would take months to read a single book this way!

One day in 1821, Captain Charles Barbier came to Louis's school. Captain Barbier had worked out a way for his soldiers to use raised dots to send messages in the dark. In his night-writing system, a different pattern of dots represented each sound. The dots were pushed into heavy sheets of paper with a long, pointed tool called a stylus. When the paper was turned over, raised dots could be felt on the other side.

Portrait of Louis Braille

But there were so many sounds in the French language that it took almost a hundred dots to write out a simple word. Night-writing also took up far too much room. Most of all, it was hard to learn and to feel.

Night-writing might have worked well for notes on the battlefield, but it was no way to make books for the blind. Did that mean the dots were a failure? Louis did not think so.

490 eTextbook This lesson is available in the *eTextbook*.

# 2 Exploring Problem Solving 30

## Using Student Pages

With the class, read the story on student page 490, which tells how Louis Braille invented a practical way for people without sight to read. The story also brings out some important points about problem solving.

During or after the story, ask questions such as the following:

- **What problem did Louis try to solve?** He tried to find a way for people who are blind to read that would be practical for making and reading whole books.
- **Did Louis solve the problem right away?** No, at one point in the story, three years go by while he's working on the problem.
- **In the system that simply used regular letters that were raised from the page, why might Qs feel like Os and Os feel like Cs?** These letters all have round shapes and if you miss a small part, you might think it was a different letter.
- **In Captain Barbier's night-writing system, did each pattern of dots stand for a letter?** No, each pattern stood for a sound.
- **Why wasn't the night-writing system useful for books for those without sight?** Possible answers: It took a lot of dots to make even a simple word; it took up a lot of room; it was hard to learn and to feel.
- **Did Louis throw out all the ideas from the night-writing system because it did not work?** No, he kept the idea of using raised dots.
- **What did you learn about problem solving from the story?** Possible answer: the importance of not giving up

Student Page

Louis decided he was going to work out a way for the blind to *really* read and write with dots. He tried not to waste a single minute. Even on vacation, he worked on his dots.

Three years went by. Sometimes Louis got so tired he could hardly lift his hand. Again and again, he simplified Captain Barbier's pattern of dots. But still they were not simple enough.

Then Louis had a very different idea. What if he used dots in a new way—not to stand for sounds, but to stand for letters?

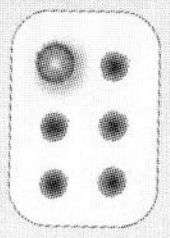

First Louis took a pencil and marked six dots on a heavy piece of paper. Then he took his stylus and raised one of the dots.

That would stand for the letter *a*. Louis made letter after letter. And when he was finished, Louis Braille's alphabet of dots looked like the illustration below.

**The Braille Alphabet**

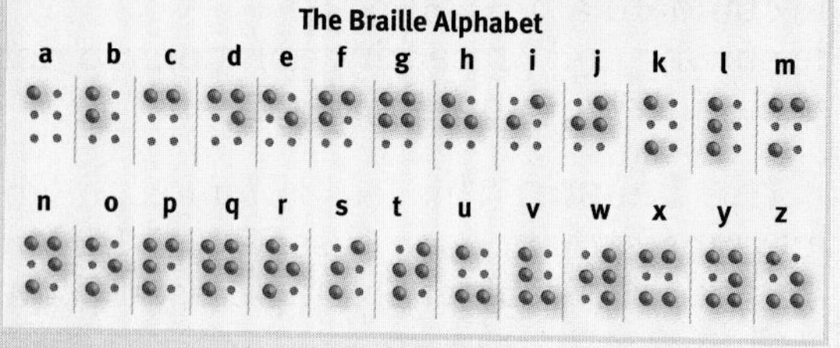


Edited excerpts from *Louis Braille: The Boy Who Invented Books for the Blind.*

1. Why do you think that only one letter is made with a single dot? Because it might be difficult to distinguish different letters if they were also made with one dot.
2. Why wouldn't a system based on a grid of four dots instead of six dots work? There wouldn't be enough different arrangements to make all twenty-six letters.

Chapter 10 491

Student Page

# Exploring Problem Solving

You can write messages in braille by making dots with a pencil on grid paper. Press hard. Turn the paper over.

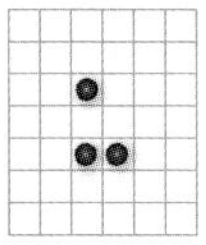

Be careful. What happens to the pattern of dots when you flip the page? Try making the letter *u* in braille to find out.

**Solve** these problems.

3. In the regular alphabet, which lowercase letters will stay the same when you flip the page? *i, l, m, o, v, w, x*. The letters *n, t,* and *u* might also qualify, depending on the way they are written.
4. In the regular alphabet, which lowercase letters will become a different letter when you flip the page? *b* becomes *d*, and *d* becomes *b*; *p* becomes *q*, and *q* becomes *p*
5. In the braille alphabet, which letters will become a different letter when you flip the page? *d* becomes *f*, and *f* becomes *d*; *h* becomes *j*, and *j* becomes *h*; *e* becomes *i*, and *i* becomes *e*
6. Suppose you flip the page as shown here, so it is around a horizontal line instead of around a vertical line. Which braille letters will stay the same, and which will become different letters? *k, l, o, r, w, x,* and *y* stay the same; *e* and *i* become each other, and so do *d, j, m, u, p,* and *v*

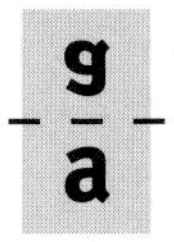


492 eTextbook This lesson is available in the *eTextbook*.

Read, discuss, and answer Problems 1 and 2 with the class. Then tell students they are going to have the opportunity to experiment with writing and reading with Louis Braille's alphabet.

Have students turn to page 492. Demonstrate how to write braille letters by making heavy dots on graph paper and then turning over the page to "read" the dot pattern by feeling it. Give the students graph paper and have them each try to make the pattern for the letter *u*, as suggested on page 492.

Have students work individually or in pairs on Problems 3–6.

## 3 Reflect

15

**Knowledge Age Skills**

**Effective Communication** Discuss with the class their experiences with writing and reading the dot patterns of the braille alphabet, and discuss their answers to Problems 3–6. Discuss the following points:

- Some patterns stay the same no matter which way they are flipped. These patterns have at least two lines of symmetry.
- Using the term *reflect* or *flip* may not be clear enough unless you specify the line that you are reflecting or flipping over. For example, the braille letter *g* would stay the same when flipped if the axis of reflection is between the two rows of dots.

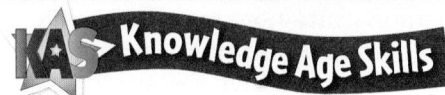

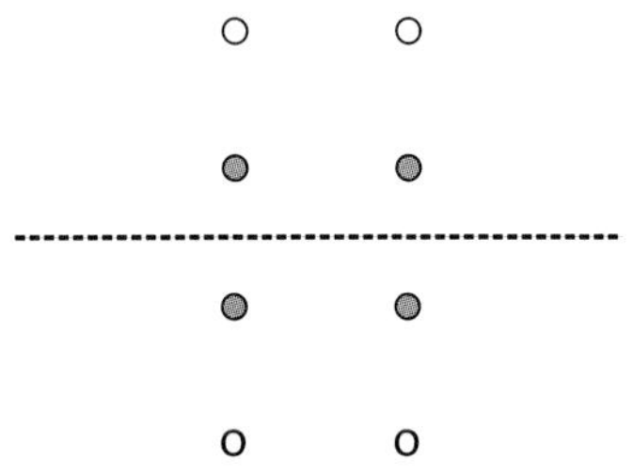

### Extensions

- Have students compare the braille system to the system of raised standard letters described at the beginning of the story. They can write a few braille letters and a few standard letters to test how easy it is to recognize them by feeling.
- Have students research other versions of the braille alphabet, such as one based on an array of eight dots.

## 4 Assess

10

When evaluating student work, focus not only on the correctness of the answer but also on students' thinking and communication. Some questions to consider include the following:

- Did the student understand the problem depicted in the story?
- Could the student recognize which letters would transform into other letters and which would stay the same when flipped?
- Could the student describe transformations clearly?

# Cumulative Review

## Assign Pages 493–494

Use this Cumulative Review as a review of concepts and skills that students have previously learned.

Here are different ways you can assign these problems to your students as they work through the chapter:

- For each lesson in the chapter, assign a set of Cumulative Review problems to be completed as practice or for homework.
  - Lesson 10.7—Problems 1–8
  - Lesson 10.8—Problems 9–10
  - Lesson 10.9—Problems 11–14
  - Lesson 10.10—Problems 15–18
  - Lesson 10.11—Problems 19–22
  - Lesson 10.12—Problems 23–25
  - Lesson 10.13—Problems 26–27
  - Lesson 10.14—Problems 28–30
- At any point during the chapter, assign part or all of the Cumulative Review problems to be completed as practice or for homework.

### Cumulative Review

**Problems 1–8** review converting customary units, Lesson 6.6.

**Problems 9–10** review ordering decimals, Lesson 9.4.

**Problems 11–14** review using relation signs, Lesson 2.4.

**Problems 15–18** review percents, Lessons 7.2, 7.3, and 7.8.

**Problems 19–22** review equivalent fractions, Lesson 8.8.

**Problems 23–25** review function rules and ordered pairs, Lesson 4.7.

**Problems 26–27** review perimeter and area, Lesson 6.1.

**Problems 28–30** review finding missing factors, Lessons 3.9 and 3.13.

### Monitoring Student Progress

**If . . .** students miss more than one problem in a section,

Student Page

## Cumulative Review

**Converting Customary Units** Lesson 6.6

**Convert** these measurements.

1. 3 pounds is how many ounces? 48
2. If there are 16 ounces in 1 pint, how many ounces are in 12 pints? 192
3. How many cups are in 1 gallon? 16
4. 6 gallons is equal to how many quarts? 24
5. Shonda weighs 65 pounds. How many ounces does she weigh? 1,040
6. How many feet are in 7 yards? 21
7. How many inches are in 76 feet? 912
8. How many fluid ounces are in 1 gallon? 128

**Ordering Decimals** Lesson 9.4

**What** are the next three numbers in the patterns below?

9. 1.2, 2.4, 4.8, 9.6, 19.2, ■ 38.4, 76.8, 153.6
10. 15.5, 14.0, 12.5, 11.0, 9.5, 8.0, ■ 6.5, 5.0, 3.5

**Using Relation Signs** Lesson 2.4

**Fill** in the correct sign: <, >, or =.

11. $6 \times 7 + 3$ ■ $9 \times 5$ =
12. $100 - 96 \times 2$ ■ $28 \div 4$ >
13. $300 + 300$ ■ $54 + 3,000$ <
14. $9 \div 3$ ■ $25 - 16$ <

**Percents** Lessons 7.2, 7.3, and 7.8

**Solve** the following problems.

15. 0.50 of 32 = ■ 16
16. $\frac{3}{4}$ of 44 = ■ 33
17. 25% of 32 = ■ 8
18. 10% of 700 = ■ 70



Student Page

## Cumulative Review

**Equivalent Fractions** Lesson 8.8

**Write** *yes* if the mixed number and improper fraction are equivalent, and *no* if they are not.

19. $2\frac{1}{2} = \frac{5}{2}$ yes
20. $\frac{10}{6} = 2\frac{1}{3}$ no
21. $7\frac{2}{5} = \frac{39}{5}$ no
22. $6\frac{3}{4} = \frac{27}{4}$ yes

**Function Rules and Ordered Pairs** Lesson 4.7

**Find** the function.

23. $x \rightarrow \times 4 \rightarrow y$

| $x$ | $y$ |
|---|---|
| 6 | 24 |
| 8 | 32 |
| 12 | 48 |
| 15 | 60 |

24. $x \rightarrow \div 3, +4 \rightarrow y$

| $x$ | $y$ |
|---|---|
| 30 | 14 |
| 24 | 12 |
| 18 | 10 |
| 12 | 8 |

25. $x \rightarrow -8 \rightarrow y$

| $x$ | $y$ |
|---|---|
| 15 | 7 |
| 20 | 12 |
| 25 | 17 |
| 30 | 22 |

**Perimeter and Area** Lesson 6.1

**Find** area and perimeter in the following situations.

26. Cindy's room is 12 feet by 14 feet; her friend Alyse's room is 16 feet by 13 feet. Which room has a greater area and by how many square feet? Alyse's room; 40 sq. ft bigger
27. Edward wants to frame a piece of his art work. The painting is 53 centimeters by 32 centimeters. How many centimeters around should the frame be? 170 cm

**Finding Missing Factors** Lessons 3.9 and 3.13

**Solve** for *n*.

28. $3 \times n = 21$ $n = 7$
29. $n \times 12 = 48$ $n = 4$
30. $n \times n = 9$ $n = 3$

# Cumulative Review

Review

## Assign Pages 493–494

Use this Cumulative Review as a review of concepts and skills that students have previously learned.

Here are different ways you can assign these problems to your students as they work through the chapter:

- For each lesson in the chapter, assign a set of Cumulative Review problems to be completed as practice or for homework.
  - Lesson 10.7—Problems 1–8
  - Lesson 10.8—Problems 9–10
  - Lesson 10.9—Problems 11–14
  - Lesson 10.10—Problems 15–18
  - Lesson 10.11—Problems 19–22
  - Lesson 10.12—Problems 23–25
  - Lesson 10.13—Problems 26–27
  - Lesson 10.14—Problems 28–30
- At any point during the chapter, assign part or all of the Cumulative Review problems to be completed as practice or for homework.

### Cumulative Review

**Problems 1–8** review converting customary units, Lesson 6.6.

**Problems 9–10** review ordering decimals, Lesson 9.4.

**Problems 11–14** review using relation signs, Lesson 2.4.

**Problems 15–18** review percents, Lessons 7.2, 7.3, and 7.8.

**Problems 19–22** review equivalent fractions, Lesson 8.8.

**Problems 23–25** review function rules and ordered pairs, Lesson 4.7.

**Problems 26–27** review perimeter and area, Lesson 6.1.

**Problems 28–30** review finding missing factors, Lessons 3.9 and 3.13.

### Monitoring Student Progress

**If . . .** students miss more than one problem in a section,

Student Page

## Cumulative Review

**Converting Customary Units** Lesson 6.6

**Convert** these measurements.

1. 3 pounds is how many ounces? 48
2. If there are 16 ounces in 1 pint, how many ounces are in 12 pints? 192
3. How many cups are in 1 gallon? 16
4. 6 gallons is equal to how many quarts? 24
5. Shonda weighs 65 pounds. How many ounces does she weigh? 1,040
6. How many feet are in 7 yards? 21
7. How many inches are in 76 feet? 912
8. How many fluid ounces are in 1 gallon? 128

**Ordering Decimals** Lesson 9.4

**What** are the next three numbers in the patterns below?

9. 1.2, 2.4, 4.8, 9.6, 19.2, ▒ 38.4, 76.8, 153.6
10. 15.5, 14.0, 12.5, 11.0, 9.5, 8.0, ▒ 6.5, 5.0, 3.5

**Using Relation Signs** Lesson 2.4

**Fill** in the correct sign: <, >, or =.

11. $6 \times 7 + 3$ ▒ $9 \times 5$ =
12. $100 - 96 \times 2$ ▒ $28 \div 4$ >
13. $300 + 300$ ▒ $54 + 3{,}000$ <
14. $9 \div 3$ ▒ $25 - 16$ <

**Percents** Lessons 7.2, 7.3, and 7.8

**Solve** the following problems.

15. 0.50 of 32 = ▒ 16
16. $\frac{3}{4}$ of 44 = ▒ 33
17. 25% of 32 = ▒ 8
18. 10% of 700 = ▒ 70



Student Page

## Cumulative Review

**Equivalent Fractions** Lesson 8.8

**Write** *yes* if the mixed number and improper fraction are equivalent, and *no* if they are not.

19. $2\frac{1}{2} = \frac{5}{2}$ yes
20. $\frac{10}{6} = 2\frac{1}{3}$ no
21. $7\frac{2}{5} = \frac{39}{5}$ no
22. $6\frac{3}{4} = \frac{27}{4}$ yes

**Function Rules and Ordered Pairs** Lesson 4.7

**Find** the function.

23. $x \rightarrow \times 4 \rightarrow y$

| $x$ | $y$ |
|---|---|
| 6 | 24 |
| 8 | 32 |
| 12 | 48 |
| 15 | 60 |

24. $x \rightarrow \div 3, +4 \rightarrow y$

| $x$ | $y$ |
|---|---|
| 30 | 14 |
| 24 | 12 |
| 18 | 10 |
| 12 | 8 |

25. $x \rightarrow -8 \rightarrow y$

| $x$ | $y$ |
|---|---|
| 15 | 7 |
| 20 | 12 |
| 25 | 17 |
| 30 | 22 |

**Perimeter and Area** Lesson 6.1

**Find** area and perimeter in the following situations.

26. Cindy's room is 12 feet by 14 feet; her friend Alyse's room is 16 feet by 13 feet. Which room has a greater area and by how many square feet? Alyse's room; 40 sq. ft bigger
27. Edward wants to frame a piece of his art work. The painting is 53 centimeters by 32 centimeters. How many centimeters around should the frame be? 170 cm

**Finding Missing Factors** Lessons 3.9 and 3.13

**Solve** for *n*.

28. $3 \times n = 21$  $n = 7$
29. $n \times 12 = 48$  $n = 4$
30. $n \times n = 9$  $n = 3$

# Wrap-Up

## 1 Discuss 5

### Concept/Question Board

Review the Concept/Question Board with students.

- Discuss students' contributions to the Concept side of the Board.
- Have students repose their questions, and lead a discussion to find satisfactory answers.

## Chapter Projects

Provide an opportunity for students who have worked on one or more of the chapter projects outlined on page 447C to share their work with the class. Allow each student or student group five minutes to present or discuss their projects. For formal assessment, use the rubrics found in ***Across the Curriculum Math Connections;*** the rubric for **Write a Shape Poem in Uncontracted Braille** is on page 105, and the rubric for **Design a New Writing System** is on page 111. For informal assessment, use the following rubric and questions.

| | Exceeds Expectations | Meets Expectations | Minimally Meets Expectations |
|---|---|---|---|
| Applies mathematics in real-world situations: | ❑ | ❑ | ❑ |
| Demonstrates strong engagement in the activity: | ❑ | ❑ | ❑ |

### Write a Shape Poem in Uncontracted Braille

LANGUAGE ARTS

- What object did you choose for your shape poem? Why?
- Does your poem reflect the object that you chose?
- How does Braille help blind people to read?
- Was it difficult to write your shape poem in uncontracted Braille? Why or why not?
- Could you read the poem that your partner gave you? Why or why not?
- Do you think a blind person would be able to read your poem? Why or why not?

### Design a New Writing System

SCIENCE WebQuest

- How did you design your writing system?
- What shapes and translations, rotations, and reflections of shapes did you use?
- How do languages allow people to communicate?
- Did you create a written, geometry-based language that another person can understand?
- What features of your language make it possible or not possible for someone else to understand?
- Would you like to use your language instead of English for written communications? Why or why not?
- Why do you think many modern languages use letters instead of pictures or picture-like symbols?

## 2 Assign Student Pages 25

### Key Ideas Review ✓ UNDERSTANDING

Have students complete the Review questions independently or in small groups. Then discuss each question as a class.

#### Possible Answers

**Problem 1** Problems 1–4 involve recognizing basic geometric figures. The answer is an angle.

**Problem 2** The answer is a line.

**Problem 3** The answer is a ray.

**Problem 4** The answer is perpendicular lines.

**Problem 5** This exercise involves students being able to recognize a *net* and to decide what figure is made when all the pieces are placed accordingly. This net is a dodecahedron.

Extended Response

**Problem 6** This problem requires students to use their knowledge of parallel and perpendicular lines. There are a few possible answers to this problem. The sign containing parallel lines can be the rhombus or square, and the sign with no parallel lines can be the triangle or pentagon.

**Problem 7** This exercise involves students' knowledge of *lines of symmetry*. A line of symmetry is a line dividing a figure into two congruent pieces. Some possible examples include the following:

- A square has four lines of symmetry.
- A pentagon has five lines of symmetry.

Extended Response

**Problem 8** This problem involves students' knowledge of a vertex, face, and edge. Students should mention that a pentagonal pyramid has six faces, six vertices, and ten edges, and that a triangular pyramid has four faces, four vertices, and six edges. The base of the triangular pyramid is a triangle, and the base of the pentagonal pyramid is a pentagon.

Student Page

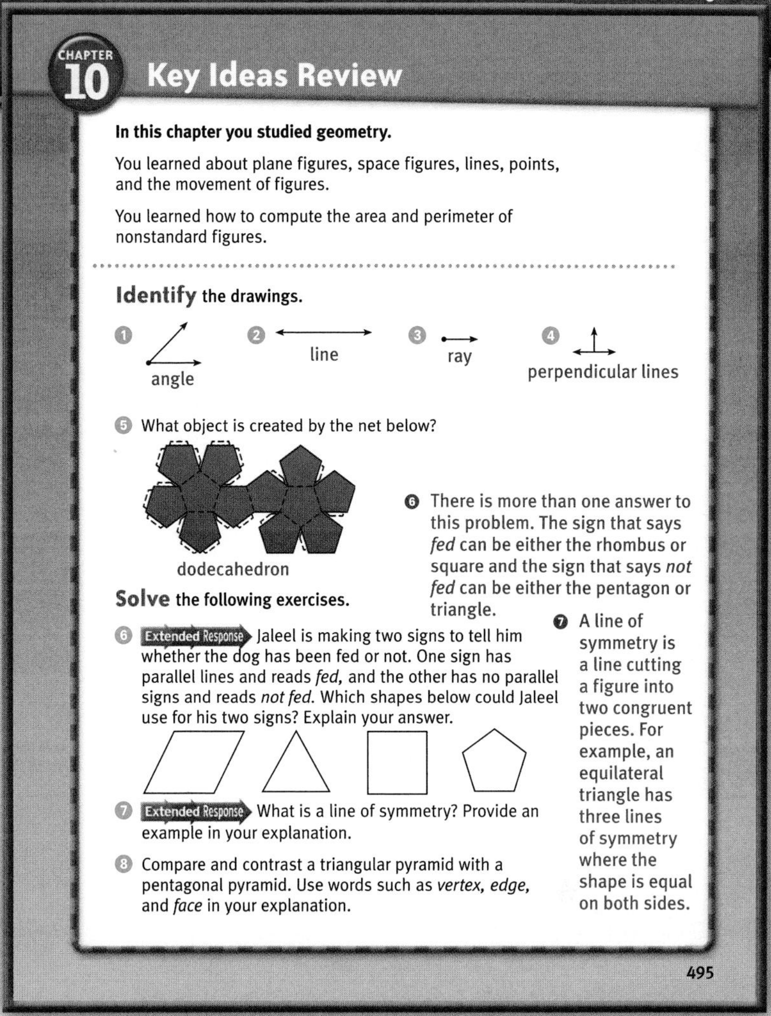

CHAPTER 10 Key Ideas Review

**In this chapter you studied geometry.**

You learned about plane figures, space figures, lines, points, and the movement of figures.

You learned how to compute the area and perimeter of nonstandard figures.

**Identify** the drawings.

1. angle
2. line
3. ray
4. perpendicular lines

5. What object is created by the net below?

dodecahedron

**Solve** the following exercises.

6. Extended Response Jaleel is making two signs to tell him whether the dog has been fed or not. One sign has parallel lines and reads *fed*, and the other has no parallel signs and reads *not fed*. Which shapes below could Jaleel use for his two signs? Explain your answer.

7. Extended Response What is a line of symmetry? Provide an example in your explanation.

8. Compare and contrast a triangular pyramid with a pentagonal pyramid. Use words such as *vertex, edge,* and *face* in your explanation.

6 There is more than one answer to this problem. The sign that says *fed* can be either the rhombus or square and the sign that says *not fed* can be either the pentagon or triangle.

7 A line of symmetry is a line cutting a figure into two congruent pieces. For example, an equilateral triangle has three lines of symmetry where the shape is equal on both sides.

495

# CHAPTER 10 Review

## Chapter Review

Use this Chapter 10 Review as a preliminary chapter test to identify areas in which each student is having difficulty or in which the class may need help. If students do well on the Chapter 10 Review, you may wish to skip directly to the next chapter. If not, you may want to spend time helping students overcome their individual difficulties before they take the Chapter Test.

Each set of problems reviews concepts from one or more lessons in the chapter. Students can refer to a specific lesson for additional instruction if they need help. You can also use this information to assign additional practice based on the previous lesson concepts.

Have students complete pages 496–497 on their own. For review purposes, you may want to do some of the word problems on page 497 as a class.

### Monitoring Student Progress

**Problems 1–3 Lessons 10.1 and 10.3**

**If . . .** students miss more than one of the problems about lines,

**Then . . .** check to see that the students know the definitions. Use examples when explaining these to students. Also have students demonstrate some of the examples.

**Problems 4–8 Lessons 10.2 and 10.4**

**If . . .** students cannot identify the angles and shapes,

**Then . . .** create a sample wall chart with the class in which students name all the characteristics of squares. For example,

**Characteristics of a Square**
- quadrilateral
- all sides congruent or equal
- all angles congruent or equal
- both pairs of opposite sides parallel

Have groups create individual charts for various angles and shapes.

**Problems 9–10 Lesson 10.5**

**If . . .** students have difficulty identifying types of triangles,

**Then . . .** extend the *Characteristics of . . .* charts to include the types of triangles.

**Problems 11–14 Lesson 10.6**

**If . . .** students have difficulty with the radius and diameter problems,

**Then . . .** review the key terms, and use the terms in sentences.

**Problems 15–16 Lesson 10.9**

**If . . .** students miss more than one line of symmetry,

**Then . . .** assess to make sure they understand the term. Students may also need more practice in finding lines of symmetry.

**Problems 17–20 Lessons 10.11–10.12**

**If . . .** students have difficulty recognizing faces, edges, and vertices,

**Then . . .** provide them more opportunities to use the language as well as practice using the solid figures.

Student Page

CHAPTER 10

# Chapter Review

Lessons 10.1 and 10.3 **Answer** the following questions.

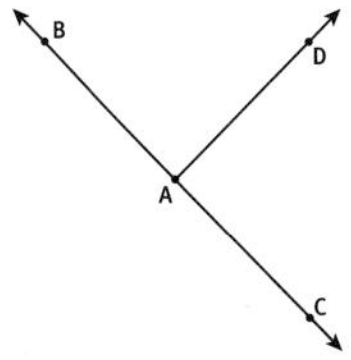


1. Name the ray. AD
2. Name the line. BC
3. Tell whether the lines are parallel, perpendicular, or neither. perpendicular

Lesson 10.2 **Label** the following angles as *acute, obtuse,* or *right.*

4.  obtuse
5.  acute
6. 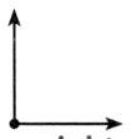 right

Lesson 10.4 **Name** the following shapes.

7. 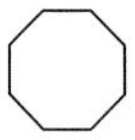 octagon
8. 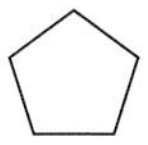 pentagon

Lesson 10.5 **Identify** the triangle according to its sides and angles.

9. 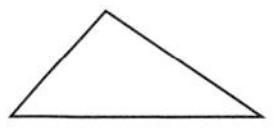 scalene obtuse
10. 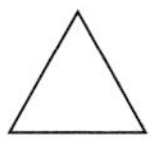 equilateral acute

Lesson 10.6 **Identify** the following parts of this circle.

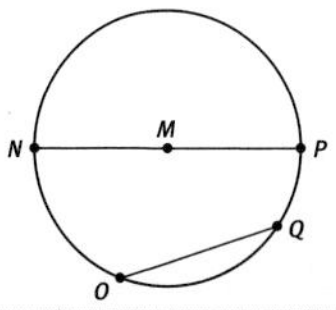


11. Line Segment NM radius
12. Line Segment NP diameter
13. Line Segment OQ chord
14. What is the center of the circle? point *M*



eTextbook This lesson is available in the *eTextbook.*

Student Page

Lesson 10.9

**Trace** and copy the figures. Find out how many lines of symmetry in each figure.

15.  4
16. 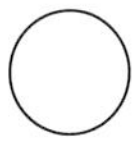 infinite number

Lessons 10.11 and 10.12

**Fill** in the following table about pyramids.
*V* = Vertex, *E* = Edge, *F* = Face

| | Name of polyhedron | Illustration of Model | *V* | *E* | *F* |
|---|---|---|---|---|---|
| 17 | Triangular pyramid |  | 4 | 6 | 4 |
| 18 | Square pyramid |  | 5 | 8 | 5 |
| 19 | Pentagonal pyramid |  | 6 | 10 | 6 |

20. **Extended Response** Name two patterns you see in the table above. Possible answers: The edges increase by two when the vertices and faces increase by one. The vertices and faces are equal numbers.

## 3 Chapter Tests 40

## Practice Test

### Student Pages 498–501

- The Chapter 10 Practice Test on ***Student Edition*** pages 498–501 provides an opportunity to formally evaluate students' proficiency with concepts developed in this chapter.
- The content is similar to the Chapter 10 Review in standardized format.

**Problem 25** Extended Response

Students should find the table and the visuals of the space figures useful in answering the questions that follow. Both the graphic representation of the space figures and the numeric pattern in the number of faces, edges, and vertices become more apparent when the information is presented in a table format.

Student Page

## CHAPTER 10 Practice Test

**Show** one line of symmetry for the figure shown.

1. 
One line possible, vertical line through the center of the arrow

2. 
Two lines are possible, either horizontal or vertical through center of figure.

3. 
Four lines are possible, either horizontal or vertical through center of figure; and two diamonds through the center of the figure.

**Use** the figure to answer the questions below.

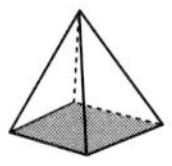

4. How many edges does this figure have? 8
5. How many vertices does this figure have? 5
6. Sketch this figure rotated 90°.

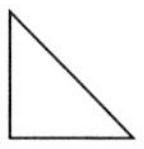

Figure may be rotated 90° either clockwise or counter clockwise.

7. Draw a triangle with two acute angles. Check that two angles are acute.

 Textbook This lesson is available in the ***eTextbook.***

Student Page

**Select** the correct answer.

8. What is another name for a half-line?
Ⓐ angle Ⓑ line segment
● ray Ⓓ vertex

9. What is the term for two lines that never intersect?
● parallel lines
Ⓑ perpendicular lines
Ⓒ square lines
Ⓓ straight lines

10. Which of the following is a quadrilateral?
Ⓐ octagon
Ⓑ pentagon
Ⓒ hexagon
● rhombus

11. What instrument is used to measure a line segment?
Ⓐ calculator Ⓑ compass
Ⓒ protractor ● ruler

12. What is the name of any line segment that intersects the perimeter of a circle in two places?
● chord
Ⓑ circumference
Ⓒ diameter
Ⓓ perimeter

13. Which word best describes the triangles shown below?

Ⓐ equilateral ● congruent
Ⓒ right Ⓓ similar

14. What is the term for an angle that measures less than 90°?
● acute Ⓑ obtuse
Ⓒ scalene Ⓓ triangle

15. Wanda is hanging a poster on the wall. After she hangs it, she decides to turn the poster 90° to the left. What kind of transformation is this?
Ⓐ flip Ⓑ reflection
● rotation Ⓓ translation

16. Which word best describes the squares shown below?
Ⓐ congruent Ⓑ equilateral
Ⓒ forward ● similar

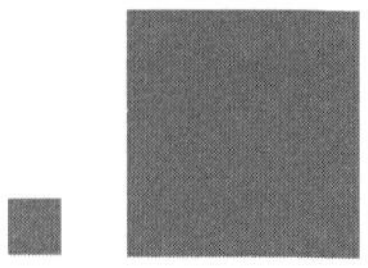

Student Page

# CHAPTER 10 Practice Test

17. How many faces does a cube have?
Ⓐ 4 ● 6
Ⓒ 8 Ⓓ 10

18. How many vertices does a square pyramid have?
Ⓐ 2 Ⓑ 3
Ⓒ 4 ● 5

19. Which of these shows a line of symmetry?

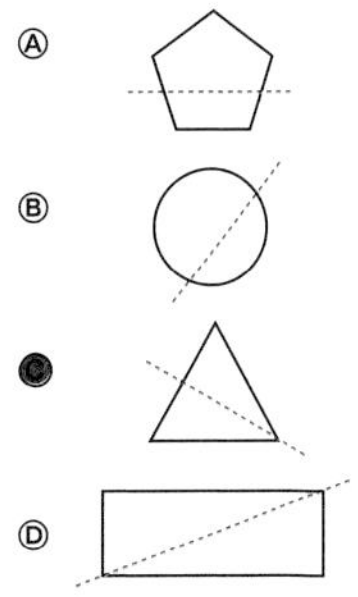

Ⓐ
Ⓑ
●
Ⓓ

20. How many dimes are in $21.30?
Ⓐ 3 Ⓑ 30
Ⓒ 210 ● 213

21. What is the least common multiple of 5 and 3?
Ⓐ 5 Ⓑ 9
Ⓒ 12 ● 15

22. Which symbol makes the statement true?
17 + 3 ▒ 3 × 6
Ⓐ = Ⓑ <
● >

23. Jenny had some marbles to give away. She gave 12 marbles to each of her 7 friends. How many marbles did Jenny have to give away?
● 84 Ⓑ 77
Ⓒ 72 Ⓓ 60

24. Which fraction is equivalent to $\frac{3}{8}$?
Ⓐ $\frac{6}{12}$ Ⓑ $\frac{3}{4}$
Ⓒ $\frac{6}{15}$ ● $\frac{9}{24}$


eTextbook This lesson is available in the *eTextbook*.

Student Page

**Extended Response** **Fill** in the table below. Then answer the questions that follow.

| Name of Polyhedron | Illustration of Model | Vertices | Edges | Faces |
|---|---|---|---|---|
| triangular prism | | 6 | 9 | 5 |
| rectangular prism | | 8 | 12 | 6 |
| pentagonal prism | | 10 | 15 | 7 |

25. What relationship do you notice between:
   a. the base of the polyhedron and the number of vertices? The number of vertices is double the number of sides in the base.
   b. the number of vertices and the number of edges in a polyhedron? Students should note that the ratio of vertices to edges is 2:3.
   c. the number of vertices, edges, and faces in a polyhedron? The number of vertices + faces = the number of edges + 2.



## Chapter Test COMPUTING

- For further evaluation instead of or in addition to this test, you may wish to have students take the Chapter 10 Test provided in ***Assessment.***

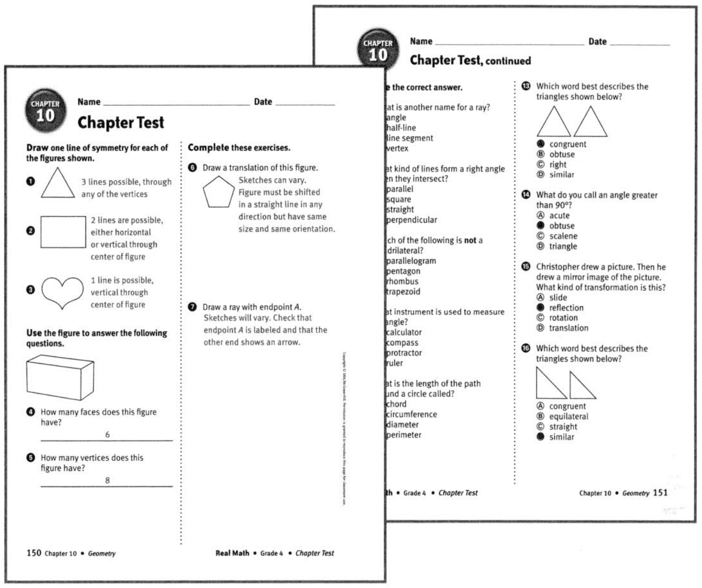
CHAPTER 10 Name ____ Date ____
Chapter Test
Draw one line of symmetry for each of the figures shown.
1 3 lines possible, through any of the vertices
2 2 lines are possible, either horizontal or vertical through center of figure
3 1 line is possible, vertical through center of figure
Use the figure to answer the following questions.
4 How many faces does this figure have? 6
5 How many vertices does this figure have? 8
Complete these exercises.
6 Draw a translation of this figure. Sketches can vary. Figure must be shifted in a straight line in any direction but have same size and same orientation.
7 Draw a ray with endpoint *A*. Sketches will vary. Check that endpoint *A* is labeled and that the other end shows an arrow.
150 Chapter 10 • *Geometry* Real Math • Grade 4 • *Chapter Test*

CHAPTER 10 Name ____ Date ____
Chapter Test, continued
e the correct answer.
at is another name for a ray? angle half-line line segment vertex
at kind of lines form a right angle n they intersect? parallel square straight perpendicular
ch of the following is **not** a drilateral? parallelogram pentagon rhombus trapezoid
at instrument is used to measure angle? calculator compass protractor ruler
at is the length of the path und a circle called? chord circumference diameter perimeter
13 Which word best describes the triangles shown below? ● congruent Ⓑ obtuse Ⓒ right Ⓓ similar
14 What do you call an angle greater than 90°? Ⓐ acute ● obtuse Ⓒ scalene Ⓓ triangle
15 Christopher drew a picture. Then he drew a mirror image of the picture. What kind of transformation is this? Ⓐ slide ● reflection Ⓒ rotation Ⓓ translation
16 Which word best describes the triangles shown below? Ⓐ congruent Ⓑ equilateral Ⓒ straight ● similar
th • Grade 4 • *Chapter Test* Chapter 10 • *Geometry* 151

**Assessment, pages 150–151**

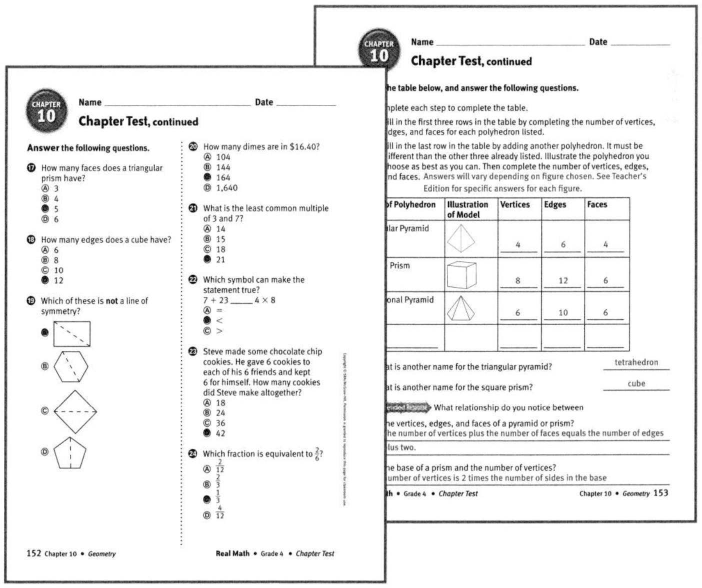
CHAPTER 10 Name ____ Date ____
Chapter Test, continued
Answer the following questions.
17 How many faces does a triangular prism have? Ⓐ 3 Ⓑ 4 ● 5 Ⓓ 6
18 How many edges does a cube have? Ⓐ 6 Ⓑ 8 Ⓒ 10 ● 12
19 Which of these is **not** a line of symmetry? ● Ⓑ Ⓒ Ⓓ
20 How many dimes are in $16.40? Ⓐ 104 Ⓑ 144 ● 164 Ⓓ 1,640
21 What is the least common multiple of 3 and 7? Ⓐ 14 Ⓑ 15 Ⓒ 18 ● 21
22 Which symbol can make the statement true? 7 + 23 ____ 4 × 8 Ⓐ = ● < Ⓒ >
23 Steve made some chocolate chip cookies. He gave 6 cookies to each of his 6 friends and kept 6 for himself. How many cookies did Steve make altogether? Ⓐ 18 Ⓑ 24 Ⓒ 36 ● 42
24 Which fraction is equivalent to $\frac{2}{6}$? Ⓐ $\frac{2}{12}$ Ⓑ $\frac{2}{3}$ ● $\frac{1}{3}$ Ⓓ $\frac{4}{12}$
152 Chapter 10 • *Geometry* Real Math • Grade 4 • *Chapter Test*

CHAPTER 10 Name ____ Date ____
Chapter Test, continued
he table below, and answer the following questions.
nplete each step to complete the table.
ill in the first three rows in the table by completing the number of vertices, dges, and faces for each polyhedron listed.
ill in the last row in the table by adding another polyhedron. It must be ifferent than the other three already listed. Illustrate the polyhedron you hoose as best as you can. Then complete the number of vertices, edges, nd faces. Answers will vary depending on figure chosen. See Teacher's Edition for specific answers for each figure.

| f Polyhedron | Illustration of Model | Vertices | Edges | Faces |
|---|---|---|---|---|
| lar Pyramid | | 4 | 6 | 4 |
| Prism | | 8 | 12 | 6 |
| onal Pyramid | | 6 | 10 | 6 |
| | | | | |

at is another name for the triangular pyramid? tetrahedron
at is another name for the square prism? cube
What relationship do you notice between
e vertices, edges, and faces of a pyramid or prism? he number of vertices plus the number of faces equals the number of edges lus two.
e base of a prism and the number of vertices? umber of vertices is 2 times the number of sides in the base
th • Grade 4 • *Chapter Test* Chapter 10 • *Geometry* 153

**Assessment, pages 152–153**

**Assess and Differentiate**

 **Assess** Use *eAssess* to record and analyze evidence of student understanding.

## A Gather Evidence

Use the Daily Class Assessment Records in *Assessment* or *eAssess* to record Informal and Formal Assessments.

**Informal Assessment**

☑ **Key Ideas Review** UNDERSTANDING

Did the student
- ❑ answer questions?
- ❑ pose new questions?
- ❑ extend the discussion?
- ❑ provide insight?

**Informal Assessment**

☑ **Project** APPLYING

Did the student
- ❑ meet the project objectives?
- ❑ communicate clearly?
- ❑ complete the project accurately?
- ❑ connect mathematics to real-world situations?

**Formal Assessment**

☑ **Chapter Test** COMPUTING

Score the test, and record the results.

## B Summarize Findings

Analyze and summarize assessment data for each student. Determine which Chapter Follow-Up is appropriate for each student. Use the Student Assessment Record in *Assessment* or *eAssess* to update assessment records.

## C Chapter Follow-Up ● DIFFERENTIATE INSTRUCTION

Based on your observations, use these teaching strategies for chapter follow-up.

| ENRICH | PRACTICE | RETEACH | INTERVENTION |
|---|---|---|---|
| **If . . .** students demonstrate **secure understanding** of chapter concepts,<br><br>**Then . . .** have them move on to the next chapter. | **If . . .** students exhibit **competent understanding** of chapter concepts,<br><br>**Then . . .** have them move on to the next chapter. | **If . . .** students demonstrate **emerging understanding** of chapter concepts,<br><br>**Then . . .** move on to the next chapter, but continue to provide cumulative review. | **If . . .** students demonstrate **minimal understanding** of chapter concepts,<br><br>**Then . . .** intensive intervention is needed before they start the next chapter. |

CHAPTER 10

# Teacher Reflection

## Lesson Study

Reflect on each of the lessons you taught in this chapter. Rate each one on the following scale, then consider ways to maintain or improve positive teaching experiences in the future.

| Lessons | Very Effective | Effective | Less Effective | What Worked | Ways to Improve |
|---|---|---|---|---|---|
| 10.1 Lines | | | | | |
| 10.2 Angles | | | | | |
| 10.3 Parallel, Perpendicular, and Intersecting Lines | | | | | |
| 10.4 Quadrilaterals and Other Polygons | | | | | |
| 10.5 Triangles | | | | | |
| 10.6 Circles | | | | | |
| 10.7 Congruence and Similarity | | | | | |
| 10.8 Rotation, Translation, and Reflection | | | | | |
| 10.9 Lines of Symmetry | | | | | |
| 10.10 Space Figures | | | | | |
| 10.11 The Five Regular Polyhedra | | | | | |
| 10.12 Pyramids and Prisms | | | | | |
| 10.13 Calculating Area | | | | | |
| 10.14 Measuring and Calculating Perimeter | | | | | |

CHAPTER 11 Overview

## Lessons



# Dividing Greater Numbers

## Teaching for Understanding

***This chapter focuses on learning to divide greater numbers.*** A long division algorithm is developed step-by-step in real-world context to promote understanding rather than memorization.

## Prerequisite Skills and Concepts

- Subtracting Multidigit Numbers • Division Facts with Remainders
- Multiplying by a One- or Two-Digit Number

## Dividing Greater Numbers Skills Trace

| Before Grade 4 | Grade 4 | After Grade 4 |
|---|---|---|
| **Grades K–1**<br>Informally and formally introduced to subtraction<br>**Grade 2**<br>Informally introduced to division concepts<br>**Grade 3**<br>Formally introduced to division concepts and facts | **Chapter 3** reviewed division facts and introduced division with remainders.<br>**This chapter** develops strategies to divide greater numbers by one- or two-digit divisors.<br>**Chapter 12** uses division for finding average. | Review how to divide greater numbers and the application of knowledge of division to divide decimals and satisfy equations |

## Problem Solving

Problem solving is in every lesson. This chapter includes the following:

**CHAPTER INTRODUCTION** Students solve a problem that uses the relationship between multiplication and division to estimate the Mayflower's size (pp. 502I–503C).

**EXPLORING PROBLEM SOLVING** The first lesson provides a specific focus on the Make a Plan strategy (pp. 522–523A). The second lesson provides an opportunity to analyze data to use division and proportional reasoning (pp. 538–540A).

## Games

Develop reasoning skills, and provide extensive practice.

**Four Cube Division Game** (Lesson 11.3)

# Background

## Multidigit Division

### The Division Algorithm

- The standard algorithm for division involves estimating the greatest digit in the quotient, finding the product of the divisor and this digit, and then subtracting the result from the dividend.
- As with the algorithms for addition and subtraction, the same steps work for numbers with any number of digits.
- Also, as with the other computational algorithms, the division algorithm is introduced in the context of a story to help students understand what each step means. The long form of the algorithm is introduced first, followed by successively more streamlined forms to get to the standard short form. The longer forms not only help the students understand the algorithm, they help prepare students for the algorithm for multidigit divisors.

### Checking Division

- The inverse relationship between multiplication and division (as with addition and subtraction) is an important mathematical idea that, among other things, allows us to do various computations without knowing the usual algorithm or facts. For example, to divide 132 by 11, we can simply search for a number that can be multiplied by 11 to get 132.
- This also provides an important way to check to see if a computation has been done correctly. With multiple-choice tests, often estimation and checking by multiplication will eliminate the need to do a division problem.

### Divisibility Rules

A number $n$ is divisible by a number $m$ if and only if $n \div m$ gives a whole number and there is no remainder.

**DIVISIBILITY BY 2** A number is divisible by 2 if its last digit is divisible by 2 (the last digit must be 0, 2, 4, 6, or 8). For example, 326 is divisible by 2 because 6 is divisible by 2.

**DIVISIBILITY BY 3** A number is divisible by 3 if the sum of its digits is divisible by 3. The number 492,603 has a digit-sum of 24. Because 24 is divisible by 3, we know 492,603 is divisible by 3.

**DIVISIBILITY BY 5** We can recognize a number that is divisible by 5 because its last digit must be either a 0 or a 5. We know 1,450 is divisible by 5 because it has a 0 as its last digit.

**DIVISIBILITY BY 9** A number is divisible by 9 if the sum of its digits is divisible by 9. For example, the number 325,620 must be divisible by 9 because its digits add up to 18.

**DIVISIBILITY BY 11** A number is divisible by 11 if the sum of the digits in "odd" places is equal to the sum of the digits in "even" places. For example, in 4,521, the first and third digits add up to 6, and the second and fourth digits add up to 6, so the number is divisible by 11. A two-digit number is divisible by 11 if the two digits are the same, as in 22 and 77.

### Multiples of 9

- Consider any number, say 85,374. It can be written like this:
  $N = (8 \times 10{,}000) + (5 \times 1{,}000) + (3 \times 100) + (7 \times 10) + 4$

The sum of its digits, S, is $8 + 5 + 3 + 7 + 4$.

- Suppose we subtract the sum of the digits from the number like this:
  $(8 \times 10{,}000) + (5 \times 1{,}000) + (3 \times 100) + (7 \times 10) + 4 - (8 + 5 + 3 + 7 + 4)$

We know that 10,000 of anything minus 1 of that thing is 9,999 of them. So the difference between the number 85,374 and the sum of its digits is $(N - S) = (9{,}999 \times 8) + (999 \times 5) + (99 \times 3) + (9 \times 7)$

Since each of the terms has a factor of 9 ($9{,}999 = 9 \times 1{,}111$, and so on), using the distributive law, we know that any number minus the sum of its digits is divisible by 9. But, if $N - S$ is divisible by 9, then, again using the distributive law, either both N and S are divisible by 9 or neither is.

# What Research Says

## About Division

### How Children Learn Division

Multiplication and division are inverse operations. Therefore, knowledge and fluency with multiplication can support the child's development of strategies with division. Fourth-grade students will focus on acquiring and using multiplication and division strategies efficiently, even while developing recognition of common contexts for the operations of multiplication and division. As the students develop meaning and fluency for use of these operations, they will also develop a greater understanding of the commutative, associative, and distributive properties as they apply to multiplication.

### Learning Trajectories for Division

Finding and using patterns aids in learning multiplication and division facts with understanding. Children typically follow an observable developmental progression in learning to multiply and divide numbers with recognizable stages or levels. This developmental path can be described as part of a learning trajectory.

Key steps from the learning trajectory for Multiplication and Division for children in Grades 3 and 4 are described below. For the complete trajectory, see Appendix B.

| Level | Description |
|---|---|
| Skip Counter ×/÷ | As children develop an understanding of multiplication and division they begin to use skip counting for multiplication and for measurement division (finding how many groups). For example, given twenty blocks, four to each person, and asked how many people, the child skip counts by 4, holding up one finger for each count of 4. A child at this level also uses trial and error for partitive division (finding out how many in each group). |
| Deriver ×/÷ | Children use strategies and derived combinations and solve multidigit problems by operating on tens and ones separately. For example, a child at this level may explain "7 × 6, five 7s is 35, so 7 more is 42." |
| Multidigit ×/÷ | Children begin to use multiple strategies for multiplication and division, from compensating to paper-and-pencil procedures. For example, a child becoming fluent in multiplication might explain that "19 times 5 is 95, because twenty 5s is 100, and one less 5 is 95." |

### Research-Based Teaching Strategies

As students gain proficiency and understanding with multiplication, it is then appropriate and relevant to introduce division as the inverse operation to multiplication. Encourage students to share their discoveries concerning the relationship between multiplication and division, focusing in particular on partitioning or factor patterns. Activities such as the use of arrays, formation of equal groups within a collection, or patterns that become obvious when using function machines can all provide rich experiences that will generate important student discoveries. These discoveries can then be shared in mathematical conversations concerning multiplication and division patterns.

### RESEARCH IN ACTION

**Division** Throughout Chapter 11 students will develop strategies, concepts, and procedures for division.

**Algorithm** In Chapter 11 the step-by-step procedures commonly used for performing division with one- and two-digit divisors will be considered both procedurally and conceptually.

**Remainders** In Chapter 11 students will explore situations where the result of division includes a remainder. They learn the meaning of a remainder by modeling division problems and exploring the size of remainders given a particular divisor.

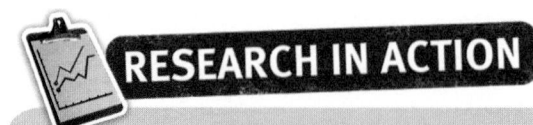

## Vocabulary

**composite number** (Lesson 11.6) any number composed of more than two factors, not including itself and 1

**dividend** (Lesson 3.11) the number that is to be divided

**divisible** (Lesson 11.7) capable of being divided without a remainder

**divisor** (Lesson 3.11) the number the dividend is to be divided by

**estimation** (Lesson 1.1) a judgment or opinion, as of the value, quality, extent, size, or cost of something

**factor** (Lesson 3.12) numbers you multiply to get a product

**inverse** (Lesson 4.5) opposite

**prime number** (Lesson 11.6) any number composed of only two factors—the number itself and 1

**quotient** (Lesson 3.10) the answer to a division problem

**remainder** (Lesson 3.11) the number that is leftover after dividing

**unit cost** (Lesson 11.8) the cost of one out of a number of goods or services

## English Learners

### Cognates

For English learners, a quick way to acquire new English vocabulary words is to build on what is known in the primary language.

| English | Spanish |
|---|---|
| divisor | divisor |
| division | división |
| dividend | dividendo |
| quotient | cociente |

### Access Vocabulary

English learners may understand words in different contexts or not understand idioms. Review chapter vocabulary for this concern. For example:

| | |
|---|---|
| inverse relationship | one operation undoes the other |
| What is left? | An amount that remains is left. |
| arrays | rectangular arrangements of qualities in rows and columns |

CHAPTER 11 Overview

# Chapter Planner

| Lessons | Objectives | NCTM Standards | State Standards |
|---|---|---|---|
| **11.1 Dividing by a One-Digit Divisor** pages 504A–507B 60 minutes | **Explore strategies for dividing greater numbers** by a one-digit divisor by applying knowledge of division | Number and Operations<br>Communication<br>Representation | |
| **11.2 Division: Written Form** pages 508A–509A 60 minutes | **Develop strategies to shorten division procedures** by learning shorter ways to divide | Number and Operations<br>Problem Solving<br>Communication | |
| **11.3 Checking Division** pages 510A–513A 60 minutes | **Explore strategies to check division exercises** by using multiplication to check quotients | Number and Operations<br>Algebra | |
| **11.4 Division: Short Form** pages 513A–515A 60 minutes | **Expand awareness of division** by learning a "short form" for finding quotients | Number and Operations<br>Problem Solving<br>Representation | |
| **11.5 Division Patterns** pages 516A–517A 60 minutes | **Practice dividing with one-digit divisors** while learning to solve problems using shortcuts | Number and Operations<br>Algebra<br>Problem Solving | |
| **11.6 Prime and Composite Numbers** pages 518A–519A 60 minutes | **Expand knowledge of factoring** by exploring strategies for deciphering prime and composite numbers | Number and Operations<br>Problem Solving<br>Representation | |
| **11.7 Finding Factors** pages 520A–521A 60 minutes | **Develop factoring strategies** by applying divisibility rules | Number and Operations<br>Problem Solving | |
| **11.8 Unit Cost** pages 526A–527A 60 minutes | **Explore division strategies** by finding unit costs of products and deciding which purchases will save money | Number and Operations<br>Problem Solving | |
| **11.9 Using Inverses** pages 528A–531B 60 minutes | **Explore the relationships between multiplication and division** by reviewing functions and graphing | Number and Operations | |
| **11.10 Estimating Quotients** pages 532A–533A 60 minutes | **Develop strategies to estimate general quotients** by applying multiplication strategies | Problem Solving | |
| **11.11 Dividing by a Two-Digit Divisor** pages 534A–535A 60 minutes | **Explore strategies of division using a two-digit divisor** by estimating then finding quotients | Number and Operations | |
| **11.12 Applying Mathematics** pages 536A–537A 60 minutes | **Practice division skills** by applying these skills to real-world situations | Number and Operations<br>Problem Solving | |

| Vocabulary | Manipulatives and Materials | Games to reinforce skills and concepts |
|---|---|---|
| divisor | • Response Wheels<br>• Play money<br>• Envelopes (optional)<br>• Base-Ten blocks (optional) | |
| dividend<br>quotient<br>remainder | • Response Wheels<br>• Play money<br>• Base-Ten blocks (optional) | |
| divisor<br>quotient | • Response Wheels<br>• Number Cubes<br>• Play money<br>• Base-Ten blocks (optional) | Four Cube Divison Game (New) |
| quotient | • Response Wheels<br>• Number Cubes<br>• Base-Ten blocks | Four Cube Divison Game (Lesson 11.3) |
| remainder | • Geoboards and overhead geoboard<br>• Response Wheels<br>• Number Cubes | Four Cube Divison Game (Lesson 11.3) |
| prime number<br>composite number | • Response Wheels | Four Cube Divison Game (Lesson 11.3) |
| factor<br>divisible | • Response Wheels<br>• Graph paper (optional) | |
| unit cost | • Response Wheels<br>• Number Cubes<br>• Play money (optional)<br>• Food ads (optional)<br>• Restaurant menus (optional) | Four Cube Divison Game (Lesson 11.3) |
| inverse | • Response Wheels | |
| estimation | • Response Wheels<br>• Base-Ten materials | |
| divisor | • Response Wheels<br>• Play money | |
| quotient | • Response Wheels<br>• Number Cubes | Four Cube Divison Game (Lesson 11.3) |

# Additional Resources

## Differentiated Instruction

***Intervention Support Guide*** provides instruction for the following prerequisite skills:

- Lesson 11.A Subtracting Multidigit Numbers
- Lesson 11.B Division Facts with Remainders
- Lesson 11.C Multiplying by a One- or Two-Digit Number

***Enrichment Support Guide***

***Practice***

***Reteach Support Guide***

***English Learner Support Guide***

## Technology

The following electronic resources are available:

**ePlanner** Lessons 11.1–11.12

**ePresentation** Lessons 11.1–11.12

**eTextbook** Lessons 11.1–11.12

**eAssess** Lessons 11.1–11.12

**eMathTools** **Coins and Money** Lessons 11.1–11.3, 11.8; **Base-Ten Blocks** Lessons 11.3–11.4, 11.10

# Chapter Planner, continued

| Problem Solving | When to Use | Objective | NCTM Standards | Skills Covered |
|---|---|---|---|---|
| **Chapter Introduction** pages 502I–503C 15–30 minutes | Use after the Chapter 11 Pretest | Introduce chapter concepts in a problem-solving setting | Connections<br>Problem Solving | Division,<br>Multiplication,<br>Problem Solving |
| **Exploring Problem Solving** pages 522–523A 30–45 minutes | Use any time during the chapter | Explore methods of solving nonroutine problems | Number and Operations<br>Reasoning and Proof | Multiplication,<br>Division,<br>Problem Solving |
| **Exploring Problem Solving** pages 538–540A 45–60 minutes | Use any time after the first Exploring Problem Solving | Develop logical reasoning while integrating reading skills with mathematics | Number and Operations<br>Reasoning and Proof | Division, Fractions |

| Review | When to Use | Objective | NCTM Standards | Skills Covered |
|---|---|---|---|---|
| **Cumulative Review** pages 524–525 15–30 minutes | Use any time after Lesson 11.7 | Review concepts and skills taught earlier in the year | Number and Operations<br>Measurement<br>Geometry | Classifying Figures<br>Multiplication, Division<br>Measuring Length, Adding Fractions, Rounding Decimals |
| **Cumulative Review** pages 541–542 15–30 minutes | Use any time after Lesson 11.12 | Review concepts and skills taught earlier in the year | Measurement<br>Geometry | Converting Metric Measurements, Geometry, Multiplication, Division |
| **Chapter 11 Review** pages 544A–545 30–45 minutes | Use after Lesson 11.12 | Review concepts and skills taught in the chapter | Problem Solving<br>Number and Operations | Multiplication,<br>Division |

| Assessment | When to Use | Objective | NCTM Standards | Skills Covered |
|---|---|---|---|---|
| **Informal Assessment** (p. 504A–537A) Rubrics | At the end of the lesson | Provide daily evaluation of math proficiency | Problem Solving<br>Reasoning and Proof<br>Communication | Computing, Understanding, Reasoning, Applying, Engaging |
| **Pretest** (*Assessment* p. 155) 15–30 minutes | Use following or in place of the Chapter 10 Review | Provide assessment or additional practice of the chapter concepts | Number and Operations<br>Problem Solving | Multiplication,<br>Division, Fractions |
| **Individual Oral Assessment** (p. 525A) 5 minutes per student | Begin after Lesson 11.7 | Provide alternate means of assessing students' progress | Communication<br>Number and Operations | Division |
| **Mastery Checkpoint** (*Assessment* p. T75) 5 minutes per student | Use after or in place of the Chapter 11 Review | Provide assessment or additional practice of the chapter concepts | Number and Operations | Division with Greater Numbers |
| **Chapter 11 Practice Test** (pp. 546–549A) 30–45 minutes | Use after or in place of the Chapter 11 Review | Provide assessment or additional practice of the chapter concepts | Problem Solving<br>Number and Operations | Division, Factoring, Functions |
| **Chapter 11 Test** (*Assessment* pp. 163–166) 30–45 minutes | Use after or in place of the Chapter 11 Review | Provide assessment or additional practice of the chapter concepts | Number and Operations,<br>Problem Solving | Division, Factoring, Functions |

# Technology Resources and Support

Visit SRAonline.com for online versions of the ***Real Math eSuite.***

## Technology for Teachers

| | |
|---|---|
| **Presentation** | Lessons 11.1–11.12 Use the ***ePresentation*** to interactively present chapter content. |
| **Planner** | Use the Chapter and Lesson Planners to outline activities and time frames for Chapter 11. |
| **Assess** | Students can take the following assessment in ***eAssess:***<br>• Chapter Pretest<br>• Mastery Checkpoint Lesson 11.5<br>• Chapter Test<br>Teachers can record results and print reports for all assessments in this chapter. |
| **MathTools** | **Coins and Money** Lessons 11.1–11.3, 11.8<br>**Base-Ten Blocks** Lessons 11.3–11.4, 11.10 |

## Technology for Students

| | |
|---|---|
| **Textbook** | An electronic, interactive version of the ***Student Edition*** is available for all lessons in Chapter 11. |
| **MathTools** | **Coins and Money** Lessons 11.1–11.3, 11.8<br>**Base-Ten Blocks** Lessons 11.3–11.4, 11.10 |
| SRA TECH KNOWLEDGE | ***TechKnowledge*** Level 4 provides lessons that specifically teach the Unit 10 Internet and Unit 4 Drawing and Graphics applications that students can use in this project. |

CHAPTER 11 Introduction

# Dividing Greater Numbers

## 1 Introduce Chapter 11 5

### Chapter Objectives

Explain to students that in this chapter they will build on what they already know about division. They will

- learn shorter ways to divide.
- learn to decipher prime and composite numbers.
- learn about the relationship between multiplication and division.

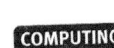

### Pretest COMPUTING

Administer the Pretest in ***Assessment.***

The Pretest for Chapter 11 covers the following prerequisite skills:

- Division with remainders (Problems 1–2)
- Three-digit by two-digit multiplication (Problems 3–4)
- Addition and subtraction of fractions (Problems 5–8)
- Common multiples and factors (Problems 9–10)
- Function tables (Problem 11)

The Pretest also covers the following topics from this chapter:

- Division by one-digit numbers (Problems 12–18)
- Prime and composite numbers (Problems 19–20)
- Unit cost (Problems 21–22)
- Inverses (Problems 23–24)

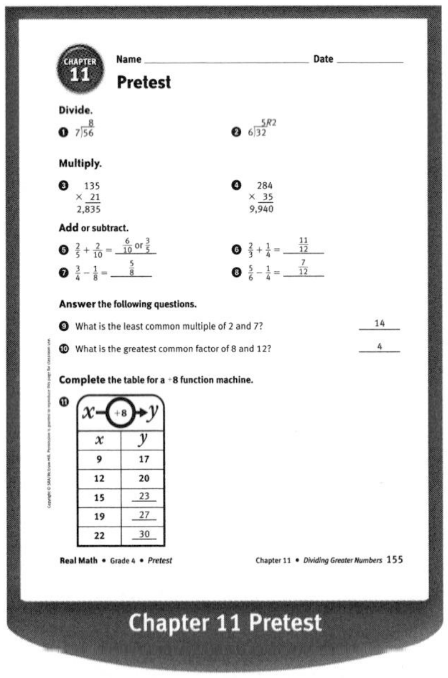
CHAPTER 11 Name ______ Date ______

**Pretest**

**Divide.**

1. $7\overline{)56}$ 8
2. $6\overline{)32}$ 5R2

**Multiply.**

3. 135 × 21 = 2,835
4. 284 × 35 = 9,940

**Add or subtract.**

5. $\frac{2}{5} + \frac{2}{10} = \frac{6}{10}$ or $\frac{3}{5}$
6. $\frac{2}{3} + \frac{1}{4} = \frac{11}{12}$
7. $\frac{3}{4} - \frac{1}{8} = \frac{5}{8}$
8. $\frac{5}{6} - \frac{1}{4} = \frac{7}{12}$

**Answer the following questions.**

9. What is the least common multiple of 2 and 7? 14
10. What is the greatest common factor of 8 and 12? 4

**Complete the table for a +8 function machine.**

11. x → +8 → y

| x | y |
|---|---|
| 9 | 17 |
| 12 | 20 |
| 15 | 23 |
| 19 | 27 |
| 22 | 30 |

Real Math • Grade 4 • *Pretest* Chapter 11 • *Dividing Greater Numbers* 155

Chapter 11 Pretest

### Access Prior Knowledge UNDERSTANDING

Have the students look at page 502 and share what they know about the Pilgrims and the Mayflower. Ask questions such as the following:

- **About how many years ago did the Mayflower sail to the New World?** about 400 years ago
- **How big do you think the Mayflower was?** Let students speculate. They will be determining possible sizes in the activity on page 503.

## 2 Exploring Problem Solving 20

### Tell Students In Today's Lesson They Will

- read information about how ships were built over 400 years ago.
- use that information to figure out how large the Mayflower might have been.

## Using Student Pages

1. Read with the students the information on page 503 about the Mayflower II, the full-size replica of the Mayflower. Explain the following:
   - When the Mayflower was built, shipbuilders did not draw detailed plans as they do today. So we cannot hope to find out the size of the Mayflower from its plans.
   - No one is sure what happened to the Mayflower, but many historians think that it ended up being sold for scrapwood.
2. Go over the problem and information on page 503. Ask questions such as the following:
   - **How could you write the information from the shipbuilder's notebook as an equation?** Possible answer: $L \times B \times D \div 100 = T$
   - **Is the breadth less than or greater than the depth?** greater than
   - **About how many times as great?** Possible answers: about 2 times; about $2\frac{1}{2}$ times; between 2 and $2\frac{1}{2}$ times
   - **How could you write the information about ship proportions in a shorter form?** Possible answer: L is between $2 \times B$ and $3 \times B$. D is between $\frac{2}{5}$ of B and $\frac{1}{2}$ of B.
3. Have students work in groups to determine possible dimensions for the Mayflower. Provide help as needed. Encourage students to use whatever problem-solving strategy they think will work. See the sample strategy in Reflect. Encourage students to estimate.

   Students may be interested to know that a scale model of the Mayflower was built in 1926 based on the information presented on page 503. Researchers determined that the actual Mayflower had a keel length of 64 feet, a breadth of 26 feet, and a depth of 11 feet.

Student Page

# CHAPTER 11 Dividing Greater Numbers

**In This Chapter You Will Learn**
- about shorter ways to divide.
- how to make sense of prime and composite numbers.
- about the relationships between multiplication and division.

Student Page

## Problem Solving

No one knows the exact dimensions of the Mayflower. When the Mayflower II was built in 1957, the designer used information from many sources to make it as close to the original as possible. SOCIAL STUDIES

Imagine you were the person chosen to design the Mayflower II. What size would you make the ship? Here is information about the size of ships in the early 1600s. Use it to estimate the dimensions of the original Mayflower. Pilgrim William Bradford wrote that the Mayflower could carry about 180 tons.

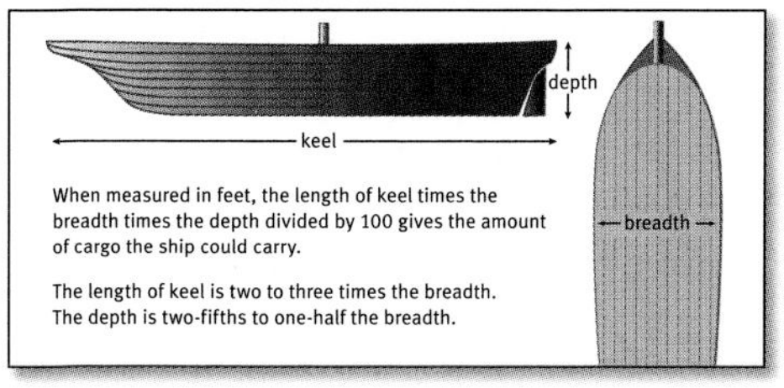


When measured in feet, the length of keel times the breadth times the depth divided by 100 gives the amount of cargo the ship could carry.

The length of keel is two to three times the breadth. The depth is two-fifths to one-half the breadth.

**Work** with your group to decide what dimensions you would use for the Mayflower II.

1. Copy and complete this table to show your results. Answers shown are examples only.

| Dimensions in feet | | | Product | Product ÷ 100 |
|---|---|---|---|---|
| length of keel | breadth | depth | | |
| 70 | 25 | 10 | 17,500 | 175 |

2. How did you decide what dimensions to use?

503

## CyberSolver

To extend problem solving, have students use the Internet to find the answers to the following questions:

- **How far did the Mayflower travel to get to the New World?**
- **How long did it take the Mayflower to cross the Atlantic Ocean?**
- **What else is known about the Mayflower and its passengers?**

Students can search for information using key words such as *Mayflower* and *Pilgrims*. The following Web site contains information about the Mayflower and the Pilgrims: http://www.americanrevolution.org/may4.html.

## Concept/Question Board APPLYING

### Questions

Have students write three questions they have about dividing greater numbers and how they can be used. Then have them select one question to post on the Question side of the Board.

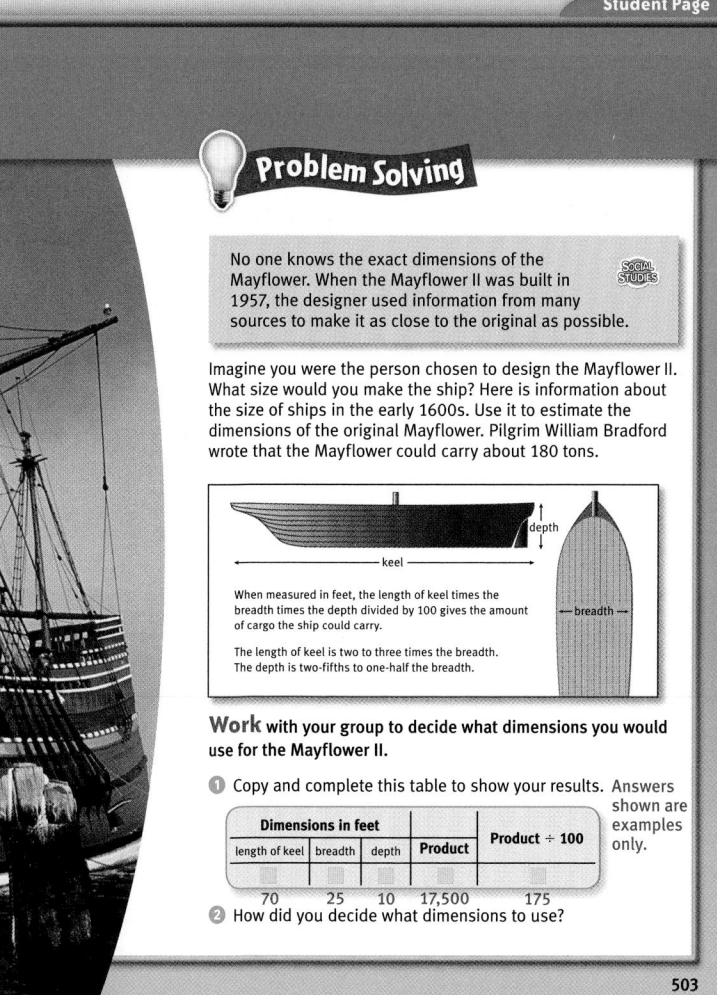

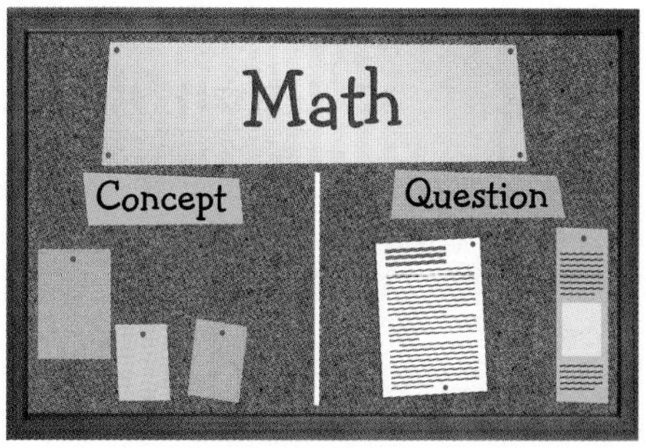


### Concepts

As students work through the chapter, have them collect examples of how dividing greater numbers is used in everyday situations. For each example, have students write problems that relate to the item(s). Have them display their examples on the Concept side of the Board.

Suggest the following:

- play money
- photograph of a cake
- a maximum occupancy sign

### Answers

Throughout the chapter, have students post answers to the questions and solutions to the problems on the Board.

# CHAPTER 11 Introduction

## 3 Reflect

5

### Knowledge Age Skills

**Effective Communication** Have groups present the dimensions they came up with and the method they used to find them. Record all results on the board. After each group presents, ask questions such as the following:

- **Did your dimensions fit all the information on page 503?**
- **Is your group's answer the same as any other group's answer?**

Afterward, discuss why groups came up with different answers and how they can all be correct.

## Sample Solution Strategies

### Work Backward and Guess, Check, and Adjust

Students might work backward to see that the product of the keel length, breadth, and depth must be about the same as the product of 180 and 100, or about 18,000. Then they can use Guess, Check, and Adjust to find three numbers that have a product of about 18,000 and are in the range of the given ratios.

## Home Connection

At this time, you may want to send home the letter on pages 42–45 of ***Home Connection.*** This letter describes what students will be learning and what activities they can do at home to support their work in school.

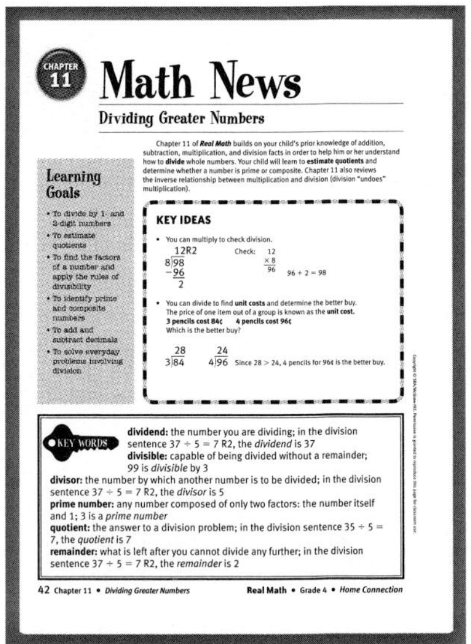

CHAPTER 11 **Math News**

**Dividing Greater Numbers**

Chapter 11 of ***Real Math*** builds on your child's prior knowledge of addition, subtraction, multiplication, and division facts in order to help him or her understand how to **divide** whole numbers. Your child will learn to **estimate quotients** and determine whether a number is prime or composite. Chapter 11 also reviews the inverse relationship between multiplication and division (division "undoes" multiplication).

**Learning Goals**

- To divide by 1- and 2-digit numbers
- To estimate quotients
- To find the factors of a number and apply the rules of divisibility
- To identify prime and composite numbers
- To add and subtract decimals
- To solve everyday problems involving division

**KEY IDEAS**

- You can multiply to check division.
  8)98 = 12R2; 98 − 96 = 2. Check: 12 × 8 = 96; 96 + 2 = 98
- You can divide to find **unit costs** and determine the better buy. The price of one item out of a group is known as the **unit cost.**
  **3 pencils cost 84¢ 4 pencils cost 96¢**
  Which is the better buy?
  3)84 = 28 4)96 = 24 Since 28 > 24, 4 pencils for 96¢ is the better buy.

**KEY WORDS**

**dividend:** the number you are dividing; in the division sentence $37 \div 5 = 7$ R2, the *dividend* is 37
**divisible:** capable of being divided without a remainder; 99 is *divisible* by 3
**divisor:** the number by which another number is to be divided; in the division sentence $37 \div 5 = 7$ R2, the *divisor* is 5
**prime number:** any number composed of only two factors: the number itself and 1; 3 is a *prime number*
**quotient:** the answer to a division problem; in the division sentence $35 \div 5 = 7$, the *quotient* is 7
**remainder:** what is left after you cannot divide any further; in the division sentence $37 \div 5 = 7$ R2, the *remainder* is 2

42 Chapter 11 • *Dividing Greater Numbers* **Real Math** • Grade 4 • *Home Connection*

Home Connection page 42

# 4 Assess and Differentiate

eAssess Use ***eAssess*** to record and analyze evidence of student understanding.

## A Gather Evidence

Use the Daily Class Assessment Records in ***Assessment*** or ***eAssess*** to record daily observations.

### Informal Assessment

**Access Prior Knowledge**

Did the student UNDERSTANDING

- ❑ make important observations?
- ❑ extend or generalize learning?
- ❑ provide insightful answers?
- ❑ pose insightful questions?

### Informal Assessment

**Concept/Question Board**

Did the student APPLYING

- ❑ apply learning in new situations?
- ❑ contribute concepts?
- ❑ contribute answers?
- ❑ connect mathematics to real-world situations?

### Formal Assessment

**Pretest** COMPUTING

Review student answers in each problem set.

- ❑ Division with remainders (Problems 1–2)
- ❑ Three-digit by two-digit multiplication (Problems 3–4)
- ❑ Addition and subtraction of fractions (Problems 5–8)
- ❑ Common multiples and factors (Problems 9–10)
- ❑ Function table (Problem 11)
- ❑ Division by one-digit numbers (Problems 12–18)
- ❑ Prime and composite numbers (Problems 19–20)
- ❑ Unit cost (Problems 21–22)
- ❑ Inverses (Problems 23–24)

## B Summarize Findings

Analyze and summarize assessment data for each student. Determine which Assessment Follow-Up is appropriate for each student. Use the Student Assessment Record in ***Assessment*** or ***eAssess*** to update assessment records.

## C Assessment Follow-Up • DIFFERENTIATE INSTRUCTION

| ENRICH | PRACTICE | RETEACH | INTERVENTION | ENGLISH LEARNER |
|---|---|---|---|---|
| **If . . .** students demonstrate a secure understanding of chapter concepts, **Then . . .** move quickly through the chapter or use ***Enrichment*** Lessons 11.1–11.12 as assessment follow-up to extend and apply understanding. | **If . . .** students grasp chapter concepts with competent understanding, **Then . . .** use ***Practice*** Lessons 11.1–11.12 as lesson follow-up to develop fluency. | **If . . .** students have prerequisite understanding but demonstrate emerging understanding of chapter concepts, **Then . . .** use ***Reteach*** Lessons 11.1, 11.2, 11.9, and 11.11 to reteach lesson concepts. | **If . . .** students are not competent with prerequisite skills, **Then . . .** use ***Intervention*** Lessons 11.A–11.C before each lesson to develop fluency with prerequisite skills. | Use ***English Learner Support Group*** Lessons 11.1–11.12 for strategies to preteach lesson vocabulary and concepts. |

# Chapter Projects

## Math Across the Curriculum

Preview the chapter projects with students. Assign or have students choose from the projects to extend and enrich concepts in this chapter.

### Plan a Voyage to the New World

SOCIAL STUDIES WebQuest

4 weeks

**MATH OBJECTIVE**
To reinforce studies of division

**SOCIAL STUDIES OBJECTIVE**
To reinforce studies of early exploration and settlement

**TECHNOLOGY OBJECTIVE**
To use a spreadsheet program to calculate data

Have students use technology to organize information about colonial travel and calculate costs for the voyage and settlement.

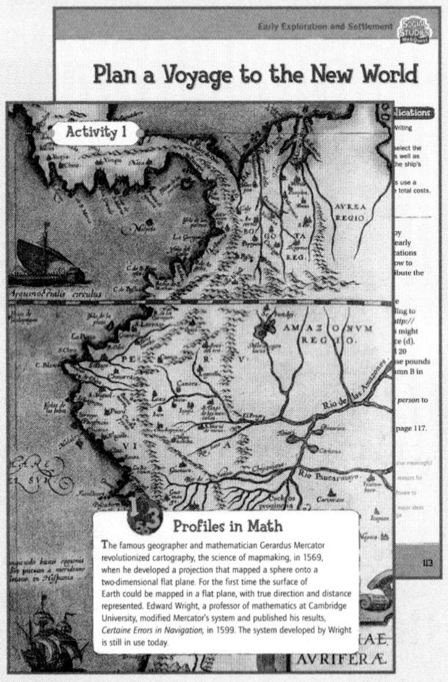


Students use the Internet to investigate:

- names of colonies
- number of colonists
- provisions and supplies needed for the journey, and long-term settlement

For specific step-by-step instructions for this project, see ***Across the Curriculum Math Connections*** pages 112–117.

#### Knowledge Age Skills

**High-Level Responsibility** Students play a role in determining costs for an entire colonization project.

**Problem Formulation, Planning, and Strategizing** Students formulate a plan for how to estimate costs.

TECH KNOWLEDGE *TechKnowledge* Level 4 provides lessons that teach the Unit 10 Internet and Unit 7 Spreadsheet applications students can use in this project.

### Plan Meals as Christopher Columbus's Cook

LANGUAGE ARTS

2–3 weeks

**MATH OBJECTIVE**
To reinforce studies of division by planning meals using division

**LANGUAGE ARTS OBJECTIVE**
To reinforce studies of historical fiction by writing log entries as Christopher Columbus's cook

**TECHNOLOGY OBJECTIVE**
To use a word processing program to write text

Have students use mathematics to plan meals as Christopher Columbus's cook. To broaden the language arts concept, have students reference historical information from works you are currently studying.

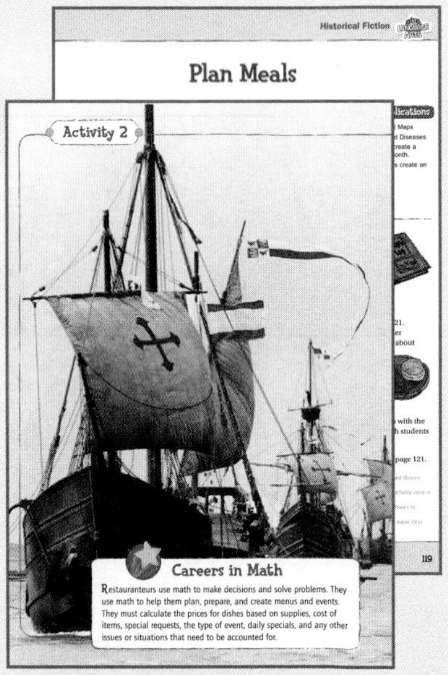


As part of the project, students should consider the following issues:

- the historical time period
- life on a ship in Columbus's time
- the food eaten in Columbus's time
- how to plan meals for a ship voyage
- the type of supplies available on a long ship voyage
- the planning required for meals over the length of a voyage
- the division skills required to plan meals for a voyage

For specific step-by-step instructions for this project, see ***Across the Curriculum Math Connections*** pages 118–121.

#### Knowledge Age Skills

**Problem Formulation, Planning, and Strategizing** Students plan and strategize to plan meals as Christopher Columbus's cook.

**Creative Work with Ideas** Students explore the information within the role of a ship's cook.

## Lesson Planner

**OBJECTIVES**
- To introduce a division algorithm for one-digit divisors
- To demonstrate why the division algorithm works

**NCTM STANDARDS**

**Number and Operations**
Divide by a one-digit number

**Communication**
Act out and discuss a story

**Representation**
Apply mathematical representations to solve division problems

**MATERIALS**
- *Response Wheels
- *Play money
- Envelopes (optional)
- *Base-Ten blocks (optional)

**TECHNOLOGY**

**Presentation** Lesson 11.1
**MathTools** Coins and Money

**TEST PREP**

**Cumulative Review**
Mental Math reviews basic facts in all four operations.

**Writing + Math**
Journal

*Manipulative Kit Item

# Dividing by a One-Digit Divisor

**Context of the Lesson** This, the first of twelve lessons on division, focuses on dividing by a one-digit divisor. This lesson develops a long form of the division algorithm through the use of a story that students can act out. You may wish to spend more than one day on this lesson.

In Lesson 11.4 students will learn a shorter form of the algorithm. By the end of this unit, students should be proficient in determining when to divide, in using some form of the algorithm to divide whole numbers by one-digit divisors, and in interpreting quotients and remainders.

See page 502B for Math Background for teachers for this lesson.

## Planning for Learning • DIFFERENTIATE INSTRUCTION

### INTERVENTION

**If . . .** students lack the prerequisite skill of subtracting multidigit numbers,

**Then . . .** teach ***Intervention*** Lesson 11.A.

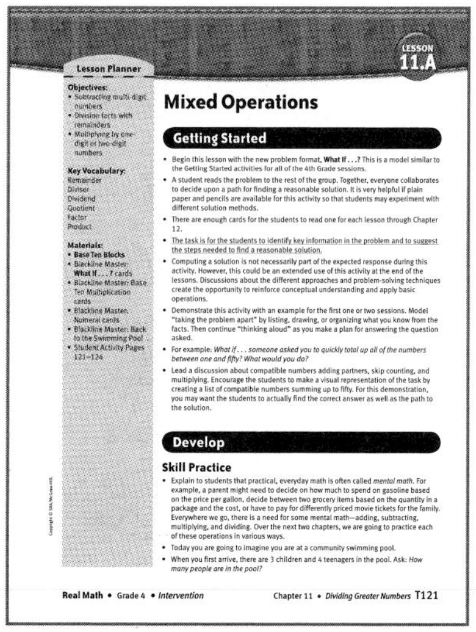
LESSON 11.A
Mixed Operations
Getting Started
Develop
Skill Practice

Intervention Lesson 11.A

### ENGLISH LEARNER

Preview

**If . . .** students need language support,

**Then . . .** use Lesson 11.1 in ***English Learner Support Guide*** to preview lesson concepts and vocabulary.

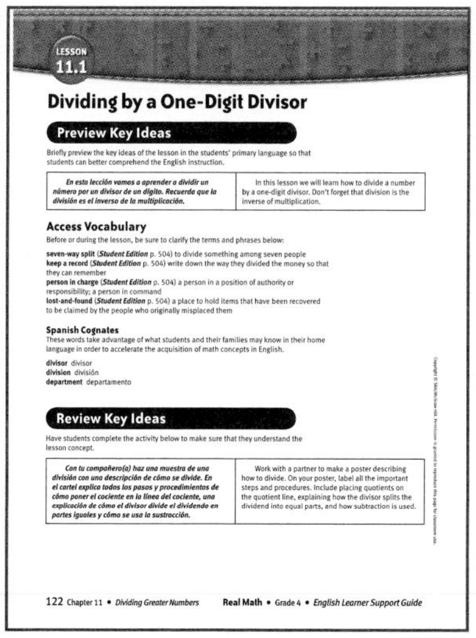
LESSON 11.1
Dividing by a One-Digit Divisor
Preview Key Ideas
Access Vocabulary
Spanish Cognates
Review Key Ideas

English Learner Lesson 11.1

### ENRICH

**If . . .** students are proficient in the lesson concepts,

**Then . . .** encourage them to try to find a shorter way to divide.

### PRACTICE

**If . . .** students would benefit from additional practice,

**Then . . .** extend Strategy Building before assigning the student pages.

### RETEACH

**If . . .** students are having difficulty understanding division by a one-digit number,

**Then . . .** extend Strategy Building before assigning the student pages.

**Access Vocabulary**
**seven-way split** to divide something among seven people
**keep a record** writing down the way something is done to remember it

**Spanish Cognates**
**divisor** divisor
**division** división

# Teaching Lesson 11.1

## Mental Math 5

Review RESPONSE WHEEL Provide practice with basic facts in all four operations. Focus on the inverse relationship between multiplication and division, using exercises such as the following:

| | | | |
|---|---|---|---|
| **a.** $30 \div 6 = 5$ | $5 \times 6 = 30$ | **b.** $17 - 9 = 8$ | $8 + 9 = 17$ |
| **c.** $4 + 5 = 9$ | $9 - 5 = 4$ | **d.** $18 \div 3 = 6$ | $3 \times 6 = 18$ |
| **e.** $14 - 8 = 6$ | $6 + 8 = 14$ | **f.** $4 \times 7 = 28$ | $28 \div 4 = 7$ |

## 1 Develop 40

**Tell Students In Today's Lesson They Will**
learn how to divide a number by a one-digit divisor.

### Strategy Building eMathTools ENGAGING Small Group

Have students role-play the activity from page 504 in groups of seven. (If you have groups with more than seven students, have the extra students keep records of what the group is doing.)

- Give each group of students the following play money: 8 \$100 bills, 3 \$10 bills, and 6 \$1 bills. You may also have students use ***eMathTools: Coins and Money.*** Tell the students that, in this activity, the bank only has bills and coins that are powers of 10, such as 100, 10, and 1.
- Ask students to divide the money equally among themselves and to keep a record of the process they used to do this. After students have divided the money equally, ask them to describe the process they used.

### Using Student Pages UNDERSTANDING Whole Group

Read the beginning of *Seven-Way Split* aloud with the class. Then work through the remainder of pages 504–507 with the class.

# 2 Assign Student Pages

10

**Pages 504–505** APPLYING

Whole Group

Questions on pages 504–505 should be discussed and answered in the Using Student Pages section. The activities and ideas depicted on these pages lead into the exercises on pages 506–507.

Student Page

LESSON 11.1 **Dividing by a One-Digit Divisor**

## Key Ideas

**There are different ways to divide a larger number by a one-digit divisor.**

### Seven-Way Split

Rosa and six of her friends were playing outside one day when they found an envelope. Inside the envelope were 8 \$100-bills, 3 \$10-bills, and 6 \$1-bills.

1. How much money is there altogether? \$836

The seven children took the money to the police station and gave it to the person in charge of the lost-and-found department.

After thirty days, nobody had claimed the money, so the police gave it back to the children. They agreed to divide the money equally.

"How should we divide the money?" asked Matt.

"Let's each take a \$100 bill," replied Luis.

Each of the 7 children took 1 \$100-bill.

The children decided to keep a record of what they were doing.

7)836 This shows that they divided 836 into 7 equal parts.

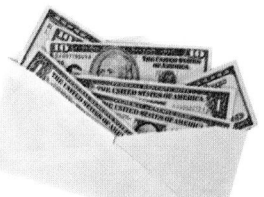

504

Textbook This lesson is available in the *eTextbook*.

Student Page

Each child took \$100. They wrote this on the top of the record.

```
  100
7)836   ← This is how much each child has taken so far.
```

Now they had used up \$700, leaving \$136. They kept track of this at the bottom of the record.

```
  100
7)836
- 700   ← This is how much they have taken altogether. 7 × 100 = 700
  136   ← This is how much they have left to divide. 836 − 700 = 136
```

Now the 7 children have 1 \$100-bill, 3 \$10-bills, and 6 \$1-bills left to share. "How should we divide the rest of the money?" asked Kelli.

"We don't have enough \$100 bills for each of us to take one," said Nasim.

Kelli suggested they take the extra \$100 bill to the bank and exchange it for 10 \$10-bills.

2. How many \$10 bills will they have if they do this? 13

At the bank, they exchanged the \$100 bill for 10 \$10-bills. Then they had 13 \$10-bills.

"We can each take 1 \$10-bill and have 6 left over," said Jolette.

The children each took 1 \$10-bill. Then they recorded it.

```
   10
  100
7)836
- 700   ← This is how much they have taken altogether. 7 × 100 = 700
  136
-  70
   66   ← This is how much they have left to divide. 136 − 70 = 66
```

3. How much money does each child have at this point? \$110
4. How many \$10 bills are left in the pile? 6
5. How many \$10 bills could each child take? There are not enough for each of the 7 children to take 1.
6. How much money is left in the pile altogether? \$66

## Assign Student Pages, continued

### Pages 506–507

Small Group

Have students complete pages 506–507 in pairs.

**Monitoring Student Progress**

**If . . .** students are confused during the story or don't understand how money relates to the algorithm,

**Then . . .** model how to use the base-ten blocks to divide, and then have students use the blocks to do the dividing.

---

LESSON 11.1 • Dividing by a One-Digit Divisor

The children now had too few $10 bills to divide equally. They decided the best way to divide the remaining 6 $10-bills was to exchange them for $1 bills.

The children then exchanged the 6 $10-bills for $1 bills at the bank.

⑦ How many $1 bills did they have altogether?   66

⑧ How many $1 bills should each child get?   9

⑨ How many $1 bills are left?   3

Now their record looks like this:

Each child took 9 $1-bills (or $9).

$$\begin{array}{r} 9 \\ 10 \\ 100 \\ 7\overline{)836} \\ -700 \\ \hline 136 \\ -70 \\ \hline 66 \\ -63 \\ \hline 3 \end{array}$$

$7 \times 9 = 63$

There are 3 $1-bills left.

Matt suggested they exchange the remaining $3 for 10 dimes, and divide the dimes among themselves. Jolette suggested they buy a pack of stickers with the extra $3 and split the stickers. They had a vote and decided to get the stickers.

Before dividing up their stickers, Kelli wanted to be sure she had gotten the right amount of money.

⑩ How much money should Kelli have?   $119

⑪ How much money should each child have?   $119

⑫ What is $7 \times \$119$?   $833

⑬ Why is the amount of money $3 less than the total amount they found ($836)?   There was $3 left over after each child took $119.

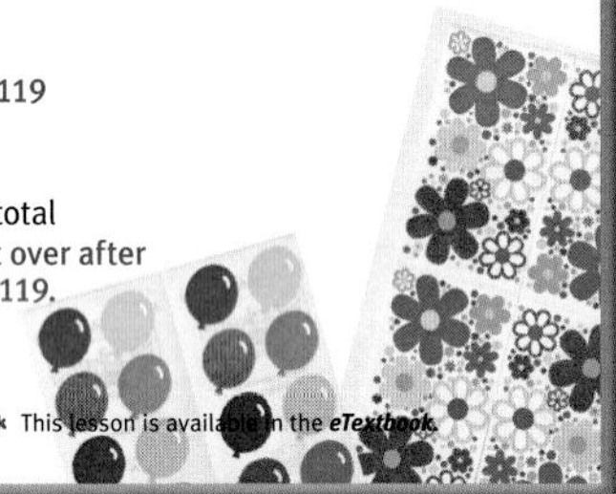

506

 Textbook  This lesson is available in the eTextbook.

---

The steps the children took looked like this:

**Step 1**

$$\begin{array}{r} 100 \\ 7\overline{)836} \\ -700 \\ \hline 136 \end{array}$$

**Step 2**

$$\begin{array}{r} 10 \\ 100 \\ 7\overline{)836} \\ -700 \\ \hline 136 \\ -70 \\ \hline 66 \end{array}$$

**Step 3**

$$\begin{array}{r} 9 \\ 10 \\ 100 \\ 7\overline{)836} \\ 700 \\ \hline 136 \\ -70 \\ \hline 66 \\ -63 \\ \hline 3 \end{array}$$

The answer is 119 with a remainder of 3.

**Try** these problems on your own.   SOCIAL STUDIES

⑭ Divide $845 among 5 children.   $169

⑮ Divide $1,086 among 3 children.   $362

⑯ Divide $5,237 among 4 children.   $1,309 R$1

Writing + Math   **Journal**

Write a few sentences to explain how to divide by a one-digit divisor.

Students' answers will vary. Look to see that they have explained proper procedures involved in division.


---

# 3 Reflect

5

## Guided Discussion REASONING

Ask students if they think a division procedure similar to the one you used in this lesson would work to divide any number by a one-digit number (other than 0).

If somebody says no, ask for an example of when it would not work. Then if someone offers an example, solve the problem and look for a way to make the problem more difficult. For example; if a student provides 123 ÷ 3, then change the problem to 123 ÷ 4. This way students can see the quotient is not a whole number and a remainder will be left.

Writing + Math Journal

Students should provide an accurate description of how to divide. Look for students to identify procedures such as placing quotients on the quotient line, explaining how the divisor splits the dividend into equal parts, and how subtraction is used.

**Curriculum Connection:** Students interested in money and economics may be interested in researching the topic online or at the library.

**Cumulative Review:** For review of three–digit by two–digit multiplication, assign Problems 1–2 on student page 524.

**Family Involvement:** Assign the ***Practice, Reteach,*** or ***Enrichment*** activities depending on the needs of your students.

**Concept/Question Board:** Have students look for examples of problems using division by a one-digit number and post them on the Concept/Question Board.

**Math Puzzler:** Joey runs 1 mile every morning. The first morning he ran, it took him 11 minutes. If he improves his time by 5 seconds every day, how quickly will he run the mile 3 weeks later? 9 minutes and 15 seconds

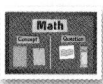

# 4 Assess and Differentiate

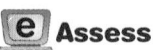

**e Assess** Use ***eAssess*** to record and analyze evidence of student understanding.

## A Gather Evidence

Use the Daily Class Assessment Records in ***Assessment*** or ***eAssess*** to record daily observations.

### Portfolio Assessment

**Journal**

Did the student REASONING

- ❑ provide a clear explanation?
- ❑ communicate reasons and strategies?
- ❑ choose appropriate strategies?
- ❑ argue logically?

### Formal Assessment

**Student Pages**

Did the student UNDERSTANDING

- ❑ make important observations?
- ❑ extend or generalize learning?
- ❑ provide insightful answers?
- ❑ pose insightful questions?

## B Summarize Findings

Analyze and summarize assessment data for each student. Determine which Assessment Follow-Up is appropriate for each student. Use the Student Assessment Record in ***Assessment*** or ***eAssess*** to update assessment records.

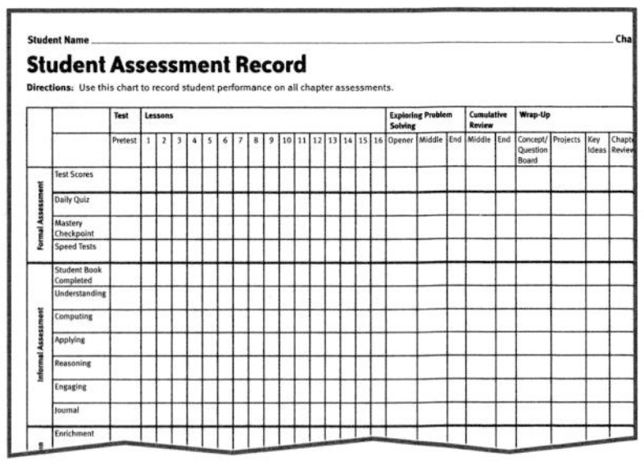


**Assessment Page T41**

## C Assessment Follow-Up • DIFFERENTIATE INSTRUCTION

Based on your observations, use these teaching strategies for assessment follow-up.

### INTERVENTION

Review student performance on ***Intervention*** Lesson 11.A to see if students have mastered prerequisite skills for this lesson.

### ENGLISH LEARNER

**Review**

Use Lesson 11.1 in ***English Learner Support Guide*** to review lesson concepts and vocabulary.

### ENRICH

**If . . .** students are proficient in the lesson concepts,

**Then . . .** encourage them to work on the chapter projects or ***Enrichment*** Lesson 11.1.

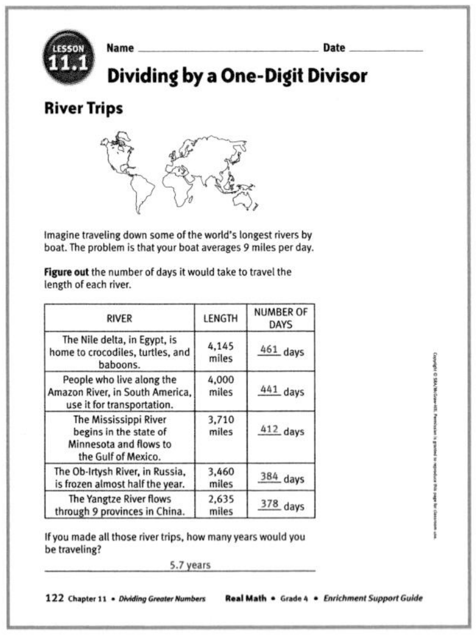


Enrichment Lesson 11.1

### PRACTICE

**If . . .** students would benefit from additional practice,

**Then . . .** assign ***Practice*** Lesson 11.1.

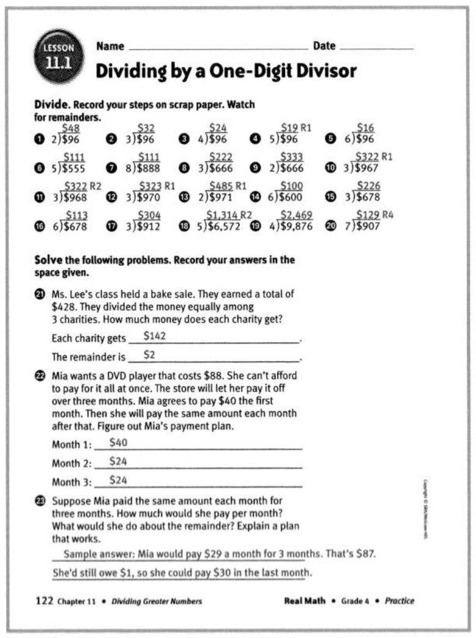


Practice Lesson 11.1

### RETEACH

**If . . .** students struggle with the division algorithm,

**Then . . .** reteach the concept using ***Reteach*** Lesson 11.1.

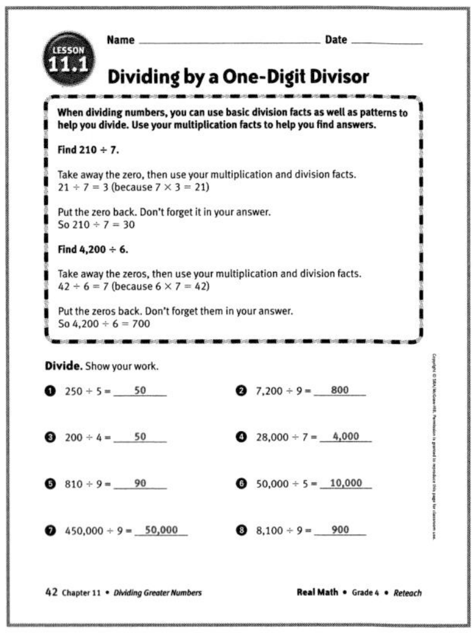


Reteach Lesson 11.1

## Lesson Planner

**OBJECTIVES**
- To develop deeper student understanding of the division algorithm
- To develop a shorter procedure for dividing

**NCTM STANDARDS**

**Number and Operations**
Divide by a one-digit number

**Problem Solving**
Solve word problems

**Communication**
Work in small groups to solve problems

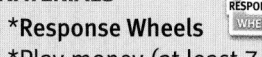

**MATERIALS**
- *Response Wheels
- *Play money (at least 7 $1,000 bills, 45 $100 bills, 36 $10 bills, and 48 $1 bills per group)
- *Base-Ten blocks (optional)

**TECHNOLOGY**
e **Presentation** Lesson 11.2
e **MathTools** Coins and Money

**TEST PREP**

**Cumulative Review**
- Mental Math reviews basic facts with all four operations.
- Problems 1–6 review money.
- All problems review subtraction.

**Extended Response**
Problem 6

**Writing + Math**
Journal

*Manipulative Kit Item

# Division: Written Form

**Context of the Lesson** This is the second of twelve lessons on division with greater numbers. This lesson expands on strategies taught in Lesson 3.11. While this lesson develops a shortened form for doing division, a method that is shorter will be developed in Lesson 11.4.

See page 502B for Math Background for teachers for this lesson.

## Planning for Learning • DIFFERENTIATE INSTRUCTION

### INTERVENTION

**If . . .** students lack the prerequisite skill of dividing with remainders,

**Then . . .** teach ***Intervention*** Lesson 11.B.

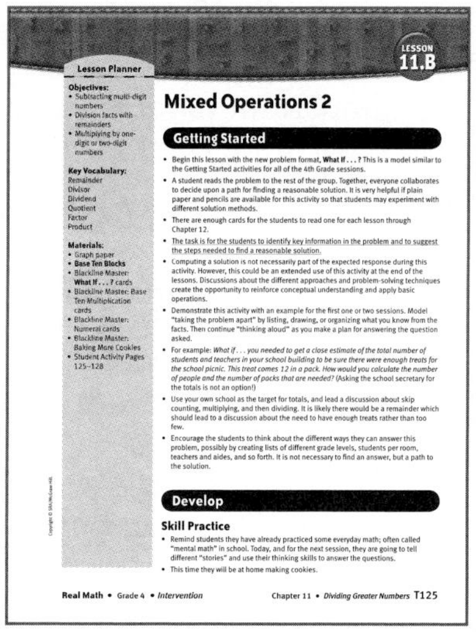
Lesson Planner
LESSON 11.B
Mixed Operations 2
Getting Started
Develop
Skill Practice
Real Math • Grade 4 • Intervention Chapter 11 • Dividing Greater Numbers T125

Intervention Lesson 11.B

### ENGLISH LEARNER

**Preview**

**If . . .** students need language support,

**Then . . .** use Lesson 11.2 in ***English Learner Support Guide*** to preview the lesson concepts and vocabulary.

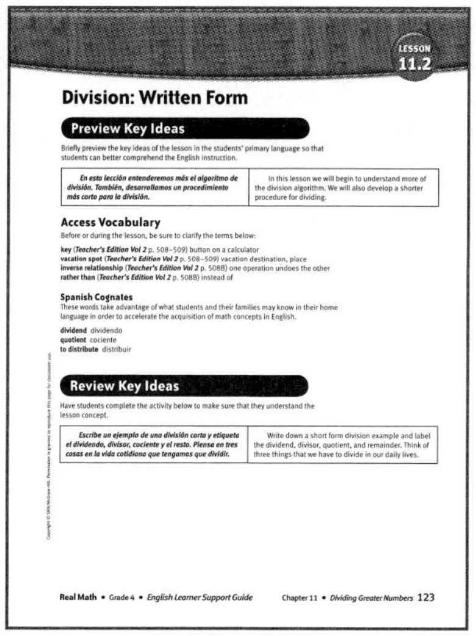
LESSON 11.2
Division: Written Form
Preview Key Ideas
Access Vocabulary
Spanish Cognates
Review Key Ideas
Real Math • Grade 4 • English Learner Support Guide Chapter 11 • Dividing Greater Numbers 123

English Learner Lesson 11.2

### ENRICH

**If . . .** students are proficient in the lesson concepts,

**Then . . .** encourage them to explore division using ***eMathTools.***

### PRACTICE

**If . . .** students would benefit from additional practice,

**Then . . .** extend Strategy Building before assigning the student pages.

### RETEACH

**If . . .** students are having difficulty understanding the written form of division,

**Then . . .** extend Guided Discussion before assigning the student pages.

**Vocabulary**

**dividend \div´ i dend\ *n.*** the number you are dividing

**quotient \kwō´ shənt\ *n.*** the answer to a division problem

**remainder \ri mān´ dər\ *n.*** what is left after you cannot divide a number any further

**Access Vocabulary**

**key** a button on a calculator

**inverse relationship** one operation undoes the other

**What is left?** An amount that remains is left.

**Spanish Cognates**

**dividend** dividendo

**quotient** cociente

# Teaching Lesson 11.2

## Mental Math

5

RESPONSE WHEEL

Provide practice in basic facts, such as the following. Focus on the inverse relationship between multiplication and division.

**a.** $3 \times 8 = 24$ $24 \div 8 = 3$
**b.** $9 \times 7 = 63$ $63 \div 9 = 7$
**c.** $6 \times 8 = 48$ $48 \div 8 = 6$
**d.** $4 + 8 = 12$ $12 - 8 = 4$
**e.** $7 \times 6 = 42$ $42 \div 7 = 6$
**f.** $9 + 4 = 13$ $13 - 4 = 9$

## 1 Develop

30

**Tell Students In Today's Lesson They Will**
learn a shorter way to divide.

Whole Group

### Guided Discussion e MathTools UNDERSTANDING

Present a new division problem to the class.

Working with the entire class, have students tell you what each step should be and how to record each step. Show them the three alternative ways of recording as shown below. Students may use play money or ***eMathTools: Coins and Money*** if they wish.

**1.** For example, 7 people wish to share $8,936 equally. How should they do it?

First, each takes $1,000, using $7,000 and leaving $1,936:

$$\begin{array}{r} 1000 \\ 7\overline{)8936} \\ -7000 \\ \hline 1936 \end{array} \qquad \begin{array}{r} 1\phantom{000} \\ 7\overline{)8936} \\ -7000 \\ \hline 1936 \end{array} \qquad \begin{array}{l} \phantom{0}1 \\ 7\overline{)8936} \\ -7 \\ \hline \phantom{0}19 \end{array}$$

Explain that rather than writing all the zeros and rewriting digits that are not going to be used in the next step, we can just think about what would happen as we multiply and subtract. We will write only those numbers we need now.

**2.** Tell students they may write as much or as little in each step as makes them comfortable. For example, in the third form above, each person would take 1,000, so 7,000 would be subtracted from 8,936, leaving 1,936. If we write the 1 and the 7 in the thousands place we will know what those mean. That would leave 1,936 to be distributed, but in our next step we will be using only the 19 hundreds, so we do not have to write everything.

Continue this process, writing in all three forms as you go. When you are finished you should have the three forms shown on page 509.

### Strategy Building ENGAGING

Small Group

Divide students into groups of three. Each person in the group will have a different responsibility for each problem. For example, the first student creates a division word problem with a one-digit divisor and multidigit dividend. The second student will solve the problem. The third student will check the second student's work. Then the duties will switch so everyone in the group creates a problem, solves a problem, and checks a problem.

## 2 Assign Student Pages

20

**Pages 508–509** APPLYING

Small Group

Have students work on page 508 individually or in small groups. If you prefer small groups, group members should take turns keeping the records, making the transactions, and acting as the banker. Each member should check to see that the banker and the record keeper carry out and record each transaction correctly. The finished record for each problem should look like the last step shown in the examples on page 509.

Students may complete page 509 independently or in small groups. When students begin recording their own division to solve Problems 7–18 on page 509, have them use the shortest form they feel comfortable with. If you have students work in groups for these problems, each student should keep his or her own record of each problem. Remind students that it is important to record zeros in the quotient whenever they occur.

#### Monitoring Student Progress

| If . . . | Then . . . |
|---|---|
| students display difficulty with multiplication or division facts, | have them use the Fact Helpers in the Student Handbook. |

Student Page

## LESSON 11.2 Division: Written Form

### Key Ideas

**There are shorter ways to show the steps when you divide.**

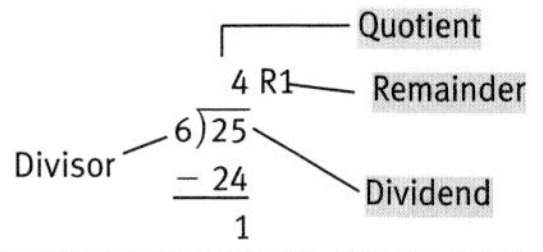


**Using** play money, work in groups to solve these problems. One person in each group should be the banker who exchanges bills. One person should keep the record. Everyone should help solve the problems and check to see that each record is correct.

1. If 6 people want to divide $948 equally, how much should each person get? How many dollars will be left over? $158; $0 left over
2. If 7 people want to divide $364 equally, how much should each person get? How many dollars will be left over? $52; $0 left over
3. If 4 people want to divide $7,433 equally, how much should each person get? How many dollars will be left over? $1,858; $1 left over
4. If 5 people want to divide $2,707 equally, how much should each person get? How many dollars will be left over? $541; $2 left over
5. If 9 people want to divide $4,536 equally, how much should each person get? How many dollars will be left over? $504; $0 left over
6. Extended Response A group of people wants to divide $641 equally. How much money should each person get? How many dollars will be left over? It depends on the number of people in the group.



Textbook This lesson is available in the *eTextbook.*

Student Page

If you wish, you may keep your records in a shorter form.

| Long Form | Shorter Form | |
|---|---|---|
| | With Zeros | Without Zeros |
| 1,276 Remainder 4 | Be careful to put the answers in the correct column. | Subtract and "bring down" only the next digit. Be careful to put the answers in the correct columns. |
| 6 | | |
| 70 | | |
| 200 | | |
| 1000 | 1,276 R4 | 1,276 R4 |
| 7)8936 | 7)8936 | 7)8936 |
| − 7000 | − 7000 | − 7 |
| 1936 | 1936 | 19 |
| − 1400 | − 1400 | − 14 |
| 536 | 536 | 53 |
| − 490 | − 490 | − 49 |
| 46 | 46 | 46 |
| − 42 | − 42 | − 42 |
| 4 | 4 | 4 |

**Complete** these exercises.

7. 7)350 50
8. 5)100 20
9. 6)91 15 R1
10. 3)515 171 R2
11. 2)41312 20,656
12. 3)46 15 R1
13. 5)744 148 R4
14. 4)806 201 R2
15. 9)729 81
16. 7)91 13
17. 8)420 52 R4
18. 5)52364 10,472 R4

Writing + Math Journal

Compare and contrast the three forms of division as shown above. What are the differences among them?

Possible answer: The steps are consolidated, and writing is avoided as we move toward the shorter form without zeros.



## 3 Reflect

5

### Guided Discussion REASONING

Whole Group

Ask students to discuss the following problem:

Joe, Peter, and Carl divided 59,059 by 7. Joe got an answer of 8,437; Peter got an answer of 8,448; and Carl got an answer of 8,439. Sarah doesn't know how to divide, but she figured out a way to decide who was correct. What did she do? She probably multiplied each of the numbers by 7 to see whether any provided a product of 59,059.

### Extended Response

**Problem 6** Students should recognize that the problem cannot be solved without knowing how many students are in the group.

**Writing + Math Journal**

Students' answers should consist of similarities and differences they notice in the three styles of division. Possible answers: in the short form without zeros, the subtraction problems consist of two digits that are divided, whereas the short form with zeros involves larger numbers to be divided. All are a form of division leading to the correct quotient.

**Cumulative Review:** For review of fractions and rational numbers, assign Problems 3–5 on student page 524.

**Family Involvement:** Assign the ***Practice, Reteach,*** or ***Enrichment*** activities depending on the needs of your students.

**Concept/Question Board:** Have students look for examples of problems using division and post them on the Concept/Question Board.

**Math Puzzler:** Miguel wants to divide 97 by 8 on his calculator, but the division symbol key won't work. How else can he use his calculator to find the answer? One way is to enter 97, then subtract 8 over and over until the display shows a number less than 8, keeping track of how many times 8 is subtracted.

# 4 Assess and Differentiate

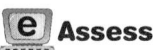

**e Assess** Use ***eAssess*** to record and analyze evidence of student understanding.

## A Gather Evidence

Use the Daily Class Assessment Records in ***Assessment*** or ***eAssess*** to record daily observations.

### Informal Assessment

**Mental Math**

Did the student COMPUTING
- ❑ respond accurately?
- ❑ respond quickly?
- ❑ respond with confidence?
- ❑ self-correct?

### Portfolio Assessment

**Extended Response**

Did the student REASONING
- ❑ provide a clear explanation?
- ❑ communicate reasons and strategies?
- ❑ choose appropriate strategies?
- ❑ argue logically?

## B Summarize Findings

Analyze and summarize assessment data for each student. Determine which Assessment Follow-Up is appropriate for each student. Use the Student Assessment Record in ***Assessment*** or ***eAssess*** to update assessment records.

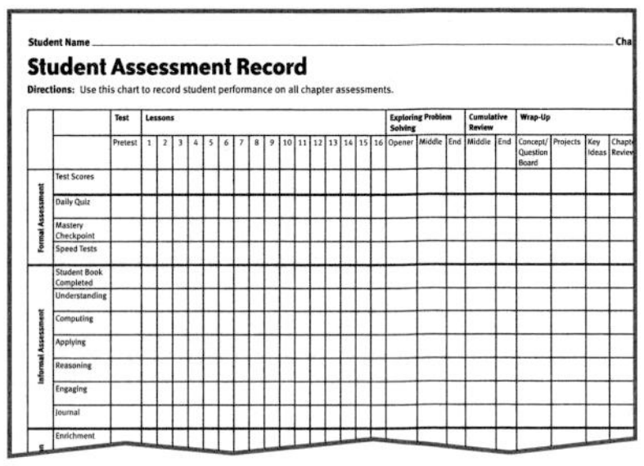
Student Name
Student Assessment Record

**Assessment Page T41**

## C Assessment Follow-Up • DIFFERENTIATE INSTRUCTION

Based on your observations, use these teaching strategies for assessment follow-up.

### INTERVENTION

Review student performance on ***Intervention*** Lesson 11.B to see if students have mastered prerequisite skills for this lesson.

### ENGLISH LEARNER

**Review**

Use Lesson 11.2 in ***English Learner Support Guide*** to review lesson concepts and vocabulary.

### ENRICH

**If . . .** students are proficient in the lesson concepts,

**Then . . .** encourage them to work on the chapter projects or ***Enrichment*** Lesson 11.2.

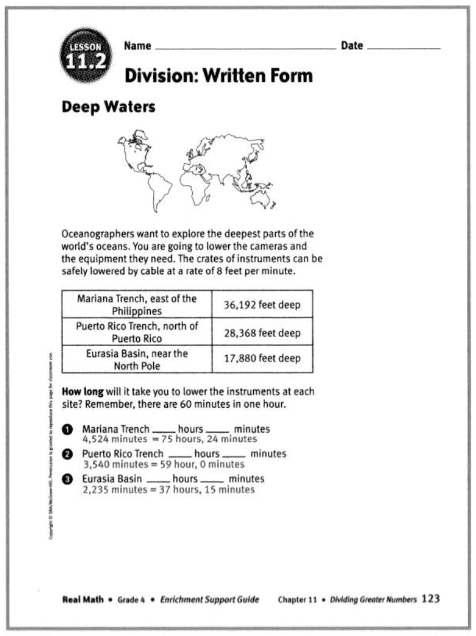
LESSON 11.2 Name Date
Division: Written Form
Deep Waters

**Enrichment Lesson 11.2**

### PRACTICE

**If . . .** students would benefit from additional practice,

**Then . . .** assign ***Practice*** Lesson 11.2.

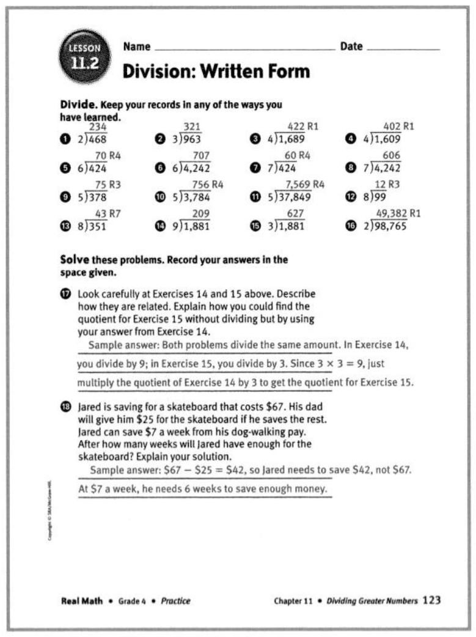
LESSON 11.2 Name Date
Division: Written Form

**Practice Lesson 11.2**

### RETEACH

**If . . .** students are having difficulty understanding the written form of division,

**Then . . .** reteach the concept using ***Reteach*** Lesson 11.2.

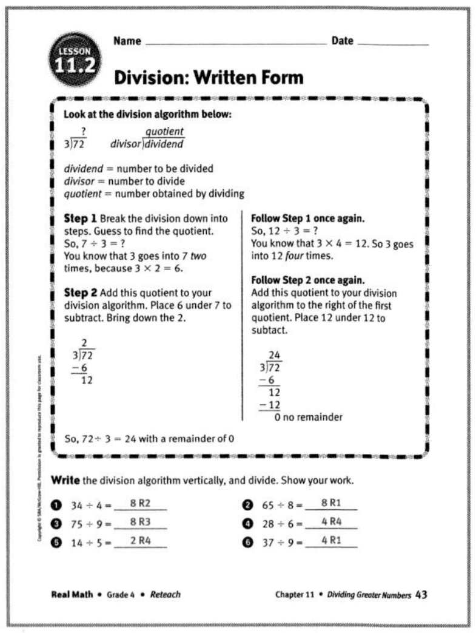
LESSON 11.2 Name Date
Division: Written Form

**Reteach Lesson 11.2**

### Objectives
- To provide more practice in dividing by one-digit divisors
- To review the inverse relationship between multiplication and division
- To practice the division algorithm by finding missing digits in completed exercises

### NCTM Standards
**Number and Operations**
- Divide by a one-digit number
- Multiply a two-digit number by a one-digit number

**Algebra**
Solve problems with missing digits

### Materials
- ***Response Wheels**
- ***Number Cubes** (two 0–5 and two 5–10)
- *Play money (optional)
- *Base-Ten blocks (optional)

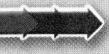

### Technology
**e Presentation** Lesson 11.3

### Test Prep
**Cumulative Review**
Mental Math reviews multiplication and division (Lesson 3.1–3.7 and 3.10–3.11).

**Multistep Problems**
Problem 22

**Extended Response**
Problem 22

**Writing + Math**
Journal

*Manipulative Kit Item

# Checking Division

**Context of the Lesson** This is the third of twelve lessons on division with greater numbers. In this lesson, students' knowledge of division will be broadened through the use of multiplication to check quotients. In Lesson 5.8 students learned how to multiply two-digit numbers by one-digit numbers. This skill will be reviewed as students multiply quotients by divisors to see if the product is equal to the dividend.

See page 502B for Math Background for teachers for this lesson.

## Planning for Learning • DIFFERENTIATE INSTRUCTION

### INTERVENTION

**If . . .** students lack the prerequisite skill of multiplying by a one-digit or two-digit number,

**Then . . .** teach ***Intervention*** Lesson 11.C.

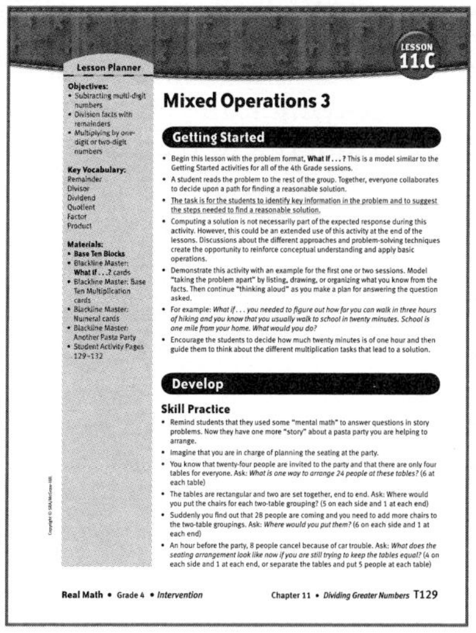


Intervention Lesson 11.C

### ENGLISH LEARNER

**Preview**

**If . . .** students need language support,

**Then . . .** use Lesson 11.3 in ***English Learner Support Guide*** to preview lesson concepts and vocabulary.

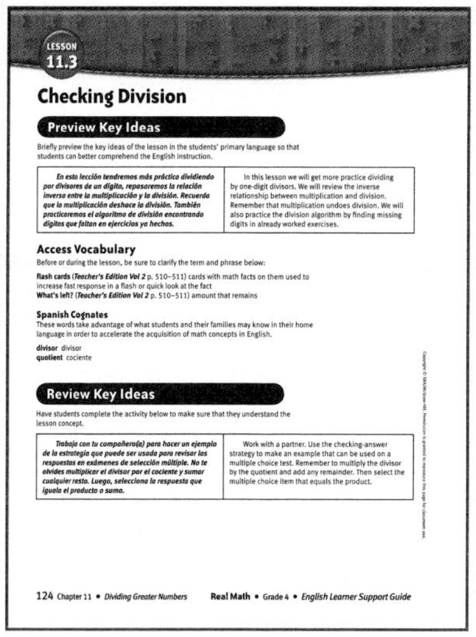


English Learner Lesson 11.3

### ENRICH

**If . . .** students are proficient in the lesson concepts,

**Then . . .** encourage them to devise variations of the **Four Cube Division Game.**

### PRACTICE

**If . . .** students would benefit from additional practice,

**Then . . .** extend either of the Guided Discussion sections.

### RETEACH

**If . . .** students are having difficulty understanding how to check division problems,

**Then . . .** extend the Checking Division Guided Discussion before assigning the student pages.

**Access Vocabulary**
**flash cards** cards with math facts on them used to increase response time with a quick look, or flash, at the card

**Spanish Cognates**
**divisor** divisor
**quotient** cociente

# Teaching Lesson 11.3

## Mental Math

5

Review RESPONSE WHEEL Provide exercises, such as those below, that show the inverse relationship between multiplication and division. Include multidigit problems students can solve mentally.

| | |
|---|---|
| **a.** $5 \times 50 = 250$ | $250 \div 5 = 50$ |
| **b.** $240 \times 20 = 4{,}800$ | $4{,}800 \div 20 = 240$ |
| **c.** $50 \times 20 = 1{,}000$ | $1{,}000 \div 50 = 20$ |
| **d.** $60 \times 8 = 480$ | $480 \div 8 = 60$ |
| **e.** $30 \times 400 = 1{,}200$ | $1{,}200 \div 30 = 400$ |
| **f.** $9 \times 700 = 6{,}300$ | $6300 \div 9 = 700$ |

## 1 Develop

20

### Tell Students In Today's Lesson They Will

learn how to use multiplication to check answers to division exercises.

## Guided Discussion UNDERSTANDING

Whole Group

### Checking Division

Explain that because multiplication and division are inverse operations (one operation undoes the other), you can use multiplication to check division problems by multiplying the divisor by the quotient. Guide students in discovering how to check division using multiplication. Ask questions such as the following:

- **What is 693 ÷ 7?** 99
- **We can check whether 99 is correct by multiplying the quotient by the divisor. What is the divisor?** 7 **What is the quotient?** 99
- **What is 7 × 99?** 693
- **What do you notice about the product of the divisor and quotient?** It's the same number as the dividend in the original division problem, which means the answer is correct.

Explain that when there is a remainder, the remainder must be added to the product of the divisor and the quotient to check the answer. Ask questions such as the following:

- **What is 295 ÷ 8?** 36 R7
- **How do we check to see if the answer is correct?** Multiply the divisor by the quotient.
- **What do we do with the remainder?** Add it to the product of the divisor and the quotient.
- **What is 36 × 8?** 288
- **What is the sum of the remainder and 288?** 295
- **What do you notice about the sum of the remainder and the product of the divisor and quotient?** It's the same number as the dividend in the original division problem, which means the answer is correct.

Discuss how this strategy of checking answers can be used to find correct answers on a multiple-choice test. All students have to do is multiply the divisor by the quotient and add the remainder (if there is one) and the choice that equals the product or the sum they got is the correct answer.

## Guided Discussion

Whole Group

### Finding Missing Digits

Discuss how to solve the missing-digits problems on pages 511–512. Explain to students that they can go directly to the missing digit and work from there rather than starting at the beginning. Complete a few examples on the board so students are exposed to the kind of thinking required to solve such problems.

For example, to find the missing digit in the following problem, ask students questions such as the following:

- **How many 3s are there in 16? What number multiplied by 3 would give 15?** 5. So the missing digit is 5 because $3 \times 5 = 15$.

```
  1□5R2
3)467
 -3
  16
 -15
   17
  -15
    2
```

## Skill and Strategy Building ENGAGING

Whole Group

**Game** **Four Cube Division Game**

Demonstrate the **Four Cube Division Game** on page 513 by playing it in front of the class with a volunteer. Then invite two students to play a round for the class. Tell students they will play the game after they finish the student pages.

# 2 Assign Student Pages

## Pages 510–511 APPLYING

Have students complete the problems on pages 510–511 independently.

### Monitoring Student Progress

**If . . .** students have trouble with division or multiplication facts,

**Then . . .** have them practice in school or at home, using flash cards, practice devices (such as a calculator), games, or some other appropriate method. Check the students regularly until they are proficient at answering pairs of questions such as *How many 7s are in 57?* and *What's left?* You may refer them to the Fact Helpers in the Student Handbook.

---

LESSON
**11.3** **Checking Division**

### Key Ideas

You can check whether a division problem was done correctly by using multiplication.

If there is no remainder, multiply the divisor by the quotient. If the product of the divisor and the quotient equals the dividend, your answer is correct.

$$3\overline{)861} = 287$$

Check:
$$\begin{array}{r} 287 \\ \times\ 3 \\ \hline 861 \end{array}$$

If the division problem has a remainder in the answer, multiply the divisor by the quotient, and then add the remainder. If the product of the divisor and the quotient plus the remainder equals the dividend, your answer is correct.

$$7\overline{)97} = 13\ R6$$

Check:
$$\begin{array}{r} 13 \\ \times\ 7 \\ \hline 91 \end{array} \longrightarrow 91 + 6 = 97$$

**Practice** division. When there is a remainder, show it. Make sure to check your answers.

1. $3\overline{)296}$  98 R2
2. $4\overline{)6128}$  1,532
3. $6\overline{)144}$  24
4. $8\overline{)232}$  29
5. $9\overline{)241}$  26 R7
6. $5\overline{)125}$  25
7. $4\overline{)64}$  16
8. $3\overline{)62}$  20 R2
9. $6\overline{)2141}$  356 R5

 **Textbook** This lesson is available in the *eTextbook*.

---

**Find** the missing digit.

10.
$$\begin{array}{r} 29 \\ 5\overline{)145} \\ -10 \\ \hline \blacksquare 5 \quad 4 \\ -45 \\ \hline 0 \end{array}$$

11.
$$\begin{array}{r} 103\ R1 \\ 9\overline{)928} \\ -9 \\ \hline 02 \\ -0 \\ \hline 28 \\ -2\blacksquare \quad 7 \\ \hline 1 \end{array}$$

12.
$$\begin{array}{r} 1\blacksquare3\ R2 \quad 0 \\ 9\overline{)929} \\ -9 \\ \hline 02 \\ -0 \\ \hline 29 \\ -27 \\ \hline 2 \end{array}$$

13.
$$\begin{array}{r} 4\blacksquare\ R1 \quad 4 \\ 7\overline{)309} \\ -28 \\ \hline 29 \\ -28 \\ \hline 1 \end{array}$$

14.
$$\begin{array}{r} 104 \\ \blacksquare\overline{)624} \quad 6 \\ -6 \\ \hline 02 \\ -0 \\ \hline 24 \\ -24 \\ \hline 0 \end{array}$$

15.
$$\begin{array}{r} 18\blacksquare\ R1 \\ 4\overline{)721} \quad 0 \\ -4 \\ \hline 32 \\ -32 \\ \hline 01 \\ -0 \\ \hline 1 \end{array}$$

16.
$$\begin{array}{r} 84\ R6 \\ 8\overline{)67\blacksquare} \quad 8 \\ -64 \\ \hline 38 \\ -32 \\ \hline 6 \end{array}$$

17.
$$\begin{array}{r} 10\blacksquare\ R7 \quad 0 \\ 9\overline{)907} \\ -9 \\ \hline 00 \\ -0 \\ \hline 07 \\ -0 \\ \hline 7 \end{array}$$

18.
$$\begin{array}{r} 1\blacksquare1\ R6 \quad 2 \\ 8\overline{)974} \\ -8 \\ \hline 17 \\ -16 \\ \hline 14 \\ -8 \\ \hline 6 \end{array}$$

19.
$$\begin{array}{r} 287\ R1 \\ \blacksquare\overline{)862} \quad 3 \\ -6 \\ \hline 26 \\ -24 \\ \hline 22 \\ -21 \\ \hline 1 \end{array}$$

20.
$$\begin{array}{r} 115\ R\blacksquare \quad 3 \\ 8\overline{)923} \\ -8 \\ \hline 12 \\ -8 \\ \hline 43 \\ -40 \\ \hline 3 \end{array}$$

21.
$$\begin{array}{r} 26\blacksquare\ R2 \quad 6 \\ 3\overline{)800} \\ -6 \\ \hline 20 \\ -18 \\ \hline 20 \\ -18 \\ \hline 2 \end{array}$$

 Multistep **22** **Extended Response** A boat delivered 500 bags of wheat to the 7 Unangan families who live on the Aleutian Islands. They had to discard 18 of those bags because they got too wet on the boat. How many bags should each family take so that each family gets the same amount of wheat? How could the 7 families share the remaining bags if each bag has 50 pounds of wheat?

Each family should get 68 bags with 6 bags left over. If each bag weighs 50 pounds, the remaining 6 bags would hold 300 pounds of wheat altogether. The 300 pounds could be divided so that each family gets 42 pounds with 6 pounds left.

# Assign Student Pages, continued

**Pages 512–513** APPLYING

Have students complete page 512 on their own or with a partner.

### As Students Finish

Game ✓ **Four Cube Division Game**

Student Page

LESSON 11.3 • Checking Division

23.
1▢5 R1 (3)
5)676
− 5
17
− 15
26
− 25
1

24.
1▢7 R2 (3)
6)824
− 6
22
− 18
44
− 42
2

25.
134 R1
4)537
− 4
13
− 1▢ (2)
17
− 16
1

26.
269 R2
3)8▢9 (0)
− 6
20
− 18
29
− 27
2

27.
▢4 R1 (3)
9)307
− 27
37
− 36
1

28.
1▢9 R6 (0)
8)878
− 8
07
− 0
78
− 72
6

29.
20▢ R3 (1)
4)807
− 8
00
− 0
07
− 4
3

30.
1▢3 R1 (0)
2)207
− 2
00
− 0
07
− 6
1

31.
109
7)763
− ▢ (7)
06
− 0
63
− 63
0

32.
50
9)450
− 4▢ (5)
00
− 0
0

33.
209
3)627
− 6
0▢ (2)
− 0
27
− 27
0

34.
100 R3
7)703
− 7
00
− 0
0▢ (3)
− 00
3

Writing + Math **Journal**

Write instructions for yourself about how to check a division problem. How do the instructions change when there is a remainder involved?

Students should mention that they multiply the quotient by the divisor. If the product is equal to the dividend, the quotient is correct. If a remainder is included, the remainder is added to the product.

512 eTextbook This lesson is available in the *eTextbook*.

Student Page

**Division and Strategies Practice**

## Four Cube Division Game

**Players:** two or more

**Materials:**
***Number Cubes***:
two 0–5 (red),
two 5–0 (blue)

**Object:** To get the least quotient

**Math Focus:** Dividing by one-digit divisors and place value

**HOW TO PLAY**

1. Roll all four cubes. If you roll a 10, roll that cube again.
2. Make a division problem using three of the rolled numbers as a three-digit dividend and the other number as the divisor. Zero may not be used as the first number of the dividend, and it cannot be used as the divisor.
3. Find the quotient.
4. The player with the least quotient wins the round. If two players have the same quotient, then the player with the least remainder is the winner.

**SAMPLE GAME**

| Jose rolled: | Cathy rolled: | Seth rolled: |
|---|---|---|
| 3 4 9 8 | 2 8 3 5 | 1 0 9 5 |
| 38 R6<br>9)348 | 29 R3<br>8)235 | 11 R6<br>9)105 |

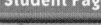

Seth won.

**Other Ways To Play This Game**

- The least remainder wins.
- The greatest quotient wins.

Chapter 11 • Lesson 3 513

## 3 Reflect

5

### Guided Discussion

MathTools REASONING Small Group

Have students demonstrate how to check whether 51 R5 is the correct answer to 362 ÷ 7.

Provide students with other exercises, such as to 702 ÷ 6, to solve using the base-ten blocks.

Ask a question, such as the following:

Philip's little sister doesn't know how to divide, but she knows how to multiply, add, and subtract. Philip said, "I have a feeling you can tell me what 623 divided by 7 is." Using only pencil and paper, she got the answer in less than five minutes. How did she do it? One possibility: she multiplied until she found the answer. 7 × 100 = 700 (too big); 7 × 90 = 630 (too big, but close); 7 × 80 = 560 (much too small); 7 × 88 = 616 (too small); 7 × 89 = 623.

### Extended Response

**Problem 22** Students should mention that each family should get 68 bags with 6 bags left over. If each bag weighs 50 pounds, the remaining 6 bags would hold 300 pounds of wheat. That could be divided so each family gets 42 pounds with 6 pounds left over.

### Writing + Math Journal

Students should mention that they need to multiply the quotient by the divisor. If the product equals the dividend, the quotient is correct. If a remainder is included, the remainder should be added to the product. By explaining this in words, students will be able to better understand how to check the answers to division problems.

**Curriculum Connection:** Students may be interested in studying the Unangan people of the Aleutian Islands. Have students study the geography of the land and hypothesize why the Unangan people would have wheat delivered to them.

**Cumulative Review:** For review of division, assign Problems 6–14 on student page 524.

**Family Involvement:** Assign the ***Practice, Reteach,*** or ***Enrichment*** activities depending on the needs of your students.

Encourage students to play the **Four Cube Division Game** at home with friends or relatives.

**Concept/Question Board:** Have students look for additional examples of problems using division and post them on the Concept/Question Board.

**Math Puzzler:** A number falls between 100 and 300. The sum of its digits is 12. If you divide the number by 3 or by 5, there is a two-digit quotient and no remainder. If you divide the number by 2 or by 4, there is a two-digit quotient and a remainder of 1. What is the number? (Allow students to use calculators to find the solution to this problem.) 165

# 4 Assess and Differentiate

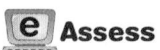

**e Assess** Use ***eAssess*** to record and analyze evidence of student understanding.

## A Gather Evidence

Use the Daily Class Assessment Records in ***Assessment*** or ***eAssess*** to record daily observations.

### Performance Assessment

**Game**

Did the student APPLYING

- ❑ apply learning in new situations?
- ❑ contribute concepts?
- ❑ contribute answers?
- ❑ connect mathematics to real-world situations?

### Informal Assessment

**Guided Discussion**

Did the student UNDERSTANDING

- ❑ make important observations?
- ❑ extend or generalize learning?
- ❑ provide insightful answers?
- ❑ pose insightful questions?

## B Summarize Findings

Analyze and summarize assessment data for each student. Determine which Assessment Follow-Up is appropriate for each student. Use the Student Assessment Record in ***Assessment*** or ***eAssess*** to update assessment records.

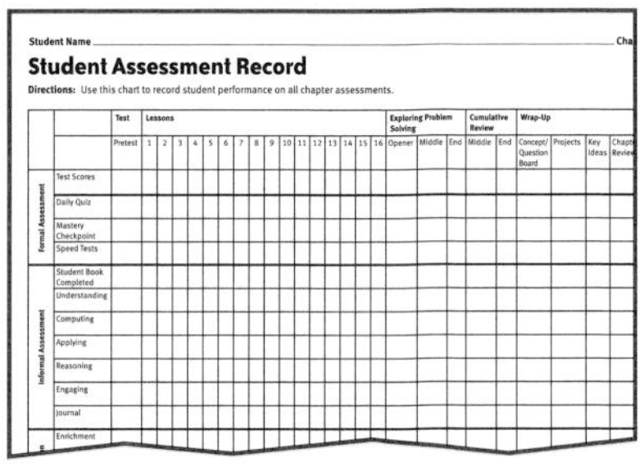
Student Name

Student Assessment Record

Directions: Use this chart to record student performance on all chapter assessments.

Assessment Page T41

## C Assessment Follow-Up • DIFFERENTIATE INSTRUCTION

Based on your observations, use these teaching strategies for assessment follow-up.

### INTERVENTION

Review student performance on ***Intervention*** Lesson 11.C to see if students have mastered prerequisite skills for this lesson.

### ENGLISH LEARNER

**Review**

Use Lesson 11.3 in ***English Learner Support Guide*** to review lesson concepts and vocabulary.

### ENRICH

**If . . .** students are proficient in the lesson concepts,

**Then . . .** encourage them to work on the chapter projects or ***Enrichment*** Lesson 11.3.

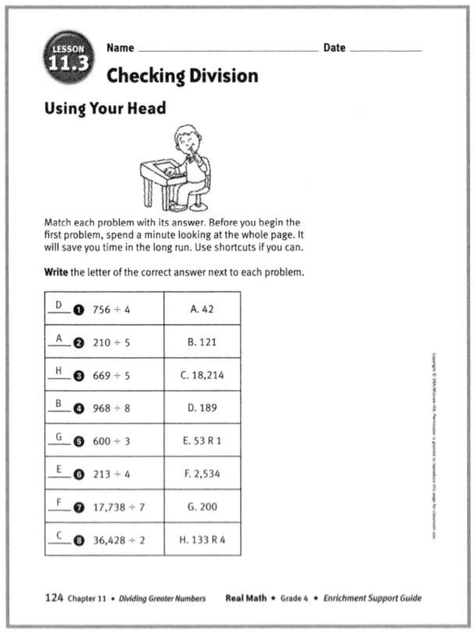
LESSON 11.3 Name ______ Date ______

Checking Division

Using Your Head

Match each problem with its answer. Before you begin the first problem, spend a minute looking at the whole page. It will save you time in the long run. Use shortcuts if you can.

**Write** the letter of the correct answer next to each problem.

| | |
|---|---|
| D 1 756 ÷ 4 | A. 42 |
| A 2 210 ÷ 5 | B. 121 |
| H 3 669 ÷ 5 | C. 18,214 |
| B 4 968 ÷ 8 | D. 189 |
| G 5 600 ÷ 3 | E. 53 R 1 |
| E 6 213 ÷ 4 | F. 2,534 |
| F 7 17,738 ÷ 7 | G. 200 |
| C 8 36,428 ÷ 2 | H. 133 R 4 |

124 Chapter 11 • *Dividing Greater Numbers* **Real Math** • Grade 4 • *Enrichment Support Guide*

Enrichment Lesson 11.3

### PRACTICE

**If . . .** students would benefit from additional practice,

**Then . . .** assign ***Practice*** Lesson 11.3.

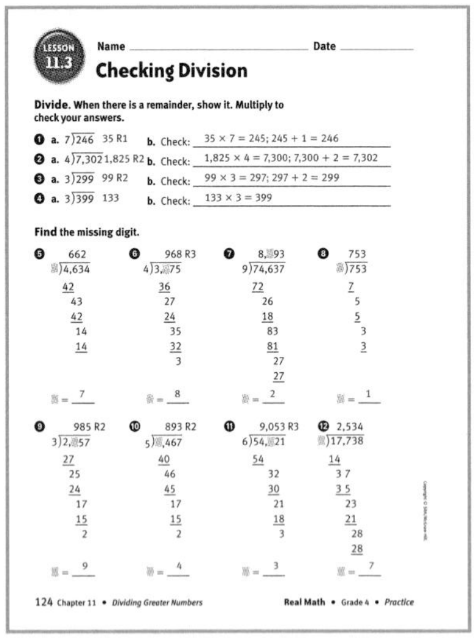
LESSON 11.3 Name ______ Date ______

Checking Division

**Divide.** When there is a remainder, show it. Multiply to check your answers.

1. a. 7)246 35 R1 b. Check: $35 \times 7 = 245; 245 + 1 = 246$
2. a. 4)7,302 1,825 R2 b. Check: $1,825 \times 4 = 7,300; 7,300 + 2 = 7,302$
3. a. 3)299 99 R2 b. Check: $99 \times 3 = 297; 297 + 2 = 299$
4. a. 3)399 133 b. Check: $133 \times 3 = 399$

Find the missing digit.

5. 662, ▒)4,634 — ▒ = 7
6. 968 R3, 4)3,▒75 — ▒ = 8
7. 8,▒93, 9)74,637 — ▒ = 2
8. 753, ▒)753 — ▒ = 1
9. 985 R2, 3)2,▒57 — ▒ = 9
10. 893 R2, 5)▒,467 — ▒ = 4
11. 9,053 R3, 6)54,▒21 — ▒ = 3
12. 2,534, ▒)17,738 — ▒ = 7

124 Chapter 11 • *Dividing Greater Numbers* **Real Math** • Grade 4 • *Practice*

Practice Lesson 11.3

### RETEACH

**If . . .** students struggle with the missing-digit problems,

**Then . . .** have them work through the problems on their own and compare their steps to the steps in the book to find the missing digit.

## Lesson Planner

# Overview LESSON 11.4

### Objectives
- To introduce the "short form" division algorithm
- To provide practice in division and in checking division by multiplying

### NCTM Standards
**Number and Operations**
Solve problems involving division

**Problem Solving**
Apply appropriate strategies to solve problems

**Representation**
Select and apply mathematical representations to solve problems

### Materials
- ***Response Wheels**
- ***Number Cubes** (0–5 and 5–10)
- Base-Ten blocks (optional)

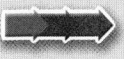

### Technology
**Presentation** Lesson 11.4
**MathTools Base-Ten Blocks**

### Test Prep
**Cumulative Review**
Mental Math reviews inverse operations with multiplication and division (Lesson 4.5).

**Extended Response**
Problem 20

*Manipulative Kit Item

# Division: Short Form

**Context of the Lesson** This is the fourth of twelve lessons on division using greater numbers. This lesson will expand the students' awareness of division by presenting a "short form" for following the standard division algorithms. Students should be encouraged to check their work by using strategies they learned from Lesson 11.3.

See page 502B for Math Background for teachers for this lesson.

## Planning for Learning • DIFFERENTIATE INSTRUCTION

### INTERVENTION

**If . . .** students lack the prerequisite skill of dividing facts with remainders,

**Then . . .** teach ***Intervention*** Lesson 11.B.

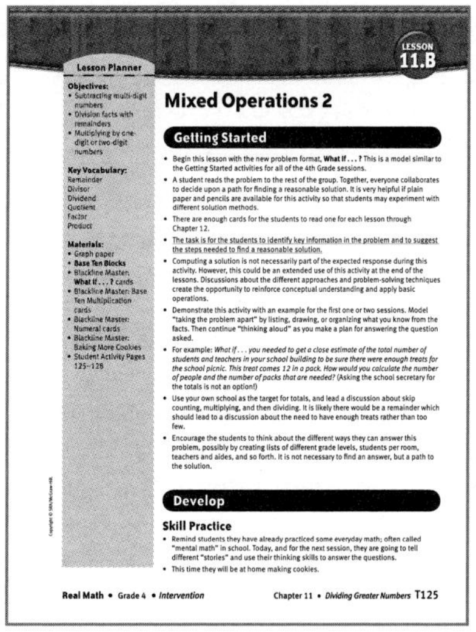
Lesson Planner
LESSON 11.B
Mixed Operations 2
Getting Started
Develop
Skill Practice
Real Math • Grade 4 • Intervention Chapter 11 • Dividing Greater Numbers T125

Intervention Lesson 11.B

### ENGLISH LEARNER

Preview

**If . . .** students need language support,

**Then . . .** use Lesson 11.4 in ***English Learner Support Guide*** to preview lesson concepts and vocabulary.

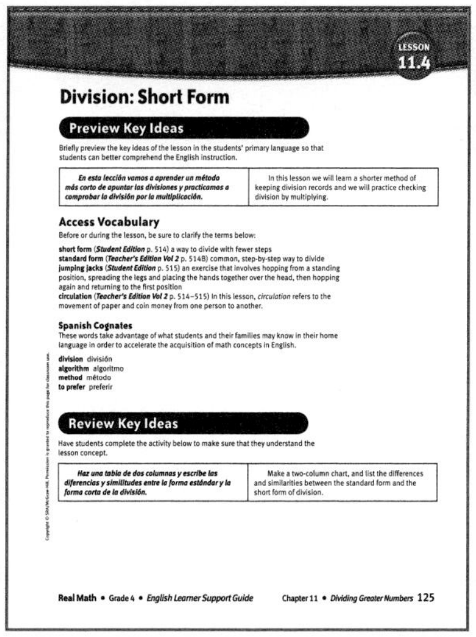
LESSON 11.4
Division: Short Form
Preview Key Ideas
Access Vocabulary
Spanish Cognates
Review Key Ideas
Real Math • Grade 4 • English Learner Support Guide Chapter 11 • Dividing Greater Numbers 125

English Learner Lesson 11.4

### ENRICH

**If . . .** students are proficient in the lesson concepts,

**Then . . .** encourage them to create new variations of the **Four Cube Division Game.**

### PRACTICE

**If . . .** students would benefit from additional practice,

**Then . . .** extend Guided Discussion before assigning the student pages.

### RETEACH

**If . . .** students are having difficulty understanding how to divide using a shortened form,

**Then . . .** extend Guided Discussion before assigning the student pages.

### Access Vocabulary
**short form** a way to divide with fewer steps
**standard form** common step-by-step way to divide

### Spanish Cognates
**algorithm** algoritmo

# Teaching Lesson 11.4

## Mental Math 5

Review RESPONSE WHEEL To emphasize inverse operations, give students pairs of related multidigit multiplication and division exercises such as the following. Present exercises one at a time, leaving previous exercises on the board.

| | | |
|---|---|---|
| **a.** | $30 \times 70 = 2{,}100$ | $2{,}100 \div 30 = 70$ |
| **b.** | $60 \times 80 = 4{,}800$ | $4{,}800 \div 80 = 60$ |
| **c.** | $40 \times 90 = 3{,}600$ | $3{,}600 \div 90 = 40$ |
| **d.** | $50 \times 10 = 500$ | $500 \div 50 = 10$ |
| **e.** | $90 \times 60 = 5{,}400$ | $5{,}400 \div 60 = 90$ |
| **f.** | $90 \times 90 = 8{,}100$ | $8{,}100 \div 90 = 90$ |

## 1 Develop 20

### Tell Students In Today's Lesson They Will

learn a shorter method of keeping division records.

### Guided Discussion UNDERSTANDING

Whole Group

Tell students they are going to learn how to do an even shorter form of division. Write an exercise, such as the one below, in two different columns on the board:

$$6\overline{)8527}$$

Walk the class through the process of finding the quotient using a standard division process in one column, as well as the shortened form in the other column. (For the shortened form, leave spaces in between the digits of the dividend.)

1. The first step is to find out how many 6s are in 8. For both procedures, the 1 will be placed above the 8 on the quotient line.

   Show the process of placing the 6 below the 8 and subtracting. For the shortened form, let the students know they will subtract in their heads (6 from 8 is 2) and place the number 2 in the upper left corner of the 5.

$$\begin{array}{r} 1\phantom{\ {}^25\ 2\ 7} \\ 6\overline{)8\ {}^25\ 2\ 7} \end{array}$$

2. Now complete the next step for the standard form ($25 \div 6 = 4$, 3 goes on the quotient line, while 24 is subtracted from 25, leaving 1). For the shortened form, divide 25 by 6 and place the 4 above the 5.

$$\begin{array}{r} 1\ \ 4\phantom{\ 2\ 7} \\ 6\overline{)8\ {}^25\ 2\ 7} \end{array}$$

   $4 \times 6 = 24$; subtract 24 from 25 to get 1. The 1 goes in the upper left-hand corner of the next digit in the dividend.

$$\begin{array}{r} 1\ \ 4\phantom{\ {}^12\ 7} \\ 6\overline{)8\ {}^25\ {}^12\ 7} \end{array}$$

3. Then complete the next step for the standard form ($12 \div 6 = 2$, so 2 goes on the quotient line while 12 is subtracted from 12). The shortened form should do the same; however, it will look like this:

$$\begin{array}{r} 1\ \ 4\ \ 2\phantom{\ {}^07} \\ 6\overline{)8\ {}^25\ {}^12\ {}^07} \end{array}$$

4. The final step in the standard form can now be completed ($7 \div 6 = 1$, so place the 1 on the quotient line; $7 - 6 = 1$, so 1 also goes in the remainder). For the shortened form, attempt to condense the steps into one, so it will look like this:

$$\begin{array}{r} 1\ \ 4\ \ 2\ \ 1 \quad \text{R1} \\ 6\overline{)8\ {}^25\ {}^12\ {}^07} \end{array}$$

Show students where each step occurs in the shortened form as well as the standard form.

Ask questions such as the following:

- **How did we get the little 2 beside the 5 in the dividend?** subtracting 6 from 8
- **Do we still divide, multiply, and then subtract?** yes

If students have difficulty, try one of the following problems, but this time ask for volunteers to assist.

$5\overline{)6492}$ $3\overline{)3760}$ $4\overline{)6406}$

## 2 Assign Student Pages 30

### Pages 514–515 UNDERSTANDING

Have students complete page 514 with a partner. If students show they have attempted the shortened form but prefer the longer method, then allow them to use it.

#### Monitoring Student Progress

**If . . .** students have trouble with the shortest algorithm form,

**Then . . .** go through the process with them slowly by using the ***eMathTools: Base-Ten Blocks.*** At each step, ask them the meaning of the numbers they are writing. Let them use the longer form if they prefer it.

### As Students Finish

Game **Four Cube Division Game**

Student Page

LESSON 11.4 **Division: Short Form**

## Key Ideas

**There is an even shorter method of showing the steps when you divide.**

| Short Form | Shorter Form | |
|---|---|---|
| 1<br>7)8936<br>− 7<br>19 | 1<br>7)8 ¹9 3 6 | There is one 7 in 8. (Write 1 in the answer above the 8.) The remainder is 1. (Write a small 1 in front of the 9.) |
| 12<br>7)8936<br>− 7<br>19<br>− 14<br>53 | 1 2<br>7)8 ¹9 ⁵3 6 | There are two 7s in 19. (Write 2 in the answer above the 9.) The remainder is 5. (Write a 5 in front of the 3.) |
| 127<br>7)8936<br>− 7<br>19<br>− 14<br>53<br>− 49<br>46 | 1 2 7<br>7)8 ¹9 ⁵3 ⁴6 | There are seven 7s in 53. (Write a 7 in the answer above the 3.) The remainder is 4. (Write a 4 in front of the 6.) |
| 1,276 R4<br>7)8936<br>− 7<br>19<br>− 14<br>53<br>− 49<br>46<br>− 42<br>4 | 1,2 7 6 R4<br>7)8 ¹9 ⁵3 ⁴6 | There are six 7s in 46. (Write a 6 in the answer above the 6.) The remainder is 4. (Write R4 in the answer.) |



eTextbook This lesson is available in the ***eTextbook***.

Student Page

**Divide.** Use whichever method you prefer. Check your answers to the first five exercises by multiplying.

1. 7)343 **Check:** Does 7 × quotient = 343? 49
2. 6)174 **Check:** Does 6 × quotient = 174? 29
3. 2)317 **Check:** Does (2 × quotient) + remainder = 317? 158 R1
4. 5)812 **Check:** Does (5 × quotient) + remainder = 812? 162 R2
5. 9)342 **Check:** Does 9 × quotient = 342? 38

**Divide.** Use shortcuts when you can.

6. 3)876 292
7. 4)512 128
8. 4)1000 250
9. 8)54 6 R6
10. 5)476 95 R1
11. 1)42506 42,506
12. 6)372 62
13. 0)15 no answer
14. 2)471 235 R1
15. 4)1003 250 R3
16. 3)4621 1,540 R1
17. 4)685 171 R1
18. Ambrose did 273 jumping jacks in 7 minutes. How many jumping jacks did Ambrose do each minute? 39
19. Phyliss spent 4 hours on the beach looking for money that people had dropped. In the first hour she found 73¢. In the second hour she found 15¢. In the third hour she found \$2.84 (284¢), and in the last hour she found \$2 (200¢). How much did she find altogether? About how much did she find per hour?

    19 \$5.72 was the total amount with an average of \$1.43 (143¢) found each hour
20. **Extended Response** Mrs. Mustafa decided to give her collection of coins to the neighborhood children. She had 783 coins. If she gave 4 coins to each child, how many children got 4 coins? Were there any left over? If so, what should she do with those? Do you think this is a fair way to give out her coins? 195 children could receive 4 coins and there would be 3 left over. One possibility is for Mrs. Mustafa to give her coins away in groups of 3s, then she could provide 261 children with coins. The fairness of what Mrs. Mustafa did depends on whether the coins were of equal value or not.



# 3 Reflect

5

## Guided Discussion REASONING

Whole Group

Discuss the similarities and differences between the shorter and shortest forms of the division algorithm. Have students demonstrate both forms to solve 435 ÷ 6. 72 R3

Discuss students' answers to Problem 13 on page 515. Ask questions such as the following:

- **Did you get an answer to Problem 13?** no
- **Is there any answer that would work?** no
- **Can it ever be that 0 × a number = 15?** no

There is no number you can multiply by 0 to get 15.

Division by 0 is not allowed.

## Extended Response

**Problem 20** Answers should say 195 children could receive 4 coins each and there would be 3 left over. Students' solutions as to what Mrs. Mustafa could do will vary. One possibility is for Mrs. Mustafa to give her coins away in groups of 3s. Then she could provide 261 children with coins.

SOCIAL STUDIES **Curriculum Connection:** Students may be interested in researching money that was in circulation in the past or money in circulation in foreign countries. Students can research online or at the library.

Review **Cumulative Review:** For review of rounding decimals, assign Problems 15–23 on student page 524.

**Family Involvement:** Assign the ***Practice, Reteach,*** or ***Enrichment*** activities depending on the needs of your students.

Encourage students to play the **Four Cube Division Game** at home with friends or relatives.

**Concept/Question Board:** Have students look for additional examples using division and post them on the Concept/Question Board.

**Math Puzzler:** Using the digits 4, 3, 2, and 1, form a division problem that has a two-digit quotient and a remainder. Digits may repeat, and each digit must appear at least once (explain there are several possible answers). One possible solution is 43 ÷ 2 = 21 R1.

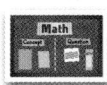

# 4 Assess and Differentiate

**e Assess** Use ***eAssess*** to record and analyze evidence of student understanding.

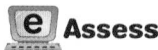

## A Gather Evidence

Use the Daily Class Assessment Records in ***Assessment*** or ***eAssess*** to record daily observations.

### Informal Assessment

**✓ Concept/Question Board**

Did the student **APPLYING**

- ❑ apply learning in new situations?
- ❑ contribute concepts?
- ❑ contribute answers?
- ❑ connect mathematics to real-world situations?

### Formal Assessment

**✓ Student Pages**

Did the student **UNDERSTANDING**

- ❑ make important observations?
- ❑ extend or generalize learning?
- ❑ provide insightful answers?
- ❑ pose insightful questions?

## B Summarize Findings

Analyze and summarize assessment data for each student. Determine which Assessment Follow-Up is appropriate for each student. Use the Student Assessment Record in ***Assessment*** or ***eAssess*** to update assessment records.

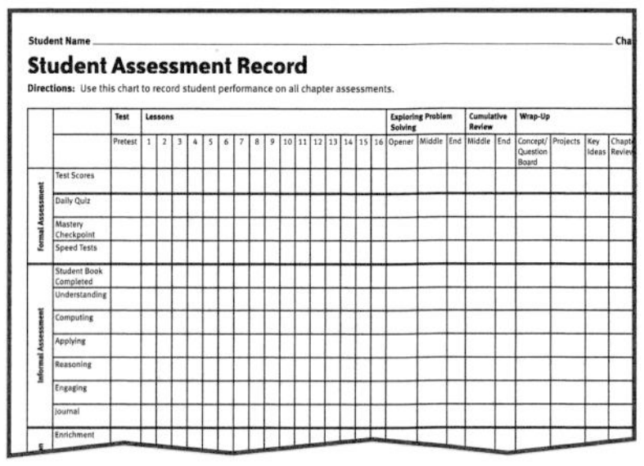


**Assessment Page T41**

## C Assessment Follow-Up • DIFFERENTIATE INSTRUCTION

Based on your observations, use these teaching strategies for assessment follow-up.

### INTERVENTION

Review student performance on ***Intervention*** Lesson 11.B to see if students have mastered prerequisite skills for this lesson.

### ENGLISH LEARNER

**Review**

Use Lesson 11.4 in ***English Learner Support Guide*** to review lesson concepts and vocabulary.

### ENRICH

**If . . .** students are proficient in the lesson concepts,

**Then . . .** encourage them to work on the chapter projects or ***Enrichment*** Lesson 11.4.

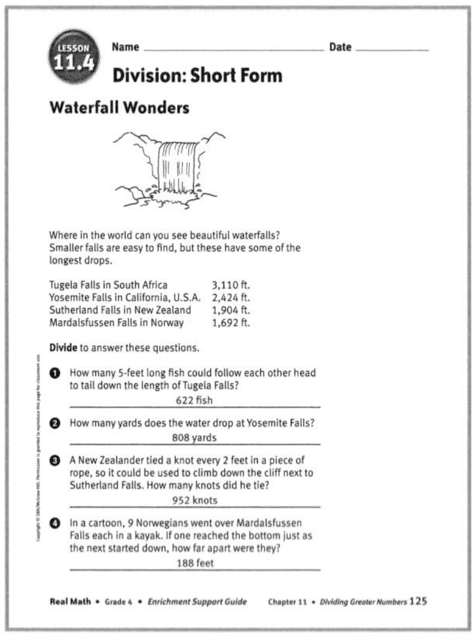

LESSON 11.4 Name ______ Date ______

**Division: Short Form**

**Waterfall Wonders**

Where in the world can you see beautiful waterfalls? Smaller falls are easy to find, but these have some of the longest drops.

| | |
|---|---|
| Tugela Falls in South Africa | 3,110 ft. |
| Yosemite Falls in California, U.S.A. | 2,424 ft. |
| Sutherland Falls in New Zealand | 1,904 ft. |
| Mardalsfussen Falls in Norway | 1,692 ft. |

**Divide** to answer these questions.

1. How many 5-feet long fish could follow each other head to tail down the length of Tugela Falls? 622 fish
2. How many yards does the water drop at Yosemite Falls? 808 yards
3. A New Zealander tied a knot every 2 feet in a piece of rope, so it could be used to climb down the cliff next to Sutherland Falls. How many knots did he tie? 952 knots
4. In a cartoon, 9 Norwegians went over Mardalsfussen Falls each in a kayak. If one reached the bottom just as the next started down, how far apart were they? 188 feet

**Real Math** • Grade 4 • *Enrichment Support Guide* Chapter 11 • *Dividing Greater Numbers* 125

Enrichment Lesson 11.4

### PRACTICE

**If . . .** students would benefit from additional practice,

**Then . . .** assign ***Practice*** Lesson 11.4.

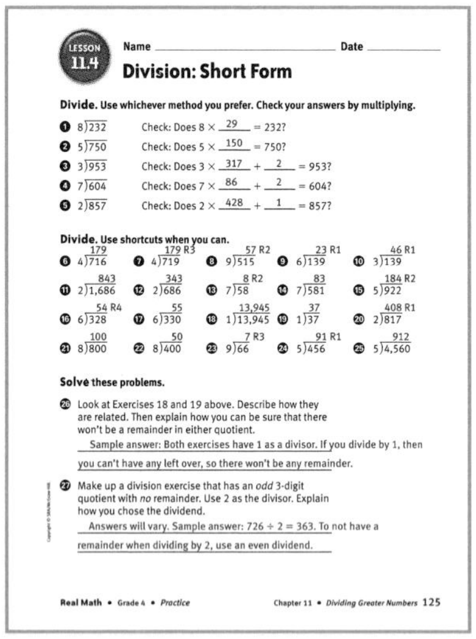

LESSON 11.4 Name ______ Date ______

**Division: Short Form**

**Divide.** Use whichever method you prefer. Check your answers by multiplying.

1. 8)232 Check: Does 8 × 29 = 232?
2. 5)750 Check: Does 5 × 150 = 750?
3. 3)953 Check: Does 3 × 317 + 2 = 953?
4. 7)604 Check: Does 7 × 86 + 2 = 604?
5. 2)857 Check: Does 2 × 428 + 1 = 857?

**Divide.** Use shortcuts when you can.

6. 4)716 = 179
7. 4)719 = 179 R3
8. 9)515 = 57 R2
9. 6)139 = 23 R1
10. 3)139 = 46 R1
11. 2)1,686 = 843
12. 2)686 = 343
13. 7)58 = 8 R2
14. 7)581 = 83
15. 5)922 = 184 R2
16. 6)328 = 54 R4
17. 6)330 = 55
18. 1)13,945 = 13,945
19. 1)37 = 37
20. 2)817 = 408 R1
21. 8)800 = 100
22. 8)400 = 50
23. 9)66 = 7 R3
24. 5)456 = 91 R1
25. 5)4,560 = 912

**Solve these problems.**

26. Look at Exercises 18 and 19 above. Describe how they are related. Then explain how you can be sure that there won't be a remainder in either quotient.
Sample answer: Both exercises have 1 as a divisor. If you divide by 1, then you can't have any left over, so there won't be any remainder.
27. Make up a division exercise that has an *odd* 3-digit quotient with *no* remainder. Use 2 as the divisor. Explain how you chose the dividend.
Answers will vary. Sample answer: 726 ÷ 2 = 363. To not have a remainder when dividing by 2, use an even dividend.

**Real Math** • Grade 4 • *Practice* Chapter 11 • *Dividing Greater Numbers* 125

Practice Lesson 11.4

### RETEACH

**If . . .** students struggle with the shortest-form algorithm,

**Then . . .** remind them that they don't have to use this form. This is a shorter method for when they are comfortable with dividing. They may not feel comfortable using this form at all.

## Lesson Planner

**OBJECTIVES**
- To provide practice dividing with one-digit divisors
- To identify division patterns and use them to help find answers

**NCTM STANDARDS**

**Number and Operations**
Solve problems involving division

**Algebra**
Identify and describe division patterns

**Problem Solving**
Apply appropriate strategies to solve problems

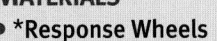

**MATERIALS**
- ***Response Wheels**
- ***Two Number Cubes** (two 0–5 and two 5–10)

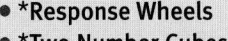

**TECHNOLOGY**
**Presentation** Lesson 11.5

**TEST PREP**

**Cumulative Review**
Mental Math reviews multiplication and division as inverse operations (Lesson 4.5).

**Extended Response**
Problem 40

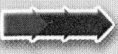

### Looking Ahead

Create two overhead transparencies for the overhead projector, the first showing a 5 × 6 array in Xs, and the second showing a 4 × 5 array in Os. This will be used to explain Problem 15 for Lesson 11.6. Leave some room between the columns because the two overhead transparencies will be laid over each other to create the image.

*Manipulative Kit Item

# Division Patterns

**Context of the Lesson** This is the fifth lesson on division with greater numbers. This lesson asks students to demonstrate their ability to spot patterns among various exercises. Students can use these patterns to replace steps with shortcuts leading to a quotient. Review from a variety of lessons including Lesson 3.10 (multiplication and division facts) and Lesson 5.2 (multiples of 10) will be called upon here. This lesson contains a Mastery Checkpoint.

See page 502B for Math Background for teachers for this lesson.

## Planning for Learning • DIFFERENTIATE INSTRUCTION

### INTERVENTION

**If . . .** students lack the prerequisite skill of dividing with remainders,

**Then . . .** teach the ***Intervention*** Lesson 11.B.

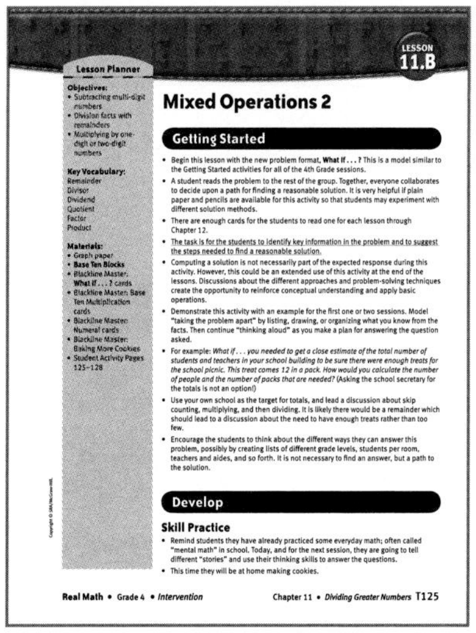
LESSON 11.B
Mixed Operations 2

Intervention Lesson 11.B

### ENGLISH LEARNER

**Preview**

**If . . .** students need language support,

**Then . . .** use Lesson 11.5 in ***English Learner Support Guide*** to preview lesson concepts and vocabulary.

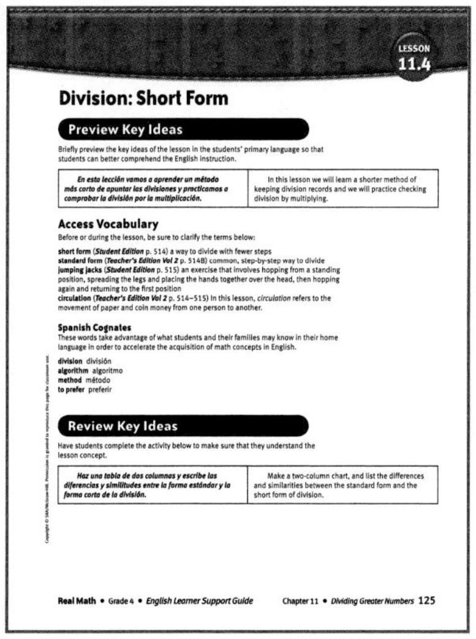
LESSON 11.4
Division: Short Form

English Learner Lesson 11.5

### ENRICH

**If . . .** students are proficient in the lesson concepts,

**Then . . .** encourage students to develop new strategies for playing the **Four Cube Division Game.**

### PRACTICE

**If . . .** students would benefit from additional practice,

**Then . . .** extend Guided Discussion before assigning the student pages.

### RETEACH

**If . . .** students are having difficulty understanding division patterns,

**Then . . .** extend Guided Discussion before assigning the student pages.

### Access Vocabulary

**target** circle-shaped goal in a dart game

**Spanish Cognates**
**concept** concepto
**pattern** patrón

# Teaching Lesson 11.5

## Mental Math 5

Review · Response Wheel

Provide practice with multiplication and division as inverse operations. Present problems such as the following on the board:

**a.** $3 \times 30 = 90$ $90 \div 30 = 3$
**b.** $8 \times 90 = 720$ $720 \div 90 = 8$
**c.** $300 \times 6 = 1{,}800$ $1{,}800 \div 300 = 6$
**d.** $60 \times 40 = 2{,}400$ $2{,}400 \div 40 = 60$
**e.** $75 \times 10 = 750$ $750 \div 75 = 10$
**f.** $70 \times 90 = 6{,}300$ $6{,}300 \div 70 = 90$

## 1 Develop 20

### Tell Students In Today's Lesson They Will

practice dividing with one-digit divisors, and learn how patterns can help you find answers.

### Guided Discussion UNDERSTANDING

Whole Group

Discuss the fact that, when students solve similar problems, they may notice patterns that can help them find answers more quickly.

Write a series of similar exercises, such as the following, on the board:

$6\overline{)10}$ $6\overline{)100}$ $6\overline{)1000}$ $6\overline{)10000}$

Invite volunteers to go to the board to write answers using remainders. 1 R4; 16 R4; 166 R4; 1666 R4

- **What patterns do you see?** Students should notice that each time the dividend was multiplied by 10, the quotient was 6 greater than 10 times the previous quotient, but the remainder was still 4. Answers such as, "There is one more 6 in the quotient" should be accepted.

Use the pattern to have students decide what the answer would be to $6\overline{)100000}$ and $6\overline{)1000000}$. 16666 R4 and 166666 R4 respectively

Repeat this exercise with other possible patterns, such as $100 \div 4 = 25$; $1{,}000 \div 4 = 250$; $10{,}000 \div 4 = 2{,}500$, and so on. Note that the quotient is multiplied by 10 when the dividend is.

## 2 Assign Student Pages 30

### Pages 516–517 APPLYING

Have students complete pages 516–517 independently. Allow students to use any algorithmic form with which they feel comfortable. They should see the division patterns on page 516 and solve these problems quickly without the use of an algorithm.

#### Monitoring Student Progress

**If . . .** students make errors when subtracting numbers,

**Then . . .** review the subtraction algorithm using the Manipulative Algorithm Development section in the Handbook in the ***Teacher's Edition***.

### As Students Finish

Game **Four Cube Division Game**

Student Page

LESSON 11.5 **Division Patterns**

**Key Ideas**

**When you solve similar problems, you may notice patterns that can help you find answers.**

**Divide.** Remember to write any remainders.

| | | |
|---|---|---|
| 1. 3)10 3 R1 | 2. 3)100 33 R1 | 3. 3)1000 333 R1 |
| 4. 2)10 5 | 5. 2)100 50 | 6. 2)1000 500 |
| 7. 4)100 25 | 8. 4)1000 250 | 9. 4)10,000 2,500 |
| 10. 5)10 2 | 11. 5)100 20 | 12. 5)1000 200 |
| 13. 6)100 16 R4 | 14. 6)101 16 R5 | 15. 6)102 17 |
| 16. 6)103 17 R1 | 17. 9)1000 111 R1 | 18. 9)2000 222 R2 |
| 19. 9)3000 333 R3 | 20. 2)246 123 | 21. 1)2520 2,520 |
| 22. 2)2520 1,260 | 23. 3)2520 840 | 24. 4)2520 630 |
| 25. 2)210 105 | 26. 3)210 70 | 27. 5)210 42 |
| 28. 7)210 30 | 29. 8)210 26 R2 | 30. 9)210 23 R3 |

516 Textbook This lesson is available in the ***eTextbook***.

Student Page

**Divide** to solve for *n*.

31. $210 \div 7 = n$ $n = 30$
32. $200 \div 8 = n$ $n = 25$
33. $100 \div 4 = n$ $n = 25$
34. $72 \div 9 = n$ $n = 8$
35. $80 \div 5 = n$ $n = 16$
36. $900 \div 6 = n$ $n = 150$
37. $2{,}871 \div 9 = n$ $n = 319$
38. $1{,}024 \div 8 = n$ $n = 128$

**Solve** these problems.

39. Anika wants to give a toy dinosaur to each of the 28 people coming to her party. The dinosaurs she wants to give come in packages of 8.
    a. How many packages does she need to buy? 4
    b. How many dinosaurs will she have left over? 4

40. Extended Response Winter Elementary School ordered 141 notebooks to be divided equally among 6 classrooms. How many notebooks were given to each classroom? Discuss how the remaining notebooks could be divided equally. 23; there are 3 books left over that cannot be divided. They could be saved for emergencies, such as if books are lost or damaged or if new students start school there.

Chapter 11 • Lesson 5 517

## 3 Reflect

5

### Guided Discussion REASONING

Whole Group

Discuss the patterns students found on page 516.
Ask questions such as the following:

- **What is one pattern you found?** Possible answer: There is one 3 in the quotient for every 0 that appears in the dividend. The remainder is always 1.
- **How did you find the pattern?** Students may say they divided and compared the quotients.
- **How did knowing the pattern help you to solve other similar problems?** Students may say once they found the quotient to smaller problems, the larger dividends extended the rule from the previous problem.
- **Are you fairly sure the pattern will always work? Why?** Students should say yes. One possibility is that the pattern will work as long as the dividend and divisor stay consistent.

Use Mastery Checkpoint 22 found in ***Assessment*** to evaluate student mastery of dividing by a one-digit number.

### Extended Response

**Problem 40** Students should say each classroom gets 23 notebooks. The notebooks leftover cannot be divided equally.

**Cumulative Review:** For review of reading a ruler, assign Problems 24–25 on student page 525.

**Family Involvement:** Assign the ***Practice, Reteach,*** or ***Enrichment*** activities depending on the needs of your students.

Encourage students to play the **Four Cube Division Game** at home with friends or relatives.

**Concept/Question Board:** Encourage students to continue to post questions, answers, and examples on the Concept/Question Board.

**Math Puzzler:** Marissa played darts on a target like the one below. On her first turn the five darts earned a total of 34 points. On her next turn she earned the same total but in a different way. Where did Marissa's darts land on each turn? four 8s and one 2 on one turn, three 8s and two 5s on the other turn

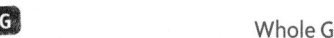

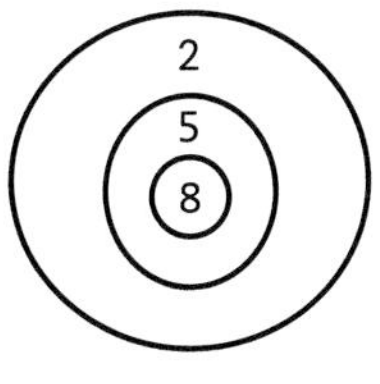

# 4 Assess and Differentiate

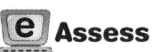

**e Assess** Use ***eAssess*** to record and analyze evidence of student understanding.

## A Gather Evidence

Use the Daily Class Assessment Records in ***Assessment*** or ***eAssess*** to record daily observations.

### Formal Assessment

**Mastery Checkpoint**

Did the student APPLYING
- ❑ use correct procedures?
- ❑ respond with at least eighty-percent accuracy?

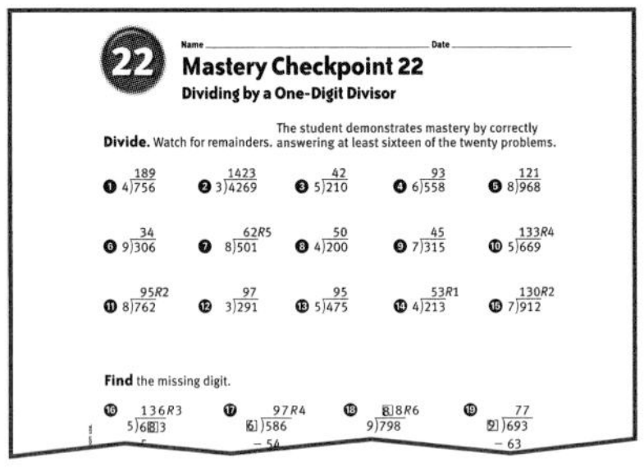
22 Name Date
Mastery Checkpoint 22
Dividing by a One-Digit Divisor
The student demonstrates mastery by correctly answering at least sixteen of the twenty problems.
**Divide.** Watch for remainders.
1. 4)756 = 189 2. 3)4269 = 1423 3. 5)210 = 42 4. 6)558 = 93 5. 8)968 = 121
6. 9)306 = 34 7. 8)501 = 62R5 8. 4)200 = 50 9. 7)315 = 45 10. 5)669 = 133R4
11. 8)762 = 95R2 12. 3)291 = 97 13. 5)475 = 95 14. 4)213 = 53R1 15. 7)912 = 130R2
**Find** the missing digit.

Assessment Page T75

## B Summarize Findings

Analyze and summarize assessment data for each student. Determine which Assessment Follow-Up is appropriate for each student. Use the Student Assessment Record in ***Assessment*** or ***eAssess*** to update assessment records.

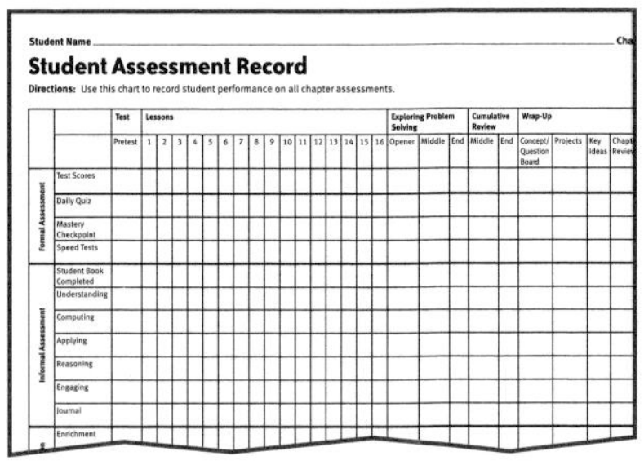
Student Name
Student Assessment Record

Assessment Page T41

## C Assessment Follow-Up • DIFFERENTIATE INSTRUCTION

Based on your observations, use these teaching strategies for assessment follow-up.

### INTERVENTION

Review student performance on ***Intervention*** Lesson 11.B to see if students have mastered prerequisite skills for this lesson.

### ENGLISH LEARNER

**Review**

Use Lesson 11.5 in ***English Learner Support Guide*** to review lesson concepts and vocabulary.

### ENRICH

**If . . .** students are proficient in the lesson concepts,

**Then . . .** encourage them to work on the chapter projects or ***Enrichment*** Lesson 11.5.

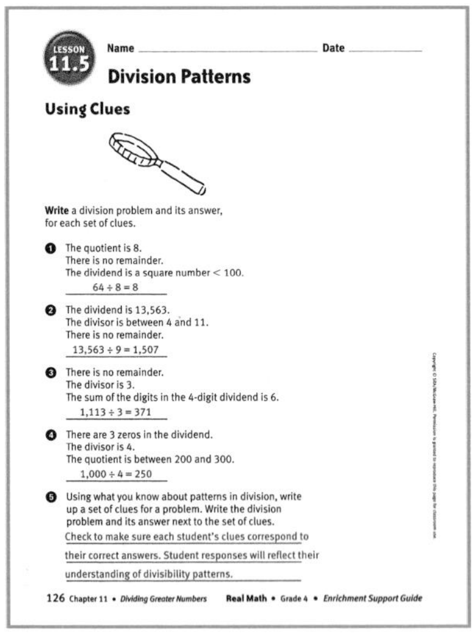
LESSON 11.5 Name Date
Division Patterns
Using Clues
Write a division problem and its answer, for each set of clues.
1. The quotient is 8. There is no remainder. The dividend is a square number < 100. 64 ÷ 8 = 8
2. The dividend is 13,563. The divisor is between 4 and 11. There is no remainder. 13,563 ÷ 9 = 1,507
3. There is no remainder. The divisor is 3. The sum of the digits in the 4-digit dividend is 6. 1,113 ÷ 3 = 371
4. There are 3 zeros in the dividend. The divisor is 4. The quotient is between 200 and 300. 1,000 ÷ 4 = 250
5. Using what you know about patterns in division, write up a set of clues for a problem. Write the division problem and its answer next to the set of clues. Check to make sure each student's clues correspond to their correct answers. Student responses will reflect their understanding of divisibility patterns.
126 Chapter 11 • Dividing Greater Numbers Real Math • Grade 4 • Enrichment Support Guide

Enrichment Lesson 11.5

### PRACTICE

**If . . .** students would benefit from additional practice,

**Then . . .** assign ***Practice*** Lesson 11.5.

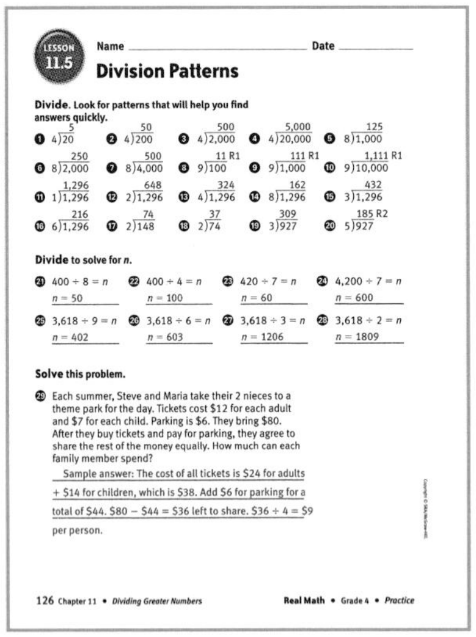
LESSON 11.5 Name Date
Division Patterns
Divide. Look for patterns that will help you find answers quickly.
1. 4)20 = 5 2. 4)200 = 50 3. 4)2,000 = 500 4. 4)20,000 = 5,000 5. 8)1,000 = 125
6. 8)2,000 = 250 7. 8)4,000 = 500 8. 9)100 = 11 R1 9. 9)1,000 = 111 R1 10. 9)10,000 = 1,111 R1
11. 1)1,296 = 1,296 12. 2)1,296 = 648 13. 4)1,296 = 324 14. 8)1,296 = 162 15. 3)1,296 = 432
16. 6)1,296 = 216 17. 2)148 = 74 18. 2)74 = 37 19. 3)927 = 309 20. 5)927 = 185 R2
Divide to solve for n.
21. 400 ÷ 8 = n, n = 50 22. 400 ÷ 4 = n, n = 100 23. 420 ÷ 7 = n, n = 60 24. 4,200 ÷ 7 = n, n = 600
25. 3,618 ÷ 9 = n, n = 402 26. 3,618 ÷ 6 = n, n = 603 27. 3,618 ÷ 3 = n, n = 1206 28. 3,618 ÷ 2 = n, n = 1809
Solve this problem.
29. Each summer, Steve and Maria take their 2 nieces to a theme park for the day. Tickets cost $12 for each adult and $7 for each child. Parking is $6. They bring $80. After they buy tickets and pay for parking, they agree to share the rest of the money equally. How much can each family member spend?
Sample answer: The cost of all tickets is $24 for adults + $14 for children, which is $38. Add $6 for parking for a total of $44. $80 − $44 = $36 left to share. $36 ÷ 4 = $9 per person.
126 Chapter 11 • Dividing Greater Numbers Real Math • Grade 4 • Practice

Practice Lesson 11.5

### RETEACH

**If . . .** students are having difficulty finding the division patterns,

**Then . . .** have them work with a partner to find the patterns without actually solving the problems. Then one student should solve the algorithm while the other watches for errors. If the partner detects an error, the students should correct it together before they switch roles.

## Lesson Planner

### OBJECTIVES
- To reintroduce factoring
- To introduce the concepts of prime numbers and composite numbers

### NCTM STANDARDS
**Number and Operations**
- Know that some numbers have exactly two factors (1 and the number itself) and are called *prime numbers*
- Know that some numbers have more than two factors (not including 1 and itself) and are called *composite numbers*

**Problem Solving**
Apply appropriate strategies to solve problems

**Representation**
Create representations to organize and communicate mathematical ideas

### MATERIALS
- *Response Wheels
- *Number Cubes (two 0–5 and two 5–10)
- Overhead projector
- The two transparencies referenced in Lesson 11.5

### TECHNOLOGY
**e Presentation** Lesson 11.6

### TEST PREP
**Cumulative Review**
Mental Math reviews basic facts and the use of parentheses (Lessons 3.10 and 3.13).

**Extended Response**
Problems 2, 15, and 16

**Writing + Math**
Journal

*Manipulative Kit Item

# Prime and Composite Numbers

**Context of the Lesson** This lesson offers a conceptual application of both the relationship between multiplication and division and of rectangular arrays as a concrete illustration of factors. Factors were introduced in Lesson 3.9. Students should be able to apply that knowledge to prime and composite numbers.

See page 502B for Math Background for teachers for this lesson.

## Planning for Learning • DIFFERENTIATE INSTRUCTION

### INTERVENTION
**If . . .** students lack the prerequisite skill of multiplying by a one- or two-digit number,

**Then . . .** teach ***Intervention*** Lesson 11.C.

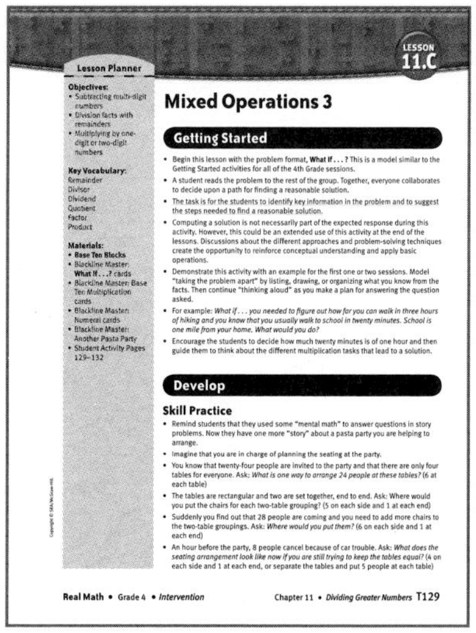

LESSON 11.C

Lesson Planner

**Objectives:**
- Subtracting multi-digit numbers
- Division facts with remainders
- Multiplying by one-digit or two-digit numbers

**Key Vocabulary:**
Remainder
Divisor
Dividend
Quotient
Factor
Product

**Materials:**
- **Base Ten Blocks**
- Blackline Master: **What If. . .?** cards
- Blackline Master: Base Ten Multiplication cards
- Blackline Master: Numeral cards
- Blackline Master: Another Pasta Party
- Student Activity Pages 129–132

**Mixed Operations 3**

**Getting Started**
- Begin this lesson with the problem format, **What If . . . ?** This is a model similar to the Getting Started activities for all of the 4th Grade sessions.
- A student reads the problem to the rest of the group. Together, everyone collaborates to decide upon a path for finding a reasonable solution.
- The task is for the students to identify key information in the problem and to suggest the steps needed to find a reasonable solution.
- Computing a solution is not necessarily part of the expected response during this activity. However, this could be an extended use of this activity at the end of the lessons. Discussions about the different approaches and problem-solving techniques create the opportunity to reinforce conceptual understanding and apply basic operations.
- Demonstrate this activity with an example for the first one or two sessions. Model "taking the problem apart" by listing, drawing, or organizing what you know from the facts. Then continue "thinking aloud" as you make a plan for answering the question asked.
- For example: *What if . . . you needed to figure out how far you can walk in three hours of hiking and you know that you usually walk to school in twenty minutes. School is one mile from your home. What would you do?*
- Encourage the students to decide how much twenty minutes is of one hour and then guide them to think about the different multiplication tasks that lead to a solution.

**Develop**

**Skill Practice**
- Remind students that they used some "mental math" to answer questions in story problems. Now they have one more "story" about a pasta party you are helping to arrange.
- Imagine that you are in charge of planning the seating at the party.
- You know that twenty-four people are invited to the party and that there are only four tables for everyone. Ask: *What is one way to arrange 24 people at these tables?* (6 at each table)
- The tables are rectangular and two are set together, end to end. Ask: Where would you put the chairs for each two-table grouping? (5 on each side and 1 at each end)
- Suddenly you find out that 28 people are coming and you need to add more chairs to the two-table groupings. Ask: *Where would you put them?* (6 on each side and 1 at each end)
- An hour before the party, 8 people cancel because of car trouble. Ask: *What does the seating arrangement look like now if you are still trying to keep the tables equal?* (4 on each side and 1 at each end, or separate the tables and put 5 people at each table)

**Real Math** • Grade 4 • *Intervention* Chapter 11 • *Dividing Greater Numbers* T129

Intervention Lesson 11.C

### ENGLISH LEARNER
Preview

**If . . .** students need language support,

**Then . . .** use Lesson 11.6 in ***English Learner Support Guide*** to preview lesson concepts and vocabulary.

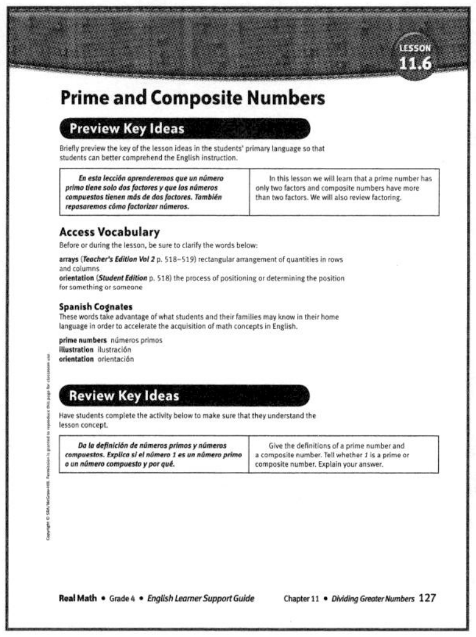

LESSON 11.6

**Prime and Composite Numbers**

**Preview Key Ideas**

Briefly preview the key of the lesson ideas in the students' primary language so that students can better comprehend the English instruction.

| | |
|---|---|
| ***En esta lección aprenderemos que un número primo tiene solo dos factores y que los números compuestos tienen más de dos factores. También repasaremos cómo factorizar números.*** | In this lesson we will learn that a prime number has only two factors and composite numbers have more than two factors. We will also review factoring. |

**Access Vocabulary**

Before or during the lesson, be sure to clarify the words below:

**arrays** (***Teacher's Edition Vol 2*** p. 518–519) rectangular arrangement of quantities in rows and columns
**orientation** (***Student Edition*** p. 518) the process of positioning or determining the position for something or someone

**Spanish Cognates**

These words take advantage of what students and their families may know in their home language in order to accelerate the acquisition of math concepts in English.

**prime numbers** números primos
**illustration** ilustración
**orientation** orientación

**Review Key Ideas**

Have students complete the activity below to make sure that they understand the lesson concept.

| | |
|---|---|
| ***Da la definición de números primos y números compuestos. Explica si el número 1 es un número primo o un número compuesto y por qué.*** | Give the definitions of a prime number and a composite number. Tell whether *1* is a prime or composite number. Explain your answer. |

**Real Math** • Grade 4 • *English Learner Support Guide* Chapter 11 • *Dividing Greater Numbers* 127

English Learner Lesson 11.6

### ENRICH
**If . . .** students are proficient in the lesson concepts,

**Then . . .** encourage them to create a new chapter project.

### PRACTICE
**If . . .** students would benefit from additional practice,

**Then . . .** extend Skill Building before assigning student pages.

### RETEACH
**If . . .** students are having difficulty understanding prime and composite numbers,

**Then . . .** extend Guided Discussion before assigning the student pages.

**Vocabulary**
**prime number *n.*** any number composed of two factors—the number itself and 1
**composite number *n.*** any number composed of more than two factors

**Access Vocabulary**
**arrays** rectangular arrangement of qualitites in rows and columns

**Spanish Cognates**
**prime numbers** números primos
**illustration** ilustración

# Teaching Lesson 11.6

## Mental Math 5

Orally present exercises such as the following. For example, say *take fourteen plus seven; divide that by three, and add three*. Students should perform operations in order from left to right, as each new term is introduced. (Don't be concerned with order of operation rules, and don't read the parentheses.)

**a.** $(14 + 7) \div 3 + 3 = 10$
**b.** $15 - 10 + 4 - 1 = 8$
**c.** $(6 + 16 + 20) \div 6 = 7$
**d.** $18 - 9 - 3 + 2 = 8$
**e.** $(81 \div 9 - 1) \div 2 = 4$
**f.** $(3 + 2) \times 6 - 1 = 29$
**g.** $6 \times 8 \div 6 \times 2 = 16$
**h.** $5 \times 9 + 5 - 10 = 40$
**i.** $72 \div 9 \times 6 \div 8 = 6$
**j.** $2 \times 2 \times 2 \times 2 = 16$

## 1 Develop 25

**Tell Students In Today's Lesson They Will**
learn about prime and composite numbers and review factoring.

### Strategy Building ENGAGING Small Group

- Explain that, even though there have been fifty stars on the American flag since 1960, there were only twenty stars on the flag from 1818–1836. Have students work individually or in small groups. Instruct them to create different ways twenty stars could be arranged into a rectangle on the flag.
- After about five minutes, regroup as a class and allow the groups to quickly display the different ways they arranged the stars to create a rectangle.
- Write a list of students' findings on the board. Possible answers are arrays of 1 by 20, 20 by 1, 2 by 10, 10 by 2, 4 by 5, and 5 by 4.

### Guided Discussion UNDERSTANDING Whole Group

Discuss how eleven stars might be displayed on a flag. Students should realize there are only two ways the stars can be put into a rectangular array: 1 by 11 and 11 by 1.

- Use these examples to illustrate prime and composite numbers.
- Define prime numbers as numbers that have exactly 2 factors, 1 and the number itself (such as 11).
- Define composite numbers as numbers that have more than two factors (such as 4 or 6).

Ask questions such as the following:

- **What is a factor? (If necessary, review what a factor is.)** A factor of a number is any number that divides the number without a remainder. For example, two factors of 8 are 2 and 4 because 8 can be divided by both 2 and 4 without remainders.
- **What are the factors of 20?** 1, 2, 4, 5, 10, and 20
- **What are the factors of 11?** 1 and 11
- **Is 20 a prime number or a composite number? Why?** a composite number because it has more than two factors
- **Is 11 a prime number or a composite number? Why?** a prime number because it has only two factors, 1 and 11

### Skill Building UNDERSTANDING Whole Group

Give students a few minutes to list or draw all possible rectangles that could be made with the following:

- thirteen stars 2 rectangles: 1 by 13, 13 by 1
- twelve stars 6 rectangles: 1 by 12, 12 by 1, 2 by 6, 6 by 2, 3 by 4, 4 by 3
- twenty-eight stars 6 rectangles: 1 by 28, 28 by 1, 2 by 14, 14 by 2, 4 by 7, 7 by 4

Ask questions such as the following:

- **What are the factors of 13?** 1 and 13
- **Is 13 prime or composite?** prime
- **What are the factors of 12?** 1, 2, 3, 4, 6, and 12
- **Is 12 prime or composite?** composite
- **What are the factors of 28?** 1, 2, 4, 7, 14, and 28
- **Is 28 prime or composite?** composite
- **What can you say about prime numbers?** Possible answer: a prime number always has only two factors—one and the number itself.
- **What can you say about composite numbers?** Possible answers: You can make more than two rectangular arrays with a composite number of stars; composite numbers always have more than two factors.
  (Note: Some students may argue that a 1 by 11 rectangle and an 11 by 1 rectangle are identical.)

## 2 Assign Student Pages 20

**Pages 518–519** APPLYING
Students should complete pages 518–519 on their own.

**As Students Finish**

Game **Four Cube Division Game**

Student Page

LESSON 11.6 Prime and Composite Numbers

## Key Ideas

**A prime number has only two factors—1 and the number itself. A composite number has more than two factors.**

Looking at the number of rectangular arrays we can make from a group of stars can help you understand prime and composite numbers. Prime numbers have exactly two possible rectangles, and composite numbers have more than two rectangles when orientation is considered.

Before 1959 the United States flag had 48 stars. They were arranged in 6 rows of 8 stars each.

Because 48 is a composite number, there are other ways to make a rectangle, such as 1 row of 48, 2 rows of 24, 3 rows of 16, and 4 rows of 12. You could make four more by turning these rectangles to show 48 rows of 1, 24 rows of 2, 16 rows of 3, and 12 rows of 4. The flag would have 8 rows of 6 if hung vertically.

The first flag of the United States had 13 stars. Because 13 is a prime number, there are exactly two ways to arrange a flag with 13 stars to make a rectangle—1 by 13 or 13 by 1.

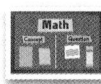

**Answer** the following questions.

1. List all possible rectangles that could be made with
   - **a.** 1 star $1 \times 1$
   - **b.** 2 stars $1 \times 2$ or $2 \times 1$
   - **c.** 3 stars $1 \times 3$ or $3 \times 1$
   - **d.** 4 stars $1 \times 4$ or $4 \times 1$ or $2 \times 2$
   - **e.** 5 stars $1 \times 5$ or $5 \times 1$
   - **f.** 6 stars $1 \times 6$ or $6 \times 1$; $2 \times 3$ or $3 \times 2$



Textbook This lesson is available in the *eTextbook*.

Student Page

2. How many rectangles did you list for 2, 3, and 5 stars? 2 each
3. Do you think there are other numbers for which there are only two rectangles (or one rectangle in two rotations)? If so, list three of them. yes; possible answers: 7, 29, and 53
4. List five prime numbers. Possible answers: 5, 17, 31, 43, and 61
5. List five composite numbers. Possible answers: 4, 6, 24, 32, 40
6. Is the number 1 prime or composite? neither

Remember, a factor of a number is any number that divides the number without leaving a remainder. For example, two factors of 36 are 9 and 4. You can divide 36 by either 9 or 4, and there will be no remainder.

7. List the factors of the following numbers:
   - **a.** 1 1
   - **b.** 2 1, 2
   - **c.** 3 1, 3
   - **d.** 4 1, 2, 4
   - **e.** 5 1, 5
   - **f.** 6 1, 2, 3, 6
8. How many factors does 2 have? 2
9. What are the factors of 8? 1, 2, 4, 8
10. List all the numbers that you think have just one factor. The only number with one factor is 1.
11. List four numbers that have exactly two factors. Possible answers: 2, 3, 5, 7
12. List six numbers that have more than two factors. Possible answers: 4, 6, 8, 9, 10, 12
13. How many factors do prime numbers have? 2
14. How many factors do composite numbers have? more than 2
15. Extended Response Why might $(6 \times 5) + (5 \times 4)$ remind someone of the United States flag? Explain your answer.
16. Extended Response Design a new flag that has 48 stars. Then write three or four sentences telling why your design is appropriate for the new flag.

15. The flag has five rows of six stars $(5 \times 6)$ and four rows of five stars $(4 \times 5)$, which, together, make 50 stars.

Writing + Math **Journal**

Write your own definitions of a prime number and a composite number to help you remember what those words mean.

Answers must mention that a prime number is a number with only two factors, while a composite number has more than two factors.





# 3 Reflect

10

## Guided Discussion REASONING

Whole Group

Have students describe the difference between a prime number and a composite number and give examples of each. Extend the discussion to include odd and even numbers by asking questions such as the following:

- **Explain what an odd number is, and give some examples.** a whole number that does not have a factor of 2, such as 3, 15 or 89
- **Explain what an even number is, and give some examples.** a whole number that has factors of 2, such as 4, 32, or 68
- **Are all odd numbers prime numbers? Why?** No, because an odd number can have more than two factors.
- **Are all even numbers composite numbers? Explain.** Yes (except for the number 2) because an even number is always divisible by 2.

Tell students that we don't include 1 among either the prime or composite numbers.

## Extended Response

**Problem 15** Show the transparencies suggested in the Looking Ahead section of the previous lesson. Display the $5 \times 6$ configuration first. Then put the $4 \times 5$ configuration on top of the $5 \times 6$ configuration. Explain that $5 \times 6 = 30$, $4 \times 5 = 20$, and that $30 + 20 = 50$, which is the number of stars on the United States flag.

**Problem 16** Arrays could be arranged in various ways: $6 \times 8$, $8 \times 6$, $4 \times 12$, $12 \times 4$, $24 \times 2$, $2 \times 24$, $1 \times 48$, or $48 \times 1$.

Writing + Math **Journal**

Answers should explain that a prime number is composed of only two factors—the number itself and 1. A composite number is composed of more than two factors, including itself and the 1.

**Cumulative Review:** For review of lines and angles, assign Problems 26–28 on student page 525.

**Family Involvement:** Assign the ***Practice, Reteach,*** or ***Enrichment*** activities depending on the needs of your students.

Encourage students to play the **Four Cube Division Game** at home with friends or relatives.

**Concept/Question Board:** Encourage students to continue to post questions, answers, and examples on the Concept/Question Board.

**Math Puzzler:** What two prime numbers can you add together to make another prime number? Possible answers: $2 + 3 = 5$; $2 + 5 = 7$; $2 + 17 = 19$ What do you notice about one of these numbers in every case? one of them must be 2

# 4 Assess and Differentiate

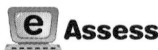

**e Assess** Use ***eAssess*** to record and analyze evidence of student understanding.

## A Gather Evidence

Use the Daily Class Assessment Records in ***Assessment*** or ***eAssess*** to record daily observations.

### Informal Assessment

**Skill Building**

Did the student UNDERSTANDING

- ❑ make important observations?
- ❑ extend or generalize learning?
- ❑ provide insightful answers?
- ❑ pose insightful questions?

### Portfolio Assessment

**Extended Response**

Did the student REASONING

- ❑ provide a clear explanation?
- ❑ communicate reasons and strategies?
- ❑ choose appropriate strategies?
- ❑ argue logically?

## B Summarize Findings

Analyze and summarize assessment data for each student. Determine which Assessment Follow-Up is appropriate for each student. Use the Student Assessment Record in ***Assessment*** or ***eAssess*** to update assessment records.

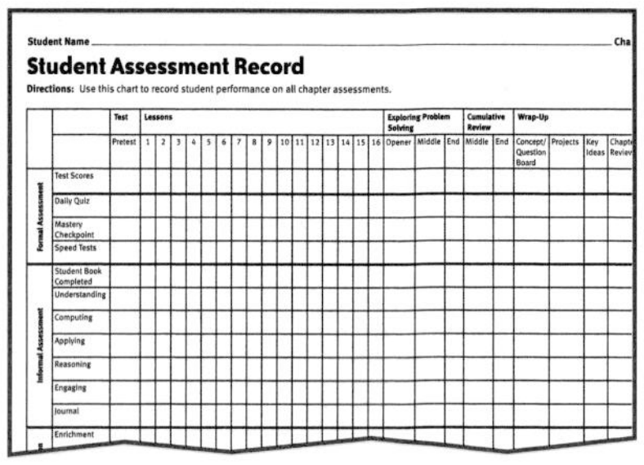
Student Assessment Record

Assessment Page T41

## C Assessment Follow-Up • DIFFERENTIATE INSTRUCTION

Based on your observations, use these teaching strategies for assessment follow-up.

### INTERVENTION

Review student performance on ***Intervention*** Lesson 11.C to see if students have mastered prerequisite skills for this lesson.

### ENGLISH LEARNER

**Review**

Use Lesson 11.6 in ***English Learner Support Guide*** to review lesson concepts and vocabulary.

### ENRICH

**If . . .** students are proficient in the lesson concepts,

**Then . . .** encourage them to work on the chapter projects or ***Enrichment*** Lesson 11.6.

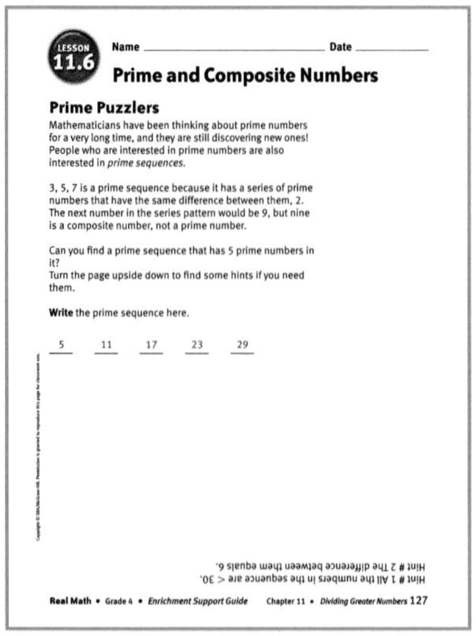
LESSON 11.6 Name ______ Date ______

**Prime and Composite Numbers**

**Prime Puzzlers**

Mathematicians have been thinking about prime numbers for a very long time, and they are still discovering new ones! People who are interested in prime numbers are also interested in *prime sequences.*

3, 5, 7 is a prime sequence because it has a series of prime numbers that have the same difference between them, 2. The next number in the series pattern would be 9, but nine is a composite number, not a prime number.

Can you find a prime sequence that has 5 prime numbers in it?
Turn the page upside down to find some hints if you need them.

**Write** the prime sequence here.

5 11 17 23 29

Hint # 2 The difference between them equals 6.
Hint # 1 All the numbers in the sequence are < 30.

**Real Math** • Grade 4 • *Enrichment Support Guide* Chapter 11 • *Dividing Greater Numbers* 127

Enrichment Lesson 11.6

### PRACTICE

**If . . .** students would benefit from additional practice,

**Then . . .** assign ***Practice*** Lesson 11.6.

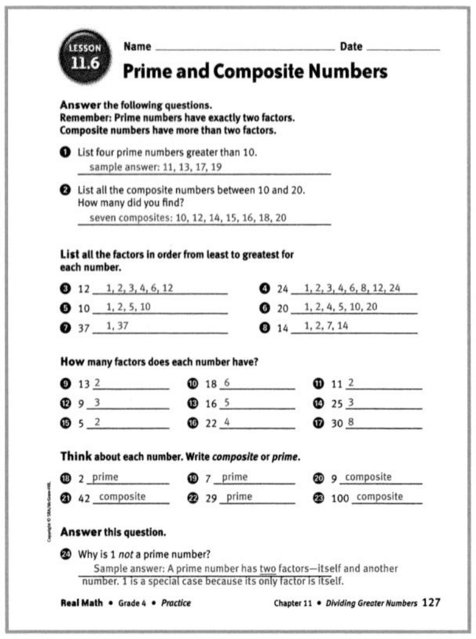
LESSON 11.6 Name ______ Date ______

**Prime and Composite Numbers**

**Answer** the following questions.
Remember: Prime numbers have exactly two factors.
Composite numbers have more than two factors.

1. List four prime numbers greater than 10.
sample answer: 11, 13, 17, 19
2. List all the composite numbers between 10 and 20. How many did you find?
seven composites: 10, 12, 14, 15, 16, 18, 20

**List all the factors in order from least to greatest for each number.**

3. 12 1, 2, 3, 4, 6, 12
4. 24 1, 2, 3, 4, 6, 8, 12, 24
5. 10 1, 2, 5, 10
6. 20 1, 2, 4, 5, 10, 20
7. 37 1, 37
8. 14 1, 2, 7, 14

**How many factors does each number have?**

9. 13 2
10. 18 6
11. 11 2
12. 9 3
13. 16 5
14. 25 3
15. 5 2
16. 22 4
17. 30 8

**Think about each number. Write *composite* or *prime*.**

18. 2 prime
19. 7 prime
20. 9 composite
21. 42 composite
22. 29 prime
23. 100 composite

**Answer this question.**

24. Why is 1 *not* a prime number?
Sample answer: A prime number has two factors—itself and another number. 1 is a special case because its only factor is itself.

**Real Math** • Grade 4 • *Practice* Chapter 11 • *Dividing Greater Numbers* 127

Practice Lesson 11.6

### RETEACH

**If . . .** students are having difficulty with composite numbers,

**Then . . .** have them practice their basic math facts, which will help them find factors.

# Finding Factors

**Context of the Lesson** This is the seventh lesson on division using greater numbers. In this lesson students will gain knowledge through the use of rules to identify factors of numbers. Students' sense of numbers will increase, allowing greater flexibility in areas such as fractions and division. Prior knowledge needed for this lesson includes multiplication and squaring facts (Lessons 3.2–3.7), prime and composite numbers (Lesson 11.6), and knowledge of area (Lesson 6.1).

See page 502B for Math Background for teachers for this lesson.

## Objectives

- To help students recall and recognize various ways to decide whether a two-digit number has factors of 2, 5, 10, 3, 9, or 11
- To help students discover that if they know rules for finding these factors and the square facts, there is only one composite number less than 100 that is not obviously composite

## NCTM Standards

**Number and Operations**

- Know that some numbers have exactly two factors and are called *prime numbers*
- Know that some numbers have more than two factors and are called *composite numbers*
- Identify factors of whole numbers to 100

**Problem Solving**

Apply appropriate strategies to solve problems

## Materials

- *Response Wheels
- Graph paper (optional)

## Technology

**Presentation** Lesson 11.7

## Test Prep

**Cumulative Review**
Mental Math reviews multiplication and addition facts (Lesson 3.10).

**Multistep Problems**
Problems 2–4

**Extended Response**
Problems 2–4

*Manipulative Kit Item

## Planning for Learning • DIFFERENTIATE INSTRUCTION

### INTERVENTION

**If . . .** students lack the prerequisite skill of dividing with remainders,

**Then . . .** teach ***Intervention*** Lesson 11.B.

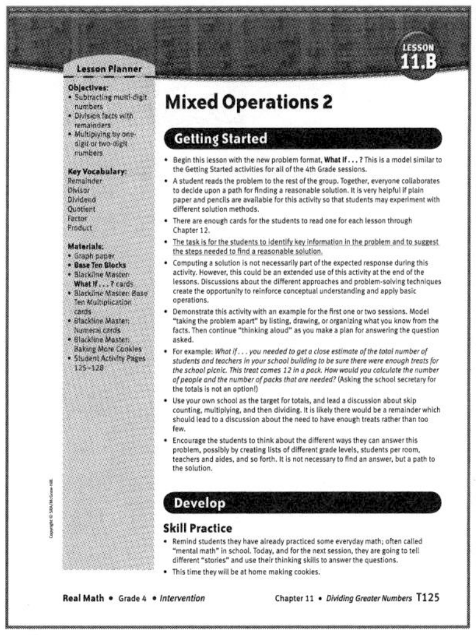


Intervention Lesson 11.B

### ENGLISH LEARNER

**Preview**

**If . . .** students need language support,

**Then . . .** use Lesson 11.7 in ***English Learner Support Guide*** to preview lesson concepts and vocabulary.

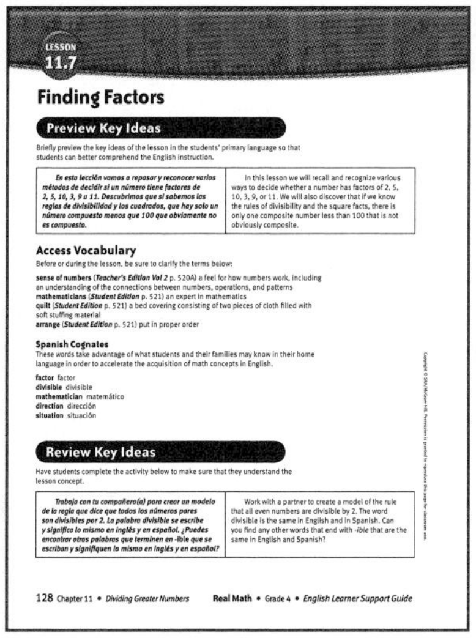


English Learner Lesson 11.7

### ENRICH

**If . . .** students are proficient in the lesson concepts,

**Then . . .** encourage students to work on their projects.

### PRACTICE

**If . . .** students would benefit from additional practice,

**Then . . .** extend Skill Practice before assigning the student pages.

### RETEACH

**If . . .** students are having difficulty understanding factors,

**Then . . .** extend Strategy Building before assigning the students pages.

### Vocabulary

**divisible \di viz´ ə bəl\ *adj.*** One number is divisible by another if it can be divided without a remainder.

### Access Vocabulary

**number sense** a feel for how numbers work, including an understanding of the connections between the numbers, operations, and patterns

### Spanish Cognates

**factor** factor
**divisible** divisible

# Teaching Lesson 11.7

## Mental Math

5

Review | RESPONSE WHEEL

Practice multiplication facts involving the numbers 9 and 3 paired with problems that involve finding the sum of the digits of each product. Provide problems such as the following:

| | | | |
|---|---|---|---|
| **a.** 9 × 7 63 | **b.** 6 + 3 9 | **c.** 9 × 9 81 | **d.** 8 + 1 9 |
| **e.** 4 × 9 36 | **f.** 3 + 6 9 | **g.** 3 × 7 21 | **h.** 2 + 1 3 |
| **i.** 3 × 20 60 | **j.** 6 + 0 6 | **k.** 3 × 12 36 | **l.** 3 + 6 9 |

## 1 Develop

20

### Tell Students In Today's Lesson They Will

learn various ways to decide which factors make up a number.

### Strategy Building

UNDERSTANDING — Whole Group

In this activity, make sure students understand that we are talking about whole numbers, such as 0, 1, 2, 3, 4, and so on.

- Write the following numbers on the board: 27, 36, and 81.

  Explain that we say these numbers are divisible by 9 because they can be divided by 9 with no remainder. For example: 27 ÷ 9 = 3 so, 27 is divisible by 9.

- **Ask the students to list some numbers that are divisible by 9.** Possible answers: 9, 18, 27, 36, 45, 54, and so on
- **Do you notice anything interesting about the sum of the digits of these numbers?** The sum of the digits of a number with a factor of 9 is 9 (at least up to 90).
- Write 9 × 11 on the board. Ask groups to determine if the rule about the sum of the digits applies in this case. 99, No, because the sum of 9 and 9 is 18.
- **How can the rule be modified so it is more accurate?** The sum of the digits of a number divisible by 9 is also divisible by 9 (the sum isn't necessarily the number 9 itself). A number is divisible by 9 if and only if the sum of its digits is divisible by 9.
- Have students determine if a similar divisibility rule exists for the number 3. If so, what is it? Yes, a number is divisible by 3 if and only if the sum of its digits is divisible by 3.
- Have students determine if divisibility rules exist for 10, 5, and 2.

### Guided Discussion

UNDERSTANDING — Whole Group

Have students share their findings about rules of divisibility for 10, 5, and 2. Follow up with questions such as the following. Have students use the board or overhead projector to show examples that illustrate their answers.

- **If a number is divisible by 10, is it also divisible by 5?** Yes, because 10 is divisible by 5. Example: 30 ÷ 10 = 3; 30 ÷ 5 = 6
- **If 5 is added to a number that is divisible by 10, then is that number divisible by 5?** Yes. Example: 50 + 5 = 55; 55 ÷ 5 = 11
- **How can we recognize a number that is divisible by 5?** if it ends in 0 or 5
- **Is a number divisible by 10 also divisible by 2?** Yes. 20 ÷ 10 = 2; 20 ÷ 2 = 10
- **If we add a number that is divisible by 2, such as 2, 4, 6, or 8, to a number that is divisible by 10, will the sum be divisible by 2?** Yes. 6 + 40 = 46; 46 ÷ 2 = 23
- **How do we recognize an even number?** The number ends in 0, 2, 4, 6, or 8. Examples: 34, 86, 450
- **An even number is always going to be divisible by what number?** 2; Examples: 16 ÷ 2 = 8; 10 ÷ 2 = 5
- **What do you notice about numbers less than 100 that are divisible by 11?** The two digits are the same. Examples: 77, 33, 99

### Skill Practice

COMPUTING — Whole Group

THUMBS UP

Have students respond with thumbs-up or thumbs-down to questions about divisibility of numbers less than or equal to 100.

Ask questions such as the following:

- **Is 36 divisible by 2?** up
- **Is 36 divisible by 3?** up
- **Is 36 divisible by 9?** up
- **Is 36 divisible by 5?** down
- **Is 90 divisible by 5?** up
- **Is 90 divisible by 11?** down

## 2 Assign Student Pages

25

### Pages 520–521 APPLYING

Have students complete pages 520 and 521 in groups of two or three.

Review Problem 1 with the class. Ask questions such as the following:

- **Can you find a number for which you don't know a factoring rule?** 7
- **Can you find another number that can be multiplied by 7 to produce a product less than 100, for which you also don't know a rule?** 13; When students multiply 7 and 13 together they will get 91. This is the only composite number less than 100 that is not obviously composite from the rules given.

#### Monitoring Student Progress

| | |
|---|---|
| **If . . .** students have trouble writing numbers in factored form, | **Then . . .** have them refer to their list of prime and composite numbers. |

### As Students Finish

If students finish early, encourage them to find factors of numbers greater than 100.

LESSON 11.7 **Finding Factors**

## Key Ideas

**There are easy ways to decide whether numbers have certain factors. The words *factor* and *divisible* are related; one may say 3 is a factor of 12 or 12 is divisible by 3.**

- An even number is a number divisible by 2. We can recognize even numbers because their last digit must be divisible by 2 (the last digit must be 0, 2, 4, 6, or 8). For example, 50 has a 0 as its last digit, therefore it is divisible by 2.
- A number is divisible by 3 if the sum of its digits is divisible by 3. The number 492,603 has a sum of digits equal to 24. Because 24 is divisible by 3, the number 492,603 is divisible by 3.
- We can recognize that a number is divisible by 5 by its last digit, which must be either 0 or 5. Because 75 has 5 as its last digit, it is divisible by 5.
- A two-digit number is divisible by 11 if the two digits are equal to each other. Take 33, for example: 3 = 3, so 33 is divisible by 11.
- Also, you know the squares of all numbers up to 10. For example, $7^2 = 49$. So, you can recognize perfect squares up to 100.
- If a number is divisible by 4, 6, 8, or 9, you will know it is divisible by one of its factors.

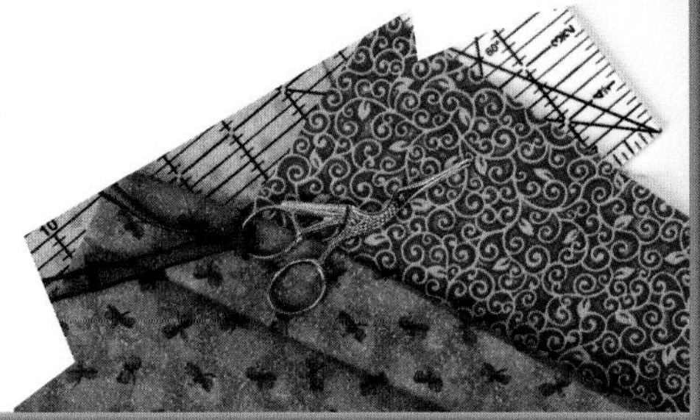





**Answer** the following questions.

1. There is one and only one composite number less than 100 whose factors cannot be easily identified using the information shown above. What must its factors be? What is the number?

   ❶ The only possible factors not covered by the preceding hints are 7 and 13, so the number is 91.

2. Multistep **Extended Response** When you rewrite a composite number in completely factored form with nothing but prime factors, you repeat factors that occur more than once. For example, $24 = 2 \times 2 \times 2 \times 3$ and $36 = 2 \times 2 \times 3 \times 3$. Explain why you think mathematicians decided to define a prime number as a number having exactly two factors (1 and itself).

   ❷ If 1 were a prime number, there would not be a unique way of writing a number as a product of primes.

3. Multistep **Extended Response** Sam has to pack boxes in a truck. The boxes are 3 feet by 4 feet by 5 feet. The truck is 9 feet tall, 30 feet long, and 12 feet wide. What is the best way for Sam to pack the boxes? (Which way should the boxes be arranged?) How many boxes can Sam fit in the truck? See Reflect in the *Teacher's Edition*.

4. Multistep SOCIAL STUDIES **Extended Response** Abigail is making a quilt. She would like the final quilt to be 76 inches long and 54 inches wide, including a 2-inch border around it. She intends to sew pieces of cloth together that are 5 inches by 6 inches, and wants all the strips to be arranged in the same direction. Which way should she arrange the pieces of cloth? How many pieces will she need altogether? How might her ability to factor help Abigail in this situation? See Reflect in the *Teacher's Edition*.





# 3 Reflect

10

## Guided Discussion REASONING

Whole Group

■ **How does knowing rules of divisibility help you determine whether numbers have certain factors.** Possible answer: By knowing a divisibility rule, we can rule out or be sure that certain numbers are factors. Divisibility rules save us time and effort in recognizing factors.

### Extended Response

**Problem 2** If 1 were a prime number, you would presumably have to write an infinite number of factors of 1 for every number. To avoid this, mathematicians created a definition of prime and composite that excludes 1 as a either prime or composite.

**Problem 3** Because 5 is a factor of 30, and 4 is a factor of 12, it is best to arrange the boxes with the 5-foot sides parallel to the 30-foot side of the truck and the 4-foot sides parallel to the 12-foot sides of the truck. Since 3 is a factor of 9, you can fit the boxes snugly in three layers with six rows of three columns or 54 boxes. Because there is no wasted space, you could also divide the volume of the truck (3,240 cu. feet) by the volume of a box (60 cu. feet).

**Problem 4** After subtracting the 2-inch border from all the sides, the quilt measures 72 inches by 50 inches. Since 6 is a factor of 72 and 5 is a factor of 50, the strips should be arranged with the 6-inch sides going the same direction as the 72-inch side, while the 5-inch sides go the same direction as the 50-inch side. There should be twelve strips in each column and ten strips in each row, with 120 strips in all.

SOCIAL STUDIES **Curriculum Connection:** Students may be interested in researching the importance of quilt making in different cultures, such as the Amish or native Hawaiians. Research can be done online or at the library.

Review **Cumulative Review:** For review of adding and subtracting fractions, assign Problems 29–32 on student page 525.

**Family Involvement:** Assign the ***Practice, Reteach,*** or ***Enrichment*** activities depending on the needs of your students.

Encourage students to play the **Four Cube Division Game** at home with friends or relatives.

**Concept/Question Board:** Encourage students to continue to post questions, answers, and examples on the Concept/Question Board.

**Math Puzzler:** Replace the letters with digits to make the division problem work. If a letter appears more than once, replace it with the same digit each time. $TAP \div A = UP$ More than one answer is possible: one could be 150 ÷ 5 = 30

# 4 Assess and Differentiate

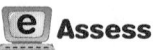

**e Assess** Use ***eAssess*** to record and analyze evidence of student understanding.

## A Gather Evidence

Use the Daily Class Assessment Records in ***Assessment*** or ***eAssess*** to record daily observations.

### Performance Assessment

**Strategy Building**

Did the student UNDERSTANDING
- ❑ make important observations?
- ❑ extend or generalize learning?
- ❑ provide insightful answers?
- ❑ pose insightful questions?

### Informal Assessment

**Skill Practice**

Did the student COMPUTING
- ❑ respond accurately?
- ❑ respond quickly?
- ❑ respond with confidence?
- ❑ self-correct?

## B Summarize Findings

Analyze and summarize assessment data for each student. Determine which Assessment Follow-Up is appropriate for each student. Use the Student Assessment Record in ***Assessment*** or ***eAssess*** to update assessment records.

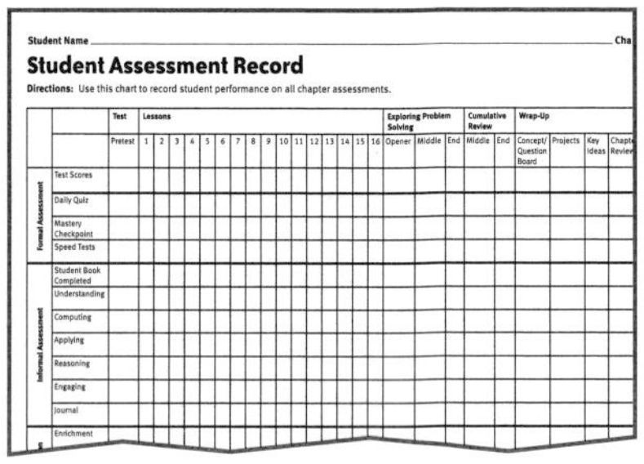


**Assessment Page T41**

## C Assessment Follow-Up • DIFFERENTIATE INSTRUCTION

Based on your observations, use these teaching strategies for assessment follow-up.

### INTERVENTION

Review student performance on ***Intervention*** Lesson 11.B to see if students have mastered prerequisite skills for this lesson.

### ENGLISH LEARNER

**Review**

Use Lesson 11.7 in ***English Learner Support Guide*** to review lesson concepts and vocabulary.

### ENRICH

**If . . .** students are proficient in the lesson concepts,

**Then . . .** encourage them to work on the chapter projects or ***Enrichment*** Lesson 11.7.

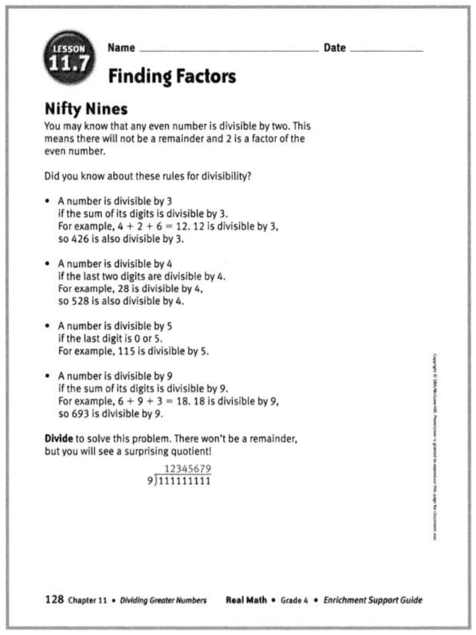

LESSON 11.7 Name ______ Date ______

**Finding Factors**

**Nifty Nines**

You may know that any even number is divisible by two. This means there will not be a remainder and 2 is a factor of the even number.

Did you know about these rules for divisibility?

- A number is divisible by 3 if the sum of its digits is divisible by 3. For example, 4 + 2 + 6 = 12. 12 is divisible by 3, so 426 is also divisible by 3.
- A number is divisible by 4 if the last two digits are divisible by 4. For example, 28 is divisible by 4, so 528 is also divisible by 4.
- A number is divisible by 5 if the last digit is 0 or 5. For example, 115 is divisible by 5.
- A number is divisible by 9 if the sum of its digits is divisible by 9. For example, 6 + 9 + 3 = 18. 18 is divisible by 9, so 693 is divisible by 9.

**Divide** to solve this problem. There won't be a remainder, but you will see a surprising quotient!

$9\overline{)111111111}$ = 12345679

128 Chapter 11 • *Dividing Greater Numbers* **Real Math** • Grade 4 • *Enrichment Support Guide*

Enrichment Lesson 11.7

### PRACTICE

**If . . .** students would benefit from additional practice,

**Then . . .** assign ***Practice*** Lesson 11.7.

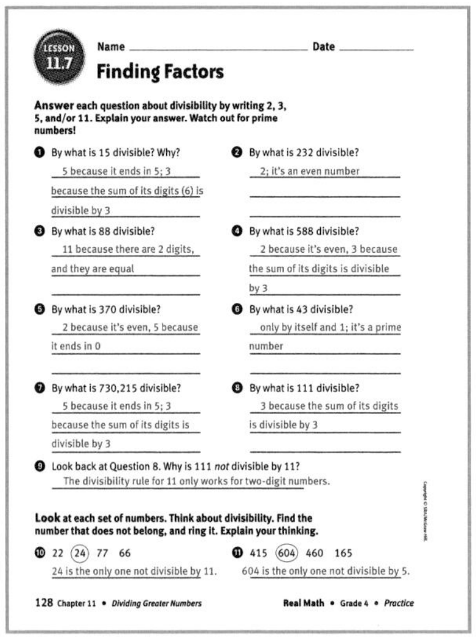

LESSON 11.7 Name ______ Date ______

**Finding Factors**

**Answer each question about divisibility by writing 2, 3, 5, and/or 11. Explain your answer. Watch out for prime numbers!**

1. By what is 15 divisible? Why? 5 because it ends in 5; 3 because the sum of its digits (6) is divisible by 3
2. By what is 232 divisible? 2; it's an even number
3. By what is 88 divisible? 11 because there are 2 digits, and they are equal
4. By what is 588 divisible? 2 because it's even, 3 because the sum of its digits is divisible by 3
5. By what is 370 divisible? 2 because it's even, 5 because it ends in 0
6. By what is 43 divisible? only by itself and 1; it's a prime number
7. By what is 730,215 divisible? 5 because it ends in 5; 3 because the sum of its digits is divisible by 3
8. By what is 111 divisible? 3 because the sum of its digits is divisible by 3
9. Look back at Question 8. Why is 111 *not* divisible by 11? The divisibility rule for 11 only works for two-digit numbers.

**Look at each set of numbers. Think about divisibility. Find the number that does not belong, and ring it. Explain your thinking.**

10. 22 (24) 77 66 — 24 is the only one not divisible by 11.
11. 415 (604) 460 165 — 604 is the only one not divisible by 5.

128 Chapter 11 • *Dividing Greater Numbers* **Real Math** • Grade 4 • *Practice*

Practice Lesson 11.7

### RETEACH

**If . . .** students are having difficulty finding factors,

**Then . . .** when factoring, have students use a factoring tree, which will help students break down a number into prime factors.

CHAPTER 11 Problem Solving

# Exploring Problem Solving

### Objectives

- To compare two plans of using division to solve a problem that involve historical data
- To explore how order can matter in some computations
- To analyze the Make a Plan Strategy
- To see the importance of checking whether or not a plan makes sense

**Context of the Lesson** In this lesson, students use what they have been learning about division to make comparisons. Building on the Chapter Introduction, students compare the crowdedness of the Mayflower before and after new passengers arrived from another ship. Later in the chapter, they will use division to analyze the voyage of the Mayflower.

## 1 Develop

5

### Tell Students In Today's Lesson They Will

- read a challenging problem about how crowded it was on the Mayflower.
- look at two different plans for solving the same problem.
- determine why one of the plans will work and why one will not.
- solve the problem with their group and share how they solved it.

## Guided Discussion

Read the problem and information on page 522 with the class. To make sure students understand the problem, ask questions such as the following:

- **Why did the Mayflower end up with more passengers than originally planned?** The ship that was traveling with the Mayflower was not seaworthy, so many of its passengers joined the Mayflower.
- **How many passengers did the Mayflower have originally?** 60
- **How many passengers did the Mayflower have after she took on passengers from the Speedwell?** 102
- **As a result, did the Mayflower get more crowded or less crowded?** more
- **On average, did each passenger have more room or less room?** less
- **What is the problem asking you to find?** how much less room there was per passenger as a result of the new passengers coming on board
- **What other information do you have besides the number of passengers?** the dimensions of the passenger sections on the Mayflower

Student Page

## Exploring Problem Solving

When the Mayflower first set off for the New World, she had 60 passengers and a companion boat, the Speedwell. After the Speedwell sprang some leaks, many of its passengers joined the already crowded Mayflower, which then carried 102 passengers across the Atlantic Ocean.

On average, about how much less area was there for each passenger after the Mayflower took on passengers from the Speedwell?

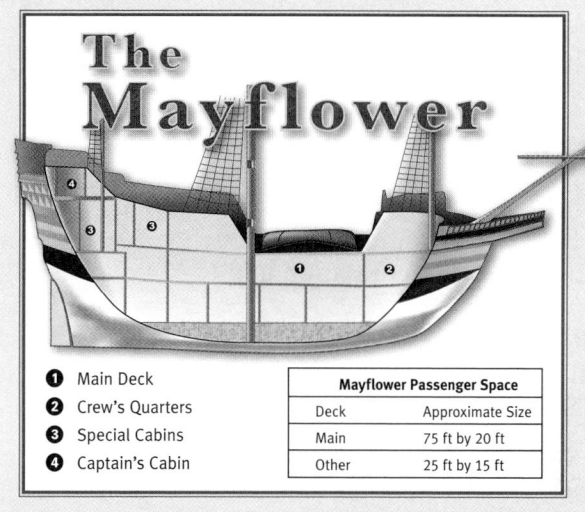

1 Main Deck
2 Crew's Quarters
3 Special Cabins
4 Captain's Cabin

| Mayflower Passenger Space | |
|---|---|
| Deck | Approximate Size |
| Main | 75 ft by 20 ft |
| Other | 25 ft by 15 ft |



Textbook This lesson is available in the *eTextbook.*

Student Page

**Miguel solved the problem this way:**

*I Made a Plan to solve the problem.*

*My Plan*
*A. Find the total area for passengers.*
*B. Divide to find the area for each passenger after passengers came from the Speedwell.*
*C. Divide to find the area for each passenger before passengers came from the Speedwell.*
*D. Find the difference.*

**Think** about Miguel's strategy. Answer these questions. See *Teacher's Edition.*

1. How can Miguel find the total area in Step A?
2. What should Miguel divide by in Steps B and C?

**Ashlee solved the problem this way:**

*I made a different plan.*

*My Plan*
*A. Find the total area for passengers.*
*B. Find how many new passengers joined the Mayflower.*
*C. Divide the total area by the number of new passengers.*

**Think** about Ashlee's strategy. Answer these questions.

3. In Step C, what number will Ashlee divide by? 42, (or 40 if she rounds)
4. If you were finding the area per passenger when there were just 60 passengers, what number would you divide the area by? 60
5. Which will give a greater result, dividing the area by 60 or by 42? 42
6. How do your answers to Problems 3–5 show that Ashlee's plan does not make sense?
7. How would you solve the problem? The area per passenger decreased by about 12 or 13 sq. ft.

6. If you follow Ashlee's plan, you'll find that the area per passenger decreased by more than what it was to start with. That can't be.

# 2 Exploring Problem Solving 20

## Using Student Pages

Discuss Miguel's strategy. Give students time to think about Problems 1–2, then discuss them. Please note that the dimensions of the passenger sections are approximations. The decks were not rectangles, and the widths given are considered to be the width at the widest point.

## Answers to Problems 1 and 2

### Problem 1

Multiply 75 × 20 to find the area of the main deck, multiply 25 × 15 to find the other area, then add the two areas together.

### Problem 2

In each step, he should divide by the number of passengers: by 102 in Step B and by 60 in Step C.

Have the class read and think about Ashlee's plan. Discuss whether it seems to make sense at first glance. Next, give students time to think about Problems 3–6, and then discuss them. Discuss the following point:
A plan may sound reasonable even though it does not make sense. That is why it is important to look at the results. If the results do not make sense, there may be something wrong with the way the plan was carried out, or there may be something wrong with the plan itself.

## Answer to Problem 6

What Ashlee is proposing:

$$\frac{\text{Area}}{60} - \frac{\text{Area}}{102} = \frac{\text{Area}}{42}$$

If students try this with simpler numbers, for example, $\frac{1}{5} - \frac{1}{8} = \frac{1}{3}$, they should see even more clearly why Ashlee's plan does not make sense because the area per passenger decreased by more than what it was to start with.

Have students work in pairs or small groups to solve Problem 7. Encourage students to approximate, since the data given is an approximation itself.

## Answer to Problem 7

The area per passenger decreased by about 12 or 13 square feet.

# 3 Reflect 10

**KAS Knowledge Age Skills**

**Effective Communication** Have groups present their solutions and methods to Problem 7. After each method is presented, ask questions such as the following:

- Did the group check its results?
- What did you like about the method or the way it was presented?
- How crowded was the Mayflower?

Give students a graphic sense of the conditions on the Mayflower. Under your guidance, have one or more volunteers use tape or other material to mark off on the floor the area that each passenger had. As you point to the area, explain the following:

- In this area each person would sleep, eat, store his or her belongings, change clothes, groom himself or herself, prepare food, and so on.
- The passengers were on the Mayflower for more than half a year, counting the time they were on board while waiting to leave England and the time they were on board after reaching the New World while they were deciding where to settle.

# 4 Assess 10

When evaluating student work, focus not only on the correctness of the answer but also on whether students thought rationally about the problem and the various solutions presented. Some questions to consider include the following:

- Did the student understand the problem?
- Did the student show all the steps his or her group took in solving the problem?
- Could the student explain why Ashlee's strategy would not work and why it did not make sense?
- Did the student look back to see if the reasoning and the answer made sense?

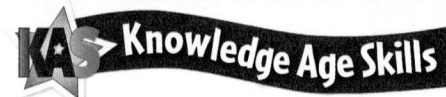

# Cumulative Review

## Assign Pages 524–525

Use this Cumulative Review as a review of concepts and skills that students have previously learned.

Here are different ways you can assign these problems to your students as they work through the chapter:

- For each lesson in the chapter, assign a set of Cumulative Review problems to be completed as practice or for homework.
  - Lesson 11.1—Problems 1–2
  - Lesson 11.2—Problems 3–5
  - Lesson 11.3—Problems 6–14
  - Lesson 11.4—Problems 15–23
  - Lesson 11.5—Problems 24–25
  - Lesson 11.6—Problems 26–28
  - Lesson 11.7—Problems 29–32
- At any point during the chapter, assign part or all of the Cumulative Review problems to be completed as practice or for homework.

### Cumulative Review

**Problems 1–2** review three-digit by two-digit multiplication, Lesson 6.5.

**Problems 3–5** review fractions and rational numbers, Lesson 8.3.

**Problems 6–14** review division, Lessons 3.10–3.11.

**Problems 15–23** review rounding decimals, Lesson 9.5.

**Problems 24–25** review reading a ruler, Lesson 8.12.

**Problems 26–28** review lines and angles, Lessons 10.2, 10.3, 10.6, and 10.9.

**Problems 29–32** review adding and subtracting fractions, Lessons 8.12 and 8.13.

### Monitoring Student Progress

**If . . .** students miss more than one problem in a section, **Then . . .** refer to the indicated lesson for remediation suggestions.

Student Page

## Cumulative Review

Multiplication: Three-Digit by Two-Digit Lesson 6.5

**Solve** each problem.

1. 565 × 32 = ■ 18,080
2. 710 × 854 = ■ 606,340

Fractions and Rational Numbers Lesson 8.3

**Write** two equivalent fractions for each of the following.

3. $\frac{2}{4}$ Some possible answers are $\frac{1}{2}, \frac{4}{8}, \frac{5}{10}$
4. $\frac{2}{3}$ Some possible answers are $\frac{4}{6}, \frac{8}{12}, \frac{16}{24}$
5. $\frac{5}{6}$ Some possible answers are $\frac{10}{12}, \frac{15}{18}, \frac{20}{24}$

Division Lesson 3.10–3.11

**Solve.**

6. 35 ÷ 13 = ■ 2 R9
7. 25 ÷ 8 = ■ 3 R1
8. 64 ÷ 4 = ■ 16
9. 19 ÷ 2 = ■ 9 R1
10. 33 ÷ 9 = ■ 3 R6
11. 74 ÷ 5 = ■ 14 R4
12. 56 ÷ 2 = ■ 28
13. 98 ÷ 6 = ■ 16 R2
14. 212 ÷ 3 = ■ 70 R2

Metric Units Lesson 9.7

**Round** the following decimals to the nearest tenth.

15. 0.14 0.1
16. 9.15 9.2
17. 125.65 125.7
18. 65.09 65.1
19. 8.47 8.5
20. 0.0589 0.1
21. 0.921 0.9
22. 18.38 18.4
23. 5.888 5.9



eTextbook This lesson is available in the *eTextbook*.

Student Page

Representing Fractions Greater than 1 Lesson 8.11

**Measure** the following lengths to the nearest $\frac{1}{8}$ of an inch.

24. —— $\frac{4}{8}$ inch or $\frac{1}{2}$ inch
25. ———————— 4 inches

Lines and Angles Lessons 10.2, 10.3, 10.6, and 10.9

**Think** carefully about these geometry problems.

26. Which of these lines are parallel? Lines *CD* and *AB*

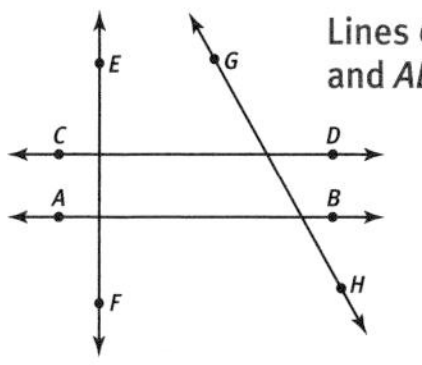


27. The line segment in the circle below appears to be which of the following?

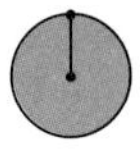

a. chord b. diameter
(c.) radius d. circumference

28. Label the acute angles in object *WXYZ*.

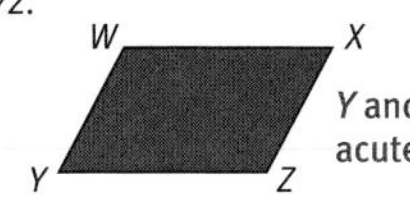


*Y* and *X* are acute angles

Adding and Subtracting Fractions Lessons 8.15–8.16

**Add** or subtract these fractions.

29. $6\frac{1}{2} + 6\frac{2}{4} =$ ■ 13
30. $6 - 1\frac{1}{5} =$ ■ $4\frac{4}{5}$
31. $7\frac{3}{8} + 11\frac{7}{10} =$ ■ $18\frac{43}{40}$ or $19\frac{3}{40}$
32. $22\frac{2}{9} - 12\frac{3}{4} =$ ■ $9\frac{17}{36}$

## Mid-Test

# Individual Oral Assessment

## Purpose of the Test

The Individual Oral Assessment is designed to measure students' growing knowledge of chapter concepts. It is administered to each student individually, and it requires oral responses from each student. The test takes about five minutes to complete.

See ***Assessment*** for detailed instructions for administering and interpreting the test, and record students' answers on the Student Assessment Recording Sheet.

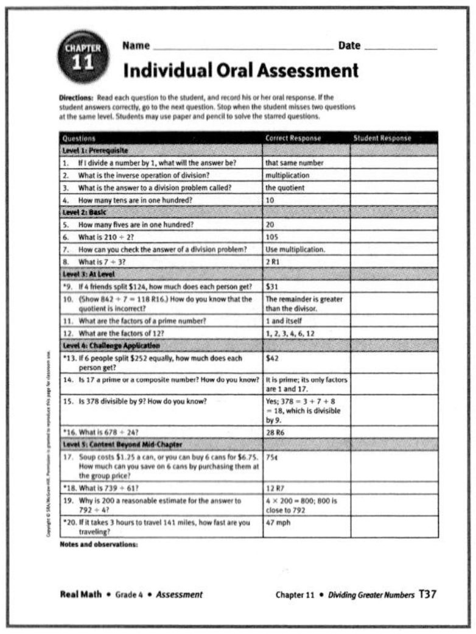


**Assessment Page T37**

### Directions

Read each question to the student, and record his or her oral response. If the student answers correctly, go to the next question. Stop when the student misses two questions at the same level. Students may use paper and pencil to solve the starred questions.

## Questions

### Level 1: Prerequisite

1. If I divide a number by 1, what will the answer be? that same number
2. What is the inverse operation of division? multiplication
3. What is the answer to a division problem called? the quotient
4. How many tens are in one hundred? 10

### Level 2: Basic

5. How many fives are in one hundred? 20
6. What is 210 ÷ 2? 105
7. How can you check the answer of a division problem? Use multiplication.
8. What is 7 ÷ 3? 2 R1

### Level 3: At Level

*9. If 4 friends split $124, how much does each person get? $31

10. (Show 842 ÷ 7 = 118 R16.) How do you know that the quotient is incorrect? The remainder is greater than the divisor.

11. What are the factors of a prime number? 1 and itself

12. What are the factors of 12? 1, 2, 3, 4, 6, 12

### Level 4: Challenge Application

*13. If 6 people split $252 equally, how much does each person get? $42

14. Is 17 a prime or a composite number? How do you know? It is prime; its only factors are 1 and 17.

15. Is 378 divisible by 9? How do you know? Yes; 378 = 3 + 7 + 8 = 18, which is divisible by 9.

*16. What is 678 ÷ 24? 28 R6

### Level 5: Content Beyond Mid-Chapter

17. Soup costs $1.25 a can, or you can buy 6 cans for $6.75. How much can you save on 6 cans by purchasing them at the group price? 75¢

*18. What is 739 ÷ 61? 12 R7

19. Why is 200 a reasonable estimate for the answer to 792 ÷ 4? 4 × 200 = 800; 800 is close to 792

*20. If it takes 3 hours to travel 141 miles, how fast are you traveling? 47 mph

## Lesson Planner

**OBJECTIVES**
- To provide practice in using division to find unit costs and determine better buys
- To develop number sense in response to how money is spent

**NCTM STANDARDS**

**Number and Operations**
Use division to figure out how much one item out of a group would cost

**Problem Solving**
Apply appropriate strategies to solve problems

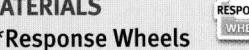

**MATERIALS**
- ***Response Wheels**
- ***Number Cubes** (two 0–5 and two 5–10)
- *Play money (optional)
- Food ads (optional)
- Restaurant menus (optional)

**TECHNOLOGY**
**e Presentation** Lesson 11.8
**e MathTools** Coins and Money

**TEST PREP**

**Cumulative Review**
Mental Math reviews inverse operations with multiplication and division (Lesson 3.10).

**Multistep Problems**
Problems 3, 8, and 11

**Extended Response**
Problems 3 and 8

**Writing + Math**
Journal

*Manipulative Kit Item

# Unit Cost

**Context of the Lesson** This is the eighth of twelve lessons on division using greater numbers. Students will use their knowledge of division to examine situations in which buying larger quantities of items may cost less. For these problems, students must decide which option is the most cost effective.

See page 502B for Math Background for teachers for this lesson.

## Planning for Learning • DIFFERENTIATE INSTRUCTION

### INTERVENTION

**If . . .** students lack the prerequisite skill of dividing with remainders,

**Then . . .** teach ***Intervention*** Lesson 11.B.

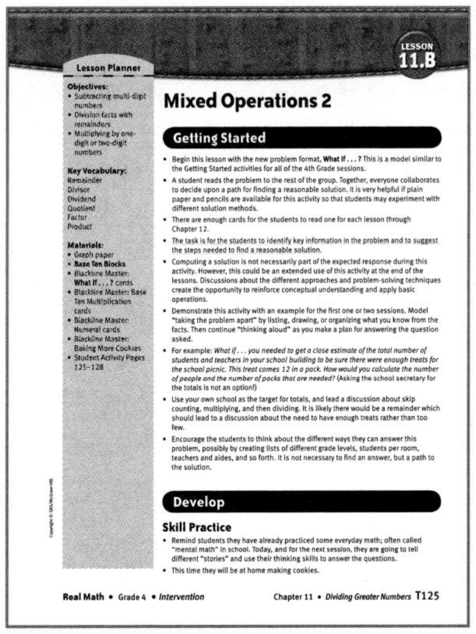


Intervention Lesson 11.B

### ENGLISH LEARNER

Preview

**If . . .** students need language support,

**Then . . .** use Lesson 11.8 in ***English Learner Support Guide*** to preview lesson concepts and vocabulary.

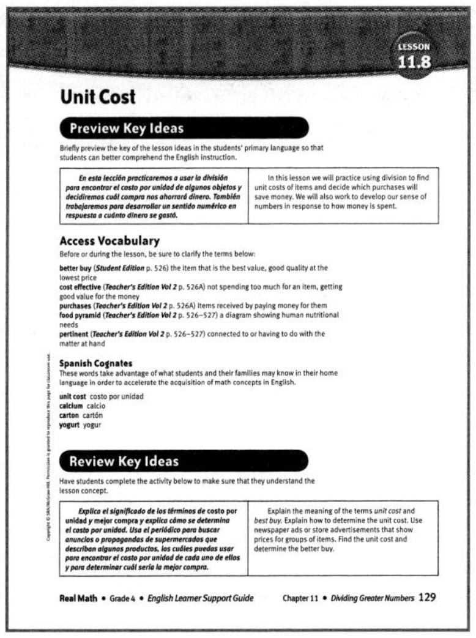


English Learner Lesson 11.8

### ENRICH

**If . . .** students are proficient in the lesson concepts,

**Then . . .** encourage them to explore division using ***eMathTools.***

### PRACTICE

**If . . .** students would benefit from additional practice,

**Then . . .** extend Guided Discussion before assigning student pages.

### RETEACH

**If . . .** students are having difficulty understanding how to find unit cost,

**Then . . .** extend Guided Discussion before assigning the student pages.

**Vocabulary**
**unit cost** ***n.*** The cost of one out of a number of equally priced goods.

**Access Vocabulary**
**better buy** the item that is the best value and quality at the lowest price
**cost effective** not spending too much money; getting a good value

**Spanish Cognates**
**unit cost** costo por unidad

# Teaching Lesson 11.8

## Mental Math 5

Review RESPONSE WHEEL To emphasize inverse operations, give students pairs of related multidigit multiplication and division problems such as the following:

**a.** $80 \times 30 = 2{,}400$ $2{,}400 \div 30 = 80$
**b.** $6 \times 50 = 300$ $300 \div 6 = 50$
**c.** $7 \times 20 = 140$ $140 \div 20 = 7$
**d.** $8 \times 40 = 320$ $320 \div 40 = 8$
**e.** $90 \times 20 = 1{,}800$ $1{,}800 \div 90 = 20$
**f.** $40 \times 80 = 3{,}200$ $3{,}200 \div 80 = 40$

## 1 Develop 15

### Tell Students In Today's Lesson They Will

learn to find unit costs of items and decide which purchases will save money.

### Guided Discussion UNDERSTANDING

Whole Group

Explain that students are going to learn how to figure unit cost by dividing. Start by asking a question such as the following:

- **Without doing any arithmetic, which do you think is a better buy—2 books for \$10 or 3 for \$12?** Keep track of students' opinions on the board.

Discuss the concept of a "better buy" as a situation in which you purchase a group of items and the cost of one item out of the group is less than the cost of one of the same item out of a second smaller group of items.

- **How much does 1 book cost if you buy books in groups of 2? How did you figure that out?** \$5 because you can divide 10 by 2 to get 5
- **How much does 1 book cost when you buy books in groups of 3? How did you figure that out?** \$4 because you can divide 12 by 3 to get 4

The cost of 1 book is the unit cost, and it was found by using division. Ask a question such as the following:

- **Is buying 3 books for \$4 a better buy than 2 books for \$10?** You are actually paying less per book when you buy them in groups of three, but if you do not want the third book you may prefer to buy only two.

## 2 Assign Student Pages 30

**Page 527** APPLYING

Have students complete page 527 independently. After students finish the problems on page 527, discuss them together.

### Monitoring Student Progress

**If . . .** students have trouble with the word problems,

**Then . . .** encourage them to draw pictures, use play money, or use ***eMathTools: Coins and Money*** to show the situation described in each problem.

### As Students Finish

Game **Four Cube Division Game**

**RESEARCH IN ACTION**

"The multiplication and division algorithms are complex embedded methods that are not easy to understand or carry out. They demand high levels of skill in multiplying a multidigit number by a single-digit number within complex embedded formats in which multiplying and adding alternate."

Fuson, Karen F. "Developing Mathematical Power in Whole Number Operations" in Kilpatrick, Jeremy, Martin, W. Gary, and Schifter, Deborah, eds. *A Research Companion to Principles and Standards for School Mathematics.* Reston, VA: National Council of Teachers of Mathematics, Inc. 2003. pp.85.

Student Page

LESSON 11.8 **Unit Cost**

## Key Ideas

**You can find the unit cost of an item by dividing.**

Sometimes you can get a better price for each item when you buy the item in larger amounts. The price of one item out of the group is called the *unit cost*. You can use division to find the unit cost. Look at the example below.

Heather wants to buy soup. The store offers 2 cans of vegetable soup for 72¢ or 3 cans of the same kind of soup for 96¢.

How much does the soup cost per can if you buy it in groups of two cans?

*Per* means "for each." We can find the cost for each can by dividing 72 by 2.

How much does soup cost per can if you buy it in groups of 3 cans? We can find the cost per can by dividing 96 by 3.

$$2\overline{)72}\ \text{quotient } 36 \qquad 3\overline{)96}\ \text{quotient } 32$$

The soup costs 36¢ per can when you buy it in groups of 2 cans.

The soup costs 32¢ per can when you buy it in groups of 3. It costs 4¢ less per can when you buy it in groups of 3 than when you buy it in groups of 2.

526

Textbook This lesson is available in the *eTextbook*.

Student Page

**Answer** the following questions.

Rosan wants to buy rice. A 2-kilogram bag costs $1.20 (120¢).

A 5-kilogram bag costs $2.65 (256¢).

1. How much per kilogram does rice in 2-kilogram bags cost? 60¢
2. How much per kilogram does rice in 5-kilogram bags cost? 53¢
3. Multistep Extended Response Which has a smaller unit cost? Why? the 5-kg bag; it costs less per kg
4. If 7 pencils cost 91¢, how much is it per pencil? 13¢
5. HEALTH Milk contains calcium, which is necessary for strong bones. If 3 quarts of milk cost $1.74 (174¢), how much is it per quart? 58¢
6. If 4 apples cost 92¢, how much is it per apple? 23¢
7. If 6 oranges cost $1.32 (132¢), how much is it per orange? 22¢
8. Multistep Extended Response An 8-pound turkey costs $9.50 (950¢). A 9-pound turkey costs $11.40 (1,140¢). Which turkey costs less per pound? Why? the 8-pound turkey; it costs almost 8¢ less per pound
9. If 3 pads of paper cost $1.38 (138¢) altogether, how much is it per pad? 46¢
10. If an 8-bottle carton of juice costs $3.84 (384¢), how much is it per bottle? 48¢
11. Multistep Lena needs to buy 24 containers of yogurt for her classmates. She can buy 1 at 55¢, or she can buy a 12-pack of yogurt for $5.80 (580¢). How much money can she save by buying 12-packs? 160¢ or $1.60
12. If 10 pencil erasers cost $1.20 (120¢), how much is it per eraser? 12¢

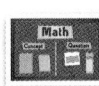

Writing + Math **Journal**

Why is it important to know the unit cost of an item?

Possible answer: Knowing the unit price may save you money if you want to buy more than one of the same item.

Chapter 11 • Lesson 8 527

# 3 Reflect

10

## Guided Discussion REASONING

Whole Group

- Have students explain how to determine unit cost.
- Present a situation such as the following:

  A group of students is selling newspapers on the corner of West St. and High St. The first paper is 50¢ and each additional paper can be purchased for 10¢. At South St. and Main St., another group of students is selling newspapers for 35¢ each. Who do you think will sell more papers? Which group has created a better buy? Students may say the group of students on West and High have created the better buy since the customer pays less if they buy multiple papers, therefore will sell more. Students can also argue that the second group will sell more because people do not want two copies of the same newspaper.

## Extended Response REASONING

**Problem 3** The 5-kilogram bag costs less per kilogram. However, students may say they do not need a 5-kilogram bag, making the 2-kilogram bag the better buy.

**Problem 8** The 8-pound turkey costs less per pound; it could be the better buy depending on the number of people eating it.

Writing + Math **Journal**

Knowing the unit price provides consumers with pertinent information affecting their decisions about how to spend their money. This skill will help people save money on goods and services in the long run.

HEALTH **Curriculum Connections:** Students interested in foods may research the food pyramid. From there they can create a balanced menu for themselves.

Review **Cumulative Review:** For review of converting metric units, assign Problems 1–4 on student page 541.

**Family Involvement:** Assign the ***Practice, Reteach,*** or ***Enrichment*** activities depending on the needs of your students. Encourage students to play the **Four Cube Division Game** at home with friends or relatives.

**Concept/Question Board:** Have students attempt to answer any unanswered questions on the Concept/Question Board.

**Math Puzzler:** Replace each blank with a different digit to form a division problem that you can check.

☐71 ÷ 4 = ☐9☐ R3   771 ÷ 4 = 192 R3

# 4 Assess and Differentiate

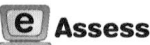

**e Assess** Use ***eAssess*** to record and analyze evidence of student understanding.

## A Gather Evidence

Use the Daily Class Assessment Records in ***Assessment*** or ***eAssess*** to record daily observations.

### Portfolio Assessment

**Journal**

Did the student **REASONING**

- ❑ provide a clear explanation?
- ❑ communicate reasons and strategies?
- ❑ choose appropriate strategies?
- ❑ argue logically?

### Informal Assessment

**Concept/Question Board**

Did the student **ENGAGING**

- ❑ pay attention to others' contributions?
- ❑ contribute information and ideas?
- ❑ improve on a strategy?
- ❑ reflect on and check the accuracy of his or her work?

## B Summarize Findings

Analyze and summarize assessment data for each student. Determine which Assessment Follow-Up is appropriate for each student. Use the Student Assessment Record in ***Assessment*** or ***eAssess*** to update assessment records.

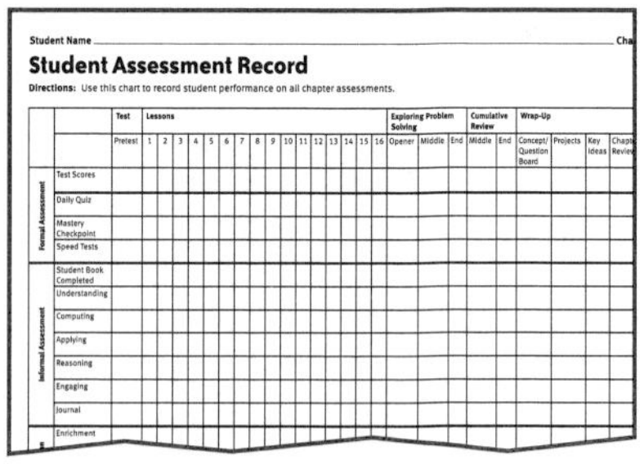
Student Name
**Student Assessment Record**
Directions: Use this chart to record student performance on all chapter assessments.

**Assessment Page T41**

## C Assessment Follow-Up • DIFFERENTIATE INSTRUCTION

Based on your observations, use these teaching strategies for assessment follow-up.

### INTERVENTION

Review student performance on ***Intervention*** Lesson 11.B to see if students have mastered prerequisite skills for this lesson.

### ENGLISH LEARNER

**Review**

Use Lesson 11.8 in ***English Learner Support Guide*** to review lesson concepts and vocabulary.

### ENRICH

**If . . .** students are proficient in the lesson concepts,

**Then . . .** encourage them to work on the chapter projects or ***Enrichment*** Lesson 11.8.

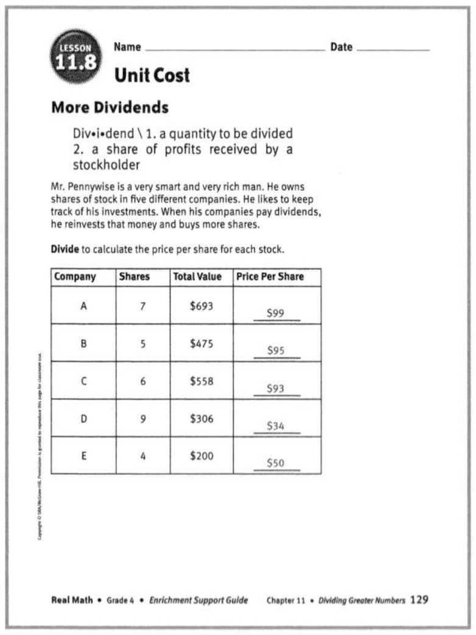
LESSON 11.8 Name ________ Date ________

**Unit Cost**

**More Dividends**

Div•i•dend \ 1. a quantity to be divided 2. a share of profits received by a stockholder

Mr. Pennywise is a very smart and very rich man. He owns shares of stock in five different companies. He likes to keep track of his investments. When his companies pay dividends, he reinvests that money and buys more shares.

**Divide** to calculate the price per share for each stock.

| Company | Shares | Total Value | Price Per Share |
|---|---|---|---|
| A | 7 | $693 | $99 |
| B | 5 | $475 | $95 |
| C | 6 | $558 | $93 |
| D | 9 | $306 | $34 |
| E | 4 | $200 | $50 |

Real Math • Grade 4 • *Enrichment Support Guide* Chapter 11 • *Dividing Greater Numbers* 129

Enrichment Lesson 11.8

### PRACTICE

**If . . .** students would benefit from additional practice,

**Then . . .** assign ***Practice*** Lesson 11.8.

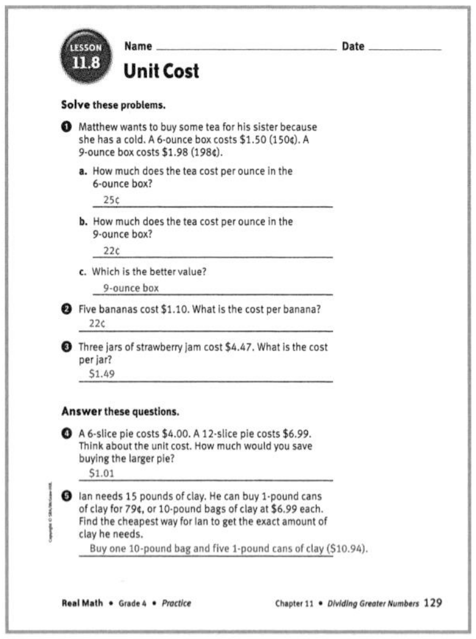
LESSON 11.8 Name ________ Date ________

**Unit Cost**

**Solve these problems.**

1. Matthew wants to buy some tea for his sister because she has a cold. A 6-ounce box costs $1.50 (150¢). A 9-ounce box costs $1.98 (198¢).
   a. How much does the tea cost per ounce in the 6-ounce box? 25¢
   b. How much does the tea cost per ounce in the 9-ounce box? 22¢
   c. Which is the better value? 9-ounce box
2. Five bananas cost $1.10. What is the cost per banana? 22¢
3. Three jars of strawberry jam cost $4.47. What is the cost per jar? $1.49

**Answer these questions.**

4. A 6-slice pie costs $4.00. A 12-slice pie costs $6.99. Think about the unit cost. How much would you save buying the larger pie? $1.01
5. Ian needs 15 pounds of clay. He can buy 1-pound cans of clay for 79¢, or 10-pound bags of clay at $6.99 each. Find the cheapest way for Ian to get the exact amount of clay he needs. Buy one 10-pound bag and five 1-pound cans of clay ($10.94).

Real Math • Grade 4 • *Practice* Chapter 11 • *Dividing Greater Numbers* 129

Practice Lesson 11.8

### RETEACH

**If . . .** students are struggling with finding unit cost,

**Then . . .** have them work the division problem as they have learned, and then compare the answers. Have students use play money to model the division required in each situation presented in the lesson. Have them record their actions in the standard algorithmic form.

## Lesson Planner

**OBJECTIVES**
- To review the inverse relationship of multiplication and division
- To review functions and graphing
- To demonstrate how to use a graph to solve related division problems

**NCTM STANDARDS**

**Number and Operations**
Demonstrate the relationship between multiplication and division

**Representation**
Use a graph to represent conversions between dollars and yen

**MATERIALS**
*Response Wheels

**TECHNOLOGY**
**Presentation** Lesson 11.9

**TEST PREP**

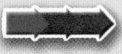

**Cumulative Review**
Mental Math reviews inverse operations with multiplication and division (Lesson 4.5).

**Extended Response**
Problem 21

*Manipulative Kit Item

# Using Inverses

**Context of the Lesson** This is the first of two lessons that review the inverse relationship between multiplication and division. This relationship was recently reintroduced in Chapter 3 and has been the focus of many Mental Math exercises. These two lessons show students a way to solve multidigit divisor problems by estimating and multiplying. The lessons will also broaden students' understanding of division.

See page 502B for Math Background for teachers for this lesson.

## Planning for Learning • DIFFERENTIATE INSTRUCTION

### INTERVENTION

**If . . .** students lack the prerequisite skill of multiplying by a one- or a two-digit number,

**Then . . .** teach ***Intervention*** Lesson 11.C.

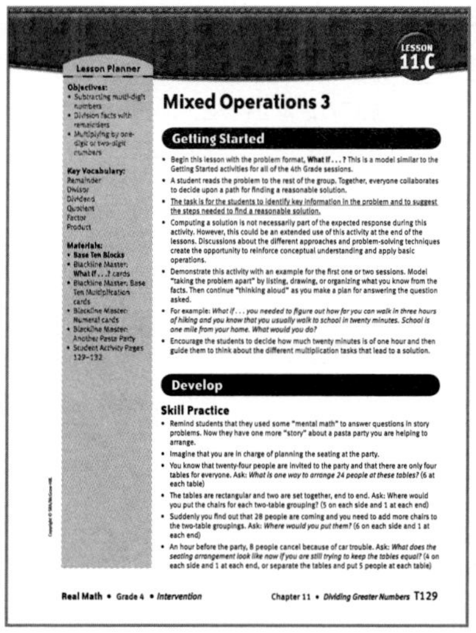
LESSON 11.C

Mixed Operations 3

Getting Started

Develop

Skill Practice

Intervention Lesson 11.C

### ENGLISH LEARNER

Preview

**If . . .** students need language support,

**Then . . .** use Lesson 11.9 in ***English Learner Support Guide*** to preview lesson concepts and vocabulary.

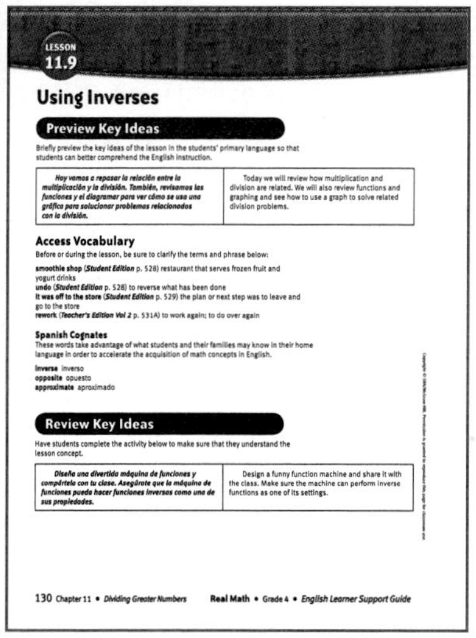
LESSON 11.9

Using Inverses

Preview Key Ideas

Access Vocabulary

Spanish Cognates

Review Key Ideas

English Learner Lesson 11.9

### ENRICH

**If . . .** students are proficient in the lesson concepts,

**Then . . .** encourage them to explore the relationship between multiplication and division using ***eMathTools.***

### PRACTICE

**If . . .** students would benefit from additional practice,

**Then . . .** extend Strategy Building before assigning the student pages.

### RETEACH

**If . . .** students are having difficulty understanding inverses of division,

**Then . . .** extend Strategy Building before assigning the student pages.

### Access Vocabulary

**currency** something used as a means of exchange or payment, such as money

**Spanish Cognates**
**inverse** inverso
**opposite** opuesto

# Teaching Lesson 11.9

## Mental Math

5

RESPONSE WHEEL Have students practice using corresponding pairs of multidigit multiplication and division problems such as the following:

| | |
|---|---|
| **a.** $9 \times 20 = 180$ | $180 \div 9 = 20$ |
| **b.** $8 \times 30 = 240$ | $240 \div 30 = 8$ |
| **c.** $3 \times 50 = 150$ | $150 \div 50 = 3$ |
| **d.** $40 \times 80 = 3{,}200$ | $3200 \div 80 = 40$ |
| **e.** $70 \times 60 = 4{,}200$ | $4200 \div 60 = 70$ |
| **f.** $90 \times 60 = 5{,}400$ | $5400 \div 90 = 60$ |

## 1 Develop

25

**Tell Students In Today's Lesson They Will**

review how multiplication and division are related.

### Using Student Pages

UNDERSTANDING Whole Group

Because this lesson is taught in the form of a story, students will need to have their books open to page 528. The story, which continues through page 529, shows how to use a graph of the multiplication function ×105 to approximate a quotient for dividing by 105. Have the students follow along in their books as the class reads aloud the story.

Pause to let students discuss and answer the questions. Make sure students understand how to convert dollars to yen by multiplying the number of dollars by 105.

When you discuss the table on page 529, point out that it is like a function machine chart for the ×105 function. In Lesson 4.5 students made and completed tables in this form:

| ×105 | |
|---|---|
| *x* | *y* |
| 0 | 0 |
| 10 | 1,050 |
| 100 | 10,500 |

If possible, draw a grid like the one on page 529 on the board or display one on an overhead transparency. Have students plot the three points (0,0), (10, 1,050), and (100, 10,500). Explain to students that any ordered pair generated from the dollar to yen function, ×105, will fall on the line that connects these three points.

As you get to the part of the story where Mindy uses the graph to find that $65 equals about 6,825 yen, demonstrate the procedure she used as indicated by the arrows on the graph on page 529. Choose a different amount to convert to yen, such as $30. Have a student find 30 on the *x*-axis, move his or her finger up the graph until it meets the line, and then go across to the *y*-axis. The answer is a little more than 3,150.

Check to be sure students understand how to use the graph to convert dollars to yen. Ask questions such as the following:

- **How does the graph show that it makes sense for Keesha to get 2,205 yen for her $21?** Possible answer: because you can round 21 to 20, which, according to the graph, is about 2,205 yen; the answer is not exact, but it is close
- **If Jordan had $45, about how many yen could he get?** about 4725; Emphasize that a small graph like the one in the book will provide only approximate answers.

As you read page 530, demonstrate how Mindy reads the graph *backward* to divide. Model moving your finger up and across as you ask a question such as the following:

- **How many yen is $65 worth?** about 6,825

As you retrace your finger's path across and down, ask a question such as the following:

- **How many dollars is 1500 yen worth?** about $14; Emphasize again that a small graph like this provides only approximate answers.

Do a problem similar to those on page 530, such as the following:

- **About how many dollars does an art supply kit cost if the price tag reads 5,250 yen?** approximately $50

### Strategy Building

ENGAGING Small Group

Review inverse, or opposite, function machines, and remind students that they worked with inverse function machines in Lesson 4.5.

Have students work on some exercises in small groups and then discuss their answers as a class. Students should be able to explain what to do to find x or y and prove their answers are correct.

Possible questions include the following:

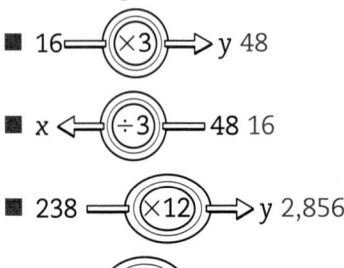

- 16 → (×3) → y 48
- x ← (÷3) ← 48 16
- 238 → (×12) → y 2,856
- x ← (÷12) ← 2,856 238

# 2 Assign Student Pages

25

### Pages 528–529 APPLYING

Pages 528–529 were covered in the Using Student Pages section. Students should notice the story uses an example of a function, a review from Chapter 4.

**RESEARCH IN ACTION**

"Algorithms and their properties are important mathematical ideas that all students need to understand. An algorithm is a reliable step-by-step procedure for solving problems. To perform arithmetic calculations, children must learn how numerical algorithms work... algorithms, when well understood, can serve as a valuable basis for reasoning about mathematics."

Kilpatrick, J., Swafford, J. and Findell, B. eds. *Adding It Up: Helping Children Learn Mathematics*. Washington, D.C.: National Reasearch Council/National Academy Press, 2001, pp.414.

Student Page

LESSON 11.9 **Using Inverses**

## Key Ideas

**Multiplication and division are inverse operations. This means they "undo" each other (the exception is dividing with a remainder).**

### It's a Yen Thing

SOCIAL STUDIES

Landon and his parents moved to Japan. He was there for three months before flying home to visit his friends, Mindy, Keesha, Tyler, and Jordan.

The friends met at a smoothie shop, and while they were paying for their food, Landon pulled out some yen, which is Japanese currency.

Mindy asked, "What is that?"

"It's called yen. It's what I use to pay for things in Japan," replied Landon.

"Can you use it here?" Keesha questioned.

Landon answered, "No, I can't. The yen isn't worth the same amount as the American dollar."

"It's not?" they replied with puzzled looks.

"Nope. When we first moved, we had to go to a bank and exchange our dollars for yen. At the time, I had 5 dollars, and the banker gave me 525 yen," Landon added.

"WOW!" replied Tyler. "You could buy a lot of things with 525 dollars."

"It's not that easy. Since we get more yen for our dollars, things cost a greater number of yen than number of dollars," Landon replied.

"So how much is one American dollar worth?" asked Jordan.

"It's worth about 105 yen," Landon said.

528 Textbook This lesson is available in the *eTextbook*.

Student Page

Keesha asked, "So if we were in Japan, I could exchange my 2 $1-dollar bills for 210 yen?"

| Dollars | Yen |
|---|---|
| 0 | 0 |
| 10 | 1,050 |
| 100 | 10,500 |

"That's right," Landon replied.

"I have an idea," said Mindy. "Let's make a graph so we can see how many yen we could get for our dollars and compare how much things cost here to how much they cost in Japan."

"Okay," they all agreed.

First they made a chart using numbers that were easy to multiply.

Next Landon and his friends made a graph of the ordered pairs on the chart: (0, 0); (10, 1,050); and (100, 10,500). They drew a straight line through the points.

"I have $65," said Jordan. "About how many yen could I get?"

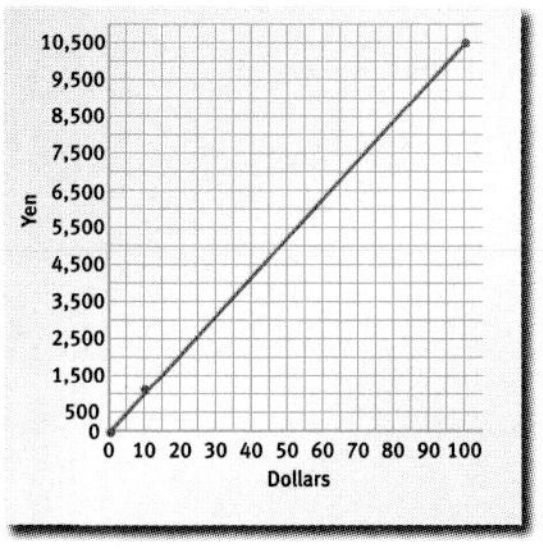


"Simple," said Mindy. "Find 65 on the sideways axis, go straight up to the line, then go across to the up-and-down axis."

Jordan watched Mindy put her finger on 65 then move it up and over. He said, "My 65 dollars are worth about 6,825 yen."

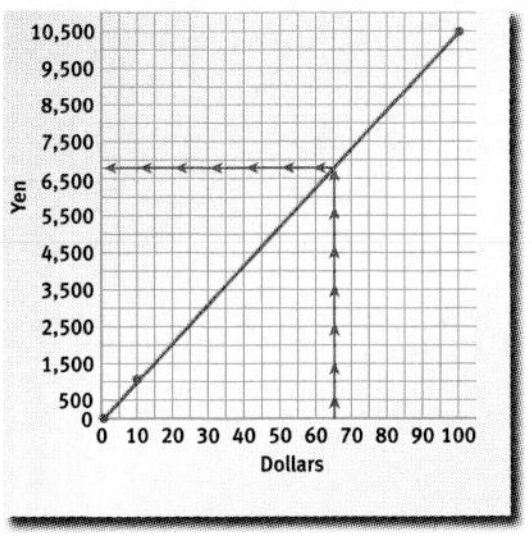


They all calculated the exchange of their dollars for yen and used the graph to check their amounts. Next it was off to the store with their graph.

# Assign Student Pages, continued

### Pages 530–531 APPLYING

Have students complete pages 530–531 independently. Students should realize they will not have to divide by two-digit numbers in order to solve Problems 9 to 20.

#### Monitoring Student Progress

**If . . .** students do not understand how to use the inverse of a multiplication problem to solve a division problem (for example, $13 \times 75 = 975$, so $975 \div 13 = 75$),

**Then . . .** relate this inverse relationship to the way in which the students have been checking the quotients. Ask, for example, *How do you check $8 \div 4 = 2$?* Work with small numbers until students see the relationship, then move on to greater numbers.

Student Page

LESSON 11.9 • Using Inverses

At the store, Tyler saw a radio. He showed it to Landon, who said it would cost about 3,000 yen in Japan.

"That's too much money," Tyler said.

"It's not as much as it sounds," Landon said. "You have to divide 3,000 by 105 to find out how much that is in dollars."

"But we don't know how to divide by big numbers like 105," said Tyler.

"We can use our graph to get an approximate answer," said Tyler. "Remember, dividing is the opposite, or inverse, of multiplication. So, if we can use the graph to multiply, we can just do the opposite to divide. Look."

"I see," said Tyler. "So 3,000 yen are worth a little more than $28."

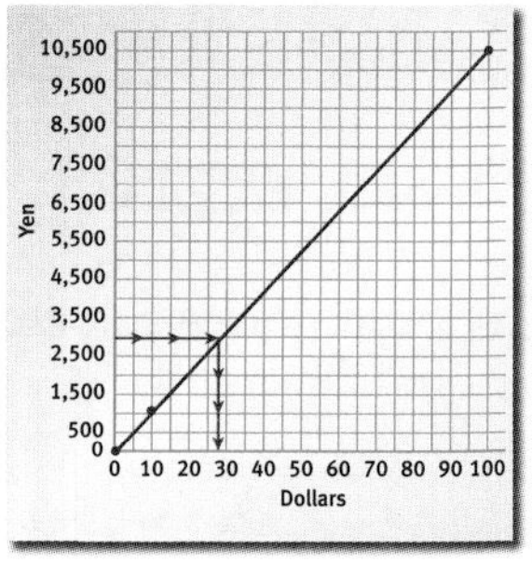


**Use** the graph to approximate how many dollars each of these items costs.

1. Running suit—2,625 yen $25
2. Baseball glove—1,575 yen $15
3. Shirt—945 yen $9
4. Bicycle—8,295 yen $79
5. Calculator—525 yen $5
6. CD player—3,570 yen $34
7. Video game system—9,725 yen $93
8. Video game—5,200 yen $50

Textbook This lesson is available in the *eTextbook.*

Student Page

**Remember:**

If you put 35 into a ×23 machine, 805 will come out.

35 → (×23) → 805

A ÷23 machine does the opposite. If you put in 805, then 35 will come out.

805 → (÷23) → 35

**Find** the value of *x* or *y*. You may be able to avoid some computing if you see a pattern.

9. 20 → (×25) → y  y = 500
10. 500 → (÷25) → x  x = 20
11. 13 → (×75) → y  y = 975
12. 975 → (÷75) → x  x = 13
13. 92 → (×10) → y  y = 920
14. 920 → (÷10) → x  x = 92
15. 63 → (×12) → y  y = 756
16. 756 → (÷12) → x  x = 63
17. 3 → (×752) → y  y = 2,256
18. 2,256 → (÷752) → x  x = 3
19. 6 → (×375) → y  y = 2,250
20. 2,250 → (÷375) → x  x = 6
21. **Extended Response** What patterns do you see in the exercises above? Explain. The answers to the problems on the left will enable you to solve the problems on the right.

Writing + Math **Journal**

Explain in detail how multiplication can be used to help solve a division problem.

## 3 Reflect 5

### Guided Discussion REASONING

Individual

Have students demonstrate how to use the graph of a multiplication function to divide.

Have students make larger yen-dollar graphs and rework the problems on page 530. Students should see the answers become more accurate when they use larger graphs, which will help them learn to choose appropriate scales.

### Extended Response

**Problem 21** Students should see the answers to the problems on the left will help them solve the problems on the right by identifying the inverse.

### Writing + Math Journal

Students should explain how using estimation and the inverse operation can help solve a division problem.

**Curriculum Connection:** Students interested in finding more out about Japan and its rich culture may research this topic online or at the library.

**Cumulative Review:** For review of common multiples and common factors, assign Problems 5–10 on student page 541.

**Family Involvement:** Assign the ***Practice, Reteach,*** or ***Enrichment*** activities depending on the needs of your students.

Encourage students to play the **Four Cube Division Game** at home with friends or relatives.

**Concept/Question Board:** Have students attempt to answer any unanswered questions on the Concept/Question Board.

**Math Puzzler:** Alana shared some peanuts with her friends. First she gave Rashid 6 peanuts. Then she gave Beth half of the peanuts that were left. Next, Damon got half the peanuts that were left, plus 1 more. Alana ate the last 6 peanuts herself. How many peanuts did Alana start with? $(6 + 7 + 1) \times 2 + 6 = 34$

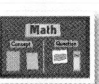

# 4 Assess and Differentiate

**e Assess** Use ***eAssess*** to record and analyze evidence of student understanding.

## A Gather Evidence

Use the Daily Class Assessment Records in ***Assessment*** or ***eAssess*** to record daily observations.

### Informal Assessment

**✓ Mental Math**

Did the student **COMPUTING**
- ❑ respond accurately?
- ❑ respond quickly?
- ❑ respond with confidence?
- ❑ self-correct?

### Formal Assessment

**✓ Student Pages**

Did the student **UNDERSTANDING**
- ❑ make important observations?
- ❑ extend or generalize learning?
- ❑ provide insightful answers?
- ❑ pose insightful questions?

## B Summarize Findings

Analyze and summarize assessment data for each student. Determine which Assessment Follow-Up is appropriate for each student. Use the Student Assessment Record in ***Assessment*** or ***eAssess*** to update assessment records.

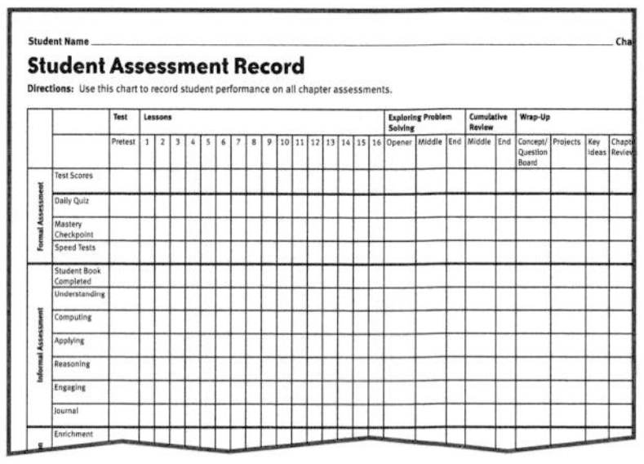


**Assessment Page T41**

## C Assessment Follow-Up • DIFFERENTIATE INSTRUCTION

Based on your observations, use these teaching strategies for assessment follow-up.

### INTERVENTION

Review student performance on ***Intervention*** Lesson 11.C to see if students have mastered prerequisite skills for this lesson.

### ENGLISH LEARNER

**Review**

Use Lesson 11.9 in ***English Learner Support Guide*** to review lesson concepts and vocabulary.

### ENRICH

**If . . .** students are proficient in the lesson concepts,

**Then . . .** encourage them to work on the chapter projects or ***Enrichment*** Lesson 11.9.

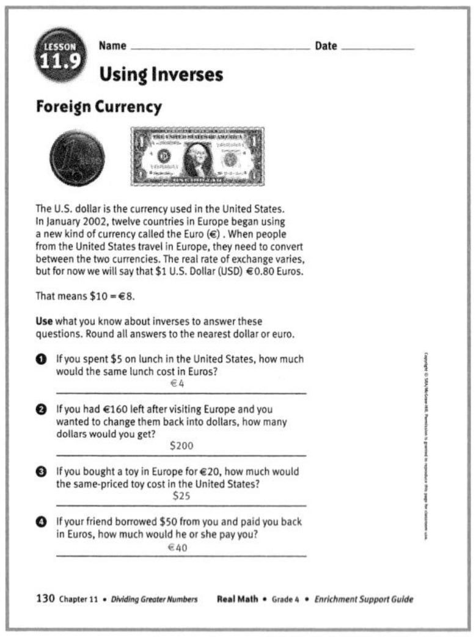

LESSON 11.9 Name ______ Date ______

**Using Inverses**

**Foreign Currency**

The U.S. dollar is the currency used in the United States. In January 2002, twelve countries in Europe began using a new kind of currency called the Euro (€). When people from the United States travel in Europe, they need to convert between the two currencies. The real rate of exchange varies, but for now we will say that $1 U.S. Dollar (USD) €0.80 Euros.

That means $10 = €8.

**Use** what you know about inverses to answer these questions. Round all answers to the nearest dollar or euro.

1. If you spent $5 on lunch in the United States, how much would the same lunch cost in Euros? €4
2. If you had €160 left after visiting Europe and you wanted to change them back into dollars, how many dollars would you get? $200
3. If you bought a toy in Europe for €20, how much would the same-priced toy cost in the United States? $25
4. If your friend borrowed $50 from you and paid you back in Euros, how much would he or she pay you? €40

130 Chapter 11 • *Dividing Greater Numbers* **Real Math** • Grade 4 • *Enrichment Support Guide*

Enrichment Lesson 11.9

### PRACTICE

**If . . .** students would benefit from additional practice,

**Then . . .** assign ***Practice*** Lesson 11.9.

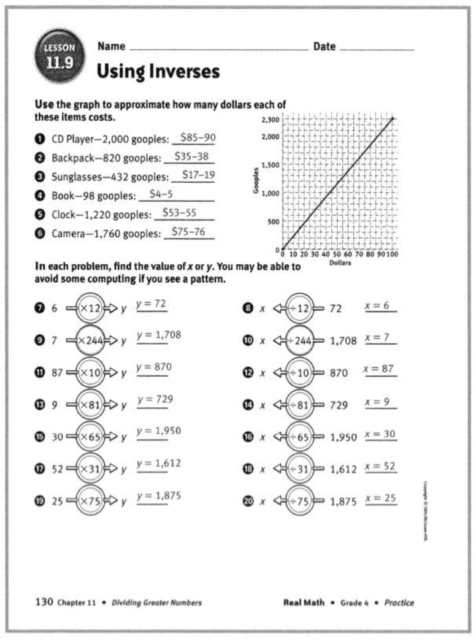

LESSON 11.9 Name ______ Date ______

**Using Inverses**

**Use the graph to approximate how many dollars each of these items costs.**

1. CD Player—2,000 googles: $85–90
2. Backpack—820 googles: $35–38
3. Sunglasses—432 googles: $17–19
4. Book—98 googles: $4–5
5. Clock—1,220 googles: $53–55
6. Camera—1,760 googles: $75–76



**In each problem, find the value of *x* or *y*. You may be able to avoid some computing if you see a pattern.**

7. 6 ×12 y — y = 72
8. x ÷12 72 — x = 6
9. 7 ×244 y — y = 1,708
10. x ÷244 1,708 — x = 7
11. 87 ×10 y — y = 870
12. x ÷10 870 — x = 87
13. 9 ×81 y — y = 729
14. x ÷81 729 — x = 9
15. 30 ×65 y — y = 1,950
16. x ÷65 1,950 — x = 30
17. 52 ×31 y — y = 1,612
18. x ÷31 1,612 — x = 52
19. 25 ×75 y — y = 1,875
20. x ÷75 1,875 — x = 25

130 Chapter 11 • *Dividing Greater Numbers* **Real Math** • Grade 4 • *Practice*

Practice Lesson 11.9

### RETEACH

**If . . .** students struggle with division,

**Then . . .** have them relate multiplication to division using ***Reteach*** Lesson 11.9.

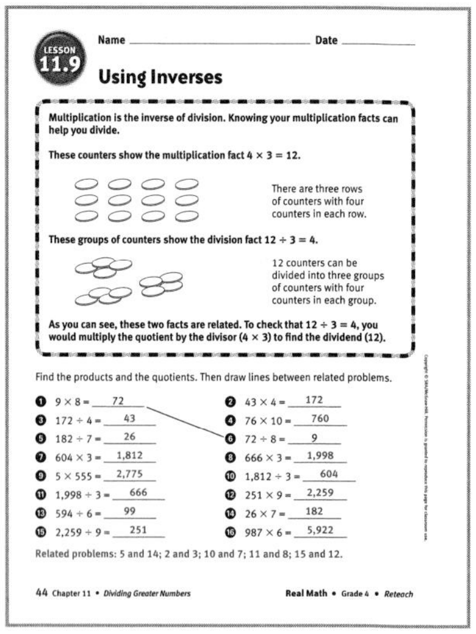

LESSON 11.9 Name ______ Date ______

**Using Inverses**

**Multiplication is the inverse of division. Knowing your multiplication facts can help you divide.**

**These counters show the multiplication fact 4 × 3 = 12.**

There are three rows of counters with four counters in each row.

**These groups of counters show the division fact 12 ÷ 3 = 4.**

12 counters can be divided into three groups of counters with four counters in each group.

**As you can see, these two facts are related. To check that 12 ÷ 3 = 4, you would multiply the quotient by the divisor (4 × 3) to find the dividend (12).**

Find the products and the quotients. Then draw lines between related problems.

1. 9 × 8 = 72
2. 43 × 4 = 172
3. 172 ÷ 4 = 43
4. 76 × 10 = 760
5. 182 ÷ 7 = 26
6. 72 ÷ 8 = 9
7. 604 × 3 = 1,812
8. 666 × 3 = 1,998
9. 5 × 555 = 2,775
10. 1,812 ÷ 3 = 604
11. 1,998 ÷ 3 = 666
12. 251 × 9 = 2,259
13. 594 ÷ 6 = 99
14. 26 × 7 = 182
15. 2,259 ÷ 9 = 251
16. 987 × 6 = 5,922

Related problems: 5 and 14; 2 and 3; 10 and 7; 11 and 8; 15 and 12.

44 Chapter 11 • *Dividing Greater Numbers* **Real Math** • Grade 4 • *Reteach*

Reteach Lesson 11.9

## Lesson Planner

**Objectives**
- To show the relationship between multiplication and division
- To show how to use multiplication strategies to estimate quotients

**NCTM Standards**

**Problem Solving**
Find answers to problems

**Number and Operations**
Estimate quotients

**Materials**
- *Response Wheels
- *Base-ten materials

**Technology**

**Presentation** Lesson 11.10
**MathTools** Base-Ten Blocks

**Test Prep**

**Cumulative Review**
Mental Math reviews multiplication facts (Lesson 3.10).

**Extended Response**
Problem 19

*Manipulative Kit Item

# Estimating Quotients

**Context of the Lesson** This is the tenth of twelve lessons on division. Students will use their knowledge of multiplication and division to estimate quotients for various exercises in this lesson. In the prior lesson, inverse operations were used to find the answer to division problems. Students will call upon those skills again in this chapter. They will also be required to use multiplication of multidigit numbers, introduced in Chapter 6 (Lessons 2 and 5).

See page 502B for Math Background for teachers for this lesson.

## Planning for Learning • DIFFERENTIATE INSTRUCTION

### INTERVENTION

**If . . .** students lack the prerequisite skill of multiplying by a one-digit or two-digit number,

**Then . . .** teach ***Intervention*** Lesson 11.C.

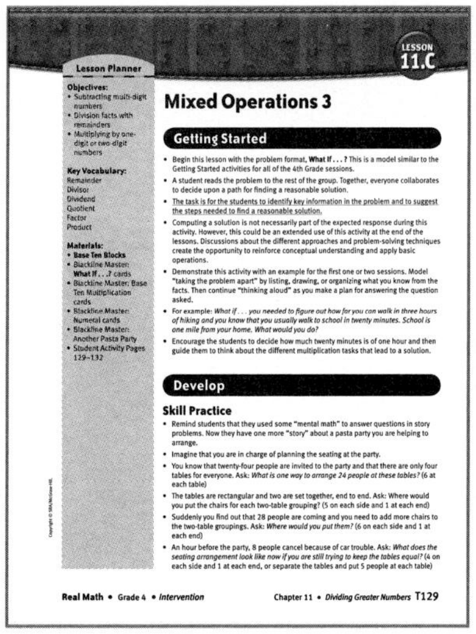


Intervention Lesson 11.C

### ENGLISH LEARNER

Preview

**If . . .** students need language support,

**Then . . .** use Lesson 11.10 in ***English Learner Support Guide*** to preview lesson concepts and vocabulary.

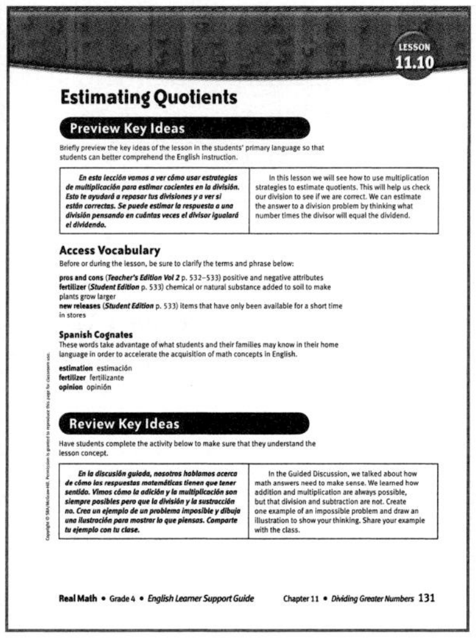


English Learner Lesson 11.10

### ENRICH

**If . . .** students are proficient in the lesson concepts,

**Then . . .** encourage them to explore division using ***eMathTools.***

### PRACTICE

**If . . .** students would benefit from additional practice,

**Then. . .** extend Guided Discussion before assigning the student pages.

### RETEACH

**If . . .** students are having difficulty understanding the estimation of quotients,

**Then . . .** extend Guided Discussion before assigning the student pages.

**Access Vocabulary**
**pros and cons** the positive and negative details about something

**Spanish Cognates**
**estimation** estimación
**opinion** opinión

# Teaching Lesson 11.10

## Mental Math

5

Review RESPONSE WHEEL Practice simple related multiplication facts, such as the following:

| | | |
|---|---|---|
| **a.** 7 × 8 56 | **b.** 70 × 8 560 | **c.** 700 × 8 5,600 |
| **d.** 7 × 800 5,600 | **e.** 10 × 23 230 | **f.** 100 × 23 2,300 |
| **g.** 4 × 12 48 | **h.** 40 × 12 480 | **i.** 4 × 120 480 |
| **j.** 40 × 120 4,800 | **k.** 10 × 21 210 | **l.** 11 × 21 231 |

## 1 Develop

25

**Tell Students In Today's Lesson They Will**
use multiplication to estimate quotients.

### Guided Discussion UNDERSTANDING

Whole Group

Review the inverse relationship between multiplication and division. Use this idea to lead into a discussion about how it is possible to use multiplication to estimate answers to division problems. Ask questions such as the following:

- **What is the relationship between multiplication and division?** They are inverse operations whenever both are possible.
- **Is it always possible to find an answer to a division problem?** If a student says no, it's not always possible, ask for an example. If they say yes, give examples where division is impossible or doesn't make sense. For example: To find the answer to 12 ÷ 6, we look for a number we can multiply by 6 to get 12, or 2. If we want to know the answer for 10 ÷ 0, we have to find a number we can multiply by 0 to get 10. There is no such number, since 0 times any number is 0.

Explain to students that when division is possible, we can often estimate the answer using multiplication. We can think of a number that can be multiplied by the divisor to equal the dividend.

For example, suppose we want to know the quotient when 30,000 is divided by 271. We know that 100 times 271 is 27,100. So, 110 × 271 must be 27,100 + 2,710 or 29,810, and 120 × 271 = 32,520. The quotient must be between 110 and 120, probably much closer to 110. Since 111 × 271 = 30,081, the quotient is between 110 and 111.

Work through several other examples with students, such as 12,000 ÷ 356. between 33 and 34

## 2 Assign Student Pages

20

**Pages 532–533** APPLYING

Have students work on pages 532–533 with a partner.

Problems 1–8 have been ordered in a way that will help the students notice patterns in their work. These patterns will reduce the steps needed to find a product.

In Problem 2 students should see 9 × 271 is 2,168 + 271 or 2,439 (for Problem 1 they found that 8 × 271 = 2,168). Another option is to multiply 10 × 271 which is 2,710 and subtract 271 to get the same answer.

By multiplying the answers for Problems 1–8 by 10, students will create numbers that the correct answers will fall between for Problems 9–14. However, for Problem 14 there is more than one such number.

Students should realize that the last digit of the product of a number multiplied by 271 will be the same as the last digit of the multiplier—so 98 is the only possible answer for Problem 14.

Student Page

LESSON 11.10 **Estimating Quotients**

## Key Ideas

**We can often estimate an answer to a division problem by using our knowledge of related multiplication facts. Sometimes the estimate is all we need.**

**Find** an easy way to do the multiplication. They may help you estimate answers to the division questions below.

1. $271 \times 8 =$ ☐ 2,168
2. $271 \times 9 =$ ☐ 2,439
3. $271 \times 10 =$ ☐ 2,710
4. $271 \times 11 =$ ☐ 2,981
5. $271 \times 12 =$ ☐ 3,252
6. $271 \times 13 =$ ☐ 3,523
7. $271 \times 14 =$ ☐ 3,794
8. $271 \times 15 =$ ☐ 4,065

**Decide** which answer is correct in each exercise below. Multiplying each of the answers for Exercises 1–8 by 10 may help.

9. $23{,}577 \div 271 =$ ☐
   a. 8
   b. 94
   (c.) 87
   d. 117
10. $39{,}295 \div 271 =$ ☐
   (a.) 145
   b. 125
   c. 150
   d. 86
11. $33{,}875 \div 271 =$ ☐
   a. 145
   (b.) 125
   c. 111
   d. 97
12. $28{,}184 \div 271 =$ ☐
   a. 64
   b. 94
   c. 128
   (d.) 104
13. $35{,}772 \div 271 =$ ☐
   a. 172
   b. 112
   (c.) 132
   d. 122
14. $26{,}558 \div 271 =$ ☐
   (a.) 98
   b. 99
   c. 100
   d. 101



eTextbook This lesson is available in the *eTextbook*.

Student Page

**Solve** the following problems.

Review 15. Brian wants to add some CDs to his collection. Groovy Tunes is having a sale in which new releases are three for $33. The Music Cellar is offering a deal in which you buy two CDs at regular price ($15) and get a third at half-off the regular price. What is the cost per CD at each store? Which store offers a lower price per CD?

15. Groovy Tunes = $11 per CD; Music Cellar = $12.50 per CD; Groovy Tunes

16. Wholesum Whole Wheat Crackers cost $3.17 for a 12-ounce box and $3.98 for a 16-ounce box. Which size box is less expensive per ounce? 16-ounce box

Science 17. A bag of fertilizer costs $28.73 and will cover about 500 square yards. Kaitlyn needs to fertilize a 7,809-square-yard area. How many bags of fertilizer does she need? 16 bags

18. Two cars started with full tanks of gasoline and drove around the same track at exactly 40 miles per hour. The first car drove 676 miles and required 18 gallons. The other went 861 miles and required 21 gallons. Which car traveled more miles per gallon of gasoline? the second car

19. Extended Response Larry hires a painter to paint the outside of his house. The painter charges $1.25 per square foot of wall painted. Larry's house has about 1,200 square feet of outside wall, but he can afford to spend only $1,000 to paint the house. Does Larry have enough money to paint the whole outside of his house? Explain your answer. See *Teacher's Edition.*

20. Abigail drinks 6 ounces of orange juice each day. About how long will a 64-ounce bottle of orange juice last her? about 11 days

# 3 Reflect

10

## Guided Discussion

REASONING

Whole Group

Go over Problem 16 to show how quotients can often be compared by using proportional reasoning instead of dividing. Ask questions such as the following:

- **How many more ounces do you get in the larger box?** 4 ounces
- **What fraction of the small box is that?** $\frac{1}{3}$

So, if you buy the large box, you get $\frac{1}{3}$ more.

- **Do you pay $\frac{1}{3}$ more when you buy the large box? How can you tell by approximating?** Help students see that $\frac{1}{3}$ of $3.17 is more than $1, but they are paying less than $1 extra to buy the large box.

So, when you buy the large box, you are getting $\frac{1}{3}$ more crackers, but you're paying less than $\frac{1}{3}$ extra.

- **What does that tell you about which box costs less per ounce?** The large box must cost less per ounce, since you're increasing the amount you get more than you're increasing the amount you pay.

## Extended Response

**Problem 19** For 1,000 square feet, the painter would charge $1,250, so Larry can't afford to paint the whole outside of his house. An alternate method: if the painter only charged $1 per square foot, it would still cost over $1,000 ($1,200).

**Curriculum Connection:** Discuss with students the pros and cons of using fertilizers on lawns or farms. A pro can be that it helps grass or vegetation grow; whereas a con is that it can have a negative impact on the animals and the environment. Students may be interested in doing more research online or at the library.

**Cumulative Review:** For review of different kinds of lines, assign Problems 11–15 on student page 542.

**Family Involvement:** Assign the ***Practice, Reteach,*** or ***Enrichment*** activities depending on the needs of your students.
Encourage students to play the **Four Cube Division Game** at home with friends or relatives.

**Concept/Question Board:** Have students attempt to answer any unanswered questions on the Concept/Question Board.

**Math Puzzler:** Ms. Lev's class is putting on a play and needs to set up 48 chairs for guests. They want to make at least two rows, but no more than eight, with the same number of chairs in each row. Find all the possible ways they can arrange the chairs. two rows of 24 chairs, three rows of 16 chairs, four rows of 12 chairs, six rows of 8 chairs, and eight rows of 6 chairs

# 4 Assess and Differentiate

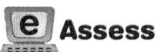

**e Assess** Use ***eAssess*** to record and analyze evidence of student understanding.

## A Gather Evidence

Use the Daily Class Assessment Records in ***Assessment*** or ***eAssess*** to record daily observations.

### Informal Assessment
**✓ Guided Discussion**

Did the student REASONING
- ❑ provide a clear explanation?
- ❑ communicate reasons and strategies?
- ❑ choose appropriate strategies?
- ❑ argue logically?

### Informal Assessment
**✓ Concept/Question Board**

Did the student ENGAGING
- ❑ pay attention to others' contributions?
- ❑ contribute information and ideas?
- ❑ improve on a strategy?
- ❑ reflect on and check the accuracy of his or her work?

## B Summarize Findings

Analyze and summarize assessment data for each student. Determine which Assessment Follow-Up is appropriate for each student. Use the Student Assessment Record in ***Assessment*** or ***eAssess*** to update assessment records.

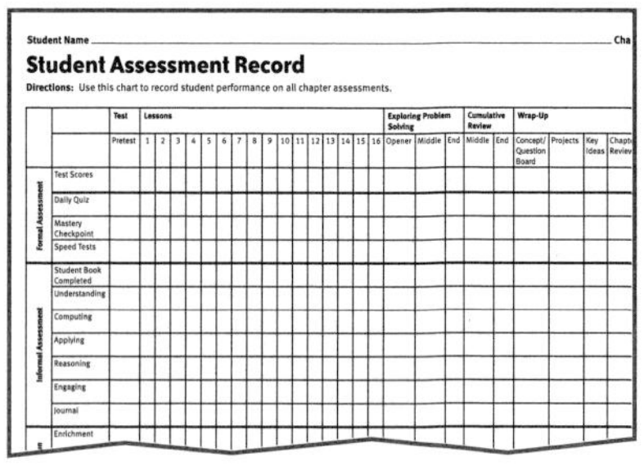
Student Name
Student Assessment Record
Directions: Use this chart to record student performance on all chapter assessments.

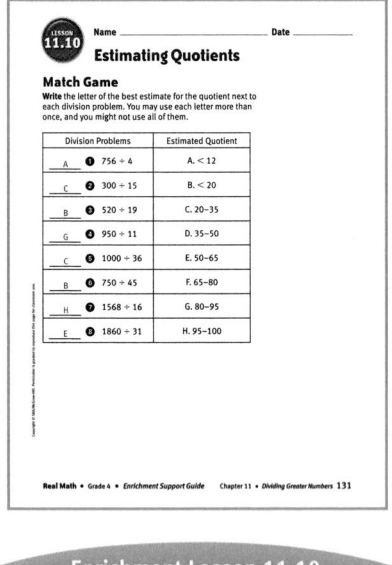

**Assessment Page T41**

## C Assessment Follow-Up • DIFFERENTIATE INSTRUCTION

Based on your observations, use these teaching strategies for assessment follow-up.

### INTERVENTION

Review student performance on ***Intervention*** Lesson 11.C to see if students have mastered prerequisite skills for this lesson.

### ENGLISH LEARNERS

**Review**

Use Lesson 11.10 in ***English Learner Support Guide*** to review lesson concepts and vocabulary.

### ENRICH

**If . . .** students are proficient in the lesson concepts,

**Then . . .** encourage them to work on the chapter projects or ***Enrichment*** Lesson 11.10.

LESSON 11.10 Name ______ Date ______

**Estimating Quotients**

**Match Game**

**Write** the letter of the best estimate for the quotient next to each division problem. You may use each letter more than once, and you might not use all of them.

| Division Problems | Estimated Quotient |
|---|---|
| A ❶ 756 ÷ 4 | A. < 12 |
| C ❷ 300 ÷ 15 | B. < 20 |
| B ❸ 520 ÷ 19 | C. 20–35 |
| G ❹ 950 ÷ 11 | D. 35–50 |
| C ❺ 1000 ÷ 36 | E. 50–65 |
| B ❻ 750 ÷ 45 | F. 65–80 |
| H ❼ 1568 ÷ 16 | G. 80–95 |
| E ❽ 1860 ÷ 31 | H. 95–100 |

Real Math • Grade 4 • *Enrichment Support Guide* Chapter 11 • *Dividing Greater Numbers* 131

**Enrichment Lesson 11.10**

### PRACTICE

**If . . .** students would benefit from additional practice,

**Then . . .** assign ***Practice*** Lesson 11.10.

LESSON 11.10 Name ______ Date ______

**Estimating Quotients**

**The multiplication table gives products with 346. Use the products in the table to help you with the following exercises.**

| 346 × | 2 | 3 | 4 | 5 | 6 | 7 | 8 | 9 | 10 |
|---|---|---|---|---|---|---|---|---|---|
| = | 692 | 1038 | 1384 | 1730 | 2076 | 2422 | 2768 | 3144 | 3460 |

**For each division exercise below, estimate to find the best answer. Several answers are given but only one is close to the actual solution.**

| | | a. | b. | c. | d. |
|---|---|---|---|---|---|
| ❶ | 6,288 ÷ 346 = | a. 10 | b. 12 | c. 15 | (d.) 18 |
| ❷ | 9,828 ÷ 346 = | a. 2 | b. 20 | (c.) 28 | d. 31 |
| ❸ | 13,498 ÷ 346 = | (a.) 39 | b. 35 | c. 30 | d. 28 |
| ❹ | 21,796 ÷ 346 = | a. 70 | b. 68 | c. 66 | (d.) 63 |
| ❺ | 24,520 ÷ 346 = | a. 7 | (b.) 70 | c. 77 | d. 707 |
| ❻ | 18,928 ÷ 346 = | a. 47 | (b.) 52 | c. 59 | d. 61 |
| ❼ | 73,892 ÷ 346 = | (a.) 203 | b. 302 | c. 180 | d. 401 |
| ❽ | 32,396 ÷ 346 = | a. 98 | (b.) 92 | c. 89 | d. 83 |
| ❾ | 17,108 ÷ 346 = | a. 40 | (b.) 47 | c. 54 | d. 62 |
| ❿ | 25,844 ÷ 346 = | a. 66 | b. 70 | (c.) 73 | d. 77 |
| ⓫ | 38,584 ÷ 346 = | a. 10 | b. 95 | c. 101 | (d.) 106 |
| ⓬ | 30,940 ÷ 346 = | a. 80 | b. 85 | (c.) 89 | d. 93 |

**Solve this problem.**

⓭ A gallon of paint covers about 400 square feet. Mr. Morano's garage has about 1850 square feet of wall area. If Mr. Morano wants to paint three coats, how much paint should he buy? Explain.

Sample answer: 3 × 1850 = 5550; Mr. Morano needs enough paint to cover 5550 square feet. At 400 square feet per gallon, Mr. Morano needs at least 14 gallons of paint.

Real Math • Grade 4 • *Practice* Chapter 11 • *Dividing Greater Numbers* 131

**Practice Lesson 11.10**

### RETEACH

**If . . .** students are having difficulty understanding how to estimate quotients,

**Then . . .** teach them another way to estimate a quotient by using compatible numbers. For example, estimate 460 ÷ 9.

What is a number near 460 that could be easily divided by 9? Try 450. Or, ask yourself, 9 times what number is about 460? Try 50.

$450 \div 9 = 50$

Or $9 \times 5 = 45$, so $9 \times 50 = 450$

So, 460 ÷ 9 is about 50.

## Lesson Planner

**OBJECTIVES**
To learn procedures to divide using a two-digit divisor

**NCTM STANDARDS**
**Number and Operations**
Divide numbers by a two-digit divisor

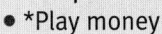

**MATERIALS**
- ***Response Wheels**
- *Play money

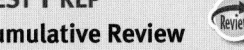

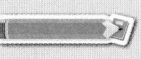

**TECHNOLOGY**
**Presentation** Lesson 11.11
**MathTools Coins and Money** and **Base-Ten Blocks**

**TEST PREP**
**Cumulative Review**
Mental Math reviews multiplication facts (Lesson 3.10).
**Writing + Math**
Journal

*Manipulative Kit Item

# Dividing by a Two-Digit Divisor

**Context of the Lesson** This is the eleventh lesson on division using greater numbers. Division can be difficult for students to learn quickly. The process in this chapter is broken down into manageable parts so students can see what is taking place at each step. For the rest of this chapter (and in parts of Chapter 12) students will be asked to call on their skills to solve division problems involving two-digit divisors. Grade 5 of ***Real Math*** also covers two-digit divisors.

See page 502B for Math Background for teachers for this lesson.

## Planning for Learning • DIFFERENTIATE INSTRUCTION

### INTERVENTION

**If . . .** students lack the prerequisite skill of subtracting multidigit numbers,

**Then . . .** teach ***Intervention*** Lesson 11.C.

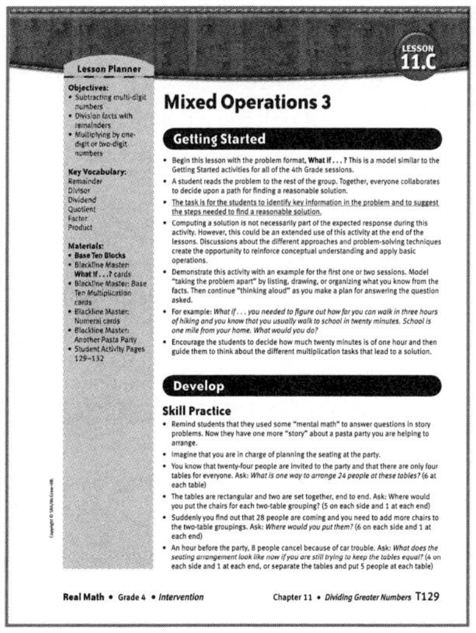
Lesson Planner
LESSON 11.C
Mixed Operations 3
Getting Started
Develop
Skill Practice
Real Math • Grade 4 • Intervention
Chapter 11 • Dividing Greater Numbers T129

Intervention Lesson 11.C

### ENGLISH LEARNER

Preview

**If . . .** students need language support,

**Then . . .** use Lesson 11.11 in ***English Learner Support Guide*** to preview lesson concepts and vocabulary.

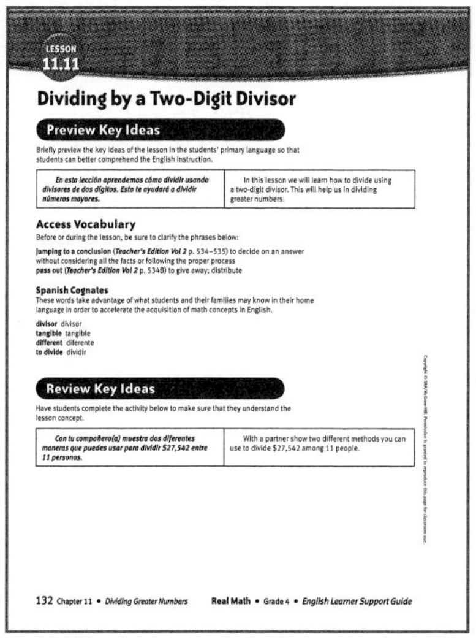
LESSON 11.11
Dividing by a Two-Digit Divisor
Preview Key Ideas
Access Vocabulary
Spanish Cognates
Review Key Ideas
132 Chapter 11 • Dividing Greater Numbers
Real Math • Grade 4 • English Learner Support Guide

English Learner Lesson 11.11

### ENRICH

**If . . .** students are proficient in the lesson concepts,

**Then . . .** encourage them to create a new project.

### PRACTICE

**If . . .** students would benefit from additional practice,

**Then . . .** extend Strategy Building before assigning the student pages.

### RETEACH

**If . . .** students are having difficulty understanding division by a two-digit divisor,

**Then . . .** extend Guided Discussion before assigning the student pages.

**Access Vocabulary**
**exchange** giving or taking one thing in return for another
**distribute** to give out something in appropriate amounts or to the appropriate people

**Spanish Cognates**
**divisor** divisor

## Mental Math 5

Review RESPONSE WHEEL Practice multiplication facts and missing-factor exercises such as the following:

a. 6 × 7 42
b. 7 × 6 42
c. 8 × 7 56
d. 7 times what is 49? 7
e. 8 times what is 24? 3
f. 10 times what is 70? 7
g. What times 6 is 48? 8
h. What times 4 is 32? 8

## 1 Develop 25

### Tell Students In Today's Lesson They Will

learn how to divide by a two-digit divisor.

### Guided Discussion UNDERSTANDING Whole Group

Develop a procedure similar to the procedure used in Lesson 11.1 to divide by any size divisor. Change the numbers to conform to the actual number of students in your class. Here is a sample. Play money should be distributed as the numbers are divided equally. Students may also use ***eMathTools: Coins and Money.***

1. We have 23 students in the class today. Suppose we have $57,495 to divide equally among all of you. The money is in 5 $10,000 bills, 7 $1,000 bills, 4 $100 bills, 9 $10 bills, and 5 $1 dollar bills.
   - **Can you each take 1 $10,000 bill?** no
   - **What should we do?** exchange the 5 $10,000 bills for 50 $1,000 bills.
   - **Then how many $1,000 bills can each of you take?** 2
   - **How many are left?** 11

   Suggest that this will be easier if you keep records. Write the numbers as a division exercise like this:

   23)57495

2. Write the 2 above the 7 in the thousands column and the 46 under the 57. Subtract 46 from 57, leaving 11. Avoid using commas in the algorithm.
   - **Are there enough $1,000 bills for each of you to take one?** no
   - **What should we do?** Exchange the thousand-dollar bills for hundreds.
   - **How many hundreds do we have altogether?** 110 + 4 = 114
   - **Estimate to find how many of the 114 $100 bills each of you should take.** 4; if someone suggests 5, multiply to show that would require 115 $100 bills.
3. Have a volunteer distribute four $100 bills to each student. Count the bills remaining; there should be 22 $100 bills. Record this step on the board.
   Ask questions such as the following:
   - **Can we distribute 22 $100 bills to everyone?** no
   - **What should we change our 22 $100 bills to?** $10 bills
   - **How many tens do we have altogether?** 229
   - **Estimate how many $10 bills you will each get if we exchange the $100 bills for $10 bills.** 9
4. Have a volunteer pass out the 229 $10 bills equally among the 23 students (there will be same left over). Record this step on the board.
   Point out to the class that there are 22 $10 bills left.
   Ask questions such as the following:
   - **Can we exchange these for $1 bills?** yes
   - **How many will we have?** 225
   - **Estimate how many bills you each get.** 9
9. Have a volunteer give 9 $1 bills to each student. Record this step on the board. This is how the problem should look:

```
     2499
 23)57495
   -46
    114
    -92
     229
    -207
      225
     -207
       18
```

   Ask questions such as the following:
   - **How much money do we have left over?** 18 $1 bills
   - **How much money did each of you get?** $2,499

   Explain that this process will work with any divisor, no matter how great, but most people do this kind of division with a calculator or other technology.

### Strategy Building ENGAGING Small Group

Have students get into groups of three. Provide students with exercises involving greater numbers being divided by two-digit divisors. An example could be

5,278 ÷ 19 =

Each person in the group will have a role to complete; however, before problem solving begins they should all agree on an estimated answer and write it down. One student will record the steps. A second student will use play money, base-ten blocks, or ***eMathTools: Base-Ten Blocks*** to separate the problem into something tangible. The third student will check their answer.

## 2 Assign Student Pages 25

### Pages 534–535 APPLYING

Have students complete the exercises on page 534 in small groups.

### As Students Finish

Encourage students to discuss with other early finishers any quick ways they found to complete the exercises without doing the long division.

Student Page

LESSON 11.11 **Dividing by a Two-Digit Divisor**

**Key Ideas**

**You already know the process for multidigit division.**

Mrs. Trimmer has 80,346 play dollars for her 27 students. How can she divide the money equally among them? She begins with 8 ten-thousand-dollar bills, 3 hundred-dollar bills, 4 ten-dollar bills, and 6 one-dollar bills.

```
    2
27)80346
  -54
   26
```

Since 27 students cannot share 8 ten-thousand-dollar bills equally, Mrs. Trimmer exchanged them for 80 thousand-dollar bills. She placed 2 on each student's desk (using 54), and had 26 thousand-dollar bills left over.

```
    29
27)80346
  -54
   263
  -243
    20
```

Mrs. Trimmer then exchanged the 26 thousand-dollar bills for hundred-dollar bills, so she had 263 hundred-dollar bills altogether. She knew she could not give 10 hundred-dollar bills to every student, because she would need to have 270; so she placed nine on every student's desk. Mrs. Trimmer used 243 hundred-dollar bills and had 20 left over.

```
    297
27)80346
  -54
   263
  -243
    204
   -189
     15
```

She then exchanged her 20 hundred-dollar bills for ten-dollar bills, giving her 204 ten-dollar bills. Mrs. Trimmer then distributed 7 ten-dollar bills to every student, using 189 of them and leaving her with 15.

```
    2975
27)80346
  -54
   263
  -243
    204
   -189
     156
    -135
      21
```

Mrs. Trimmer then exchanged her 15 ten-dollar bills for one-dollar bills. Altogether she had 156 one-dollar bills. After passing out 5 to each student, she noticed she had used 135 and had 21 left over.

According to Mrs. Trimmer's calculations, each student can have $2,975, and she will still have $21 left over.

534 eTextbook This lesson is available in the *eTextbook*.

Student Page

**Give** the answer to the nearest whole number.

1. 591,592 ÷ 73 8,104
2. 14,501 ÷ 17 853
3. 14,501 ÷ 853 17
4. 16,207 ÷ 853 19
5. 56,088 ÷ 123 456
6. 71,572 ÷ 29 2,468
7. 3,000 ÷ 34 88 R8
8. 8,946 ÷ 7 1,278
9. 8,946 ÷ 69 129 R45
10. 8,946 ÷ 71 126

**Choose** the correct answer using whatever method you wish.

11. 62,748 ÷ 83 — **a.** 7,561 **c.** 756 (circled) **b.** 76 **d.** 124
12. 62,748 ÷ 756 — **a.** 802 **c.** 803 **b.** 83 (circled) **d.** 97
13. 8,559 ÷ 9 — **a.** 95.1 **c.** 9.51 (circled) **b.** 951 **d.** 952
14. 3,741 ÷ 43 — **a.** 87 (circled) **c.** 124 **b.** 42 **d.** 186
15. 3,741÷ 87 — **a.** 102 **c.** 63 **b.** 123 **d.** 43 (circled)
16. 40,584 ÷ 89 — **a.** 114 **c.** 406 **b.** 456 (circled) **d.** 514
17. 40,584 ÷ 114 — **a.** 356 (circled) **c.** 89 **b.** 456 **d.** 890
18. 5,978 ÷ 7 — **a.** 458 **c.** 845 **b.** 584 **d.** 854 (circled)
19. 11,739 ÷ 13 — **a.** 173 **c.** 93 **b.** 403 **d.** 903 (circled)
20. Fancile drove 578 miles and used 17 gallons of gasoline. How many miles did she go on each gallon of gasoline? — **a.** 17 **c.** 34 (circled) **b.** 24 **d.** 104

Writing + Math **Journal**

Explain any shortcuts you may have found to help solve Exercises 1–20, such as estimation, using information from a previous exercise, or another method.

Chapter 11 • Lesson 11 535

# 3 Reflect

5

## Guided Discussion APPLYING

Whole Group

Ask students to explain procedures they used or might have used to complete the exercises on page 534.

Some methods that may have been used include the following:

**Problem 3** from Problem 2 we know 17 × 853 = 14,501, therefore the answer is 17.

**Problem 11** 6,400 ÷ 8 is 800, so the answer should be a little less than 800.

**Problem 12** If the answer to Problem 11 is right, this answer has to be 83.

**Problem 13** Use short division or notice the last digit has to be a 1 if we are to multiply it by 9 and get something that ends with a 9.

**Problem 14** Using estimation, the answer has to be a little less than 90. Also, the answer must end in a 7 to get a units digit of 1.

**Problem 15** If the answer for Problem 14 is correct, the answer to this problem must be 43.

**Problem 16** Estimation: 4,058 ÷ 9 is about 450, so 456 is probably right. This can be checked using multiplication.

**Problem 17** Using estimation, the answer must be close to but less than 400 because 114 was rounded down to make the estimate. Note that students who answer 114 for Problem 16 and 89 for Problem 17 have picked up a pattern of looking at exercises in pairs and are jumping to a conclusion. A simple estimate should have convinced them they were wrong.

**Problem 18** Short division. Also, the answer must end in 4 to get 8 in the ones place so only b or d could be correct, and b is much too small.

Writing + Math **Journal**

For some possible answers, refer to the Reflect section above.

**Cumulative Review:** For review of percents, assign Problems 16–20 on student page 542.

**Family Involvement:** Assign the ***Practice, Reteach,*** or ***Enrichment*** activities depending on the needs of your students.

Encourage students to play the **Four Cube Division Game** at home with friends or relatives.

**Concept/Question Board:** Have students attempt to answer any unanswered questions on the Concept/Question Board.

**Math Puzzler:** Make a magic square out of the digits 2–10 so that the sum of each row and diagonal is 18. Possible answer: first row: 7, 8, 3; second row: 2, 6, 10; third row: 9, 4, 5

# 4 Assess and Differentiate

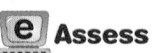

**e Assess** Use ***eAssess*** to record and analyze evidence of student understanding.

## A Gather Evidence

Use the Daily Class Assessment Records in ***Assessment*** or ***eAssess*** to record daily observations.

### Performance Assessment

**Strategy Building**

Did the student UNDERSTANDING

- ❑ make important observations?
- ❑ extend or generalize learning?
- ❑ provide insightful answers?
- ❑ pose insightful questions?

### Informal Assessment

**Guided Discussion**

Did the student APPLYING

- ❑ apply learning in new situations?
- ❑ contribute concepts?
- ❑ contribute answers?
- ❑ connect mathematics to real-world situations?

## B Summarize Findings

Analyze and summarize assessment data for each student. Determine which Assessment Follow-Up is appropriate for each student. Use the Student Assessment Record in ***Assessment*** or ***eAssess*** to update assessment records.

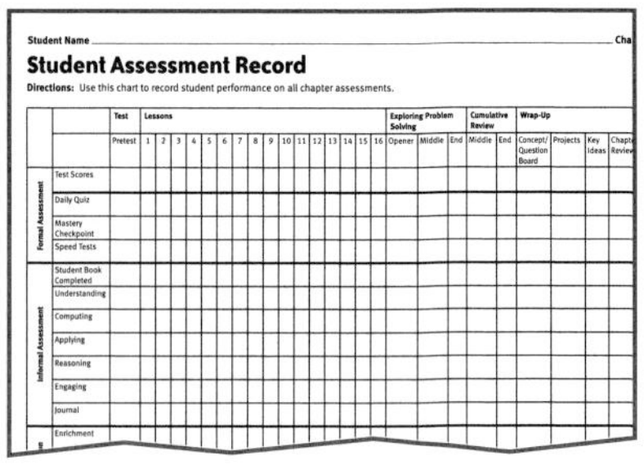
Student Assessment Record

**Assessment Page T41**

## C Assessment Follow-Up • DIFFERENTIATE INSTRUCTION

Based on your observations, use these teaching strategies for assessment follow-up.

### INTERVENTION

Review student performance on ***Intervention*** Lesson 11.A to see if students have mastered prerequisite skills for this lesson.

### ENGLISH LEARNER

**Review**

Use Lesson 11.11 in ***English Learner Support Guide*** to review lesson concepts and vocabulary.

### ENRICH

**If . . .** students are proficient in the lesson concepts,

**Then . . .** encourage them to work on the chapter projects or ***Enrichment*** Lesson 11.11.

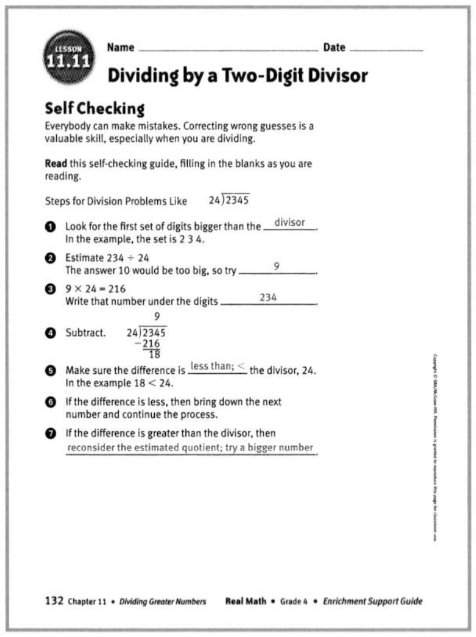
LESSON 11.11 Dividing by a Two-Digit Divisor — Self Checking

Enrichment Lesson 11.11

### PRACTICE

**If . . .** students would benefit from additional practice,

**Then . . .** assign ***Practice*** Lesson 11.11.

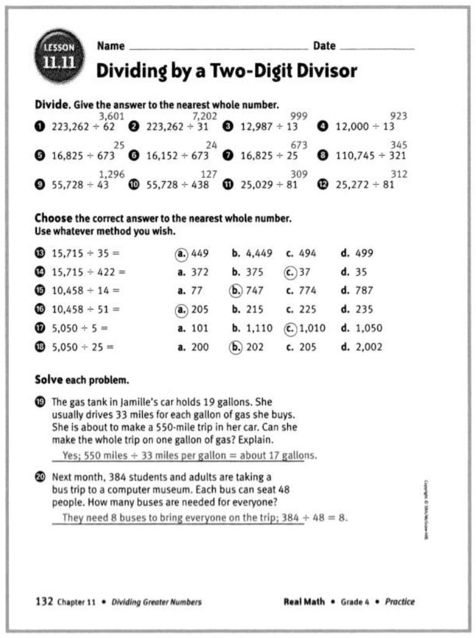
LESSON 11.11 Dividing by a Two-Digit Divisor

Practice Lesson 11.11

### RETEACH

**If . . .** students are having difficulty understanding division,

**Then . . .** reteach the concept using ***Reteach*** Lesson 11.11.

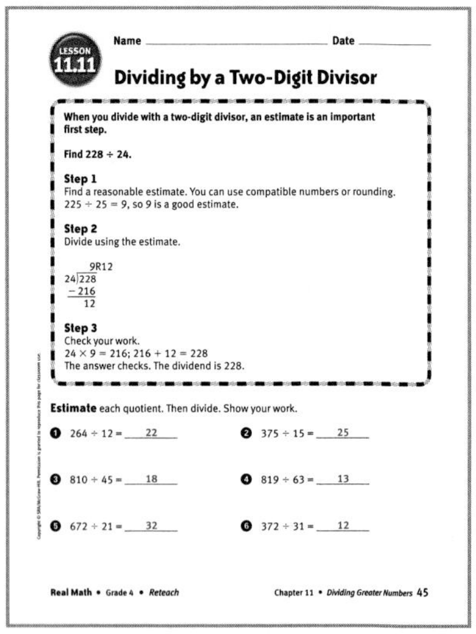
LESSON 11.11 Dividing by a Two-Digit Divisor

Reteach Lesson 11.11

## Lesson Planner

**Objectives**
- To provide practice in solving word problems that focus on interpreting answers to multiplication and division, including the meaning of answers
- To provide practice in dividing by one-digit divisors

**NCTM Standards**

**Problem Solving**
Solve word problems

**Number and Operations**
Find quotients

**Materials**

***Number Cubes** (two 0–5 and two 5–10)

**Technology**

**Presentation** Lesson 11.12

**Test Prep**

**Cumulative Review**
Mental Math reviews approximating answers (Lessons 2.6 and 5.6).

**Extended Response**
Problems 5 and 25

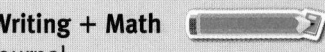

**Writing + Math**
Journal

*Manipulative Kit Item

# Applying Mathematics

**Context of the Lesson** This is the final lesson covering division using greater numbers. In this lesson, students are asked to use the knowledge they have acquired throughout this chapter to solve real-world problems. The exercises in the ***Student Edition*** will review much of what was covered in previous lessons. The division operation will appear again in the first lesson of Chapter 12, in which students will learn about averaging. Division will appear in the next level of the ***Real Math*** series in a variety of ways.

See page 502B for Math Background for teachers for this lesson.

## Planning for Learning • DIFFERENTIATE INSTRUCTION

### INTERVENTION

**If . . .** students lack the prerequisite skill of dividing with remainders,

**Then . . .** teach ***Intervention*** Lesson 11.B.

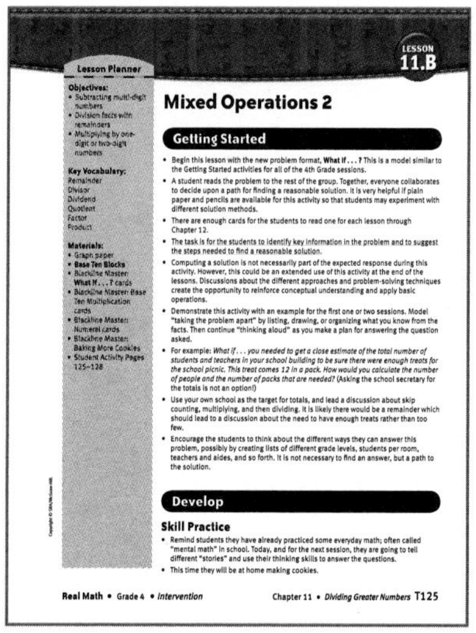

LESSON 11.B

Lesson Planner

**Objectives:**
- Subtracting multi-digit numbers
- Division facts with remainders
- Multiplying by one-digit or two-digit numbers

**Key Vocabulary:**
Remainder
Divisor
Dividend
Quotient
Factor
Product

**Materials:**
- Graph paper
- **Base Ten Blocks**
- Blackline Master: **What If . . . ?** cards
- Blackline Master: Base Ten Multiplication cards
- Blackline Master: Numeral cards
- Blackline Master: Baking More Cookies
- Student Activity Pages 125–128

**Mixed Operations 2**

**Getting Started**
- Begin this lesson with the new problem format, **What If . . . ?** This is a model similar to the Getting Started activities for all of the 4th Grade sessions.
- A student reads the problem to the rest of the group. Together, everyone collaborates to decide upon a path for finding a reasonable solution. It is very helpful if plain paper and pencils are available for this activity so that students may experiment with different solution methods.
- There are enough cards for the students to read one for each lesson through Chapter 12.
- The task is for the students to identify key information in the problem and to suggest the steps needed to find a reasonable solution.
- Computing a solution is not necessarily part of the expected response during this activity. However, this could be an extended use of this activity at the end of the lessons. Discussions about the different approaches and problem-solving techniques create the opportunity to reinforce conceptual understanding and apply basic operations.
- Demonstrate this activity with an example for the first one or two sessions. Model "taking the problem apart" by listing, drawing, or organizing what you know from the facts. Then continue "thinking aloud" as you make a plan for answering the question asked.
- For example: *What if . . . you needed to get a close estimate of the total number of students and teachers in your school building to be sure there were enough treats for the school picnic. This treat comes 12 in a pack. How would you calculate the number of people and the number of packs that are needed?* (Asking the school secretary for the totals is not an option!)
- Use your own school as the target for totals, and lead a discussion about skip counting, multiplying, and then dividing. It is likely there would be a remainder which should lead to a discussion about the need to have enough treats rather than too few.
- Encourage the students to think about the different ways they can answer this problem, possibly by creating lists of different grade levels, students per room, teachers and aides, and so forth. It is not necessary to find an answer, but a path to the solution.

**Develop**

**Skill Practice**
- Remind students they have already practiced some everyday math; often called "mental math" in school. Today, and for the next session, they are going to tell different "stories" and use their thinking skills to answer the questions.
- This time they will be at home making cookies.

Real Math • Grade 4 • *Intervention* Chapter 11 • *Dividing Greater Numbers* T125

Intervention Lesson 11.B

### ENGLISH LEARNER

Preview

**If . . .** students need language support,

**Then . . .** use Lesson 11.12 in ***English Learner Support Guide*** to preview lesson concepts and vocabulary.

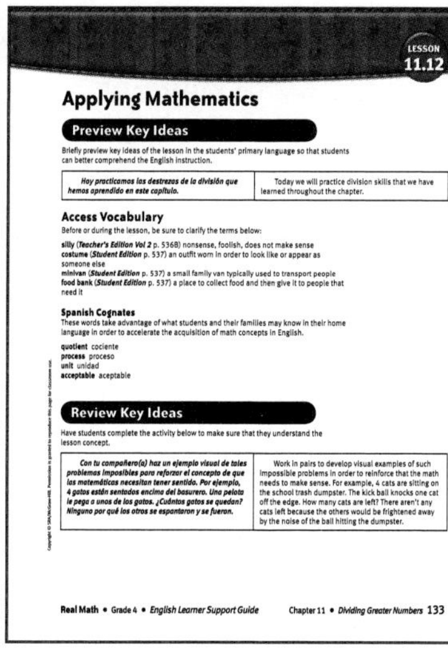

LESSON 11.12

**Applying Mathematics**

**Preview Key Ideas**

Briefly preview key ideas of the lesson in the students' primary language so that students can better comprehend the English instruction.

| | |
|---|---|
| ***Hoy practicamos las destrezas de la división que hemos aprendido en este capítulo.*** | Today we will practice division skills that we have learned throughout the chapter. |

**Access Vocabulary**

Before or during the lesson, be sure to clarify the terms below:

**silly** (***Teacher's Edition Vol 2*** p. 536B) nonsense, foolish, does not make sense
**costume** (***Student Edition*** p. 537) an outfit worn in order to look like or appear as someone else
**minivan** (***Student Edition*** p. 537) a small family van typically used to transport people
**food bank** (***Student Edition*** p. 537) a place to collect food and then give it to people that need it

**Spanish Cognates**

These words take advantage of what students and their families may know in their home language in order to accelerate the acquisition of math concepts in English.

**quotient** cociente
**process** proceso
**unit** unidad
**acceptable** aceptable

**Review Key Ideas**

Have students complete the activity below to make sure that they understand the lesson concept.

| | |
|---|---|
| ***Con tu compañero(a) haz un ejemplo visual de tales problemas imposibles para reforzar el concepto de que las matemáticas necesitan tener sentido. Por ejemplo, 4 gatos están sentados encima del basurero. Una pelota le pega a unos de los gatos. ¿Cuántos gatos se quedan? Ninguno por qué los otros se espantaron y se fueron.*** | Work in pairs to develop visual examples of such impossible problems in order to reinforce that the math needs to make sense. For example, 4 cats are sitting on the school trash dumpster. The kick ball knocks one cat off the edge. How many cats are left? There aren't any cats left because the others would be frightened away by the noise of the ball hitting the dumpster. |

Real Math • Grade 4 • *English Learner Support Guide* Chapter 11 • *Dividing Greater Numbers* 133

English Learner Lesson 11.12

### ENRICH

**If . . .** students are proficient in the lesson concepts,

**Then . . .** encourage them to create variations of the **Four Cube Division Game.**

### PRACTICE

**If . . .** students would benefit from additional practice,

**Then . . .** extend Guided Discussion before assigning student pages.

### RETEACH

**If . . .** students are having difficulty understanding how to use multiplication and division to solve word problems,

**Then . . .** extend Guided Discussion before assigning student pages.

**Vocabulary**
Review from Lesson 3.10:
**quotient**

**Access Vocabulary**
**real-world situations** examples that are familiar because we encounter them in our regular day

**Spanish Cognates**
**quotient** cociente

## Mental Math

5

THUMBS UP

Provide problems and answers, such as the following, in all four operations. Students should show thumbs-up for correct or possibly correct answers and thumbs-down for obviously wrong answers.

**a.** 300 + 50 = 1,500 down
**b.** 900 − 400 = 500 up
**c.** 30 × 40 = 1,200 up
**d.** 50 × 50 = 2,500 up
**e.** 500 ÷ 50 = 100 down
**f.** 90 − 50 = 30 down
**g.** 40 + 800 = 940 down
**h.** 3,000 ÷ 100 = 30 up
**i.** 6 × 500 = 300 down
**j.** 300 − 75 = 280 down

## 1 Develop

15

**Tell Students In Today's Lesson They Will**
practice division skills they have learned throughout this chapter.

### Guided Discussion

UNDERSTANDING

Whole Group

Discuss and review with students what they have learned so far about division, including the long form, the two short forms, how to check division problems, and so on.

Tell students that thinking about this knowledge will help them solve the problems in this lesson.

Discuss how some math problems present situations in which the arithmetic results in an answer that is quite silly. For example, if 5 people are in a room and half of them leave. The arithmetic would suggest $2\frac{1}{2}$ people are still in the room, but this is not possible. Ask students to think of similar problems where the data must be wrong.

## 2 Assign Student Pages

30

**Pages 536–537** APPLYING

Have students complete pages 536–537 individually or in groups of two.

**As Students Finish**

Game **Four Cube Division Game**

Student Page

LESSON 11.12 **Applying Mathematics**

**Key Ideas**

**You can use multiplication and division to solve many different kinds of problems.**

**Solve** these problems. Check to see that your answers make sense.

1. Mr. Quincy paid $1.05 (105¢) for 7 onions. How much did each onion cost? 15¢
2. Antonio bought 9 glass beads for 72¢. How much should 10 glass beads cost? 80¢
3. The grocery store sells 2 cans of cat food for $1.38 (138¢). How much would 1 can of cat food cost? 69¢
4. Greg drove for 8 hours. He traveled about 45 miles each hour. About how many miles did he drive? 360 miles
5. Extended Response Christy has 27 stickers. She wants to divide the stickers equally among 5 friends. See *Teacher's Edition.*
   - **a.** How many stickers should she give each friend? 5
   - **b.** Will there be any stickers left over? yes
   - **c.** What should she do with them? Possible answer: keep them for herself

**Divide.** Use shortcuts when you can.

| | | |
|---|---|---|
| 6. 6)480 80 | 7. 7)523 74 R5 | 8. 5)35 7 |
| 9. 8)326 40 R6 | 10. 2)632 316 | 11. 9)720 80 |
| 12. 9)722 80 R2 | 13. 3)426 142 | 14. 8)223 27 R5 |
| 15. 9)751 83 R4 | 16. 8)222 27 R6 | 17. 8)56 7 |
| 18. 3)471 157 | 19. 3)472 157 R1 | 20. 3)219 73 |

536 eTextbook This lesson is available in the *eTextbook*.

Student Page

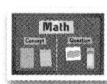

**Solve** these problems.

21. Mr. Taylor has 443 yards of fabric for the school play's costumes. He can make a complete costume from 8 yards of fabric. How many costumes can he make altogether? 55
22. There are 443 people who will ride to the convention. Each minivan can take 8 people. How many minivans will be needed to take everyone to the convention? 56
23. The Art Club will contribute a total of $443 to a local food bank. They decide that each of the 8 members will contribute an equal amount. How much should each person contribute? $56
24. Each basketball team must have exactly 8 players (5 regulars and 3 substitutes). If 443 people want to play, how many teams will there be? 55
25. Extended Response What is similar and what is different about your answers to Problems 21–24? Why are the answers different? Explain. See *Teacher's Edition.*
26. Monica can do 7 difficult mathematics problems in 1 hour. About how many hours will she need to do 21 difficult problems? 3 hours
27. Marta talked for 9 extra minutes on her cell phone. She was charged 657 cents ($6.57) for the extra time. How much did she pay for each extra minute? 73¢
28. Omar drove his car 318 miles in 6 hours. How many miles per hour did he drive? 53 mph

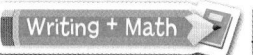

Writing + Math **Journal**

Describe a situation for which it is suitable to use estimation in regard to division. Then describe a time when an exact answer would be needed in regard to division.

Chapter 11 • Lesson 12 537

# 3 Reflect

10

## Guided Discussion REASONING

Whole Group

Discuss the word problems with the class. In discussing Problems 21–24 on page 537, most students will say the problems used the same numbers but in different situations. Although the quotient and the remainder were the same in each case, the specifics of the situation determined how to interpret the numbers.

Also have students explain the process for checking answers to division problems.

## Extended Response

**Problem 5** One possible solution is for her to keep the stickers for herself.

**Problem 25** Look to see that the students have stated the divisor and dividend are the same, but the answers differ because the situations differ.

Writing + Math **Journal**

One possible situation in which estimating is acceptable is when you're looking for unit cost of an item while shopping. Also, a time to be exact would be when a measurement needs to be divided for a project.

**Curriculum Connection:** Students may be interested in researching the distances different cars can travel on one tank of gas. They can find out what types of cars get the best gas mileage and which ones get the worst gas mileage. This information can be found online or at a local library.

**Cumulative Review:** For review of square facts, assign Problems 21–30 on student page 542.

**Family Involvement:** Assign the ***Practice, Reteach,*** or ***Enrichment*** activities depending on the needs of your students.

Encourage students to play the **Four Cube Division Game** at home with friends or relatives.

**Concept/Question Board:** Have students attempt to answer any unanswered questions on the Concept/Question Board.

**Math Puzzler:** Use only the digits 1, 2, 4, and 8 to create two fractions. Their sum must equal 1. $1/2 + 4/8 = 1$

# 4 Assess and Differentiate

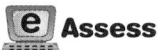

**e Assess** Use ***eAssess*** to record and analyze evidence of student understanding.

## A Gather Evidence

Use the Daily Class Assessment Records in ***Assessment*** or ***eAssess*** to record daily observations.

### Informal Assessment

**✓ Mental Math**

Did the student COMPUTING
- ❑ respond accurately?
- ❑ respond quickly?
- ❑ respond with confidence?
- ❑ self-correct?

### Portfolio Assessment

**✓ Journal**

Did the student REASONING
- ❑ provide a clear explanation?
- ❑ communicate reasons and strategies?
- ❑ choose appropriate strategies?
- ❑ argue logically?

## B Summarize Findings

Analyze and summarize assessment data for each student. Determine which Assessment Follow-Up is appropriate for each student. Use the Student Assessment Record in ***Assessment*** or ***eAssess*** to update assessment records.

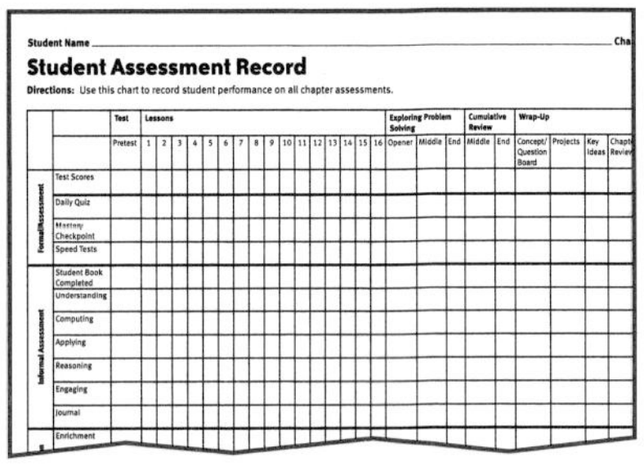
Student Assessment Record

Directions: Use this chart to record student performance on all chapter assessments.

**Assessment Page T41**

## C Assessment Follow-Up • DIFFERENTIATE INSTRUCTION

Based on your observations, use these teaching strategies for assessment follow-up.

### INTERVENTION

Review student performance on ***Intervention*** Lesson 11.B to see if students have mastered prerequisite skills for this lesson.

### ENGLISH LEARNERS

**Review**

Use Lesson 11.12 in ***English Learner Support Guide*** to review lesson concepts and vocabulary.

### ENRICH

**If . . .** students are proficient in the lesson concepts,

**Then . . .** encourage them to work on the chapter projects or ***Enrichment*** Lesson 11.12.

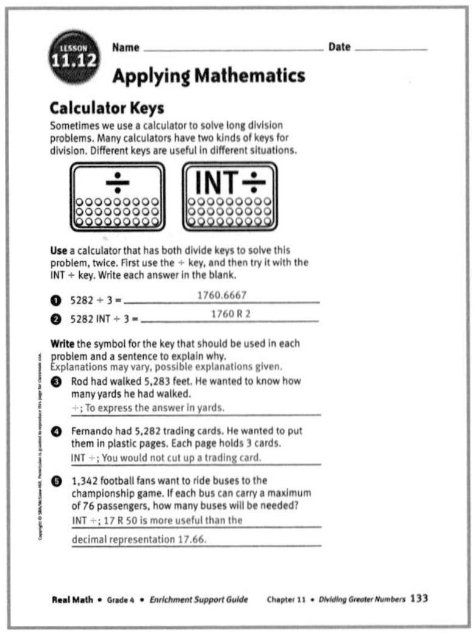
LESSON 11.12 Name ______ Date ______

Applying Mathematics

Calculator Keys

Sometimes we use a calculator to solve long division problems. Many calculators have two kinds of keys for division. Different keys are useful in different situations.

÷ INT÷

**Use** a calculator that has both divide keys to solve this problem, twice. First use the ÷ key, and then try it with the INT ÷ key. Write each answer in the blank.

1. 5282 ÷ 3 = 1760.6667
2. 5282 INT ÷ 3 = 1760 R 2

**Write** the symbol for the key that should be used in each problem and a sentence to explain why.
Explanations may vary, possible explanations given.

3. Rod had walked 5,283 feet. He wanted to know how many yards he had walked.
÷; To express the answer in yards.
4. Fernando had 5,282 trading cards. He wanted to put them in plastic pages. Each page holds 3 cards.
INT ÷; You would not cut up a trading card.
5. 1,342 football fans want to ride buses to the championship game. If each bus can carry a maximum of 76 passengers, how many buses will be needed?
INT ÷; 17 R 50 is more useful than the decimal representation 17.66.

Real Math • Grade 4 • Enrichment Support Guide    Chapter 11 • Dividing Greater Numbers 133

Enrichment Lesson 11.12

### PRACTICE

**If . . .** students would benefit from additional practice,

**Then . . .** assign ***Practice*** Lesson 11.12.

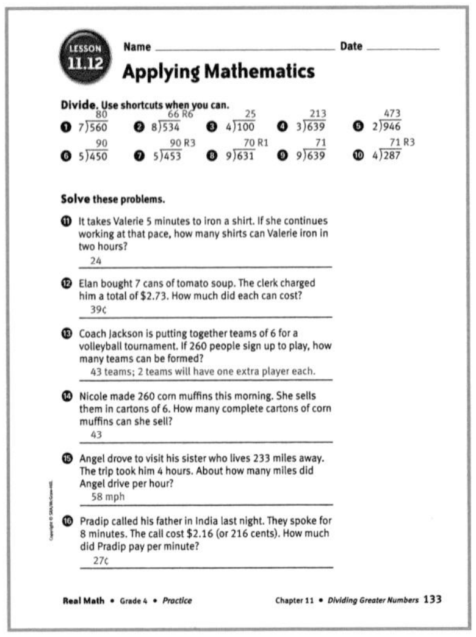
LESSON 11.12 Name ______ Date ______

Applying Mathematics

Divide. Use shortcuts when you can.

1. 7)560 — 80
2. 8)534 — 66 R6
3. 4)100 — 25
4. 3)639 — 213
5. 2)946 — 473
6. 5)450 — 90
7. 5)453 — 90 R3
8. 9)631 — 70 R1
9. 9)639 — 71
10. 4)287 — 71 R3

Solve these problems.

11. It takes Valerie 5 minutes to iron a shirt. If she continues working at that pace, how many shirts can Valerie iron in two hours?
24
12. Elan bought 7 cans of tomato soup. The clerk charged him a total of $2.73. How much did each can cost?
39¢
13. Coach Jackson is putting together teams of 6 for a volleyball tournament. If 260 people sign up to play, how many teams can be formed?
43 teams; 2 teams will have one extra player each.
14. Nicole made 260 corn muffins this morning. She sells them in cartons of 6. How many complete cartons of corn muffins can she sell?
43
15. Angel drove to visit his sister who lives 233 miles away. The trip took him 4 hours. About how many miles did Angel drive per hour?
58 mph
16. Pradip called his father in India last night. They spoke for 8 minutes. The call cost $2.16 (or 216 cents). How much did Pradip pay per minute?
27¢

Real Math • Grade 4 • Practice    Chapter 11 • Dividing Greater Numbers 133

Practice Lesson 11.12

### RETEACH

**If . . .** students are having difficulty interpreting remainders,

**Then . . .** help them learn to analyze the meaning of a remainder as it applies to the situation.
For example, in Problem 22, the quotient 55 R3 does not answer the question of how many minivans to use. Guide students to see that 55 is the number of full vans. The remainder represents three people who will still need rides. Help them to see that the remainder means another van is needed to transport the remaining people.

# Exploring Problem Solving

**Objectives**

- To analyze travel data from a historic voyage in order to gain a better understanding of the event
- To use division and proportional reasoning to find and compare rates
- To relate division and fractions
- To explore solving and presenting solutions to nonroutine problems

**Context of the Lesson** This lesson provides an opportunity for students to use their understanding of division to analyze a historic voyage. It also builds on the Mayflower theme established in earlier lessons in this chapter.

## 1 Develop

5

**Tell Students In Today's Lesson They Will**

- read about the Mayflower's voyage to the New World.
- figure out how fast the Mayflower traveled.
- solve problems about the food supply on the Mayflower.

## Guided Discussion

Recall previous discussions about the Mayflower in earlier lessons in this chapter. Then go over the synopsis of the Mayflower voyage and the maps on student page 538 with the class. During or after the story, ask questions such as the following:

- **Why are several routes shown on the first map?** Students may remember from page 522 the ill-fated attempts of the Speedwell to sail with the Mayflower.
- **Based on the story, do you think the Mayflower sailed a direct route from England to the New World?** No. For one thing, the ship drifted when the sails had to be taken down during heavy storms.

Students may be interested to know that the Mayflower's passengers were heading to New York, where they intended to settle. Without modern navigation tools, the Mayflower ended up several hundred miles off course. The rest is indeed history.

Student Page

**Exploring Problem Solving**

### Incredible Journey

On September 6, 1620, after a month and a half of false starts, the Mayflower and her 60 passengers finally sailed from the English port of Plymouth. Unaware of how they would change history, the voyagers headed across the Atlantic Ocean to a new life in a new world.

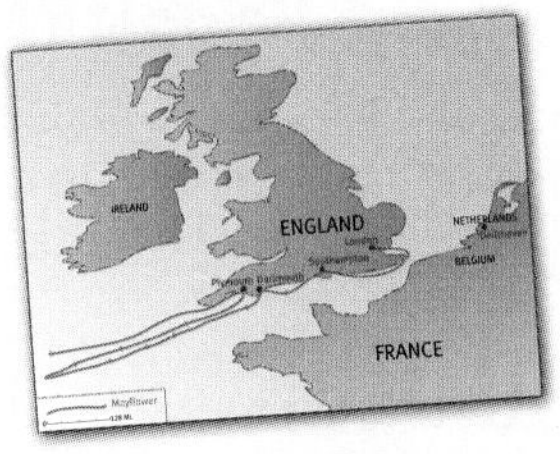


For a while, some seasickness was the only disturbance on the Mayflower. But by October, storms rocked the ship, forcing the crew to take down her sails. Tossed by heavy waves, the ship drifted until clear weather allowed the sails to be hoisted once again.

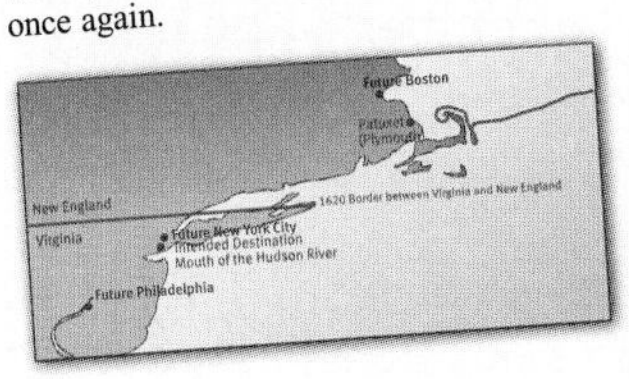


At last, the weary travelers caught sight of what is now Cape Cod and landed there on November 11. It would be another month before the ship would actually land at the place the Pilgrims would call Plymouth.

538 Textbook This lesson is available in the *eTextbook*.

# 2 Exploring Problem Solving 30

## Using Student Pages

Have students turn to page 539. Discuss the purpose of a map scale and how to use it. Then have the class work in groups to answer Problems 1–5, or work on them as a class.

## Answers to Problems 1–5

### Problem 1

It took 66 days; 67 days is also acceptable if students decide to start with the morning of September 6 and end with the evening of November 11.

### Problem 2

It is about 3,300 miles. Any answer from 3,000 to 3,500 miles is reasonable, depending on how closely students measure or estimate.

### Problem 3

The ship went about 2 miles per hour. A calculation might look like this: Since 100 miles a day would result in 6,600 miles in 66 days, then half of that speed would result in 3,300 miles per day. So the average speed was about 50 miles per day, or 50 miles in 24 hours, which is about 2 miles per hour.

### Problem 4

Students should figure it to be about $\frac{1}{3}$ of the total distance. If they answered 3,300 miles in Problem 2, then they should answer about 1,100 miles here.

### Problem 5

The actual average speed was greater, because the ship traveled more than 3,300 miles in 66 days.

**Student Page**

No one knows how many miles the Mayflower traveled because her exact route is still a mystery. But we know she traveled at least as far as the distance from England to the coast of Massachusetts.

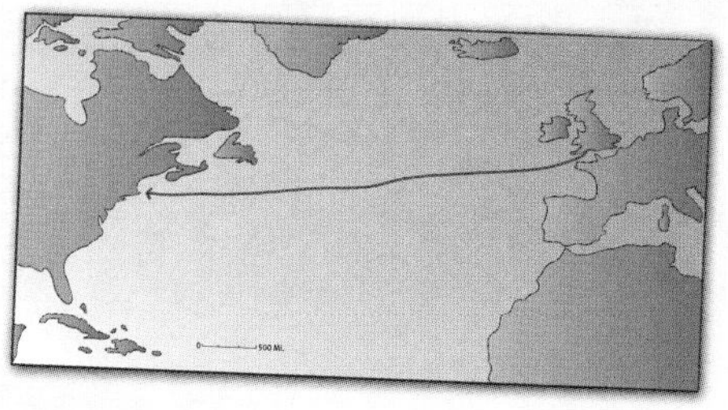

**Work** with your group to solve these problems. Use the map and the information in the story. See *Teacher's Edition* for answers.

1. How many days did it take the Mayflower to cross the Atlantic Ocean?
2. How far is it from Plymouth, England, to Cape Cod, Massachusetts?
3. In miles per hour, at about what rate did the Mayflower make her way toward the New World?
4. Suppose the Mayflower had headed for the New World steadily at that rate. About how far from England would she have been on September 28?
5. Since the Mayflower did not travel a direct route from England to Massachusetts, was the average speed of the Mayflower greater than or less than your answer to Problem 3? How do you know?

Chapter 11 539

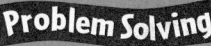

Student Page

## Exploring Problem Solving

We do not know the exact supplies that the Mayflower carried. Some historians think that the Pilgrims probably followed the advice of someone who had already journeyed to the New World—Captain John Smith.

In a pamphlet, Captain Smith suggested what clothing, food, tools, and bedding travelers should bring. Captain Smith's food list was supposed to be enough for one man for one year. Part of this list is shown.

About 2 barrels of wheat
About $\frac{1}{2}$ barrel of peas
About $\frac{1}{2}$ barrel of oats
2 gallons of vinegar
1 gallon of salad oil
Bacon
Cheese
Sugar, spice, and fruit

About 250 lbs　About 150 lbs

**Work** in groups to discuss and solve these problems. **Compare your answers with those of other groups.** See *Teacher's Edition.*

6. Did Captain Smith's list provide more or less than $1\frac{1}{2}$ pounds of wheat each day for one person? How do you know?
7. About what fraction of a pound of oats per day does the list provide for? Explain.
8. Suppose you were on the Mayflower and had brought the food that Captain Smith recommended. When you arrived in Massachusetts, about how much salad oil would you expect to have left? Explain.

540　Textbook This lesson is available in the *eTextbook.*

Go over the information on page 540 with the class. Ask questions such as the following:

- **How long was the food on the list supposed to last for one person?** one year
- **Why would someone recommend a year's supply of food for a voyage that takes only about two months?** The voyage could take much longer due to bad weather or the ship going off course. Also, food is eaten while getting ready for the trip, which in the Mayflower's case was several months. Travelers would need food when they reached the New World. The Mayflower passengers had to live on board the ship for a month or longer while a settlement location was chosen.
- **About how many pounds of wheat are recommended?** about 500 pounds
- **About how many pounds of oats are recommended?** about 75 pounds

Have the students work in groups to answer Problems 6–8. Provide help as needed.

## Answers to Problems 6–8

### Problem 6

It provided a little less. Students might reason as follows: 1 pound per day for 365 days is 365 pounds, and a half-pound per day for 365 days is about 180 pounds. So, a pound and a half per day would total more than 500 pounds. That means a supply of 500 pounds for a year comes to less than $1\frac{1}{2}$ pounds a day. Alternatively, students might look at the fraction $\frac{500}{365}$, and see that it is less than $1\frac{1}{2}$.

### Problem 7

It provides about $\frac{1}{5}$ of a pound. The supply of oats is about 75 pounds. Students may see that $5 \times 75$ is close to 365, so 75 is about $\frac{1}{5}$ of 365. So, if a pound per day lasts 75 days, then $\frac{1}{5}$ of a pound a day would last 5 times as long, or about one year. To help students see this, you might work with them to make a table like the following:

| Pounds of food | How many days the food will last if the amount eaten is | |
|---|---|---|
| | 1 lb per day | $\frac{1}{5}$ lb per day |
| 1 | 1 | 5 |
| 2 | 2 | 10 |
| 3 | 3 | 15 |
| 75 | 75 | 375 |

### Problem 8

After 2 months, you would have used about $\frac{2}{12}$, or $\frac{1}{6}$, of the salad oil. You would expect to have about $\frac{5}{6}$ of a gallon left.

## 3 Reflect

10

### Knowledge Age Skills

**Effective Communication** Discuss with the class their answers to Problems 6–8. Discuss the following points:

- Estimation is often sufficient to solve a problem.
- In place of division, students can often use multiplication along with the Guess, Check, and Adjust Strategy.

## 4 Assess

15

When evaluating student work, focus not only on the correctness of the answer but also on students' thinking and communication. Some questions to consider include the following:

- Did the student interpret the map and use the scale in an appropriate way when trying to find actual distances?
- Did the student use division or other appropriate methods to find a rate?
- Did the student use estimation to solve the problem?

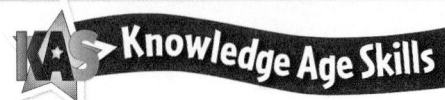

# Cumulative Review

Review

## Assign Pages 541–542

Use this Cumulative Review as a review of concepts and skills that students have previously learned.

Here are different ways you can assign these problems to your students as they work through the chapter:

- For each lesson in the chapter, assign a set of Cumulative Review problems to be completed as practice or for homework.
  - Lesson 11.8—Problems 1–4
  - Lesson 11.9—Problems 5–10
  - Lesson 11.10—Problems 11–15
  - Lesson 11.11—Problems 16–20
  - Lesson 11.12—Problems 21–30
- At any point during the chapter, assign part or all of the Cumulative Review problems to be completed as practice or for homework.

### Cumulative Review

**Problems 1–4** review comparing decimals, Lesson 9.3.

**Problems 5–10** review common multiples and common factors, Lesson 3.12.

**Problems 11–15** review types of lines, Lesson 10.3.

**Problems 16–20** review percentages, Lessons 7.2, 7.3 and 7.8.

**Problems 21–30** review square facts, Lessons 3.4 and 3.13.

### Monitoring Student Progress

**If . . .** students miss more than one problem in a section, **Then . . .** refer to the indicated lesson for remediation suggestions.

Student Page

## Cumulative Review

**Comparing Decimals** Lesson 9.3

**Select** the unequal measurement from each list.

1. 625 centimeters; 6.25 meters; $6\frac{1}{4}$ meters; 625 millimeters — 625 millimeters
2. 50 centimeters; 5 centimeters; 0.5 meter; 0.005 millimeters — 5 centimeters
3. 10.15 meters; 10 meters and 15 centimeters; 1,015 centimeters; 10,015 millimeters — 10,015 millimeters
4. 75 centimeters; 750 millimeters; $\frac{3}{4}$ meter; 7,500 millimeters — 7,500 millimeters

**Common Multiples and Common Factors** Lesson 3.12

**Select** the least common multiple for each set of numbers.

5. 3 and 2 — a. 5 (b.) 6 c. 12 d. 8
6. 4 and 6 — a. 5 b. 6 (c.) 12 d. 16
7. 5 and 10 — a. 5 b. 15 (c.) 10 d. 50

**Select** the greatest factor for each set of numbers.

8. 12 and 15 — (a.) 3 b. 6 c. 5 d. 27
9. 18 and 30 — (a.) 6 b. 3 c. 22 d. 180
10. 24 and 4 — a. 2 b. 48 (c.) 4 d. 28



Student Page

## Cumulative Review

**Parallel, Perpendicular, and Intersecting Lines** Lesson 10.3

**Write** *perpendicular, intersecting,* or *parallel* for the following line segments.

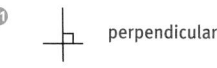

11. 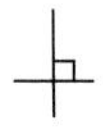 perpendicular
12.  intersecting
13.  intersecting
14.  perpendicular
15. 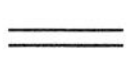  parallel

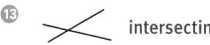

**Percents** Lessons 7.2, 7.3, and 7.8

**Solve** these problems.

16. 10% of 45 = ■ 4.5
17. $\frac{1}{8}$ of 320 = ■ 40
18. 0.25 of 400 = ■ 100
19. 50% of 25 = ■ 12.5
20. 12.5% of 24 = ■ 3

**Square Facts** Lessons 3.4 and 3.13

**Multiply** to find the answers.

21. What is the area of a square with a length of 6 cm? 36 $cm^2$
22. $3^2$ = ■ 9
23. $12^2$ = ■ 144
24. $4 + (9 \times 3)$ = ■ 31
25. $(64 \div 16) + 6$ = ■ 10
26. $9^2$ = ■ 81
27. Is the following number sentence true or false? true $7 + (5 \times 3) = 11 \times 2 + 0$
28. $7^2$ = ■ 49
29. $(72 \div 6) - 8$ = ■ 4
30. Is the following number sentence true or false? false $3 + (5^2) = (2 \times 6) \times 2$

# Wrap-Up

## 1 Discuss

5

### Concept/Question Board

Review the Concept/Question Board with students.

- Discuss students' contributions to the Concept side of the Board.
- Have students repose their questions, and lead a discussion to find satisfactory answers.

## Chapter Projects

Provide an opportunity for students who have worked on one or more of the chapter projects outlined on page 503C to share their work with the class. Allow each student or student group five minutes to present or discuss their projects. For formal assessment, use the rubrics found in ***Across the Curriculum Math Connections;*** the rubric for **Plan a Voyage to the New World** is on page 117, and the rubric for **Plan Meals as Christopher Columbus's Cook** is on page 121. For informal assessment, use the following rubric and questions.

| | Exceeds Expectations | Meets Expectations | Minimally Meets Expectations |
|---|---|---|---|
| Applies mathematics in real-world situations: | ❑ | ❑ | ❑ |
| Demonstrates strong engagement in the activity: | ❑ | ❑ | ❑ |

### Plan a Voyage to the New World

SOCIAL STUDIES WebQuest

- What did you name your colony? Why?
- How many people will settle in your colony? What size is your colony?
- Did you list all of the supplies that you would need for the colony? What else would you have included?
- What was the total cost per person to create a new settlement?
- What factors might you consider when selecting colonists to join you in the voyage to a new settlement?
- Do you think that it is possible to anticipate all the supplies that are needed? Why or why not?
- What skills do you think it takes to become the leader of a new settlement or colony?

### Plan Meals as Christopher Columbus's Cook

abc LANGUAGE ARTS

- What are some of the differences between the food eaten during Columbus's time and the food you eat today?
- How did you plan how much food you would need for a week?
- How did you divide the food for the week?
- What information did you include in your log entries? What other information could you have included?
- Was it difficult planning meals for a week? Why or why not?
- Would you like to have been a cook on Christopher Columbus's ship? Why or why not?

# 2 Assign Student Pages 25

## Key Ideas Review ✓ UNDERSTANDING

Have students complete the Review questions independently or in small groups. Then discuss each question as a class.

### Possible Answers

**Problem 1** Problems 1–3 ask students to use their knowledge of dividing greater numbers. The answer is A.

**Problem 2** The answer is C. This problem focuses on the placement of the decimal point within the quotient.

**Problem 3** The answer is B. This problem focuses on the *remainder* within division of greater numbers.

**Problem 4** The answers are 1, 2, 3, 4, 6, 8, 12, and 24. *Factors* are numbers multiplied to get a product.

**Problem 5** This exercise requires students to know what prime and composite numbers are. A prime number has two factors, one and itself. For example:

- 3
- 5

A composite number has more than two factors. For example:

- 4
- 6

Extended Response

**Problem 6** Students could say that multiplication is the inverse of division; therefore, the quotient can be estimated and then multiplied by the divisor. If the product of those numbers is equal to the dividend, then the quotient has been found.

Extended Response

**Problem 7** This exercise asks students to find quotients and to see the pattern of those quotients. Students should recognize that 6 is added to the end of the quotients as the dividend is multiplied by 10.

Extended Response

**Problem 8** This problem involves students' knowledge of how to compute unit cost. Students could say that if the unit cost is $0.60 and there are 6 in a pack, the cost for the entire pack is close to $3.60.

Extended Response

**Problem 9** This problem asks students to explain how to check a quotient that has a remainder. Students should mention that the quotient is multiplied by the divisor, and the remainder is then added to the product of the two numbers.

Extended Response

**Problem 10** In the quotient, the decimal point is located between the same place values that it was in the dividend.

Student Page

## CHAPTER 11 Key Ideas Review

**In this chapter you discovered how to divide greater numbers.**

You learned strategies to find factors of greater numbers.

You learned many ways to divide greater numbers.

**Use** multiplication or division to select the correct answer.

| (1) 3)858 | (2) 4)6.80 | (3) 54)9167 |
|---|---|---|
| (a.) 286 | a. 170 | a. 169 R 44 |
| b. 266 | b. 17.0 | (b.) 169 R 41 |
| c. 267 R 1 | (c.) 1.70 | c. 168 R 41 |

(4) List all the factors for 24. 1, 2, 3, 4, 6, 8, 12, and 24

Extended Response **Solve** each problem.

(5) What is the difference between a prime and a composite number? Provide an example of each. (5) Prime numbers have two factors, 1 and itself, whereas composite numbers have more than two factors. For example, 3 is prime and 4 is composite.

(6) How can multiplication be used to solve a division problem?

(7) Solve the three exercises below and explain what pattern you notice.

6)100 6)1000 6)10000

(7) 16 R 4, 166 R 4, 1,666 R 4; 6 is added to the end of each quotient as another 0 is added to the dividend.

(8) If a 6-pack of yogurt costs $3.54, is it reasonable to estimate that one container of yogurt would cost $0.60? Explain why or why not. (8) It is reasonable because $0.6 \times 6 = 3.60$.

(9) How do you check to see if a quotient with a remainder is correct? (9) The quotient is multiplied by the divisor and the remainder is then added to the product of the two numbers.

(10) Where is the decimal point placed in the quotient of a division problem? (10) The decimal point is placed between the same placeholders as in the dividend.

543

# CHAPTER 11 Review

## Chapter Review

Use this Chapter 11 Review as a preliminary chapter test to identify areas in which each student is having difficulty or in which the class may need help. If students do well on the Chapter 11 Review, you may wish to skip directly to the next chapter. If not, you may want to spend time helping students overcome their individual difficulties before they take the Chapter Test.

Each set of problems reviews concepts from one or more lessons in the chapter. Students can refer to a specific lesson for additional instruction if they need help. You can also use this information to assign additional practice based on the p revious lesson concepts.

Have students complete pages 544–545 on their own. For review purposes, you may want to do some of the word problems on page 545 as a class.

### Monitoring Student Progress

**Problems 1–4 Lesson 11.1 and 11.4**

**If . . .** students miss more than one of these division problems,

**Then . . .** assess students individually. The **Four Cube Division Game** in Lesson 11.3, which reinforces the skill of dividing by one-digit divisors and using place value, also provides extra practice.

**Problems 5–8 Lesson 11.3**

**If . . .** students miss more than one of these problems involving checking answers to division problems,

**Then . . .** reteach the method for checking a division problem. Give students a chance to discuss this method and why it works.

**Problems 9–12 Lesson 11.6**

**If . . .** students miss more than one of these prime numbers,

**Then . . .** make sure students know the definition of a prime number. Give students more practice with finding factors.

**Problems 13–15 Lesson 11.8–11.9**

**If . . .** students miss more than one of these word problems,

**Then . . .** assess students individually to see if they are having difficulty understanding the problem or if they are not using the proper method to solve the problem.

**Problems 16–20 Lessons 11.11–11.12**

**If . . .** students miss more than one of these division problems,

**Then . . .** provide extra instruction. Allow students to use drawings to help them.

Student Page

# CHAPTER 11 Chapter Review

Lessons 11.1 and 11.4 **Solve.**

1. 36 ÷ 4 = 9
2. A zoo received 6,921 pounds of meat for the tigers. If there are 8 tigers, how much meat does each tiger get? 865 pounds with 1 pound left over
3. 6,129 ÷ 8 = 766 R 1
4. The Palmers paid $2,864 for 4 people to fly from Detroit to Montgomery. How much did the Palmers pay for each ticket? $716

Lesson 11.3 **Check the following problems. If a problem is wrong, correct it. If it is correct, then write *okay* on your paper.**

5. 312 ÷ 4 = 78 okay
6. 6300 ÷ 7 = 900 okay
7. 7923 ÷ 4 = 198 R 3 1980 R 3
8. 257 ÷ 2 = 128 R 1 okay

Lesson 11.6 **Study each set of numbers and list any prime numbers falling between the set of numbers.**

9. 12–18 13 and 17
10. 1–6 2, 3, and 5
11. 20–29 23
12. 6–15 7, 11, and 13

Lessons 11.8 and 11.9 **Answer the following questions.**

13. Michael and Kim went on a 3-hour hike. They covered 14.25 miles in that time. About how far did they go each hour? 4.75 miles
14. Terrell needs 64 brownies for a party. At the bakery, one brownie is $0.55 or he can buy 85 brownies for $32.
    **a.** Which selection will save Terrell money? 85 brownies for $32
    **b.** How much money would he save? $3.20
15. Bobbi is buying a new car and spreading the payments over four years. If the car costs $12,500, about how much is she paying each month? $260.42



Textbook This lesson is available in the *eTextbook.*

Student Page

Lessons 11.11 and 11.12

**Select a good estimate for the following problems, then find the exact answer.**

16. 7,832 ÷ 12 = ▢
    **a.** 80
    **(b.)** 800 652 R 8
    **c.** 8,000
17. 98,206 ÷ 16 = ▢
    **a.** 50
    **b.** 500
    **(c.)** 5,000 6,137 R 14
18. 397 ÷ 22 = ▢
    **(a.)** 20 18 R 1
    **b.** 200
    **c.** 2
19. 4012 ÷ 26 = ▢
    **a.** 10
    **(b.)** 100 154 R 8
    **c.** 1,000

20. Extended Response Ronnie is comparing two cars. Look at the chart below to help him decide which car is best for his needs.

| Car | Gas: Miles Per Tank | Gas Tank Capacity | Price | Cost to Operate Per Mile |
|---|---|---|---|---|
| STC 300 | 405 | 15 gal | $12,525 | $0.35 |
| XZ 550 | 494 | 19 gal | $13,650 | $0.33 |

**a.** Which car can go farther on 1 gallon of gas? STC 300

**b.** The bank told Ronnie he can get a loan for 36 months on the STC 300 or for 4 years on the XZ 550. Which car would cost less per month? XZ 550

# CHAPTER 11 Assessment

## 3 Chapter Tests 40

### Practice Test

**Student Pages 546–549**

- The Chapter 11 Practice Test on ***Student Edition*** pages 546–549 provides an opportunity to formally evaluate students' proficiency with concepts developed in this chapter.
- The content is similar to the Chapter 11 Review in standardized format.

**Problem 28** Extended Response

Students should be encouraged to solve Problem 28 by using division although some may still find it easier to make groups of equal numbers. In part c, students are to think of alternate ways to solve the problem. For those students who find it easier to form groups of equal size, they should recognize that division is also an alternative.

Student Page

CHAPTER 11 **Practice Test**

**Answer** the following questions.

1. How many factors do prime numbers have? What are they? 2, 1, and the number itself
2. Give five composite numbers. Possible answers: 4, 6, 8, 9, 10

**Rewrite** each number in completely factored form.

3. 8 $2 \times 2 \times 2 = 2^3$
4. 11 factored
5. 28 $2 \times 2 \times 7 = 2^2 \times 7$
6. 36 $2 \times 2 \times 3 \times 3 = 2^2 \times 3^2$

**Solve** each problem below.

7. Eight people want to divide \$3,365 equally. How much should each person get? How many dollars will be left over? \$420 each, \$5 left over
8. Mary drove 512 miles and used 16 gallons of gas. How many miles did Mary drive on one gallon of gasoline? 32
9. Jane bought 6 scented erasers for 72¢. How much should 8 erasers cost her? 96¢

546 Textbook This lesson is available in the *eTextbook*.

Student Page

**Divide.**

10. $4\overline{)458}$
    - Ⓐ 11 R1 ● 114 R2
    - Ⓒ 115 Ⓓ 141
11. $9\overline{)8325}$
    - ● 925 Ⓑ 825
    - Ⓒ 936 Ⓓ 936 R1
12. $6\overline{)2124}$
    - Ⓐ 404 Ⓑ 35 R2
    - Ⓒ 345 ● 354
13. $5\overline{)10000}$
    - ● 2000 Ⓑ 20
    - Ⓒ 200 Ⓓ 2200
14. 6,232 ÷ 19
    - Ⓐ 3,228 Ⓑ 382
    - ● 328 Ⓓ 618
15. 11,568 ÷ 24
    - Ⓐ 548 Ⓑ 248
    - Ⓒ 4,482 ● 482

**Solve** for *n*.

16. $600 \div 6 = n$
    - Ⓐ 1,000 Ⓑ 111
    - ● 100 Ⓓ 1
17. $6000 \div 6 = n$
    - ● 1000 Ⓑ 111
    - Ⓒ 100 Ⓓ 10

**Find** the value of *x* or *y*.

18. *X* ← ÷24 ← 264
    - ● 11 Ⓑ 6,336
    - Ⓒ 3,663 Ⓓ 636
19. 23 → ×152 → *y*
    - Ⓐ 3,344 Ⓑ 3,369
    - ● 3,496 Ⓓ 4,486

Real Math • Chapter 11 547

Student Page

# CHAPTER 11 Practice Test

**Select** the correct answer.

**20.** What is the greatest common factor of 15 and 21?

Ⓐ 1 ● 3

Ⓒ 5 Ⓓ 7

**21.** What is $\frac{1}{10}$ of 300?

Ⓐ 3 Ⓑ 10

● 30 Ⓓ 3000

**22.** ▭ meters = 6 centimeters

Ⓐ 60 Ⓑ 6

Ⓒ 0.6 ● 0.06

**23.** 20 meters = ▭ millimeters

● 20,000 Ⓑ 200

Ⓒ 0.2 Ⓓ 0.002

**24.** What is the area of the rectangle shown below?

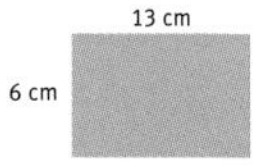


Ⓐ 19 square centimeters

Ⓑ 26 square centimeters

● 78 square centimeters

Ⓓ 87 square centimeters

**25.** Which number is a prime number?

Ⓐ 27 ● 31

Ⓒ 16 Ⓓ 44

**26.** Which number is a composite number?

Ⓐ 3 Ⓑ 17

Ⓒ 43 ● 51

**27.** Which pair of numbers contains a prime and a composite number?

Ⓐ 2 and 7 Ⓑ 3 and 83

Ⓒ 9 and 55 ● 4 and 67



eTextbook This lesson is available in the ***eTextbook***.

Student Page

Extended Response **Solve** the problem below. Explain how you found each answer.

**28.** John brought a bag of buttons to school for an art project. The bag had 132 buttons inside. He gave an equal number of buttons to each of his 19 classmates and to himself.

**a.** How many buttons did each student get?
Each student received 6 buttons.

**b.** Did John have any buttons left over? If so, how many?
John had 12 buttons left over.

**c.** Explain two different methods that John could use to know how many buttons to give himself and each of his classmates.

**d.** Marshall joined the art project. Does John have enough buttons to give Marshall as many as the other classmates received?

c. Answers will vary. Possible answers include: Make 20 groups, put buttons in each group until all groups are equal with not enough buttons to make another full round; use multiplication to find multiplication fact closest to 132 (20 × 6); use division.

d. Yes. The others each received 6 buttons. John has 12 buttons left.



## Chapter Test ☑ COMPUTING

- For further evaluation instead of or in addition to this test, you may wish to have students take the Chapter 11 Test provided in ***Assessment***.

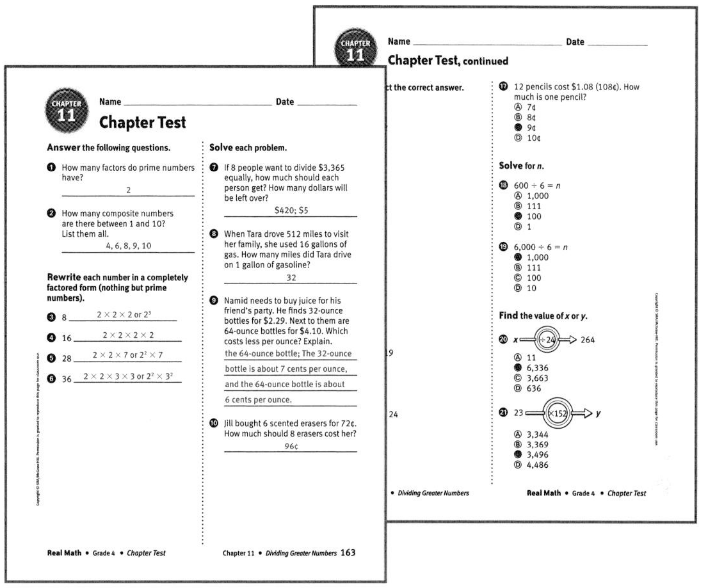

Assessment, pages 163–164

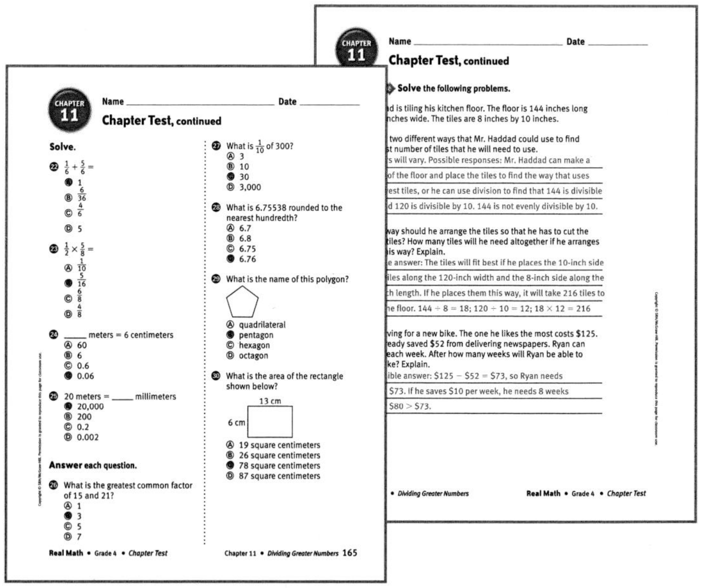

Assessment, pages 165–166

# 4 Assess and Differentiate

**e Assess** Use ***eAssess*** to record and analyze evidence of student understanding.

## A Gather Evidence

Use the Daily Class Assessment Records in ***Assessment*** or ***eAssess*** to record Informal and Formal Assessments.

### Informal Assessment

**Key Ideas Review** UNDERSTANDING

Did the student
- ❑ answer questions?
- ❑ pose new questions?
- ❑ extend the discussion?
- ❑ provide insight?

### Informal Assessment

**Project** APPLYING

Did the student
- ❑ meet the project objectives?
- ❑ communicate clearly?
- ❑ complete the project accurately?
- ❑ connect mathematics to real-world situations?

### Formal Assessment

**Chapter Test** COMPUTING

Score the test, and record the results.

## B Summarize Findings

Analyze and summarize assessment data for each student. Determine which Chapter Follow-Up is appropriate for each student. Use the Student Assessment Record in ***Assessment*** or ***eAssess*** to update assessment records.

## C Chapter Follow-Up • DIFFERENTIATE INSTRUCTION

Based on your observations, use these teaching strategies for chapter follow-up.

| ENRICH | PRACTICE | RETEACH | INTERVENTION |
|---|---|---|---|
| **If . . .** students demonstrate **secure understanding** of chapter concepts,<br>**Then . . .** have them move on to the next chapter. | **If . . .** students exhibit **competent understanding** of chapter concepts,<br>**Then . . .** have them move on to the next chapter. | **If . . .** students demonstrate **emerging understanding** of chapter concepts,<br>**Then . . .** move on to the next chapter, but continue to provide cumulative review. | **If . . .** students demonstrate **minimal understanding** of chapter concepts,<br>**Then . . .** intensive intervention is needed before they start the next chapter. |

CHAPTER 11

# Teacher Reflection

## Lesson Study

Reflect on each of the lessons you taught in this chapter. Rate each one on the following scale, then consider ways to maintain or improve positive teaching experiences in the future.

| Lessons | Very Effective | Effective | Less Effective | What Worked | Ways to Improve |
|---|---|---|---|---|---|
| 11.1 Dividing by a One-Digit Divisor | | | | | |
| 11.2 Division: Written Form | | | | | |
| 11.3 Checking Division | | | | | |
| 11.4 Division: Short Form | | | | | |
| 11.5 Division Patterns | | | | | |
| 11.6 Prime and Composite Numbers | | | | | |
| 11.7 Finding Factors | | | | | |
| 11.8 Unit Cost | | | | | |
| 11.9 Using Inverses | | | | | |
| 11.10 Estimating Quotients | | | | | |
| 11.11 Dividing by a Two-Digit Divisor | | | | | |
| 11.12 Applying Mathematics | | | | | |

CHAPTER 12 Overview

## Lessons



# Organizing and Interpreting Data

## Teaching for Understanding

***This chapter focuses on introducing statistical analysis of average, mode, median, and range as well as ways to read and create graphs.*** Students see information in various ways and begin to learn the basics of statistics. Average (or mean) is taught as an "evening out" process as well as the traditional way of computation.

## Prerequisite Skills and Concepts

- Dividing by a One-Digit Number
- Approximating Products and Quotients
- Reading Graphs

## Organizing and Interpreting Data Skills Trace

| Before Grade 4 | Grade 4 | After Grade 4 |
|---|---|---|
| **Grades K–1** Formally introduced to making and analyzing graphs<br>**Grades 2–3** Informally introduced to range and mode; formally introduced to vertical and horizontal bar graphs | **Chapter 4** developed strategies for working with graphs.<br>**Chapter 11** explored strategies for dividing greater numbers.<br>**This chapter** introduces average (mean), median, mode, and range as computations for statistical analysis. | Practice with collecting data to make circle graphs, bar graphs, and multiple-line graphs and development of strategies for statistical awareness |

### Problem Solving

Problem solving is in every lesson. This chapter includes the following:

**CHAPTER INTRODUCTION** Students solve a problem that uses average to determine a site to buy from the California Gold Rush of 1848 (pp. 550I–551C).

**EXPLORING PROBLEM SOLVING** The first lesson requires students to apply what they know about mean, median, and mode (pp. 564–565). The second lesson allows students to explore results of different sampling methods by applying computation and geometrical abilities (pp. 575–576A).

### Games

Develop reasoning skills, and provide extensive practice.

**Four Cube Division Game** (Lesson 11.3), **Cubo** (Lesson 3.14), **Harder Snake Game Mat** (Lesson 4.4), **Fracto I Game Mat** (Lesson 8.5)

# Math Background

## Using Data

### What is Data Analysis?

*Describing data involves reading displays of data (e.g., tables, lists, graphs); that is, finding information explicitly stated in the display, recognizing graphical conventions and making direct connections between the original data and the display. The process is essentially what has been called* reading the data. . . *The process of organizing, and reducing, data incorporates mental actions such as ordering, grouping, and summarizing. Data reduction also includes the use of representative measures of center (often termed* measures of central tendency) *such as mean, mode, or median, and measures of spread such as range or standard deviation.*

(Kilpatrick, J.; Swafford, J.; and Findell, B. eds. *Adding It Up: Helping Children Learn Mathematics.* Washington, D.C.: National Research Council/National Academy Press, 2001, p. 289.)

Collecting, organizing, displaying, and interpreting data, as well as using the information to make decisions and predictions, are skills that students will use throughout their lives. Statistical instruction should be carried out in a spirit of investigation and exploration so students can understand the data they have gathered or received. Students should develop not only the routine skills of tabulating and graphing results, but also at a higher level, the ability to detect patterns and trends in poorly organized data either before or after reorganization.

### Measures of Central Tendency

**MEAN** The *mean* can be found by adding the numbers in a set and dividing by the number of addends.

**MEDIAN** The *median* is the middle number in a set when the numbers are arranged in numerical order. If there are an even number of numbers in the set, the median is halfway between the two middle numbers.

**MODE** The *mode* is the most frequently occurring number in a set. A set may have more than one mode. If all numbers occur the same number of times, the set has no mode.

### Tools for Organizing Data

**BAR GRAPH** A *bar graph* is a chart with bars whose lengths are proportional to the quantities they represent.

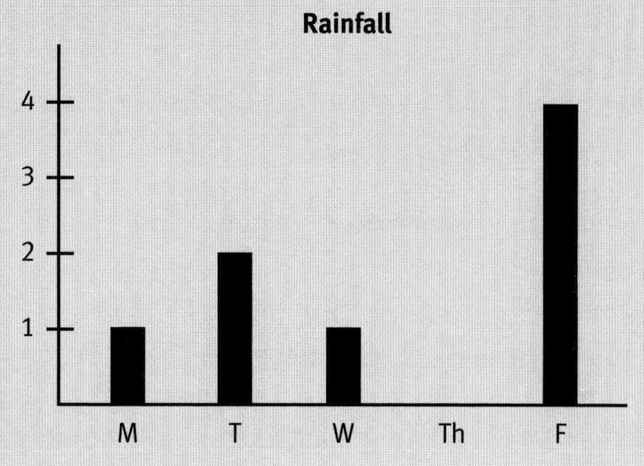


**CIRCLE GRAPH** A *circle graph* is a circular graph having radii dividing the circle into sectors proportional in angle and area to the relative size of the quantities represented.

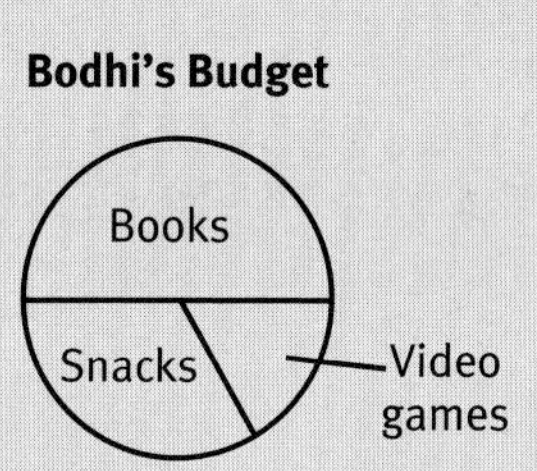


**TREE DIAGRAM** A *tree diagram* shows possible choices at each decision point, or "branch."

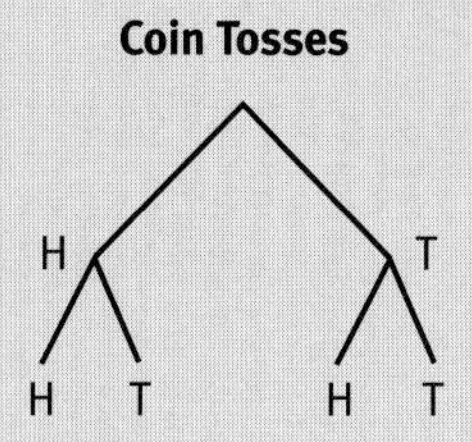

# What Research Says

## About Data Analysis and Probability

### How Children Learn Data Analysis and Probability

*Data analysis contains one big idea: classifying, organizing, representing, and using information to ask and answer questions. The developmental continuum for data analysis includes growth in classifying and counting to sort objects and quantify their groups.... Children eventually become capable of simultaneously classifying and counting, for example, counting the number of colors in a group of objects....*

*After gathering data to answer questions, children's initial representations often do not use categories. Their interest in data is on the particulars.... Thus, children should use physical objects to make graphs, then picture graphs, then line plots, and finally bar graphs that include grid lines to facilitate reading frequencies. By second grade most children should be able to organize and display data through both simple numerical summaries such as counts, tables, and tallies, and graphical displays, including picture graphs, line plots, and bar graphs. They can compare parts of the data, make statements about the data as a whole, and generally determine whether the graphs answer the questions posed initially.*

(Clements, Douglas and Sarama, J. eds. *Engaging Young Children in Mathematics: Standards for Early Childhood Mathematics Education*. Mahwah, New Jersey: Lawrence Erlbaum Associates, Publishers, 2004. p. 56)

### Research-Based Teaching Strategies

**Research-Based Teaching Strategies**

*Elementary school students have difficulty analyzing and interpreting data. In one study, 80% of the first and second graders interviewed gave idiosyncratic or incomplete responses when they attempted to analyze data from a line plot and a bar graph. In another study, almost all the fourth and fifth graders could describe bar graphs, but fewer could interpret them, and many fewer still could use the graphs to predict.*

(Kilpatrick, J.; Swafford, J.; and Findell, B. eds. *Adding It Up: Helping Children Learn Mathematics*. Washington, D.C.: National Research Council/National Academy Press, 2001, p. 291.)

Students need a variety of experiences for creating, interpreting, and working with different representations of data such as in tables, bar graphs, circle graphs, line graphs and tree charts or diagrams. They need opportunities to

### Research-Based, continued

identify and study examples of graphs and tables found in their own environment, such as those found in newspapers, magazines, textbooks, and on cereal boxes.

Students need an opportunity to pose questions relevant to their own life and to collect their own data. They will also need opportunities to use data already collected, perhaps by their teachers or schools, or use other existing data sets such as those used to represent census or weather data on the Internet. If students collect their own data, they need to decide how the data could best be gathered, whether by conducting a survey or making observations or measurements.

Students should develop an appreciation of the role that analysis of data plays in answering questions for us. By analyzing data, students will develop an awareness and appreciation of averages and other measures of central tendency (median, mode, and range). From discussions that grow out of their analysis of the data, students will share discoveries they uncover from the data, discuss functional relationships represented by the data, and determine the reasonableness of their interpretations of the data.

### RESEARCH IN ACTION

**Data** In Chapter 12 procedures commonly used for gathering data will be explored by students.

**Classification** Throughout Chapter 12 students will develop strategies, concepts, and procedures for classifying and organizing data in order to use the data to ask and answer questions.

**Representations of Data** Within Chapter 12 students will create, interpret, and work with different representations of data such as date from tables, bar and circle graphs, and tree charts or diagrams.

**Reasonableness** In Chapter 12 students will interpret data, describe patterns, and share explanations to support and justify the reasonableness of their observations or conclusions.

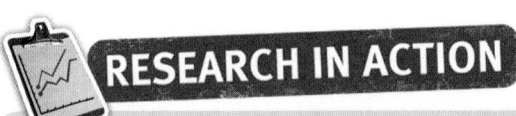

## Vocabulary

**average** (Lesson 12.1) the typical or usual amount, which is found by dividing the sum of two or more quantities by the number of quantities

**degree** (Lesson 12.6) the unit of measurement for angles

**graph** (Lesson 12.5) a diagram showing the relationship between two or more sets of data

**inverse** (Lesson 4.5) opposite

**mean** (Lesson 12.1) another name for average

**median** (Lesson 12.2) the middle number in a set of data when all numbers are arranged in order

**mode** (Lesson 12.2) the number appearing most frequently in a set of data

**range** (Lesson 12.2) the difference between the greatest and least numbers in a set of data

**scale** (Lesson 4.9) the series of evenly spaced marks on an axis line that shows the range of numbers covered by the graph

**outcome** (Lesson 12.7) a result or consequence

## English Learners

### Cognates

For English learners, a quick way to acquire new English vocabulary words is to build on what is known in the primary language.

| English | Spanish |
|---|---|
| data | datos |
| graph | gráfica |
| interpret | interpreter |
| range | rango |

### Access Vocabulary

English learners may understand words in different contexts or not understand idioms. Review chapter vocabulary for this concern. For example:

| | |
|---|---|
| "evened out" | distributing items to make all piles even or equal |
| above average | more than average |
| bar graph | a visual display of information |

# Chapter Planner

| Lessons | Objectives | NCTM Standards | State Standards |
|---|---|---|---|
| 12.1 **Finding Averages** pages 552A–555B 60 minutes | **Begin to develop the concept of average** by applying division | Number and Operations<br>Problem Solving | |
| 12.2 **Mean, Median, Mode, and Range** pages 556A–559B 60 minutes | **Explore statistical analysis** by introducing median, mode, and range while practicing mean | Number and Operations<br>Problem Solving | |
| 12.3 **Using Mathematics** pages 560A–561A 60 minutes | **Practice interpreting data** by examining real-world situations | Number and Operations<br>Problem Solving | |
| 12.4 **Choosing Reasonable Answers** pages 562A–563A 60 minutes | **Explore strategies to solve multiple-choice exercises** by using knowledge of estimation and the inverse operation | Number and Operations | |
| 12.5 **Using a Bar Graph** pages 568A–569A 60 minutes | **Practice creating and reading bar graphs** by solving problems related to the graphs | Number and Operations<br>Problem Solving<br>Data Analysis and Probability | |
| 12.6 **Interpreting Circle Graphs** pages 570A–571A 60 minutes | **Develop strategies to read circle graphs** while comparing them to bar graphs | Data Analysis and Probability | |
| 12.7 **Tree Diagrams** pages 572A–573A 60 minutes | **Explore probability strategies** by designing tree diagrams | Number and Operations<br>Data Analysis and Probability | |

| Vocabulary | Manipulatives and Materials | Games to reinforce skills and concepts |
| --- | --- | --- |
| average<br>mean | • Response Wheels<br>• Rulers<br>• 20 books or other counting materials | |
| median<br>mode<br>mean | • Response Wheels<br>• Number Cubes<br>• Sticky notes | Four Cube Division Game (Lesson 11.3) |
| | • Index cards<br>• Tape measure<br>• Number Cubes | Four Cube Division Game (Lesson 11.3) |
| inverse | • Response Wheels<br>• Harder Snake Game Mats<br>• Number Cubes | Cubo (Lesson 3.14)<br>Four Cube Division Game (Lesson 11.3)<br>Harder Snake Game (Lesson 4.4) |
| graph<br>scale | • Large sheets of paper or poster board<br>• Number Cubes | Cubo (Lesson 3.14) |
| degree | • Response Wheels<br>• Colored overhead projector pens or chalk<br>• Fracto I Game Mats<br>• Number Cubes<br>• 30 counters of the same color | Fracto I Game (Lesson 8.5) |
| outcome | • Number Cubes | Four Cube Division Game (Lesson 11.3) |

# Additional Resources

## Differentiated Instruction

*Intervention Support Guide* provides instruction for the following prerequisite skills:

- Lesson 12.A Dividing by a One-Digit Number
- Lesson 12.B Approximating Products and Quotients
- Lesson 12.C Reading Graphs

*Enrichment Support Guide*

*Practice*

*Reteach Support Guide*

*English Learner Support Guide*

## Technology

The following electronic resources are available:

e **Planner** Lessons 12.1–12.7

e **Presentation** Lessons 12.1–12.7

e **Textbook** Lessons 12.1–12.7

e **Assess** Lessons 12.1–12.7

e **MathTools** **Calculator** Lessons 12.1–12.4; **Spreadsheet** Lesson 12.5; **Graphing Tool** Lesson 12.6

# Chapter Planner continued

| Problem Solving | When to Use | Objective | NCTM Standards | Skills Covered |
|---|---|---|---|---|
| **Chapter Introduction**<br>pages 550I–551C **15–30 minutes** | Use after the Chapter 12 Pretest | Introduce chapter concepts in a problem-solving setting | Reasoning and Proof<br>Communication<br>Data Analysis | Problem Solving<br>Data Analysis |
| **Exploring Problem Solving**<br>pages 564–565A **30–45 minutes** | Use any time during the chapter | Explore methods of solving nonroutine problems | Problem Solving<br>Number and Operations | Data Analysis |
| **Exploring Problem Solving**<br>pages 574–576A **45–60 minutes** | Use any time after the first Exploring Problem Solving | Develop logical reasoning while integrating reading skills with mathematics | Problem Solving<br>Connections<br>Data Analysis | Data Analysis |

| Review | | | | |
|---|---|---|---|---|
| **Cumulative Review**<br>pages 566–567 **15–30 minutes** | Use any time after Lesson 12.4 | Review concepts and skills taught earlier in the year | Geometry,<br>Number and Operations | Rounding<br>Division<br>Fractions<br>Multiplication<br>Geometry |
| **Cumulative Review**<br>pages 577–578 **15–30 minutes** | Use any time after Lesson 12.7 | Review concepts and skills taught earlier in the year | Measurement<br>Numbers and Operations | Subtraction<br>Division<br>Measuring Length |
| **Chapter 5 Review**<br>pages 580A–581 **30–45 minutes** | Use after Lesson 12.7 | Review concepts and skills taught in the chapter | Number and Operations<br>Data Analysis | Data Analysis<br>Division |

| Assessment | | | | |
|---|---|---|---|---|
| **Informal Assessment**<br>(pp. 552A–573A) **Rubrics** | Use at the end of the lesson | Provide daily evaluation of math proficiency | Problem Solving<br>Reasoning and Proof<br>Communication | Computing, Understanding, Reasoning, Applying, Engaging |
| **Pretest**<br>(*Assessment* p. 168) **15–30 minutes** | Use after or in place of the Chapter 11 Review | Provide assessment or additional practice of the chapter concepts | Data Analysis<br>Number and Operations | Computing Averages<br>Data Analysis |
| **Individual Oral Assessment**<br>(p. 567A) **5 minutes per student** | Begin after Lesson 12.4 | Provide alternate means of assessing students' progress | Data Analysis<br>Number and Operations | Data Analysis<br>Computing Average |
| **Chapter 12 Practice Test**<br>(pp. 582–585A) **30–45 minutes** | Use after or in place of the Chapter 12 Review | Provide assessment or additional practice of the chapter concepts | Data Analysis<br>Number and Operations<br>Problem Solving | Data Analysis<br>Fractions<br>Decimals<br>Computing Average |
| **Chapter 12 Test**<br>(*Assessment* pp. 174–177) **30–45 minutes** | Use after or in place of the Chapter 12 Review | Provide assessment or additional practice of the chapter concepts | Data Analysis<br>Number and Operations | Data Analysis<br>Fractions<br>Decimals<br>Computing Average |

# Technology Resources and Support

Visit SRAonline.com for online versions of the ***Real Math eSuite.***

## Technology for Teachers

| | |
|---|---|
| **Presentation** | Lessons 12.1–12.7 Use the ***e-Presentation*** to interactively present chapter content. |
| **Planner** | Use the Chapter and Lesson Planners to outline activities and time frames for Chapter 12. |
| **Assess** | Students can take the following assessment in ***eAssess:***<br>• Chapter Pretest<br>• Chapter Test<br>Teachers can record results and print reports for all assessments in this chapter. |
| **MathTools** | **Calculator** Lessons 12.1–12.4<br>**Spreadsheet** Lesson 12.5<br>**Graphing Tool** Lesson 12.6 |

## Technology for Students

| | |
|---|---|
| **Textbook** | An electronic, interactive version of the ***Student Edition*** is available for all lessons in Chapter 12. |
| **MathTools** | **Calculator** Lesson 12.1–12.4<br>**Spreadsheet** Lesson 12.5<br>**Graphing Tool** Lesson 12.6 |
| SRA TECH KNOWLEDGE | ***TechKnowledge*** Level 4 provides lessons that specifically teach the Unit 10 Internet, Unit 3 Word Processing, and Unit 8 Database applications that students can use while working on this chapter's projects. |

# Organizing and Interpreting Data

## 1 Introduce Chapter 12 (5)

### Chapter Objectives

Explain to students that in this chapter they will build on what they already know about geometry. They will

- find averages.
- compare circle graphs and bar graphs.
- design tree diagrams.

### Pretest ✓ COMPUTING

Administer the Pretest in ***Assessment.***

The Pretest for Chapter 12 covers the following prerequisite skills:

- Multidigit addition with decimals (Problems 1–4)
- Multidigit multiplication (Problems 5–6)
- Division (Problems 7–10)
- Number lines (Problem 11)
- Probability experiments (Problems 12–13)

The Pretest also covers the following topics from this chapter:

- Averages (Problems 14–15)
- Mean, median, mode, and range (Problems 16–19)
- Tree diagrams (Problem 20)

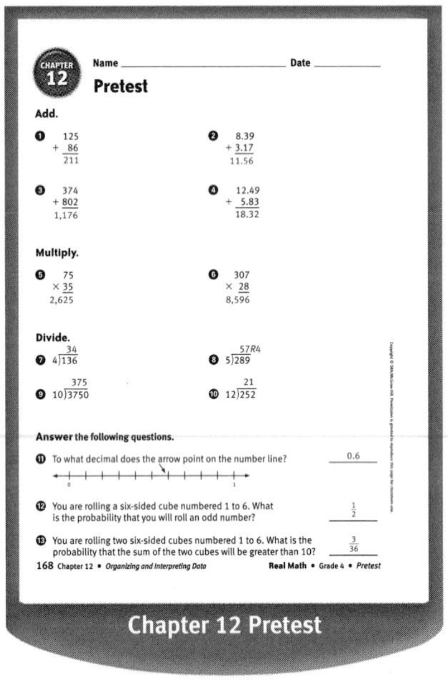

CHAPTER 12 Name ______ Date ______

**Pretest**

**Add.**

1. 125 + 86 = 211
2. 8.39 + 3.17 = 11.56
3. 374 + 802 = 1,176
4. 12.49 + 5.83 = 18.32

**Multiply.**

5. 75 × 35 = 2,625
6. 307 × 28 = 8,596

**Divide.**

7. 4)136 = 34
8. 5)289 = 57 R4
9. 10)3750 = 375
10. 12)252 = 21

**Answer the following questions.**

11. To what decimal does the arrow point on the number line? 0.6
12. You are rolling a six-sided cube numbered 1 to 6. What is the probability that you will roll an odd number? $\frac{1}{2}$
13. You are rolling two six-sided cubes numbered 1 to 6. What is the probability that the sum of the two cubes will be greater than 10? $\frac{3}{36}$

168 Chapter 12 • *Organizing and Interpreting Data* **Real Math** • Grade 4 • *Pretest*

Chapter 12 Pretest

### Access Prior Knowledge ✓ UNDERSTANDING

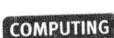

Have students look at page 550 and share what they know about the California Gold Rush. Ask questions such as the following:

- **What do you think is going on in the photo?**
- **About how many years ago was gold first discovered in California?** about 150 years ago; gold was discovered in 1848

## 2 Exploring Problem Solving (20)

### Tell Students In Today's Lesson They Will

- read about how the California Gold Rush began.
- look at the gold found in two different places.
- decide which site they would want to buy.

### Using Student Pages

Read the information on page 551 with the students. Tell the students that each site yields about a nugget a day. Then go over the problem. Ask questions such as the following:

- **Look at the gold nuggets from site B. How many different sizes are there?** 4
- **If the smallest-nugget weighs 1 ounce, how many ounces do you think the next larger-size nugget weighs?** about 2 ounces
- **Which site has shown a more consistent production of gold?** Site A, but with the exception of one very productive day, site B has been very consistent as well.
- **Was the same method used to extract gold at each site?** This information is unknown.

Discuss Problems 1–4 with the students. Have students work in groups to answer Problem 5. Provide help as needed, and encourage students to estimate.

### Answers to Problems 3 and 5

#### Problem 3

Students might use visual estimation and some direct comparison to see that site A would produce more gold in eight days than site B. For example, students can draw or imagine five more piles from site A like the three that are already shown. Each pile from site A is greater than any of the seven small piles from site B. The one large pile from site B is not large enough to make up the difference.

#### Problem 5

Students may offer several reasons for choosing either site. Site A appears to be more productive on a regular basis, and because it has not been mined as long, it is less likely to have been depleted. On the other hand, site B has a potential for yielding a large quantity of gold in a single day, and perhaps there are more of these productive areas within the site. To make matters even more uncertain, no information is given about how much material had to be sifted through in order to extract the gold at either site. Suppose the miners at one of the sites had used only small pans to extract gold. Then switching to more efficient equipment such as sluice boxes or rocker boxes would raise the daily yield considerably at that site.

Student Page

CHAPTER 12

# Organizing and Interpreting Data

**In This Chapter You Will Learn**

- about finding averages.
- how to compare circle graphs and bar graphs.
- how to design tree diagrams.

Student Page

## Problem Solving

The year was 1848. James Wilson Marshall was building a sawmill along the American River near what is now Sacramento, California. On a cold January morning, Marshall spotted a few metallic flakes glistening in the sun. He wrapped them in a handkerchief and took them to his boss, John Sutter. The yellow specks were almost pure gold.

REAL WORLD

Within months of Marshall's discovery, thousands of miners began the greatest gold rush in history. By the time the rush ended, it had yielded nearly $2 billion in gold.

Imagine you have just arrived in California in 1849. You hear many stories from miners about the best places to find gold. This illustration shows how much gold has been retrieved each day so far from two different sites.

**Answer** these questions. (Note: Each piece of gold represents one day's worth of mining.)

1. How many days has each site been mined? A: 3 days, B: 8 days
2. Which site has yielded more gold so far? Site B
3. If both sites kept producing gold at the same rate, which site would produce more gold in 8 days? Explain. See *Teacher's Edition.*
4. On average, which site produces more gold each day? Site A
5. If you could buy either site for the same price, which would you choose? Why? See *Teacher's Edition.*

551

## CyberSolver

To extend problem solving, have students use the Internet to find the answers to the following questions:

- **Where do people look for gold today?**
- **How do they use modern technology to help them?**

Students can search for information using key words such as *gold prospecting* and *mining gold*. The following are Web sites students can visit:
http://www.mpm.edu/research/geology/gold_lore05.html and
http://collections.ic.gc.ca/cariboo/teacher/goldpro2.htm.

## Concept/Question Board

APPLYING

### Questions

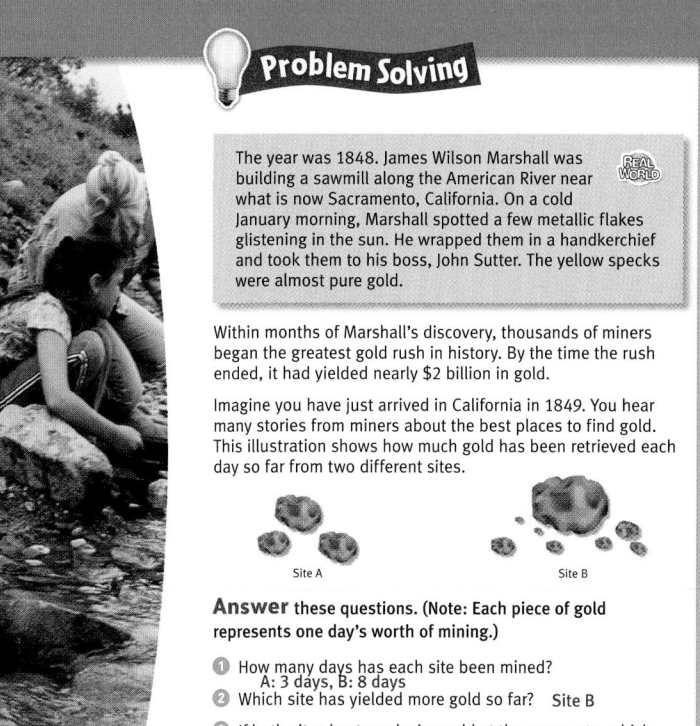

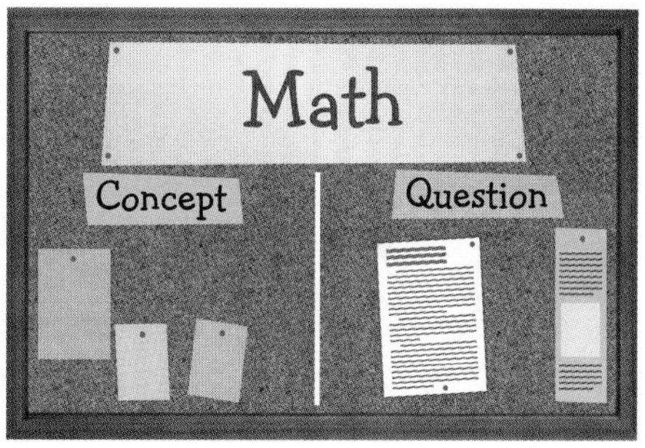


Have students write three questions they have about organizing and interpreting data and how it can be used. Then have them select one question to post on the Question side of the Board.

### Concepts

As students work through the chapter, have them collect examples of how organizing and interpreting data is used in everyday situations. For each example, have students write problems that relate to the item(s). Have them display their examples on the Concept side of the Board.

Suggest the following:

- growth chart of a child
- class test results
- population statistics

### Answers

Throughout the chapter, have students post answers to the questions and solutions to the problems on the Board.

## 3 Reflect

5

### Knowledge Age Skills

**Effective Communication** Have groups present their answers and reasons to Problem 5. After each group presents, ask questions such as the following:

- **Did you give specific reasons for your decision?**
- **Were there additional factors that you could have considered?**

Afterward, discuss why groups came up with different answers and how they can all be reasonable.

## Home Connection

At this time, you may want to send home the letter on pages 46–49 of ***Home Connection.*** This letter describes what students will be learning and what activities they can do at home to support their work in school.

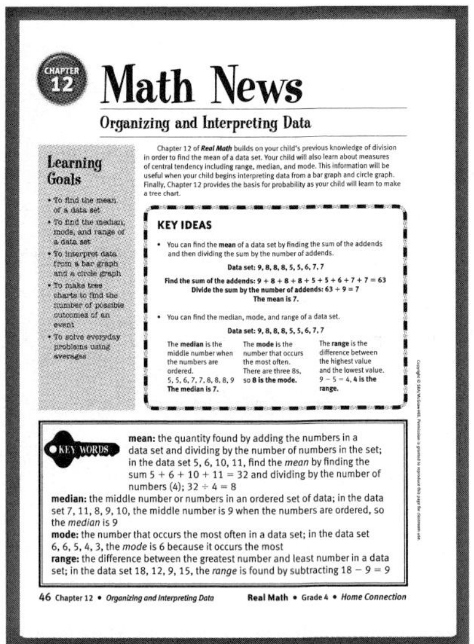

CHAPTER 12

# Math News

**Organizing and Interpreting Data**

**Learning Goals**

- To find the mean of a data set
- To find the median, mode, and range of a data set
- To interpret data from a bar graph and a circle graph
- To make tree charts to find the number of possible outcomes of an event
- To solve everyday problems using averages

Chapter 12 of ***Real Math*** builds on your child's previous knowledge of division in order to find the mean of a data set. Your child will also learn about measures of central tendency including range, median, and mode. This information will be useful when your child begins interpreting data from a bar graph and circle graph. Finally, Chapter 12 provides the basis for probability as your child will learn to make a tree chart.

**KEY IDEAS**

- You can find the **mean** of a data set by finding the sum of the addends and then dividing the sum by the number of addends.

**Data set: 9, 8, 8, 8, 5, 5, 6, 7, 7**

**Find the sum of the addends: 9 + 8 + 8 + 8 + 5 + 5 + 6 + 7 + 7 = 63**
**Divide the sum by the number of addends: 63 ÷ 9 = 7**
**The mean is 7.**

- You can find the median, mode, and range of a data set.

**Data set: 9, 8, 8, 8, 5, 5, 6, 7, 7**

The **median** is the middle number when the numbers are ordered. 5, 5, 6, 7, 7, 8, 8, 8, 9 **The median is 7.**

The **mode** is the number that occurs the most often. There are three 8s, so **8 is the mode.**

The **range** is the difference between the highest value and the lowest value. 9 − 5 = 4, **4 is the range.**

KEY WORDS

**mean:** the quantity found by adding the numbers in a data set and dividing by the number of numbers in the set; in the data set 5, 6, 10, 11, find the *mean* by finding the sum 5 + 6 + 10 + 11 = 32 and dividing by the number of numbers (4); 32 ÷ 4 = 8

**median:** the middle number or numbers in an ordered set of data; in the data set 7, 11, 8, 9, 10, the middle number is 9 when the numbers are ordered, so the *median* is 9

**mode:** the number that occurs the most often in a data set; in the data set 6, 6, 5, 4, 3, the *mode* is 6 because it occurs the most

**range:** the difference between the greatest number and least number in a data set; in the data set 18, 12, 9, 15, the *range* is found by subtracting 18 − 9 = 9



46 Chapter 12 • *Organizing and Interpreting Data* **Real Math** • Grade 4 • *Home Connection*

Home Connection page 46

# 4 Assess and Differentiate

**e Assess** Use ***eAssess*** to record and analyze evidence of student understanding.

## A Gather Evidence

Use the Daily Class Assessment Records in ***Assessment*** or ***eAssess*** to record daily observations.

### Informal Assessment

**Access Prior Knowledge**

Did the student UNDERSTANDING

- ❑ make important observations?
- ❑ extend or generalize learning?
- ❑ provide insightful answers?
- ❑ pose insightful questions?

### Informal Assessment

**Concept/Question Board**

Did the student APPLYING

- ❑ apply learning in new situations?
- ❑ contribute concepts?
- ❑ contribute answers?
- ❑ connect mathematics to real-world situations?

### Formal Assessment

**Pretest** COMPUTING

Review student answers in each problem set.

- ❑ Multidigit addition with decimals (Problems 1–4)
- ❑ Multidigit multiplication (Problems 5–6)
- ❑ Division (Problems 7–10)
- ❑ Number lines (Problem 11)
- ❑ Probability experiments (Problems 12–13)
- ❑ Averages (Problems 14–15)
- ❑ Mean, median, mode, and range (Problems 16–19)
- ❑ Tree diagrams (Problem 20)

## B Summarize Findings

Analyze and summarize assessment data for each student. Determine which Assessment Follow-Up is appropriate for each student. Use the Student Assessment Record in ***Assessment*** or ***eAssess*** to update assessment records.

## C Assessment Follow-Up • DIFFERENTIATE INSTRUCTION

**ENRICH**

**If . . .** students demonstrate a secure understanding of chapter concepts,

**Then . . .** move quickly through the chapter or use ***Enrichment*** Lessons 12.1–12.7 as assessment follow-up to extend and apply understanding.

**PRACTICE**

**If . . .** students grasp chapter concepts with competent understanding,

**Then . . .** use ***Practice*** Lessons 12.1–12.7 as lesson follow-up to develop fluency.

**RETEACH**

**If . . .** students have prerequisite understanding but demonstrate emerging understanding of chapter concepts,

**Then . . .** use ***Reteach*** Lessons 12.1 and 12.2 to reteach lesson concepts.

**INTERVENTION**

**If . . .** students demonstrate minimal understanding readiness for chapter concept and/or are not competent with prerequisite skills,

**Then . . .** use ***Intervention*** Lessons 12.A–12.C before each lesson to develop fluency with prerequisite skills.

**ENGLISH LEARNER**

Use ***English Learner*** Lessons 12.1–12.7 for strategies to preteach lesson vocabulary and concepts.

# Math Across the Curriculum

Preview the chapter projects with students. Assign or have students choose from the projects to extend and enrich concepts in this chapter.

## Organize Information about the Yukon Gold Rush

SCIENCE WebQuest

### Math Objective
To reinforce studies of how to find the mean, median, mode, and range

### Science Objective
To reinforce studies of how to construct a table to organize data

### Technology Objective
To create a database to organize data about the Yukon Gold Rush

Have students use technology to collect, record, and organize data about the Yukon Gold Rush.

Students use the Internet to investigate:

- how prospectors reached the Pacific Northwest and cities from which they left
- supplies and mining methods

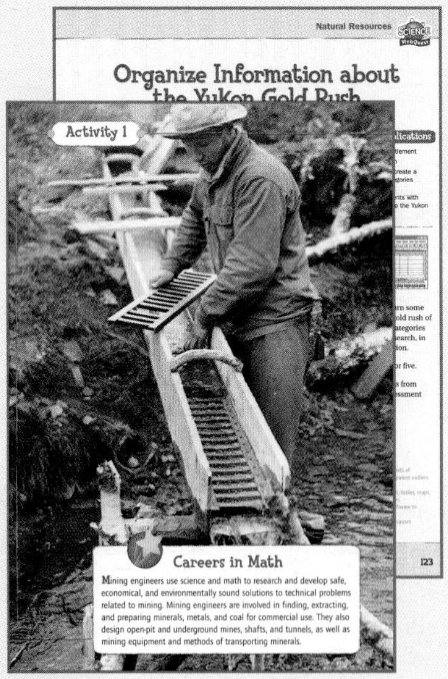


For specific step-by-step instructions for this project, see ***Across the Curriculum Math Connections*** pages 122–127.

**Knowledge Age Skills**

**Problem Formulation, Planning, and Strategizing** Students collect information and strategize how to organize it.

**Effective Communication** Students organize information in a statistical format that is clear and concise.

***TechKnowledge*** Level 4 provides lessons that teach Unit 10 Internet, Unit 3 Word Processing, and Unit 8 Database applications.

## Create a Presentation about the Texas Oil Industry

ART

1–2 weeks

### Math Objective
To reinforce studies of graphing skills by creating a bar graph to enhance a presentation

### Fine Arts Objective
To reinforce studies of the use music and sounds to enhance a presentation

### Technology Objective
To create a bar graph in a spreadsheet and insert it into a presentation

Have students use mathematics to create a bar graph to be used in a presentation about the Texas oil industry.

As part of the project, students should consider the following issues:

- details related to the history of the Texas oil industry
- statistics about the oil industry that would be best illustrated in a bar graph
- using appropriate sound and music clips to enhance a presentation

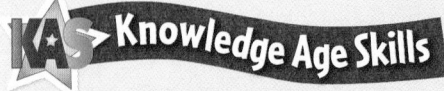

For specific step-by-step instructions for this project, see ***Across the Curriculum Math Connections*** pages 128–131.

**Knowledge Age Skills**

**High-Level Responsibility** Students must take information about the Texas oil industry and filter out useful facts to be used in presentations.

**Effective Communication** Students select appropriate sound and music clips to enhance the effectiveness of presentations.

## Lesson Planner

### Objectives
- To teach the concept of average (mean) and how to compute it
- To provide another common application of division

### NCTM Standards
**Number and Operations**
Find the average from a set of data

**Problem Solving**
Find solutions to problems

### Materials
- *Response Wheels
- 20 books and other counting materials
- **Number Cubes* (one 0–5 and one 5–10)

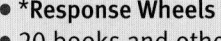

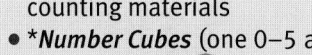

### Technology
**Presentation** Lesson 12.1

### Test Prep
**Cumulative Review**
Mental Math reviews division facts (Lesson 3.10).

**Extended Response**
Problems 3, 6, and 10–13

*Manipulative Kit Item

# Finding Averages

**Context of the Lesson** This is the first of three lessons on measures of central tendency. In this lesson, students are exposed to averages in the natural context involving "evening things out," as well as in the traditional context of adding numbers together then dividing that sum by the quantity of numbers. This is the first lesson in the ***Real Math*** series that explicitly exposes students to the idea of an average.

See page 550B for Math Background for teachers for this lesson.

## Planning for Learning • DIFFERENTIATE INSTRUCTION

### INTERVENTION

**If . . .** students lack the prerequisite skill of dividing by a one-digit number,

**Then . . .** teach ***Intervention*** Lesson 12.A.

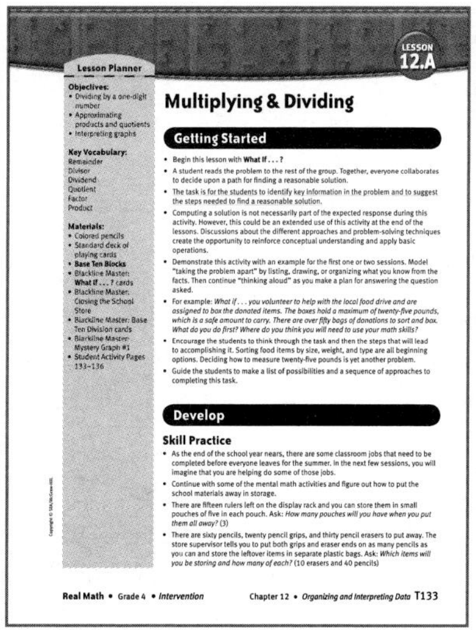


Intervention Lesson 12.A

### ENGLISH LEARNER

**Preview**

**If . . .** students need language support,

**Then . . .** use Lesson 12.1 in ***English Learner Support Guide*** to preview lesson concepts and vocabulary.

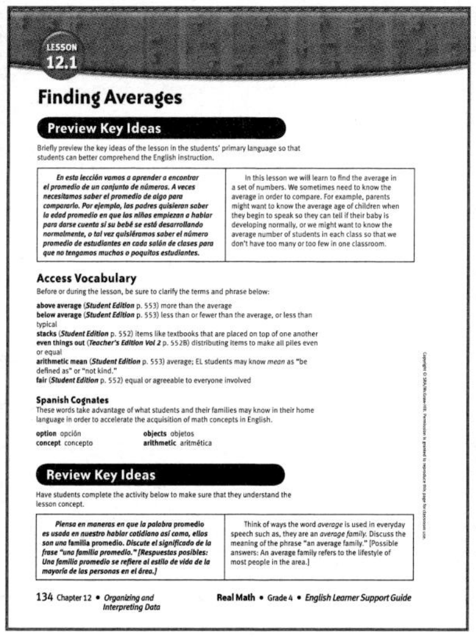


English Learner Lesson 12.1

### ENRICH

**If . . .** students are proficient in the lesson concepts,

**Then . . .** encourage them to attempt the chapter projects.

### PRACTICE

**If . . .** students would benefit from additional practice,

**Then . . .** extend Guided Discussion before assigning the student pages.

### RETEACH

**If . . .** students have difficulty understanding how to compute averages,

**Then . . .** extend Guided Discussion before assigning the student pages.

### Vocabulary
**average** **\av´ rij** ***n.*** the amount found by dividing the sum of a set of numbers by the quantity of numbers
**mean** **\mēn** ***n.*** another name for average

### Access Vocabulary
**arithmetic mean** "evened out"

**Spanish Cognates**
**objects** objetos
**arithmetic** aritmética

## Mental Math 5

Review RESPONSE WHEEL Provide practice in division with exercises such as the following:

| | |
|---|---|
| **a.** 70 ÷ 7 = 10 | **g.** 77 ÷ 7 = 11 |
| **b.** 48 ÷ 6 = 8 | **h.** 480 ÷ 6 = 80 |
| **c.** 360 ÷ 6 = 60 | **i.** 56 ÷ 8 = 7 |
| **d.** 560 ÷ 8 = 70 | **j.** 72 ÷ 8 = 9 |
| **e.** 720 ÷ 80 = 9 | **k.** 7200 ÷ 80 = 90 |
| **f.** 24 ÷ 3 = 8 | **l.** 2,400 ÷ 3 = 800 |

## 1 Develop 25

**Tell Students In Today's Lesson They Will**
learn how to find an average from a set of numbers.

### Guided Discussion UNDERSTANDING Whole Group

Illustrate the concept of *average* using an example such as the following:

Call five students to the front of the classroom. Hand the first student 3 books, the second student 1 book, the third student 10 books, the fourth student 2 books, and the fifth student 4 books. Ask questions such as the following:

- **Which stack of books would you like to carry home from school?** Answers may vary, but the smallest pile seems likely.
- **Do you think it would be fair to make each person carry the stack I handed out to them?** no
- **How could we even things out?** Answers will vary. Possible answers: Have the person with the most books give half to the person with the fewest books; redistribute the books; give each person the same number.

Ask a student who has not been previously involved to move a stack of books from one pile to another to help even out the stacks. Continue this until each of the first five students has the same number of books (4). Ask questions such as the following:

- **Since there are 4 books in each pile, how many are there total?** 20
- **Suppose there were 9 books in each pile. How many would there be in all?** 45
- **How did you find that answer?** multiplied 9 × 5
- **What operation undoes multiplication?** division
- **If we started with a total of 90 books and wanted to distribute them fairly, how many books should each person get?** 18
- **How do you know?** because we are dividing 90 books into 5 piles; 90 ÷ 5 = 18 books in each pile

Explain that when we add a group of different numbers and divide by the number of numbers, we get what is called the mean or average of the amounts. In this instance we add the number of books and divide by the number of stacks to get an average of 4 books per stack. Ask questions such as the following:

- **If I distributed 30 stickers to 6 students, what would the average number of stickers per student be?** 5
- **If I gave 3 of those stickers to the first person, 3 to the second, 3 to the third, 3 to the fourth, 3 to the fifth, and 15 to the last person, what would the average number of stickers be?** 5
- **If I gave 1 to the third person and 29 to the fifth person, what would the average number of stickers for the 6 people be?** 5
- **How can you find the answer?** Add up all the stickers then divide that sum by the total number of people.

Note that all problems in this chapter have been created so that the average is a whole number—which does not always happen in real-life situations.

# 2 Assign Student Pages

25

## Pages 552–553 APPLYING

Small Group

Have students open their books to pages 552–553 and complete Problems 1–9 in small groups. As students work through the first few problems, you may want to provide counters so students can model the number of tokens purchased and manipulate them to get a feeling for averages.

Student Page

LESSON 12.1 **Finding Averages**

### Key Ideas

**You have discovered that you can sometimes find the average of the number of objects in several sets by moving objects from one set to another.**

The teacher needs five students to help her move five stacks of textbooks. The numbers of textbooks in each pile are 6, 16, 3, 11, and 4.

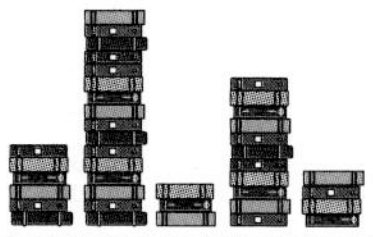

Which pile of textbooks would you prefer to carry?

Would it be fair for some students to have to carry larger stacks of books?

Perhaps the stacks can be divided evenly so that each student can carry the same number of textbooks.

First, let's take 4 textbooks from the stack of 16 and put them in the middle stack of 3 textbooks.

The new stack sizes are 6, 12, 7, 11, and 4.

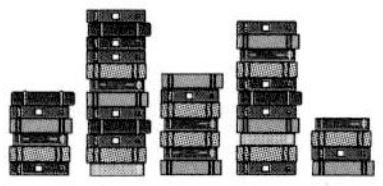

Can we make that fairer? Suppose we take 2 textbooks from the stack of 12 and 2 textbooks from the stack of 11, and put them in the pile of 4 textbooks.

The new stack sizes are 6, 10, 7, 9, and 8. That's much better.

Can we improve more? Yes—take 1 from the stack of 9 textbooks and put it on the stack of 7 textbooks.

The new stack sizes are 6, 10, 8, 8, and 8. That seems pretty fair.

Still, let's take 2 books from the stack of 10 and put them on the stack of 6 textbooks.

The new stack sizes are 8, 8, 8, 8, and 8. Now each stack has 8 textbooks.

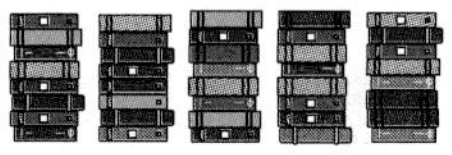

That seems fair.

552 **eTextbook** This lesson is available in the ***eTextbook***.

Student Page

1. Since there are now 8 textbooks in each stack, how many textbooks are there altogether? 64
2. If we know the total number of books from the start, how can we figure out the number of textbooks to put in each stack? Think—what undoes multiplication? division
3. **Extended Response** How would you distribute the books equally if there were 3 more students? See ***Teacher's Edition.***

Counting all the textbooks and dividing by the number of piles produces a number called the arithmetic mean, or just the mean. Sometimes this number is also called the average.

Let's apply the concept of average to the following example.

There were 7 people who purchased train tokens. This chart shows how many tokens each person purchased

| Name | Number of Train Tokens |
|---|---|
| Marcia | 7 |
| Cindy | 6 |
| Peter | 13 |
| Alice | 14 |
| Jan | 10 |
| Greg | 16 |
| Bobby | 18 |

Cindy said, "I wish I had as many tokens as everybody else."

Alice suggested that they all put their tokens together and then take an equal amount.

**Answer the following questions.**

4. How many tokens do the 7 people have in all? 84
5. How many would each person get if they put all their tokens together and then each took an equal number? 12
6. **Extended Response** Do you think anyone might object to Alice's suggestion? Who? Why? See ***Teacher's Edition.***
7. Which people purchased an above-average number of tokens? Peter, Alice, Greg, and Bobby
8. Which people purchased a below-average number of tokens? Marcia, Cindy, and Jan
9. Which people purchased exactly the average number of tokens? no one

Chapter 12 • Lesson 1 553

# Assign Student Pages, continued

## Pages 554–555 APPLYING

Review an example like those at the top of page 555 to ensure that students can find the average of a set of numbers. Then have students complete page 555 independently.

### Monitoring Student Progress

As students work on page 555, watch for the following:

**If . . .** students have difficulty calculating averages for Problems 14–28,

**Then . . .** encourage students to use base-ten materials to even out the number of items, similar to the example on page 552 of the ***Student Edition.***

### As Students Finish

Game **Don't Go Over 1,000 Game**

Student Page

LESSON 12.1 • Finding Averages

**Explain** what you think about each statement. Which ones make sense? Which statements don't make sense? Explain your reasons. Extended Response For Problems 10–13, see *Teacher's Edition.*

10. Kenny used to live at 600 Elm Street. Now he lives at 200 Elm Street. On average he has lived at 400 Elm Street.
11. Hannah is 14 years old. She used to be 6 years old. Her average age is 10.
12. SOCIAL STUDIES The average number of children in each family in the United States 100 years ago was about 3. Now the average number of children in each family in the United States is a little less than 1. So, families have fewer people now than they did 100 years ago.
13. Gina was 140 centimeters tall on her tenth birthday. On her fourteenth birthday she was 180 centimeters tall. She grew an average of 10 centimeters a year from age ten to age fourteen.

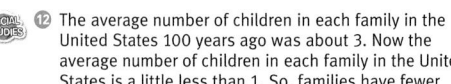

554

Textbook This lesson is available in the *eTextbook.*

Student Page

Find the average of 10, 7, 9, 4, and 10.

First add the numbers. 10 + 7 + 9 + 4 + 10 = 40

How many numbers were added? 5

Then divide the sum by how many numbers were added. $5\overline{)40}$ = 8

The average for 10, 7, 9, 4, and 10 is 8.

Another option is to move 2 from each 10 to the 4, and move 1 from 9 to 7.

**Find** the average of each set of numbers. Use shortcuts when you can.

14. 3, 4, 5, 6, 7 5
15. 4, 2, 8, 16, 0, 5, 12, 17, 25, 11 10
16. 13, 14, 15, 16, 17 15
17. 44, 44, 44, 44, 44, 44, 44, 44 44
18. 30, 40, 50, 60, 70 50
19. 27, 103, 59, 68, 112, 96, 84, 11 70
20. 125, 39, 247, 362, 189, 154 186
21. 82, 57, 49, 63, 85, 42 63
22. 2,843; 2,844; 2,845; 2,846; 2,847 2,845
23. 25, 64, 27, 39, 15 34

**Which** of the following groups has a greater average, **a** or **b**? Explain how you know.

24. **a.** 121, 174, 156, 29 (**b.**) 119, 173, 153, 27
25. **a.** 45, 16, 18, 93, 21, 5 (**b.**) 45, 16, 18, 93, 21, 9
26. **a.** 1, 15, 61, 28, 39, 12, 12 (**b.**) 28, 39, 16, 22, 18, 19, 33

**Solve** these problems.

27. Alma jumped double Dutch during recess. Her first attempt lasted 48 seconds, her second attempt lasted 39 seconds, and her final attempt lasted 72 seconds. What was her average time? 53 seconds
28. Carolyn sells hot dogs at the ballpark. She sold 192 on Monday, 160 on Tuesday, 233 on Friday, 220 on Saturday, and 260 on Sunday. There were no games on Wednesday or Thursday. What was the average number of hot dogs Carolyn sold each day that she worked? 213 hot dogs

Chapter 12 • Lesson 1 555

## 3 Reflect

5

### Guided Discussion

REASONING

Whole Group

Discuss the problems on page 554 with the class. The purpose of the discussion is to help students recognize that there is more to using averages than adding and dividing. Encourage students to give and defend their opinions. Provide adequate time to discuss each situation and identify why it does or does not make sense. Discuss shortcuts to find the average in Problems 14, 17, 18, and 22. Ask questions such as the following:

- **Could you find a shortcut in Problem 17? If so, what did you do?** Yes; all the numbers were the same, so there was no need to find the average.
- **Could you find a shortcut in Problem 14? If so, what did you do?** Yes; Possible answers: Students may have noticed that if you take 2 from 7 and add it to 3, and take 1 from 6 and add it to 4, then all the numbers become 5. Notice that 3 + 7 = 10 and 4 + 6 = 10, which is 5 doubled, so the average of 7 and 3 is 5; and the average of 4 and 6 is 5. The average of 5 is also 5; therefore, the average of the numbers altogether is 5.
- **Can you use this same shortcut in Problem 18?** yes
- **What is the answer?** 50
- **How did you find the answer?** Possible answer: It is the same as Problem 14 with all the numbers multiplied by 10; 30 + 70 = 100 and 40 + 60 = 100, which is 50 doubled. Therefore, since the average of each pair of numbers is 50, and the middle number is 50, the average of all the numbers is 50.
- **Do you see a similar shortcut in Problem 22?** yes
- **What is the answer?** 2,845
- **What did you do?** Possible answer: It is the same as Problem 14 with 2,840 added to each number as shown: 2,840 + 3; 2,840 + 4; 2,840 + 5; 2,840 + 6; 2,840 + 7. The answer is 2,840 + (average of 3, 4, 5, 6, and 7) = 2,840 + 5 or 2,845.

### Extended Response

**Problem 3** Each student would carry fewer books. They would all have 5 books instead of 8.

**Problem 6** Students should claim that Peter, Greg, and Bobby are most likely to object because they bought more tokens than everyone else.

**Problem 10** Finding the average does not make sense in this situation because addresses are numbers representing places, not quantities.

**Problem 11** An average should not be used in this situation because the age of one person does not have an average.

**Problem 12** An average can be taken from the number of children per family in the United States; however, it is impossible to have a fraction of a child.

**Problem 13** An average can be used to describe the amount of growth over time for a specific person or object.

SOCIAL STUDIES **Curriculum Connection:** Students may be interested in studying the population of foreign countries and hypothesizing why these places are different from the United States.

Review **Cumulative Review:** For review of rounding decimals, assign Problems 1–6 on student page 566.

**Family Involvement:** Assign the ***Practice, Reteach,*** or ***Enrichment*** activities depending on the needs of your students. Encourage students to play the **Don't Go Over 1,000 Game** with a friend or relative.

**Concept/Question Board:** Have students look for additional examples using average or mean and post them on the Concept/Question Board.

**Math Puzzler:** A hungry caterpillar ate 55 leaves in 5 days. Each day the caterpillar ate 3 more leaves than it ate the day before. How many leaves did the caterpillar eat on the first day? (Allow students to use calculators to find the solution.) 5

# 4 Assess and Differentiate

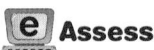

**eAssess** Use ***eAssess*** to record and analyze evidence of student understanding.

## A Gather Evidence

Use the Daily Class Assessment Records in ***Assessment*** or ***eAssess*** to record daily observations.

### Informal Assessment

**✓ Guided Discussion**

Did the student UNDERSTANDING

- ❑ make important observations?
- ❑ extend or generalize learning?
- ❑ provide insightful answers?
- ❑ pose insightful questions?

### Portfolio Assessment

**✓ Extended Response**

Did the student REASONING

- ❑ provide a clear explanation?
- ❑ communicate reasons and strategies?
- ❑ choose appropriate strategies?
- ❑ argue logically?

## B Summarize Findings

Analyze and summarize assessment data for each student. Determine which Assessment Follow-Up is appropriate for each student. Use the Student Assessment Record in ***Assessment*** or ***eAssess*** to update assessment records.

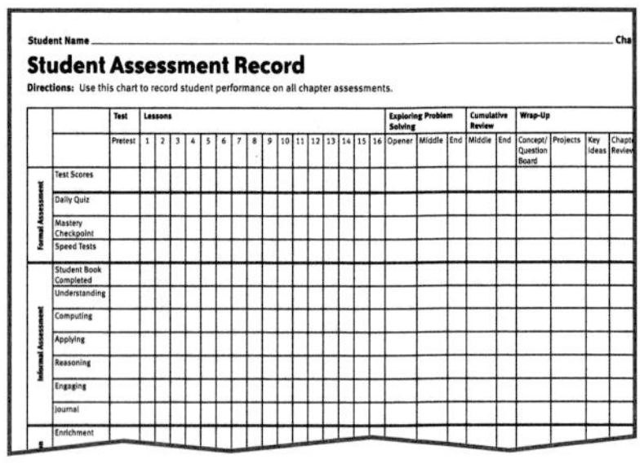


**Assessment Page T41**

## C Assessment Follow-Up • DIFFERENTIATE INSTRUCTION

Based on your observations, use these teaching strategies for assessment follow-up.

### INTERVENTION

Review student performance on ***Intervention*** Lesson 12.A to see if students have mastered prerequisite skills for this lesson.

### ENGLISH LEARNER

**Review**

Use Lesson 12.1 in the ***English Learner Support Guide*** to review lesson concepts and vocabulary.

### ENRICH

**If . . .** students are proficient in the lesson concepts,

**Then . . .** encourage them to work on chapter projects or ***Enrichment*** Lesson 12.1.

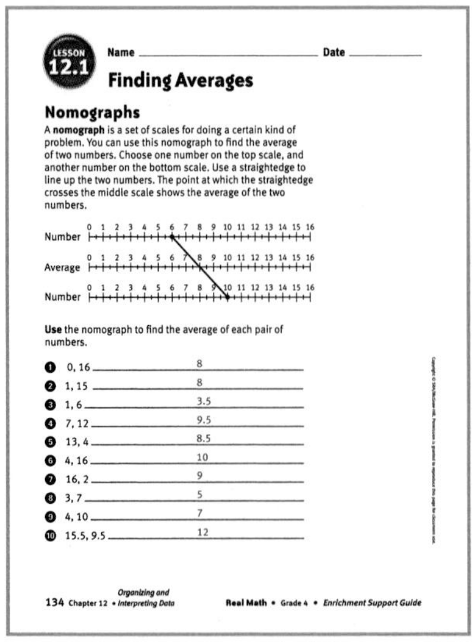

LESSON 12.1 Name ______ Date ______

**Finding Averages**

**Nomographs**

A **nomograph** is a set of scales for doing a certain kind of problem. You can use this nomograph to find the average of two numbers. Choose one number on the top scale, and another number on the bottom scale. Use a straightedge to line up the two numbers. The point at which the straightedge crosses the middle scale shows the average of the two numbers.



**Use** the nomograph to find the average of each pair of numbers.

1. 0, 16 ___8___
2. 1, 15 ___8___
3. 1, 6 ___3.5___
4. 7, 12 ___9.5___
5. 13, 4 ___8.5___
6. 4, 16 ___10___
7. 16, 2 ___9___
8. 3, 7 ___5___
9. 4, 10 ___7___
10. 15.5, 9.5 ___12___

134 Chapter 12 • *Organizing and Interpreting Data* **Real Math** • Grade 4 • *Enrichment Support Guide*

Enrichment Lesson 12.1

### PRACTICE

**If . . .** students would benefit from additional practice,

**Then . . .** assign ***Practice*** Lesson 12.1.

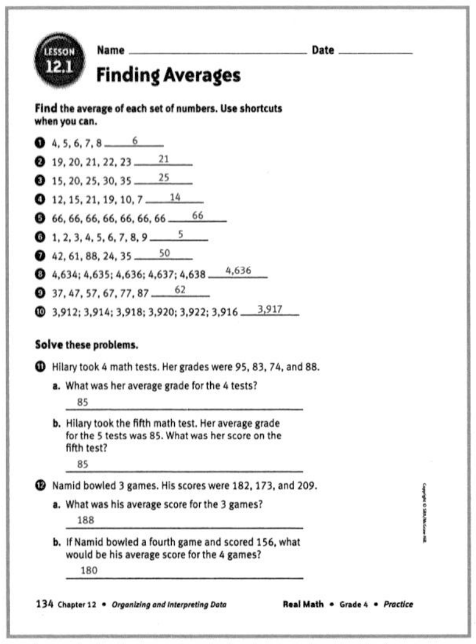

LESSON 12.1 Name ______ Date ______

**Finding Averages**

**Find the average of each set of numbers. Use shortcuts when you can.**

1. 4, 5, 6, 7, 8 ___6___
2. 19, 20, 21, 22, 23 ___21___
3. 15, 20, 25, 30, 35 ___25___
4. 12, 15, 21, 19, 10, 7 ___14___
5. 66, 66, 66, 66, 66, 66, 66 ___66___
6. 1, 2, 3, 4, 5, 6, 7, 8, 9 ___5___
7. 42, 61, 88, 24, 35 ___50___
8. 4,634; 4,635; 4,636; 4,637; 4,638 ___4,636___
9. 37, 47, 57, 67, 77, 87 ___62___
10. 3,912; 3,914; 3,918; 3,920; 3,922; 3,916 ___3,917___

**Solve these problems.**

11. Hilary took 4 math tests. Her grades were 95, 83, 74, and 88.
    a. What was her average grade for the 4 tests? ___85___
    b. Hilary took the fifth math test. Her average grade for the 5 tests was 85. What was her score on the fifth test? ___85___
12. Namid bowled 3 games. His scores were 182, 173, and 209.
    a. What was his average score for the 3 games? ___188___
    b. If Namid bowled a fourth game and scored 156, what would be his average score for the 4 games? ___180___

134 Chapter 12 • *Organizing and Interpreting Data* **Real Math** • Grade 4 • *Practice*

Practice Lesson 12.1

### RETEACH

**If . . .** students have difficulty understanding how to compute averages,

**Then . . .** reteach the concept using ***Reteach*** Lesson 12.1.

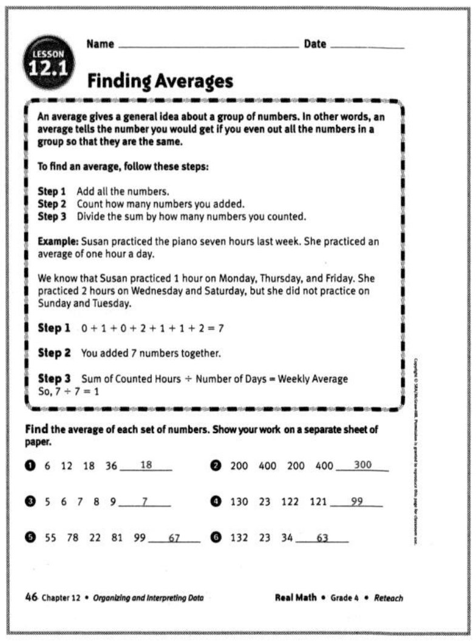

LESSON 12.1 Name ______ Date ______

**Finding Averages**

**An average gives a general idea about a group of numbers. In other words, an average tells the number you would get if you even out all the numbers in a group so that they are the same.**

**To find an average, follow these steps:**

**Step 1** Add all the numbers.
**Step 2** Count how many numbers you added.
**Step 3** Divide the sum by how many numbers you counted.

**Example:** Susan practiced the piano seven hours last week. She practiced an average of one hour a day.

We know that Susan practiced 1 hour on Monday, Thursday, and Friday. She practiced 2 hours on Wednesday and Saturday, but she did not practice on Sunday and Tuesday.

**Step 1** $0 + 1 + 0 + 2 + 1 + 1 + 2 = 7$

**Step 2** You added 7 numbers together.

**Step 3** Sum of Counted Hours ÷ Number of Days = Weekly Average
So, $7 \div 7 = 1$

**Find the average of each set of numbers. Show your work on a separate sheet of paper.**

1. 6 12 18 36 ___18___
2. 200 400 200 400 ___300___
3. 5 6 7 8 9 ___7___
4. 130 23 122 121 ___99___
5. 55 78 22 81 99 ___67___
6. 132 23 34 ___63___

46 Chapter 12 • *Organizing and Interpreting Data* **Real Math** • Grade 4 • *Reteach*

Reteach Lesson 12.1

# Mean, Median, Mode, and Range

**Context of the Lesson** This is the second of three lessons on measures of central tendency. This lesson explores the concepts of median, mode, and range while building on the foundation of mean discussed in the previous lesson.

See page 550B for Math Background for teachers for this lesson.

### Objectives
- To introduce two measures of central tendency (median and mode), as well as range
- To provide practice computing and considering mean, median, mode, and range
- To illustrate how outliers can change the range and measures of central tendencies

### NCTM Standards
**Number and Operations**
Compute for mean, median, mode, and range

**Problem Solving**
Solve problems involving mean, median, mode, and range

**Data Analysis and Probability**
Use appropriate statistical methods to analyze data

### Materials
- *Response Wheels
- Sticky notes
- *Number Cubes (one 0–5 and one 5–10)

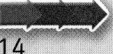

### Technology
**ePresentation** Lesson 12.2

### Test Prep
**Cumulative Review**
Mental Math reviews addition and subtraction of multidigit numbers (Lesson 2.3).

**Extended Response**
Problems 11, 13, and 14

**Writing + Math**
Journal

### Looking Ahead
Prepare index cards with video game scores from Strategy Building in Lesson 12.3. You will create 12 cards with the scores so students can hold them and move to different locations in the room.

*Manipulative Kit Item

## Planning for Learning • DIFFERENTIATE INSTRUCTION

### INTERVENTION
**If . . .** students lack the prerequisite skill of dividing by a one-digit number,

**Then . . .** teach ***Intervention*** Lesson 12.A.

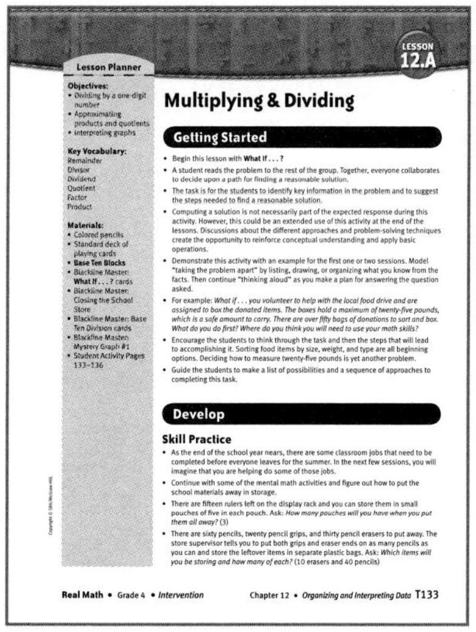


Intervention Lesson 12.A

### ENGLISH LEARNER
Preview

**If . . .** students need language support,

**Then . . .** use Lesson 12.2 in the ***English Learner Support Guide*** to preview lesson concepts and vocabulary.

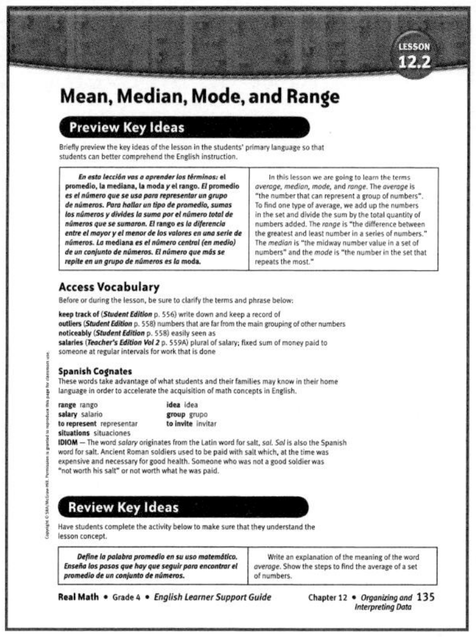


English Learner Lesson 12.2

### ENRICH
**If . . .** students are proficient in the lesson concepts,

**Then . . .** encourage them to explore game variations.

### PRACTICE
**If . . .** students would benefit from additional practice,

**Then . . .** extend Strategy Building before assigning the students pages.

### RETEACH
**If . . .** students have difficulty understanding the analysis of statistics,

**Then . . .** extend Guided Discussion before assigning the students pages.

### Vocabulary
**median \mē´ dē ən\ *n.*** the middle number in a set of data
**mode \mōd\ *n.*** the number appearing most frequently in a set of data
**range \rānj\ *n.*** the difference between the greatest and least numbers in a set of data

### Access Vocabulary
**above average** more than average
**below average** less than or fewer than average
**stray outlier** numbers that are far from the main grouping of data

### Spanish Cognates
**range** rango
**salary** salario

# Teaching Lesson 12.2

## Mental Math

5

Review RESPONSE WHEEL Use exercises such as the following to provide practice with addition and subtraction as inverse operations. Emphasize speedy response.

| | |
|---|---|
| **a.** 40 + 50 = 90 | 90 − 50 = 40 |
| **b.** 35 + 35 = 70 | 70 − 35 = 35 |
| **c.** 84 + 84 = 168 | 168 − 84 = 84 |
| **d.** 377 + 200 = 577 | 577 − 377 = 200 |
| **e.** 123 + 321 = 444 | 444 − 321 = 123 |
| **f.** 425 + 425 = 850 | 850 − 425 = 425 |
| **g.** 9,000 + 7,000 = 16,000 | 16,000 − 7,000 = 9,000 |
| **h.** 1,562 + 3,000 = 4,562 | 4,562 − 3,000 = 1,562 |
| **i.** 606 + 707 = 1,313 | 1,313 − 606 = 707 |
| **j.** 44,000 + 35,000 = 79,000 | 79,000 − 35,000 = 44,000 |

## 1 Develop

25

### Tell Students In Today's Lesson They Will

compute median, mode, and range.

### Guided Discussion UNDERSTANDING

Whole Group

Write the numbers 3, 4, and 5 on the board or on an overhead projector transparency with plenty of room to compute. Ask questions such as the following:

- **If I gave you the numbers 3, 4, and 5, how would you find the mean?** add them then divide by 3, or reduce the 5 by 1 and increase the 3 by 1

Place 1 on the left and 7 on the right of your list. Then ask questions such as the following:

- **What would you do if I added 1 and 7 to the list?** move 3 from the 7 to the 1, or add the numbers then divide by 5

Place another 1 on the left and another 7 on the right.

- **Do you think the mean would be the same now? Why?** Yes; answers will vary. Possible answers: 1 + 7 = 8 and 8 ÷ 2 = 4, so it wouldn't change; the mean is still 4; the set is balanced on both sides.

Place another 1 on the left and 97 on the right. Then ask questions such as the following:

- **Do you think this list would have the same mean?** no
- **Why not?** Possible answers: because 1 + 97 = 98 and 98 ÷ 2 > 4; because 97 is far greater than the other numbers; because moving 3 from 97 to 1 still leaves 94 along with all 4s.
- **What is the mean now?** 14
- **How did you find the answer?** added the numbers then divided by 7
- **How would you describe why the mean changed?** Possible answers: We're finding the number in the middle; we're finding the balance point; the number was way off compared to the others.

Explain that sometimes one stray number can change the mean significantly. These numbers are referred to as *outliers*. You may want to mention that we sometimes leave out these outliers when finding the mean. Go on to tell the class that when we have a list of numbers that are in order from least to greatest, we call the middle number the *median*. Refer back to the seven numbers on the board (1, 1, 3, 4, 5, 7, and 97). Then ask questions such as the following:

- **What is the median of these seven numbers?** 4
- **How do you know?** It is in the middle.

Next, explain to students that if a list contains an even amount of numbers, the average of the two numbers in the middle is taken to find the median. For example, in the list 2, 3, 5, 7, 9, and 12, the median is (5 + 7) ÷ 2 = 6. Now ask questions such as the following:

- **Suppose your list was 8 and 10. What is the median?** 9
- **What is the median of 1, 2, 3, 11, 12, and 13?** 7

Go on to explain that mode is the number that occurs most often in a set of data. Then ask questions such as the following:

- **What is the mode for the following: 1, 3, 2, 7, 8, 3, 6, and 5?** 3
- **What is the mode for the following: 1, 2, 3, 11, 12, and 15?** When two or more numbers appear the same number of times, we say each is a mode, but we don't usually use this concept when no two numbers are the same.
- **What is the mode for the following: 3, 4, 3, 5, 2, 2, 7, and 9?** 3 and 2

Finally, the range of a set of values is the difference between the greatest and least values in the list. In the list 3, 6, 9, and 12, the range is 12 − 3 = 9. Ask questions such as the following:

- **What is the range for 3, 4, 3, 5, 2, 2, 7, and 9?** 7

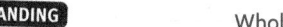

## Strategy Building UNDERSTANDING

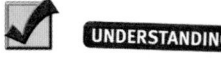

Small Group

### Finding Mean, Median, Mode, and Range in the Classroom

Select a piece of information from each student that can be measured in numbers and that varies from student to student. For example, ask for the number of pets that students have at home, the number of people who live at their residence, and so on.

Provide each student with a sticky note to record their number, and have them place the sticky note on the board in a row or column.

Have the class write down the numbers on everyone's sticky note on a sheet of paper.

Divide the class into small groups and have them compute the mean, median, mode, and range for their data.

Remind students that the problems in their book have been created to result in averages containing whole numbers; however, for this activity, their averages may not be whole numbers.

Note that this activity could also be done by dividing the class into groups before each number is recorded. Then have each group find the total number of items being measured for this activity, which would allow students the convenience of computing fewer numbers while making their data more specific to various groups.

## 2 Assign Student Pages

25

### Pages 556–557 APPLYING

Small Group

Students should use pages 556–557 as a reference for the vocabulary terms median, mode, and range. These pages also describe situations where these terms are applied.

Student Page

LESSON 12.2

## Mean, Median, Mode, and Range

### Key Ideas

**Mean, median, and mode are numbers that, in some situations are used to represent all the members of a set of data.**

Yolanda's mother wants to get an idea of how often Yolanda uses the telephone. She asked Yolanda to keep track of her calls for 9 days. The number of calls she made each day were 0, 2, 3, 3, 3, 4, 4, 5, 12.

What number best describes how many calls Yolanda usually makes each day?

We have begun to learn about ways to use a single number to describe a group of numbers. The *mean,* which we learned about in the last lesson, is one way to find out. In this lesson we will explore other ways. Let's review.

What is the mean number of calls Yolanda made?

The average, or mean, number of calls is 4 because Yolanda made a total of 36 calls in 9 days, and $36 \div 9 = 4$.

Sometimes people think the number that appears most often is the best number to use to describe a group of numbers. The number that appears most often is called the mode.

What is the mode of the number of times per day Yolanda made telephone calls?

Since 3 is the number of calls Yolanda made most often, the mode is 3.



Textbook This lesson is available in the *eTextbook.*

Student Page

What is the mode of the following set of numbers?

9, 4, 5, 5, 6, 9, 12, 7, 8, 5, 9

The numbers 5 and 9 are both modes because they occur most often.

Sometimes a set of data will have more than one mode. In such a case, you should report all modes.

Another number often used to describe a set of numbers is the median. The median is the number in the middle when a set of numbers is placed in order from least to greatest.

What is the median number of calls Yolanda made each day?

0, 2, 3, 3, 3, 4, 4, 5, 12

If Yolanda puts the number of calls in order from least to greatest, the middle number is 3, which is the median.

When there is an odd number of numbers, there is always a middle number.

But what do we do when there is an even number of numbers?

Since we are looking for the middle number, we can take the mean of the two numbers in the middle. Then this number will be in the middle of the set.

2, 4, 5, 7, 8, 9

In this case, the two middle numbers in the list would be 5 and 7, so their mean, 6, is the median.

2, 4, 5, 6, 7, 8, 9

## Assign Student Pages, continued

**Pages 558–559** APPLYING — Small Group

Have students complete pages 558–559 in small groups.

### As Students Finish

**Game** **Four Cube Division Game**

Student Page



Another way to use a single number to describe a set of numbers is called the range. The range is the difference between the greatest and least numbers in the set.

What is the range for the number of daily phone calls Yolanda made?

Since the greatest number of calls that Yolanda made in one day is 12 and the least number is 0, we find the range by subtracting 12 − 0 = 12.

Let's look at Yolanda's number of calls one more time.

0, 2, 3, 3, 3, 4, 4, 5, 12

Notice that one of the numbers is much greater than the others. On one of the days Yolanda made 12 phone calls! Perhaps she was inviting people to a party that day and needed to make more calls than usual. A number that lies noticeably outside the other numbers is called an *outlier.* Sometimes we may not want to include outliers when we calculate a mean.

What would our mean be if we removed the number 12?

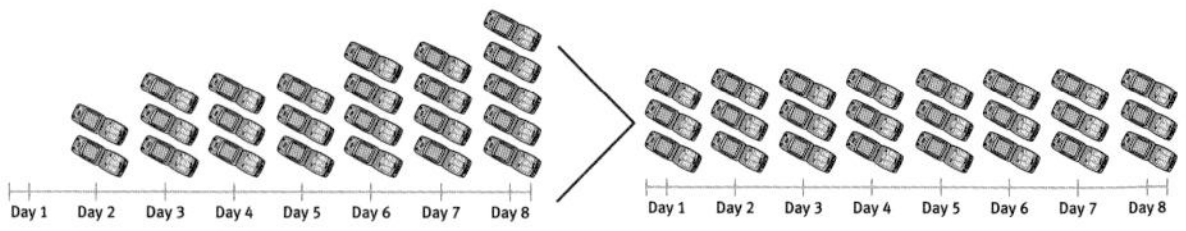


0, 2, 3, 3, 3, 4, 4, 5 — 3, 3, 3, 3, 3, 3, 3, 3

Without the one day of 12 calls, there were 24 calls made over 8 days. To find the mean, we need to divide 24 by 8.

0 + 2 + 3 + 3 + 3 + 4 + 4 + 5 = 24 — 24 ÷ 8 = 3

So, instead of a mean of 4 calls per day, we have a mean of 3 calls per day. One number can have a significant effect.



eTextbook This lesson is available in the *eTextbook.*

Student Page

**Find** the mean, median, mode, and range.

1. 9, 10, 11, 12, 28 — 14; 11; none; 19
2. 1, 1, 1, 5, 7 — 3; 1; 1; 6
3. 1, 2, 2, 3, 3, 3, 4, 4, 4, 4, 5, 5, 5, 5, 5, 6, 6, 6, 6, 7, 7, 7, 8, 8, 9 — 5; 5; 5; 8
4. 2, 3, 4, 7, 7, 8, 11 — 6; 7; 7; 9
5. 7, 12, 3, 8, 4, 5, 0, 6, 0 — 5; 5; 0; 12
6. 9, 9, 9, 6, 0, 1, 3, 1, 2, 0 — 4; 2.5; 9; 9
7. 12, 4, 12, 0, 8, 4, 13, 4, 6, 8, 5, 8 — 7; 7; 8 and 4; 13

X-Press is a small phone company with 9 employees, including the owner. These are their yearly salaries:

$16,000; $16,000; $16,000; $16,000; $18,000; $19,000; $20,000; $21,000; $65,000

**Answer** these questions. SOCIAL STUDIES

8. What is the average, or mean, salary of the 9 employees? $23,000
9. What is the median salary of the employees? $18,000
10. What is the mode of the salaries of the employees? $16,000
11. Extended Response Of the mean, the median, and the mode, which do you think best describes the salaries of the X-Press employees? See Reflect in the *Teacher's Edition.*
12. What is the range of salaries? $49,000
13. Extended Response Explain what would happen to the mean, median, mode, and range if a new employee made $23,000 per year. See Reflect in the *Teacher's Edition.*
14. Extended Response Would you consider any of the salaries to be an outlier? If so, explain how the data should be handled and what would result. See Reflect in the *Teacher's Edition.*

Writing + Math **Journal**

Explain two ways to determine the average of a set of numbers and give examples of when you would want to use each. See Reflect in the *Teacher's Edition.*

# 3 Reflect 5

## Guided Discussion UNDERSTANDING

Whole Group

Place a line-plot on the board to show the number of letters each student has in his or her name.

Ask the class what conclusions they can draw from the line-plot by having them create factual sentences from the data shown on the board. Students should be able to incorporate words such as *mean, mode, maximum, range,* and *minimum*.

## Extended Response

**Problem 11** Look for thoughtful reasoning behind students' answers. For example, finding the mean would best represent all the employees.

**Problem 13** Students should explain that the mean and mode would not change because 23,000 was the original average. However, the median *would* change because there is an even number of salaries, so the median is between the two middle values.

**Problem 14** Students should explain that the $65,000 salary is an outlier from the rest of the employees' salaries. If this salary is removed from the original mean, then the average would fall to $17,750, while the mode would stay the same.

**Writing + Math Journal**

Students should respond that one way is to add the numbers then divide by the amount of numbers. The other way is to even out the numerical values. Examples for each will vary.

**Curriculum Connection:** Students discussed average salaries of employees in this lesson. Students may be interested in researching the occupations with the highest average salaries in the United States and comparing them with salaries for similar occupations in other countries.

**Cumulative Review:** For review of multidigit multiplication and division of whole numbers, assign Problems 7–15 on student page 566.

**Family Involvement:** Assign the ***Practice, Reteach,*** or ***Enrichment*** activities depending on the needs of your students.

Encourage students to play the **Four Cube Division Game** with a friend or relative.

**Concept/Question Board:** Have students look for additional examples of mean, mode, median, and range, and post them on the Concept/Question Board.

**Math Puzzler:** Joe and Flo were returning books to the library. Flo said, "If you give me one of your books, I'll have twice as many books as you. But if I give you one of my books, we'll both have the same number of books." How many books did Joe and Flo each have? Joe had 5 books, and Flo had 7 books.

# 4 Assess and Differentiate

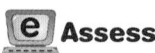

**e Assess** Use ***eAssess*** to record and analyze evidence of student understanding.

## A Gather Evidence

Use the Daily Class Assessment Records in ***Assessment*** or ***eAssess*** to record daily observations.

### Informal Assessment

**✓ Strategy Building**

Did the student UNDERSTANDING

- ❑ make important observations?
- ❑ extend or generalize learning?
- ❑ provide insightful answers?
- ❑ pose insightful questions?

### Portfolio Assessment

**✓ Extended Response**

Did the student REASONING

- ❑ provide a clear explanation?
- ❑ communicate reasons and strategies?
- ❑ choose appropriate strategies?
- ❑ argue logically?

## B Summarize Findings

Analyze and summarize assessment data for each student. Determine which Assessment Follow-Up is appropriate for each student. Use the Student Assessment Record in ***Assessment*** or ***eAssess*** to update assessment records.

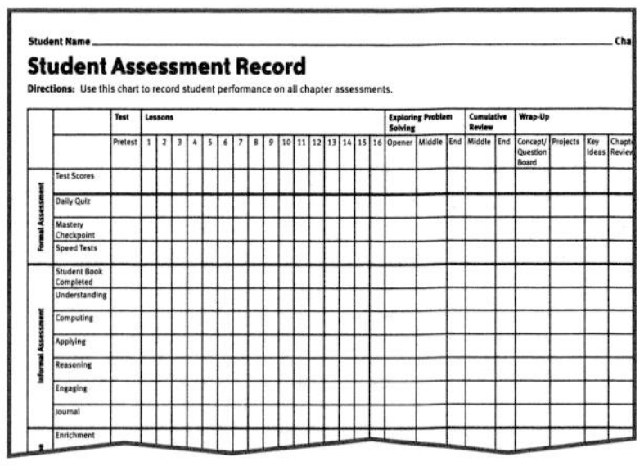
Student Name
Student Assessment Record

**Assessment Page T41**

## C Assessment Follow-Up • DIFFERENTIATE INSTRUCTION

Based on your observations, use these teaching strategies for assessment follow-up.

### INTERVENTION

Review student performance on ***Intervention*** Lesson 12.A to see if they have mastered prerequisite skills for this lesson.

### ENGLISH LEARNER

**Review**

Use Lesson 12.2 in ***English Learner Support Guide*** to preview lesson concepts and vocabulary.

### ENRICH

**If . . .** students are proficient in the lesson concepts,

**Then . . .** encourage them to work on chapter projects or ***Enrichment*** Lesson 12.2.

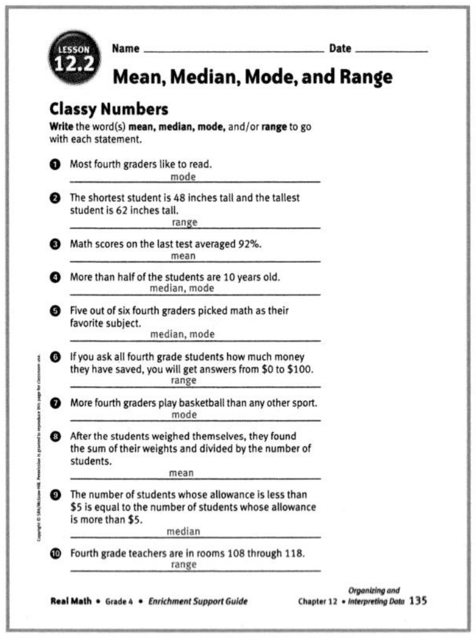
LESSON 12.2 Name ________ Date ________

**Mean, Median, Mode, and Range**

**Classy Numbers**

**Write** the word(s) **mean, median, mode,** and/or **range** to go with each statement.

1. Most fourth graders like to read. mode
2. The shortest student is 48 inches tall and the tallest student is 62 inches tall. range
3. Math scores on the last test averaged 92%. mean
4. More than half of the students are 10 years old. median, mode
5. Five out of six fourth graders picked math as their favorite subject. median, mode
6. If you ask all fourth grade students how much money they have saved, you will get answers from $0 to $100. range
7. More fourth graders play basketball than any other sport. mode
8. After the students weighed themselves, they found the sum of their weights and divided by the number of students. mean
9. The number of students whose allowance is less than $5 is equal to the number of students whose allowance is more than $5. median
10. Fourth grade teachers are in rooms 108 through 118. range

Real Math • Grade 4 • *Enrichment Support Guide* Chapter 12 • *Organizing and Interpreting Data* 135

Enrichment Lesson 12.2

### PRACTICE

**If . . .** students would benefit from additional practice,

**Then . . .** assign ***Practice*** Lesson 12.2.

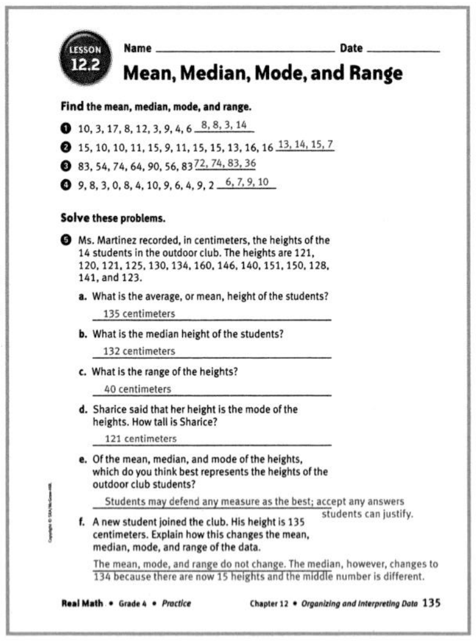
LESSON 12.2 Name ________ Date ________

**Mean, Median, Mode, and Range**

**Find the mean, median, mode, and range.**

1. 10, 3, 17, 8, 12, 3, 9, 4, 6 8, 8, 3, 14
2. 15, 10, 10, 11, 15, 9, 11, 15, 15, 13, 16, 16 13, 14, 15, 7
3. 83, 54, 74, 64, 90, 56, 83 72, 74, 83, 36
4. 9, 8, 3, 0, 8, 4, 10, 9, 6, 4, 9, 2 6, 7, 9, 10

**Solve these problems.**

5. Ms. Martinez recorded, in centimeters, the heights of the 14 students in the outdoor club. The heights are 121, 120, 121, 125, 130, 134, 160, 146, 140, 151, 150, 128, 141, and 123.
   a. What is the average, or mean, height of the students? 135 centimeters
   b. What is the median height of the students? 132 centimeters
   c. What is the range of the heights? 40 centimeters
   d. Sharice said that her height is the mode of the heights. How tall is Sharice? 121 centimeters
   e. Of the mean, median, and mode of the heights, which do you think best represents the heights of the outdoor club students? Students may defend any measure as the best; accept any answers students can justify.
   f. A new student joined the club. His height is 135 centimeters. Explain how this changes the mean, median, mode, and range of the data. The mean, mode, and range do not change. The median, however, changes to 134 because there are now 15 heights and the middle number is different.

Real Math • Grade 4 • *Practice* Chapter 12 • *Organizing and Interpreting Data* 135

Practice Lesson 12.2

### RETEACH

**If . . .** students have difficulty understanding the analysis of statistics,

**Then . . .** reteach the concept using ***Reteach*** Lesson 12.2.

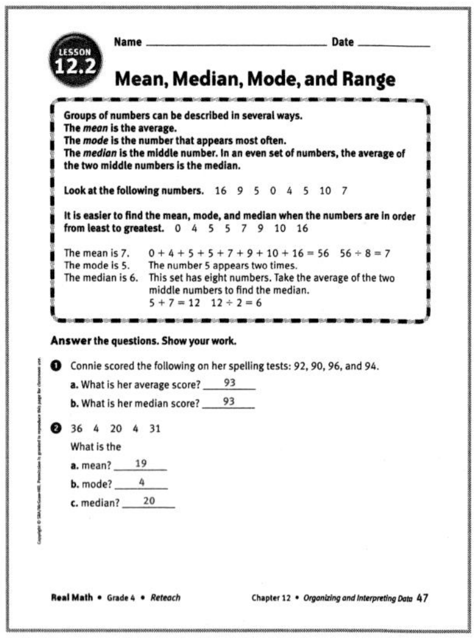
LESSON 12.2 Name ________ Date ________

**Mean, Median, Mode, and Range**

**Groups of numbers can be described in several ways.**
**The *mean* is the average.**
**The *mode* is the number that appears most often.**
**The *median* is the middle number. In an even set of numbers, the average of the two middle numbers is the median.**

**Look at the following numbers.** 16 9 5 0 4 5 10 7

**It is easier to find the mean, mode, and median when the numbers are in order from least to greatest.** 0 4 5 5 7 9 10 16

The mean is 7. $0 + 4 + 5 + 5 + 7 + 9 + 10 + 16 = 56$ $56 \div 8 = 7$
The mode is 5. The number 5 appears two times.
The median is 6. This set has eight numbers. Take the average of the two middle numbers to find the median. $5 + 7 = 12$ $12 \div 2 = 6$

**Answer the questions. Show your work.**

1. Connie scored the following on her spelling tests: 92, 90, 96, and 94.
   a. What is her average score? 93
   b. What is her median score? 93
2. 36 4 20 4 31
   What is the
   a. mean? 19
   b. mode? 4
   c. median? 20

Real Math • Grade 4 • *Reteach* Chapter 12 • *Organizing and Interpreting Data* 47

Reteach Lesson 12.2

## Lesson Planner

**OBJECTIVES**
- To help students understand the meaning of average and to help them begin to make predictions based on average
- To provide practice solving word problems

**NCTM STANDARDS**

**Problem Solving**
Find solutions to problems regarding average

**Number and Operations**
Compute solutions to real-world situations

**Data Analysis and Probability**
Use appropriate statistical methods to analyze data

**MATERIALS**
- Index cards
- ***Number Cubes** (one 0–5 and one 5–10)

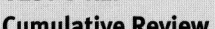

**TECHNOLOGY**
**e Presentation** Lesson 12.3

**TEST PREP**

**Cumulative Review**
- Mental Math reviews estimation among mathematical operations (Lessons 1.1, 2.6, 6.10, and 11.10).
- Problem 2 reviews area (Lesson 6.1).
- Problem 6 reviews converting customary units (Lesson 6.6).

**Extended Response**
Problem 4

**Writing + Math**
Journal

*Manipulative Kit Item

# Using Mathematics

**Context of the Lesson** This is the last of three lessons on measurements of central tendency. This lesson extends students' knowledge of the material from the previous two lessons by creating real-world situations in which they can interpret data.

See page 550B for Math Background for teachers for this lesson.

## Planning for Learning • DIFFERENTIATE INSTRUCTION

### INTERVENTION

**If . . .** students lack the prerequisite skill of approximating products and quotients,

**Then . . .** teach ***Intervention*** Lesson 12.B.

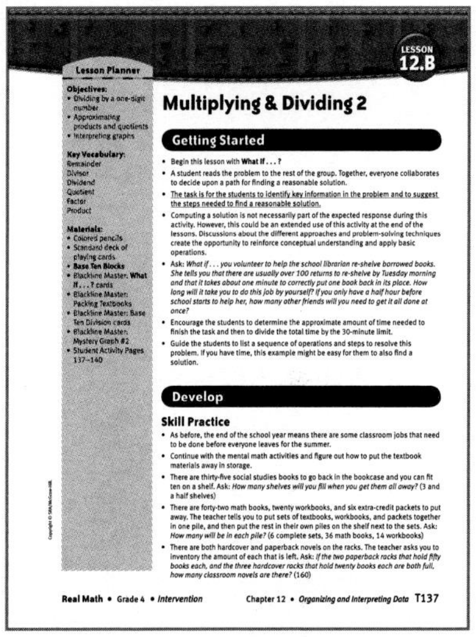


Intervention Lesson 12.B

### ENGLISH LEARNER

**Preview**

**If . . .** students need language support,

**Then . . .** use Lesson 12.3 in the ***English Learner Support Guide*** to preview lesson concepts and vocabulary.

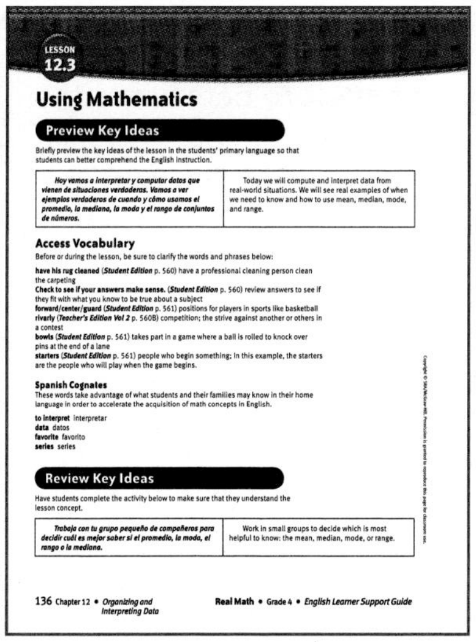


English Learner Lesson 12.3

### ENRICH

**If . . .** students are proficient in the lesson concepts,

**Then . . .** encourage them to create new game strategies.

### PRACTICE

**If . . .** students would benefit from additional practice,

**Then . . .** extend Strategy Building before assigning the student pages.

### RETEACH

**If . . .** students have difficulty understanding how to base decisions on statistics,

**Then . . .** extend Strategy Building before assigning the student pages.

**Access Vocabulary**
**Check to see if your answers make sense** Review the answers to see if they fit with what you know about a subject.

**Spanish Cognates**
**interpret** interpretar
**data** datos

# Teaching Lesson 12.3

## Mental Math 5

THUMBS UP Provide students with addition, subtraction, multiplication, and division exercises in which they need to estimate the answers. Have them show thumbs-up for correct or possibly correct answers and thumbs-down for obviously wrong answers. Use examples such as the following:

**a.** $400 \times 3 = 20$ down
**b.** $900 \div 30 = 200$ down
**c.** $543 \times 35 = 54{,}000$ down
**d.** $922 - 420 = 502$ up
**e.** $402 \times 55 = 36{,}075$ down
**f.** $850 - 440 = 410$ up
**g.** $460 + 460 = 1{,}120$ down
**h.** $745 + 840 = 1{,}585$ up
**i.** $780 \times 100 = 7{,}800$ down
**j.** $877 - 398 = 211$ down

## 1 Develop 25

**Tell Students In Today's Lesson They Will**
interpret and compute data from real-world situations.

### Strategy Building UNDERSTANDING

Small Group

Divide the class into small groups, then present a problem, such as the following, on the board: Suppose Misha and his friend Akiko have a video game rivalry and want to determine the better player. Misha played 7 games with scores of 2,101; 5,620; 4,202; 4,808; 4,178; 4,105; and 4,232. Akiko played 5 games and scored 4,343; 3,998; 4,988; 4,702; and 5,199. Ask each group of students to solve questions such as the following:

- **How could you decide who the better player is? What would be the best option?** Possible answers: decide who has the highest score; decide who has the best average; decide who has the best median. If you went by high score alone, Misha would win. However, if you were choosing a teammate for a video game tournament, you might be interested in best average or the highest median.
- **Why would picking the person with the most points be a bad decision?** because Misha played more games

Rather than listing scores on the board or overhead projector transparency, write each of the scores on an index card and hand the cards out to different students. Have students with Misha's scores stand on one side of the room and those with Akiko's stand on the other.

Have students arrange themselves in order from least to greatest score.

| | | | | Median | | | | Total | Mean |
|---|---|---|---|---|---|---|---|---|---|
| Misha | 2,101 | 4,105 | 4,178 | 4,202 | 4,232 | 4,808 | 5,620 | 29,246 | 4,178 |
| Akiko | 3,998 | 4,343 | | 4,702 | | 4,988 | 5,199 | 23,230 | 4,646 |

Have groups find solutions to mathematical questions such as the following:

- **How do we find the median?** Put the numbers in order from least to greatest—the middle number is the median.
- **What is Misha's median?** 4,202
- **What is Akiko's median?** 4,702
- **How do we find the mean or average?** Possible answer: Add all the scores for each person then divide that sum by their number of games.
- **What is Misha's average?** 4,178
- **What is Akiko's average?** 4,646
- **How do you find the range?** Subtract the smallest score from the greatest score.
- **What is Misha's range of scores?** 3,519
- **What is Akiko's range of scores?** 1,201
- **How do you know who played more consistently?** The person with the smallest range of scores, Akiko, played more consistently because her scores were closer together than Misha's.
- **Can you explain another reason why Akiko may have had a smaller range?** because she played fewer games than Misha
- **How would you summarize this discussion about who is the better player?** Answers will vary. Misha has the highest score, but Akiko has the better average and the greatest median.

## 2 Assign Student Pages 25

**Pages 560–561** APPLYING

Have students complete pages 560–561 individually.

**As Students Finish**

Game **Four Cube Division Game**

Student Page

LESSON 12.3 Using Mathematics

**Key Ideas**

**Mean, median, mode, and range can be used to help interpret data.**

**Solve these problems. Check to see if your answers make sense and fit the given situations.**

1. There were 9 people who took a 40-word spelling test. Their scores were 39, 38, 30, 39, 26, 31, 35, 7, and 34.
   - **a.** What was the average score? 31
   - **b.** How many people had above-average scores? 5
   - **c.** How many people had below-average scores? 3
   - **d.** How many people had average scores? 1

2. Review Mr. Epstein knows his living room rug is rectangular and that its area is 42 square meters.
   - **a.** He knows his rug is 6 meters wide, but he cannot remember how long it is. How long is the rug? 7 meters
   - **b.** If the local cleaner charges \$2.53 (253¢) for each square meter of rug, how much will it cost Mr. Epstein to have his rug cleaned? \$106.26 (10,626¢)

3. Ms. McConnell heard that the cabbages at her favorite store weigh about 1 kilogram (1,000 grams). She bought 9 cabbages and weighed them. Their weights were 932 grams; 961 grams; 982 grams; 989 grams; 994 grams; 996 grams; 1,008 grams; 1,087 grams; and 1,096 grams.
   - **a.** How many of the 9 cabbages weighed more than 1 kilogram? 3
   - **b.** What was the average weight of the 9 cabbages? 1,005 g (1.005 kg)
   - **c.** Would it cost Ms. McConnell less to buy the cabbages for 65¢ per cabbage or for 65¢ per kilogram? 65¢ per cabbage

560 eTextbook This lesson is available in the *eTextbook*.

Student Page

4. **Extended Response** When Roland bowls, he bowls a series of three games. The last 7 nights he went bowling, his total scores for three games were 561, 570, 572, 568, 430, 564, and 571. See *Teacher's Edition.*
   - **a.** Could Roland's average score for a series of 3 games be 400? Could it be 430? 600? 572? See *Teacher's Edition.*
   - **b.** Make your best estimate of Roland's average score for the last 7 nights he bowled. Then calculate the average to see how close you were. cooler than usual
   - **c.** What do you think Roland's score will be the next night he bowls? Explain your reasoning. See Reflect in the *Teacher's Edition.*

5. READING The temperature in Columbus, Ohio has varied greatly over the past 14 days. The high temperatures for each day were 31°F, 27°F, 31°F, 33°F, 44°F, 59°F, 62°F, 33°F, 33°F, 34°F, 36°F, 35°F, 33°F, and 42°F.
   - **a.** What was the average high temperature of this 14-day period? 38°F
   - **b.** Over the past 100 years, the average daily high temperature in Columbus for this particular 14-day period has been 53°F. Would you say that this same period this year is warmer than usual, cooler than usual, or about average? cooler than usual

6. Review The table below shows the height of the 5 starters for a professional basketball team.
   - **a.** What is the mean height of the team? 6 feet 5 inches
   - **b.** What is the range in height of the team? 1 foot

| Position | Height |
|---|---|
| Center | 7 feet |
| Forward | 6 feet 8 inches |
| Forward | 6 feet 5 inches |
| Guard | 6 feet 4 inches |
| Guard | 6 feet |

Writing + Math **Journal**

Explain how to find mean, median, mode, and range.

Chapter 12 • Lesson 3 561

## 3 Reflect

5

### Guided Discussion REASONING

Whole Group

Discuss Roland's bowling score in Problem 4, and ask questions such as the following:

- **Is 570 a better guess than Roland's average of 548? Why or why not?** Yes; the outlier (430) dropped his average.
- **How consistent of a bowler would you say Roland is?** very consistent
- **How many of his series of games were significantly different from the rest?** one—the 430 series

### Extended Response

**Problem 4a** Roland's score could not be 400 because 400 is lower than the least score. The score could not be 430 because 430 equals the lowest score. The score could also not be 600 because 600 is greater than the greatest score.

**Problem 4c** One possibility is Roland's score will probably be between 560 and 580 because he had only one game out of seven below 560, and the average of the remaining games was about 568.

Writing + Math **Journal**

Mean can be found by either evening the numbers out or computing the sum of a set of numbers then dividing by the amount of numbers. Median can be found by finding the middle number. Mode is the number appearing most often in the set, and the range is the difference between the greatest and least numbers.

SOCIAL STUDIES **Curriculum Connection:** In this lesson, students discussed temperatures. Students may enjoy reading *Antartica: Journeys to the South Pole,* a heroic adventure of battling the harsh weather of the South Pole.

Review **Cumulative Review:** For review of addition and subtraction of fractions, assign Problems 16–19 on student page 566.

**Family Involvement:** Assign the ***Practice, Reteach,*** or ***Enrichment*** activities depending on the needs of your students.

Encourage students to play the **Four Cube Division Game** with a friend or relative.

**Concept/Question Board:** Have students look for additional examples of mean, mode, median, and range, and post them on the Concept/Question Board.

**Math Puzzler:** Dori spent \$4.00 to buy 2 magazines. One magazine cost 50¢ less than the other. How much did each magazine cost? \$1.75 and \$2.25

# 4 Assess and Differentiate

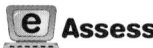

**e Assess** Use ***eAssess*** to record and analyze evidence of student understanding.

## A Gather Evidence

Use the Daily Class Assessment Records in ***Assessment*** or ***eAssess*** to record daily observations.

### Informal Assessment
**Strategy Building**

Did the student UNDERSTANDING
- ❑ make important observations?
- ❑ extend or generalize learning?
- ❑ provide insightful answers?
- ❑ pose insightful questions?

### Informal Assessment
**Mental Math**

Did the student COMPUTING
- ❑ respond accurately?
- ❑ respond quickly?
- ❑ respond with confidence?
- ❑ self-correct?

## B Summarize Findings

Analyze and summarize assessment data for each student. Determine which Assessment Follow-Up is appropriate for each student. Use the Student Assessment Record in ***Assessment*** or ***eAssess*** to update assessment records.

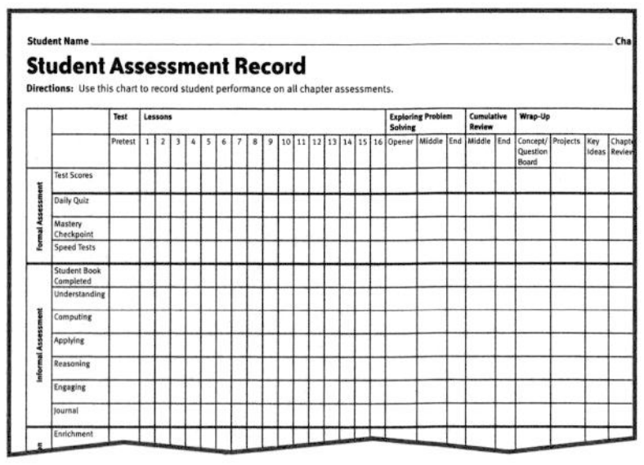


Assessment Page T41

## C Assessment Follow-Up • DIFFERENTIATE INSTRUCTION

Based on your observations, use these teaching strategies for assessment follow-up.

### INTERVENTION

Review student performance using ***Intervention*** Lesson 12.B to see if they have mastered the prerequisite skills for this lesson.

### ENGLISH LEARNER

**Review**

Use Lesson 12.3 in ***English Learner Support Guide*** to preview lesson concepts and vocabulary.

### ENRICH

**If . . .** students are proficient in the lesson concepts,

**Then . . .** encourage them to work on chapter projects or ***Enrichment*** Lesson 12.3.

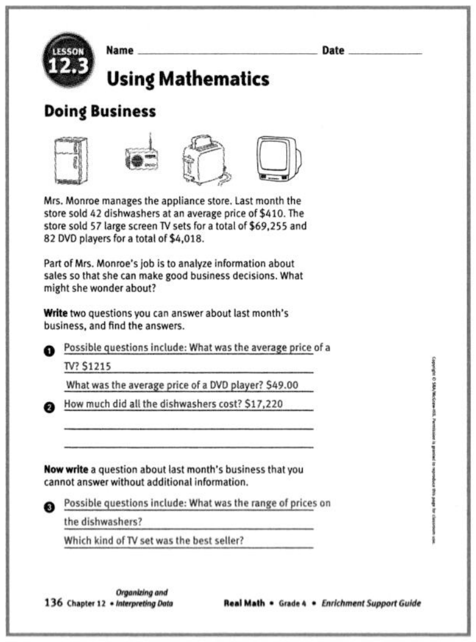
LESSON 12.3 Name ______ Date ______

**Using Mathematics**

**Doing Business**

Mrs. Monroe manages the appliance store. Last month the store sold 42 dishwashers at an average price of $410. The store sold 57 large screen TV sets for a total of $69,255 and 82 DVD players for a total of $4,018.

Part of Mrs. Monroe's job is to analyze information about sales so that she can make good business decisions. What might she wonder about?

**Write** two questions you can answer about last month's business, and find the answers.

1. Possible questions include: What was the average price of a TV? $1215
   What was the average price of a DVD player? $49.00
2. How much did all the dishwashers cost? $17,220

**Now write** a question about last month's business that you cannot answer without additional information.

3. Possible questions include: What was the range of prices on the dishwashers?
   Which kind of TV set was the best seller?

136 Chapter 12 • *Organizing and Interpreting Data* **Real Math** • Grade 4 • *Enrichment Support Guide*

Enrichment Lesson 12.3

### PRACTICE

**If . . .** students would benefit from additional practice,

**Then . . .** assign ***Practice*** Lesson 12.3.

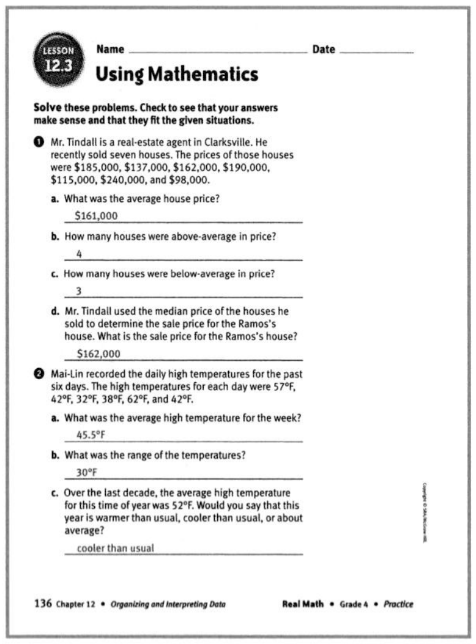
LESSON 12.3 Name ______ Date ______

**Using Mathematics**

**Solve these problems. Check to see that your answers make sense and that they fit the given situations.**

1. Mr. Tindall is a real-estate agent in Clarksville. He recently sold seven houses. The prices of those houses were $185,000, $137,000, $162,000, $190,000, $115,000, $240,000, and $98,000.
   a. What was the average house price? $161,000
   b. How many houses were above-average in price? 4
   c. How many houses were below-average in price? 3
   d. Mr. Tindall used the median price of the houses he sold to determine the sale price for the Ramos's house. What is the sale price for the Ramos's house? $162,000
2. Mai-Lin recorded the daily high temperatures for the past six days. The high temperatures for each day were 57°F, 42°F, 32°F, 38°F, 62°F, and 42°F.
   a. What was the average high temperature for the week? 45.5°F
   b. What was the range of the temperatures? 30°F
   c. Over the last decade, the average high temperature for this time of year was 52°F. Would you say that this year is warmer than usual, cooler than usual, or about average? cooler than usual

136 Chapter 12 • *Organizing and Interpreting Data* **Real Math** • Grade 4 • *Practice*

Practice Lesson 12.3

### RETEACH

**If . . .** students struggle with their answers to word problems,

**Then . . .** have them reread the problem and make sure that their answers are logical.

## Lesson Planner

**OBJECTIVES**
- To provide practice in approximating answers to division problems using the inverse operation of multiplication
- To provide practice in solving word problems

**NCTM STANDARDS**

**Number and Operations**
Use various techniques to approximate products

**Problem Solving**
Solve problems

**MATERIALS**
- ***Response Wheels**
- *Copies of the **Harder Snake Game Mat**
- ***Number Cubes** (one 0–5 and one 5–10)

**TECHNOLOGY**

**Presentation** Lesson 12.4
**MathTools** Calculator

**TEST PREP**

**Cumulative Review**
- Mental Math reviews finding patterns in larger exercises by referring to basic facts (Lesson 3.10).
- Problems 1–10 reviews division of greater numbers and division patterns (Lessons 11.4 and 11.5).

**Multistep Problems**
Problems 16 and 20

*Manipulative Kit Item

# Choosing Reasonable Answers

**Context of the Lesson** This lesson continues to expand students' understanding of the appropriate use of division and other operations to solve problems. Students will use strategies, such as estimation and the inverse operation, to solve a number of multiple-choice exercises. Good estimation skills often reduce the amount of errors found in everyday calculations. Also, students can use estimation to eliminate some wrong answers when taking multiple-choice tests, thereby allowing greater opportunity to guess the correct answers. Estimation of quotients was introduced in Lesson 11.10, and using the inverse of division to check quotients was taught in Lesson 11.3.

See page 550B for Math Background for teachers for this lesson.

## Planning for Learning • DIFFERENTIATE INSTRUCTION

### INTERVENTION

**If . . .** students lack the prerequisite skill of approximating products and quotients,

**Then . . .** teach ***Intervention*** Lesson 12.B.

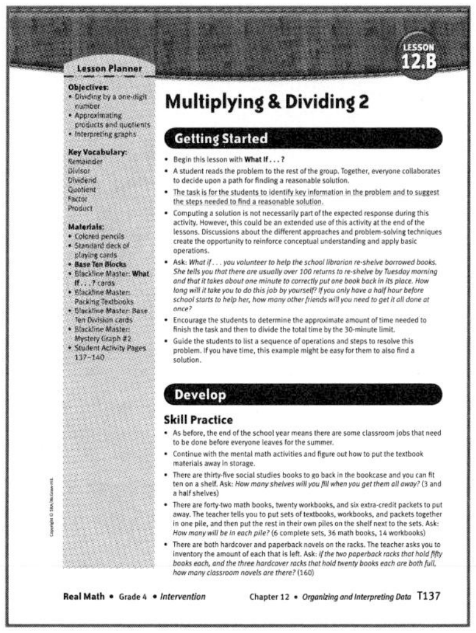
Lesson Planner
Multiplying & Dividing 2
Getting Started
Develop
Skill Practice

Intervention Lesson 12.B

### ENGLISH LEARNER

**Preview**

**If . . .** students need language support,

**Then . . .** use Lesson 12.4 in the ***English Learner Support Guide*** to preview lesson concepts and vocabulary.

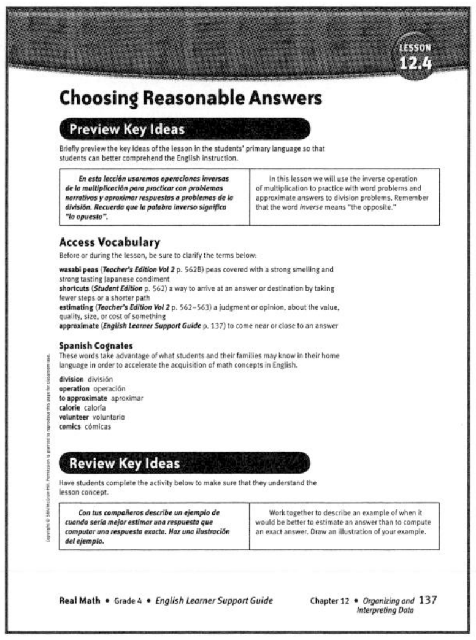
Choosing Reasonable Answers
Preview Key Ideas
Access Vocabulary
Spanish Cognates
Review Key Ideas

English Learner Lesson 12.4

### ENRICH

**If . . .** students are proficient in the lesson concepts,

**Then . . .** encourage them to create alternative strategies.

### PRACTICE

**If . . .** students would benefit from additional practice,

**Then . . .** extend Guided Discussion before assigning the student pages.

### RETEACH

**If . . .** students have difficulty understanding how to choose reasonable answers,

**Then . . .** extend Guided Discussion before assigning the student pages.

**Access Vocabulary**
**shortcuts** taking fewer steps
**simpler facts** math facts already memorized

**Spanish Cognates**
**division** división
**operation** operación

## Mental Math 5

Review · RESPONSE WHEEL

Provide exercises, such as the following, involving all four operations and multidigit numbers:

**a.** $8 \times 3 = 24$
**b.** $8 + 3 = 11$
**c.** $2,400 \div 30 = 80$
**d.** $24 \div 8 = 3$
**e.** $1,100 - 300 = 800$
**f.** $240 \div 80 = 3$

## 1 Develop 25

### Tell Students In Today's Lesson They Will

use estimation and the inverse operation to compute or select correct answers.

### Guided Discussion APPLYING

Whole Group

Write a few problems, such as the following, on the board or overhead projector. You may wish to demonstrate calculations on the ***eMathTools: Calculator.*** For each question, have someone read the question aloud and then ask a volunteer to give the answer and a strategy for solving the problem.

- **Charla went to the Korean market to buy her favorite snack, wasabi peas. If she spent $3.30 for a 6-pack, how much did she pay for each snack?** 55¢
- **Justin drove to his friend's new house and wondered how fast he had traveled. If he drove 150 miles before lunch and then another 210 miles in a total of $6\frac{1}{2}$ hours (with a $\frac{1}{2}$ hour break for lunch), how fast was he driving on average?** 60 miles per hour
- **Usak went to the used bookstore and bought 7 of his favorite comics for $17.01. What was the average cost per comic book?** $2.43

## 2 Assign Student Pages 25

### Pages 562–563 APPLYING

Have students complete pages 562–563 independently. As students begin page 562, encourage them to look for patterns and relationships among the numbers.

### As Students Finish

Game **Cubo, Four Cube Division Game, Harder Snake Game Mat**

**RESEARCH IN ACTION**

"Procedural fluency and conceptual understanding are often seen as competing for attention in school mathematics. But pitting skill against understanding creates a false dichotomy. . . the two are interwoven. Understanding makes learning skills easier, less susceptible to common errors, and less prone to forgetting. By the same token, a certain level of skill is required to learn many mathematical concepts with understanding, and using procedures can help strengthen and develop that understanding."

Kilpatrick, J., Swafford, J. and Findell, B. eds. *Adding It Up: Helping Children Learn Mathematics.* Washington, D.C.: National Research Council/National Academy Press, 2001, p. 122

Student Page

## LESSON 12.4 Choosing Reasonable Answers

### Key Ideas

**You can find answers to division problems by using other operations.**

For example, what is 7)213 to the nearest tenth?
**a.** 30.4 **b.** 3.4 **c.** 200.4 **d.** 35.4

One way to solve the problem is to think about multiplication.

First, we can easily eliminate 3.4 and 200.4 since $7 \times 3.4$ is much less than 213, and $7 \times 200.4$ is way too much. This leaves only two possibilities, 30.4 and 35.4.

$7 \times 3 = 21$ so $7 \times 30 = 210$

This means the answer is very close to 30.

$7 \times 35 = 245$ so 35.4 is too great a number.

$$7\overline{)213.0} = 30.4$$

Review **Choose** the correct answer. Use shortcuts when you can.

1. 1)350
 a. 27
 b. 35
 c. 270
 (d.) 350
2. 10)350
 a. 27
 (b.) 35
 c. 270
 d. 350
3. 15)60
 (a.) 4
 b. 3
 c. 2
 d. 5
4. 2)10
 a. 2
 b. 3
 c. 4
 (d.) 5
5. 20)100
 a. 2
 b. 3
 c. 4
 (d.) 5
6. 3)100
 a. 3.3
 b. 30.3
 (c.) 33.3
 d. 3.4
7. 33)100
 (a.) 3 R1
 b. 30 R1
 c. 33 R1
 d. 3 R2
8. 7)67
 a. 9.4
 (b.) 9.6
 c. 9.5
 d. 8.5
9. 18)90
 a. 3
 b. 4
 (c.) 5
 d. 6
10. 11)132
 (a.) 12
 b. 14
 c. 16
 d. 18



Textbook This lesson is available in the ***eTextbook***.

Student Page

**Solve** these problems. Check your answers to see if they make sense.

11. Claire and her 3 friends wanted to share 36 taquitos equally. How many should each person get? 9
12. Dr. Lin rode a train 171 miles from Fargo, ND, to St. Cloud, MN. The trip lasted 3 hours. What was the average speed of the train? 57 mph
13. Venus can record about 16 songs on a CD. If she wants to record 204 songs, how many CDs will she need? 13 CDs
14. Gregory can buy a 12-pack of juice bottles for $5.88 (or 588¢). What is the cost for each bottle of juice if he buys a 12-pack? 49¢
15. Nolan plays in a hockey league. In the first 6 games, he played a total of 252 minutes. How many minutes does Nolan average in each game? 42
16. Multistep Hari bought 9 goldfish that cost 89¢ each. The tax was 48¢. He gave the cashier a $10 bill. How much change should he get back? 151¢ or $1.51
17. SCIENCE Stratosphere Giant in Rockefeller Forest in California is the tallest living tree at 4,428 inches. How high is this tree in feet? 369 feet
18. A sea turtle lays eggs each year. The first year the sea turtle laid 154 eggs. Last year the turtle laid 97 eggs. This year the turtle laid 121 eggs. What is the average number of eggs laid each year? 124
19. Kimberly and Jorge left the school on their bikes at the same time. Kimberly rode $2\frac{1}{2}$ miles and Jorge rode $1\frac{1}{2}$ miles. How far apart were they? can't tell
20. Multistep Kwan ate 530 calories for lunch and 610 calories for dinner. His total calorie intake for the day was 1,500. How many calories did Kwan have for breakfast? 360 calories

**Note:** Not enough calories for a growing child.

## 3 Reflect

5

### Guided Discussion

Whole Group

Have students select the answer to a multiple-choice test question without computing and explain how they chose their answer.

Use an example such as:

17)4301

**a.** 23
**b.** 28
**c.** 250
**d.** 253
**e.** 263

Since 30 × 17 = 510, a and b are too small. And we know 250 × 17 would end in 0, so c can be eliminated. Since 260 × 17 = 4,420 we can see 263 is too big. Thus, the answer is d.

**Curriculum Connection:** Students interested in studying sequoias can research them online or at the library.

**Cumulative Review:** For review of geometry, assign Problems 20–30 on student page 567.

**Family Involvement:** Assign the ***Practice, Reteach,*** or ***Enrichment*** activities depending on the needs of your students.

Encourage students to play **Cubo** or the **Four Cube Division Game** with a friend or relative.

**Concept/Question Board:** Have students continue to post questions, answers, and examples on the Concept/Question Board.

**Math Puzzler:** Austin has 27 rabbits. How can he put the rabbits in 4 cages so that he has an odd number of rabbits in each cage? (Hint: There is a trick to solving this puzzle.) Answers will vary. One possibility is to put 9 rabbits in each of 3 cages, then put the 3 cages inside 1 large cage.

# 4 Assess and Differentiate

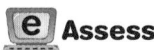

**e Assess** Use ***eAssess*** to record and analyze evidence of student understanding.

## A Gather Evidence

Use the Daily Class Assessment Records in ***Assessment*** or ***eAssess*** to record daily observations.

### Informal Assessment

**Guided Discussion**

Did the student APPLYING

- ❑ apply learning in new situations?
- ❑ contribute concepts?
- ❑ contribute answers?
- ❑ connect mathematics to real-world situations?

### Performance Assessment

**Game**

Did the student ENGAGING

- ❑ pay attention to others' contributions?
- ❑ contribute information and ideas?
- ❑ improve on a strategy?
- ❑ reflect on and check the accuracy of his or her work?

## B Summarize Findings

Analyze and summarize assessment data for each student. Determine which Assessment Follow-Up is appropriate for each student. Use the Student Assessment Record in ***Assessment*** or ***eAssess*** to update assessment records.

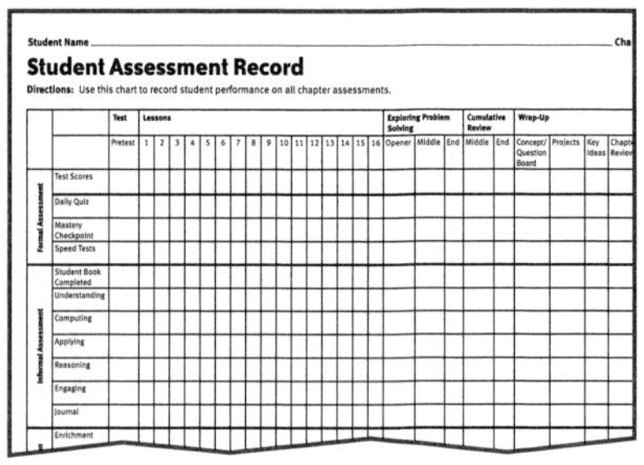
Student Assessment Record

**Assessment Page T41**

## C Assessment Follow-Up • DIFFERENTIATE INSTRUCTION

Based on your observations, use these teaching strategies for assessment follow-up.

### INTERVENTION

Review student performance on ***Intervention*** Lesson 12.B to see if they have mastered prerequisite skills for this lesson.

### ENGLISH LEARNER

**Review**

Use Lesson 12.4 in ***English Learner Support Guide*** to preview lesson concepts and vocabulary.

### ENRICH

**If . . .** students are proficient in the lesson concepts,

**Then . . .** encourage them to work on chapter projects or ***Enrichment*** Lesson 12.4.

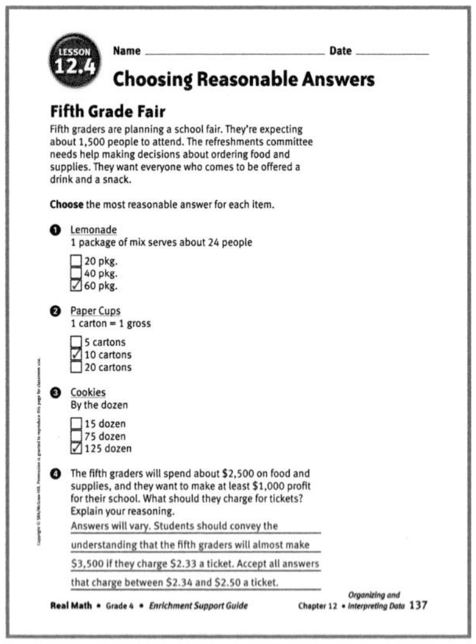
LESSON 12.4 Name ________ Date ________

**Choosing Reasonable Answers**

**Fifth Grade Fair**

Fifth graders are planning a school fair. They're expecting about 1,500 people to attend. The refreshments committee needs help making decisions about ordering food and supplies. They want everyone who comes to be offered a drink and a snack.

**Choose** the most reasonable answer for each item.

1. Lemonade
   1 package of mix serves about 24 people
   ☐ 20 pkg.
   ☐ 40 pkg.
   ☑ 60 pkg.
2. Paper Cups
   1 carton = 1 gross
   ☐ 5 cartons
   ☑ 10 cartons
   ☐ 20 cartons
3. Cookies
   By the dozen
   ☐ 15 dozen
   ☐ 75 dozen
   ☑ 125 dozen
4. The fifth graders will spend about $2,500 on food and supplies, and they want to make at least $1,000 profit for their school. What should they charge for tickets? Explain your reasoning.
   Answers will vary. Students should convey the understanding that the fifth graders will almost make $3,500 if they charge $2.33 a ticket. Accept all answers that charge between $2.34 and $2.50 a ticket.

Real Math • Grade 4 • *Enrichment Support Guide* Chapter 12 • *Organizing and Interpreting Data* 137

Enrichment Lesson 12.4

### PRACTICE

**If . . .** students would benefit from additional practice,

**Then . . .** assign ***Practice*** Lesson 12.4.

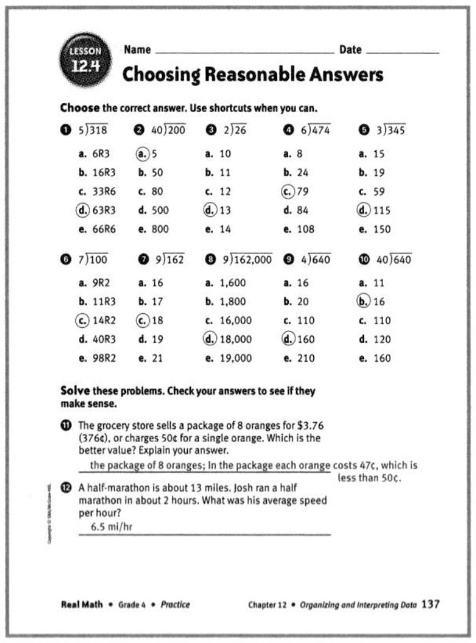
LESSON 12.4 Name ________ Date ________

**Choosing Reasonable Answers**

**Choose** the correct answer. Use shortcuts when you can.

| 1. 5)318 | 2. 40)200 | 3. 2)26 | 4. 6)474 | 5. 3)345 |
|---|---|---|---|---|
| a. 6R3 | (a.) 5 | a. 10 | a. 8 | a. 15 |
| b. 16R3 | b. 50 | b. 11 | b. 24 | b. 19 |
| c. 33R6 | c. 80 | c. 12 | (c.) 79 | c. 59 |
| (d.) 63R3 | d. 500 | (d.) 13 | d. 84 | (d.) 115 |
| e. 66R6 | e. 800 | e. 14 | e. 108 | e. 150 |

| 6. 7)100 | 7. 9)162 | 8. 9)162,000 | 9. 4)640 | 10. 40)640 |
|---|---|---|---|---|
| a. 9R2 | a. 16 | a. 1,600 | a. 16 | a. 11 |
| b. 11R3 | b. 17 | b. 1,800 | b. 20 | (b.) 16 |
| (c.) 14R2 | (c.) 18 | c. 16,000 | c. 110 | c. 110 |
| d. 40R3 | d. 19 | (d.) 18,000 | (d.) 160 | d. 120 |
| e. 98R2 | e. 21 | e. 19,000 | e. 210 | e. 160 |

**Solve** these problems. Check your answers to see if they make sense.

11. The grocery store sells a package of 8 oranges for $3.76 (376¢), or charges 50¢ for a single orange. Which is the better value? Explain your answer.
    the package of 8 oranges; In the package each orange costs 47¢, which is less than 50¢.
12. A half-marathon is about 13 miles. Josh ran a half marathon in about 2 hours. What was his average speed per hour?
    6.5 mi/hr

Real Math • Grade 4 • *Practice* Chapter 12 • *Organizing and Interpreting Data* 137

Practice Lesson 12.4

### RETEACH

**If . . .** students have difficulty with visualizing the word problems,

**Then . . .** have them draw pictures or act out the situations.

# Exploring Problem Solving

**Objectives**
- To formulate a problem by restating a question in mathematical terms
- To compare visual models of mean, median, and mode
- To consider whether the mean, median, or mode best suits a given situation

**Context of the Lesson** In this lesson, students use what they have been learning about mean, median, and mode to solve a nonroutine problem. The problem revisits the California Gold Rush theme that was established in the Chapter Introduction and raised again later in the second Problem Solving in Chapter 12.

## 1 Develop 5

**Tell Students In Today's Lesson They Will**
- pretend they have found gold at several sites.
- look at different ways to decide where to set up a camp for visiting the sites.

## Guided Discussion

Remind students of the activity they did on page 551 in which they compared two gold deposits. As questions such as the following:

- **What did you compare from the two gold mines?** the amount of gold that was retrieved
- **Would you rather own a gold mine that produced about the same amount of gold each day or one that varied from day to day?**

Student Page

### Exploring Problem Solving

Imagine you are a forty-niner who has found deposits of gold at seven different sites along a stream. Your helpers are panning gold at each of the sites. You want to set up a base camp so that you can be nearby in case you are needed. Where should you set up the camp?

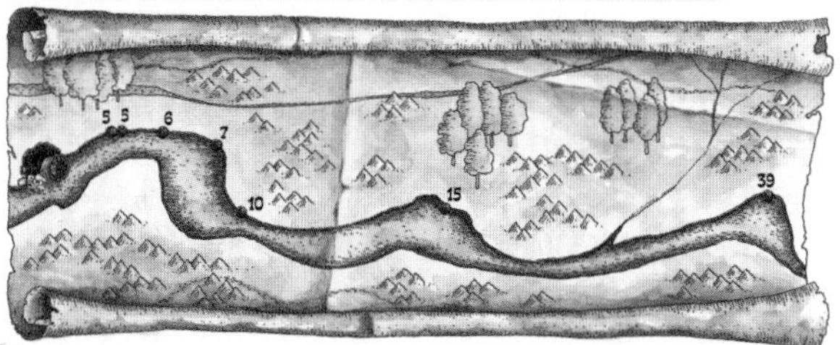


**Yoko solved the problem this way:**

*I decided to first Define the Problem in a mathematical way. I think the camp should be an average distance from all the sites. I am going to find the mean.*

5+5+6+

**Think** about Yoko's strategy. Answer these questions.

1. What sum do you think Yoko will get? Why?
2. What will Yoko do next to find the mean? divide the sum (77) by the number of sites (7)
3. What number will she end up with? 11
4. Where do you think Yoko will say the camp should be? Do you think that is a good idea? Why or why not?

1 77; to find the mean distance from the mill, she will first add the distance of each site from the mill.

11 miles from the mill. Opinions and reasons will vary.



Textbook This lesson is available in the *eTextbook*.

Student Page

**Greg solved the problem this way:**

*I decided to find the mean also. But I think that one of the sites is too far away to visit often.*

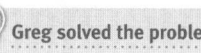

5 + 5 + 6 + 7 + 10 + 15 =

**Jack and Soledad solved the problem in different ways:**

*Jack thought the camp should be at the median distance from the mill.*

*Soledad thought it should be at the mode.*

**Think** about all the different ways to solve the problem. Answer these questions.

5. Where will Greg suggest putting the camp? 6 miles from the mill, or between 6 and 7 miles from the mill
6. Which solution do you prefer, Yoko's or Greg's? Why?
7. Where do you think Jack will suggest putting the camp?
8. Where do you think Soledad will suggest putting the camp? 5 miles from the mill, because that is the mode of all the distances.
9. Whose solution was the easiest to carry out? Soledad's or Jack's; their solutions do not require any calculation.
10. Copy the map and show the four places that you think Yoko, Greg, Jack, and Soledad will recommend. Where do you think the camp should be? Why?

7 10 miles from the mill, because that's the median distance. Some students may say 7 miles from the mill, if Jack decides to exclude the most distant site.

## 2 Exploring Problem Solving 25

### Using Student Pages

Read the problem and information on page 564 with the class. To make sure students understand the problem, ask questions such as the following:

- **Would the site 29 miles from the mill be a good spot for setting up the camp? Why not?** You would be close to one site but very far from all the others. That would make visiting the sites costly and time consuming.
- **What do you think is meant by the word *best* in this problem?** Allow students to offer different definitions.
- **Based on your definition of *best*, how would you find the best place for the camp?** Allow students to offer suggestions, but encourage them to relate their answer to their definitions of *best*.

Discuss Yoko's strategy. Give students time to think about Problems 1–4, then discuss them. Allow students to disagree about whether placing the camp 11 miles from the mill is a good idea. See the discussion points in the Reflect section.

Have students turn to student page 565 and examine the three other methods of solving the problem. Give students time to think about Problems 5–9, then discuss them.

Have students work in pairs on Problem 10. Check to see that students are placing the camp correctly according to the four different solution methods presented. Provide help as needed.

## 3 Reflect 10

**Knowledge Age Skills**

**Effective Communication** Draw the map on the board, and have volunteers mark the four suggested locations based on the four different methods of approaching the problem. Discuss students' opinions about where the camp should be and why. As students use the terms *mean, median, mode,* and *outlier,* refer to the map on the board, which provides a visual model for each of these concepts.

Discuss the following points:

- There is no single correct answer to this problem. Reasonable arguments can be presented for any of the locations, although each location has its advantages and disadvantages.
- The need to formulate or define a problem comes up more frequently in real life than students may realize.
- In this problem, students do not have much information from which to decide what *best* means. They can make assumptions about what kind of traveling they will need to do.
- Some students may say that the average (mean) is the best to use because it feels like it makes the distances as "evened out" as possible.
- Some students may agree with Greg and say that it is just not worth worrying about the site that is so far away. They could visit it once in a while, but they should not sacrifice close supervision of the other sites by taking so much time to travel to this outlying site.
- Some may prefer the median because it is so easy to determine, and the camp would be located at one of the sites. The median also has the advantage of not letting one distant site have too big of an effect on where the camp is placed.
- Some students may defend the mode because then the camp would be located where two of the sites are, and it would also be close to some of the other sites.

## 4 Assess 10

When evaluating student work, focus not only on the correctness of the answer but also on whether students thought rationally about the problem and the various solutions presented. Some questions to consider include the following:

- Did the student understand the problem?
- Did the student show an understanding of mean, median, and mode?
- Did the student explain why he or she preferred using the mean, median, or mode in the given situation?
- Did the student look back to see if the reasoning made sense?

# Cumulative Review

## Assign Pages 566–567

Use this Cumulative Review as a review of concepts and skills that students have previously learned.

Here are different ways you can assign these problems to your students as they work through the chapter:

- For each lesson in the chapter, assign a set of Cumulative Review problems to be completed as practice or for homework.
  - Lesson 12.1—Problems 1–6
  - Lesson 12.2—Problems 7–15
  - Lesson 12.3—Problems 16–19
  - Lesson 12.4—Problems 20–30
- At any point during the chapter, assign part or all of the Cumulative Review problems to be completed as practice or for homework.

### Cumulative Review

**Problems 1–6** review rounding decimals, Lesson 9.5.

**Problems 7–15** review multidigit multiplication and division, Lessons 6.2, 6.5, and 11.1.

**Problems 16–19** review addition and subtraction of fractions, Lesson 8.14.

**Problems 20–30** review geometry, Lessons 10.1–10.10.

### Monitoring Student Progress

**If . . .** students miss more than one problem in a section, **Then . . .** refer to the indicated lesson for remediation suggestions.

Student Page

## Cumulative Review

**Metric Units** Lesson 9.7

**Round** the following problems to the nearest hundredth.

1. 0.2687 0.27
2. 16.9752 16.98
3. 45.002 45.00
4. 699.999 700.00
5. 57.31069 57.31
6. 185.478 185.48

**Multiplying and Dividing** Lessons 6.2, 6.5, and 11.1

**Compute** the following.

7. 45 × 125 = ■ 5,625
8. 635 × 504 = ■ 320,040
9. 340 ÷ 4 = ■ 85
10. 35 × 67 = ■ 2,345
11. 616 ÷ 7 = ■ 88
12. 90 × 52 = ■ 4,680
13. 125 × 450 = ■ 56,250
14. 178 ÷ 2 = ■ 89
15. 19 × 19 = ■ 361

**Adding and Subtracting Fractions** Lesson 8.14

**Add** or subtract.

16. $4\frac{1}{4} + 6\frac{3}{6} =$ ■ $10\frac{3}{4}$
17. $12\frac{7}{8} - 1\frac{2}{9} =$ ■ $11\frac{47}{72}$
18. $4\frac{2}{5} - 3\frac{2}{10} =$ ■ $1\frac{1}{5}$ or $1\frac{2}{10}$
19. $6\frac{3}{9} + 17\frac{12}{15} =$ ■ $24\frac{2}{15}$ or $24\frac{6}{45}$

566 Textbook This lesson is available in the eTextbook.

Student Page

**Geometry** Lessons 10.1–10.10

**Identify** the following polyhedra.

20. 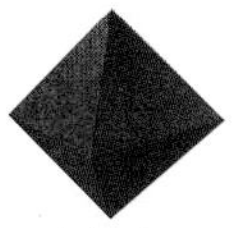
octahedron

21. 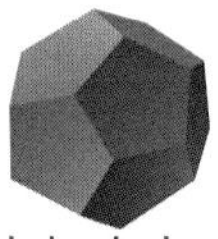
dodecahedron

22. 
cube or hexahedron

**Complete** the following.

23. How many vertices does a rectangular prism have?

8

24. How many vertices does a sphere have?
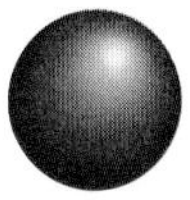
0

25. Trace and reflect the trapezoid.
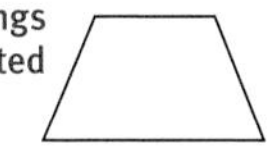
Students' drawings should be reflected horizontally or vertically.

26. Trace and rotate the pentagon.
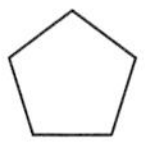
Students' drawings should be rotated.

27. Name a solid object that has two congruent curved bases. cylinder

28. How many lines of symmetry does this equilateral triangle have?

3

29. Which of these triangles are congruent?
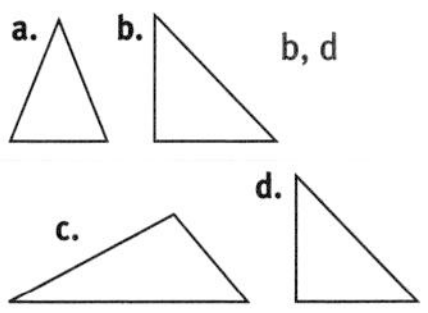

b, d

30. Which of the following shapes is not a polygon?
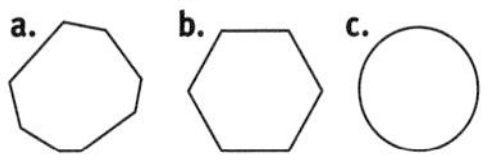

c

Real Math • Chapter 12 567

## Mid-Test

# Individual Oral Assessment

## Purpose of the Test

The Individual Oral Assessment is designed to measure students' growing knowledge of chapter concepts. It is administered to each student individually, and it requires oral responses from each student. The test takes about five minutes to complete.

See **Assessment** for detailed instructions for administering and interpreting the test, and record students' answers on the Student Assessment Recording Sheet.

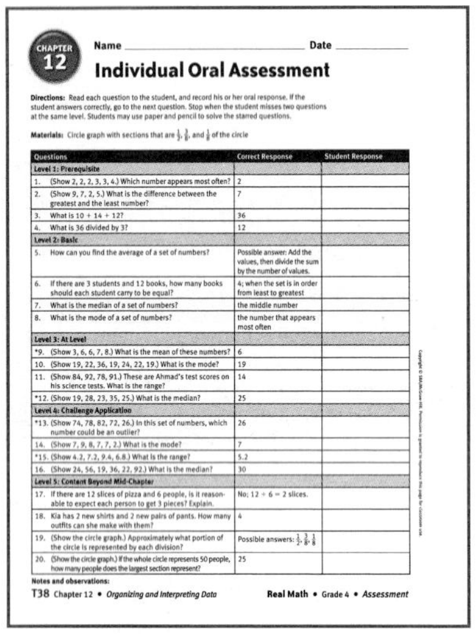

**Assessment Page T38**

## Directions

Read each question to the student, and record his or her oral response. If the student answers correctly, go to the next question. Stop when the student misses two questions at the same level. Students may use paper and pencil to solve the starred questions.

**Materials:** Circle graph with sections that are $\frac{1}{2}$, $\frac{3}{8}$, and $\frac{1}{8}$ of the circle

## Questions

### Level 1: Prerequisite

1. (Show 2, 2, 2, 3, 3, 4.) Which number appears most often? 2
2. (Show 9, 7, 2, 5.) What is the difference between the greatest and the least number? 7
3. What is 10 + 14 + 12? 36
4. What is 36 divided by 3? 12

### Level 2: Basic

5. How can you find the average of a set of numbers? Possible answer: Add the values, then divide the sum by the number of values.
6. If there are 3 students and 12 books, how many books should each student carry to be equal? 4
7. What is the median of a set of numbers? the middle number when the set is in order from least to greatest
8. What is the mode of a set of numbers? the number that appears most often

### Level 3: At Level

*9. (Show 3, 6, 6, 7, 8.) What is the mean of these numbers? 6
10. (Show 19, 22, 36, 19, 24, 22, 19.) What is the mode? 19
11. (Show 84, 92, 78, 91.) These are Ahmad's test scores on his science tests. What is the range? 14
*12. (Show 19, 28, 23, 35, 25.) What is the median? 25

### Level 4: Challenge Application

*13. (Show 74, 78, 82, 72, 26.) In this set of numbers, which number could be an outlier? 26
14. (Show 7, 9, 8, 7, 7, 2.) What is the mode? 7
*15. (Show 4.2, 7.2, 9.4, 6.8.) What is the range? 5.2
16. (Show 24, 56, 19, 36, 22, 92.) What is the median? 30

### Level 5: Content Beyond Mid-Chapter

17. If there are 12 slices of pizza and 6 people, is it reasonable to expect each person to get 3 pieces? Explain. No; 12 ÷ 6 = 2 slices
18. Kia has 2 new shirts and 2 new pairs of pants. How many outfits can she make with them? 4
19. (Show the circle graph.) Approximately what portion of the circle is represented by each division? Possible answers: $\frac{1}{2}$, $\frac{3}{8}$, $\frac{1}{8}$
20. (Show the circle graph.) If the whole circle represents 50 people, how many people does the largest section represent? 25

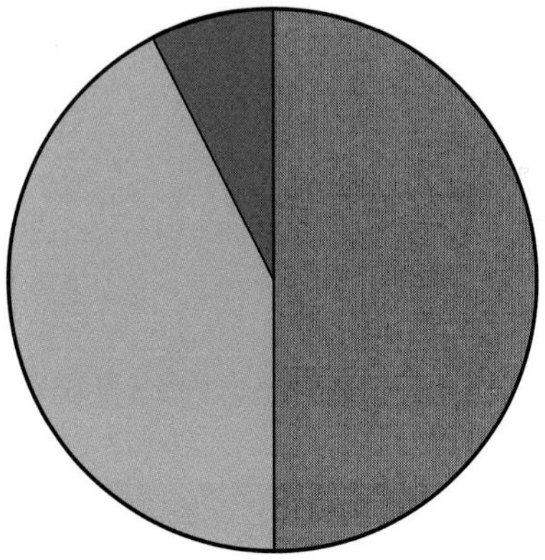

## Lesson Planner

### Objectives
- To provide practice in reading a bar graph and in solving related problems
- To provide practice in dividing with one- and two-digit divisors

### NCTM Standards
**Data Analysis and Probability**
Read bar graphs

**Number and Operations**
Divide to check products

**Problem Solving**
Find solutions to problems

### Materials
- Large sheets of paper, poster board, or transparency pages
- ***Number Cubes** (one 0–5 and one 5–10)

### Technology
**e Presentation** Lesson 12.5
**e MathTools** Graphing Tool

### Test Prep
**Cumulative Review**
Mental Math reviews estimation of answers from different operations (Lessons 2.6 and 3.10).

**Extended Response**
Problem 9

### Looking Ahead
Prepare an overhead projector transparency or a chalkboard drawing of a circle with sectors already drawn to represent the number of students in your class. For example, if there are 20 students in the class, each sector should be 18°; if there are 24 students, each sector should be 15°; for 30 students, each sector should be 12°. If you have an odd number of students, include yourself in the calculation.

*Manipulative Kit Item

# Using a Bar Graph

**Context of the Lesson** This is the first of two lessons on interpreting graphs. This lesson offers an application for division and other operations in solving problems based on data from a bar graph. Graphs were last taught in Lesson 4.15.

See page 550B for Math Background for teachers for this lesson.

## Planning for Learning • DIFFERENTIATE INSTRUCTION

### INTERVENTION
**If . . .** students lack the prerequisite skill of reading graphs,

**Then . . .** teach ***Intervention*** Lesson 12.C.

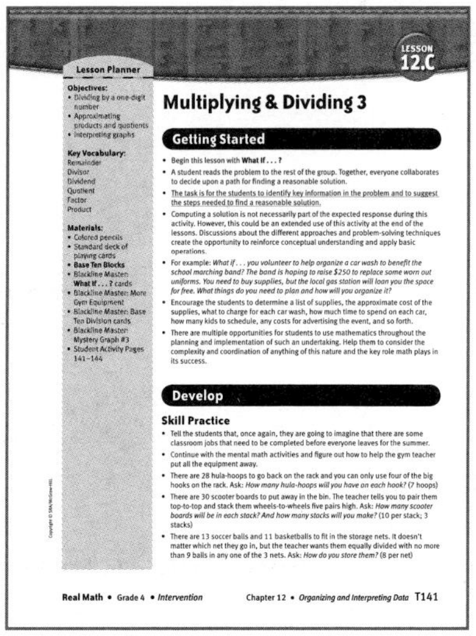
Lesson Planner
LESSON 12.C
Multiplying & Dividing 3
Getting Started
Develop
Skill Practice
Real Math • Grade 4 • Intervention    Chapter 12 • Organizing and Interpreting Data T141

Intervention Lesson 12.C

### ENGLISH LEARNER
Preview

**If . . .** students need language support,

**Then . . .** use Lesson 12.5 in ***English Learner Support Guide*** to preview lesson concepts and vocabulary.

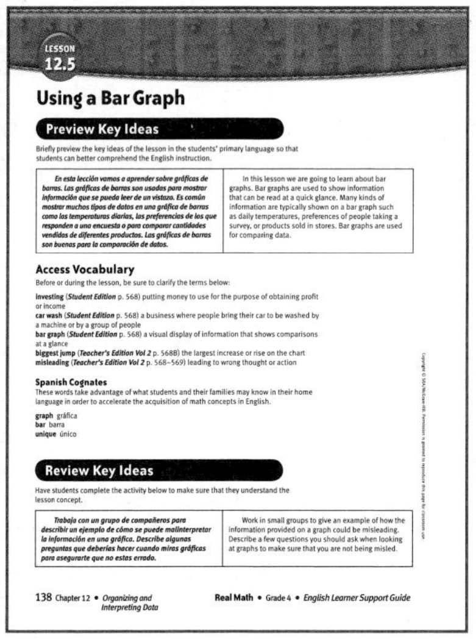
LESSON 12.5
Using a Bar Graph
Preview Key Ideas
Access Vocabulary
Spanish Cognates
Review Key Ideas
138 Chapter 12 • Organizing and Interpreting Data    Real Math • Grade 4 • English Learner Support Guide

English Learner Lesson 12.5

### ENRICH
**If . . .** students are proficient in the lesson concepts,

**Then . . .** encourage them to create new game strategies.

### PRACTICE
**If . . .** students would benefit from additional practice,

**Then . . .** extend Strategy Building before assigning the student pages.

### RETEACH
**If . . .** students have difficulty understanding how to read graphs,

**Then . . .** extend Strategy Building before assigning the student pages.

**Vocabulary**
**graph\graf\ *n.*** a diagram showing the relationship between two or more sets of data.

**Access Vocabulary**
**bar graph** A visual display of information that shows comparisons at a glance.

**Spanish Cognates**
**graph** gráphica
**bar** barra
**scale** escala

## Mental Math

5

Review THUMBS UP

Present exercises, such as the following, to provide practice with all four operations. Have students indicate thumbs-up if the answer falls within the bounds of 2,000 to 3,000 and thumbs-down if it does not.

**a.** 100 × 201 down
**b.** 300 ÷ 3 down
**c.** 2,900 + 50 up
**d.** 1,500 + 600 up
**e.** 40 × 60 up
**f.** 4,300 − 2,100 up

## 1 Develop

30

### Tell Students In Today's Lesson They Will

create and read bar graphs and answer questions related to them.

### Strategy Building

ENGAGING eMathTools Small Group

Students will create survey questions about how to improve the school or on another topic that the teacher feels comfortable with. The questions that students create will need to be in a number format to distinguish the feelings and thoughts of the surveyed population. Allow students to work in small groups to create questions about the specific topic. For example, students may ask: Which of the following best describes your feelings about the school's playground?

1. The equipment is very nice and we are lucky to have it.
2. The equipment is okay, but some should be replaced.
3. The equipment is not very good and most of it needs to be replaced.

Provide students with time to survey other members of the class about their specific issues. Remind students that they may only ask each person once.

Once the students have collected their results, have them select one or two of their questions that provide unique insight into their issue to graph. Students should create a bar graph, keeping in mind the scale and the conclusions that can be drawn from the graph. For this, you may want to provide students with poster board or transparency sheets so the groups can share their results. They may also share their results electronically on the ***eMathTools: Graphing Tool.***

### Using Student Pages

UNDERSTANDING Whole Group

Have students open their books to page 569 to look at the bar graph about official United States flags.

Ask students to answer the following questions. Be sure to demonstrate how to answer each of the questions.

- **How many stars did the first official United States flag have?** 13
- **How could you tell from the graph?** Look up the earliest year on the y-axis or side, follow the bar to the end, then slide your finger down to the x-axis to see how many stars the flag had.
  Demonstrate how to read the bar graph. Then ask questions such as the following:
- **What has been the range of the number of stars on the flag?** 37
- **How can you tell?** Subtract the least amount of stars (13) from the greatest amount (50).
- **How many stars did the United States flag have in 1848?** 30
- **In what year did the flag first have 36 stars?** 1865
- **How can you tell that from looking at the graph?** Find 36 stars on the horizontal or bottom axis and slide your finger straight up to the first bar it touches above that.
- **When did the flag have half the number of stars we have now?** 1836
- **How many stars did the flag have in 1828?** 24
- **When did our flag have exactly 41 stars? Explain why.** Never; it had 38 stars in 1877 and then added 5 more in 1890, yielding a total of 43 stars.
- **Do you know why?** Five new states were added to the union that year.
- **In which year did the biggest jump in the number of stars occur?** There were two jumps of five stars each, in 1818 and in 1890.

## 2 Assign Student Pages

20

### Pages 568–569

APPLYING

Have students complete pages 568–569 independently.

#### Monitoring Student Progress

**If . . .** students have trouble reading a bar graph,

**Then . . .** show them how to move their finger horizontally to the left from the top of the bar or vertically from the end of the bar to the bottom of the page.

### As Students Finish

Game Cubo

eMathTools Have students practice graphing using the ***eMathTools: Graphing Tool.***

Student Page

LESSON 12.5 **Using a Bar Graph**

**Key Ideas**

**Different kinds of graphs are used to show information, such as temperatures in a town or financial information for investing. It is important to read graphs carefully in order to make correct conclusions.**

Bar graphs show information that can be read quickly.

Jacob earns $8 an hour working at the Splish-Splash Car Wash. The bar graph shows the total amount of money he earned each day last week.

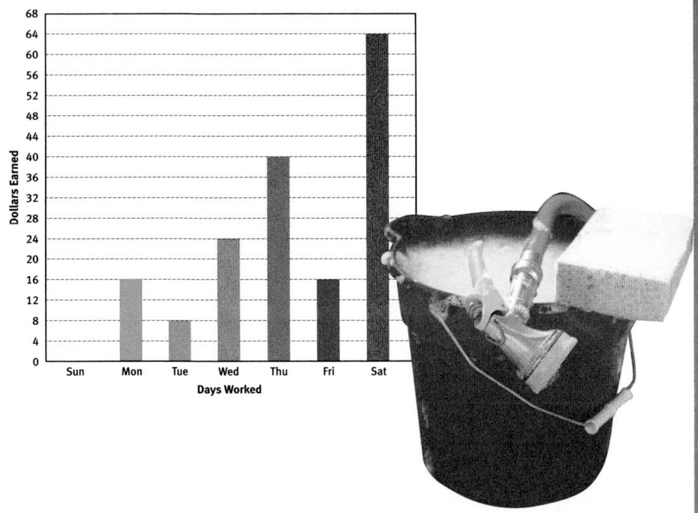


568

Textbook This lesson is available in the *eTextbook*.

Student Page

**Use** the bar graph on page 568 to answer the following questions.

1. How much money did Jacob earn on Monday? $16
2. On which day did he earn the most money? Saturday
3. How much money did Jacob earn during the entire week? $168
4. What was the average amount of money Jacob made per day for the 6 days he worked? $28
5. How many hours would Jacob have to work to make $432 in one week? 54
6. If he had earned $4 an hour, how much would Jacob have earned during the entire week? $84

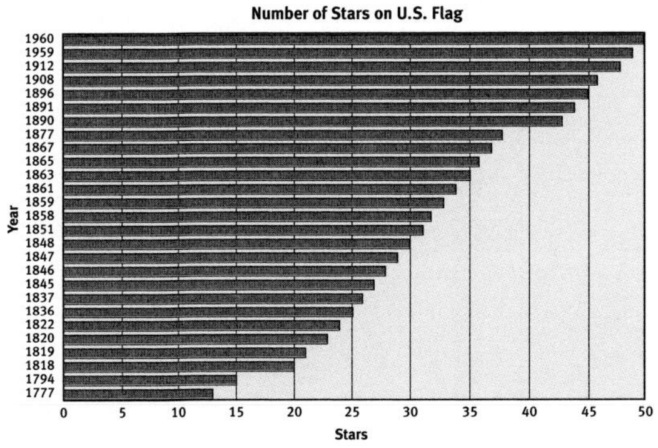


**Use** the graph above to answer these questions.

7. According to this graph, how many different United States flags were there? 27
8. In what year do you think our 21st state joined the union? 1818 or 1819
9. Extended Response Describe two other ways to display the information from this graph. Possible answers: line graph, table

Chapter 12 • Lesson 5 569

## 3 Reflect

5

## Guided Discussion

Whole Group

In reference to the graph on student page 569, ask students questions such as the following:

- **What could be misleading about this graph?** Students may find any number of things misleading about the graph. In particular, you may want to point out that, although at first glance the graph seems to indicate that the number of states was increasing fairly steadily through the years, this is not really the case. For instance, between 1912 and 1959 the number of states in the union remained constant. There was also a 13-year gap between 1877 and 1889, and then a jump of 5 new states in 1890. Other possible answers are that this graph might seem outdated because the latest year listed is 1960, or it may seem as if we gained our independence in 1777 (rather than in 1776), and there were no stars on the flag during the "in-between" years not listed on the graph.

### Extended Response

**Problem 9** Students' other choices are a line graph or a table. In a line graph, students could plot the years on the $x$-axis and the number of stars on the $y$-axis. If each year were graphed, however, this would be quite a large graph, since the range of $x$-values would be from 1777 to the present day. In a table, students could list the years in one column and the number of stars in another. This would certainly take up a lot less space, but the information would be harder to see at a glance. It would be more difficult, for instance, to quickly see if the number of stars was always increasing or if it was staying the same each year.

**Curriculum Connection:** Students may be interested in studying more about the United States flag, such as the meaning of the stripes or the colors.

**Cumulative Review:** For review of multidigit subtraction, assign Problems 1–6 on student page 577.

**Family Involvement:** Assign the ***Practice, Reteach,*** or ***Enrichment*** activities depending on the needs of your students.

Encourage students to play **Cubo** with a friend or relative.

**Concept/Question Board:** Encourage students to continue to post questions, answers, and examples on the Concept/Question Board.

**Math Puzzler:** Larry, Marco, Shari, and Tess were playing a card game. They formed partnerships, and the partners sat opposite each other at a square table. The boys were not partners. People whose names rhymed were not partners. What were the partnerships? Larry and Tess, Shari and Marco

# 4 Assess and Differentiate

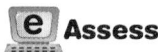

**e Assess** Use ***eAssess*** to record and analyze evidence of student understanding.

## A Gather Evidence

Use the Daily Class Assessment Records in ***Assessment*** or ***eAssess*** to record daily observations.

### Performance Assessment

**Game**

Did the student ENGAGING

- ❑ pay attention to others' contributions?
- ❑ contribute information and ideas?
- ❑ improve on a strategy?
- ❑ reflect on and check the accuracy of his or her work?

### Informal Assessment

**Student Pages**

Did the student UNDERSTANDING

- ❑ make important observations?
- ❑ extend or generalize learning?
- ❑ provide insightful answers?
- ❑ pose insightful questions?

## B Summarize Findings

Analyze and summarize assessment data for each student. Determine which Assessment Follow-Up is appropriate for each student. Use the Student Assessment Record in ***Assessment*** or ***eAssess*** to update assessment records.

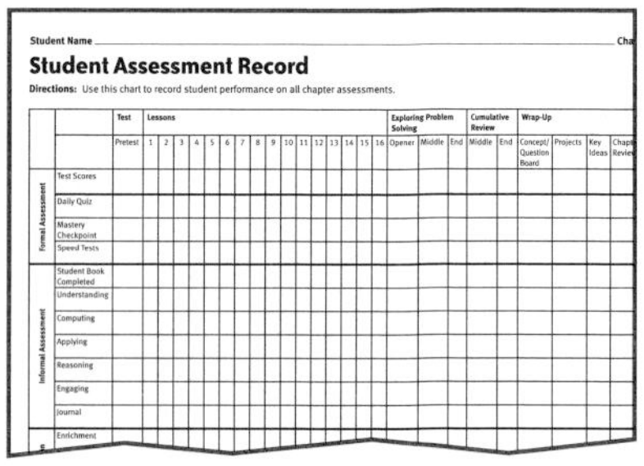


**Assessment Page T41**

## C Assessment Follow-Up • DIFFERENTIATE INSTRUCTION

Based on your observations, use these teaching strategies for assessment follow-up.

### INTERVENTION

Review student performance on ***Intervention*** Lesson 12.C to see if they have mastered prerequisite skills for this lesson.

### ENGLISH LEARNER

**Review**

Use Lesson 12.5 in ***English Learner Support Guide*** to review lesson concepts and vocabulary.

### ENRICH

**If . . .** students are proficient in the lesson concepts,

**Then . . .** encourage them to work on chapter projects or ***Enrichment*** Lesson 12.5.

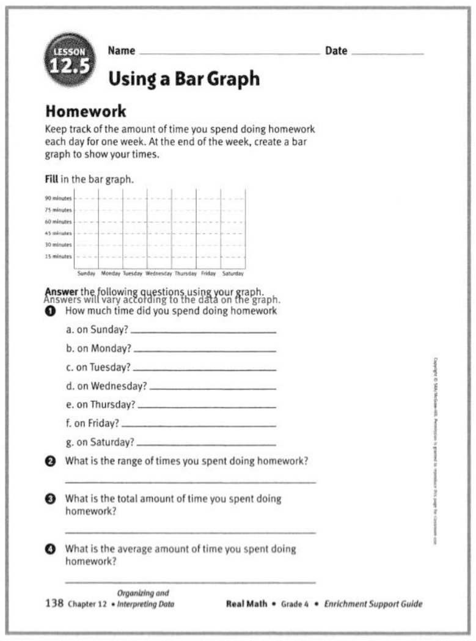
LESSON 12.5 Name ________ Date ________

**Using a Bar Graph**

**Homework**

Keep track of the amount of time you spend doing homework each day for one week. At the end of the week, create a bar graph to show your times.

**Fill** in the bar graph.

**Answer** the following questions using your graph.
Answers will vary according to the data on the graph.

1. How much time did you spend doing homework
   a. on Sunday? ________
   b. on Monday? ________
   c. on Tuesday? ________
   d. on Wednesday? ________
   e. on Thursday? ________
   f. on Friday? ________
   g. on Saturday? ________
2. What is the range of times you spent doing homework?
3. What is the total amount of time you spent doing homework?
4. What is the average amount of time you spent doing homework?

138 Chapter 12 • Organizing and Interpreting Data — Real Math • Grade 4 • Enrichment Support Guide

Enrichment Lesson 12.5

### PRACTICE

**If . . .** students would benefit from additional practice,

**Then . . .** assign ***Practice*** Lesson 12.5.

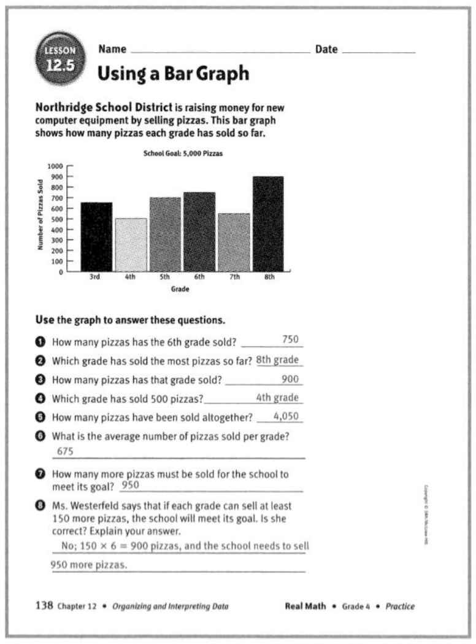
LESSON 12.5 Name ________ Date ________

**Using a Bar Graph**

**Northridge School District** is raising money for new computer equipment by selling pizzas. This bar graph shows how many pizzas each grade has sold so far.

**Use the graph to answer these questions.**

1. How many pizzas has the 6th grade sold? 750
2. Which grade has sold the most pizzas so far? 8th grade
3. How many pizzas has that grade sold? 900
4. Which grade has sold 500 pizzas? 4th grade
5. How many pizzas have been sold altogether? 4,050
6. What is the average number of pizzas sold per grade? 675
7. How many more pizzas must be sold for the school to meet its goal? 950
8. Ms. Westerfeld says that if each grade can sell at least 150 more pizzas, the school will meet its goal. Is she correct? Explain your answer. No; 150 × 6 = 900 pizzas, and the school needs to sell 950 more pizzas.

138 Chapter 12 • Organizing and Interpreting Data — Real Math • Grade 4 • Practice

Practice Lesson 12.5

### RETEACH

**If . . .** students struggle with bar graphs,

**Then . . .** have them review graphs and use some of the tips they have learned in previous chapters.

## Lesson Planner

**OBJECTIVES**
- To help students learn how to read circle graphs
- To have students compare circle graphs with other ways of presenting data

**NCTM STANDARDS**

**Data Analysis and Probability**
Decipher bar and circle graphs from data

**Problem Solving**
Solve problems

**Representation**
Use representations to organize and communicate mathematical ideas

**MATERIALS**
- *Response Wheels
- Colored overhead pens or chalk
- *Copies of the **Fracto 1 Game Mat**
- ***Number Cubes** (one 0–5 and one 5–10)

**TECHNOLOGY**

**Presentation** Lesson 12.6
**Games** Fracto
**MathTools** Graphing Tool

**TEST PREP**

**Cumulative Review**
Mental Math reviews division of greater numbers (Lessons 11.1 and 11.12).

*Manipulative Kit Item

# Interpreting Circle Graphs

**Context of the Lesson** This is the last of two lessons on interpreting graphs. In this lesson the circle graph, which is a new method of organizing and displaying data, is introduced and it is compared to a bar graph. For this lesson you will need an overhead projector transparency or a chalkboard drawing of a circle with sectors already drawn to represent the number of students in your class. For example, if there are 20 students in the class, each sector should be 18°; if there are 24 students, each sector should be 15°; and for 30 students, each sector should measure 12°. If you have an odd number of students, include yourself in the calculation.

See page 550B for Math Background for teachers for this lesson.

## Planning for Learning • DIFFERENTIATE INSTRUCTION

### INTERVENTION

**If . . .** students lack the prerequisite skill of reading graphs,

**Then . . .** teach ***Intervention*** Lesson 12.C.

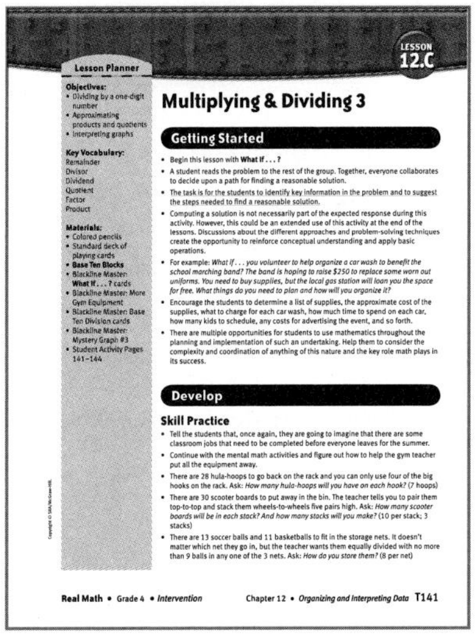
Lesson Planner
Multiplying & Dividing 3
Getting Started
Develop
Skill Practice

Intervention Lesson 12.C

### ENGLISH LEARNER

Preview

**If . . .** students need language support,

**Then . . .** use Lesson 12.6 in ***English Learner Support Guide*** to preview lesson concepts and vocabulary.

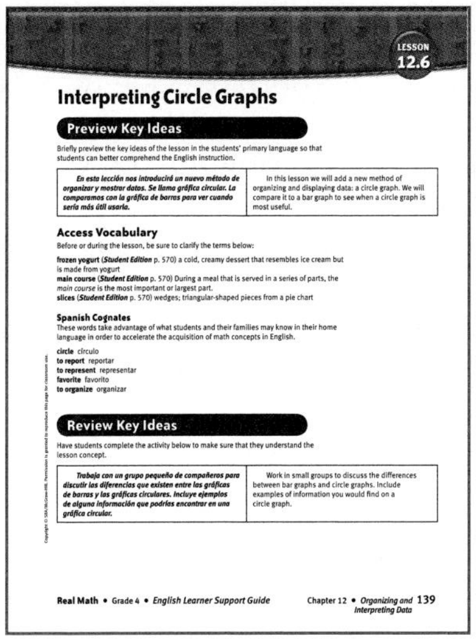
Interpreting Circle Graphs
Preview Key Ideas
Access Vocabulary
Spanish Cognates
Review Key Ideas

English Learner Lesson 12.6

### ENRICH

**If . . .** students are proficient in the lesson concepts,

**Then . . .** encourage them to create new game strategies.

### PRACTICE

**If . . .** students would benefit from additional practice,

**Then . . .** extend Strategy Building before assigning the student pages.

### RETEACH

**If . . .** students have difficulty understanding circle graphs,

**Then . . .** extend the using student pages activity before assigning the student pages.

**Vocabulary**
Review from Lesson 10.2:
**degree**

**Access Vocabulary**
**sports cards** Small collectable cards with photos of professional athletes.

**Spanish Cognates**
**to report** reportar
**a report** un reporte

# Teaching Lesson 12.6

## Mental Math

5

RESPONSE WHEEL Have students find quotients of 360 by dividing by a factor of 360, such as in the following exercises:

| | |
|---|---|
| **a.** 360 ÷ 2 = 180 | **f.** 360 ÷ 3 = 120 |
| **b.** 360 ÷ 4 = 90 | **g.** 360 ÷ 5 = 72 |
| **c.** 360 ÷ 6 = 60 | **h.** 360 ÷ 8 = 45 |
| **d.** 360 ÷ 9 = 40 | **i.** 360 ÷ 10 = 36 |
| **e.** 360 ÷ 12 = 30 | **j.** 360 ÷ 15 = 24 |

## 1 Develop

25

### Tell Students In Today's Lesson You Will

compare and interpret circle graphs and bar graphs.

Whole Group

### Strategy Building UNDERSTANDING eMathTools

Pick a topic with three or four options and ask students' opinions. For example, you might ask them to choose their favorite school subject. Ask students to decide on their favorites and then tell you their answers. Write the answers in order. For example: *mathematics, mathematics, science, mathematics, reading, reading, mathematics, history,* and so on. To save space, you may want to just write the first initial of the subject. Once you have all the answers, have one student make a tally chart of the information while another student reads the letters in order from the beginning.

Prompt students to help you pick an appropriate scale for a bar graph (make sure the biggest bar will fit), and create a bar graph on the board, overhead projector, or on the ***eMath Tools: Graphing Tool***. Then ask questions such as the following:

- **What is the most popular answer? How many students chose that option?**
- **How many squares or units should we use to represent each student if the graph is this size?** Answers will vary depending on the size of the space available.

Explain that you would like to make a circle graph of the data. To do this, you have to decide how many degrees of the circle should represent each answer. Ask questions such as the following:

- **How many degrees are there in a circle?** 360°
- **How do we figure out what part of the circle should represent each answer?** Divide the circle into as many parts as there are students. For example, if there are 24 students, then each answer should be shown with $\frac{1}{24}$ of the circle.

Have students use a calculator to figure out how many degrees represent each student. Ask a question such as the following:

- **If there are ▒ students, how many degrees does each student get?** Answers will vary. Divide 360 by the number of students. For 24 students, that is 15 degrees.

Tell students that you have already divided the circle into segments of that size (sectors). If the circle was made assuming all the students would be present and some were not, make up answers for those students.

Then ask how many of those segments (sectors) you should use to show each answer. Go on to ask questions such as the following:

- **How many sectors should be colored in for mathematics?** Answers will vary. For example, if 9 people liked mathematics best, you would shade 9 segments.
- **How many sectors should be colored in for history?**

### Using Student Pages UNDERSTANDING

Whole Group

Have students open their books to page 570, and ask volunteers to read page 570.

Point out the various ways to graphically display data. Go on to ask questions such as the following:

- **From the tally chart and bar graph, is it easy to tell which flavor was most popular?** yes
- **Is it easier to tell whether any flavor had a majority from the bar graph or the circle graph?** The circle graph should seem easier to most students.
- **Have you seen circle graphs before? Where?** Answers will vary. Possible answers include in newspapers or on television.
- **Why would we want to use a circle graph instead of another graph?** Circle graphs are useful to represent percentage data of a whole, while bar graphs are better to compare more than one piece of information.

## 2 Assign Student Pages

25

### Pages 570–571 APPLYING

Small Group

Have students complete pages 570–571 in small groups.

#### Monitoring Student Progress

| If . . . | Then . . . |
|---|---|
| **If . . .** some groups have a great deal of trouble, | **Then . . .** you may want to discuss the questions with the class as a whole. Bar *E* is about 5.5 times as tall as bar *F*, but, even though the bars in Figure 6 are shorter than the bars in Figure 5, the ratio of *E* to *F* is only about 5 or 6 to 1, whereas the ratio of *K* to *L* is closer to 15 to 1 (14 to 1). |

### As Students Finish

Game **Fracto I Game Mat**

eGames *Fracto*

eMathTools Have students practice graphing using the ***Graphing Tool***.

Student Page

LESSON 12.6 Interpreting Circle Graphs

## Key Ideas

**When we report data, we try to organize it so it can be easily understood. Circle graphs are often a good option to display data in an easily understandable way.**

Suppose we asked the students in Ms. Anelich's class what their favorite frozen yogurt flavors are.

We can make a tally chart of the information (Figure 1) or a bar graph (Figure 2). We can also make a circle graph (Figure 3). Each of these graphs is easier to understand than just listing the flavors in the order they were mentioned. Do you see that all three graphs represent the same data?

| | |
|---|---|
| chocolate | 卌 III |
| banana | III |
| vanilla | 卌 II |
| strawberry | II |

Figure 1

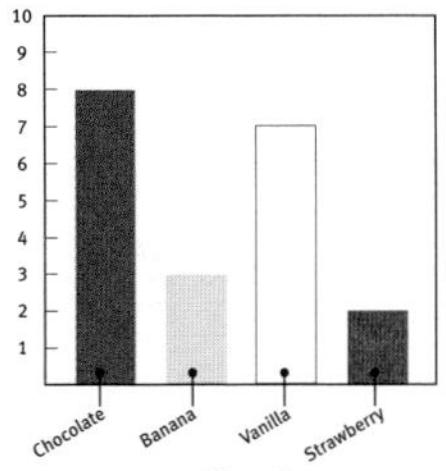

Figure 2

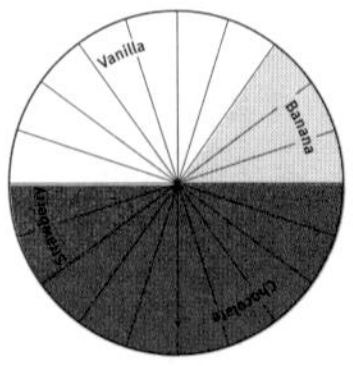

Figure 3

**Match** the data with the graphs on the next page.

Students in a school were asked to choose the main course, drink, and dessert for a party. These are their choices:

| Main Course | Students | Drink | Students | Dessert | Students |
|---|---|---|---|---|---|
| Hamburger | 33 | Milk | 42 | Apple | 15 |
| Hot Dog | 6 | Orange Juice | 3 | Pear | 15 |
| Cheese Sandwich | 12 | Cranberry Juice | 6 | Grapes | 12 |
| Tofu Chili | 9 | Grape Juice | 9 | Watermelon | 18 |



eTextbook This lesson is available in the *eTextbook*.

Student Page

1. Decide which two graphs represent the main course, which two represent the drinks, and which two show dessert choices. Then, write each of the 24 letters followed by the food or drink each represents.
2. How many students responded altogether? 60
3. How many units tall are bars A, E, and K? 18, 33, 42
4. If we broke our circle into 60 equal slices or sectors, what would the measure of each sector be in degrees? Explain how you arrived at this answer. 6°; divide 360° by 60
5. How many degrees are in the angles for R, T, and Z? (Remember, there are 360° in a circle.) 252°; 108°; 198°

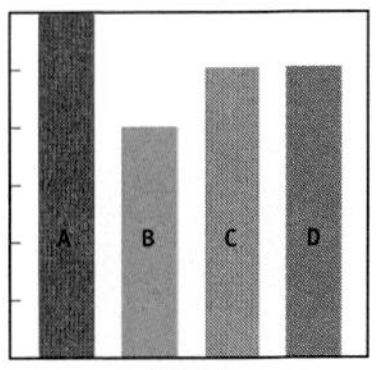

Figure 4

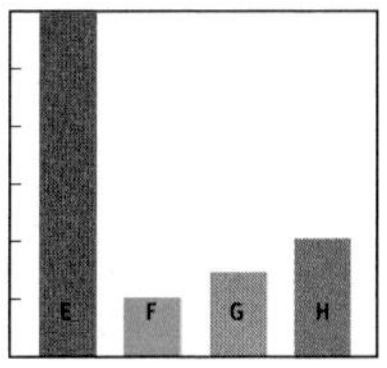

Figure 5

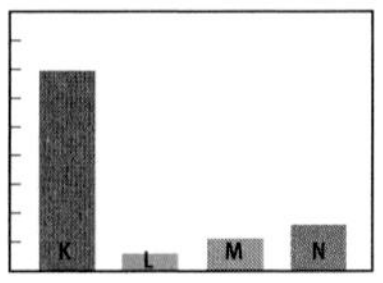

Figure 6

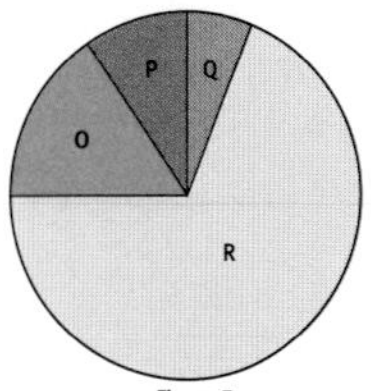

Figure 7

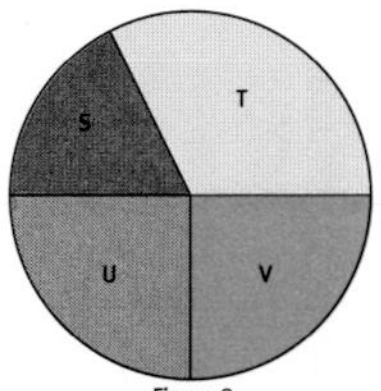

Figure 8

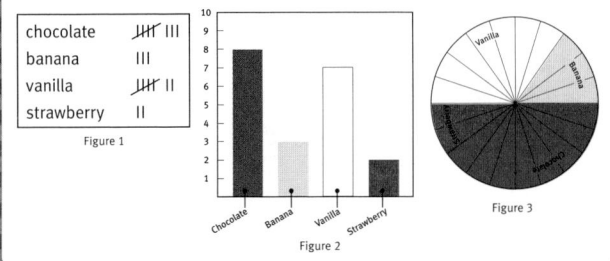

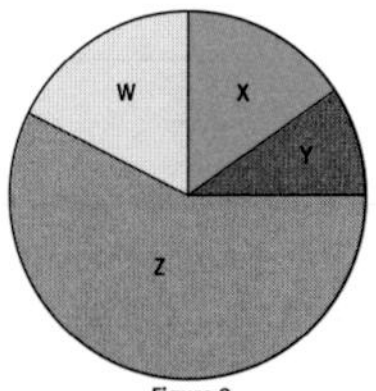

Figure 9

1. A. watermelon; B. grapes; C. apples or pears; D. apples or pears; E. hamburger; F. hot dog; G. tofu chili; H. cheese sandwich; K. milk; L. orange juice; M. cranberry juice; N. grape juice; O. grape juice; P. cranberry juice; Q. orange juice; R. milk; S. grapes; T. watermelon; U. apples or pears; V. apples or pears; W. cheese sandwich; X. tofu chili; Y. hot dog; Z. hamburger



# 3 Reflect

5

## Guided Discussion REASONING

Whole Group

Reintroduce students to the concept of percent in this new context by asking questions such as the following:

- **What does the word *percent* mean?** per 100
- **How many students responded to the questions about the party?** 60
- **If 6 students out of 60 said they wanted hot dogs, how would you figure out what fraction of the total that is?** Divide 6 by 60 and reduce the fraction to $\frac{1}{10}$ (one-tenth).
- **What percentage of the total is that?** 10%
- **How much of the circle will that take up?** one-tenth

Ask similar questions, such as the following, for the other food preferences:

- **How do we know 25% of the students chose pears for dessert?** Possible answer: On the circle graph, pears were $\frac{1}{4}$ of the total (25%) or 15 out of 60 is 25%.
- **If 3 of the 60 students decided to drink water instead of the drinks offered, what percentage of the total would that be?** 5%
- **Since there are 60 students altogether, how many students make 100% of the group?** 60
- **How many students make 50% of the group?** 30
- **How many students make 55% of the group?** 33, which is the number of students that make up 50% plus the number of students that make up 5%.
- **Is it easier to see the section representing 70% than the section representing 55% on the circle graphs?** Yes, since segment R is clearly a greater percentage of its circle than segment Z. On the other hand, it seems much more difficult to see that bar K represents 70% of its population.

## Extended Response REASONING

**Problem 4** Students should notice that when the circle is broken into 60 slices, each slice is 6°. The answer can be found by dividing 360 by 60.

**Cumulative Review:** For review of division, assign Problems 7–14 on student page 578.

**Family Involvement:** Assign the ***Practice, Reteach,*** or ***Enrichment*** activities depending on the needs of your students. Encourage students to play **Fracto** with a friend or relative.

**Concept/Question Board:** Have students attempt to answer any unanswered questions on the Concept/Question Board.

**Math Puzzler:** Barry, Gary, and Larry are brothers. If you add their ages, the sum is 53. What will the sum of their ages be 10 years from now? 83

# 4 Assess and Differentiate

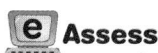

**e Assess** Use ***eAssess*** to record and analyze evidence of student understanding.

## A Gather Evidence

Use the Daily Class Assessment Records in ***Assessment*** or ***eAssess*** to record daily observations.

### Informal Assessment
**✓ Strategy Building**

Did the student UNDERSTANDING
- ❑ make important observations?
- ❑ extend or generalize learning?
- ❑ provide insightful answers?
- ❑ pose insightful questions?

### Informal Assessment
**✓ Mental Math**

Did the student COMPUTING
- ❑ respond accurately?
- ❑ respond quickly?
- ❑ respond with confidence?
- ❑ self-correct?

## B Summarize Findings

Analyze and summarize assessment data for each student. Determine which Assessment Follow-Up is appropriate for each student. Use the Student Assessment Record in ***Assessment*** or ***eAssess*** to update assessment records.

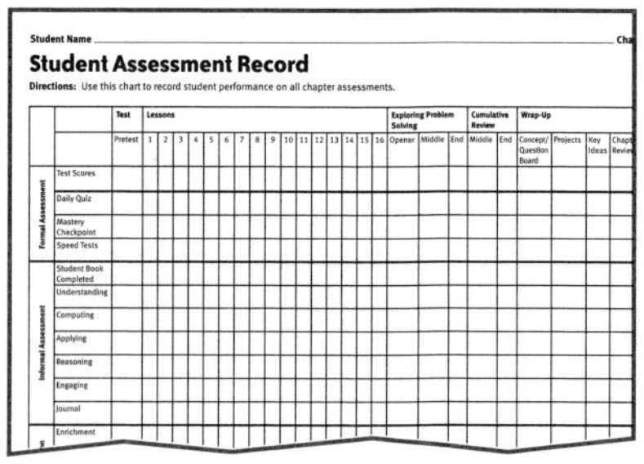
Student Name
Student Assessment Record
Directions: Use this chart to record student performance on all chapter assessments.

**Assessment Page T41**

## C Assessment Follow-Up • DIFFERENTIATE INSTRUCTION

Based on your observations, use these teaching strategies for assessment follow-up.

### INTERVENTION

Review student performance on ***Intervention*** Lesson 12.C to see if they have mastered prerequisite skills for this lesson.

### ENGLISH LEARNER

**Review**

Use Lesson 12.6 in ***English Learner Support Guide*** to review lesson concepts and vocabulary.

### ENRICH

**If . . .** students are proficient in the lesson concepts,

**Then . . .** encourage them to work on chapter projects or ***Enrichment*** Lesson 12.6.

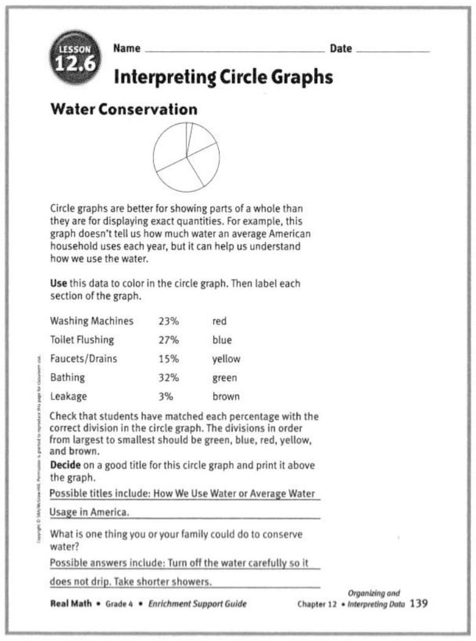
LESSON 12.6 Name ______ Date ______

**Interpreting Circle Graphs**

**Water Conservation**

Circle graphs are better for showing parts of a whole than they are for displaying exact quantities. For example, this graph doesn't tell us how much water an average American household uses each year, but it can help us understand how we use the water.

**Use** this data to color in the circle graph. Then label each section of the graph.

| | | |
|---|---|---|
| Washing Machines | 23% | red |
| Toilet Flushing | 27% | blue |
| Faucets/Drains | 15% | yellow |
| Bathing | 32% | green |
| Leakage | 3% | brown |

Check that students have matched each percentage with the correct division in the circle graph. The divisions in order from largest to smallest should be green, blue, red, yellow, and brown.

**Decide** on a good title for this circle graph and print it above the graph.

Possible titles include: How We Use Water or Average Water Usage in America.

What is one thing you or your family could do to conserve water?

Possible answers include: Turn off the water carefully so it does not drip. Take shorter showers.

Real Math • Grade 4 • *Enrichment Support Guide* Chapter 12 • *Organizing and Interpreting Data* 139

Enrichment Lesson 12.6

### PRACTICE

**If . . .** students would benefit from additional practice,

**Then . . .** assign ***Practice*** Lesson 12.6.

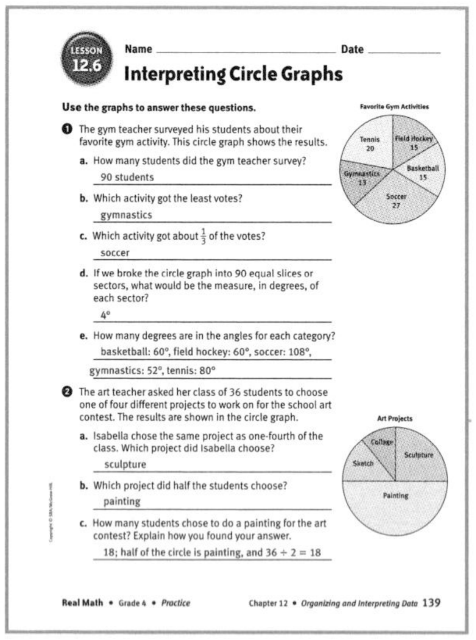
LESSON 12.6 Name ______ Date ______

**Interpreting Circle Graphs**

**Use the graphs to answer these questions.**



1. The gym teacher surveyed his students about their favorite gym activity. This circle graph shows the results.
   a. How many students did the gym teacher survey? 90 students
   b. Which activity got the least votes? gymnastics
   c. Which activity got about $\frac{1}{3}$ of the votes? soccer
   d. If we broke the circle graph into 90 equal slices or sectors, what would be the measure, in degrees, of each sector? 4°
   e. How many degrees are in the angles for each category? basketball: 60°, field hockey: 60°, soccer: 108°, gymnastics: 52°, tennis: 80°
2. The art teacher asked her class of 36 students to choose one of four different projects to work on for the school art contest. The results are shown in the circle graph.
   a. Isabella chose the same project as one-fourth of the class. Which project did Isabella choose? sculpture
   b. Which project did half the students choose? painting
   c. How many students chose to do a painting for the art contest? Explain how you found your answer. 18; half of the circle is painting, and $36 \div 2 = 18$



Real Math • Grade 4 • *Practice* Chapter 12 • *Organizing and Interpreting Data* 139

Practice Lesson 12.6

### RETEACH

**If . . .** students struggle with circle graphs,

**Then . . .** show them that each segment of a circle graph represents a portion of a total, just as a percentage is a part of 100.

**Objectives**
- To introduce tree diagrams
- To provide students with experience in understanding and creating tree diagrams

**NCTM Standards**

**Number and Operations**
Review multidigit multiplication and division

**Data Analysis and Probability**
Display data on a tree diagram

**Representations**
Create representations to organize mathematical ideas

**Materials**
***Number Cubes** (two 0–5)

**Technology**
**Presentation** Lesson 12.7

**Test Prep**

**Cumulative Review**
Mental Math reviews equivalent fractions (Lesson 8.7).
- Problems 1–3 review probability (Lesson 8.4).
- Problems 4–11 review multidigit multiplication (Lessons 5.1, 5.8, and 6.5).
- Problems 12–16 review division by a one-digit divisor (Lesson 11.1).

**Extended Response**
Problem 3

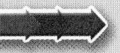

*Manipulative Kit Item

# Tree Diagrams

**Context of the Lesson** This is the final lesson on organizing data. It extends the representation for probability by using tree diagrams to reinforce systematic counting of outcomes. Students will be asked to call upon their knowledge of probability from Chapter 8.

See page 550B for Math Background for teachers for this lesson.

## Planning for Learning • DIFFERENTIATE INSTRUCTION

### INTERVENTION

**If . . .** students lack the prerequisite skill of reading graphs,

**Then . . .** teach ***Intervention*** Lesson 12.C.

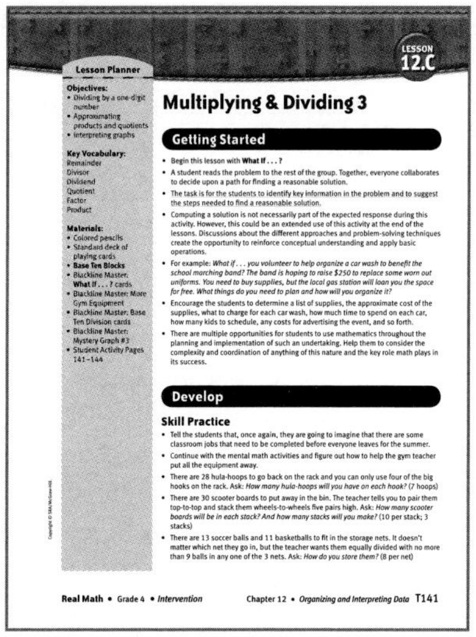
Lesson Planner

LESSON 12.C

Multiplying & Dividing 3

Getting Started

Develop

Skill Practice

Real Math • Grade 4 • Intervention — Chapter 12 • Organizing and Interpreting Data T141

Intervention Lesson 12.C

### ENGLISH LEARNER

Preview

**If . . .** students need language support,

**Then . . .** use Lesson 12.7 in the ***English Learner Support Guide*** to preview lesson concepts and vocabulary.

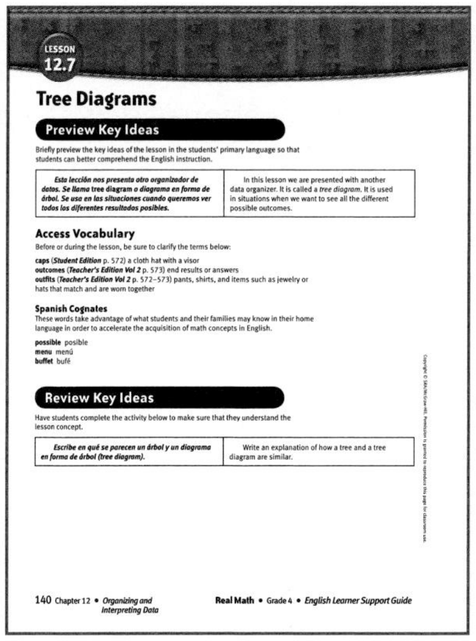
LESSON 12.7

Tree Diagrams

Preview Key Ideas

Access Vocabulary

Spanish Cognates

Review Key Ideas

140 Chapter 12 • Organizing and Interpreting Data — Real Math • Grade 4 • English Learner Support Guide

English Learner Lesson 12.7

### ENRICH

**If . . .** students are proficient in the lesson concepts,

**Then . . .** encourage them to attempt the chapter projects.

### PRACTICE

**If . . .** students would benefit from additional practice,

**Then . . .** extend Skill Practice before assigning the student pages.

### RETEACH

**If . . .** students have difficulty understanding tree diagrams,

**Then . . .** extend Guided Discussion before assigning the student pages.

### Access Vocabulary

**cap** A cloth hat with a visor.
**side dishes** These are foods that are prepared to accompany the main dish, usually meat. Some side dishes include a starch like mashed potatoes or rice, or a cooked vegetable like string beans or corn.

**Spanish Cognates**
**information** información
**menu** menú

# Teaching Lesson 12.7

## Mental Math 5

THUMBS UP Provide practice with equivalent fractions. Place two fractions on the board or say them aloud to the class, using the following as examples. Have students show thumbs-up for equivalent fractions or thumbs-down for fractions that are not equivalent.

**a.** $\frac{1}{2}$ and $\frac{5}{10}$ up
**b.** $\frac{1}{3}$ and $\frac{5}{15}$ up
**c.** $\frac{5}{9}$ and $\frac{10}{20}$ down
**d.** $\frac{4}{9}$ and $\frac{1}{2}$ down
**e.** $\frac{6}{8}$ and $\frac{3}{4}$ up
**f.** $\frac{3}{4}$ and $\frac{8}{16}$ down
**g.** $\frac{12}{15}$ and $\frac{4}{5}$ up
**h.** $\frac{8}{16}$ and $\frac{2}{3}$ down
**i.** $\frac{1}{4}$ and $\frac{4}{16}$ up
**j.** $\frac{3}{5}$ and $\frac{12}{20}$ up

## 1 Develop 25

**Tell Students In Today's Lesson They Will**
create tree diagrams from a set of data.

### Guided Discussion UNDERSTANDING

Whole Group

Students will be creating a tree diagram for all possible sums of two 0–5 ***Number Cubes.*** Start by asking questions such as the following:

- **Using two 0–5 *Number Cubes* and adding the numbers together, what is the least possible sum you could get using the two cubes?** 0
- **What is the greatest possible sum you could get?** 10
- **If these numbers are the greatest and least possible sum, is it possible to make all of the numbers in between (1–9)?** yes

Write the numbers 0–10 on the board. Then ask questions such as the following:

- **What would be a good way to keep track of all the possibilities?** Answers will vary. One possible answer is to record the numbers on paper.

Introduce the tree diagram as a way to display all possible sums. Go on to ask questions such as the following:

- **If you roll the first cube and get 0, how many different numbers could you roll with the second cube?** six—0, 1, 2, 3, 4, 5

Show students how to record the six possible outcomes when the first roll is 0. An example is shown below.

| First cube | Second cube | |
|---|---|---|
| 0 | 0 → | 0 + 0 = 0 |
| | 1 → | 1 + 0 = 1 |
| | 2 → | 2 + 0 = 2 |
| | 3 → | 3 + 0 = 3 |
| | 4 → | 4 + 0 = 4 |
| | 5 → | 5 + 0 = 5 |

Have students work in pairs to complete tree diagrams of all the possible sums for two rolls of the ***Number Cubes.***

### Skill Practice ENGAGING

Small Group

Have students get into small groups to create a tree diagram for information that the teacher deems fit, such as selections from a dinner buffet.

Allow students the opportunity to share their tree diagrams with all possible outcomes to the class.

## 2 Assign Student Pages 25

**Pages 572–573** APPLYING

Have students complete the problems on pages 572–573 individually. The exercises on page 573 are a review of multidigit multiplication and division from Chapters 6 and 11.

**As Students Finish**

Game **Four Cube Division Game**

**RESEARCH IN ACTION**

"Different measures of center appear to be important for different students; all need eventually to understand the different measures and their purposes."

Kilpatrick, J., Swafford, J. and Findell, B. eds. *Adding It Up: Helping Children Learn Mathematics.* Washington, D.C.: National Research Council/National Academy Press, 2001, p. 290.

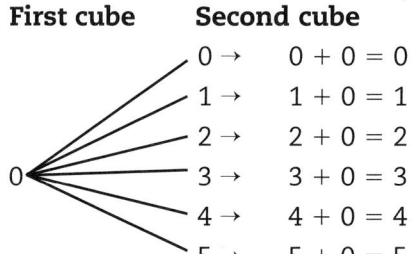

Student Page

LESSON 12.7 Tree Diagrams

## Key Ideas

**A tree diagram (sometimes called a tree chart) is a good way of keeping track of information.**

If you had three shirts and three pairs of shorts, you could make a tree diagram of the number of outfits you had altogether.

Draw a tree diagram for 3 pairs of shorts (brown, yellow, and blue) paired with 3 different shirts (orange, blue, and plaid).

How many outfits are possible with 3 shirts and 3 pairs of shorts?

If you also include 3 caps, how many outfits would you have now?

572 eTextbook This lesson is available in the ***eTextbook.***

Student Page

You and a friend are going to design a deli lunch menu.

Use a 0–5 ***Number Cube*** to roll for the number of types of sandwiches you will have. (If you roll a 1 or a 0, roll again.)

Next, roll to see how many side dishes you will provide. (If you roll a 1 or a 0, roll again.)

By combining one type of sandwich and one side dish, how many different lunches can you make?

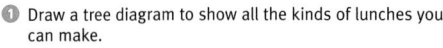

Review
1. Draw a tree diagram to show all the kinds of lunches you can make.
2. If you provided 3 different drinks on your lunch menu, how many different lunches could a customer choose from? Answers will vary depending on the numbers rolled.
3. Extended Response How would adding another option to the lunch menu affect your tree diagram? Create a new chart to see how many outcomes would exist now. Answers will vary depending on the numbers rolled.

Review **Solve** the following.

4. $100 \times 15 = n$ $n = 1{,}500$
5. $5 \times 100 = n$ $n = 500$
6. $5 \times 10{,}000 = n$ $n = 50{,}000$
7. $51 \times 1{,}000 = n$ $n = 51{,}000$
8. $100 \times 969 = n$ $n = 96{,}900$
9. $479 \times 23 = n$ $n = 11{,}017$
10. $648 \times 251 = n$ $n = 162{,}648$
11. $216 \times 415 = n$ $n = 89{,}640$

Review **Fill** in the missing digit.

| 12 | 13 | 14 | 15 | 16 |
|---|---|---|---|---|
| 1☐8 R3 (0) | 62 R3 | 74 R ☐ (7) | 23 R2 | 40 R ☐ (2) |
| 5)543 | 7)437 | 8)599 | 9)209 | 8)322 |
| − 5 | − 42 | − 56 | − 18 | − 32 |
| 43 | 1☐7 | 39 | 29 | 2 |
| − 40 | − 14 | − 32 | − 27 | |
| 3 | 3 | 7 | 2☐ | |

Chapter 12 • Lesson 7 573

# 3 Reflect 5

## Guided Discussion REASONING

Whole Group

Look at the tree diagrams for outfits of shorts, shirts, and caps. Ask questions such as the following:

- **How many different outfits can be made with just 1 shirt and 3 different pairs of shorts?** 3
- **With 3 pairs of shorts and 3 different shirts?** 9
- **With just shorts, shirts, and caps?** 27
- **What do you notice about the total number of outfit combinations that you can make each time you add a different article of clothing? Why?** When you add a new article of clothing, the number of combinations is multiplied by the number of options for the item.

## Extended Response

**Problem 3** A third menu item would allow for more possible outcomes.

**Curriculum Connection:** In this lesson students referred to clothing commonly found in the United States. Students can study the cultural diversity reflected in clothing from other cultures.

**Cumulative Review:** For review of reading a ruler, assign Problems 15–22 on student page 578.

**Family Involvement:** Assign the ***Practice, Reteach,*** or ***Enrichment*** activities depending on the needs of your students.

Encourage students to play the **Four Cube Division Game** with a friend or relative.

**Concept/Question Board:** Have students attempt to answer any unanswered questions on the Concept/Question Board.

**Math Puzzler:** Kristina makes a beaded necklace with this repeating pattern: red bead, green bead, yellow bead, yellow bead, green bead, yellow bead. The finished necklace will have 174 beads. How many of each color will she use? 29 red, 58 green, and 87 yellow beads

# 4 Assess and Differentiate

e Assess Use ***eAssess*** to record and analyze evidence of student understanding.

## A Gather Evidence

Use the Daily Class Assessment Records in ***Assessment*** or ***eAssess*** to record daily observations.

### Informal Assessment

**✓ Guided Discussion**

Did the student REASONING

- ❑ provide a clear explanation?
- ❑ communicate reasons and strategies?
- ❑ choose appropriate strategies?
- ❑ argue logically?

### Informal Assessment

**✓ Mental Math**

Did the student COMPUTING

- ❑ respond accurately?
- ❑ respond quickly?
- ❑ respond with confidence?
- ❑ self-correct?

## B Summarize Findings

Analyze and summarize assessment data for each student. Determine which Assessment Follow-Up is appropriate for each student. Use the Student Assessment Record in ***Assessment*** or ***eAssess*** to update assessment records.

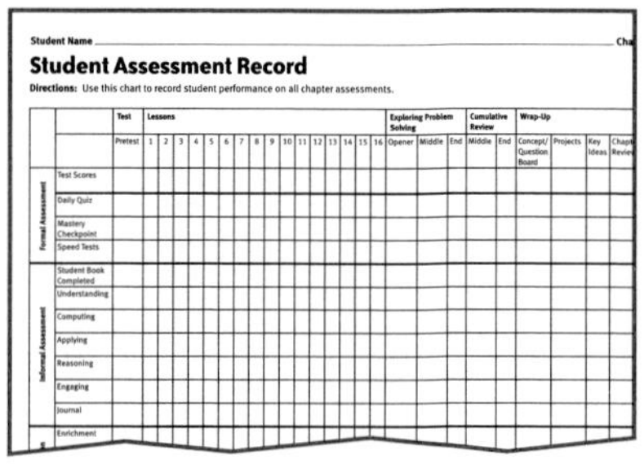
Student Assessment Record

**Assessment Page T41**

## C Assessment Follow-Up • DIFFERENTIATE INSTRUCTION

Based on your observations, use these teaching strategies for assessment follow-up.

### INTERVENTION

Review student performance on ***Intervention*** Lesson 12.C to see if they have mastered prerequisite skills for this lesson.

### ENGLISH LEARNER

**Review**

Use Lesson 12.7 in ***English Learner Support Guide*** to review lesson concepts and vocabulary.

### ENRICH

**If . . .** students are proficient in the lesson concepts,

**Then . . .** encourage them to work on chapter projects or ***Enrichment*** Lesson 12.7.

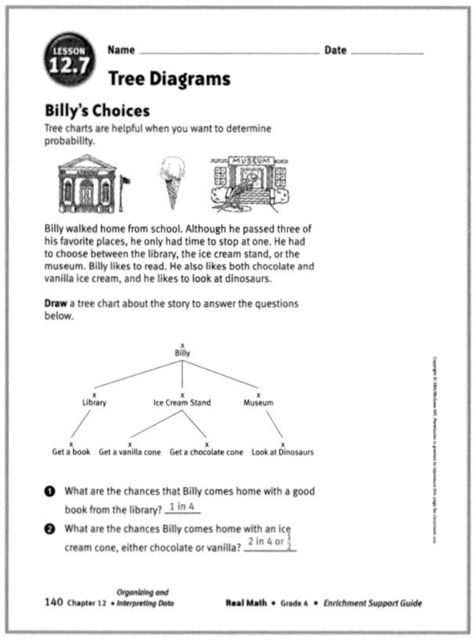
LESSON 12.7 Name Date

Tree Diagrams

Billy's Choices

Tree charts are helpful when you want to determine probability.

Billy walked home from school. Although he passed three of his favorite places, he only had time to stop at one. He had to choose between the library, the ice cream stand, or the museum. Billy likes to read. He also likes both chocolate and vanilla ice cream, and he likes to look at dinosaurs.

**Draw** a tree chart about the story to answer the questions below.



1. What are the chances that Billy comes home with a good book from the library? 1 in 4
2. What are the chances Billy comes home with an ice cream cone, either chocolate or vanilla? 2 in 4 or $\frac{1}{2}$

140 Chapter 12 • *Organizing and Interpreting Data* Real Math • Grade 4 • *Enrichment Support Guide*

Enrichment Lesson 12.7

### PRACTICE

**If . . .** students would benefit from additional practice,

**Then . . .** assign ***Practice*** Lesson 12.7.

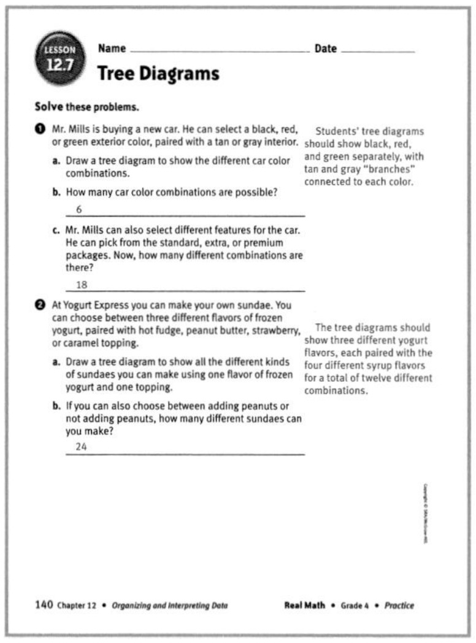
LESSON 12.7 Name Date

Tree Diagrams

**Solve these problems.**

1. Mr. Mills is buying a new car. He can select a black, red, or green exterior color, paired with a tan or gray interior.
   a. Draw a tree diagram to show the different car color combinations. Students' tree diagrams should show black, red, and green separately, with tan and gray "branches" connected to each color.
   b. How many car color combinations are possible? 6
   c. Mr. Mills can also select different features for the car. He can pick from the standard, extra, or premium packages. Now, how many different combinations are there? 18
2. At Yogurt Express you can make your own sundae. You can choose between three different flavors of frozen yogurt, paired with hot fudge, peanut butter, strawberry, or caramel topping.
   a. Draw a tree diagram to show all the different kinds of sundaes you can make using one flavor of frozen yogurt and one topping. The tree diagrams should show three different yogurt flavors, each paired with the four different syrup flavors for a total of twelve different combinations.
   b. If you can also choose between adding peanuts or not adding peanuts, how many different sundaes can you make? 24

140 Chapter 12 • *Organizing and Interpreting Data* Real Math • Grade 4 • *Practice*

Practice Lesson 12.7

### RETEACH

**If . . .** students struggle with multiplication and division problems,

**Then . . .** have them review the various techniques discussed for each of the types of problems.

Student Page

# Exploring Problem Solving

**Objectives**

- To analyze sampling techniques used in modern gold prospecting
- To interpret results of different sampling methods
- To explore solving and presenting solutions to nonroutine problems

**Context of the Lesson** In this lesson, which builds on the work that students have been doing with organizing and interpreting data, students apply computation and geometry to problems about sampling. The theme of the California Gold Rush that was introduced in the Chapter Introduction is continued in this lesson.

## 1 Develop

5

### Tell Students In Today's Lesson They Will

- read about how the search for gold has changed in 150 years.
- solve problems about looking for gold.
- figure out which prize to choose on a television game show.

## Guided Discussion

Have students discuss how advances in technology have changed different jobs. Ask questions such as the following:

- **How has technology helped students and teachers?**
- **What can people do if their job requires them to learn new skills?**
- **Does technology always make a job easier to complete?**

**Exploring Problem Solving**

Times have changed, but the lure of gold has not. You can still prospect for gold on your own, though the chances of finding any are very slim.

WANTED
Senior Geologist
A mining company with extensive mineral holdings has an opening for a Senior Geologist to manage a gold exploration program.
Candidate should have
• an advanced degree in geology or related earth science
• a minimum of 15 years experience, of which at least five years should be as a Project Manager
Salary negotiable.

In the days of the California Gold Rush, miners might have found visible rock that contained $\frac{1}{2}$ ounce or more of gold per ton. But that easy gold has been taken. Nowadays, prospectors are happy to find rock that contains $\frac{1}{10}$ of an ounce of gold per ton, and the rock is likely to be hidden underground. If prospectors find a promising rock formation, then they need machines to help them. The machines dig out and crush millions of tons of rock. They also contain thousands of gallons of liquid chemicals, which remove the microscopic particles of gold.

574 eTextbook This lesson is available in the *eTextbook*.

# 2 Exploring Problem Solving 30

## Using Student Pages

Have students look at the job posting on page 574. Then read the rest of the information on page 574 with the class. Ask questions such as the following:

- **What makes finding gold more complicated today than in the days of the Gold Rush?** Easily visible areas of high gold concentrations have already been mined, leaving deposits that contain gold in less concentrated forms, which is harder to find and more expensive to extract.
- **In the days of the Gold Rush, how much gold might a lucky prospector find in one ton of rock?** half an ounce
- **Nowadays how much gold might a lucky prospector find in one ton of rock?** one-tenth of an ounce
- **How many times more concentrated was a lucky find in the days of the Gold Rush than a promising find today?** five times

Although students already know that the miners of the 1849 California Gold Rush sifted through river gravel to extract gold, they may not know that a law passed in 1866 granted people the right to claim these deposits. As the gold in these gravel deposits was taken, prospectors looked upstream to find the source of the gold, which was often in rock formations. In 1872 another law gave people the right to claim such deposits. The claims could be as large as 1,500 feet by 600 feet.

Review the information on page 575 with the class. This information provides an example of how sampling is actually used in modern prospecting. Then read, discuss, and answer Problems 1–3 with the class.

## Answers to Problems 1–3

### Problem 1

50 samples; with 100 feet between lines, the grid would be $10 \times 5$.

### Problem 2

Answers may range from 2,500 to 3,000. Students might consider a square that is one mile on each side, or about 5,000 feet on each sides. If students make a grid with 100 feet between lines, they would get a $50 \times 50$ grid, which would have about 2,500 intersections, or sampling points.

### Problem 3

Not really. Any reasonable rectangle with an area of one square mile will have have the same number of intersections. If the region is irregularly shaped, it still will have about the same number. Students might see this better by taking a sheet of graph paper and cutting it into irregular pieces then reassembling them into an irregularly shaped region.

Student Page

It usually takes a team of geologists and a lot of money and time to find gold today. If you were leading such a team, you might follow these steps to find gold.

### How to Locate Gold

A. **Select a target area.** Choose an old mine that may have hard-to-get gold that you can recover with modern machines and methods. Or look for volcanic hot springs. The target area you select might be more than 100 square miles.

B. **Take surface samples.** Dig lots of small holes all over the target area. From each hole, take out about a pound of dirt, and send it to a laboratory to find out how much gold it contains.

C. **Stake a claim.** Narrow your search to the most promising areas and get mining rights to them.

D. **Take more surface samples.** On these most promising sections, lay out a grid. Space the grid lines 100 feet apart and take a new sample at every point where two grid lines meet.

E. **Drill for samples.** Decide on the most favorable site and drill to collect underground samples.

F. **Get the gold.** If the results from drilling are good, it's time to start mining the gold you have found.

**Solve** these problems. See *Teacher's Edition.*

1. According to Step D, about how many samples should you take from a rectangular region that is 1,000 feet long and 500 feet wide?
2. According to Step D, about how many samples should you take from a region with an area of one square mile?
3. Does your answer to Problem 1 depend on the shape of the region?

Student Page

# Exploring Problem Solving

GOLD RUSH
MINE 1
MINE 2
MINE 3
Welcome to ***Gold Rush,*** the show where each contestant gets a chance to win a gold mine filled with 500 nuggets.
Each mine is different. Some have a lot of gold. Some have a lot of iron. You get to choose. And before you choose, you can take a sample from each mine.
Whoever chooses the most golden mine gets to take it home. Choose well—a mine is a terrible thing to waste.


Here is what the contestants do.

| Contestant | Sampling Action | Result | Decision |
|---|---|---|---|
| A | Took one nugget from each mine. | Red mine — gold nugget<br>Blue mine — iron nugget<br>Green mine — iron nugget | Chose Red mine |
| B | Grabbed a handful of nuggets from the **front** of each pile. | Red mine — 1 gold, the rest iron<br>Blue mine — 1 iron, the rest gold<br>Green mine — 4 gold, 5 iron | Chose Blue mine |
| C | Grabbed a handful of nuggets from the **back** of each pile. | Red mine — 6 gold, 2 iron<br>Blue mine — all iron<br>Green mine — 4 gold, 4 iron | Chose Red mine |

**Work** in groups to discuss and solve these problems. See the *Teacher's Edition.*

4. If you were Contestant A, would you have wanted to change your decision after seeing Contestant B's results?
5. Why do you think Contestants B and C got such different results?
6. Why do you think Contestant C chose the Red mine?

576 eTextbook This lesson is available in the ***eTextbook.***

With the class, read and discuss the game show described on page 576. You may want to have some volunteers act out the game rules to make sure everyone understands them. Point out that only the contestant or contestants who choose the richest mine get to keep the gold.

After students understand how the game is played, have them work in groups on Problems 4–6.

## Answers to Problems 4–6

### Problem 4

After seeing Contestant B's results, most people would want to change their choice because the new results give much more information.

### Problem 5

Contestants B and C could have gotten different results just by chance. But it is also possible that the mix of nuggets was different at the front and rear of each mine. Since the Blue mine had mostly gold nuggets near the front (as Contestant B found) and none at the rear, it is likely that the host tried to fool the contestants by placing a few gold nuggets near the front of a mine filled with iron.

### Problem 6

Contestant C probably chose the Red mine because it yielded the most gold nuggets.

## 3 Reflect

10

### Knowledge Age Skills

**Effective Communication** Have groups present and explain their answers to selected questions from page 576. Ask questions such as the following:

- **Do you understand the reasoning?**
- **Do you agree with the reasoning? Why or why not?**

## 4 Assess

5

When evaluating student work, focus not only on the correctness of the answer but also on students' thinking and communication. Some questions to consider include the following:

- Did the student understand the purpose of sampling?
- Did the student interpret sampling data in reasonable ways?
- Did the student use data to support a conclusion?

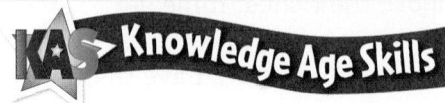

# Cumulative Review

## Assign Pages 577–578

Use this Cumulative Review as a review of concepts and skills that students have previously learned.

Here are different ways you can assign these problems to your students as they work through the chapter:

- For each lesson in the chapter, assign a set of Cumulative Review problems to be completed as practice or for homework.
  - Lesson 12.5—Problems 1–6
  - Lesson 12.6—Problems 7–14
  - Lesson 12.7—Problems 15–22
- At any point during the chapter, assign part or all of the Cumulative Review problems to be completed as practice or for homework.

### Cumulative Review

**Problems 1–6** review multidigit subtraction, Lesson 2.2.

**Problems 7–14** review division, Lessons 11.3–11.4.

**Problems 15–22** review reading a ruler, Lesson 8.12.

#### Monitoring Student Progress

**If . . .** students miss more than one problem in a section, **Then . . .** refer to the indicated lesson for remediation suggestions.

Student Page

## Cumulative Review

Multidigit Subtraction Lesson 2.2

**Solve.**

1. 6001 − 989 = ■ 5,012
2. 652 − 364 = ■ 288
3. 601 − 89 = ■ 512
4. 129 − 28 = ■ 101
5. Jasmine won $3,000 in a school raffle. She gave 10% to charity. Then she bought two outfits for $75 each, a pair of shoes for $60, four DVDs at $12 each, and dinner for her family for $127. How much of her winnings are left? $2,315
6. Cameron is creating a budget so that he will spend his money wisely. He thinks he may have made a mistake with his calculations. Check his work and explain if he is correct or not. Cameron's monthly salary is $1,500.

| Bill | Cost | Amount Left after Bill Is Paid |
|---|---|---|
| Phone | $32 | $1,468 |
| Cable | $36 | $1,432 |
| Electricity/Gas | $89 | $1,343 |
| Car | $317 | $1,034 |
| Groceries | $200 | $834 |
| Entertainment | $160 | $674 |
| Rent | $450 | $224 |

He did make a mistake. When subtracting 317 from 1,343 the answer should be $1,026, not $1,034.



Student Page

## Cumulative Review

Division Lessons 11.3–11.4

**Divide** and check your answers.

7. 363 ÷ 10 = ■ 36 R3; 36 × 10 + 3 = 363
8. 78 ÷ 12 = ■ 6 R6; 6 × 12 + 6 = 78
9. 625 ÷ 8 = ■ 78 R1; 78 × 8 + 1 = 625
10. 906 ÷ 3 = ■ 302; 302 × 3 = 906
11. 165 ÷ 12 = ■ 13 R9; 13 × 12 + 9 = 165
12. 210 ÷ 7 = ■ 30; 30 × 7 = 210
13. 733 ÷ 15 = ■ 48 R13; 48 × 15 + 13 = 733
14. 1,200 ÷ 400 = ■ 3; 400 × 3 = 1,200

Representing Fractions Greater than 1 Lesson 8.11

**Measure** each line segment to the nearest $\frac{1}{2}$ inch.

15. ———— $1\frac{1}{2}$ in.
16. ———— 3 in.
17. ———— $\frac{1}{2}$ in.
18. ———— 2 in.

**Measure** each line to the nearest $\frac{1}{4}$ of an inch.

19. ———— $1\frac{3}{4}$ in.
20. ———— $4\frac{1}{4}$ in.
21. ———— $2\frac{2}{4}$ or $2\frac{1}{2}$ in.
22. ———— $\frac{1}{4}$ in.



eTextbook This lesson is available in the *eTextbook*.

# Wrap-Up

## 1 Discuss

5

### Concept/Question Board

Review the Concept/Question Board with students.

- Discuss students' contributions to the Concept side of the Board.
- Have students repose their questions, and lead a discussion to find satisfactory answers.

## Chapter Projects

Provide an opportunity for students who have worked on one or more of the chapter projects outlined on page 551C to share their work with the class. Allow each student or student group five minutes to present or discuss their projects. For formal assessment, use the rubrics found in ***Across the Curriculum Math Connections;*** the rubric for **Organize Information about the Yukon Gold Rush** is on page 127, and the rubric for **Create a Presentation about the Texas Oil Industry** is on page 131. For informal assessment, use the following rubric and questions.

| | Exceeds Expectations | Meets Expectations | Minimally Meets Expectations |
|---|---|---|---|
| Applies mathematics in real-world situations: | ❑ | ❑ | ❑ |
| Demonstrates strong engagement in the activity: | ❑ | ❑ | ❑ |

### Organize Information about the Yukon Gold Rush

SCIENCE WebQuest

- What category of information about the Yukon Gold Rush did you choose? Why?
- Did you have any problems transforming information from sources into numerical forms?
- How did you organize the information about your category in a database?
- How did you calculate the mean, median, mode, and range of your data?
- Were you able to organize the information for the category you chose in a database?
- If you had to choose another category, which one would you choose? Why?
- What could another person learn from reading your database?

### Create a Presentation about the Texas Oil Industry

ART

- What information did you give about the Texas oil industry? What else could you have included?
- Does your information show the growth of the oil industry in Texas?
- How did you create and place your bar graph into your presentation?
- Did the bar graph help you with your presentation? Why or why not? How else could you have shown the information?

## 2 Assign Student Pages

25

### Key Ideas Review

UNDERSTANDING

Have students complete the Review questions independently or in small groups. Then discuss each question as a class.

#### Possible Answers

**Problem 1** The answer is 89 percent. *Mean* is found by adding all the numbers, and then dividing that sum by the amount of numbers.

**Problem 2** The answer is 14 points. *Range* is the difference between the least and greatest numbers.

**Problem 3** The answer is 89 percent. *Median* is the middle number in a set of data when the numbers are arranged in order from least to greatest.

**Problem 4** Yes; it is 91 percent. *Mode* is the number occurring most often in a set of data.

**Problem 5** Check students' tree diagrams. There are nine different combinations for Gervice to choose from.

**Problem 6** Students should see there are nine selections for Gervice to make.

Student Page

CHAPTER 12

## Key Ideas Review

**In this chapter you recorded and interpreted data.**

You learned to read data on graphs.

You learned the meaning of words such as *mean, median, mode,* and *range.*

**Use Odessa's grades to answer the questions.**

| SUBJECT | GRADE |
|---|---|
| Reading | 85% |
| Spelling | 86% |
| Language Arts | 88% |
| Social Studies | 91% |
| English | 92% |
| Handwriting | 98% |
| Science | 84% |
| Math | 91% |

1. What is Odessa's mean percent for all the subjects above? 89%
2. What is the range of data displayed on the report card? 14 points
3. What is the median percent from Odessa's report card? 89%
4. Does this report card have a mode? If so, what is it? yes, 91%

**Solve.**

5. Gervice has enough money for a pizza with one topping. Below is a list of toppings he likes and the type of crust he likes. Create a tree diagram to show all the possible types of pizzas he can have.

| Toppings | Crusts |
|---|---|
| pepperoni | thin |
| green peppers | traditional |
| sausage | deep dish |

6. How many options are there? 9

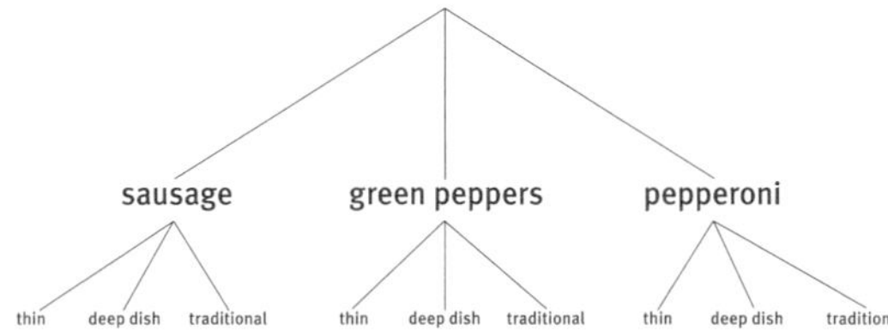


579

CHAPTER 12

# Review

## Chapter Review

Use this Chapter 12 Review as a preliminary chapter test to identify areas in which each student is having difficulty or in which the class may need help. If students do well on the Chapter 12 Review, you may wish to skip directly to the next chapter. If not, you may want to spend time helping students overcome their individual difficulties before they take the Chapter Test.

Each set of problems reviews concepts from one or more lessons in the chapter. Students can refer to a specific lesson for additional instruction if they need help. You can also use this information to assign additional practice based on the previous lesson concepts.

Have students complete pages 580–581 on their own. For review purposes, you may want to do some of the word problems on page 581 as a class.

### Monitoring Student Progress

**Problems 1–4 Lessons 12.1–12.2**

**If . . .** students miss more than one of these problems,

**Then . . .** assess students' understanding of the definitions of the key terms. Students may need daily exposure to these terms and their definitions. Try posting the words and their definitions in the classroom. Students may also benefit from opportunities to practice using these terms and their functions in real-life problems.

**Problems 5–7 Lesson 12.4**

**If . . .** students miss more than one of these reasonable answer problems,

**Then . . .** assess to determine whether students understand how to check a division problem. Use manipulatives, such as play money or base-ten blocks, to reteach the concept or provide extra practice.

**Problems 8–11 Lesson 12.5**

**If . . .** students miss more than one of these problems involving reading a bar graph,

**Then . . .** provide multiple opportunities to read, decipher, and answer questions based on a variety of bar graphs.

**Problems 12–13 Lesson 12.6**

**If . . .** students have difficulty answering questions based on the circle graph,

**Then . . .** provide multiple opportunities to read and answer questions based on a variety of circle graphs.

# CHAPTER 12 Chapter Review

Lessons 12.1 and 12.2 **Review** the table to see what Samantha spent on her cell phone the past few months.

| Month | Money spent on cell phone |
|---|---|
| June | $44 |
| July | $87 |
| August | $53 |
| September | $48 |
| October | $44 |

1. What is the average amount Samantha spent on her cell phone? $55.20 each month
2. What is the median amount Samantha spent on her cell phone? $48
3. What is the mode of the amount Samantha spent on her cell phone? $44
4. Are there any outliers in this set of data? If so, what are they and by how much do they affect the overall mean?

4. Yes, the $87 spent in July. Without this month the average drops $9.95.

Lesson 12.4 **Select** a reasonable answer.

5. 180 ÷ 6 = ▢
   a. 3 c. 33
   (b.) 30 d. 300
6. 562 ÷ 8 = ▢
   (a.) 70 R 2 c. 7 R 20
   b. 7 R 2 d. 70 R 8

7. A 12-pack of soda costs $3.50. One can of soda costs 75¢. Which option is less expensive for 12 cans? the 12-pack

**Use** the bar graph below to answer Problems 8–11.

Amount of Meat and Beans *Left Over* at the End of Two Weeks (lbs.)

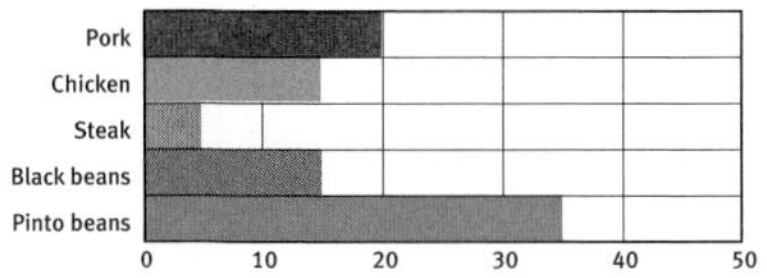


A burrito restaurant buys supplies every 2 weeks. The graph shows what was left over from the last two weeks. Customers select a type of meat and a type of bean for each burrito.






Lesson 12.5

**Answer** these questions using the bar graph on page 580.

8. What meat and bean combination do customers like the most? steak with black beans
9. Which combination of meat and beans are people least likely to order? pork with pinto beans
10. How many pounds of meat did the restaurant use over this 2-week span? 110 pounds
11. If a $\frac{1}{2}$ pound of meat is placed on every burrito, about how many burritos were made over the span of these two weeks? 200 burritos

Lesson 12.6

**Use** the circle graph to answer the following questions.

These numbers represent number of hours that Milton spent doing the following activities on a specific day.

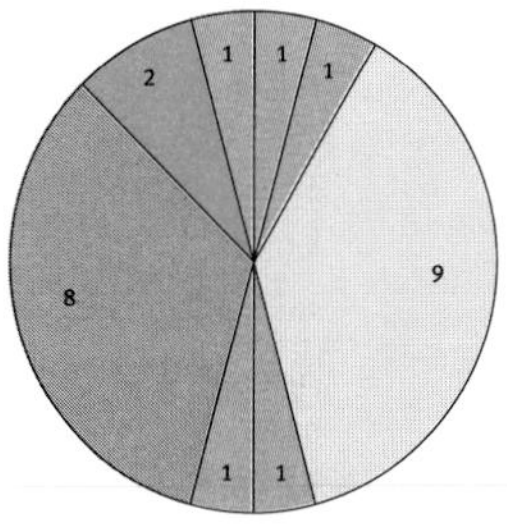


| Activity | Hours Spent |
|---|---|
| Sleeping | 9 |
| School | 8 |
| Watching T.V. | 2 |
| Piano Lesson | 1 |
| Eating Dinner | 1 |
| Doing Homework | 1 |
| Reading | 1 |
| Doing Chores | 1 |

12. If the circle was divided into 24 pieces, what would each piece measure in degrees? 15°
13. What combination of events would equal 180° on the circle graph? Possible answer: sleeping, reading, chores, and dinner

# CHAPTER 12 Assessment

## 3 Chapter Tests

40

## Practice Test

### Student Pages 582–585

- The Chapter 12 Practice Test on ***Student Edition*** pages 582–585 provides an opportunity to formally evaluate students' proficiency with concepts developed in this chapter.
- The content is similar to the Chapter 12 Review in standardized format.

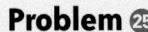

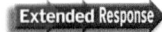

**Problem 25** Extended Response

Students can solve Problem 25 by carefully interpreting the data in the two charts shown. Students will need to compare the data in the tally chart with the data displayed in each graph. Once students have identified the chart that accurately displays the data, they can use it to analyze the data and answer the questions that follow.

Student Page

CHAPTER 12 **Practice Test**

**Use** the bar graph to answer the following questions.

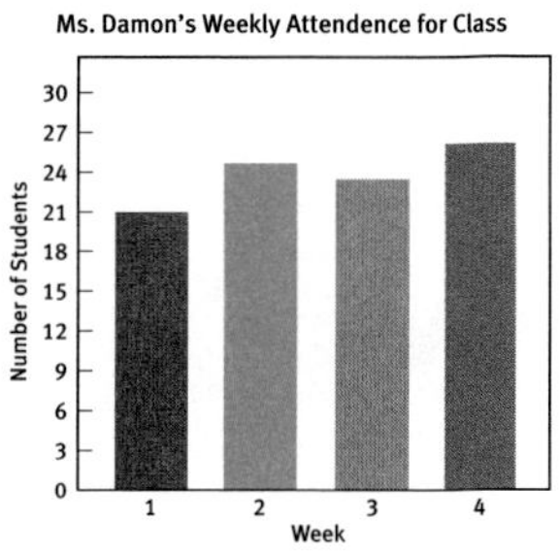


1. How many students were in class during Week 2? 25
2. What was the greatest number of students in class in any week? 26
3. In which week did the most students attend class? Week 4
4. In which week did the fewest students attend class? Week 1
5. What was the difference between the highest attendance week and the lowest attendance week? 5
6. Kevin is going to a baseball game with his dad. Kevin wants to show support for his team. He has 4 team hats and 5 team shirts. He can wear any hat with any shirt. How many different shirt and hat combinations can Kevin wear? 20
7. Make a tree diagram to show all the different shirt and hat combinations Kevin can wear.



eTextbook This lesson is available in the *eTextbook.*

Student Page

**Select** the correct answer.

8. Find the average, or mean, of these numbers.
   5, 7, 12, 4
   Ⓐ 6 ● 7
   Ⓒ 8 Ⓓ 10
9. Find the median of these numbers.
   12, 14, 15, 18, 22, 23, 25, 25
   Ⓐ 18 ● 20
   Ⓒ 22 Ⓓ 24
10. Find the mode of this set of numbers.
    14, 24, 38, 42, 24, 28
    ● 24 Ⓑ 28
    Ⓒ 32 Ⓓ 40
11. Find the range of this set of numbers.
    5, 7, 9, 10, 7, 17, 23
    Ⓐ 5 Ⓑ 12
    ● 18 Ⓓ 20

**Solve.**

12. $4\overline{)84}$
    Ⓐ 20 Ⓑ 23
    ● 21 Ⓓ 45

**Use** the following information for questions 13 through 15.

Kelly wants to know how well she is doing in reading class. Here are her grades for the term.

88, 92, 79, 88, 83

13. Based on her test scores, what is her current average in math?
    Ⓐ 84 ● 86
    Ⓒ 87 Ⓓ 88
14. What is the mode of her test scores?
    Ⓐ 79 Ⓑ 83
    ● 88 Ⓓ 92
15. What is the median of her test scores?
    Ⓐ 92 ● 88
    Ⓒ 83 Ⓓ 79
16. What is the range of her test scores?
    Ⓐ 12 ● 13
    Ⓒ 15 Ⓓ 20

Student Page

# CHAPTER 12 Practice Test

17. Which decimal number does the arrow point to on the number line?

Ⓐ 0.55 Ⓑ 0.6
● 0.65 Ⓓ 0.8

18. What is 10% of 80?
Ⓐ 2 Ⓑ 4
Ⓒ 6 ● 8

19. What is $6\frac{1}{4}$% of 80?
Ⓐ 25 Ⓑ 20
Ⓒ 10 ● 5

20. Which decimal number is equal to the fraction $\frac{1}{4}$?
● 0.25 Ⓑ 0.3
Ⓒ 0.5 Ⓓ 0.55

21. Rewrite $\frac{15}{2}$ as a mixed number.
Ⓐ $8\frac{1}{3}$ Ⓑ $7\frac{2}{3}$
● $7\frac{1}{2}$ Ⓓ $6\frac{1}{3}$

22. $\frac{15}{100} = ?$
Ⓐ 1.5 Ⓑ 1.05
● 0.15 Ⓓ 0.015

23. How many faces does this pyramid have?

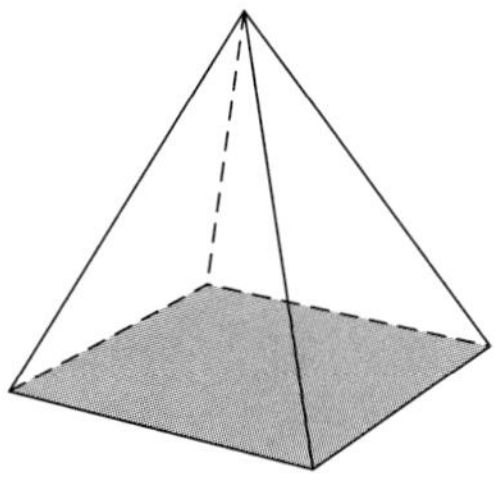

Ⓐ 4 ● 5
Ⓒ 6 Ⓓ 7

24. Which shows all of the factors of 16?
Ⓐ 1, 2, 5
Ⓑ 1, 4
Ⓒ 1, 2, 8, 10
● 1, 2, 4, 8, 16



eTextbook This lesson is available in the *eTextbook*.

Student Page

Extended Response **Answer** the following questions.

25. Dana surveyed some students in her school about their favorite fruit. First she made a tally chart of the results.

Next, she graphed her results. She made a bar graph and a circle graph.

Favorite Fruit

| | |
|---|---|
| Apples | 卌 III 卌 |
| Bananas | 卌 卌 |
| Peaches | 卌 III |
| Strawberries | 卌 卌 III 卌 |
| Watermelon | 卌 卌 卌 I |

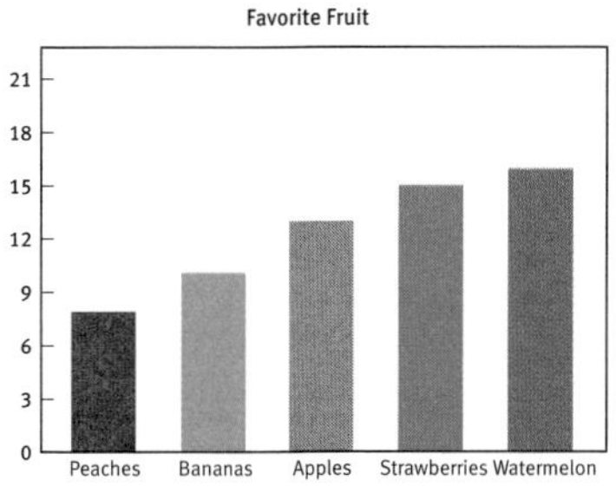


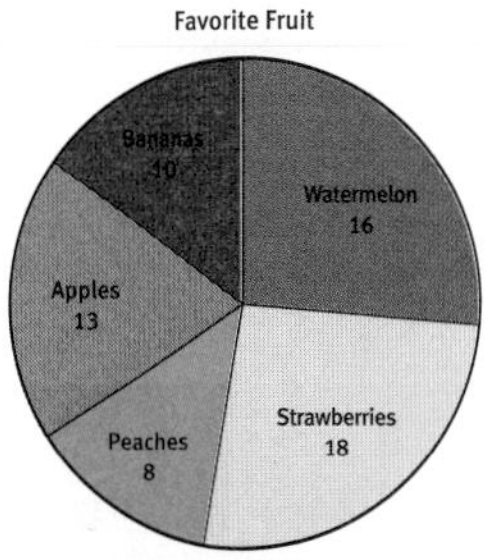


After Dana made the graphs, she realized she had used the wrong data to make one of them.

a. Which graph matches the data in the tally chart? How do you know?

b. How many students did Dana survey in all? 65

c. What fraction of the students chose apples as their favorite fruit? $\frac{1}{5}$

d. Which fruit or fruits were less popular than bananas?

a. The circle graph matches the data. Possible answer: Strawberries should be the tallest bar in the graph.

d. Peaches. The bar for peaches is shorter than the bar for bananas.



# Chapter Test COMPUTING

- For further evaluation instead of or in addition to this test, you may wish to have students take the Chapter 12 Test provided in ***Assessment***.

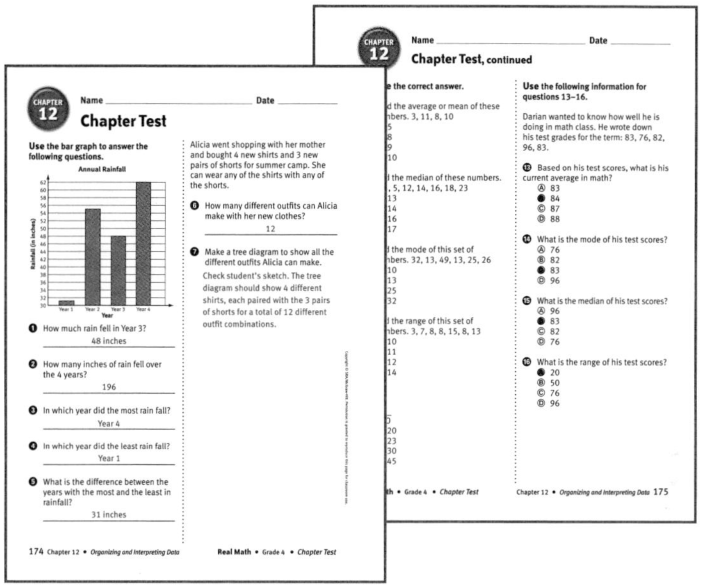

Assessment, pages 174–175

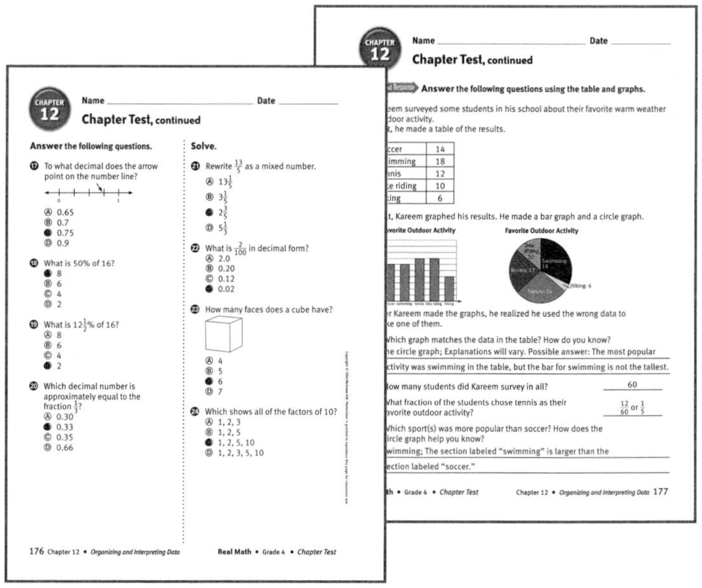

Assessment, pages 176–177

# CHAPTER 12 Assessment

## 4 Assess and Differentiate

e Assess Use ***eAssess*** to record and analyze evidence of student understanding.

### A Gather Evidence

Use the Daily Class Assessment Records in ***Assessment*** or ***eAssess*** to record Informal and Formal Assessments.

**Informal Assessment**

**Key Ideas Review** UNDERSTANDING

Did the student
- ❑ answer questions?
- ❑ pose new questions?
- ❑ extend the discussion?
- ❑ provide insight?

**Informal Assessment**

**Project** APPLYING

Did the student
- ❑ meet the project objectives?
- ❑ communicate clearly?
- ❑ complete the project accurately?
- ❑ connect mathematics to real-world situations?

**Formal Assessment**

**Chapter Test** COMPUTING

Score the test, and record the results.

### B Summarize Findings

Analyze and summarize assessment data for each student. Determine which Chapter Follow-Up is appropriate for each student. Use the Student Assessment Record in ***Assessment*** or ***eAssess*** to update assessment records.

### C Chapter Follow-Up • DIFFERENTIATE INSTRUCTION

Based on your observations, use these teaching strategies for chapter follow-up.

| ENRICH | PRACTICE | RETEACH | INTERVENTION |
|---|---|---|---|
| **If . . .** students demonstrate **secure understanding** of chapter concepts, **Then . . .** encourage them to explore math and play math games until the start of the next level of math. | **If . . .** students exhibit **competent understanding** of chapter concepts, **Then . . .** encourage them to practice math and play math games to prepare for the next level of math. | **If . . .** students demonstrate **emerging understanding** of chapter concepts, **Then . . .** encourage them to play math games and use and practice math before they begin the next level of math. Suggest that these students study and review math to be ready for the next level. | **If . . .** students demonstrate **minimal understanding** of chapter concepts, **Then . . .** encourage them to use and practice math until they start the next level of math. Advise taking a mental math class to be ready for the next level of math. |

CHAPTER 12

# Teacher Reflection

## Lesson Study

Reflect on each of the lessons you taught in this chapter. Rate each one on the following scale, then consider ways to maintain or improve positive teaching experiences in the future.

| Lessons | Very Effective | Effective | Less Effective | What Worked | Ways to Improve |
|---|---|---|---|---|---|
| 12.1 Finding Averages | | | | | |
| 12.2 Mean, Median, Mode, and Range | | | | | |
| 12.3 Using Mathematics | | | | | |
| 12.4 Choosing Reasonable Answers | | | | | |
| 12.5 Using a Bar Graph | | | | | |
| 12.6 Interpreting Circle Graphs | | | | | |
| 12.7 Tree Diagrams | | | | | |

# SRA Real Math

## Student Handbook









## Handwriting Models

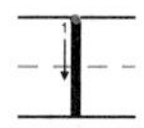

Starting point, straight down

Starting point, around right, slanting left and straight across right

Starting point, around right, in at the middle, around right

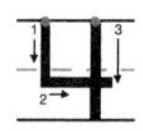

Starting point, straight down, straight across right. Starting point, straight down, crossing line

Straight down, curve around right and up. Starting point, straight across right

Starting point, slanting left, around the bottom curving up around left and into the curve

Starting point, straight across right, slanting down left

Starting point, curving left, curving down and around right, slanting up right to starting point

Starting point, curving around left all the way, straight down

Starting point, straight down. Starting point, curving left all the way around to starting point





## Problem-Solving Tips

**If you need help solving a math problem, try this:**

- Write the problem in your own words.
- Write what you are trying to find out.
- List the information you already know.
- List the information you need to find out.
- Discuss the problem with other people.
- Write possible ways you can find out what you need to know.
- Have you solved problems like this before? If so, how did you do it?
- Try to solve the problem.

**After you think you have solved the problem, ask yourself:**

- Does the answer make sense?
- Is there more than one answer?
- Is there a different way to solve the problem?
- Would a different way have been easier or better for some reason?
- What have you learned that will help you solve other problems?





## Number Line

**Number lines show numbers in order.**

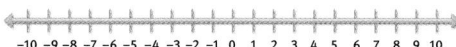

**You can use a number line to**

- count on.
- count back.
- skip count by 2s or 3s or any number.
- add.
- subtract.

## Number Names

| | | | | |
|---|---|---|---|---|
| 0 | Zero | | | |
| 1 | One | | 1st | First |
| 2 | Two | | 2nd | Second |
| 3 | Three | | 3rd | Third |
| 4 | Four | | 4th | Fourth |
| 5 | Five | | 5th | Fifth |
| 6 | Six | | 6th | Sixth |
| 7 | Seven | | 7th | Seventh |
| 8 | Eight | | 8th | Eighth |
| 9 | Nine | | 9th | Ninth |
| 10 | Ten | | 10th | Tenth |
| 11 | Eleven | Ten and one | 11th | Eleventh |
| 12 | Twelve | Ten and two | 12th | Twelfth |
| 13 | Thirteen | Ten and three | 13th | Thirteenth |
| 14 | Fourteen | Ten and four | 14th | Fourteenth |

| | | | | |
|---|---|---|---|---|
| 15 | Fifteen | Ten and five | 15th | Fifteenth |
| 16 | Sixteen | Ten and six | 16th | Sixteenth |
| 17 | Seventeen | Ten and seven | 17th | Seventeenth |
| 18 | Eighteen | Ten and eight | 18th | Eighteenth |
| 19 | Nineteen | Ten and nine | 19th | Nineteenth |
| 20 | Twenty | Two tens | 20th | Twentieth |
| 30 | Thirty | Three tens | 30th | Thirtieth |
| 40 | Forty | Four tens | 40th | Fortieth |
| 50 | Fifty | Five tens | 50th | Fiftieth |
| 60 | Sixty | Six tens | 60th | Sixtieth |
| 70 | Seventy | Seven tens | 70th | Seventieth |
| 80 | Eighty | Eight tens | 80th | Eightieth |
| 90 | Ninety | Nine tens | 90th | Ninetieth |
| 100 | One hundred | Ten tens | 100th | One hundredth |

## Handbook

# Place Value

**A place-value table tells you how many hundreds, tens, and ones. Place value is important. Look what happens when the 5 is in the hundreds place or the ones place.**

| Hundreds | Tens | Ones |
|---|---|---|
| 5 | 4 | 1 |

| Hundreds | Tens | Ones |
|---|---|---|
| 1 | 4 | 5 |

# Big Numbers

**Numbers go on forever. After trillions come quadrillions and then quintillions. A googol is written as 1 followed by 100 zeros. A googolplex is written as 1 followed by one googol zeros.**

| | |
|---|---|
| 1 | One |
| 10 | Ten |
| 100 | One hundred |
| 1,000 | One thousand |
| 10,000 | Ten thousand |
| 100,000 | One hundred thousand |
| 1,000,000 | One million |
| 10,000,000 | Ten million |
| 100,000,000 | One hundred million |
| 1,000,000,000 | One billion |
| 10,000,000,000 | Ten billion |
| 100,000,000,000 | One hundred billion |
| 1,000,000,000,000 | One trillion |





# Addition Table

**You can use the Addition Table to find basic addition and subtraction facts.**

| + | 0 | 1 | 2 | 3 | 4 | 5 | 6 | 7 | 8 | 9 | 10 |
|---|---|---|---|---|---|---|---|---|---|---|---|
| 0 | 0 | 1 | 2 | 3 | 4 | 5 | 6 | 7 | 8 | 9 | 10 |
| 1 | 1 | 2 | 3 | 4 | 5 | 6 | 7 | 8 | 9 | 10 | 11 |
| 2 | 2 | 3 | 4 | 5 | 6 | 7 | 8 | 9 | 10 | 11 | 12 |
| 3 | 3 | 4 | 5 | 6 | 7 | 8 | 9 | 10 | 11 | 12 | 13 |
| 4 | 4 | 5 | 6 | 7 | 8 | 9 | 10 | 11 | 12 | 13 | 14 |
| 5 | 5 | 6 | 7 | 8 | 9 | 10 | 11 | 12 | 13 | 14 | 15 |
| 6 | 6 | 7 | 8 | 9 | 10 | 11 | 12 | 13 | 14 | 15 | 16 |
| 7 | 7 | 8 | 9 | 10 | 11 | 12 | 13 | 14 | 15 | 16 | 17 |
| 8 | 8 | 9 | 10 | 11 | 12 | 13 | 14 | 15 | 16 | 17 | 18 |
| 9 | 9 | 10 | 11 | 12 | 13 | 14 | 15 | 16 | 17 | 18 | 19 |
| 10 | 10 | 11 | 12 | 13 | 14 | 15 | 16 | 17 | 18 | 19 | 20 |





## Handbook

# Addition and Subtraction Facts

## Addition Fact Helpers

**These strategies can help with many of the addition facts.**

| To add: | Think of: |
|---|---|
| 0 | No change |
| 1 | Counting on 1 |
| 2 | Counting on 2 |
| 4 | One less than adding 5 |
| 5 | Finger sets—one more hand |
| 6 | One more than adding 5 |
| 9 | One less than adding 10 |
| 10 | Write 1 in the tens place |

## Subtraction Fact Helpers

**These strategies can help with some of the subtraction facts. For other subtraction facts, think of the corresponding addition fact.**

| To subtract: | Think of: |
|---|---|
| 0 | No change |
| 1 | Counting back 1 |
| 5 | Finger sets—taking away one hand |
| 9 | One more than subtracting 10 |
| 10 | Subtracting 1 from the tens digit |





# Addition

## One Way to Add

```
  685
+ 267
```

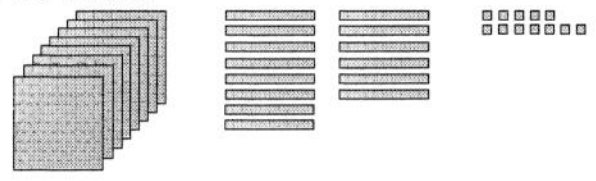

We start at the right because it is easier that way. Add ones. 5 + 7 = 12. 12 ones = 1 ten and 2 ones.

```
    1
  685
+ 267
    2
```

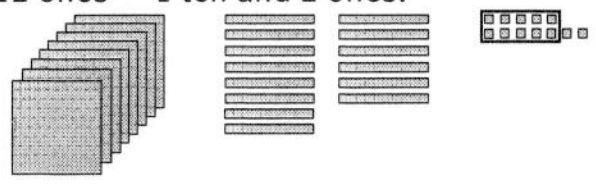

Add tens. 1 + 8 + 6 = 15. 15 tens = 1 hundred and 5 tens.

```
   11
  685
+ 267
   52
```

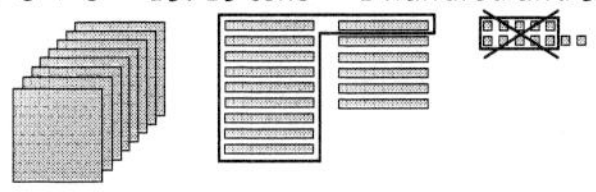

Add hundreds. 1 + 6 + 2 = 9.

```
   11
  685
+ 267
  952
```

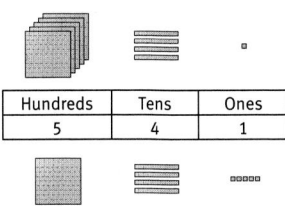

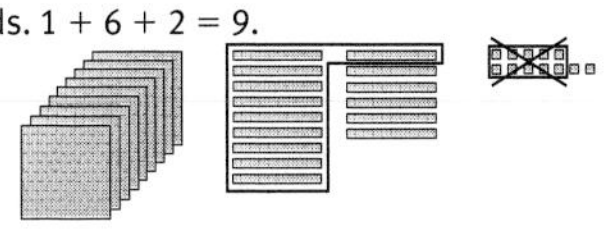

## Addition Laws

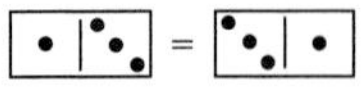

**Commutative Law of Addition**

The order of two numbers does not affect their sum. For example, the sum of 1 + 3 is the same as the sum of 3 + 1.

**Associative Law of Addition**

When adding three numbers, it does not matter whether the first pair or the last pair is added first.

$5 + 4 + 3 = (5 + 4) + 3 = 5 + (4 + 3)$

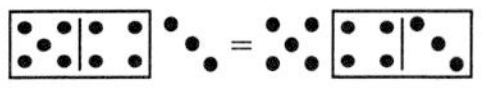

9 + 3      5 + 7

**Additive Identity**

Adding a number to 0 gives that number.

$6 + 0 = 6$

**Additive Inverse**

Adding a positive number and a negative number with the same absolute value (distance from 0) gives 0.

$4 + (-4) = 0.$





## Subtraction

### One Way to Subtract

$$\begin{array}{r} 365 \\ -\ 178 \\ \hline \end{array}$$

**Start at the right because it is easier.**

There are not enough ones to subtract 8, so rename 6 tens as 5 tens and 10 ones.

$$\begin{array}{r} {\scriptstyle 5\,15} \\ 3\not{6}\not{5} \\ -\ 178 \\ \hline \end{array}$$

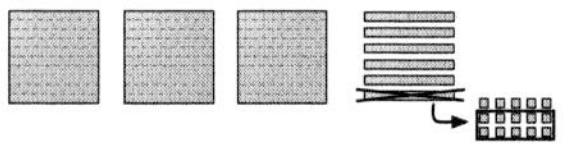

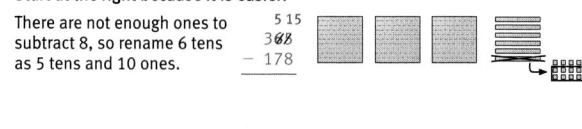

Subtract ones.

$$\begin{array}{r} {\scriptstyle 5\,15} \\ 3\not{6}\not{5} \\ -\ 178 \\ \hline 7 \end{array}$$

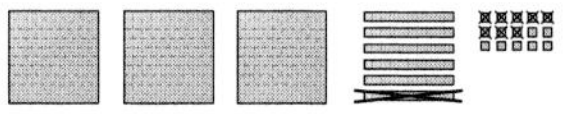

There are not enough tens to subtract 7, so rename 3 hundreds as 2 hundreds and 10 tens. Subtract tens.

$$\begin{array}{r} {\scriptstyle 2\,15\,15} \\ \not{3}\not{6}\not{5} \\ -\ 178 \\ \hline 87 \end{array}$$

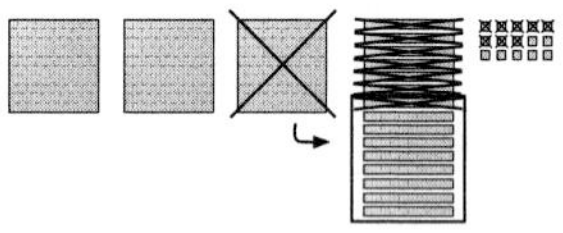

Subtract hundreds.

$$\begin{array}{r} {\scriptstyle 2\,15\,15} \\ \not{3}\not{6}\not{5} \\ -\ 178 \\ \hline 187 \end{array}$$

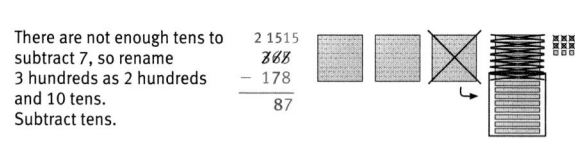

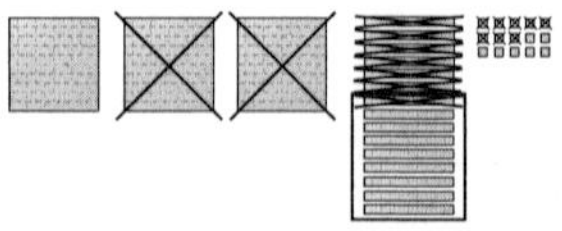







## Multiplication Table

**You can use the Multiplication Table to find basic facts.**

| × | 0 | 1 | 2 | 3 | 4 | 5 | 6 | 7 | 8 | 9 | 10 | 11 | 12 |
|---|---|---|---|---|---|---|---|---|---|---|---|---|---|
| 0 | 0 | 0 | 0 | 0 | 0 | 0 | 0 | 0 | 0 | 0 | 0 | 0 | 0 |
| 1 | 0 | 1 | 2 | 3 | 4 | 5 | 6 | 7 | 8 | 9 | 10 | 11 | 12 |
| 2 | 0 | 2 | 4 | 6 | 8 | 10 | 12 | 14 | 16 | 18 | 20 | 22 | 24 |
| 3 | 0 | 3 | 6 | 9 | 12 | 15 | 18 | 21 | 24 | 27 | 30 | 33 | 36 |
| 4 | 0 | 4 | 8 | 12 | 16 | 20 | 24 | 28 | 32 | 36 | 40 | 44 | 48 |
| 5 | 0 | 5 | 10 | 15 | 20 | 25 | 30 | 35 | 40 | 45 | 50 | 55 | 60 |
| 6 | 0 | 6 | 12 | 18 | 24 | 30 | 36 | 42 | 48 | 54 | 60 | 66 | 72 |
| 7 | 0 | 7 | 14 | 21 | 28 | 35 | 42 | 49 | 56 | 63 | 70 | 77 | 84 |
| 8 | 0 | 8 | 16 | 24 | 32 | 40 | 48 | 56 | 64 | 72 | 80 | 88 | 96 |
| 9 | 0 | 9 | 18 | 27 | 36 | 45 | 54 | 63 | 72 | 81 | 90 | 99 | 108 |
| 10 | 0 | 10 | 20 | 30 | 40 | 50 | 60 | 70 | 80 | 90 | 100 | 110 | 120 |
| 11 | 0 | 11 | 22 | 33 | 44 | 55 | 66 | 77 | 88 | 99 | 110 | 121 | 132 |
| 12 | 0 | 12 | 24 | 36 | 48 | 60 | 72 | 84 | 96 | 108 | 120 | 132 | 144 |





## Multiplication Facts

### Fact Helper Strategies

**To multiply by:**

10 Write a "0" after the number.

9 Subtract the number from 10 times the number.

0 The answer is 0.

1 The answer is the number.

2 Add the number to itself.

5 Multiply half the number by 10 if it is even. If the number is odd, multiply half of the next smaller number by 10 and add 5.

4 Double the number, and then double that answer.

3 Add the number to its double.

8 Double 4 times the number, or subtract the number from 9 times the number.

6 Double 3 times the number.

7 If you've learned all the other facts and can remember that $7 \times 7 = 49$, you know all the multiples of 7.

### Fact Families

**Fact families show how multiplication and division are related.**

| | |
|---|---|
| $2 \times 3 = 6$ | $6 \div 2 = 3$ |
| $3 \times 2 = 6$ | $6 \div 3 = 2$ |

# Handbook

## Multiplication

Think of multiplication as finding many areas.

| | 100 | 100 | 100 | 10 | 10 | 10 | 10 | 6 |
|---|---|---|---|---|---|---|---|---|
| 10 | | | | | | | | |
| 10 | | | | | | | | |
| 10 | | $300 \times 50 = 15{,}000$ | | | $40 \times 50 = 2{,}000$ | | | |
| 10 | | | | | | | | |
| 10 | | | | | | | | |
| 2 | | $300 \times 2 = 600$ | | | $40 \times 2 = 80$ | | | |

$6 \times 2 = 12$

$6 \times 50 = 300$

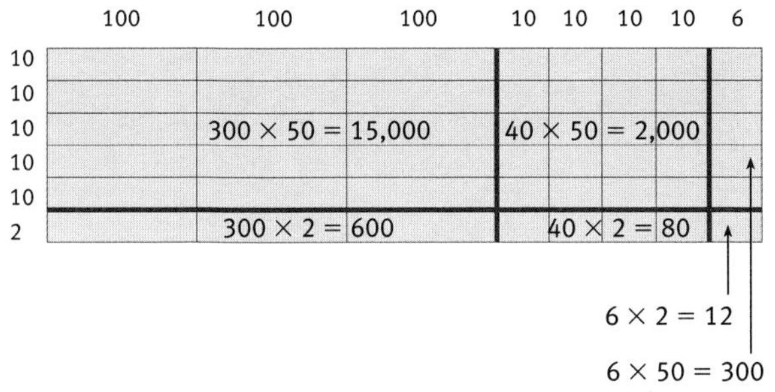

### Partial Products

Multiplying using partial products may help you keep track of place values. Starting with the rightmost column, multiply each position in the top number by the ones-column digit, then the tens-column digit, and so on. Then add the partial products to find the final product. You could start with any column, but it is easier if you start on the right.

$$\begin{array}{r} 346 \\ \times\ 52 \\ \hline \end{array}$$

| | |
|---|---|
| $2 \times 6 = 12$ | 12 |
| $2 \times 40 = 80$ | 80 |
| $2 \times 300 = 600$ | 600 |
| $50 \times 6 = 300$ | 300 |
| $50 \times 40 = 2{,}000$ | 2000 |
| $50 \times 300 = 15{,}000$ | + 15000 |
| Add partial products. | 17992 |

---

# Handbook

## A Shorter Way to Multiply

Beginning at the rightmost column, find the product. Write the ones digit of the product below the line in the ones column, and write the tens digit at the top of the tens column. Then repeat this process for each digit of the second factor.

$$\begin{array}{r} 346 \\ \times\ 52 \\ \hline \end{array}$$

Multiply 2 times the ones. $6 \times 2 = 12$
12 ones = 1 ten and 2 ones
Multiply 2 times 4 tens, and add the carried ten.
$(2 \times 4) + 1 = 9$

$$\begin{array}{r} 1 \\ 346 \\ \times\ 52 \\ \hline 2 \end{array} \qquad \begin{array}{r} 1 \\ 346 \\ \times\ 52 \\ \hline 92 \end{array}$$

Multiply 2 times 3 hundreds. $2 \times 3 = 6$

$$\begin{array}{r} 1 \\ 346 \\ \times\ 52 \\ \hline 692 \end{array}$$

Multiply 5 tens times 6 ones. $5 \times 6 = 30$
30 tens = 3 hundreds and 0 tens
Multiply 5 tens times 4 tens, and add the carried hundreds. $(5 \times 4) + 3 = 23$
23 = 2 thousands and 3 hundreds

$$\begin{array}{r} 3 \\ 346 \\ \times\ 52 \\ \hline 692 \\ 00 \end{array} \qquad \begin{array}{r} 2\,3 \\ 346 \\ \times\ 52 \\ \hline 692 \\ 300 \end{array}$$

Multiply 5 tens times 3 hundreds, and add the carried thousands. $(5 \times 3) + 2 = 17$
17 thousands = 1 ten thousand and 7 thousands

$$\begin{array}{r} 2\,3 \\ 346 \\ \times\ 52 \\ \hline 692 \\ 17300 \end{array}$$

Add partial products.

$$\begin{array}{r} 2\,3 \\ 346 \\ \times\ 52 \\ \hline 692 \\ + 17300 \\ \hline 17992 \end{array}$$

---

# Handbook

## Division

### One Way to Divide

$5\overline{)423}$

Five does not divide into 4, but it will divide into 42 eight times.

$$\begin{array}{r} 8\ \ \\ 5\overline{)423} \\ 40\ \ \end{array}$$

Subtract 40 from 42.

$$\begin{array}{r} 8\ \ \\ 5\overline{)423} \\ -40\ \ \\ \hline 2\ \ \end{array}$$

Bring down the next digit, 3.

$$\begin{array}{r} 8\ \ \\ 5\overline{)423} \\ -40\ \ \\ \hline 23 \end{array}$$

Five divides into 23 four times.

$$\begin{array}{r} 84 \\ 5\overline{)423} \\ -40\ \ \\ \hline 23 \\ 20 \end{array}$$

Subtract 20 from 23.

$$\begin{array}{r} 84 \\ 5\overline{)423} \\ -40\ \ \\ \hline 23 \\ -20 \\ \hline 3 \end{array}$$

$423 \div 5 = 84\ R3$

---

## Divisibility Patterns

### Divisibility by 2

An even number is a number divisible by 2. We can recognize even numbers because their last digit must also be divisible by 2 (the last digit must be 0, 2, 4, 6, or 8). For example, 78,950 has a 0 as its last digit; therefore, it's divisible by 2.

### Divisibility by 3

A number is divisible by 3 if the sum of its digits is divisible by 3. The number 492,603 has a digit sum of 24. Twenty-four is divisible by 3; therefore, 492,603 is divisible by 3.

### Divisibility by 5

We can recognize a number that is divisible by 5 because its last digit must be either a 0 or a 5. The number 47,825 has a 5 as its last digit; therefore, it's divisible by 5.

### Divisibility by 11

A two-digit number is divisible by 11 if the two digits are equal to each other. Take 33, for example: 3 = 3, so 33 is divisible by 11. There are patterns for divisibility by 11 for numbers greater than 100. Can you find them?

# Geometric Figures

## Plane Figures

Circle A circle is composed of all points in a plane the same distance from the center.

Polygon A polygon is a closed figure with sides that are all line segments.

Angles Angles are measured based on the amount of turn they represent. A quarter turn is a right angle. Angles of less than a quarter turn are acute angles. Angles of more than a quarter turn but less than half a turn are obtuse angles.
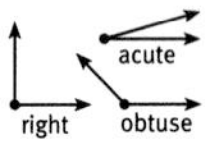


Triangle A triangle is a polygon with three sides.

## Polygons

Quadrilateral A polygon with four sides.

Rectangle A rectangle has four sides with opposite pairs of sides of equal length and four right angles.
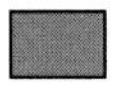

Square A square is a quadrilateral with four equal sides and four right angles.

Rhombus A rhombus is a quadrilateral with four equal sides.

Trapezoid A trapezoid is a quadrilateral with two sides parallel.

Pentagon A pentagon is a polygon with five sides.

Hexagon A hexagon is a polygon with six sides.
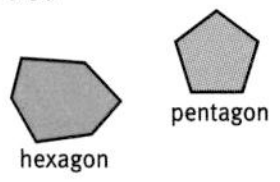


## Space Figures

Cube A cube is a space figure with six square faces.

Sphere A sphere is a space figure composed of all its points in space the same distance from its center.

Cone A cone is a space figure made by connecting every point on a circle or other plane figure to a point not on the figure.
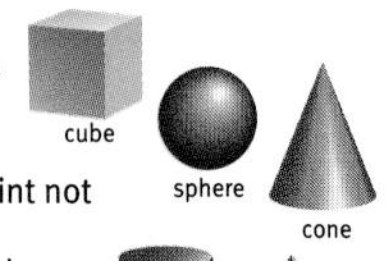


Cylinder A cylinder is a space figure with two parallel bases (usually circles).

Polyhedron A polyhedron is a closed space figure whose faces are all polygons.
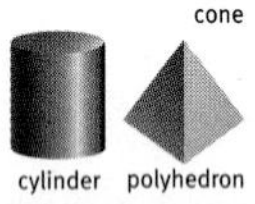






# Measurements

**Decimal and Metric Prefixes**

1000 = thousand = *kilo-*
100 = hundred = *hecto-*
10 = ten = *deca-*
0.10 = tenth = *deci-*
0.01 = hundredth = *centi-*
0.001 = thousandth = *milli-*

**The basic units in the metric system are *meter, gram,* and *liter.***

## Measuring Length

| Metric | Equivalency |
|---|---|
| 1 millimeter (mm) | 1mm: - |
| 1 centimeter (cm) | 10 millimeters |
| 1 decimeter (dm) | 10 centimeters |
| 1 meter (m) | 100 centimeters |
| 1 dekameter (dam) | 10 meters |
| 1 hectometer (hm) | 100 meters |
| 1 kilometer (km) | 1,000 meters |

| Customary | Equivalency |
|---|---|
| 1 inch (in.) | 1 inch: ———— |
| 1 foot (ft) | 12 inches |
| 1 yard (yd) | 3 feet |
| 1 mile (mi) | 5,280 feet<br>1,760 yards |

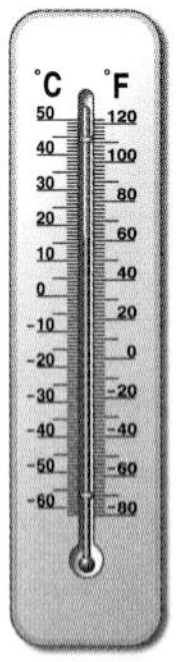


## Measuring Temperature

| Celsius | | Fahrenheit |
|---|---|---|
| 0 | Water Freezes | 32 |
| 100 | Water Boils | 212 |





## Weight (Mass)

| Metric | Equivalent |
|---|---|
| 1 gram (g) | a dollar bill weighs about 1 gram |
| 1 dekagram (dag) | 10 grams |
| 1 hectogram (hg) | 100 grams |
| 1 kilogram (kg) | 1,000 grams |
| 1 metric ton (t) | 1,000 kilograms |

| Customary | Equivalent |
|---|---|
| 1 ounce (oz) | 11 pennies weigh about 1 ounce |
| 1 pound (lb) | 16 ounces |
| 1 ton | 2,000 pounds |

## Capacity

| Metric | Equivalent |
|---|---|
| 1 milliliter (mL) | an eyedropper holds about 1 milliliter |
| 1 centiliter (cL) | 0.01 liter |
| 1 deciliter (dL) | 0.1 liter |
| 1 liter (L) | 1,000 milliliters |
| 1 dekaliter (daL) | 10 liters |
| 1 hectoliter (hL) | 100 liters |
| 1 kiloliter (kL) | 1,000 liters |

| Customary | Equivalent |
|---|---|
| 1 fluid ounce (fl oz) | approximately the volume of 1 ounce of water |
| 1 cup (c) | 8 fluid ounces |
| 1 pint (pt) | 2 cups |
| 1 quart (qt) | 2 pints |
| 1 gallon (gal) | 4 quarts |





# Time

## Months of the Year

| Month | Number of Days |
|---|---|
| January | 31 |
| February | 28, except in leap year every four years when there are 29 |
| March | 31 |
| April | 30 |
| May | 31 |
| June | 30 |
| July | 31 |
| August | 31 |
| September | 30 |
| October | 31 |
| November | 30 |
| December | 31 |

## Equivalents of Time

| | |
|---|---|
| 60 seconds | 1 minute |
| 60 minutes | 1 hour |
| 24 hours (the time it takes Earth to rotate) | 1 day |
| 7 days<br>168 hours | 1 week |
| 12 months<br>$52\frac{1}{7}$ weeks<br>365.25 days<br>(the time it takes Earth to revolve around the sun) | 1 year |

A.M. (ante meridiem; before midday) means between midnight and noon

P.M. (post meridiem; after midday) means between noon and midnight

## Military or 24-Hour Time Equivalents

| | | | | | | | |
|---|---|---|---|---|---|---|---|
| 1:00 | 1 AM | 7:00 | 7 AM | 13:00 | 1 PM | 19:00 | 7 PM |
| 2:00 | 2 AM | 8:00 | 8 AM | 14:00 | 2 PM | 20:00 | 8 PM |
| 3:00 | 3 AM | 9:00 | 9 AM | 15:00 | 3 PM | 21:00 | 9 PM |
| 4:00 | 4 AM | 10:00 | 10 AM | 16:00 | 4 PM | 22:00 | 10 PM |
| 5:00 | 5 AM | 11:00 | 11 AM | 17:00 | 5 PM | 23:00 | 11 PM |
| 6:00 | 6 AM | 12:00 | 12 Noon | 18:00 | 6 PM | 24:00 | 12 Midnight |

A.D. or C.E. means the common era, after the year 0

B.C. or B.C.E. means before the common era, before the year 0

## Handbook

# Frequency Tables

**A frequency table shows tally marks and how often each kind of data occurs in a set of data.**

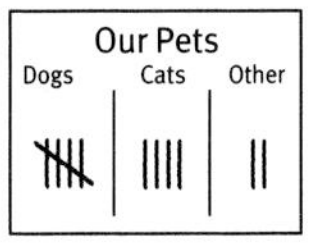


### Tally Marks

**Tally marks are used to keep count.**

### Tallies of Five

**Tally marks represent 5 when four tallies are combined with one diagonal mark.**

# Graphs

### Bar Graph

**A bar graph is a graph with bars of lengths that represent amounts.**

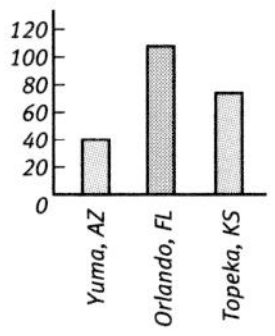


### Circle Graph

**A circle graph has sectors that represent different categories.**

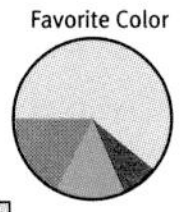


### Line Graph

**A line graph connects points to show change over time.**

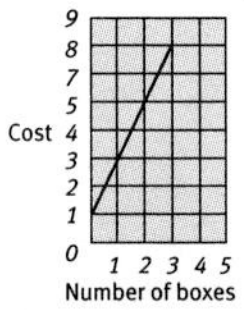






# Fractions, Decimals, and Percentages

**Fractions, decimals, and percentages are called *rational numbers* because they can be written as ratios. Whole numbers, counting numbers, integers, fractions, decimals, improper fractions, and mixed numbers are all examples of rational numbers.**

Percentages are special ratios that compare a number to 100.

A ratio is the comparison of two quantities by division, such as a fraction.

Ratios are commonly used to relate one number to another. Ratios have no labels. There are three major representations of ratios: 3 out of 4, 3:4, and $\frac{3}{4}$. Probabilities are represented most often by ratios.

The ratio of blue to red dots can be written $\frac{2}{5}$.
The ratio of blue dots to the total number of dots is $\frac{2}{7}$.

**A number line helps you think about rational numbers. You can see whole numbers, negative numbers, and fractions as belonging to the same system.**

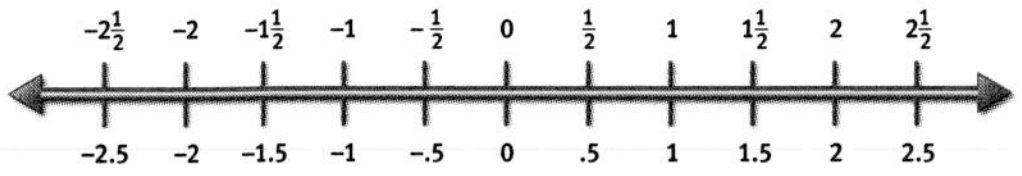


**Benchmark for Fractions, Decimals, and Percentages**

Fractions, decimals, and percentages can all represent the same rational number or part of a whole.

$1 = 1.0 = 100\%$
$\frac{3}{4} = 0.75 = 75\%$
$\frac{1}{2} = 0.5 = 50\%$
$\frac{1}{4} = 0.25 = 25\%$
$\frac{1}{8} = 0.125 = 12.5\%$

3 — *numerator*
4 — *denominator*





## Handbook

# Algebraic Functions

**A function pairs a number (the input) with a second number (the output).**
**A function table lists the pairs of numbers.**

If a girl is 3 years older than her brother, you can say:
Brother's age + 3 = Sister's age
No matter how old they are, the sister will always be three years older than her brother.

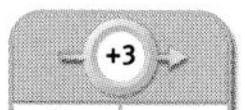


| in | out |
|---|---|
| 1 | 4 |
| 2 | 5 |
| 3 | 6 |
| 4 | 7 |
| 5 | 8 |

A **function machine** shows the input, output, and rule for a function. A **function rule** tells how the input of a function is related to the output of a function.

**Composite functions** involve more than one step in the function rule.

**Linear functions** create a straight line when graphed.

An **equation** is a mathematical statement showing that one quantity or expression is equal to another quantity or expression. These are the sentences of mathematical language.





# Math Symbols

| | | |
|---|---|---|
| + | Plus<br>Add | 7 + 3 = 10 |
| − | Minus<br>Subtract | 10 − 3 = 7 |
| × or * on the computer | Times<br>Multiply | 3 × 2 = 6 |
| ÷, ⟌, or / on the computer | Divided by | 6 ÷ 2 = 3 |
| = | Is equal to | 4 + 2 = 6 |
| ¢ | Cents | 39¢ |
| $ | Dollars | $1.00 |
| °F | Degrees Fahrenheit | 100°F |
| °C | Degrees Celsius | 25°C |
| > | Greater than | 47 > 39 |
| < | Less than | 2 + 6 < 10 |
| $4^3$ ← exponent; ↑ base | Exponents are used as a shorthand notation to show repeated multiplication. | $4^3 = 4 \times 4 \times 4 = 64$ |
| ∠ | Angle | ∠ABC |
| Δ | Triangle | ΔJKL |
| ≅ | Is congruent to | ∠ABC ≅ ∠DEF |
| ∽ | Is similar to | ΔJKL ∽ ΔABC |

# Glossary

## A

**acute angle \ə kūt'** *n.* an angle which measures between 0 and 90°

These are acute angles:

**addend \ad' end** *n.* any number or quantity that is to be added to another. For example:

35 —addend
+ 48 —addend
83 —sum

7 + 8 = 15 —sum
addend
addend

**approximate \ə prok' sə m āt'** *v.* to come near or close. **\ə prok' sə mit** *adj.* nearly correct or exact

**approximation \ə prok' sə mā' shən** *n.* something that is nearly correct, as an estimated amount

**area \âr' ē ə** *n.* the measure of the interior, or inside, of a figure. The area of this rectangle is 6 square centimeters:

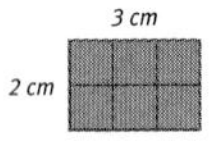


**associative \ə sō' shē ā' tiv** *adj.* a law stating that the sum or product of two or more quantities will be the same regardless of the way in which they are grouped

**average \av' rij** *n.* the typical or usual amount, which is found by dividing the sum of two or more quantities by the number of quantities

**axes** (of a graph) **\ak' sēz** *n.* the two zero lines of a graph that give the coordinates of points

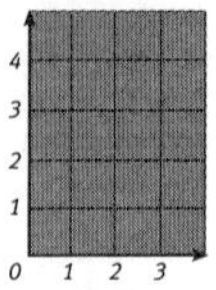


## B

**balance \bal' əns** *n.* the amount of money remaining in an account

**benchmark \bench märk** *n.* something that serves as a standard or reference by which something else can be measured or compared

## C

**centi– \sen' ti** *prefix* a hundredth of a part

**centisecond \sen' ti sek' ənd** *adj.* a hundredth $\frac{1}{100}$ of a second

**circle \sûr' kəl** *n.* a continuous, closed curved line, every point of which is equally distant from the center

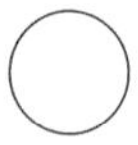

**commutative \kə mū' tə tiv** *adj.* relating to or designating a law stating that the sum or product of two or more quantities will be the same regardless of their order

**composite \kəm poz' it** *adj.* made up of various parts or elements

**composite function \kəm poz' it fungk' shən** *n.* a function with two or more operations

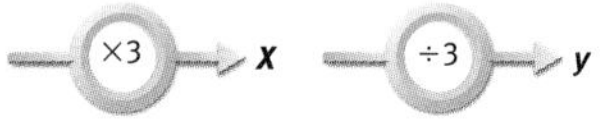


**composite number** *n.* a whole number with more than two factors (that is, factors other than itself and 1)



Student Page

# Glossary

**congruent \kən grü' ənt** *adj.* figures that are the same size and same shape; that is, they fit perfectly when placed on top of one another

These triangles are congruent:

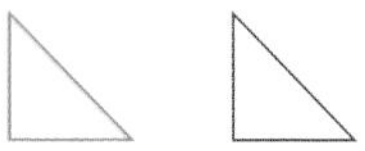

These triangles are not congruent:

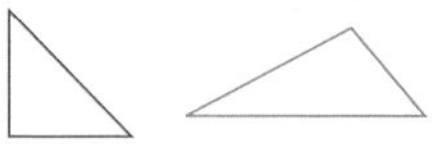

**coordinates \kō ôr' də nits** *n.* a pair of numbers that gives the location of a point on a graph; also called an ordered pair of numbers. In the figure shown, for example, the coordinates of point A are (2, 3); the *x*–coordinate is 2 and the *y*–coordinate is 3

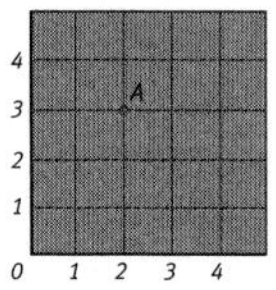


**cylinder \sil' ən dər** *n.* a solid geometric figure bounded by two equal, parallel circles and a curved surface that is formed by a straight line moving parallel to itself with its ends always on the circumferences of the circles

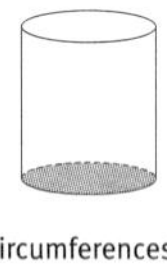

## D

**data \dā' tə, dat' ə** *pl. n.* information from which conclusions can be drawn; facts and figures

**decimal equivalent \des' ə məl i kwiv' ə lənt** *n.* decimals that name the same amount (such as the same amount as a fraction or as another decimal)

**decimal point \des' ə məl point** *n.* a dot used in separating the ones digit from the tenths digit

**denominator \di nom' ə nā' tər ** *n.* a number below the line in a fraction, indicating the number of equal parts into which the whole is divided

**deposit \dip oz' it** *v.* to put in a bank or other safe place for safekeeping. *n.* something put in a place for safekeeping

**diameter \dī am' i tər** *n.* a straight line passing through the center of a circle or sphere, from one side to the other

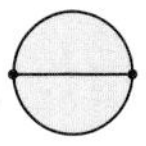

**difference \dif' rəns** *n.* remainder left after subtracting one quantity from another
For example:

43 —minuend
– 16 —subtrahend
27 —difference

10 – 7 = 3 —difference
subtrahend
minuend

**digit \dij' it ** *n.* any of the ten Arabic numerals from 0 through 9

**distributive law \di strib' yə tiv** *adj.* a law stating that a product is the same when the operation is performed on a whole set as when it is performed on the individual members of the set



Student Page

# Glossary

**dividend \div' i dend** *n.* the number that is to be divided. For example:

6 ÷ 3 = 2 — quotient
divisor
dividend

43 — quotient
divisor — 8)347 — dividend
– 32
27
–24
3

**divisible \di viz' ə bəl** *adj.* capable of being divided without a remainder

**divisor \di vī' zər** *n.* the number the dividend is to be divided by

**doubles \dub' əls** *n.* numbers that are added to themselves, such as 12 + 12 = 12 × 2 = 24

## E

**edge \ej** *n.* the segment where two faces of a space figure meet

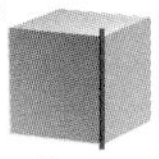

**equation \i kwā' zhən** *n.* a mathematical statement showing that one quantity or expression is equal to another quantity or expression

**equilateral triangle \ē' kwə lat' ər əl** *n.* a triangle having all sides equal in length

**equivalent fractions \i kwiv' ə lənt** *n.* fractions that name the same rational number

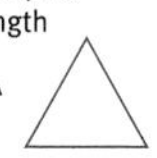

**estimate ** *n.*, **es' tə mit;** *v.*, **es' tə māt'** *n.* a judgment or opinion, as of the value, quality, extent, size, or cost of something

*v.* to form a judgment or opinion of, based on available information; calculate

**even number \ē' vən** *n.* a number that can be divided exactly by two

**exponent \ek spō' nənt** *n.* a numeral or symbol placed at the upper right side of another numeral or symbol to indicate the number of times it is to be used as a factor

## F

**face \fās** *n.* a plane figure that serves as one side of a space figure

**factor \fak' tər** *n.* number you multiply to get a product

For example: 3 (multiplier) × 5 (multiplicand) = 15 (product)

**fraction \frak' shən** *n.* a quantity expressing the division of one number by a second number, written as two numerals separated by a line

**function \fungk' shən** *n.* a relationship that pairs every element of one set with an element of a second set—for example, a relationship that pairs any number with another number

**function machine \fungk' shən mə shēn'** *n.* a machine (sometimes imaginary) that does the same thing to every number that is put into it

## G

**graph \graf** *n.* a diagram showing the relationship between two or more sets of data

**greatest common factor** *n.* the greatest factor shared by a pair of numbers

**grid \grid** *n.* a pattern of intersecting lines that divides a map or chart into small squares



Student Page

# Glossary

## H

**heptagon \hep' tə gon'** *n.* a plane figure having seven sides and seven angles

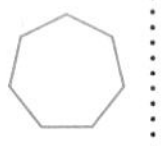

**hexagon \hek' sə gon'** *n.* a plane figure having six sides and six angles

**hundredth \hun' dridth** *n.* one of a hundred equal parts; $\frac{1}{100}$

**hypotenuse \hī pot' ə nūs'** *n.* the side of a right triangle opposite the right angle

## I

**improper fraction \im prop' ər frak' shən** *n.* a fraction whose numerator is greater than, or equal to, its denominator

**inequality \in' i kwol' i tē** *n.* mathematical statement showing that two numbers are not equal or that one number is greater than or less than another number

**inference \in' fər əns** *n.* a conclusion drawn from something that was known or hinted at

**integer \in' ti jər** *n.* any positive or negative whole number, or zero

**intersecting lines \in' tər sekt' ing** *n.* lines that meet and cross each other

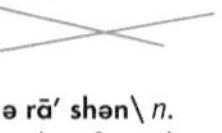

**inverse operation \in' vərs op' ə rā' shən** *n.* an operation that undoes the results of another operation; examples are multiplication and division; addition and subtraction

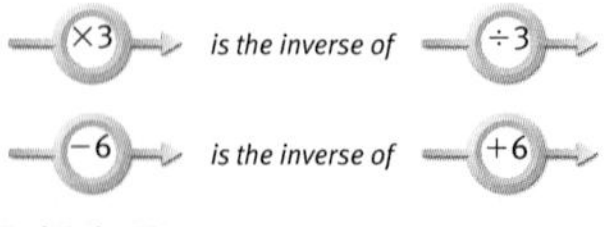


**isosceles \ī sōs' lēz** *adj.* having two equal sides. These are isosceles triangles:

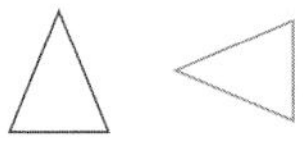

## K

**kilo– \kē' lo; kil' ō** *prefix* one thousand

**kilometer \ki lom' i tər, kil' ə mē' tər** *n.* a unit of length in the metric system equal to 1,000 meters

## L

**least common multiple** *n.* the smallest multiple of a pair of numbers

**line of symmetry** *n.* a line on which a figure can be folded into two parts that fit exactly on top of each other

**line segment \līn seg' mənt** *n.* a part of a line with two endpoints

**linear function \lin' ē ər** *n.* a function that creates a straight line when graphed

## M

**mean \mēn** *n.* another name for average

**median \mē' dē ən** *n.* the middle number in a set of data

Student Page

# Glossary

**metric system** \met′ rik sis′ təm\ *n.* a decimal system of measurement that uses the meter as the fundamental unit of length

**minuend** \min′ ū end′\ *n.* the number from which another is to be subtracted

**mixed number** \mikst num′ bər\ *n.* a number consisting of a whole number and a fraction

**mode** \mōd\ *n.* the number appearing most frequently in a set of data

**multiple** \mul′ tə pəl\ *n.* any number that is the product of that number and any whole number

**multiplicand** \mul tə pli kand′\ *n.* a number multiplied by another number, the multiplier. For example:

5 —multiplicand
× 3 —multiplier
15 —product

3 × 5 = 15 —product
multiplicand
multiplier

**multiplier** \mul′ tə plī ər\ *n.* a factor of a product

**multiply** \mul′ tə plī′\ *v.* to find the product of a number that is repeatedly added to itself (4 + 4 + 4 + 4 = 4 × 4 = 16)

## N

**negative** \neg′ tiv\ *n.* less than zero

**net** \net\ *n.* a pattern used to create a space figure

**notation** \nō tā′ shən\ *n.* a system of signs or symbols used to represent values, quantities, or other facts or information

**number line** \num′ bər līn\ *n.* a line of infinite extent whose points correspond to the real numbers according to their distance in a positive or negative direction from a point arbitrarily taken as zero

**numerator** \nü′ mə rā′ tər\ *n.* the number above the line in a fraction, indicating the number of parts being considered

## O

**obtuse angle** \əb tüs′\ *n.* an angle that is greater than 90°

These are obtuse angles:

**octagon** \ok′ tə gon′\ *n.* a polygon having eight sides and eight angles

**odd number** \od\ *n.* a number leaving a remainder of one when divided by two

**ordered pair** *n.* two numbers written so that one is considered before the other. Coordinates of points are written as ordered pairs, with the *x*-coordinate written first, then the *y*-coordinate. An example is (3, 4).

**outcome** \out′ kum\ *n.* a result or consequence

## P

**parallel lines** \par′ ə lel\ *adj.* lines that are the same distance apart and go in the same direction and never meet

**parallelogram** \par′ ə lel′ ə gram′\ *n.* a plane figure with four sides whose opposite sides are parallel and equal in length

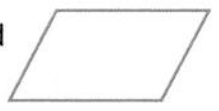



Student Page

# Glossary

**parentheses** \pə ren′ thə sēz\ *n.* curved marks ( ) used to enclose symbols or numbers to indicate which expression to evaluate first

**partial product** \pär′ shəl prod′ əkt\ *n.* the product that comes from multiplying the multiplicand by one of the digits of the multiplier. For example:

36
× 12
72 — This partial product comes from multiplying 36 by 2 ones.
+360 — This partial product comes from multiplying 36 by 1 ten.
432 — This product comes from adding the partial products.

**pattern** \pat′ ərn\ *n.* an element that is characterized by repetition

**pentagon** \pen′ tə gon′\ *n.* a polygon with five sides and five angles

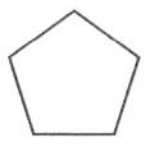

**percent** \pər sent′\ *n.* the number of parts in every hundred

**perimeter** \pə rim′ i tər\ *n.* the distance around the boundary of a closed plane figure; the perimeter of this rectangle is 6 cm.

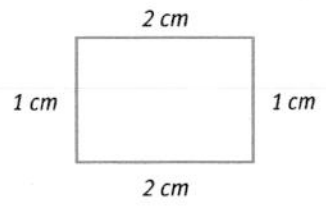


**perpendicular** \pər′ pən di′ kyə lər\ *adj.* lines that intersect at right angles

**place value** \plās val′ ū\ *n.* the value of a digit in a number

**plane** \plān\ *n.* a flat surface wholly containing every line connecting any two points on it

**plane figure** \plān fig′ yər\ *n.* a figure having only height and width

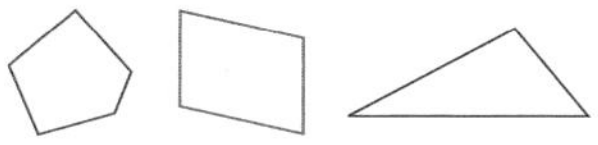

**polygon** \pä′ lē gän′\ *n.* a closed plane figure with three or more line segments as sides

**polyhedron** \pä′ lē hē′ drən\ *n.* a space figure that has only flat faces, which are polygons

**power** \pou′ ər\ *n.* the number of times a given number or expression is multiplied by itself

**prime number** *n.* a whole number that has only two factors—the number itself and 1

**prism** \priz′ əm\ *n.* a solid having two congruent and parallel faces, and whose other faces are parallelograms

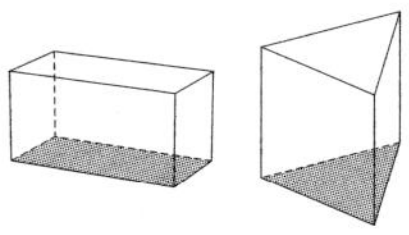

**probability** \prob′ ə bil′ i tē\ *n.* the ratio of the number of chances favoring the occurrence of a particular event to the total number of possible occurrences

**product** \prod′ əkt\ *n.* the result of multiplying two or more numbers (factors).

**profit** \prof′ it\ *n.* the amount remaining after all the costs of a business have been paid



Student Page

# Glossary

**pyramid** \pir′ ə mid\ *n.* a solid figure having a polygon for a base and triangular sides intersecting at a point

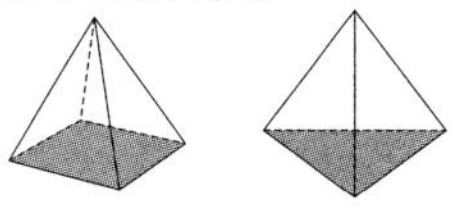

**Pythagorean Theorem** \pi thag′ ə rē′ ən thē′ ər əm\ *n.* Named for the Greek mathematician Pythagoras. For any right triangle, the square of the length of the hypotenuse is equal to the sum of the squares of the lengths of the other two sides. It is written as $a^2 + b^2 = c^2$, where c is the length of the hypotenuse and a and b are the lengths of the other sides.

## Q

**quadrilateral** \kwod′ rə lat′ ər əl\ *n.* a polygon with four sides and four angles

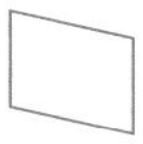

**quotient** \kwō′ shənt\ *n.* the answer to a division problem

## R

**radius** \rā′ dē əs\ *n.* a line segment going from the center to the outside of a circle or sphere

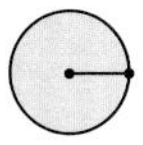

**range** \rānj\ *n.* the difference between the greatest and least numbers in a set of data

**rational number** *n.* a number that can be expressed as a quotient of two integers or as an integer (e.g. $\frac{3}{4}$, 5)

**ray** \rā\ *n.* a set of points that has one endpoint and extends forever in one direction

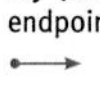

**rectangle** \rek′ tang′ gəl\ *n.* a parallelogram having four right angles

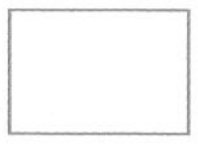

**reflection** \ri flek′ shən\ *n.* a change in location of a figure when it is flipped over a line

**regroup** \rē grüp′\ *v.* to rename a number to make adding and subtracting easier

1 15
25
− 17
8

To subtract in the ones column, 2 tens and 5 is regrouped as 1 ten and 15.

1
296
+ 442
738

After the tens column is added, 13 tens is regrouped as 1 hundred and 3 tens.

**regular polygon** *n.* a polygon with sides of equal length

**relation signs** \ri lā shən\ *n.* the three basic relation signs are > (greater than), < (less than) and = (equal to)

**remainder** \ri mān′ dər\ *n.* the number that is left over after dividing. For example, when you divide 25 by 4, the quotient is 6 with a remainder of 1.

6 R1
4)25
− 24
1



Student Page

# Glossary

**right angle** \rīt ang′ gəl\ *n.* an angle forming a 90° angle

**rotation** \rō tā′ shən\ *n.* a change in the location of a figure when it is turned around a point

**rounding** \round ing\ *v.* changing a number to another number that is easier to work with and that is close enough for the purpose

## S

**scale** \skāl\ *n.* the series of evenly spaced marks on an axis line that show the range of numbers covered by the graph

**similar** \sim′ ə lər\ *adj.* figures that have the same shape, but that differ in size

**sphere** \sfîr\ *n.* a round three–dimensional figure having all the points at an equal distance from the center



**square** \skwâr\ *n.* a plane figure having four sides of equal length and four right angles

**subtrahend** \sub′ trə hend\ *n.* the number that is to be subtracted from another

**sum** \sum\ *n.* a result obtained from addition

**symmetrical figure** \si met′ ri kəl fig′ yər\ *n.* a figure that can be divided in half so that each half is a mirror image of the other.

## T

**tenth** \tenth\ *n.* one of ten equal parts

**translation** \tranz lā′ shən\ *n.* a change in the location of a figure in which it slides without being turned

**trapezoid** \trap′ ə zoid′\ *n.* a figure having four sides with only two sides parallel

**triangle** \trī′ ang gəl′\ *n.* a plane figure with three sides and three angles

## U

**unit cost** *n.* the cost of one out of a number of equally priced goods or services

**upper and lower bounds** *n.* numbers that an answer must be less than or greater than

## V

**vertex** \vər′ teks\ *n.* 1. The point where two rays meet. 2. The point of intersection of two sides of a polygon. 3. The point of intersection of three edges of a space figure.

**volume** \vol′ ūm\ *n.* the amount of space an object can hold

## W

**withdrawal** \with drô′ əl\ *n.* the act of taking away or removing

**whole number** *n.* a number that tells how many complete things there are

## Z

**zero** \zîr′ ō\ *n.* the number that leaves any number unchanged when it is added to it

# Appendix

## Appendix A



## Appendix B



## Appendix C



## Appendix D



This appendix provides additional information about key issues in mathematics education and how they are addressed in ***Real Math.***

# About Mathematics

> **"Genuine mathematics...constitutes one of the finest expressions of the human spirit. The great areas of mathematics—algebra, real analysis, complex analysis, number theory, combinatorics, probability theory, statistics, topology, geometry, and so on—have undoubtedly arisen from our experience of the world around us, in order to systematize that experience, to give it order and coherence, and thereby to enable us to predict and perhaps control future events."**
>
> Hilton, Peter. *"Mathematics in Our Culture"* in Gullberg, Jan. Mathematics: From the Birth of Numbers. New York: W.W. Norton & Company, 1997.

Mathematics is a way of describing relationships between numbers and other measurable quantities. As the language of science, mathematics communicates ideas in universally accepted terminology. It can express simple equations or explain relationships among the farthest objects in the known universe. Mathematics has helped make advances in medicine, technology, astronomy, meteorology, biology, physics, economics, and political science.

Mathematics has two main branches: pure mathematics, the study of abstract relationships, and applied mathematics, which applies mathematical analysis to real-world problems. The relationship between pure and applied mathematics is a complex one, and is constantly shifting.

Mathematics continues to grow at a phenomenal rate. There is no end in sight, and the application of mathematics to science becomes greater all the time.

## Key Events in the Timeline of Mathematics

- Counting was the earliest mathematical activity. Early humans needed counting to keep track of herds and for trade. Early counting systems used the fingers of one or both hands, as evidenced by the predominance of the numbers 5 and 10 as the bases for most number systems today. Advances were in the concept of numbers, the invention of addition, subtraction, multiplication, and division, and concepts such as the line and the circle in geomoetry.
- **2000 B.C.** The Babylonians of ancient Mesopotamia and the ancient Egyptians developed principles of arithmetic, measurement, and calculation.
- **1400 B.C.** The first true evidence of mathematical activity in China can be found in numeration symbols on tortoise shells and oracle bones from the Shang dynasty. These inscriptions contain both tally and code symbols based on a decimal system. Early Chinese mathematics had a great influence on later civilizations.
- **1000 B.C.** The Maya used a base-20 number system, which probably descended from early times when people counted on both fingers and toes and may have been the first to have a special symbol for zero. The Maya also developed two types of calendars, calculating the length of the lunar month and the solar year with remarkable precision.
- **6th Century B.C.** The Greeks adopted elements of mathematics from the Babylonians and the Egyptians and invented abstract mathematics founded on a logical structure of definitions, axioms (propositions accepted as self-evident), and proofs. Thales and Pythagoras were famous mathemmaticians.
- **300 B.C.** Euclid, a Greek mathematician, deduced some 500 theorems comprising all the important results of Greek mathematics to that time. Euclid began by defining terms, such as line, angle, and circle. He stated ten self-evident truths, such as "The whole is greater than any of its parts."
- **1st Century A.D.** After the decline of Greece and Rome, mathematics flourished for hundreds of years in India and the Islamic world. Their mathematical masterpieces and those of the Greeks were translated into Arabic in the centers of Islamic learning, where mathematical discoveries continued during the Middle Ages. Our present numeration system, with each number having an absolute value and a place value (ones, tens, hundreds, and so forth), is known as the Hindu-Arabic system.
- **8th Century A.D.** Translators in Baghdad produced Arabic versions of Greek and Indian mathematical works. Many of the ancient Greek works on mathematics were preserved during the Middle Ages through Arabic translations and commentaries. Europe acquired much of this learning during the 12th century, when Greek and Arabic works were translated into Latin, the written language of the educated Europeans.

*"Number rules the universe."*

—Pythagoras, Greek philosopher and mathematician, 580–520 B.C.

"Mathematics is one of humanity's great achievements. By enhancing the capabilities of the human mind, mathematics has facilitated the development of science, technology, engineering, business, and government. Mathematics is also an intellectual achievement of great sophistication and beauty that epitomizes the power of deductive reasoning. For people to participate fully in society, they must know basic mathematics."

Kilpatrick, J., Swafford, J., and Findell, B. eds. *Adding It Up: Helping Children Learn Mathematics.* Washington, D.C.: National Research Council/National Academy Press, 2001, p. 1.

## SRA Real Math and Mathematics

***Real Math*** has been developed with a keen respect for the history and the beauty of mathematics. Careful attention has been paid to developing children's understanding of mathematics in a coherent and logical fashion to demonstrate the connections among the different strands and branches of mathematics. ***Real Math*** aims for children to develop a positive attitude toward mathematics. Specific abilities and understandings will be of little value to children unless accompanied by two convictions: (a) that mathematics does what it was invented to do—solve real, interesting problems; and (b) that it is a tool that can be used confidently and well. Also, we hope that students will find mathematics enjoyable to do and that they will appreciate it esthetically.

- **9th Century A.D.** Arab mathematician al-Khwārizmī wrote a systematic introduction to algebra. The English word *algebra* comes from *al-jabr* in the title. A 12th-century Latin translation of al-Khwārizmī's treatise was crucial for the later development of algebra in Europe. Al-Khwārizmī's name is the source of the word *algorithm*.
- **16th Century** Mathematicians began to use symbols to make algebraic thinking and writing more concise. These symbols included $+$, $-$, $\times$, $=$, $>$ (greater than), and $<$ (less than). The most significant innovation, by French mathematician François Viète, was the systematic use of letters for variables in equations.
- **17th Century** The founders of modern science—Nicolaus Copernicus, Johannes Kepler, Galileo, and Isaac Newton—studied the natural world as mathematicians, and they looked for its mathematical laws. Over time, mathematics grew more and more abstract as mathematicians sought to establish the foundations of their fields logically. The most important development in geometry during the 17th century was the discovery of analytic geometry by René Descartes and Pierre de Fermat, which makes it possible to study geometric figures using algebraic equations. The discovery of differential and integral calculus by Sir Isaac Newton and Gottfried Wilhelm Leibniz ranks as the crowning achievement of 17th-century mathematics. Calculus allowed the solution of many problems that had been previously insoluble, including the determination of the laws of motion and the theory of electromagnetism.
- **18th Century** During the 18th century, calculus became the cornerstone of mathematical analysis on the European continent. Mathematicians applied the discovery to a variety of problems in physics, astronomy, and engineering. In the course of doing so, they also created new areas of mathematics. The greatest mathematician of the 18th century, Leonhard Euler of Switzerland, was also the most prolific writer on mathematical subjects of all time. His treatises covered essentially the entire fields of pure and applied mathematics.
- **The 19th Century** was a period of intense mathematical activity. It began with German mathematician Carl Friedrich Gauss, considered to be the last complete mathematician because of his contributions to all branches of the field. The century saw a great effort to place all areas of mathematics on firm theoretical foundations. The support for these foundations was logic—the deduction of basic propositions from a limited set of assumptions and definitions. Mathematicians also discovered the existence of additional geometries and algebras, and more than one kind of infinity.
- **During the 20th Century** mathematics made rapid advances on all fronts. The foundations of mathematics became more solidly grounded in logic, while at the same time mathematics advanced the development of symbolic logic. Philosophy and physics, too, benefited from the contributions of mathematicians to the Relativity Theory and Quantum Theory. Indeed, mathematics achieved broader applications than ever before as new fields developed within mathematics (computational mathematics, game theory, and chaos theory), and other branches of knowledge, including economics and physics, achieved firmer grounding through the application of mathematics. Even the most abstract mathematics seemed to find application, and the boundaries between pure mathematics and applied mathematics grew ever fuzzier.

# Content Strands of Mathematics

*"One reason why mathematics enjoys special esteem, above all other sciences, is that its laws are absolutely certain and indisputable, while those of other sciences are to some extent debatable and in constant danger of being overthrown by newly discovered facts."*

—Albert Einstein, physicist, 1879–1955

## Algebra

Algebra is the branch of mathematics that uses symbols to represent arithmetic operations. Algebra extends arithmetic through the use of symbols and other notations, such as exponents and variables. Algebraic thinking involves understanding patterns, equations, and relationships, and includes concepts of functions and inverse operations. Because algebra uses symbols rather than numbers, it can produce general rules that apply to all numbers. What most people commonly think of as algebra involves the manipulation of equations and the solving of equations. Exposure to algebraic ideas can and should occur well before students first study algebra in middle school or high school. Even primary-grade students are capable of understanding many algebraic concepts. Developing algebraic thinking in the early grades smoothes the transition to algebra in middle school and high school and ensures success in future math and science courses, as well as in the workplace.

**"Algebra begins with a search for patterns. Identifying patterns helps bring order, cohesion, and predictability to seemingly unorganized situations and allows one to make generalizations beyond the information directly available. The recognition and analysis of patterns are important components of the young child's intellectual development because they provide a foundation for the development of algebraic thinking."**

Clements, Douglas and Sarama, J. eds. *Engaging Young Children in Mathematics: Standards for Early Childhood Mathematics Education.* Mahwah, New Jersey: Lawrence Erlbaum Associates, Publishers, 2004. p. 52.

### SRA Real Math and Algebra

**Goal:** Understanding of functional relationships between variables that represents real-world phenomena in a constant state of change. Children should be able to draw the graphs of functions and to derive information about functions from their graphs. They should understand the special importance of linear functions and the connection between the study of functions and the solution of equations and inequalities.

The algebra readiness strand that begins in the PreK level is designed to prepare students for future work in algebra by exposing them to algebraic thinking, including looking for patterns, using variables, working with functions, using integers and exponents, and being aware that mathematics is far more than just arithmetic.

## Arithmetic

Arithmetic, one of the oldest branches of mathematics, arises from the most fundamental of mathematical operations: counting. The arithmetic operations—addition, subtraction, multiplication, division, and placeholding—form the basis of the mathematics that we use regularly. Mastery of the basic operations with whole numbers (addition, subtraction, multiplication, and division)

**"Although some educators once believed that children memorize their 'basic facts' as conditioned responses, research now shows that children do not move from knowing nothing about sums and differences of numbers to having the basic number combinations memorized. Instead, they move through a series of progressively more advanced and abstract methods for working out the answers to simple arithmetic problems. Furthermore, as children get older, they use the procedures more and more efficiently."**

Kilpatrick, J., Swafford, J. and Findell, B. eds. Adding It Up: Helping Children Learn Mathematics. Washington, D.C.: National Research Council/National Academy Press, 2001, p. 182–183.

## Real Math and Arithmetic

**Goal:** Mastery of the basic operations with whole numbers (addition, subtraction, multiplication, and division). Whatever other skills and understandings children acquire, they must have the ability to calculate a precise answer when necessary. This fundamental skill includes not only knowledge of the appropriate arithmetic algorithms, but also mastery of the basic addition, subtraction, multiplication, and division facts and understanding of the positional notation (base ten) of the whole numbers.

Mastery Checkpoints occur throughout the program to indicate when mastery of concepts and skills is expected. Skills are introduced at least one grade level before mastery is expected and then reviewed in Mental Math and subsequent grade levels. Once taught, arithmetic skills are also integrated into other topics, such as functions and geometry.

### Data Collection and Organization

Ability to organize information to make it easier to use and the ability to interpret data and graphs.

> **"Describing data involves reading displays of data (e.g., tables, lists, graphs); that is, finding information explicitly stated in the display, recognizing graphical conventions, and making direct connections between the original data and the display. The process is essentially what has been called reading the data.... The process of organizing and reducing data incorporates mental actions, such as ordering, grouping, and summarizing. Data reduction also includes the use of representative measures of center (often termed *measures of central tendency*), such as mean, mode, or median, and measures of spread, such as range or standard deviation."**
>
> Kilpatrick, J., Swafford, J. and Findell, B. eds. *Adding It Up: Helping Children Learn Mathematics*. Washington, D.C.: National Research Council/National Academy Press, 2001, p. 289.

## Real Math and Data Organization

**Goal:** Ability to organize and arrange data for greater intelligibility. Children should develop not only the routine skills of tabulating and graphing results, but also, at a higher level, the ability to detect patterns and trends in poorly organized data, either before or after reorganization. In addition, children need to develop the ability to extrapolate and interpolate from data and from graphic representations. Children should also know when extrapolation or interpolation is justified and when it is not.

In ***Real Math*** students work with graphs beginning in PreK. In each grade, the program emphasizes understanding what data shows.

### Geometry

Geometry is the branch of mathematics that deals with the properties of space. Plane geometry is the geometry of flat surfaces, and solid geometry is the geometry of three-dimensional space figures. Geometry has many more fields, including the study of spaces with four or more dimensions.

> **"Geometry can be used to understand and to represent the objects, directions, and locations in our world, and the relationships between them. Geometric shapes can be described, analyzed, transformed, and composed and decomposed into other shapes."**
>
> Clements, Douglas and Sarama, J. eds. *Engaging Young Children in Mathematics: Standards for Early Childhood Mathematics Education.* Mahwah, New Jersey: Lawrence Erlbaum Associates, Publishers, 2004. p. 39.

## Real Math and Geometry

**Goal:** Understanding of and ability to use geometric concepts in a variety of contexts.

To appreciate how geometry can help to explain algebraic concepts.

## Measurement

Understanding of what a measurement is and how units relate to measurement.

**"Measurement is one of the main real-world applications of mathematics...counting is a type of measurement—it measures how many items in a collection. Measurement of continuous quantities involves assigning a number to attributes, such as length, area, and weight. Together, number and measurement are components of quantitative reasoning. In this vein, measurement helps connect the two realms of number and geometry, each providing conceptual support to the other."**

Clements, Douglas and Sarama, J. eds. *Engaging Young Children in Mathematics: Standards for Early Childhood Mathematics Education.* Mahwah, New Jersey: Lawrence Erlbaum Associates, Publishers, 2004. p. 43–50.

### SRA Real Math and Measurement

**Goal:** Firm understanding of magnitude with respect to measurements and of the role of units in assigning numerical magnitudes to physical quantities. Children should, for example, understand the need for standard units of measurement and know how to use appropriate measurement tools (rulers, balances, liquid volume measures, and thermometers).

In ***Real Math,*** students work extensively with estimating measures and making actual measurements. They work with both the customary system (inches, pounds, cups) and the metric system (meters, grams, liters) separately so that they develop an intuitive feel for measurements in both systems.

## Number Sense and Place Value

Understanding of the significance and use of numbers in counting, measuring, comparing, and ordering.

**"It is very important for teachers to provide children with opportunities to recognize the meaning of mathematical symbols, mathematical operations, and the patterns or relationships represented in the child's work with numbers. For example, the number sense that a child acquires should be based upon an understanding that inverse operations, such as addition and subtraction, undo the operations of the other. Instructionally, teachers must encourage their students to think beyond simply finding the answer and to actually have them think about the numerical relationships that are being represented or modeled by the symbols, words, or materials being used in the lesson."**

Kilpatrick, J., Swafford, J. and Findell, B. eds. *Adding It Up: Helping Children Learn Mathematics.* Washington, D.C.: National Research Council/National Academy Press, 2001, p. 270–271.

### SRA Real Math and Number Sense

**Goal:** Firm understanding of the significance and use of numbers in counting, measuring, comparing, and ordering. The ability to think intelligently, using numbers. This basic requirement of numeracy includes the ability to recognize given answers as absurd, without doing a precise calculation, by observing that they violate experience, common sense, elementary logic, or familiar arithmetic patterns. It also includes the use of imagination and insight in using numbers to solve problems. Children should be able to recognize when, for example, a trial-and-error method is likely to be easier to use and more manageable than a standard algorithm.

Developing number sense is a primary goal of ***Real Math*** in every grade. Numbers are presented in a variety of representations and integrated in many contexts so that students develop thorough understanding of numbers.

## Probability and Statistics

Probability and statistics deal with events where outcomes are uncertain, and they assess the likelihood of possible outcomes. Statistics is the organization and analysis of data for the purpose of simplification, comparison, and prediction.

### Real Math and Probability and Statistics

**Goal:** The ability to use probabilistic ideas in ordinary, elementary applications. Children should understand the reasons for (and something of the dangers of) using sampling techniques; they should have the ability to describe a population in terms of some simple statistic (mean, median, range); and they should understand the difference between intelligent risk taking, based on reasonable estimates of probabilities, and foolish risks, based on unsupported guesswork or wishful thinking.

## Rational Numbers—Fractions, Decimals, and Percents

Understanding fractions, decimals, and percents and their relationships to each other, including the ability to perform calculations and to use rational numbers in measurement.

**"Children need to learn that rational numbers are numbers in the same way that whole numbers are numbers. For children to use rational numbers to solve problems, they need to learn that the same rational number may be represented in different ways, as a fraction, a decimal, or a percent. Fraction concepts and representations need to be related to those of division, measurement, and ratio. Decimal and fractional representations need to be connected and understood. Building these connections take extensive experience with rational numbers over a substantial period of time. Researchers have documented that difficulties in working with rational numbers can often be traced to weak conceptual understanding....Instructional sequences in which more time is spent at the outset on developing meaning for the various representations of rational numbers and the concept of unit have been shown to promote mathematical proficiency."**

—Kilpatrick, J., Swafford, J. and Findell, B. eds. *Adding It Up: Helping Children Learn Mathematics*. Washington, D.C.: National Research Council/National Academy Press, 2001, p. 415–416.

### Real Math and Rational Numbers

**Goal:** Understanding of rational numbers and of the relationship of fractions to decimals. Included here are the ability to do appropriate calculations with fractions or decimals (or both, as in fractions of decimals); the use of decimals in (metric unit) measurements; and the multiplication of fractions as a model for the "of" relation and as a model for areas of rectangles.

**Goal:** Understanding of the meaning of rates and of their relationship to the arithmetic concept of ratio. Children should be able to calculate ratios, proportions, and percentages; understand how to use them intelligently in real-life situations; understand the common units in which rates occur (such as kilometers per hour, cents per gram); understand the meaning of per; and be able to express ratios as fractions.

In ***Real Math,*** understanding of rational numbers begins in the earliest grades with sharing activities and develops understanding of rational numbers with increasing sophistication at each grade.

# Mathematics Research Overview

**For decades, people have been studying mathematics instruction to figure out what is and what is not effective. In the last few years, two compendiums of reliable research have been published; this research is relevant, sound, and generalizable.**

Kilpatrick, J., Swafford, J. and Findell, B. eds. *Adding It Up: Helping Children Learn Mathematics.* Washington, D.C.: National Research Council/National Academy Press, 2001.

Kilpatrick, Jeremy, Martin, W. Gary, and Schifter, Deborah, eds. *A Research Companion to Principles and Standards for School Mathematics.* Reston, VA: National Council of Teachers of Mathematics, Inc. 2003.

The purpose of these books has been to synthesize the research on elementary math education to provide recommendations and advice to educators. Research can help to guide decisions about what mathematics to teach and how to teach it to improve the quality of math education and promote interest and achievement in mathematics.

## Research has helped to identify

- what mathematics should be learned in elementary school to develop a solid foundation in understanding.
- effective teaching strategies for different strands of mathematics.
- classification of the learning trajectories that describe how children learn mathematics.

*"The science of pure mathematics...may claim to be the most original creation of the human spirit."*

Alfred North Whitehead, English mathematician and philosopher, 1861–1947

## SRA Real Math and Research

***Real Math*** is based on several types of research.

1. *Field Tests.* ***Real Math*** is constantly being tested and improved. It was originally developed one grade level at a time over a 10-year period and was rigorously field-tested to ensure its effectiveness. Used in classrooms for over thirty years, the program has been revised to address current standards and the latest research in mathematics education, and continues its reliance on scientific field-testing and feedback from teachers.
2. *Research on Teaching Strategies.* ***Real Math*** seriously attends to the latest research in mathematics education. Doug Clements's and Julie Sarama's work in early childhood mathematics forms the prekindergarten level of the program, and Joan Moss's work in fractions, decimals, and percents inspired revision of the rational number strand throughout the program. A review of relevant research precedes each chapter, and research-based strategies throughout the program are identified in the ***Research in Action*** feature.
3. *Research on Learning Trajectories.* Much research has been conducted in identifying children's learning trajectories in mathematics. Developmental Levels for early mathematics are outlined in Appendix C, and relevant information for teachers about the learning trajectories precedes each chapter. ***Real Math*** activities, teaching strategies, and lesson progression supports the development of children through the developmental levels of the learning trajectories.

# Math Proficiencies

**Mathematical proficiency has five strands. These strands are not independent; they represent different aspects of a complex whole.... they are interwoven and interdependent in the development of proficiency in mathematics.**

Kilpatrick, J., Swafford, J. and Findell, B. eds. Adding It Up: Helping Children Learn Mathematics. Washington, D.C.: National Research Council/National Academy Press, 2001, p. 115–133.

*Each problem that I solved became a rule which served afterwards to solve other problems.*

René Descartes French philosopher and mathematician, 1596–1650

1. **Understanding** (Conceptual Understanding): Comprehending mathematical concepts, operations, and relations—knowing what mathematical symbols, diagrams, and procedures mean.

   *Conceptual Understanding* refers to an integrated and functional grasp of mathematical ideas. Students with conceptual understanding know more than isolated facts and methods. They understand why a mathematical idea is important and the kinds of contexts in which it is useful. They have organized their knowledge into a coherent whole, which enables them to learn new ideas by connecting those ideas to what they already know. Conceptual understanding also supports retention. Because facts and methods learned with understanding are connected, they are easier to remember and use, and they can be reconstructed when forgotten. If students understand a method, they are unlikely to remember it incorrectly.

   A significant indicator of conceptual understanding is being able to represent mathematical situations in different ways and knowing how different representations can be useful for different purposes.

   Knowledge that has been learned with understanding provides the basis for generating new knowledge and for solving new and unfamiliar problems. When students have acquired conceptual understanding in an area of mathematics, they see the connections among concepts and procedures and can give arguments to explain why some facts are consequences of others. They gain confidence, which then provides a base from which they can move to another level of understanding.

2. **Computing** (Procedural Fluency): Carrying out mathematical procedures, such as adding, subtracting, multiplying, and dividing numbers flexibly, accurately, efficiently, and appropriately.

   *Procedural Fluency* refers to knowledge of procedures, knowledge of when and how to use them appropriately, and skill in performing them flexibly, accurately, and efficiently. In the domain of numbers, procedural fluency is especially needed to support conceptual understanding of place value and the meanings of rational numbers. It also supports the analysis of similarities and differences between methods of calculating. These methods include, in addition to written procedures, mental methods for finding certain sums, differences, products, or quotients, as well as methods that use calculators, computers, or manipulative materials such as blocks, counters, or beads.

   Students need to be efficient and accurate in performing basic computations with whole numbers without always having to refer to tables or other aids. They also need to know reasonably efficient and accurate ways to add, subtract, multiply, and divide multidigit numbers, both mentally and with pencil and paper. A good conceptual understanding of place value in the base-ten system supports the development of fluency in multidigit computation. Such understanding also supports simplified but accurate mental arithmetic and more flexible ways of dealing with numbers than many students ultimately achieve.

3. **Applying** (Strategic Competence): Being able to formulate problems mathematically and to devise strategies for solving them using concepts and procedures appropriately.

   *Strategic Competence* refers to the ability to formulate mathematical problems, represent them, and solve them. This strand is similar to what has been called *problem solving* and *problem formulation.* Although students are often presented with clearly specified problems to solve in the school setting, outside of school they encounter situations in which part of the difficulty is to figure out exactly what the problem is. Then they need to formulate the problem so that they can use mathematics to solve it. Consequently, they are likely to need experience and practice in problem formulating, as well as in problem solving. They should know a variety of solution strategies, as well as which strategies might be useful for solving a specific problem.

   To represent a problem accurately, students must first understand the situation, including its key features. They then need to generate a mathematical representation of the problem that captures the core mathematical elements and ignores the irrelevant features.

Students develop procedural fluency as they use their strategic competence to choose among effective procedures. They also learn that solving challenging mathematics problems depends on the ability to carry out procedures readily, and conversely, and that problem-solving experience helps them acquire new concepts and skills.

4. **Reasoning** (Adaptive Reasoning): Using logic to explain and justify a solution to a problem or to extend from something known to something not yet known.

   *Adaptive Reasoning* refers to the capacity to think logically about the relationships among concepts and situations. Such reasoning is correct and valid, stems from careful consideration of alternatives, and includes knowledge of how to justify the conclusions. In mathematics, adaptive reasoning is the glue that holds everything together and guides learning. One uses it to navigate through the many facts, procedures, concepts, and solution methods, and to see that they all fit together in some way, that they make sense. In mathematics, deductive reasoning is used to settle disputes and disagreements. Answers are right because they follow some agreed-upon assumptions through a series of logical steps. Students who disagree about a mathematical answer need not rely on checking with the teacher, collecting opinions from their classmates, or gathering data from outside the classroom. In principle, they need only check that their reasoning is valid.

   Research suggests that students are able to display reasoning ability when three conditions are met: they have a sufficient knowledge base, the task is understandable and motivating, and the context is familiar and comfortable.

5. **Engaging** (Productive Disposition): Seeing mathematics as sensible, useful, and doable—if you work at it—and being willing to do the work.

   *Productive Disposition* refers to the tendency to see sense in mathematics, to perceive it as both useful and worthwhile, to believe that steady effort in learning mathematics pays off, and to see oneself as an effective learner and doer of mathematics. If students are to develop conceptual understanding, procedural fluency, strategic competence, and adaptive reasoning abilities, they must believe mathematics is understandable, not arbitrary; that with diligent effort, it can be learned and used; and that they are capable of figuring it out. Developing a productive disposition requires frequent opportunities to make sense of mathematics, to recognize the benefits of perseverance, and to experience the rewards of sense making in mathematics.

   Students' dispositions toward mathematics are a major factor in determining their educational success. Students who have developed a productive disposition are confident in their knowledge and ability. They see that mathematics is both reasonable and intelligible, and believe that, with appropriate effort and experience, they can learn.

## Real Math and Math Proficiency

The goals of ***Real Math*** are to develop the five interwoven proficiencies. In every lesson, activities are designed to address understanding, computing, reasoning, applying, and engaging in an integrated fashion. Most games, for example, can be thought of as one or more mathematical problems. Students must first identify that a problem or problems exist, then provide a structure of the problem and use reasoning to arrive at a solution. At the same time, students are developing fluency in arithmetic. There is little question that students demonstrate engagement with mathematics, as well, when they are playing a ***Real Math*** game. Similarly, many activities in ***Real Math*** are engaging because the situations are those that are real to students. The students are well-motivated to learn the mathematics involved in each situation.

# ***Real Math*** Computational Expectations

At every grade level, ***Real Math*** develops each strand of mathematics with understanding, teaching children to appreciate and think mathematically. Problem solving, communicating mathematically, algebra, measurement, geometry, probability, and statistics, for example, are explored in every grade. Below are the computational expectations that are developed with understanding at each grade level that build fluency with number.

## PreK

There are two key ideas emphasized in number.

1. Numbers can be used to tell us how many, describe order, and measure; they involve numerous relations, and can be represented in various ways.
2. Operations with numbers can be used to model a variety of real-world situations and to solve problems; they can be carried out in various ways.

## Grade K

- Numbers (cardinal and ordinal) through 100
- Counting; writing numerals
- Measurement with nonstandard units
- One-to-one matching
- Adding and subtracting whole numbers in the 0–100 range

## Grade 1

- Numbers 0 through 100
- Addition and subtraction concepts
- Basic addition facts (through $10 + 10$)
- Measurement with nonstandard units
- Introductory work with Multiplication, fractions, recording data, maps, and inequalities

## Grade 2

- Numbers through 10,000
- Basic addition and subtraction facts
- Multidigit addition and subtraction algorithms
- Introduction to multiplication and division
- Measurement with standard units
- Fractions of area and fractions of numbers
- Reading maps

## Grade 3

- Numbers through 1,000,000 and beyond
- Fractions and decimals
- Multiplication and division
- Multiplication facts through $10 \times 10$
- Multidigit multiplication algorithms
- Measurement
- Graphing and functions
- Adding and subtracting decimals

## Grade 4

- General multidigit multiplication algorithm
- Division by a one-digit divisor
- Addition and subtraction of common fractions
- Rounding and approximation
- Linear functions and composite and inverse functions
- Graphing such functions
- Multiplying decimals and whole numbers
- Introduction to mixed numbers

## Grade 5

- Multidigit division algorithm
- Rounding
- Linear functions and composite and inverse functions
- Graphing such functions
- Introduction of negative numbers
- Rates, ratios, and percentages
- Relation of fractions and decimals
- Addition, subtraction, and multiplication of fractions, mixed numbers, and decimals
- Division with decimal dividends and quotients

## Grade 6

- All operations with whole numbers, fractions, and decimals
- Some operations with negative numbers
- Computational shortcuts
- Compass and ruler constructions
- Nonlinear functions
- Graphing such functions
- Exponents
- Use of hand-held calculators

# Basic Facts

> **"Although some educators once believed that children memorize their 'basic facts' as conditioned responses, research now shows that children do not move from knowing nothing about sums and differences of numbers to having the basic number combinations memorized. Instead, they move through a series of progressively more advanced and abstract methods for working out the answers to simple arithmetic problems. Furthermore, as children get older, they use the procedures more and more efficiently."**
>
> Kilpatrick, J., Swafford, J. and Findell, B. eds. *Adding It Up: Helping Children Learn Mathematics.* Washington, D.C.: National Research Council/National Academy Press, 2001, p. 182–183.

The "basic" computation facts involve addition expressions in which the addends are whole numbers from 0 through 10, the corresponding subtraction expressions, multiplication expressions in which the factors are whole numbers from 0 through 10, and the corresponding division expressions. Fluency with basic facts is the ability to quickly and accurately use facts. Fluency is necessary before students can use multidigit algorithms efficiently. ***Real Math*** uses a variety of methods to ensure that students become fluent with basic facts by developing an understanding of how facts are related rather than by encouraging rote memorization.

If students have difficulty with some basic facts, you can help them by providing (or helping them discover) specific strategies for the facts they have not mastered. If students use their thinking skills and understand our base-ten number system and relationships between numbers, they can use strategies, such as the following, to help with quick and accurate recall.

Note that ***Real Math*** teaches the addition and multiplication facts systematically to emphasize the relationships between the facts, but that most of the subtraction and division facts are taught to be the inverses of the addition and multiplication facts, rather than being grouped on their own.

## Addition Fact Helpers

These strategies can help with many of the addition facts.

| To add: | Think of: |
|---|---|
| 0 | No change |
| 1 | Counting up 1 |
| 2 | Counting up 2 |
| 4 | One less than adding 5 |
| 5 | Finger sets |
| 6 | One more than adding 5 |
| 9 | One less than adding 10 |
| 10 | Write 1 in the tens place |

Other strategies which may be helpful include the following:

- **Commutative Law** (for example, 6 + 9 and 9 + 6). Students should recognize that if they can add two numbers in one order, they also know the sum in the opposite order. You can demonstrate this using concrete objects that are arranged in two different ways or a picture of two sets that is turned upside down. This realization cuts roughly in half the number of facts students need to learn.
- **Doubles** (for example, 4 + 4 and 7 + 7). Most students find the doubles facts easy to learn, since only one distinct addend is involved in each fact. The **Roll a Double Game** provides targeted practice with doubles facts.
- **Near doubles** (for example, 4 + 5, 8 + 7, and 7 + 9). When the two addends in a fact differ by 1 or 2, students can relate the fact to a doubles fact. For example, 8 + 7 must be 1 more than 7 + 7, so it is 14 + 1, or 15. One way to find 7 + 9 is to recognize that since 7 is 1 less than 8 and 9 is 1 more than 8, we know 7 + 9 = 8 + 8, or 16.
- **Sums of 10** (for example, 3 + 7 and 2 + 8). Students can become familiar with pairs of numbers that add to 10 by thinking of their fingers—raising 3 fingers then 7 fingers results in all 10 fingers being raised. The **Roll a Ten Game** provides targeted practice with the skill of recognizing sums of 10, which is useful for mental computation.
- **Remaining facts**. The strategies above will help with all facts except 8 + 3, 7 + 4, and 8 + 4. If students have trouble with these, you can demonstrate that 8 + 3 and 7 + 4 are both 1 more than 7 + 3, and that 8 + 4 = 8 + 2 + 2 = 10 + 2.
- **Subtraction**. To subtract 10 from a number between 10 and 20, simply remove the tens digit. To subtract 0, leave the number unchanged. For other subtraction facts, think of the corresponding addition fact.

## Multiplication Fact Helpers

| To multiply by: | Think: |
|---|---|
| 0 | The product is 0. |
| 1 | The product is the other number. |
| 2 | Add the number to itself. |
| 3 | Add the number to its double. |
| 4 | Double the number and then double that answer. |
| 5 | Multiply the number by 10 and take half. |
| 6 | Add the number to 5 times the number, or double three times the number. |
| 8 | Double four times the number, or double the number three times. |
| 9 | Subtract the number from 10 times the number. |
| 10 | Write a "0" after the number to indicate that number of tens. |

Other strategies which may be helpful include the following:

- **Commutative Law** (for example, 6 × 9 and 9 × 6). Students should recognize that if they can multiply two numbers in one order, they also know the product of the numbers in the opposite order. You can demonstrate this using an array that is turned sideways so that rows become columns and columns become rows. This realization cuts roughly in half the number of facts students need to learn.
- **Square facts** (for example, 3 × 3 and 7 × 7). Most students find the square facts relatively easy to learn, since only one distinct factor is involved in each fact.
- **Near squares** (for example, 8 × 7 and 6 × 8). When the two factors in a fact differ by 1 or 2, students can relate the product to a square fact. When the difference is 1, the product can be found by adding the smaller factor to its square. For example, 8 × 7 is 7 more than 7 × 7 — that is, 49 + 7 = 56. When the difference is 2, students can use the pattern $(n-1)(n+1) = n^2 - 1$. They can discover this pattern in the multiplication table even though they cannot prove it algebraically. For example, $6 \times 8 = (7 - 1)(7 + 1) = 49 - 1 = 48$.
- **Multiples of 9**. Once students are familiar with most of the multiplication facts, you may want to point out that the sum of the digits in multiples of 9 is always a multiple of 9. They can use this to check their work, or to recall a product if they can find the first digit. For example, 7 × 9 is a little less than 7 × 10, or 70, so the first digit is 6. Since 6 + 3 = 9, the product is 63. It is best not to introduce this pattern when students are first learning multiplication facts because they may inappropriately apply it to other factors. It is not true, for instance, that the sum of the digits of a multiple of 8 is a multiple of 8 (although the "rule" does also work for 3).

  Another quick way to multiply a whole number (0 through 10) by 9 is to spread out fingers and turn down the finger corresponding to the other factor (for example, the third finger to find 3 times 9). The product is "read" by counting the fingers to the left of the folded finger as tens, and the fingers to the right as ones. Two fingers and seven fingers represents 27.
- **Division**. Since the division facts do not fall neatly into patterns, the most efficient way to find division facts is to think of the corresponding multiplication fact. For example, 56 ÷ 7 = 8 because 8 × 7 = 56.

## Ways to Practice Facts

Even after students have learned all the basic facts with understanding, they need practice to retain their fluency. There are several useful ways for students to practice facts at school or at home.

- **Flash Cards**. When used appropriately, flash cards are a good way to provide either targeted practice with certain facts or general practice with all facts. Flash cards should be used by students independently or with a partner (teacher, aide, parent, or another student working on the same facts). If a student answers correctly, he or she should receive positive reinforcement. Incorrect answers should simply receive no reaction — negative reinforcement is counter-productive since it often leads to frustration.
- **Frequent "quizzing."** If a student or class is struggling with just a few facts, ask about those facts frequently throughout the day. For example, when walking around the room checking students' progress, you can say, "What's 6 × 8?" Encourage parents to do the same before and after school.
- **Games**. Playing appropriate games is an excellent way to provide practice with many facts in a brief period of time, while engaging even those students who are already fluent with basic facts.

  Good games for addition practice include **Roll a 15, Addition Table,** and **Addition Crossing.**

  Good games for multiplication practice include **Multiplication Table, Multiple Crossing,** and **Multigo.**
- **Speed Tests**. Administer speed tests periodically after most students have learned the basic facts to ensure that students are maintaining and improving their skills. Timed exercises are important because decreasing the time to think about an answer encourages automatic recall. Be sure to stress that students should work to improve their own performance, rather than comparing their results to those of others.

# Algorithms

> **"Step-by-step procedures for adding, subtracting, multiplying, or dividing numbers are called algorithms.... Learning to use algorithms for computation with multidigit numbers is an important part of developing proficiency with numbers. Algorithms are procedures that can be executed in the same way to solve a variety of problems arising from different situations and involving different numbers."**
>
> Kilpatrick, J., Swafford, J. and Findell, B. eds. *Adding It Up: Helping Children Learn Mathematics.* Washington, D.C.: National Research Council/National Academy Press, 2001, p. 196.

An algorithm is a set of steps for carrying out a procedure. There are many commonly used algorithms for addition, subtraction, multiplication, and division of multidigit numbers. ***Real Math*** guides students to discover one standard algorithm for each operation. However, if students have previously learned a different algorithm, or have figured out efficient procedures for some computations on their own, they should not be restricted to the procedures taught in class.

## Addition

A standard algorithm for addition is introduced using two sets of sticks bundled in groups of ten.

$$\begin{array}{r} 37 \\ +\ 48 \\ \hline \end{array}$$

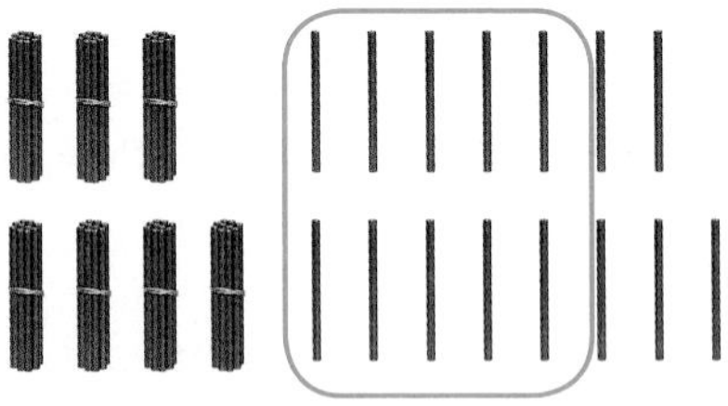

There are 7 tens and 15 ones.

We can regroup 10 ones as 1 ten.

Now there are 8 tens and 5 ones, so 37 + 48 = 85.

To avoid regrouping at the end, we can start adding with the ones place. We can record each step.

Beginning on the rightmost (ones) column, find the sum of the digits in the column. Write the ones digit of the sum below the addition line and carry the tens digit to the top of the tens column. Then repeat this process for the tens, hundreds, and so on.

$$\begin{array}{r} 684 \\ +\ 267 \\ \hline \end{array}$$

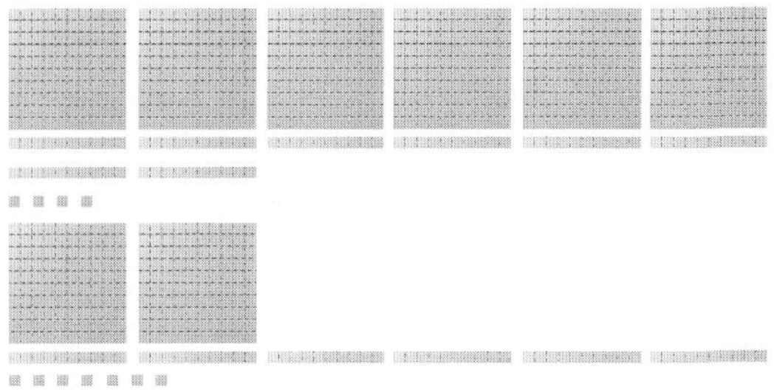

Add the ones: 4 + 7 = 11. Think, 11 ones = 1 ten and 1 one. Write the 1 one below the addition line. Write the 1 ten on top of the tens column.

$$\begin{array}{r} {}^{1}\phantom{4} \\ 684 \\ +\ 267 \\ \hline 1 \end{array}$$

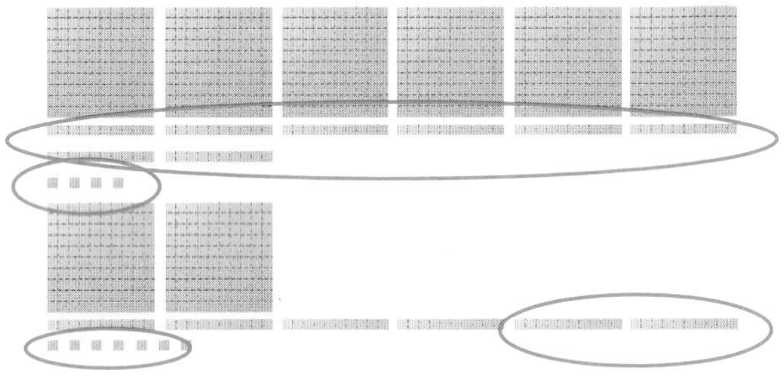

Add the tens: 1 + 8 + 6 = 15. Think, 15 tens = 1 hundred and 5 tens. Write the 5 tens below the addition line. Write the 1 hundred on top of the hundreds column.

$$\begin{array}{r} {}^{1\,1}\phantom{4} \\ 684 \\ +\ 267 \\ \hline 51 \end{array}$$

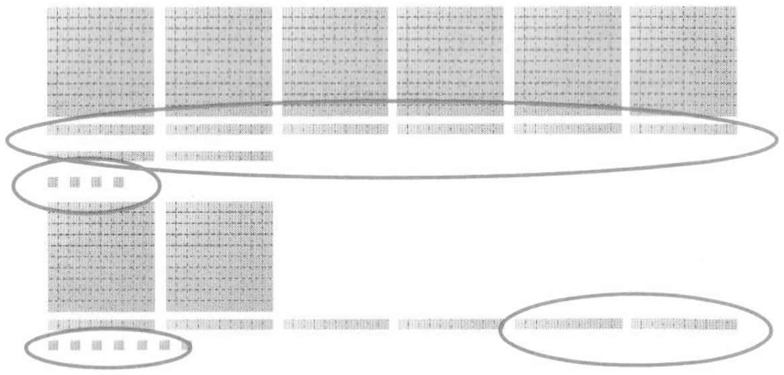

Add the hundreds.: 1 + 6 + 2 = 9. Write the 9 hundreds below the hundreds column.

$$\begin{array}{r} {}^{1\,1}\phantom{4} \\ 684 \\ +\ 267 \\ \hline 951 \end{array}$$

## Subtraction

As with the addition algorithm, a standard algorithm for subtraction is introduced using a set of sticks bundled in groups of ten.

```
  8 5
− 3 7
─────
```

There are not enough ones to take away 7.

Regroup 1 ten as 10 ones.

```
  8 5
− 3 7
─────
```

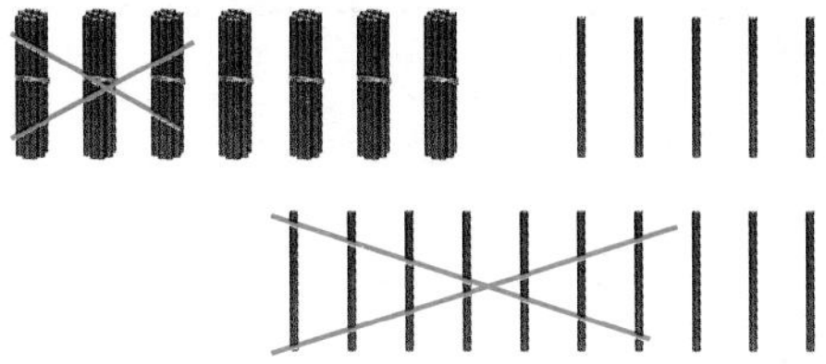

There are 4 tens and 8 ones.

85 − 37 = 48

It is easiest if we start subtracting with the ones place. We can record each step.

Beginning at the rightmost (ones) column, find the difference of that column. If the difference cannot be found, then rename the number in the next column to the left. Rewrite the tens and ones to reflect renaming. Then repeat this process for the tens, hundreds, and so on.

```
  1 1 6 5
−   4 2 8
─────────
```

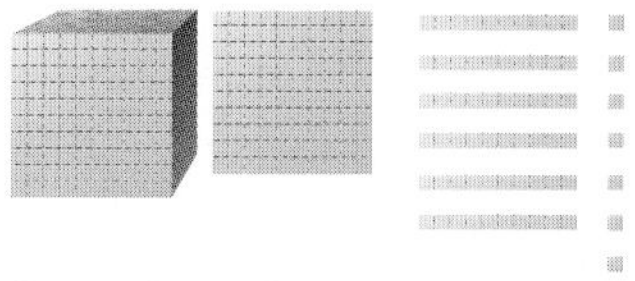

Since 8 ones cannot be taken from 5 ones, rename 6 tens as 5 tens and 10 ones.

```
      5 15
  1 1 ~~6~~ ~~5~~
−   4 2 8
─────────
```

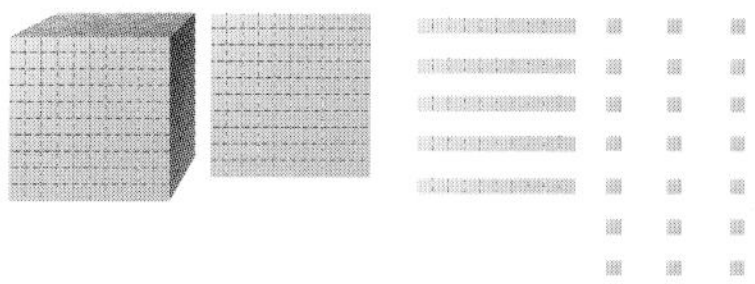

Subtract the ones.

```
      5 15
  1 1 ~~6~~ ~~5~~
−   4 2 8
─────────
        7
```

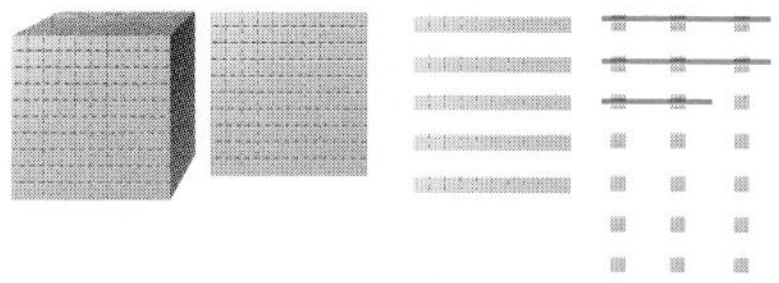

Subtract the tens.

```
      5 15
  1 1 ~~6~~ ~~5~~
−   4 2 8
─────────
      3 7
```

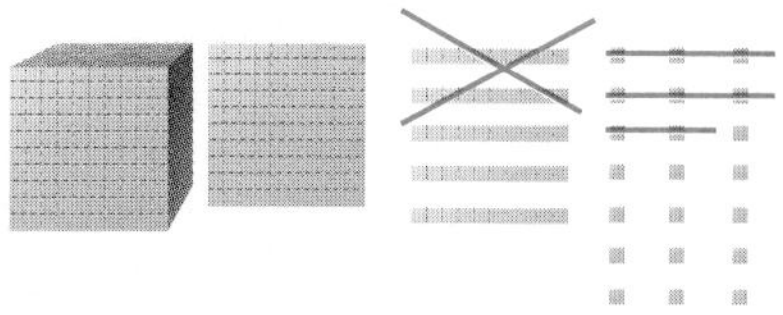

Since 4 hundreds cannot be taken from 1 hundred, rename 1 thousand as 10 hundreds.

```
      5 15
  1 1 ~~6~~ ~~5~~
−   4 2 8
─────────
      3 7
```

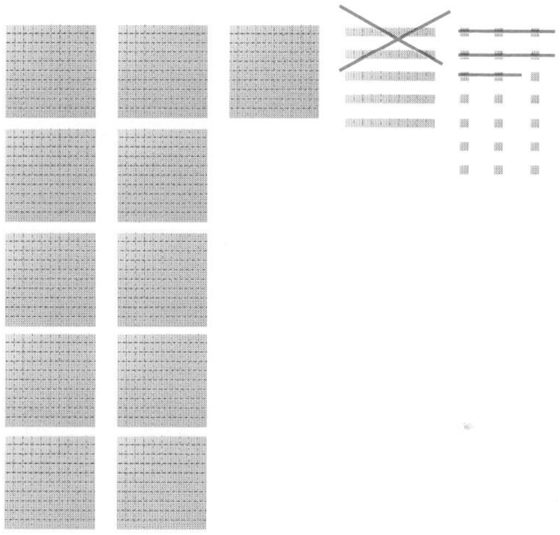

Subtract the hundreds.

```
      5 15
  1 1 ~~6~~ ~~5~~
−   4 2 8
─────────
    7 3 7
```

# Professional Development

## Multiplication

Efficient multiplication of multidigit numbers uses the Distributive Law. To multiply by a multidigit number, you can rewrite the product as a series of partial products. For example, $43 \times 8 = (40 + 3) \times 8 = (40 \times 8) - (3 \times 8) = 320 + 24 = 344$.

Products of two multidigit numbers can be found by writing each factor in expanded form and finding the products of each pair of terms. For example, $46 \times 73 = (40 + 6) \times (70 + 3) = (40 \times 70) + (40 \times 3) + (6 \times 70) + (6 \times 3)$.

***Real Math*** introduces these ideas using area models in which each partial product is shown as a separate area. The product of the numbers (the sum of the areas of each rectangle) is the sum of the partial products.

$$\begin{array}{r} 43 \\ \times \quad 8 \\ \hline 24 \\ 320 \\ \hline 344 \end{array}$$

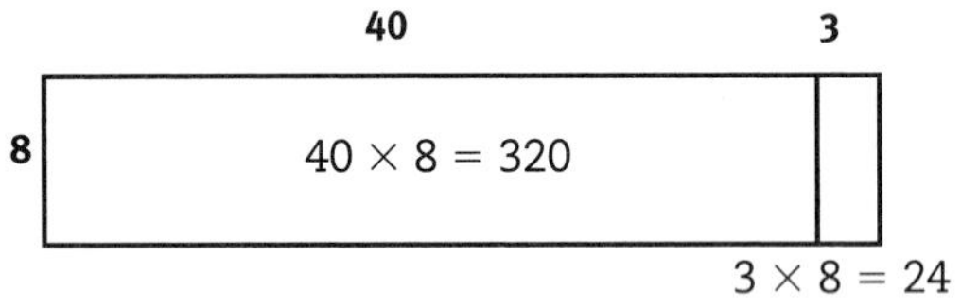


$$\begin{array}{lr} & 46 \\ & \times\ 73 \\ \hline 6 \times 3 = 18 & 18 \\ 40 \times 3 = 120 & 120 \\ 6 \times 70 = 420 & 420 \\ 40 \times 70 = 2{,}800 & 2800 \\ \hline & 3{,}358 \end{array}$$

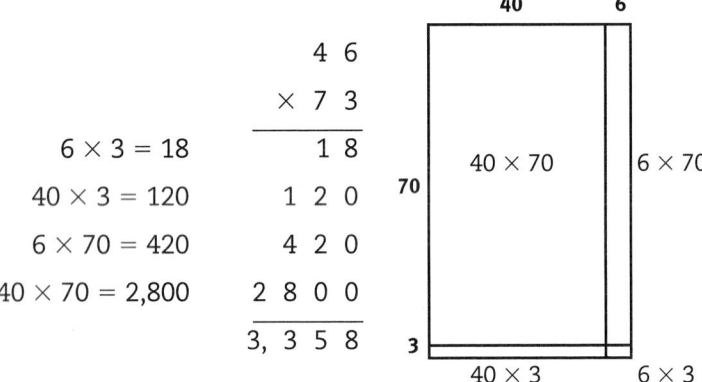

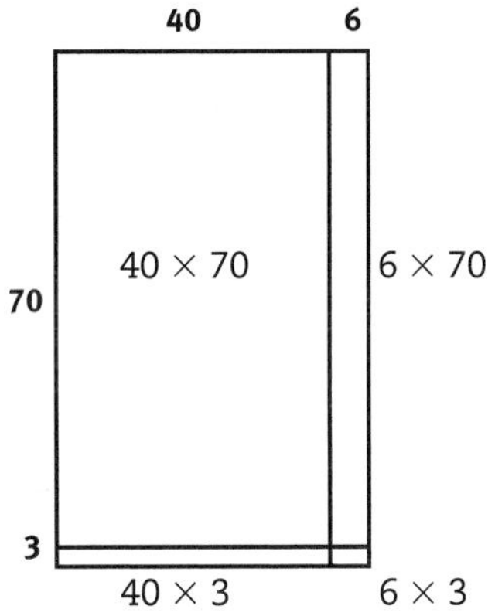


### Standard algorithm

Once students understand the idea of partial products, they are introduced to a more efficient way of recording their work.

Beginning at the rightmost column, find the product. Write the ones digit of the product below the line and carry the tens digit to the top of the tens column. Then repeat this process for each digit of the second factor.

$$\begin{array}{r} 46 \\ \times\ 73 \\ \hline \end{array}$$

Multiply 3 times the ones: $6 \times 3 = 18$.

18 ones = 1 ten and 8 ones

$$\begin{array}{r} {\scriptstyle 1}\ \ \\ 46 \\ \times\ 73 \\ \hline 8 \end{array}$$

Multiply 3 times the tens and add the carried ten:

$(4 \times 3) + 1 = 13$. Record 13 tens.

$$\begin{array}{r} {\scriptstyle 1}\ \ \\ 46 \\ \times\ 73 \\ \hline 138 \end{array}$$

Multiply 7 tens times the ones: $7 \times 6 = 42$.

42 tens = 4 hundreds and 2 tens.

$$\begin{array}{r} {\scriptstyle 1}\ \ \\ 46 \\ \times\ 73 \\ \hline 138 \\ 2\ \ \end{array}$$

Multiply 7 tens times 4 tens and add the 4 carried tens:

$(7 \times 4) + 4 = 32$

$$\begin{array}{r} {\scriptstyle 4}\ \ \\ 46 \\ \times\ 73 \\ \hline 138 \\ 322\ \ \end{array}$$

Add the partial products.

$$\begin{array}{r} {\scriptstyle 4}\ \ \\ 46 \\ \times\ 73 \\ \hline 138 \\ 322\ \ \\ \hline 3{,}358 \end{array}$$

## Division

Division with a multidigit dividend is introduced using an example in which an amount of money (expressed in \$100, \$10, and \$1 bills) is shared as equally as possible by a number of students. As students share the money, they exchange \$100 bills for \$10 bills and \$10 bills for \$1 bills as needed.

Share \$836 (8 \$100-bills, 3 \$10-bills, and 6 \$1-bills) among 7 students.

Each student gets 1 \$100-bill, so write 100 above the dividend. Now \$700 has been distributed, so subtract 700 from the total.

$$\begin{array}{r} 100 \\ 7\overline{)836} \\ -700 \\ \hline 136 \end{array}$$

Now there is 1 \$100 bill, 3 \$10 bills, and 6 \$1 bills. Exchange the 1 \$100-bill for 10 \$10-bills, to leave 13 \$1-bills.

Each student gets 1 \$10-bill, so write 10 above the dividend and subtract 70.

$$\begin{array}{r} 10 \\ 100 \\ 7\overline{)836} \\ -700 \\ \hline 136 \\ -70 \\ \hline 66 \end{array}$$

Now there are 6 \$10-bills and 6 \$1-bills left. Exchange the 6 \$10 bills for 60 \$1-bills, to leave 66 \$1-bills.

Each student gets 9 \$1-bills, so write 9 above the dividend and subtract 63 ($7 \times 9$).

$$\begin{array}{r} 9 \\ 10 \\ 100 \\ 7\overline{)836} \\ -700 \\ \hline 136 \\ -70 \\ \hline 66 \\ -63 \\ \hline 3 \end{array}$$

***The mathematical sciences particularly exhibit order, symmetry, and limitation; and these are the greatest forms of the beautiful.***

Aristotle, Greek philosopher, 384–322 B.C.

Since $100 + 10 + 9 = 119$, each student gets \$119. There will be \$3 left over.

This naturally leads to a standard algorithm which involves asking how many times the divisor divides into the thousands, hundreds, tens, and ones of the dividend.

### Standard algorithm

Once students understand the steps in division, they are introduced to progressively more efficient ways of writing them. Three different versions of the algorithm are taught. Each uses the same steps, but they differ in the amount of writing they require.

**Long Form**

1,276 Remainder 4

$$\begin{array}{r} 6 \\ 70 \\ 200 \\ 1000 \\ 7\overline{)8936} \\ -7000 \\ \hline 1936 \\ -1400 \\ \hline 536 \\ -490 \\ \hline 46 \\ -42 \\ \hline 4 \end{array}$$

**Shorter From**

With Zeros

Be careful to put the answers in the correct column.

$$\begin{array}{r} 1276 \text{ R4} \\ 7\overline{)8936} \\ -7000 \\ 1936 \\ -1400 \\ \hline 536 \\ -490 \\ \hline 46 \\ -42 \\ \hline 4 \end{array}$$

**Shorter Form**

Without Zeros

Subtract and "bring down" only the next digit. Be careful to put the answers in the correct columns.

$$\begin{array}{r} 1276 \text{ R4} \\ 7\overline{)8936} \\ -7 \\ \hline 19 \\ -14 \\ \hline 53 \\ -49 \\ \hline 46 \\ -42 \\ \hline 4 \end{array}$$

# Technology

Technology has changed the world of mathematics. Technological tools have eliminated the need for tedious calculations and have enabled significant advances in applications of mathematics. Technology can also help to make teaching more effective and efficient. Well-designed math software activities have proven effective in advancing children's math achievements. Technology can also help teachers organize planning and instruction and manage record keeping.

## *Real Math* Technology for Teachers

***ePlanner*** provides a tool to help teachers plan daily lessons and plot out year-long goals.

- Daily lesson plan with lesson and homework detail
- Weekly lesson plan
- Monthly plan
- Yearly plan with lesson detail
- Lesson summaries and electronic lessons from the ***ePresentation*** that can be accessed at home
- Program resources (blacklines, pictures of manipulatives)
- Correlation to state guidelines
- Homework Site

***ePresentation*** is an electronic presentation of all of the ***Real Math*** lessons, ***eGames,*** and ***eMathTools.*** Teachers can use this daily or periodically to vary instructional presentations.

***eAssess*** enables teachers to record, track, and report on all aspects of students' math performances and progress toward achieving state and national standards.

### Professional Development

A series of five courses that teach different aspects of instruction for math proficiency.

- Teaching for Understanding
- Teaching Computational Fluency
- Teaching Mathematical Reasoning and Problem Solving
- Teaching Applications of Mathematics
- Teaching Mathematics

Each course covers a definition of the proficiency, what teachers need to know about it, how children learn, effective strategies, differentiating instruction, and assessment.

## *Real Math* Technology for Students

Calculators: Basic arithmetic skills are essential in mathematics. It is important for students to learn how to use calculators wisely and when appropriate. It is also important that students understand arithmetic procedures and are able to do computations by hand when calculators are impractical or unavailable. To this end, ***Real Math*** teaches students how to use a calculator effectively. Children should be able to recognize when a calculator is useful and when other methods, such as mental approximation or precise calculation, are more appropriate. Students should also be expected to approximate answers and use numbers intelligently so that they can detect absurd answers that might result, for example, from pushing the wrong keys or using an inappropriate calculation.

> **"A large number of empirical studies of calculator use, including long-term studies, have generally shown that the use of calculators does not threaten the development of basic skills and that it can enhance conceptual understanding, strategic competence, and disposition toward mathematics....The question...is not whether, but how, calculators should be used."**
>
> Kilpatrick, J., Swafford, J. and Findell, B. eds. *Adding It Up: Helping Children Learn Mathematics.* Washington, D.C.: National Research Council/National Academy Press, 2001, p. 354–355.

In ***Real Math,*** students first learn arithmetic skills and only then use calculators to help them solve more complex problems using those skills. Specific instruction addresses when it is and is not appropriate to use a calculator.

## Computer Math Technology for Students

***Real Math*** develops familiarity with the nature and purpose of computers. We believe that children should have the opportunity to use computers. Whether or not children have the advantage of access to a computer, it is essential that they understand the principles on which computers function and the role they are capable of playing in our daily domestic, social, and professional lives. Children should appreciate that computers enable us to obtain numerical answers to large-scale mathematical problems easily and quickly.

***eGames,*** available within the ***eTextbook*** and ***ePresentation,*** provide electronic versions of several of the cube games and game mats. ***eGames*** are referenced in relevant lessons in the ***Teacher's Edition.***

***Building Blocks*** software provides computer math activities that address specific developmental levels of the math learning trajectories. ***Building Blocks*** software is critical to the prekindergarten level of ***Real Math*** and provides support activities for specific concepts in Grades K–6.

Some ***Building Blocks*** activities have different levels of difficulty, indicated by ranges in the Activity Names below. The list provides an overview of all of the ***Building Blocks*** activities, along with the domains, descriptions, and appropriate age ranges.

| Domain: Trajectory | Activity Name | Description | Age Range |
|---|---|---|---|
| Geometry: Composition/ Decomposition | Create a Scene | Students explore shapes by moving and manipulating them to make pictures. | 4–12 |
| Geometry: Composition/ Decomposition | Piece Puzzler I–XII and Piece Puzzler Explore | Students complete puzzles using pattern shapes. | 4–12 |
| Geometry: Imagery | Geometry Snapshots 1–8 | Students match configurations of a variety of shapes (e.g., line segments in different arrangements, 3–6 tiled shapes, embedded shapes) to corresponding configurations, given only a brief view of the goal shapes. | 5–12 |
| Geometry: Shapes (Identifying) | Memory Geometry 1–5 | Students match familiar geometric shapes (shapes in same or similar sizes, same orientation) within the framework of a "Concentration" card game. | 3–5 |
| Geometry: Shapes (Matching) | Mystery Pictures 1–6 and Mystery Pictures Free Explore | Students construct predefined pictures by selecting shapes that match a series of target shapes. | 3–8 |
| Geometry: Shapes (Parts) | Shape Parts 1–9 | Students build or fix some real-world object, exploring shape and properties of shapes. | 5–12 |
| Geometry: Shapes (Properties) | Shape Detective | Given verbal clues, students identify a shape, which then becomes part of a Mystery Picture. | 8–12 |
| Geometry: Shapes (Properties) | Shape Shop 2 | Students make quadrilaterals, beginning with a general quadrilateral and gradually moving toward those with more and more properties (a trapezoid followed by an isosceles trapezoid, then rhomboids, etc.) Similar with triangles. | 8–12 |
| Measurement: Length | Gus's Garage | Students learn about nonstandard measurement by measuring the length or height of familiar household objects with smaller tools. | 6–9 |
| Measurement: Length | Reptile Ruler | Students learn about linear measurement by using a ruler to determine the length of various reptiles. | 7–10 |
| Multiplication/Division | Arrays in Area | Students build arrays and then determine the area of those arrays. | 8–11 |
| Multiplication/Division | Comic Book Shop | Students use skip-counting to produce products that are multiples of 10s, 5s, 2s, and 3s. The task is to identify (1) the product, given a number and bundles (Grade 1) and (2) how many bundles you had to add to make the product (Grade 2). | 7–9 |
| Multiplication/Division | Field Trip | Students solve multidigit multiplication problems in a field-trip environment (e.g., equal number of students on each bus; the number of tickets are needed for all students). | 8–11 |
| Multiplication/Division | Fruit Salad (guided activity — Multiplication Problems with Counters) | Students use direct modeling to solve multiplication problems. | 6–8 |
| Multiplication/Division | Number Tools — Multidigit multiplication and missing factor problems | Students use number tools to solve multidigit multiplication and division problems. | 8–11 |
| Multiplication/Division | Numbers Tools — Multiplication Word Problems | Students use tools to solve multiplication and division problems. | 7–9 |
| Numbers: Adding and Subtracting | Barkley's Bones 1–20 | Students determine the missing addend in $X + \_\_ = Z$ problems to feed bone treats to a dog (Z = 10 or less). Students determine the missing addend in $X + \_\_ = Z$ problems (Z = 10 or less). | 5–8 |
| Numbers: Adding and Subtracting | Coin Combos | Students use coins to solve multidigit addition and subtraction problems to 100. | 7–9 |

# Professional Development

| Domain: Trajectory | Activity Name | Description | Age Range |
|---|---|---|---|
| Number: Adding and Subtracting | Double Compare 1–20 | Students compare sums of cards (to 10) to determine which sum is greater. | 5–8 |
| Number: Adding and Subtracting | Multidigit Word Problems with Tools | Students use provided tools to solve multidigit word problems. Tools include "counter" tools on mats, etc. | 8–12 |
| Number: Adding and Subtracting | Numbers Tools — Multiplication Word Problems | Students use provided tools to solve multidigit word problems. Tools include "counter" tools on mats, etc. | 7–11 |
| Number: Adding and Subtracting | Word Problems with Tools | Students use provided tools to solve word problems (totals to 20). Tools include "counter" tools on mats, etc. | 8–12 |
| Number: Adding and Subtracting and Counting | Counting Activity 1–12 | Students identify numerals (1 through10) and total number amounts (one through 20), then move forward a corresponding number of spaces on a game board, up to 100. | 3–9 |
| Number: Adding and Subtracting and Multiplication and Division | Function Machine 1–5 | Students provide inputs to a function and examine the resulting outputs to determine the definition of that function. Functions include either addition or subtraction. | 6–12 |
| Number: Comparing | Rocket Blast 1–4 | Given a number line with only initial and final endpoints labeled and a location on that line, students determine the number label for that location. | 6–12 |
| Number: Comparing and Counting | Party Time 1–2 and Party Time Free Explore | Students practice one-to-one correspondence by matching party utensils to placemats. | 4–6 |
| Number: Comparing and Multiplication and Division | Number Compare 1–5 | Students compare two cards and choose the one with the greater value. | 4–11 |
| Number: Comparing, Counting, Adding and Subtracting | Pizza Pizzazz 1–5 and Pizza Pizzazz Free Explore | Students count items, match target amounts, and explore missing addends related to toppings on pizzas. | 3–8 |
| Number: Counting (Object) | Memory Number 1–3 | Students match displays containing both numerals and collections to matching displays within the framework of a "Concentration" card game. | 4–6 |
| Number: Counting (Object) and Adding and Subtracting | Dino Shop 1–10 and Dino Shop Free Explore | Students identify the numeral that represents a target number of dinosaurs in a number frame. | 4–7 |
| Number: Counting (Objects) | Juice Box Factory | Students fill an order by counting up from a two-digit number through the next decade. | 6–8 |
| Number: Counting (Objects) | School Supply Shop | Students count school supplies, bundled in groups of ten to reach a target number up to 100. | |
| Number: Counting (Objects) | Tire Recycling | Students use skip-counting by 2s and 5s to count tires as they are moved. | 6–8 |
| Number: Counting (Strategies) | Build Stairs 1–3 | Students add stairs to a stair frame outline to reach a target height between 1 and 10. Students identify the appropriate stacks of unit cubes to fill in a series of staircase steps. Students identify the numeral that represents a missing number in a sequence. Students explore counting, sequencing, and ordering by building staircases. | 4–7 |
| Number: Counting (Strategies) | Math-O-Scope | Students identify the numbers that surround a given number in the context of a 100s chart. | 7–9 |
| Number: Counting (Strategies) | Under the Hat | Students are told how many objects there are in all, shown a number of objects not hidden, and are prompted to identify how many are hidden under a hat. | 6–9 |
| Number: Counting (Verbal) | Count and Count Free Explore | Students count up to 50 by adding cars to a racetrack one at a time. | 3–6 |
| Number: Counting (Verbal) | Before and After Math | Students identify and select numbers that come either just before or right after a target number. | 4–7 |
| Number: Subitizing | Number Snapshots 1–10 | Students match and combine collections of numbers. | 3–12 |
| Number: Subitizing (Conceptual) | Number Pictures 1–2 and Number Pictures Free Explore | Students design a picture with two types of parts (e.g., two shapes) that consists of a given number of shapes (up to five), and label the addends (i.e., the number of each type of part in the picture). | 5–8 |
| Patterning | Marching Patterns 1–3 | Students extend a linear pattern of marchers by one full repetition of an entire unit (AB patterns). | 5–7 |
| Patterning | Pattern Planes 1–3 | Students duplicate a linear pattern of flags based on an outline that serves as a guide. | 4–6 |
| Patterning | Pattern Zoo 1–3 and Free Explore | Students identify a linear pattern of fruit that matches a target pattern to feed zoo animals. | 3–6 |

# e MathTools

## Data Organization and Display Tools

- **Spreadsheet**—allows students to manage, display, sort, and calculate data. Links to the graphing tool for further data display
- **Graphing Tool**—displays data in circle graphs, line graphs, bar graphs, or coordinate grids
- **Venn Diagram**—allows students to sort data visually

## Calculation and Counting Tools

- **Calculator**—allows students to launch a calculator to perform mathematical operations
- **Function Machine**—an electronic version of a function machine that students use to solve missing variable problems
- **Multiplication and Division Table**—an interactive version of a table that highlights relationships between multiplication and division facts
- **Addition and Subtraction Table**—an interactive version of a table that highlights relationships between addition and subtraction facts
- **100 Table**—an interactive version of a table that highlights patterns and relationships among numbers
- **Number Line**—an electronic number line that allows students to skip count and see the relationships among whole numbers, fractions, decimals, and percents
- **Number Stairs**—a tool to illustrate counting in units
- **Probability Tool**—uses ***Number Cubes,*** spinners, or tumble drums to test scenarios of probability
- **Set Tool**—allows students to visually represent and manipulate different sets of objects for a variety of counting activities
- **Base-Ten Blocks**—allows students to manipulate base-ten blocks for counting
- **Coins and Money**—uses visual representations of coins and money to represent counting
- **Fraction Tool**—represents fractional units for counting and understanding relationships
- **Array Tool**—presents arrays to represent multiplication and division patterns and relationships

## Measurement and Conversion Tools

- **Stopwatch**—measures real time for development of counting and time concepts
- **Calendar**—an electronic calendar to develop concepts of time
- **Metric and Customary Conversion Tool**—converts metric and customary measurements in length, distance, mass and weight, time, temperature, and capacity
- **Estimating Proportion Tool**—allows visual representations of proportions in order to develop understanding of ratios, fractions, and decimals

## Geometric Exploration Tools

- **Tessellations**—allows students to create tessellation patterns by rotating, coloring, and tiling shapes
- **Net Tool**—allows students to manipulate 2-D shapes and then print them to create 3-D shapes
- **Shape Tools**—explores and manipulates shapes to create designs
- **Geometry Sketch Tool**—allows drawing, manipulating, and measuring a wide variety of shapes
- **Pythagorean Theorem Tool**—launches right triangles to explore the Pythagorean Theorem

# Using Games

Games

## The Role of Games

Games provide practice. They give students a way of becoming proficient in the mathematical skills to which they have been introduced. Many ***Real Math*** games do more. They offer students a chance to recognize situations, real to the student, that can be understood through mathematical thinking, which leads to the identification and solution of strategy problems. This usually leads to in-depth mathematical communication between students regarding the problem and solution.

A benefit of this development through games is that there is no need to teach students the best solution. The process of trying to find a better strategy is the useful activity.

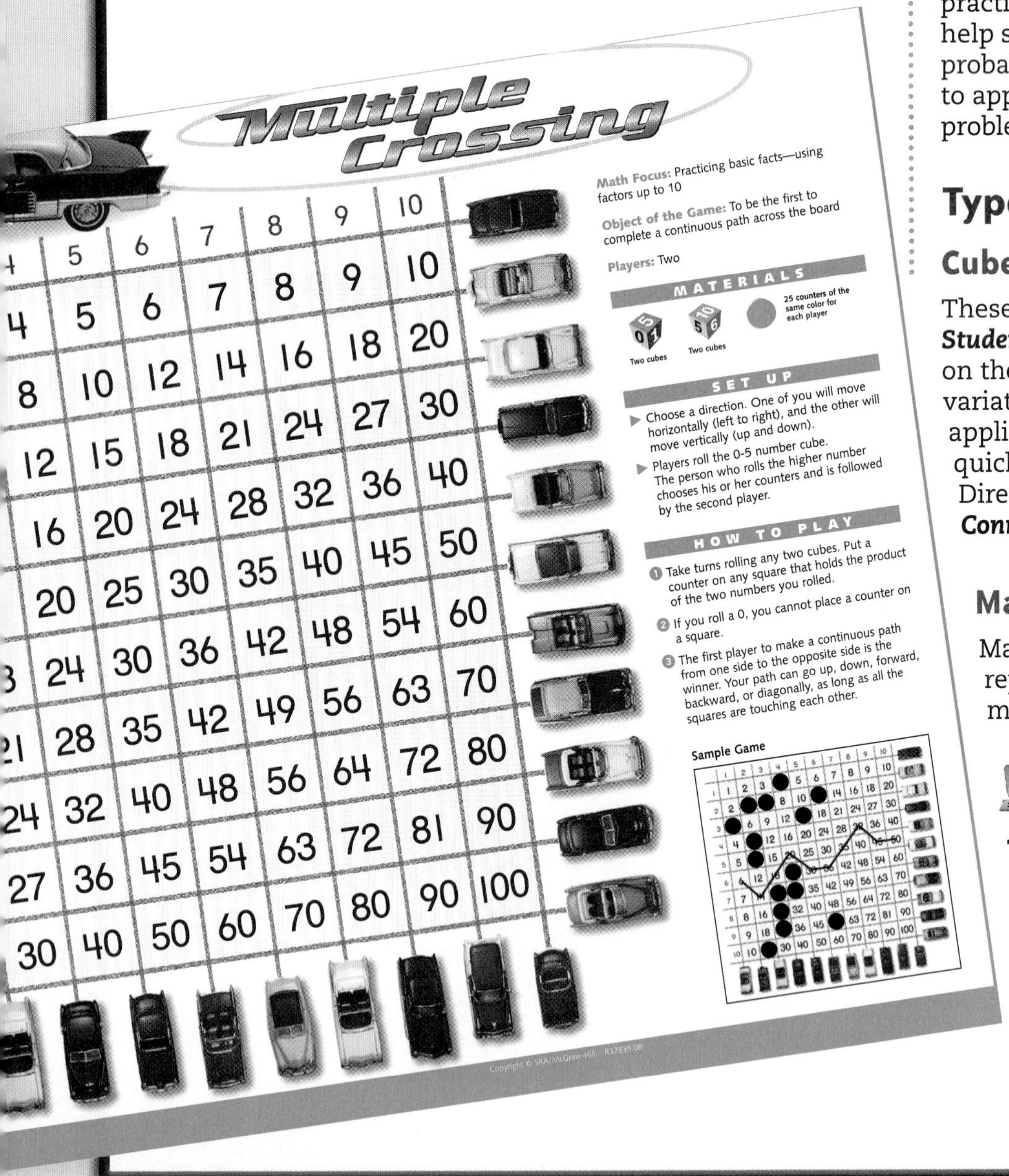


Games also afford teachers the opportunity to monitor progress. By observing game-playing sessions, teachers can assess students' computational fluency, understanding, reasoning, and engagement.

Games allow students of all levels of ability to compete fairly. Winning games requires a mix of chance, skills, and thinking strategies.

## Games and Skills

Each of the games in ***Real Math*** involves the use of specific math skills. When a lesson plan prescribes a game, it does so because the principal skills involved in that game need attention at that time. Most games provide practice in many skills. For example, nearly all the games help students develop and apply intuitive concepts of probability. Many games afford students the opportunity to apply problem-solving strategies, such as recognizing a problem, working backward, or making an approximation.

## Types of Games

### Cube Games

These games are included in appropriate lessons in the ***Student*** and ***Teacher's Editions.*** The games' rules appear on the student pages. Many of the cube games have variations that extend beyond mathematics or provide applications for new strategies. Variations can be learned quickly, making the cube games even more practical. Directions for all cube games are also reproduced in ***Home Connection,*** as well as in the **Home Connection Game Kit.**

### Mat Games

Mat games can be found in the **Game Mat Kit** and are reproduced in Appendix D of this ***Teacher's Edition.*** The mat games are referenced in appropriate lessons.

### eGames

These games are electronic versions of some of the cube games. They are referenced in appropriate lessons throughout the program. The ***eGames*** can be accessed online, on the ***eGames*** CD-ROM, or through the ***eTextbook, ePresentation,*** or ***ePlanner.***

**Building Blocks**

These electronic games are referenced in appropriate lessons throughout the lower grades of ***Real Math.*** The Pre–K level of the ***Building Blocks*** software, which includes the games appropriate for prekindergarten, is a crucial part of the Pre–K curriculum. The ***Building Blocks*** games referenced in appropriate lessons at the other grade levels reinforce key concepts.

## Choosing Games

Some lesson plans suggest a particular game, some suggest that teachers select appropriate games for students based on needed skill practice; and some suggest that students be given a free choice of games. The authors recommend that teachers maintain a balance between selecting games for students and having students choose games for themselves.

To help students choose games, teachers can make a chart of the games that have been introduced to date. The chart can be a simple list or an organized collection of game mats, titles, game rules, materials lists, and illustrations. A group of students might be put in charge of making the display and updating it whenever a new game is introduced.

When you do prescribe games, check the game directory in Appendix D. This listing of the principal skills involved in each game will help you select those games that will give each student an appropriate form of practice.

## Learning Game Rules

Rules for each game are given in the lesson in which the game is introduced. The directions for game mats are also found on the game mats. Here are some tips for making sure that games are played correctly:

- Familiarize yourself with each game before showing students how to play it. Read the instructions, and then play the game by yourself or with a colleague or friend.
- Demonstrate—do not tell—how a game is played. Even for straightforward games, oral instructions can sound complicated. Introduce a game by demonstrating it in front of the class, with you playing against the class, with you playing against one student (representing the class), or with two students (representing teams) playing against each other. The ***ePresentation*** allows teachers to present and demonstrate all games to the entire class at one time. Make sure that each student can see while you demonstrate a game.
- Verbalize the rules as you demonstrate games. End the demonstration when all the rules have been covered.
- Supervise to see that students get off to the right start after you have introduced a game.
- Let students teach other students. Those who have grasped the game rules can help those who have not.

## Organizing Successful Game Sessions

- Pair children wisely. There are times when it will be appropriate to pair children of the same ability. However, this rule should not become invariable because most games involve some luck. Furthermore, if a student who is not attentive while playing a game plays with one who is, the first student may realize that paying attention may help.
- Change groupings from day to day. Students can learn different things by playing with different partners.
- Be sure students are challenged by a game. Most games have easier and harder variations.
- Assign a referee to each group. When students get so absorbed in their own efforts that they do not follow the rules, a referee can be useful. This is particularly appropriate for kindergarten through second grade. The referee can see that the rules are followed, remind each player when it is his or her turn, settle disputes, keep track of scores, and in some games, act as a banker.
- Make game mats accessible. Store mats so they are easy for the students to find and to return without your help.
- Encourage students to play games during free time, in school, and at home, as well as during the scheduled game sessions.
- Allow students opportunities to create and name their own variations of the games. In some cases, you may want to describe a student's variation to the entire class and ask him or her to name it. Be alert, however, to avoid student-invented variations that reduce the skill practice or thinking value of the game.
- Get help during game-playing sessions. Likely candidates are parents, grandparents, teacher's aides, or students in upper grades. Be sure the helpers know the rules of the games by having them play the chosen games ahead of time.

## Game-Playing Behavior

Establishing the proper atmosphere for game playing makes the sessions more effective and easier to manage. Encourage enjoyment rather than competition. Emphasize sportsmanship, fair play, and taking turns. Beginning with the first game-playing session, teach students to control their excitement and to speak using low voices. Cubes, when rolled, should stay within a confined area. Insisting that students roll cubes on an $11 \times 8\frac{1}{2}$ pad or cardboard field reduces noise and inappropriate exuberance.

# Problem Solving

Problem solving and reasoning are fundamental math proficiencies. Without the ability to reason mathematically, identify problems, and devise appropriate strategies to solve them, computational fluency has little relevance. There are several keys to developing students' problem-solving abilities.

## 1. Use Real Problems

The first and most important step in helping students become good problem solvers is to provide opportunities to identify and solve problems that are genuinely interesting and, therefore, motivating. We call these *real problems.* To help understand what we mean by *real,* we can consider three types of problems: those that are real, those that are realistic, and those that are contrived.

**Contrived Problems** appear largely in textbooks — never in real life. They often occur when it is difficult to find an application for a particular type of computation, so a forced, contrived situation is invented. For example, knowing how much antifreeze to add to a radiator that is $\frac{4}{7}$ full and which has a 4-gallon capacity is a contrived problem. One would never know that the radiator was $\frac{4}{7}$ full, and even if one did have that piece of useless information, nobody would calculate how much antifreeze to add. They would simply fill the tank to capacity. When students encounter such problems they learn the wrong lesson — that mathematics is an endeavor that makes work, not one that saves work and solves useful problems. We avoid using contrived problems in ***Real Math.***

**Realistic Problems** mirror the kind of mathematics that people do in real life. Although not as motivating as real problems, they are an important part of a mathematics program and are the main source of word problems found in our student texts. Unit pricing, comparing or combining quantities or measures, balancing a checkbook, and learning to read a telephone bill are all examples of realistic problems.

**Real Problems** are developed from the reality of the person being asked to solve the problem; they come from the social situation of the problem solver and his or her desire to find a solution. Thus what is real to a first grader is not the same as what is real to a third grader or to an adult. The same problem may be real to one person and realistic to another who is engaged in a different activity, but if a problem is real to one person, then it can never be a contrived problem. Carefully selected games are a source of real problems because figuring out a strategy to win a game is of real interest to a school child. Thinking stories, too, can be real, because they have the proper balance of storyline, fantasy, humor, and reality, appropriate for the intended grade level. Carefully developed activities are another source of real problems.

Finding real problems is one of the more difficult challenges in curriculum development, one that we take seriously and work hard at achieving. But it is here where teachers can help immensely. One of the most important prerequisites for developing real problem-solving opportunities is to know the students — know what they are interested in and know what is real to them. And so ***Real Math*** is rich in opportunities to individualize mathematics to the interests of the students.

## 2. Develop Critical-Thinking Skills

Students must have tools that are useful for solving problems. Computational skills are, of course, important, but they are not enough. Students also need an arsenal of critical-thinking skills (sometimes called *problem-solving strategies,* and sometimes called *heuristics*) that they can call upon to solve particular problems. These skills should not be taught in isolation. Rather, students should learn to use them in different contexts. By doing so, students are more likely to recognize in which situations a particular skill will be useful and when it is not likely to be useful.

We can group critical-thinking skills into two categories — those that are useful in virtually all situations and those that are useful in specific contexts.

### Strategies for Every Problem-Solving Situation

**Identify the problem** — The first step in becoming a good problem solver is to learn how to identify when a problem does, in fact, exist. Too often in school mathematics, we give students problems to solve, even many interesting problems, but the problems are always given by the teacher or provided by the textbook—they are never identified by the student as arising from a particular context. That is not the way we encounter problems in the real world. ***Real Math*** lessons are rich in opportunities for students to identify problems.

**Understand the problem** — Without exception, students must understand each problem or physical situation and do only what makes sense to them. Applying rules in unthinking ways, using key words that avoid thinking, or using other shortcuts that subvert or eliminate understanding are all counterproductive, and although they might lead to correct answers in contrived situations, such tactics do not help students become good problem solvers, and they are not used in ***Real Math.*** There are no exceptions.

**Reflect on the problem** — Students must learn to reflect on problems both before and after solving them. Before a solution is found, students might reflect on problems that they have encountered earlier. A solution to a problem encountered earlier might offer a clue about how to structure the solution to the current problem. Good problem solvers also reflect on problems after they have been solved. What have I learned from this problem that might help with other problems? Was there an easier or a more elegant solution? Can I think of related problems that I have not yet solved? Asking such questions is likely to help students become good problem solvers. Every ***Real Math*** lesson concludes with an opportunity for students to reflect on what they have learned, expand on what they have learned, or ask new questions that arise from what they have learned.

**Revisit the problem** — Good problem solvers tend to think about a problem after they have solved it. By doing so they are likely to better understand the processes they used and see things the second and third time that they did not see the first time. One of the central roles of games in ***Real Math*** is to afford students the opportunity to revisit problems. Students do this by replaying games that allow them to formulate and reformulate winning strategies.

## Problem-Solving Strategies for Specific Situations

A partial listing of critical-thinking skills that are likely to be useful in specific contexts are the following:

Draw a Picture — Sometimes drawing a picture will help to visualize and hence understand a problem.

Look for a Pattern — Some problems can be solved by looking for and finding patterns.

Guess, Check, and Adjust — If a direct procedure cannot be found, it is sometimes useful to make an educated guess and then check to see if that answer makes sense. This procedure often involves making several successive guesses, each based on feedback from earlier guesses.

Make a Table or Graph — Organizing information in a table or graph will often reveal important trends and patterns.

Work Backward — For some problems, working backward helps to reveal a pattern or patterns.

Work an Easier Problem — If a problem appears too difficult, it sometimes helps to solve a related, but easier, problem. Solving the easier problem will often reveal strategies likely to be useful for solving the more difficult problem.

Detect Absurdities — Spotting answers that are contrary to reason, even if the correct answer is not known, is often an important part of the problem-solving process.

Ask the Right Questions — Knowing when necessary information is missing, knowing how to find the information, and knowing how to ask the right questions to find the information is often useful.

Approximate — Many problems do not require precise answers. Knowing when a precise answer is appropriate and when an approximate answer is appropriate is important, as is sufficient knowledge of the number system in order to make approximations.

## 3. Involve All Students in Problem Solving

Problem solving is an activity that must involve all students, not just those who are more able or who have mastered particular computational skills. ***Real Math*** lessons are designed to provide many such opportunities.

## 4. Include Problem Solving in Every Lesson

If students are to see the usefulness of mathematics for solving interesting problems that are relevant to their own lives, and if they are to have lots of experience solving problems, such activities must be part of every mathematics lesson — not something that is reserved for Fridays or perhaps isolated in one or two chapters of a textbook. That is why we include problem-solving opportunities in every lesson in ***Real Math.*** There are no exceptions.

## SRA Real Math and Problem Solving

***Real Math*** lessons are rich in problem-solving opportunities and are adaptable to many styles of teaching. The principal sources of problem-solving opportunities come from the following:

### Games

***Real Math*** games are a principal source of traditional skill practice. Most games do more: they give the student an opportunity to work out important mathematical ideas and strategies. Thus a student might start a game by just getting the skill practice, but after a while he or she might realize that the game involves more than practice — that a winning strategy must be developed. At that point the student has identified a problem. Because winning the game is often a real problem for the student, there is genuine motivation to find a solution. Moreover, each time the student replays the game, there is an opportunity to revisit a problem previously encountered and find alternative and more sophisticated strategies that might have been missed earlier. Although students compete with each other during game playing sessions, they often communicate their strategies to each other and discuss them.

### Thinking Stories

Thinking Stories found in kindergarten, grades one, two and three are an essential part of the ***Real Math*** approach to developing problem solving abilities; they develop creativity and common sense in the use of mathematics. The problem-solving skills that are stressed include recognizing absurd answers, recognizing obvious answers (those that don't need calculation), recognizing when a problem can be solved using mathematics and when other, non-mathematical knowledge is needed, and so on. The stories are real stories, designed to be read to the students and discussed. The various characters in the stories have peculiarities in thinking that the students come to know. Mr. Breezy, for example, is always giving more information than what is needed, while Ms. Eng is often vague and provides too little information. Thus when Mr. Breezy appears in a story, students learn to listen and think about what information is not useful; whereas when Ms. Eng appears, students learn to ask questions to get the information that she has failed to give. Because the stories are read to the students, we can use a much richer vocabulary than what would be necessary if students read the stories themselves. Thus we do not divorce language from mathematics — rather we make use of language to build problem-solving skills.

### Exploring Problem Solving

Three sets of explorations in every chapter focus specifically on introducing, comparing, and using strategies for identifying and solving problems. Students analyze solution methods and share other possible solutions.

### Activities

The many whole-class and small-group activities allow students to apply mathematics in different contexts, which are often cross-curricular. Such activities are rich in opportunities for students to communicate their ideas within their small groups and also to others from whom they are seeking information.

*Mathematics is being lazy. Mathematics is letting the principles do the work for you so that you do not have to do the work for yourself.*

George Pólya, mathematician, 1887–1985

### Computation Pages

As in most programs, pages that provide needed computation practice are included throughout ***Real Math.*** But because we frequently include groups of related exercises on these pages, students learn to look for them and use the resulting patterns to avoid tedious computations. For example, an exercise such as 54 + 73 = might be followed by 54 + 74 = and 54 + 75 =. Students who notice this pattern can compute the first sum, but then note that each successive sum is one more than the previous sum. Such patterns appear often in ***Real Math.***

### Word Problems

Realistic word problems appear frequently throughout ***Real Math.*** They illustrate situations in which mathematics is useful in the real world, and they are a source of much practice. To be certain that students understand the situations described in these problems, we never group problems of the same type together, such as giving problems, all of which call for addition. To do so would allow students to simply look for the numbers and use the indicated operation. They would not have to understand the problem and would not have to think. To encourage thinking, we include problems that include too much information, too little information, problems that can be solved by mathematics, and those that cannot. We also include problems in which an approximate answer is more useful than a precise answer, and those in which a precise answer is more useful than an approximate answer. We do not allow students to rely on key words either, because doing so allows students to avoid thinking and to apply procedures that are likely to only work with problems that appear in textbooks.

# Guided Discussion

> **"Discourse should not be confided to answers only, but should include discussion of connections to other problems, alternative representations and solution methods, the nature of justification and argumentation, and the like."**
>
> Kilpatrick, J., Swafford, J. and Findell, B. eds. *Adding It Up: Helping Children Learn Mathematics.* Washington, D.C.: National Research Council/National Academy Press. 2001, p. 425–426.

Mathematical discussions have the potential to greatly advance mathematical understanding. A good discussion provides opportunities for students to explain their thinking, to expand or challenge their understanding by listening to others' contributions, and to justify their reasoning. Good mathematical discussions enable teachers to assess and understand student thinking to inform their future instruction.

> **"Writing and talking enable learners to make their mathematical thinking visible. It is through writing and talking that teachers obtain a window into their students' thinking. Both writing and talking are tools for discovery, enabling learners to make new connections as they engage in the process. The fluid nature of talk allows for the quick brainstorming of many ideas, while the permanent quality of writing provides an important trail of our children's thinking."**
>
> Whitin, Phyllis and Whitin, David J. *Math Is Language Too.* Urbana, IL: National Council of Teachers of English. 2000, p. 17.

## Discussion Management

These points will help produce more discussions:

1. Restate some or all of what the student has said, and then ask the student to respond and verify whether or not the teacher's restatement is correct.
2. Ask students to restate someone else's reasoning, which gives the rest of the class another rendition of the first student's contribution and provides evidence that other students could and did hear. It is also evidence for the speaker's points.
3. Ask students to apply and explain their own reasoning to someone else's reasoning. This will involve more students in the discussion and will encourage student interactions.
4. Prompt students by asking for further commentary to support a position.
5. Use free time. This time allows students to think and consider answers to complicated questions before they speak.

Chapin, Suzanne, O'Connor, Catherine, and Anderson, Nancy Canavan. *Classroom Discussions: Using Math Talk to Help Students Learn.* Sausalito, CA: Math Solutions Publications, 2003, p. 12–16.

## Real Math and Guided Discussion

Guided Discussion plays a prominent role in the Develop and Reflect parts of virtually every lesson in ***Real Math.*** Routines for Guided Discussion are included in the Getting Started section of each grade level to develop effective discussion strategies.

## Questions that Promote Learning

Not all questions have the same effect. Questions help teachers learn what students are thinking, and to consider instructional implications of that knowledge. Below are ideas for formulating questions to promote learning during Guided Discussion.

**Engaging questions** to invite students to participate in a discussion

| | |
|---|---|
| Identify terms, relationships, and methods already known that are connected to the topic. | What is ________? What does ________ mean? |
| Share opinions about the topic. | What do you think about ________? |
| Relate concrete experiences that are pertinent to the topic. | Have you ever been asked to do this before? |
| Verify the results. | How do you know this is true? |

**Exploratory questions** to help students consider connections and consequences

| | |
|---|---|
| Identify a specific difficulty, and decide how to solve it. | What was the hardest part of the problem? Is there an easier way to solve it? |
| Relate personal experience in solving the problem. | What did you do in the past to solve the problem? |
| Draw analogies to other situations. | How is this the same as or different from other problems? |
| Process and record results. | Write the steps you used to solve the problem. |

**Synthesizing questions** to help students pull ideas together.

| | |
|---|---|
| Identify patterns. | What pattern do you see in everyone's results? |
| Generalize. | What is a good way to solve this problem? |
| Elaborate rules, definitions, and laws that express the generalization. | Write the steps for solving problems like this. |
| Argue, prove, or demonstrate assumptions. | Which way is the best way to solve a problem like this? How is it better? |
| Use references. | Who else solved the problem in this way? |

**Clarifying questions** to help students explain their thinking or to help you understand their thinking

| | |
|---|---|
| Reflect on examples and analyze results. | Which is the easiest/hardest/most fun way of approaching the problem, and why? |
| Provide examples. | What is an example of a problem like this? |
| Describe stages and observations. | What was the thinking process you used to solve the problem? |
| Understand and accept limitations of personal and peer knowledge, and search for other information sources. | Is there a better way? How could we find out? |

**Refocusing questions** to help students get back on track

| | |
|---|---|
| Refocusing questions are most useful when students are working in nonproductive ways. | How is this like ________? What does this say about ________? |

# Manipulatives and How to Use Them

"The use of concrete materials, sometimes termed manipulatives, for teaching mathematics is widely accepted, particularly in elementary grades. Manipulatives should always be seen as a means and not an end in themselves. They require careful use over sufficient time to allow students to build meaning and make connections....Simply putting materials on desks is not enough to guarantee students will learn appropriate mathematics. The relationship between learning and the use of manipulatives is far more complex than many mathematics educators have thought....When students use a manipulative, they need to be helped to see its relevant aspects and to link those aspects to appropriate symbolism and mathematical concepts and operations....If students do not see the connections among object, symbol, language, and idea, using a manipulative becomes just one more thing to learn rather than a process leading to a larger mathematical learning goal....The evidence indicates...that manipulatives can provide valuable support for student learning when teachers interact over time with the students to help them build links between the object, the symbol, and the mathematical idea that both represent."

Kilpatrick, J., Swafford, J. and Findell, B. eds. *Adding It Up: Helping Children Learn Mathematics.* Washington, D.C.: National Research Council/National Academy Press. 2001, p. 353–354.

*"The laws of nature are written in the language of mathematics...the symbols are triangles, circles, and other geometrical figures, without whose help it is impossible to comprehend a single word."*

Galileo Galilei, Italian astronomer and physicist, 1564–1642

## SRA Real Math and Manipulatives

The purpose of using manipulatives is to help students understand mathematics, not to get answers to problems. Too often students know rules, but do not know how or why the rules work. By explaining abstract concepts with manipulatives, students can develop and demonstrate understanding of mathematical concepts. Manipulatives are used whenever appropriate in ***Real Math.*** Each time they are used, there is also a plant to remove the need for them so that once the understanding is achieved, students focus attention on fluency and the abstract. The power of mathematics is in its abstractness.

# Professional Development

Below are common manipulatives and their principal purposes.

| Manipulatives | Description | Purpose | Concepts to Develop |
|---|---|---|---|
| Money | Pennies, nickels, dimes, quarters, half dollars, $1-, $5-, $10-, $20-, $50-, and $100-bills | Demonstrate concepts and values of money and applications of base-ten arithmetic | • Number sense<br>• Base-ten system<br>• Place value |
| Pattern Blocks | Colorful blocks in different geometric shapes (hexagons, squares, trapezoids, triangles, and parallelograms, and rhombi) and colors | Create and demonstrate different types of color and shape patterns and to explore the mathematics of tiling and tesselations | • Number sense<br>• Fractions<br>• Geometry<br>• Proportional reasoning |
| Attribute Blocks | Blocks in five shapes (circle, hexagon, rectangle, square, and triangle), different sizes, thicknesses, and colors | Build shape identification, logical thinking, and comparing and ordering concepts | • Number sense<br>• Geometry |
| Platonic Solids | Wooden 3-D cone, cube, pyramid, and sphere | Develop geometric concepts of space figures | • Geometry |
| Mirror | Small nonbreakable mirror | Develop concepts of symmetry | • Geometry |
| Geoboard | Plastic board with pegs and rubber bands laid out in a square grid | Explore shapes, area, perimeter, symmetry, design, and fractions of shapes | • Geometry<br>• Measurement |
| Protractor | Clear protractor in graduations from 0–180 degrees | Measure angles | • Geometry<br>• Measurement |
| Compass | Center point and pencil | Draw and measure circles | • Geometry<br>• Measurement |
| Gummed Tape | Adhesive paper tape | Create geometric figures and shapes | • Geometry |
| Fraction Tiles | Plastic tiles in sets of different fractional increments including $\frac{1}{8}$, $\frac{1}{4}$, $\frac{1}{3}$, $\frac{1}{2}$, and 1. | Explore parts of wholes and adding and subtracting fractions | • Number sense<br>• Fractions and rational numbers<br>• Measurement |
| Spinners | Plastic spinners | Explore probability | • Probability<br>• Number operations |
| Counters | Colored plastic disks | Explore patterns and counting | • Number sense<br>• Counting<br>• Probability<br>• Number operations |
| Base-Ten Blocks | Plastic shapes in cubes, flats, rods, and units | Explore base-ten systems, counting, and number operations | • Number sense<br>• Counting<br>• Number operation |
| Craft Sticks and Rubber Bands | Wood sticks | Explore place value and standard multidigit addition and subtraction algorithms | • Number sense<br>• Counting<br>• Number operation |
| Counters | Plastic shapes | Explore counting and ordering numbers | • Number sense<br>• Counting<br>• Number operation |
| Math-Link Cubes | Plastic cubes that nest together | Explore counting, patterns, number operations, and composing and decomposing numbers | • Number sense<br>• Counting<br>• Patterns<br>• Number operations<br>• Rational number |
| Ruler and Tape Measure | Plastic customary and metric ruler and tape measure | Explore metric and customary measurements of length | • Measurement<br>•Counting |
| Measuring Cups and Liter Pitcher | Plastic metric and customary measurement containers | Explore metric and customary measurements of capacity | • Measurement<br>• Geometry<br>• Fractions, decimals, and percents |
| Double Pan Balance and Platform Scales | Scale and balance and weight set | Explore metric and customary measurements of weight | • Measurement |
| Thermometer | Metric and Fahrenheit thermometers | Explore temperature measurements | • Measurement |
| Clock Face | Plastic analog clock face | Explore time measurements | • Measurement |
| Stopwatch | Electronic stopwatch | Explore time measurements | • Measurement<br>• Fractions, decimals, and percents |

# Differentiating Instruction

> **"In the context of education, we define *differentiation as* 'a teacher's reacting responsively to a learner's needs.' A teacher who is differentiating understands a student's need to express humor or work with a group, or to have additional teaching on a particular skill, or to delve more deeply into a particular topic....Differentiation is simply attending to the learning needs of a particular student or small group of students rather than the more typical pattern of teaching the class as though all individuals in it were basically alike. The goal of a differentiated classroom is maximum student growth and individual success."**
>
> —Tomlinson, Carol Ann and Allan, Susan Demirsky. *Leadership for Differentiating Schools and Classrooms.* Alexandria, VA: Association for Supervision and Curriculum Development. 2000, p. 4.

All students can benefit from differentiated instruction. Differentiated instruction is dependent on ongoing, daily assessment and an interest in and understanding of how children learn and develop concepts.

## How to Differentiate

Instruction can be differentiated in three key ways:

- **Content** What the teacher wants students to learn and the materials or mechanisms through which that is accomplished. Differentiating the content may entail teaching prerequisite concepts to students who need intervention or by asking questions that will cause students to think beyond the concepts covered in the lesson.
- **Process** How or what activities the students do to ensure that they use key skills to make sense of the content. Differentiating the process may include grouping students in different ways, or alternating the pace of the lesson by moving more slowly or more quickly than originally planned. It might also include stressing different modalities: visual, auditory, or kinesthetic.
- **Product** How the student will demonstrate what he or she has come to know. Differentiating the product may include assigning ***Enrichment, Practice,*** or ***Reteach*** activities to complete.

Differentiating instruction does not mean chaos or a classroom devoid of structure with everyone working on different goals. Lessons should have clearly defined purposes with students focused on one key understanding.

## Analyzing Student Needs

Teachers successful at differentiating instruction are typically in tune with individual student needs. These needs vary, and should be addressed in the context of the key ideas of the lesson. By preparing for differentiation and considering what you might do when you encounter different student needs, teachers can have materials and strategies at the ready.

For a particular concept or lesson, different students may need

- challenge.
- social interaction.
- alternative instruction.
- independence.
- personal attention.
- serious intervention.
- language support.
- creative expression.
- cooperative grouping.
- extra practice.

## SRA Real Math and Differentiated Instruction

Every lesson of ***Real Math*** begins with Planning for Learning: Differentiate Instruction ideas. These include

- ***Intervention*** that teach prerequisite skills for students who are not ready for the lesson concepts.
- ***English Learner Preview*** lesson that preview lesson concepts and vocabulary for students learning English.
- ***Enrichment*** ideas for expanding parts of the lesson if, as you are teaching, you realize students are already confident with the lesson concepts.
- ***Practice*** strategies for extending parts of the lesson, if you realize during the lesson that students would benefit from more practice.

- ***Reteach*** ideas for re-presenting and reinforcing the key teaching of the lesson, if you realize that students are not grasping the concepts.

During the lesson, Monitoring Student Progress presents tips for addressing specific concerns.

At the end of the lesson, Assessment Follow-Up provides activities to review, reteach, practice, or enrich lesson concepts depending on student performance.

### Key Principles of a Differentiated Classroom

- The teacher is clear about what matters in subject matter.
- The teacher understands, appreciates, and builds upon student differences.
- Assessment and instruction are inseparable.
- The teacher adjusts content, process, and product in response to student readiness, interests, and learning profiles.
- All students participate in respectful work.
- Students and teachers are collaborators in learning.
- Goals of a differentiated classroom are maximum growth and individual success.
- Flexibility is the hallmark of a differentiated classroom.

Tomlinson, Carol Ann and Allan, Susan Demirsky. *Leadership for Differentiating Schools and Classrooms.* Alexandria, VA: Association for Supervision and Curriculum Development. 2000, p. 48.

# Assessment

"...assessment, whether externally mandated or developed by the teacher, should support the development of students' mathematical proficiency. It needs to provide opportunities for students to learn, rather than taking time away from their learning. Assessments in which students are learning, as well as showing what they have already learned, can provide valuable information to teachers, schools, districts, and states, as well as to the students themselves. Such assessments help teachers modify their instruction to support better learning at each grade level."

Kilpatrick, J., Swafford, J. and Findell, B. eds. *Adding It Up: Helping Children Learn Mathematics*. Washington, D.C.: National Research Council/National Academy Press. 2001, p. 423.

Much has been written about the importance of assessment. The Assessment Standards book from the National Council of Teachers of Mathematics tells us that classroom assessment should

- provide a rich variety of mathematical topics and problem situations.
- give students opportunities to investigate problems in many ways.
- question and listen to students.
- look for evidence of learning from many sources.
- expect students to use concepts and procedures effectively in solving problems.

The goals of assessment are to

- improve instruction by informing teachers of the effectiveness of their lessons.
- promote growth of students by identifying where they need additional instruction and support.
- recognize accomplishments.

## Real Math and Assessment

***Real Math*** provides opportunities for formal and informal assessments and convenient ways to record, track, and report on student achievements.

## Informal Assessments

Informal assessment involves ongoing observations of student involvement in class activities. Informal assessments are tailored to evaluate students on the five areas of mathematic proficiency: computing, understanding, reasoning, applying, and engaging.

Every lesson includes two ***Assessment*** checkmarks in the ***Teacher's Edition*** next to activities tailored to reveal students' math proficiencies. These activities may include Guided Discussion, Skill Building, Strategy Building, Games, or Journals. The checkmarks alert teachers to carefully observe students during the activity. Rubric checklists in Assess and Differentiate of the lesson describe specific positive behaviors to look for as signs of development. As teachers become familiar with the rubric checklists, they can access them through memory. Teachers can record their observations in the Daily Class Assessment Records for each proficiency.

| | |
|---|---|
| Computing | • respond accurately<br>• respond quickly<br>• respond with confidence<br>• self-correct |
| Understanding | • make important observations<br>• extend or generalize learning<br>• provide insightful answers<br>• pose insightful questions |
| Reasoning | • provide a clear explanation<br>• communicate reasons and strategies<br>• chooses appropriate strategies<br>• argue logically |
| Applying | • apply learning in new situations<br>• contribute concepts<br>• contribute answers<br>• connect mathematics to real-world situations |
| Engaging | • pay attention to others' contributions<br>• contribute information and ideas<br>• improve on a strategy<br>• reflect on and check the accuracy of his or her work |

Daily checklist observations can be summarized in the Student Assessment Record for the chapter or in ***eAssess*** to provide a long-term holistic view of student proficiency. If teachers record these observations, these daily informal assessments can be powerful indicators of student proficiency, and as such help inform instruction, as well as provide feedback to students and their parents.

## Formal Assessment

There are several opportunities for formal assessment in every chapter. All assessments can be recorded further in the Student Assessment Record or in ***eAssess*** for every chapter to provide a comprehensive view of student achievement.

- **Pretests** test prerequisite and chapter concepts to provide a diagnostic assessment of student understanding for the upcoming chapter.
- **Speed Tests** appear in lessons to test computational fluency.
- **Mastery Checkpoints** provide assessments for skills that should be mastered at particular points in the program. The Mastery Checkpoint Chart provides a class view of student progress toward mastery of particular skills.
- **Oral Assessment** in the middle of the chapter is an opportunity for teachers to interact individually with students to assess their growth in proficiency. An Individual Oral Assessment recording sheet is available in ***Assessment*** for each Oral Assessment for teacher convenience.
- **Daily Quizzes** are available to provide a quick review and assessment of student understanding of lesson concepts and skills.
- **Chapter Tests** offer a way to assess student understanding of chapter content and skills.

### eAssess

The ***eAssess*** program offers a powerful way to record and track student progress. Teachers can enter data on a daily or weekly basis. The more data a teacher inputs—including records of Formal and Informal Assessments, completion of student pages, completion of projects, and additional activities—the more comprehensive and reliable the reports that can be generated will be.

Using ***eAssess,*** teachers can generate reports that show student performance in reference to the entire class, individual development, and in reference to state and/or national standards. These reports provide a comprehensive view of individual student and class performance that can provide valuable feedback for your instruction and for student and parent conferences.

More information, including masters of recording sheets and tests, can be found in ***Assessment.***

# Handwriting Models

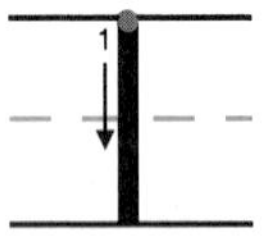

Starting point, straight down: 1

Starting point, around right, slanting left, and straight across right: 2

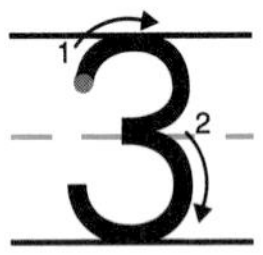

Starting point, around right, in at the middle, and around right: 3

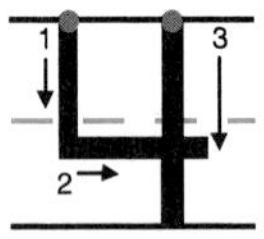

Starting point, straight down, and straight across right. Starting point, straight down, and crossing line: 4

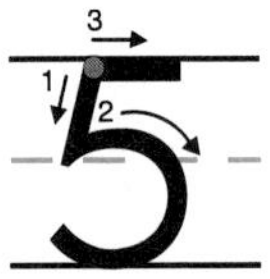

Straight down, curve around right and up. Starting point, straight across right: 5

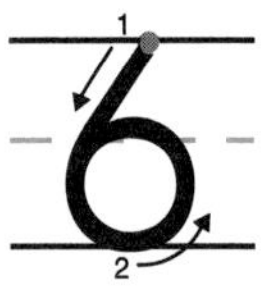

Starting point, slanting left, around the bottom curving up around left and into the curve: 6

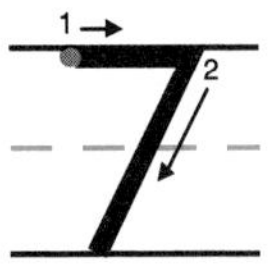

Starting point, straight across right, and slanting down left: 7

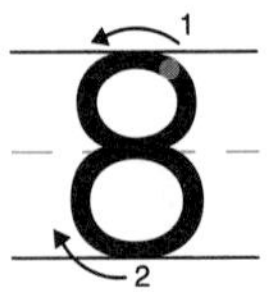

Starting point, curving left, curving down and around right, slanting up right to starting point: 8

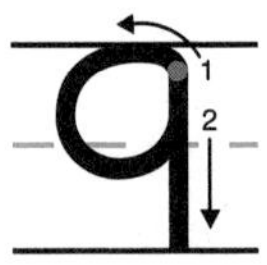

Starting point, curving around left all the way, and straight down: 9

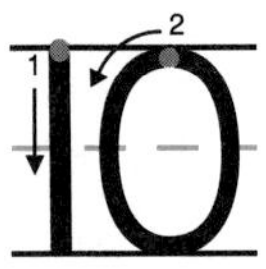

Starting point, straight down. Starting point, curving left all the way around to starting point: 10

*Students follow natural developmental progressions in learning, developing mathematical ideas in their own ways. Curriculum research has revealed sequences of activities that are effective in guiding students through these levels of thinking. These developmental paths can be described as learning trajectories. Each learning trajectory has levels of understanding, each more sophisticated than the last, and with tasks that promote growth from one level to the next. The* ***Building Blocks*** *Learning Trajectories give simple labels, descriptions, and examples of each level. Complete learning trajectories describe the goals of learning, the thinking and learning processes of students at various levels, and the learning activities in which they might engage.*

# Learning Trajectories for Primary Grades Mathematics

## Developmental Levels

The following provides the developmental levels from the first signs of development in different strands of mathematics through approximately age 8. Research shows that when teachers understand how students develop mathematics understanding, they are more effective in questioning, analyzing, and providing activities that further students' development than teachers who are unaware of the development process. Consequently students have a much richer and more successful math experience in the primary grades.

### Frequently Asked Questions (FAQ)

1. ***When are students "at" a level?*** Students are at a certain level when most of their behaviors reflect the thinking—ideas and skills—of that level. Often, they show a few behaviors from the next (and previous) levels as they learn.
2. ***Can students work at more than one level at the same time?*** Yes, although most students work mainly at one level or in transition between two levels (naturally, if they are tired or distracted, they may operate at a much lower level). Levels are not "absolute." They are "benchmarks" of complex growth that represent distinct ways of thinking. So, another way to think of them is as a sequence of different patterns of thinking. Students are continually learning, within levels and moving between them.
3. ***Can students jump ahead?*** Yes, especially if there are separate "subtopics." For example, we have combined many counting competencies into one "Counting" sequence with subtopics, such as verbal counting skills. Some students learn to count to 100 at age 6 after learning to count objects to 10 or more; some may learn that verbal skill earlier. The subtopic of verbal counting skills would still be followed.
4. ***How do these developmental levels support teaching and learning?*** The levels help teachers, as well as curriculum developers, and assess, teach, and sequence activities. *Teachers who understand learning trajectories and the developmental levels that are at their foundation are more effective and efficient.* Through planned teaching and also by encouraging informal, incidental mathematics, teachers help students learn *at an appropriate and deep level.*
5. ***Should I plan to help students develop just the levels that correspond to my students' ages?*** No! The ages in the table are typical ages when students develop these ideas. *But these are rough guides only*—students differ widely. Furthermore, the ages below are lower bounds on what students achieve without instruction. So, these are *"starting levels," not goals.* We have found that students who are provided high-quality mathematics experiences are capable of developing to levels one or more years beyond their peers.

Each column in the table, such as "Counting," represents a main developmental progression that underlies the learning trajectory for that topic.

Clements, D. H., Sarama, J., & DiBiase, A.M. *Engaging Young Students in Mathematics: Standards for Early Childhood Mathematics Education.* Mahwah, NJ: Lawrence Erlbaum Associates.

Clements, D. H., & Sarama, J. "Early Childhood Mathematics Learning." In F. K. Lester, Jr. (Ed.), *Second Handbook of Research on Mathematics Teaching and Learning.* New York: Information Age Publishing.

## Developmental Levels for Counting

The ability to count with confidence develops over the course of several years. Beginning in infancy, students show signs of understanding numbers. With instruction and number experience, most students can count fluently by age 8, with much progress in counting occurring in kindergarten and first grade. Most students follow a natural developmental progression in learning to count with recognizable stages or levels. This developmental path can be described as part of a learning trajectory.

| Age Range | Level Name | Level | Description |
|---|---|---|---|
| 1–2 | Precounter | 1 | A student at the earliest level of counting may name some numbers meaninglessly. The student may skip numbers and have no sense of sequence. |
| 1–2 | Chanter | 2 | At this level, a student may sing-song numbers, but without meaning. |
| 2 | Reciter | 3 | At this level, the student may verbally count with separate words, but not necessarily in the correct order. |
| 3 | Reciter (10) | 4 | A student at this level may verbally count to 10 with some correspondence with objects. They may point to objects to count a few items, but then lose track. |
| 3 | Corresponder | 5 | At this level, a student may keep one-to-one correspondence between counting words and objects—at least for small groups of objects laid in a line. A corresponder may answer "how many" by recounting the objects starting over with one each time. |
| 4 | Counter (Small Numbers) | 6 | At around 4 years of age, students may begin to count meaningfully. They may accurately count objects to 5 and answer the "how many" question with the last number counted. These students may count verbally to 10 and may write or draw to represent 1–5. |
| 4 | Producer—Counter to (Small Numbers) | 7 | The next level after counting small numbers is to produce a group of four objects. When asked to show four of something, for example, this student may give four objects. |
| 4 | Counter (10) | 8 | This student may count structured arrangements of objects to 10. He or she may be able to write or draw to represent 10 and may accurately count a line of nine blocks and say there are 9. |
| 4 | Just After/Just Before Counter | 9 | A student at this level may find the number just after or just before another number, but only by counting up from 1. |
| 5 | Counter and Producer—Counter to (10+) | 10 | Around 5 years of age, students may begin to count out objects accurately to 10 and then beyond to 30. They may keep track of objects that have and have not been counted, even in different arrangements. They may write or draw to represent 1 to 10 and then 20 and 30, and may give the next number to 20 or 30. |
| 5 | Counting Error Recognizer | 11 | The next level in counting is recognizing errors in others' counting and being able to eliminate most errors in one's own counting. |

| Age Range | Level Name | Level | Description |
|---|---|---|---|
| 5 | Counter Backward from 10 | 12 | Another milestone at about age 5 is being able to count backward from 10. |
| 6 | Counter from N (N+1, N−1) | 13 | Around 6 years of age, students may begin to count on, counting verbally and with objects from numbers other than 1. |
| 6 | Just After/Just Before | 14 | Another noticeable accomplishment is that students may determine the number immediately before or after another number without having to start back at 1. |
| 6 | Skip-Counting by 10s to 100 | 15 | A student at this level may count by tens to 100. They may count through decades knowing that 40 comes after 39, for example. |
| 6 | Counter to 100 | 16 | A student at this level may count by ones through 100, including the decade transitions from 39 to 40, 49 to 50, and so on. |
| 6 | Counter On Using Patterns | 17 | At this level, a student may keep track of counting acts by using numerical patterns, such as tapping as he or she counts. |
| 6 | Skip-Counter | 18 | At this level, students can count by 5s and 2s with understanding. |
| 6 | Counter of Imagined Items | 19 | At this level, a student may count mental images of hidden objects. |
| 6 | Counter On Keeping Track | 20 | A student at this level may keep track of counting acts numerically with the ability to count up one to four more from a given number. |
| 6 | Counter of Quantitative Units | 21 | At this level, a student can count unusual units, such as "wholes" when shown combinations of wholes and parts. For example, when shown three whole plastic eggs and four halves, a student at this level will say there are five whole eggs. |
| 6 | Counter to 200 | 22 | At this level, a student may count accurately to 200 and beyond, recognizing the patterns of ones, tens, and hundreds. |
| 7 | Number Conserver | 23 | A major milestone around age 7 is the ability to conserve number. A student who conserves number understands that a number is unchanged even if a group of objects is rearranged. For example, if there is a row of ten buttons, the student understands there are still ten without recounting, even if they are rearranged in a long row or a circle. |
| 7 | Counter Forward and Back | 24 | A student at this level may count in either direction and recognize that sequence of decades mirrors single-digit sequence. |

## Developmental Levels for Comparing and Ordering Numbers

Comparing and ordering sets is a critical skill for students as they determine whether one set is larger than another in order to make sure sets are equal and "fair." Prekindergartners can learn to use matching to compare collections or to create equivalent collections. Finding out how many more or fewer in one collection is more demanding than simply comparing two collections. The ability to compare and order sets with fluency develops over the course of several years. With instruction and number experience, most students develop foundational understanding of number relationships and place value at ages 4 and 5. Most students follow a natural developmental progression in learning to compare and order numbers with recognizable stages or levels. This developmental path can be described as part of a learning trajectory.

| Age Range | Level Name | Level | Description |
|---|---|---|---|
| 2 | Object Corresponder | 1 | At this early level, a student puts objects into one-to-one correspondence, but with only intuitive understanding of resulting equivalence. For example, a student may know that each carton has a straw, but does not necessarily know there are the same numbers of straws and cartons. |
| 2 | Perceptual Comparer | 2 | At this level, a student can compare collections that are quite different in size (for example, one is at least twice the other) and know that one has more than the other. If the collections are similar, the student can compare very small collections. |
| 3 | Nonverbal Comparer of Similar Items | 3 | At this level, a student can identify that different organizations of the same number of small groups are equal and different from other sets (1–4 items). For example, a student can identify ••• and •˙• as equal and different from •• or ˙•. |
| 3 | Nonverbal Comparer of Dissimilar Items | 4 | At this level, a student can match small, equal collections of dissimilar items, such as shells and dots, and show that they are the same number. |
| 4 | Matching Comparer | 5 | As students progress, they begin to compare groups of 1–6 by matching. For example, a student gives one toy bone to every dog and says there are the same number of dogs and bones. |
| 4 | Knows-to-Count Comparer | 6 | A significant step occurs when the student begins to count collections to compare. At the early levels, students are not always accurate when a larger collection's objects are smaller in size than the objects in the smaller collection. For example, a student at this level may accurately count two equal collections, but when asked, says the collection of larger blocks has more. |
| 4 | Counting Comparer (Same Size) | 7 | At this level, students make accurate comparisons via counting, but only when objects are about the same size and groups are small (about 1–5 items). |
| 5 | Counting Comparer (5) | 8 | As students develop their ability to compare sets, they compare accurately by counting, even when a larger collection's objects are smaller. A student at this level can figure out how many more or less. |
| 5 | Ordinal Counter | 9 | At this level, a student identifies and uses ordinal numbers from "first" to "tenth." For example, the student can identify who is "third in line." |

| Age Range | Level Name | Level | Description |
|---|---|---|---|
| 5 | Serial Orderer to 6+ | 10 | Students demonstrate development in comparing when they begin to order lengths marked into units (1–6, then beyond). For example, given towers of cubes, this student can put them in order, 1 to 6. Later the student begins to order collections. For example, given cards with one to six dots on them, the student can put them in order. |
| 6 | Counting Comparer (10) | 11 | This level can be observed when the student compares sets by counting, even when a larger collection's objects are smaller, up to 10. A student at this level can accurately count two collections of 9 items each, and says they have the same number, even if one collection has larger blocks. |
| 6 | Mental Number Line to 10 | 12 | As students move into this level, they begin to use mental rather than physical images and knowledge of number relationships to determine relative size and position. For example, a student at this level can answer which number is closer to 6, 4, or 9 without counting physical objects. |
| 7 | Place Value Comparer | 13 | Further development is made when a student begins to compare numbers with place value understanding. For example, a student at this level can explain that "63 is more than 59 because six tens is more than five tens, even if there are more than three ones." |
| 7 | Mental Number Line to 100 | 14 | Students demonstrate the next level in comparing and ordering when they can use mental images and knowledge of number relationships, including ones embedded in tens, to determine relative size and position. For example, when asked, "Which is closer to 45, 30 or 50?" a student at this level may say "45 is right next to 50, but 30 isn't." |
| 8+ | Mental Number Line to 1,000s | 15 | At about age 8, students may begin to use mental images of numbers up to 1,000 and knowledge of number relationships, including place value, to determine relative size and position. For example, when asked, "Which is closer to 3,500—2,000 or 7,000?"a student at this level may say "70 is double 35, but 20 is only fifteen from 35, so twenty hundreds, 2,000, is closer." |

## Developmental Levels for Recognizing Number and Subitizing (Instantly Recognizing)

The ability to recognize number values develops over the course of several years and is a foundational part of number sense. Beginning at about age 2, students begin to name groups of objects. The ability to instantly know how many are in a group, called *subitizing,* begins at about age 3. By age 8, with instruction and number experience, most students can identify groups of items and use place values and multiplication skills to count them. Most students follow a natural developmental progression in learning to count with recognizable stages or levels. This developmental path can be described as part of a learning trajectory.

| Age Range | Level Name | Level | Description |
|---|---|---|---|
| 2 | Small Collection Namer | 1 | The first sign occurs when the student can name groups of 1 to 2, sometimes 3. For example, when shown a pair of shoes, this young student says, "two shoes." |
| 3 | Nonverbal Subitizer | 2 | This level occurs when, shown a small collection (1 to 4), the student can put out a matching group nonverbally, but cannot necessarily give the number telling how many. For example, when 4 objects are shown, the student makes a set of 4 objects to "match." |
| 3 | Maker of Small Collections | 3 | At this level, a student can nonverbally make a small collection (no more than 5, usually 1 to 3) with the same number as another collection. For example, when shown a collection of 3, the student makes another collection of 3. |
| 4 | Perceptual Subitizer to 4 | 4 | Progress is made when a student instantly recognizes collections up to 4 and verbally names the number of items. For example, when shown 4 objects briefly, the student says "4." |
| 5 | Perceptual Subitizer to 5 | 5 | This level is the ability to instantly recognize collections up to 5 and verbally name the number of items. For example, when shown 5 objects, the student says "5." |

| Age Range | Level Name | Level | Description |
|---|---|---|---|
| 5 | Conceptual Subitizer to 5 | 6 | At this level, the student can verbally label all arrangements to 5, using groups. For example, a student at this level might say, "I saw 2 and 2, and so I saw 4." |
| 5 | Conceptual Subitizer to 10 | 7 | This step is when the student can verbally label most arrangements to 6, then up to 10, using groups. For example, a student at this level might say, "In my mind, I made 2 groups of 3 and 1 more, so 7." |
| 6 | Conceptual Subitizer to 20 | 8 | Next, a student can verbally label structured arrangements up to 20, using groups. For example, the student may say, "I saw 3 fives, so 5, 10, 15." |
| 7 | Conceptual Subitizer with Place Value and Skip-Counting | 9 | At this level, a student is able to use skip-counting and place value to verbally label structured arrangements. For example, the student may say, "I saw groups of tens and twos, so 10, 20, 30, 40, 42, 44, 46...46!" |
| 8+ | Conceptual Subitizer with Place Value and Multiplication | 10 | As students develop their ability to subitize, they use groups, multiplication, and place value to verbally label structured arrangements. At this level, a student may say, "I saw groups of tens and threes, so I thought, 5 tens is 50 and 4 threes is 12, so 62 in all." |

## Developmental Levels for Composing (Knowing Combinations of Numbers)

Composing and decomposing are combining and separating operations that allow students to build concepts of "parts" and "wholes." Most prekindergartners can "see" that two items and one item make three items. Later, students learn to separate a group into parts in various ways and then to count to produce all of the number "partners" of a given number. Eventually students think of a number and know the different addition facts that make that number. Most students follow a natural developmental progression in learning to compose and decompose numbers with recognizable stages or levels. This developmental path can be described as part of a learning trajectory.

| Age Range | Level Name | Level | Description |
|---|---|---|---|
| 4 | Pre-Part-Whole Recognizer | 1 | At the earliest levels of composing, a student only nonverbally recognizes parts and wholes. For example, when shown 4 red blocks and 2 blue blocks, a young student may intuitively appreciate that "all the blocks" includes the red and blue blocks, but when asked how many there are in all, the student may name a small number, such as 1. |
| 5 | Inexact Part-Whole Recognizer | 2 | A sign of development is that the student knows a whole is bigger than parts, but does not accurately quantify. For example, when shown 4 red blocks and 2 blue blocks and asked how many there are in all, the student may name a "large number," such as 5 or 10. |
| 5 | Composer to 4, then 5 | 3 | At this level, a student begins to know number combinations. A student at this level quickly names parts of any whole, or the whole given the parts. For example, when shown 4, then 1 is secretly hidden, and then shown the 3 remaining, the student may quickly say "1" is hidden. |

| Age Range | Level Name | Level | Description |
|---|---|---|---|
| 6 | Composer to 7 | 4 | The next sign of development is when a student knows number combinations to totals of 7. A student at this level quickly names parts of any whole, or the whole when given parts, and can double numbers to 10. For example, when shown 6, then 4 are secretly hidden, and then shown the 2 remaining, the student may quickly say "4" are hidden. |
| 6 | Composer to 10 | 5 | This level is when a student knows number combinations to totals of 10. A student at this level may quickly name parts of any whole, or the whole when given parts, and can double numbers to 20. For example, this student would be able to say "9 and 9 is 18." |
| 7 | Composer with Tens and Ones | 6 | At this level, the student understands two-digit numbers as tens and ones, can count with dimes and pennies, and can perform two-digit addition with regrouping. For example, a student at this level may explain, "17 and 36 is like 17 and 3, which is 20, and 33, which is 53." |

## Developmental Levels for Adding and Subtracting

Single-digit addition and subtraction is generally characterized as "math facts." It is assumed students must memorize these facts, yet research has shown that addition and subtraction have their roots in counting, counting on, number sense, the ability to compose and decompose numbers, and place value. Research has also shown that learning methods for addition and subtraction with understanding is much more effective than rote memorization of seemingly isolated facts. Most students follow an observable developmental progression in learning to add and subtract numbers with recognizable stages or levels. This developmental path can be described as part of a learning trajectory.

| Age Range | Level Name | Level | Description |
|---|---|---|---|
| 1 | Pre +/− | 1 | At the earliest level, a student shows no sign of being able to add or subtract. |
| 3 | Nonverbal +/− | 2 | The first sign is when a student can add and subtract very small collections nonverbally. For example, when shown 2 objects, then 1 object being hidden under a napkin, the student identifies or makes a set of 3 objects to "match." |
| 4 | Small Number +/− | 3 | This level is when a student can find sums for joining problems up to 3 + 2 by counting with objects. For example, when asked, "You have 2 balls and get 1 more. How many in all?" the student may count out 2, then count out 1 more, then count all 3: "1, 2, 3, 3!" |
| 5 | Find Result +/− | 4 | **Addition** Evidence of this level in addition is when a student can find sums for joining (you had 3 apples and get 3 more; how many do you have in all?) and part-part-whole (there are 6 girls and 5 boys on the playground; how many students were there in all?) problems by direct modeling, counting all, with objects. For example, when asked, "You have 2 red balls and 3 blue balls. How many in all?" the student may count out 2 red, then count out 3 blue, then count all 5.<br>**Subtraction** In subtraction, a student can also solve take-away problems by separating with objects. For example, when asked, "You have 5 balls and give 2 to Tom. How many do you have left?" the student may count out 5 balls, then take away 2, and then count the remaining 3. |
| 5 | Find Change +/− | 5 | **Addition** At this level, a student can find the missing addend (5 + _ = 7) by adding on objects. For example, when asked, "You have 5 balls and then get some more. Now you have 7 in all. How many did you get?" The student may count out 5, then count those 5 again starting at 1, then add more, counting "6, 7," then count the balls added to find the answer, 2.<br>**Subtraction** A child can compare by matching in simple situations. For example, when asked, "Here are 6 dogs and 4 balls. If we give a ball to each dog, how many dogs will not get a ball?" a student at this level may count out 6 dogs, match 4 balls to 4 of them, then count the 2 dogs that have no ball. |
| 5 | Change To *n* +/− | 6 | A significant advancement occurs when a student is able to count on. This student can add on objects to make one number into another without counting from 1. For example, when told, "This puppet has 4 balls, but she should have 6. Make it 6," the student may put up 4 fingers on one hand, immediately count up from 4 while putting up 2 fingers on the other hand, saying, "5, 6," and then count or recognize the 2 fingers. |

| Age Range | Level Name | Level | Description |
|---|---|---|---|
| 6 | Counting Strategies +/− | 7 | This level occurs when a student can find sums for joining (you had 8 apples and get 3 more...) and part-part-whole (6 girls and 5 boys...) problems with finger patterns or by adding on objects or counting on. For example, when asked "How much is 4 and 3 more?" the student may answer "4...5, 6, 7. 7!" Students at this level can also solve missing addend (3 + _ = 7) or compare problems by counting on. When asked, for example, "You have 6 balls. How many more would you need to have 8?" the student may say, "6, 7 [puts up first finger], 8 [puts up second finger]. 2!" |
| 6 | Part-Whole +/− | 8 | Further development has occurred when the student has part-whole understanding. This student can solve problems using flexible strategies and some derived facts (for example, "5 + 5 is 10, so 5 + 6 is 11"), can sometimes do start- unknown problems (_ + 6 = 11), but only by trial and error. When asked, "You had some balls. Then you get 6 more. Now you have 11 balls. How many did you start with?" this student may lay out 6, then 3, count, and get 9. The child may put 1 more, say 10, then put 1 more. The child may count up from 6 to 11, then recounts the group added, and say, "5!" |
| 6 | Numbers-in-Numbers +/− | 9 | Evidence of this level is when a student recognizes that a number is part of a whole and can solve problems when the start is unknown (_ + 4 = 9) with counting strategies. For example, when asked, "You have some balls, then you get 4 more balls, now you have 9. How many did you have to start with?" this student may count, putting up fingers, "5, 6, 7, 8, 9." The child may look at his or her fingers, and say, "5!" |
| 7 | Deriver +/− | 10 | At this level, a student can use flexible strategies and derived combinations (for example, "7 + 7 is 14, so 7 + 8 is 15") to solve all types of problems. For example, when asked, "What's 7 plus 8?" this student thinks: 7 + 8 = 7 + [7 + 1] = [7 + 7] + 1 = 14 + 1 = 15. The student can also solve multidigit problems by incrementing or combining 10s and 1s. For example, when asked "What's 28 + 35?" this student may think: 20 + 30 = 50; + 8 = 58; 2 more is 60, and 3 more is 63. Combining 10s and 1s: 20 + 30 = 50. 8 + 5 is like 8 plus 2 and 3 more, so, it is 13–50 and 13 is 63. |
| 8+ | Problem Solver +/− | 11 | As students develop their addition and subtraction abilities, they can solve by using flexible strategies and many known combinations. For example, when asked, "If I have 13 and you have 9, how could we have the same number?" this student may say, "9 and 1 is 10, then 3 more makes 13. 1 and 3 is 4. I need 4 more!" |
| 8+ | Multidigit +/− | 12 | Further development is shown when students can use composition of 10s and all previous strategies to solve multidigit +/− problems. For example, when asked, "What's 37 − 18?" this student may say, "Take 1 ten off the 3 tens; that's 2 tens. Take 7 off the 7. That's 2 tens and 0...20. I have one more to take off. That's 19." Or, when asked, "What's 28 + 35?" this child may think, 30 + 35 would be 65. But it's 28, so it's 2 less...63. |

## Developmental Levels for Multiplying and Dividing

Multiplication and division builds on addition and subtraction understanding and is dependent upon counting and place-value concepts. As students begin to learn to multiply, they make equal groups and count them all. They then learn skip-counting and derive related products from products they know. Finding and using patterns aids in learning multiplication and division facts with understanding. Students typically follow an observable developmental progression in learning to multiply and divide numbers with recognizable stages or levels. This developmental path can be described as part of a learning trajectory.

| Age Range | Level Name | Level | Description |
|---|---|---|---|
| 2 | Nonquantitive Sharer "Dumper" | 1 | Multiplication and division concepts begin very early with the problem of sharing. Early evidence of these concepts can be observed when a student dumps out blocks and gives some (not an equal number) to each person. |
| 3 | Beginning Grouper and Distributive Sharer | 2 | Progression to this level can be observed when a student is able to make small groups (fewer than 5). This student can share by "dealing out," but often only between 2 people, although he or she may not appreciate the numerical result. For example, to share 4 blocks, this student may give each person a block, check that each person has one, and repeat this. |
| 4 | Grouper and Distributive Sharer | 3 | The next level occurs when a student makes small equal groups (fewer than 6). This student can deal out equally between 2 or more recipients, but may not understand that equal quantities are produced. For example, the student may share 6 blocks by dealing out blocks to herself and a friend one at a time. |
| 5 | Concrete Modeler ×/÷ | 4 | As students develop, they are able to solve small-number multiplying problems by grouping—making each group and counting all. At this level, a student can solve division/sharing problems with informal strategies, using concrete objects—up to 20 objects and 2 to 5 people—although the student may not understand equivalence of groups. For example, the student may distribute 20 objects by dealing out 2 blocks to each of 5 people, then 1 to each, until the blocks are gone. |
| 6 | Parts and Wholes ×/÷ | 5 | A new level is evidenced when the student understands the inverse relation between divisor and quotient. For example, this student may understand "If you share with more people, each person gets fewer." |
| 7 | Skip-Counter ×/÷ | 6 | As students develop understanding in multiplication and division, they begin to use skip-counting for multiplication and for measurement division (finding out how many groups). For example, given 20 blocks, 4 to each person, and asked how many people, the student may skip-count by 4, holding up 1 finger for each count of 4. A student at this level may also use trial and error for partitive division (finding out how many in each group). For example, given 20 blocks, 5 people, and asked how many each should get, this student may give 3 to each, then 1 more, then 1 more. |
| 8+ | Deriver ×/÷ | 7 | At this level, students use strategies and derived combinations and solve multidigit problems by operating on tens and ones separately. For example, a student at this level may explain "7 × 6, five 7s is 35, so 7 more is 42." |
| 8+ | Array Quantifier | 8 | Further development can be observed when a student begins to work with arrays. For example, given 7 × 4 with most of 5 × 4 covered, a student at this level may say, "There's 8 in these 2 rows, and 5 rows of 4 is 20, so 28 in all." |
| 8+ | Partitive Divisor | 9 | This level can be observed when a student is able to figure out how many are in each group. For example, given 20 blocks, 5 people, and asked how many each should get, a student at this level may say, "4, because 5 groups of 4 is 20." |
| 8+ | Multidigit ×/÷ | 10 | As students progress, they begin to use multiple strategies for multiplication and division, from compensating to paper-and-pencil procedures. For example, a student becoming fluent in multiplication might explain that "19 times 5 is 95, because 20 fives is 100, and one less five is 95." |

## Developmental Levels for Measuring

Measurement is one of the main real-world applications of mathematics. Counting is a type of measurement which determines how many items are in a collection. Measurement also involves assigning a number to attributes of length, area, and weight. Prekindergarten students know that mass, weight, and length exist, but they do not know how to reason about these or to accurately measure them. As students develop their understanding of measurement, they begin to use tools to measure and understand the need for standard units of measure. Students typically follow an observable developmental progression in learning to measure with recognizable stages or levels. This developmental path can be described as part of a learning trajectory.

| Age Range | Level Name | Level | Description |
|---|---|---|---|
| 3 | Length Quantity Recognizer | 1 | At the earliest level, students can identify length as an attribute. For example, they might say, "I'm tall, see?" |
| 4 | Length Direct Comparer | 2 | In this level, students can physically align 2 objects to determine which is longer or if they are the same length. For example, they can stand 2 sticks up next to each other on a table and say, "This one's bigger." 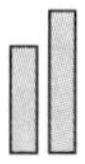 |
| 5 | Serial Orderer to 6+ | 3 | At this level, a student can order lengths, marked in 1 to 6 units. For example, given towers of cubes, a student at this level may put them in order, 1 to 6. |
| 5 | Indirect Length Comparer | 4 | A sign of further development is when a student can compare the length of 2 objects by representing them with a third object. For example, a student might compare the length of 2 objects with a piece of string. Additional evidence of this level is that when asked to measure, the student may assign a length by guessing or moving along a length while counting (without equal-length units). The student may also move a finger along a line segment, saying 10, 20, 30, 31, 32. |
| 6 | End-to-End Length Measurer | 5 | At this level, the student can lay units end-to-end, although he or she may not see the need for equal-length units. For example, a student might lay 9-inch cubes in a line beside a book to measure how long it is. |

| Age Range | Level Name | Level | Description |
|---|---|---|---|
| 7 | Length Unit Iterater | 6 | A significant change occurs when a student can use a ruler and see the need for identical units. |
| 7 | Length Unit Relater | 7 | At this level, a student can relate size and number of units. For example, the student may explain, "If you measure with centimeters instead of inches, you'll need more of them, because each one is smaller." |
| 8 | Length Measurer | 8 | As students develop measurement ability, they begin to measure, knowing the need for identical units, the relationships between different units, partitions of unit, and the zero point on rulers. At this level, the student also begins to estimate. The student may explain, "I used a meter-stick 3 times, then there was a little left over. So, I lined it up from 0 and found 14 centimeters. So, it's 3 meters, 14 centimeters in all." |
| 8 | Conceptual Ruler Measurer | 9 | Further development in measurement is evidenced when a student possesses an "internal" measurement tool. At this level, the student mentally moves along an object, segmenting it, and counting the segments. This student also uses arithmetic to measure and estimates with accuracy. For example, a student at this level may explain, "I imagine one meter-stick after another along the edge of the room. That's how I estimated the room's length to be 9 meters." |

# Developmental Levels for Recognizing Geometric Shapes

Geometric shapes can be used to represent and understand objects. Analyzing, comparing, and classifying shapes helps create new knowledge of shapes and their relationships. Shapes can be decomposed or composed into other shapes. Through their everyday activity, students build both intuitive and explicit knowledge of geometric figures. Most students can recognize and name basic two-dimensional shapes at 4 years of age. However, young students can learn richer concepts about shape if they have varied examples and nonexamples of shape, discussions about shapes and their characteristics, a wide variety of shape classes, and interesting tasks. Students typically follow an observable developmental progression in learning about shapes with recognizable stages or levels. This developmental path can be described as part of a learning trajectory.

| Age Range | Level Name | Level | Description |
|---|---|---|---|
| 2 | Shape Matcher—Basic 1 | 1 | The earliest sign of understanding shape is when a student can match basic shapes (circle, square, typical triangle) with the same size and orientation. |
| 2 | Basic 2a | 2 | A sign of development is when a student can match basic shapes with different sizes. |
| 2 | Basic 2b | 3 | This level of development is when a student can match basic shapes with different orientations. |
| 3 | Shape Prototype Recognizer and Identifier | 4 | A sign of development is when a student can recognize and name a prototypical circle, square, and, less often, a typical triangle. For example, the student names this a square. □ Some students may name different sizes, shapes, and orientations of rectangles, but also accept some shapes that look rectangular but are not rectangles. Students name these shapes "rectangles" (including the nonrectangular parallelogram). 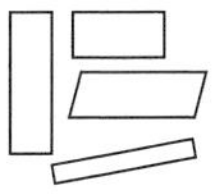 |
| 3 | Shape Matcher—3 | 5 | As students develop understanding of shape, they can match a wider variety of shapes with the same size and orientation. |
| 4 | Shape Recognizer—Basic 1 | 6 | This sign of development is when a student can recognize some nonprototypical squares and triangles and may recognize some rectangles, but usually not rhombi (diamonds). Often, the student does not differentiate sides/corners. The student at this level may name these as triangles.  |
| 4 | Constructor of Shapes from Parts 1 | 7 | A significant sign of development is when a student represents a shape by making a shape "look like" a goal shape. For example, when asked to make a triangle with sticks, the student may create the following: □. |
| 5 | Shape Recognizer—Basic 2 | 8 | As students develop understanding of shape, they recognize more rectangle sizes, shapes, and orientations of rectangles. For example, a student at this level may correctly name these shapes "rectangles." 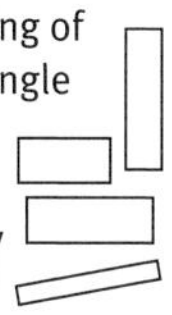 |
| 5 | Side Recognizer | 9 | A sign of development is when a student recognizes parts of shapes and identifies sides as distinct geometric objects. For example, when asked what this shape is, the student may say it is a quadrilateral (or has 4 sides) after counting and running a finger along the length of each side.  |
| 5 | Angle Recognizer | 10 | At this level, a student can recognize angles as separate geometric objects. For example, when asked, "Why is this a triangle," the child may say, "It has three angles" and count them, pointing clearly to each vertex (point at the corner). |
| 5 | Shape Recognizer—3 | 11 | As students develop, they are able to recognize most basic shapes and prototypical examples of other shapes, such as hexagon, rhombus (diamond), and trapezoid. For example, a student can correctly identify and name all the following shapes: 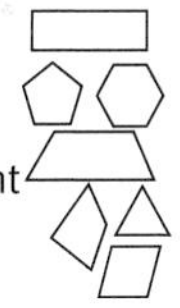 |
| 6 | Shape Identifier | 12 | At this level, the student can name most common shapes, including rhombi, "ellipses-is-not-circle." A student at this level implicitly recognizes right angles, so distinguishes between a rectangle and a parallelogram without right angles. A student may correctly name all the following shapes: 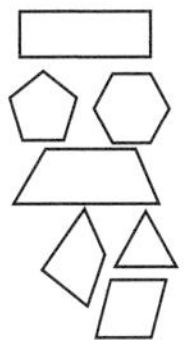 |
| 6 | Angle Matcher | 13 | A sign of development is when the student can match angles concretely. For example, given several triangles, the child may find 2 with the same angles by laying the angles on top of one another. |

# Learning Trajectories

| Age Range | Level Name | Level | Description |
|---|---|---|---|
| 7 | Parts of Shapes Identifier | 14 | At this level, the student can identify shapes in terms of their components. For example, the student may say, “No matter how skinny it looks, that’s a triangle because it has 3 sides and 3 angles.”  |
| 7 | Constructor of Shapes from Parts 2 | 15 | A significant step is when the student can represent a shape with completely correct construction, based on knowledge of components and relationships. For example, when asked to make a triangle with sticks, the student may create the following:  |
| 8 | Shape Class Identifier | 16 | As students develop, they begin to use class membership (for example, to sort) not explicitly based on properties. For example, a student at this level may say, “I put the triangles over here, and the quadrilaterals, including squares, rectangles, rhombi, and trapezoids, over there.” |
| 8 | Shape Property Identifier | 17 | At this level, a student can use properties explicitly. For example, a student may say, “I put the shapes with opposite sides that are parallel over here, and those with 4 sides but not both pairs of sides parallel over there.” |
| 8 | Angle Size Comparer | 18 | The next sign of development is when a student can separate and compare angle sizes. For example, the student may say, “I put all the shapes that have right angles here, and all the ones that have bigger or smaller angles over there.” |
| 8 | Angle Measurer | 19 | A significant step in development is when a student can use a protractor to measure angles. |
| 8 | Property Class Identifier | 20 | The next sign of development is when a student can use class membership for shapes (for example, to sort or consider shapes “similar”) explicitly based on properties, including angle measure. For example, the student may say, “I put the equilateral triangles over here, and the right triangles over here.” |
| 8 | Angle Synthesizer | 21 | As students develop understanding of shape, they can combine various meanings of angle (turn, corner, slant). For example, a student at this level could explain, “This ramp is at a 45° angle to the ground.” |

# Developmental Levels for Composing Geometric Shapes

Students move through levels in the composition and decomposition of two-dimensional figures. Very young students cannot compose shapes but then gain ability to combine shapes into pictures, synthesize combinations of shapes into new shapes, and eventually substitute and build different kinds of shapes. Students typically follow an observable developmental progression in learning to compose shapes with recognizable stages or levels. This developmental path can be described as part of a learning trajectory.

| Age Range | Level Name | Level | Description |
|---|---|---|---|
| 2 | Pre-Composer | 1 | The earliest sign of development is when a student can manipulate shapes as individuals, but is unable to combine them to compose a larger shape. |
| 3 | Pre-Decomposer | 2 | At this level, a student can decompose shapes, but only by trial and error. |
| 4 | Piece Assembler | 3 | Around age 4, a student can begin to make pictures in which each shape represents a unique role (for example, one shape for each body part) and shapes touch. A student at this level can fill simple outline puzzles using trial and error. |
| 5 | Picture Maker | 4 | As students develop, they are able to put several shapes together to make one part of a picture (for example, 2 shapes for 1 arm). A student at this level uses trial and error and does not anticipate creation of the new geometric shape. The student can choose shapes using "general shape" or side length, and fill "easy" outline puzzles that suggest the placement of each shape (but note below that the student is trying to put a square in the puzzle where its right angles will not fit). |
| 5 | Simple Decomposer | 5 | A significant step occurs when the student is able to decompose ("take apart" into smaller shapes) simple shapes that have obvious clues as to their decomposition. |
| 5 | Shape Composer | 6 | A sign of development is when a student composes shapes with anticipation ("I know what will fit!"). A student at this level chooses shapes using angles as well as side lengths. Rotation and flipping are used intentionally to select and place shapes. |
| 6 | Substitution Composer | 7 | A sign of development is when a student is able to make new shapes out of smaller shapes and uses trial and error to substitute groups of shapes for other shapes in order to create new shapes in different ways. For example, the student can substitute shapes to fill outline puzzles in different ways. |

| Age Range | Level Name | Level | Description |
|---|---|---|---|
| 6 | Shape Decomposer (with Help) | 8 | As students develop, they can decompose shapes by using imagery that is suggested and supported by the task or environment. |
| 7 | Shape Composite Repeater | 9 | This level is demonstrated when the student can construct and duplicate units of units (shapes made from other shapes) intentionally, and understands each as being both multiple, small shapes and one larger shape. For example, the student may continue a pattern of shapes that leads to tiling. |
| 7 | Shape Decomposer with Imagery | 10 | A significant sign of development is when a student is able to decompose shapes flexibly by using independently generated imagery. |
| 8 | Shape Composer—Units of Units | 11 | Students demonstrate further understanding when they are able to build and apply units of units (shapes made from other shapes). For example, in constructing spatial patterns, the student can extend patterning activity to create a tiling with a new unit shape—a unit of unit shapes that he or she recognizes and consciously constructs. For example, the student may build *T*s out of 4 squares, use 4 *T*s to build squares, and use squares to tile a rectangle. |
| 8 | Shape Decomposer — Units of Units | 12 | As students develop understanding of shape, they can decompose shapes flexibly by using independently generated imagery and planned decompositions of shapes that themselves are decompositions. |

## Developmental Levels for Comparing Geometric Shapes

As early as 4 years of age, students can create and use strategies, such as moving shapes to compare their parts or to place one on top of the other for judging whether two figures are the same shape. From Pre-K to Grade 2, they can develop sophisticated and accurate mathematical procedures for comparing geometric shapes. Students typically follow an observable developmental progression in learning about how shapes are the same and different with recognizable stages or levels. This developmental path can be described as part of a learning trajectory.

| Age Range | Level Name | Level | Description |
|---|---|---|---|
| 3 | "Same Thing" Comparer | 1 | The first sign of understanding is when the student can compare real-world objects. For example, the student may say two pictures of houses are the same or different. |
| 4 | "Similar" Comparer | 2 | Thist sign of development occurs when the student judges two shapes to be the same if they are more visually similar than different. For example, the student may say, "These are the same. They are pointy at the top." 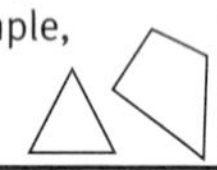 |
| 4 | Part Comparer | 3 | At this level, a student can say that two shapes are the same after matching one side on each. For example, a student may say, "These are the same" (matching the two sides).  |
| 4 | Some Attributes Comparer | 4 | As students develop, they look for differences in attributes, but may examine only part of a shape. For example, a student at this level may say, "These are the same" (indicating the top halves of the shapes are similar by laying them on top of each other).  |
| 5 | Most Attributes Comparer | 5 | At this level, the student looks for differences in attributes, examining full shapes, but may ignore some spatial relationships. For example, a student may say, "These are the same." 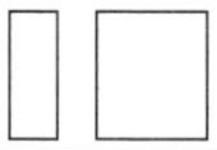 |
| 7 | Congruence Determiner | 6 | A sign of development is when a student determines congruence by comparing all attributes and all spatial relationships. For example, a student at this level may say that two shapes are the same shape and the same size after comparing every one of their sides and angles. |
| 7 | Congruence Superposer | 7 | As students develop understanding, they can move and place objects on top of each other to determine congruence. For example, a student at this level may say that two shapes are the same shape and the same size after laying them on top of each other. |
| 8 | Congruence Representer | 8 | Continued development is evidenced as students refer to geometric properties and explain transformations. For example, a student at this level may say, "These must be congruent, because they have equal sides, all square corners, and I can move them on top of each other exactly." |

## Developmental Levels for Spatial Sense and Motions

Infants and toddlers spend a great deal of time learning about the properties and relations of objects in space. Very young students know and use the shape of their environment in navigation activities. With guidance they can learn to "mathematize" this knowledge. They can learn about direction, perspective, distance, symbolization, location, and coordinates. Students typically follow an observable developmental progression in developing spatial sense with recognizable stages or levels. This developmental path can be described as part of a learning trajectory.

| Age Range | Level Name | Level | Description |
|---|---|---|---|
| 4 | Simple Turner | 1 | An early sign of spatial sense is when a student mentally turns an object to perform easy tasks. For example, given a shape with the top marked with color, the student may correctly identify which of three shapes it would look like if it were turned "like this" (90 degree turn demonstrated), before physically moving the shape. |
| 5 | Beginning Slider, Flipper, Turner | 2 | This sign of development occurs when a student can use the correct motions, but is not always accurate in direction and amount. For example, a student at this level may know a shape has to be flipped to match another shape, but flips it in the wrong direction. |
| 6 | Slider, Flipper, Turner | 3 | As students develop spatial sense, they can perform slides and flips, often only horizontal and vertical, by using manipulatives. For example, a student at this level may perform turns of 45, 90, and 180 degrees and know a shape must be turned 90 degrees to the right to fit into a puzzle. |
| 7 | Diagonal Mover | 4 | A sign of development is when a student can perform diagonal slides and flips. For example, a student at this level may know a shape must be turned or flipped over an oblique line (45 degree orientation) to fit into a puzzle. |
| 8 | Mental Mover | 5 | Further signs of development occur when a student can predict results of moving shapes using mental images. A student at this level may say, "If you turned this 120 degrees, it would be just like this one." |

## Developmental Levels for Patterning and Early Algebra

Algebra begins with a search for patterns. Identifying patterns helps bring order, cohesion, and predictability to seemingly unorganized situations and allows one to make generalizations beyond the information directly available. The recognition and analysis of patterns are important components of the young student's intellectual development because they provide a foundation for the development of algebraic thinking. Although prekindergarten students engage in pattern-related activities and recognize patterns in their everyday environment, research has revealed that an abstract understanding of patterns develops gradually during the early childhood years. Students typically follow an observable developmental progression in learning about patterns with recognizable stages or levels. This developmental path can be described as part of a learning trajectory.

| Age Range | Level Name | Level | Description |
|---|---|---|---|
| 2 | Prepatterner | 1 | A student at the earliest level does not recognize patterns. For example, a student may name a striped shirt with no repeating unit a "pattern." |
| 3 | Pattern Recognizer | 2 | At this level, the student can recognize a simple pattern. For example, a student at this level may say, "I'm wearing a pattern" about a shirt with black and white stripes. |
| 4 | Pattern Duplicator AB | 3 | A sign of development is when the student can duplicate an ABABAB pattern, although the student may have to work alongside the model pattern. For example, given objects in a row, ABABAB, the student may make his or her own ABABAB row in a different location. |
| 4 | Pattern Duplicator | 4 | At this level, the student is able to duplicate simple patterns (not just alongside the model pattern). For example, given objects in a row, ABBABBABB, the student may make his or her own ABBABBABB row in a different location. |

| Age Range | Level Name | Level | Description |
|---|---|---|---|
| 5 | Pattern Extender | 5 | A sign of development is when the student can extend simple patterns. For example, given objects in a row, ABBABBABB, he or she may add ABBABB to the end of the row. |
| 6 | Pattern Maker from *n* | 6 | As a student develops patterning, he or she is able to fill in a missing element of a pattern. For example, given objects in a row with one missing, ABBAB_ABB, he or she may identify and fill in the missing element. |
| 7 | Pattern Unit Recognizer | 7 | At this level, a student can identify the smallest unit of a pattern. For example, given objects in a row with one missing, ABBAB_ABB, he or she may identify and fill in the missing element. |

# Glossary

## A

**absolute value** The distance of a number from 0. For example, the absolute value of 7, written as |7|, is 7. The absolute value of −4, written as |−4|, is 4.

**acute angle** An angle with a measure greater than 0 degrees and less than 90 degrees.

**addend** One of the numbers being added in an addition sentence. In the sentence 41 + 27 = 68, the numbers 41 and 27 are addends.

**addition** A mathematical operation based on "putting things together." Numbers being added are called *addends*. The result of addition is called a *sum*. In the number sentence 15 + 63 = 78, the numbers 15 and 63 are addends.

**additive inverses** Two numbers whose sum is 0. For example, 9 + −9 = 0. The additive inverse of 9 is −9, and the additive inverse of −9 is 9.

**adjacent angles** Two angles with a common side that do not otherwise overlap. In the diagram, angles 1 and 2 are adjacent angles. So are angles 2 and 3, angles 3 and 4, and angles 4 and 1.

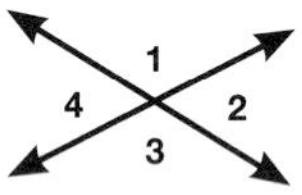


**algorithm** A step-by-step procedure for carrying out a computation or solving a problem.

**angle** Two rays with a common endpoint. The common endpoint is called the vertex of the angle.

**area** A measure of the surface inside a closed boundary. The formula for the area of a rectangle or parallelogram is $A = b \times h$, where $A$ represents the area, $b$ represents the length of the base, and $h$ the height of the figure.

**array** A rectangular arrangement of objects in rows and columns in which each row has the same number of elements and each column has the same number of elements.

**attribute** A feature such as size, shape, or color.

**average** See **mean.** The **median** and **mode** are also sometimes called the average.

**axis** (plural **axes**) A number line used in a coordinate grid.

## B

**bar graph** A graph in which the lengths of horizontal or vertical bars represent the magnitude of the data represented.

**base** See **exponential notation.**

**base** (of a parallelogram) One of the sides of a parallelogram; also, the length of this side. The length of a perpendicular line segment between the base and the side opposite the base is the height of the parallelogram.

**base** (of a polyhedron) The "bottom" face of a polyhedron; the face whose shape determines the type of prism or pyramid.

**base** (of a rectangle) One of the sides of a rectangle; also, the length of this side. The length of the side perpendicular to the base is the height of the rectangle.

**base** (of a triangle) One of the sides of a triangle; also, the length of this side. The shortest distance between the base and the vertex opposite the base is the height of the triangle.

**base ten** The commonly used numeration system, in which the ten digits 0, 1, 2,..., 9 have values that depend on the place in which they appear in a numeral (ones, tens, hundreds, and so on, to the left of the decimal point; tenths, hundredths, and so on, to the right of the decimal point).

**benchmark** A number or measure used as a standard of comparison for other numbers or measures.

**bisect** To divide a segment, angle, or figure into two parts of equal measure.

## C

**capacity** A measure of how much liquid or substance a container can hold. See also **volume.**

***centi-*** A prefix for units in the metric system meaning one hundredth.

**centimeter** (cm) In the metric system, a unit of length defined as 1/100 of a meter; equal to 10 millimeters or 1/10 of a decimeter.

**chance** The possibility of an outcome in an uncertain event. For example, in rolling a 0–5 ***Number Cube,*** there is an equal chance of rolling 1 or 4.

**circle** The set of all points in a plane that are a given distance (the radius) from a given point (the center of the circle).

**circle graph** A graph in which a circular region is divided into sectors to represent the categories in a set of data. The circle represents the whole set of data.

**circumference** The distance around a circle or sphere; also, the circle itself.

**clipped range** In a set of numbers, the range calculated without the greatest and least value, or with the two or three greatest and least values removed.

**closed figure** A figure that divides the plane into two regions, inside and outside the figure. A closed space figure divides space into two regions in the same way.

**common denominator** Any nonzero number that is a multiple of the denominators of two or more fractions.

**common factor** Any number that is a factor of two or more numbers.

**complementary angles** Two angles whose measures total 90 degrees.

**composite function** A function with two or more operations. For example, this function multiplies the input number by 5 then adds 3.

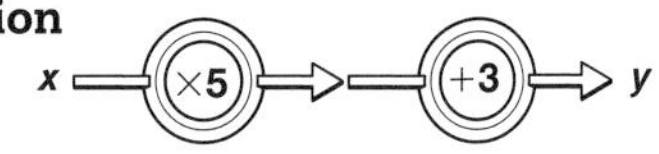


**composite number** A whole number that has more than two whole number factors. For example, 14 is a composite number because it has more than two whole number factors.

**concave** (nonconvex) **polygon** A polygon in which a line segment between two of the points on the boundary lies outside the polygon.

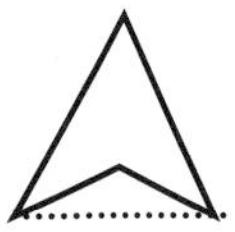

**cone** A space figure having a circular base, curved surface, and one vertex.

**congruent** Having identical sizes and shapes. Congruent figures are said to be congruent to each other.

**convex polygon** A polygon in which line segments between any two points on the boundary lie inside the polygon.

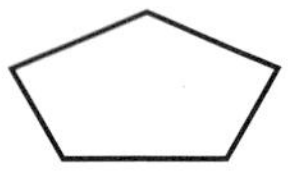

**coordinate** One of two numbers used to locate a point on a coordinate grid. See also **ordered pair.**

**coordinate grid** A device for locating points in a plane by means of ordered pairs or coordinates. A coordinate grid is formed by two number lines that intersect at their 0-points.

**corresponding angles** Two angles in the same relative position in two figures, or in similar locations in relation to a transversal intersecting two lines. In the diagram below, angles 1 and 5, 3 and 7, 2 and 6, and 4 and 8 are corresponding angles. If the lines are parallel, then the corresponding angles are congruent.

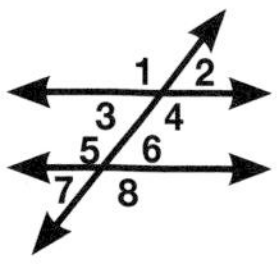


**corresponding sides** Two sides in the same relative position in two figures. In the diagram below, *AB* and A'B', BC and B'C', and AC and A'C' are corresponding sides.

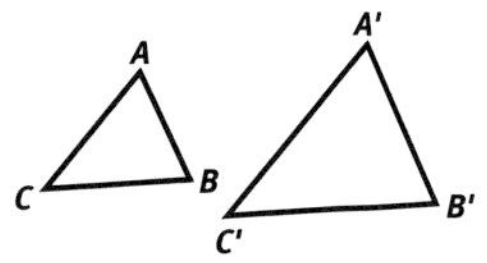


**cube** A space figure whose six faces are congruent squares that meet at right angles.

**cubic centimeter** ($cm^3$) A metric unit of volume; the volume of a cube 1 centimeter on an edge. 1 cubic centimeter is equal to 1 milliliter.

**cubic unit** A unit used in a volume and capacity measurement.

**customary system of measurement** The measuring system used most often in the United States. Units for linear measure (length, distance) include inch, foot, yard, and mile; units for weight include ounce and pound; units for capacity (amount of liquid or other substance a container can hold) include fluid ounce, cup, pint, quart, and gallon.

**cylinder** A space figure having a curved surface and parallel circular or elliptical bases that are congruent.

# D

**decimal** A number written in standard notation, usually one containing a decimal point, as in 3.78.

**decimal approximation** A decimal that is close to the value of a rational number. By extending the decimal approximation to additional digits, it is possible to come as close as desired to the value of the rational number. For example, decimal approximations of $\frac{1}{12}$ are 0.083, 0.0833, 0.08333, and so on.

**decimal equivalent** A decimal that names the same number as a fraction. For example, the decimal equivalent of $\frac{3}{4}$ is 0.75. The only rational numbers with decimal equivalents are those that can be written as fractions whose denominators have prime factors only of 2 and 5. For example, $\frac{1}{2}$, $\frac{1}{4}$, and $\frac{1}{20}$ have decimal equivalents, but $\frac{1}{6}$, $\frac{1}{7}$, and $\frac{1}{9}$ have only decimal approximations.

**degree** (°) A unit of measure for angles; based on dividing a circle into 360 equal parts. Also, a unit of measure for temperature.

**degree Celsius** (°C) In the metric system, the unit for measuring temperature. Water freezes at 0°C and boils at 100°C.

**degree Fahrenheit** (°F) In the U.S. customary system, the unit for measuring temperature. Water freezes at 32°F and boils at 212°F.

**denominator** The number of equal parts into which a whole is divided. In the fraction $\frac{a}{b}$, $b$ is the denominator. See also **numerator.**

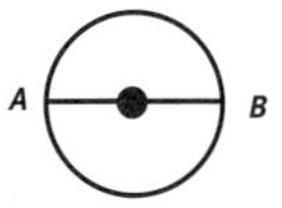


**diameter** A line segment, going through the center of a circle, that starts at one point on the circle and ends at the opposite point on the circle; also, the length of such a line segment. The diameter of a circle is twice its radius. *AB* is a diameter of this circle. See also **circle.**

**difference** The result of subtraction. In the subtraction sentence 40 − 10 = 30, the difference is 30.

**digit** In the base-ten numeration system, one of the symbols 0, 1, 2, 3, 4, 5, 6, 7, 8, 9. Digits can be used to write a numeral for any whole number in the base-ten numbering system. For example, the numeral 145 is made up of the digits 1, 4, and 5.

**distributive law** A law that relates two operations on numbers, usually multiplication and addition, or multiplication and subtraction. Distributive law of multiplication over addition: $a \times (b + c) = (a \times b) + (a \times c)$

**dividend** See **division.**

**divisibility rule** A rule that indicates whether a whole number is divisible by another whole number, without actually doing the division. For example, to tell whether a number is divisible by 3, check whether the sum of its digits is divisible by 3. The number 48 is divisible by 3 since 4 + 8 = 12, and 12 is divisible by 3.

**divisible by** One whole number is divisible by another whole number if the result of the division is a whole number (with a remainder of 0). For example, 35 is divisible by 5, because 35 divided by 5 is 7 with a remainder of 0. If a number $n$ is divisible by a number $x$, then $x$ is a factor of $n$. See also **factor of a whole number *n*.**

**division** A mathematical operation based on "equal sharing" or "separating into equal parts." The *dividend* is the total before sharing. The *divisor* is the number of equal parts or the number in each equal part. The *quotient* is the result of division. For example, in 35 ÷ 5 = 7, 35 is the dividend, 5 is the divisor, and 7 is the quotient. If 35 objects are separated into 5 equal parts, there are 7 objects in each part. If 35 objects are separated into parts with 5 in each part, there are 7 equal parts. The number left over when a set of objects is shared equally or separated into equal groups is called the *remainder*. For 35 ÷ 5, the quotient is 7 and the remainder is 0. For 36 ÷ 5, the quotient is 7 and the remainder is 1.

**divisor** See **division.**

**dodecahedron** A space figure with twelve faces, each formed by a pentagon.

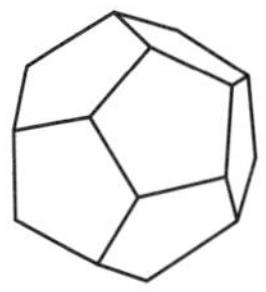

# E

**edge** The line segment where two faces of a polyhedron meet.

**endpoint** The point at either end of a line segment; also, the point at the end of a ray. Line segments are named after their endpoints; a line segment between and including points A and B is called segment *AB* or segment *BA*.

**equation** A mathematical sentence that states the equality of two expressions. For example, 3 + 7 = 10, y = x + 7, and 4 + 7 = 8 + 3 are equations.

**equilateral polygon** A polygon in which all sides are the same length.

**equivalent** Equal in value, but in a different form. For example, $\frac{1}{2}$, $\frac{2}{4}$, 0.5, and 50% are equivalent forms of the same number.

**equivalent fractions** Fractions that have different numerators and denominators but name the same number. For example, $\frac{2}{3}$ and $\frac{6}{9}$ are equivalent fractions.

**estimate** A judgment of a time, measurement, number, or other quantity that may not be exactly right.

**evaluate an algebraic expression** To replace each variable in an algebraic expression with a particular number and then calculate the value of the expression.

**evaluate a numerical expression** To carry out the operations in a numerical expression to find the value of the expression.

**even number** A whole number such as 0, 2, 4, 6, and so on, that can be divided by 2 with no remainder. See also **odd number.**

**event** A happening or occurrence. The tossing of a coin is an event.

**exponent** See **exponential notation.**

**exponential notation** A shorthand way of representing repeated multiplication of the same factor. For example, $4^3$ is exponential notation for 4 × 4 × 4. The small raised 3, called the *exponent*, indicates how many times the number 4, called the *base,* is used as a factor.

**expression** A group of mathematical symbols (numbers, operation signs, variables, grouping symbols) that represents a number (or can represent a number if values are assigned to any variables it contains).

# F

**face** A flat surface on a space figure.

**fact family** A group of addition or multiplication facts grouped together with the related subtraction or division facts. For example, 4 + 8 = 12, 8 + 4 = 12, 12 − 4 = 8, and 12 − 8 = 4 form an addition fact family. The facts 4 × 3 = 12, 3 × 4 = 12, 12 ÷ 3 = 4, and 12 ÷ 4 = 3 form a multiplication fact family.

**factor** (noun) One of the numbers that is multiplied in a multiplication expression. For example, in 4 × 1.5 = 6, the factors are 4 and 1.5. See also **multiplication.**

# Glossary

**factor** (verb) To represent a quantity as a product of factors. For example, 20 factors to $4 \times 5$, $2 \times 10$, or $2 \times 2 \times 5$.

**factor of a whole number *n*** A whole number, which, when multiplied by another whole number, results in the number *n*. The whole number *n* is divisible by its factors. For example, 3 and 5 are factors of 15 because $3 \times 5 = 15$, and 15 is divisible by 3 and 5.

**factor tree** A method used to obtain the prime factorization of a number. The original number is represented as a product of factors, and each of those factors is represented as a product of factors, and so on, until the factor string consists of prime numbers.

**fair** A coin, spinner, number cube, and so on is said to be fair if, over a large number of tosses, the results are consistent with the predictions of probability. On a fair coin, heads and tails should come up about equally often; the six sides of a fair number cube should come up about equally often.

**fair game** A game in which each player has the same chance of winning. If any player has an advantage or disadvantage (for example, by playing first), then the game is not fair.

**finger sets** An organized way taught in ***Real Math*** of showing numbers using fingers.

**formula** A general rule for finding the value of something. A formula is usually written as an equation with variables representing unknown quantities. For example, a formula for distance traveled at a constant rate of speed is $d = r \times t$, where *d* stands for distance, *r* for rate, and *t* for time.

**fraction** A number in the form $\frac{a}{b}$, where *a* and *b* are integers and *b* is not 0. Fractions are used to name part of a whole object or part of a whole collection of objects, or to compare two quantities. A fraction can represent division; for example, $\frac{2}{5}$ can be thought of as 2 divided by 5.

**frequency** The number of times an event or value occurs in a set of data.

**function machine** An imaginary machine that processes numbers according to a certain rule. A number (input) is put into the machine and is transformed into a second number (output) by application of the rule.

## G

**greatest common factor** The largest factor that two or more numbers have in common. For example, the common factors of 24 and 30 are 1, 2, 3, and 6. The greatest common factor of 24 and 30 is 6.

## H

**height** (of a parallelogram) The length of the line segment between the base of the parallelogram and the opposite side (or an extension of the opposite side), running perpendicular to the base.

**height** (of a polyhedron) The perpendicular distance between the bases of the polyhedron or between a base and the opposite vertex.

**height** (of a rectangle) The length of the side perpendicular to the side considered the base of the rectangle. (Base and height of a rectangle are interchangeable.)

**height** (of a triangle) The length of the line segment perpendicular to the base of the triangle (or an extension of the base) from the opposite vertex.

**heptagon** A polygon with seven sides.

**hexagon** A polygon with six sides.

**hypotenuse** In a right triangle, the side opposite the right angle.

## I

**icosahedron** A space figure with twenty triangular faces.

**improper fraction** A fraction that names a number greater than or equal to 1; a fraction whose numerator is equal to or greater than its denominator. Examples of improper fractions are $\frac{4}{3}$, $\frac{10}{8}$, and $\frac{4}{4}$.

**inch (in.)** In the U. S. customary system, a unit of length equal to $\frac{1}{12}$ of a foot.

**indirect measurement** Methods for determining heights, distances, and other quantities that cannot be measured or are not measured directly.

**inequality** A number sentence stating that two quantities are not equal. Relation symbols for inequalities include $<$ (is less than), $>$ (is greater than), and $\neq$ (is not equal to).

**integers** The set of integers is $\{\ldots, -4, -3, -2, -1, 0, 1, 2, 3, 4, \ldots\}$. The set of integers consists of whole numbers and their opposites.

**intersect** To meet (at a point, a line, and so on), sharing a common point or points.

**interior** The set of all points in a plane "inside" a closed plane figure, such as a polygon or circle. Also, the set of all points in space "inside" a closed space figure, such as a polyhedron or sphere.

**isosceles** Having two sides of the same length; commonly used to refer to triangles and trapezoids.

## K

***kilo-*** A prefix for units in the metric system meaning one thousand.

## L

**least common denominator** The least common multiple of the denominators of every fraction in a given set of fractions. For example, 12 is the least common denominator of $\frac{2}{3}$, $\frac{1}{4}$, and $\frac{5}{6}$. See also **least common multiple.**

**least common multiple** The smallest number that is a multiple of two or more numbers. For example, some common multiples of 6 and 8 are 24, 48, and 72. 24 is the least common multiple of 6 and 8.

**leg of a right triangle** A side of a right triangle that is not the hypotenuse.

**line** A straight path that extends infinitely in opposite directions.

**line graph** (broken-line graph) A graph in which points are connected by line segments to represent data.

**line of symmetry** A line that separates a figure into halves. The figure can be folded along this line into two parts which exactly fit on top of each other.

**line segment** A straight path joining two points, called *endpoints* of the line segment. A straight path can be described as the shortest distance between two points.

**line symmetry** A figure has line symmetry (also called *bilateral symmetry*) if a line of symmetry can be drawn through the figure.

**liter (L)** A metric unit of capacity, equal to the volume of a cube 10 centimeters on an edge. $1 \text{ L} = 1{,}000 \text{ mL} = 1{,}000 \text{ cm}^3$. A liter is slightly larger than a quart. See also **milliliter (mL).**

## M

**map scale** A proportion that compares the distance between two locations shown on a map with the actual distance between them.

**mean** A typical or central value that may be used to describe a set of numbers. It is found by adding the numbers in the set and dividing the sum by the number of numbers. The mean is often referred to as the *average*.

**median** The middle value in a set of data when the data are listed in order from least to greatest (or greatest to least). If the number of values in the set is even (so that there is no "middle" value), the median is the mean of the two middle values.

**meter (m)** The basic unit of length in the metric system, equal to 10 decimeters, 100 centimeters, and 1,000 millimeters.

**metric system of measurement** A measurement system based on the base-ten numeration system and used in most countries in the world. Units for linear measure (length, distance) include millimeter, centimeter, meter, kilometer; units for mass (weight) include gram and kilogram; units for capacity (amount of liquid or other substance a container can hold) include milliliter and liter.

**midpoint** A point halfway between two points.

***milli-*** A prefix for units in the metric system meaning one thousandth.

**milliliter (mL)** A metric unit of capacity, equal to 1/1,000 of a liter and 1 cubic centimeter.

**millimeter (mm)** In the metric system, a unit of length equal to 1/10 of a centimeter and 1/1,000 of a meter.

**minuend** See **subtraction.**

**mixed number** A number greater than 1, written as a whole number and a fraction less than 1. For example, $5\frac{1}{2}$ is equal to $5 + \frac{1}{2}$.

**mode** The value or values that occur most often in a set of data.

**multiple of a number *n*** The product of a whole number and the number *n*. For example, the numbers 0, 4, 8, 12, and 16 are all multiples of 4 because $4 \times 0 = 0$, $4 \times 1 = 4$, $4 \times 2 = 8$, $4 \times 3 = 12$, and $4 \times 4 = 16$.

**multiplication** A mathematical operation used to find the total number of things in several equal groups, or to find a quantity that is a certain number of times as much or as many as another number. Numbers being multiplied are called *factors*. The result of multiplication is called the *product*. In $8 \times 12 = 96$, 8 and 12 are the factors and 96 is the product.

**multiplicative inverses** Two numbers whose product is 1. For example, the multiplicative inverse of $\frac{2}{5}$ is $\frac{5}{2}$, and the multiplicative inverse of 8 is $\frac{1}{8}$. Multiplicative inverses are also called *reciprocals* of each other.

# N

**negative number** A number less than 0; a number to the left of 0 on a horizontal number line.

**number line** A line on which equidistant points correspond to integers in order.

**number sentence** A sentence that is made up of numerals and a relation symbol (<, >, or =). Most number sentences also contain at least one operation symbol. Number sentences may also have grouping symbols, such as parentheses.

**numeral** The written name of a number.

**numerator** In a whole divided into a number of equal parts, the number of equal parts being considered. In the fraction $\frac{a}{b}$, *a* is the numerator.

# O

**obtuse angle** An angle with a measure greater than 90 degrees and less than 180 degrees.

**octagon** An eight-sided polygon.

**octahedron** A space figure with eight faces.

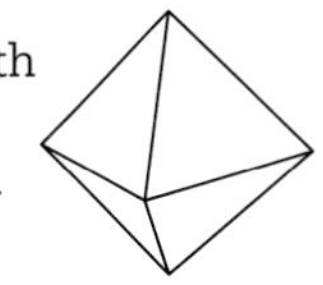

**odd number** A whole number that is not divisible by 2, such as 1, 3, 5, and so on. When an odd number is divided by 2, the remainder is 1. A whole number is either an odd number or an even number.

**opposite of a number** A number that is the same distance from 0 on the number line as the given number, but on the opposite side of 0. If *a* is a negative number, the opposite of *a* will be a positive number. For example, if $a = -5$, then $-a$ is 5. See also **additive inverses.**

**ordered pair** Two numbers in a specific order used to locate a point on a coordinate grid. They are usually written inside parentheses; for example, (2, 3). See also **coordinate.**

**ordinal number** A number used to express position or order in a series, such as first, third, tenth. People generally use ordinal numbers to name dates; for example, "May fifth" rather than "May five."

**origin** The point where the *x*- and *y*-axes intersect on a coordinate grid. The coordinates of the origin are (0, 0).

**outcome** The result of an event. Heads and tails are the two outcomes of the event of tossing a coin.

# P

**parallel lines (segments, rays)** Lines (segments, rays) going in the same direction that are the same distance apart and never meet.

**parallelogram** A quadrilateral that has two pairs of parallel sides. Pairs of opposite sides and opposite angles of a parallelogram are congruent.

**parentheses** A pair of symbols, ( and ), used to show in which order operations should be done. For example, the expression $(3 \times 5) + 7$ says to multiply 5 by 3 then add 7. The expression $3 \times (5 + 7)$ says to add 5 and 7 and then multiply by 3.

**pattern** A model, plan, or rule that uses words or variables to describe a set of shapes or numbers that repeat in a predictable way.

**pentagon** A polygon with five sides.

**percent** A rational number that can be written as a fraction with a denominator of 100. The symbol % is used to represent percent. 1% means 1/100 or 0.01. For example, "53% of the students in the school are girls" means that out of every 100 students in the school, 53 are girls.

**perimeter** The distance along a path around a plane figure. A formula for the perimeter of a rectangle is $P = 2 \times (B + H)$, where *B* represents the base and *H* is the height of the rectangle. Perimeter may also refer to the path itself.

**perpendicular** Two rays, lines, line segments, or other figures that form right angles are said to be perpendicular to each other.

**pi** The ratio of the circumference of a circle to its diameter. Pi is the same for every circle, approximately 3.14 or $\frac{22}{7}$. Also written as the Greek letter $\pi$.

**pictograph** A graph constructed with pictures or icons, in which each picture stands for a certain number. Pictographs make it easier to visually compare quantities.

**place value** A way of determining the value of a digit in a numeral, written in standard notation, according to its position, or place, in the numeral. In base-ten numbers, each place has a value ten times that of the place to its right and one-tenth the value of the place to its left.

**plane** A flat surface that extends forever.

**plane figure** A figure that can be contained in a plane (that is, having length and width but no height).

**point** A basic concept of geometry; usually thought of as a location in space, without size. Points are named with italicized capital letters.

**polygon** A closed plane figure consisting of line segments (sides) connected endpoint to endpoint. The interior of a polygon consists of all the points of the plane "inside" the polygon. An *n*-gon is a polygon with *n* sides; for example, an 8-gon has 8 sides.

**polyhedron** A closed space figure, all of whose surfaces (faces) are flat. Each face consists of a polygon and the interior of the polygon.

**power** A product of factors that are all the same. For example, $6 \times 6 \times 6$ (or 216) is called 6 to the third power, or the third power of 6, because 6 is a factor three times. The expression $6 \times 6 \times 6$ can also be written as $6^3$.

**power of 10** A whole number that can be written as a product using only 10 as a factor. For example, 100 is equal to $10 \times 10$ or $10^2$, so 100 is called 10 squared, the second power of 10, or 10 to the second power. Other powers of 10 include $10^1$, or 10, and $10^3$, or 1,000.

**precision** (of a count or measurement) An indicator of how close a count or measure is believed to be to the actual count or measure. The precision of a measurement may be improved by using measuring instruments with smaller units.

**prime factorization** A whole number expressed as a product of prime factors. For example, the prime factorization of 18 is $2 \times 3 \times 3$. A number has only one prime factorization (except for the order in which the factors are written).

**prime number** A whole number greater than 1 that has exactly two whole number factors, 1 and itself. For example, 13 is a prime number because its only factors are 1 and 13. A prime number is divisible only by 1 and itself. The first five prime numbers are 2, 3, 5, 7, and 11. See also **composite number.**

**prism** A polyhedron with two parallel faces (bases) that are the same size and shape. Prisms are classified according to the shape of the two parallel bases. The bases of a prism are connected by parallelograms that are often rectangular.

**probability** A number between 0 and 1 that indicates the likelihood that something (an event) will happen. The closer a probability is to 1, the more likely it is that an event will happen.

**product** See **multiplication.**

**protractor** A tool for measuring or drawing angles. When measuring an angle, the vertex of the angle should be at the center of the protractor and one side should be aligned with the 0 mark.

**pyramid** A polyhedron in which one face (the base) is a polygon and the other faces are formed by triangles with a common vertex (the apex). A pyramid is classified according to the shape of its base, as a triangular pyramid, square pyramid, pentagonal pyramid, and so on.

**Pythagorean Theorem** A mathematical theorem, proven by the Greek mathematician Pythagoras and known to many others before and since, that states that if the legs of a right triangle have lengths $a$ and $b$, and the hypotenuse has length $c$, then $a^2 + b^2 = c^2$.

## Q

**quadrilateral** A polygon with four sides.

**quotient** See **division.**

## R

**radius** A line segment that goes from the center of a circle to any point on the circle; also, the length of such a line segment.

**random sample** A sample taken from a population in a way that gives all members of the population the same chance of being selected.

**range** The difference between the maximum and minimum values in a set of data.

**rate** A ratio comparing two quantities with unlike units. For example, a measure such as 23 miles per gallon of gas compares mileage with gas usage.

**ratio** A comparison of two quantities using division. Ratios can be expressed with fractions, decimals, percents, or words. For example, if a team wins 4 games out of 5 games played, the ratio of wins to total games is $\frac{4}{5}$, 0.8, or 80%.

**rational number** Any number that can be represented in the form $a \div b$ or $\frac{a}{b}$, where $a$ and $b$ are integers and $b$ is positive. Some, but not all, rational numbers have exact decimal equivalents.

**ray** A straight path that extends infinitely in one direction from a point, which is called its *endpoint*.

**reciprocal** See **multiplicative inverses.**

**rectangle** A parallelogram with four right angles.

**reduced form** A fraction in which the numerator and denominator have no common factors except 1.

**reflection** A transformation in which a figure "flips" so that its image is the reverse of the original.

**regular polygon** A convex polygon in which all the sides are the same length and all the angles have the same measure.

**regular polyhedron (**plural **polyhedra)** A polyhedron with faces that are all congruent regular polygons with their interiors. The same number of faces meet at each vertex. There are five regular polyhedra:

*tetrahedron* four faces, each formed by an equilateral triangle

*cube* six faces, each formed by a square

*octahedron* eight faces, each formed by an equilateral triangle

*dodecahedron* twelve faces, each formed by a regular pentagon

*icosahedron* twenty faces, each formed by an equilateral triangle

**relation symbol** A symbol used to express the relationship between two numbers or expressions. Among the symbols used in number sentences are $=$ for "is equal to," $<$ for "is less than," $>$ for "is greater than," and $\neq$ for "is not equal to."

**remainder** See **division.**

**rhombus** A parallelogram whose sides are all the same length.

**right angle** An angle with a measure of 90 degrees, representing a quarter of a full turn.

**right triangle** A triangle that has a right angle.

**rotation** A transformation in which a figure "turns" around a center point or axis.

**rotational symmetry** Property of a figure that can be rotated around a point (less than a full, 360-degree turn) in such a way that the resulting figure exactly matches the original figure. If a figure has rotational symmetry, its order of rotational symmetry is the number of different ways it can be rotated to match itself exactly. "No rotation" is counted as one of the ways.

**rounding** Changing a number to another number that is easier to work with and is close enough for the purpose. For example, 12,924 rounded to the nearest thousand is 13,000 and rounded to the nearest hundred is 12,900.

## S

**sample** A subset of a group used to represent the whole group.

**scale** The ratio of the distance on a map or drawing to the actual distance.

**scalene triangle** A triangle in which all three sides have different lengths.

**scale drawing** An accurate picture of an object in which all parts are drawn to the same scale. If an actual object measures 32 by 48 meters, a scale drawing of it might measure 32 by 48 millimeters.

**scale model** A model that represents an object or display in proportions based on a determined scale.

**scientific notation** A method of expressing a number as the product of two factors, one of which is a number greater than or equal to 1 but less than 10, and the other of which is a power of 10. The notation is used to describe very great (or very small) numbers. For example, 4,000,000 in scientific notation is $4 \times 10^6$.

**similar figures** Figures that are exactly the same shape but not necessarily the same size.

**space figure** A figure which cannot be contained in a plane. Common space figures include the rectangular prism, square pyramid, cylinder, cone, and sphere.

**sphere** The set of all points in space that are a given distance (the radius) from a given point (the center). A ball is shaped like a sphere.

**square number** A number that is the product of a whole number and itself. The number 36 is a square number, because $36 = 6 \times 6$.

**square of a number** The product of a number multiplied by itself. For example, 2.5 squared is $(2.5)^2$.

**square root** The square root of a number *n* is a number which, when multiplied by itself, results in the number *n*. For example, 8 is a square root of 64, because $8 \times 8 = 64$.

**square unit** A unit used to measure area—usually a square that is 1 inch, 1 centimeter, 1 yard, or other standard unit of length on each side.

**standard notation** The most familiar way of representing whole numbers, integers, and decimals by writing digits in specified places; the way numbers are usually written in everyday situations.

**stem-and-leaf plot** A display of data in which digits with larger place values are named as stems, and digits with smaller place values are named as leaves.

**straight angle** An angle of 180 degrees; a line with one point identified as the vertex of the angle.

**subtraction** A mathematical operation based on "taking away" or comparing ("How much more?"). The number being subtracted is called the *subtrahend*; the number it is subtracted from is called the *minuend*; the result of subtraction is called the *difference*. In the number sentence $63 - 45 = 18$, 63 is the minuend, 45 is the subtrahend, and 18 is the difference.

**subtrahend** See **subtraction.**

**supplementary angles** Two angles whose measures total 180 degrees.

**surface area** The sum of the areas of the faces of a space figure.

**symmetrical** Having the same size and shape across a dividing line or around a point.

# T

**tessellation** An arrangement of closed shapes that covers a surface completely without overlaps or gaps.

**tetrahedron** A space figure with four faces, each formed by an equilateral triangle.

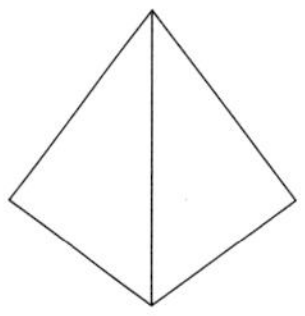

**theorem** A mathematical statement that can be proved to be true (or, sometimes, a statement that is proposed and needs to be proved). For example, the Pythagorean Theorem states that if the legs of a right triangle have lengths *a* and *b*, and the hypotenuse has length *c*, then $a^2 + b^2 = c^2$.

**transformation** An operation that moves or changes a geometric figure in a specified way. Rotations, reflections, and translations are types of transformations.

**translation** A transformation in which a figure "slides" along a line.

**transversal** A line which intersects two or more other lines.

**trapezoid** A quadrilateral with exactly one pair of parallel sides.

**tree diagram** A tool used to solve probability problems in which there is a series of events. This tree diagram represents a situation where the first event has three possible outcomes and the second event has two possible outcomes.

**triangle** A polygon with three sides. An *equilateral* triangle has three sides of the same length. An *isosceles* triangle has two sides of the same length. A *scalene* triangle has no sides of the same length.

# U

**unit (of measure)** An agreed-upon standard with which measurements are compared.

**unit fraction** A fraction whose numerator is 1. For example, $\frac{1}{2}, \frac{1}{3}$, and $\frac{1}{10}$ are unit fractions.

**unit cost** The cost of one item or one specified amount of an item. If 20 pencils cost 60¢, then the unit cost is 3¢ per pencil.

**unlike denominators** Unequal denominators, as in $\frac{3}{4}$ and $\frac{5}{6}$.

# V

**variable** A letter or other symbol that represents a number, one specific number, or many different values.

**Venn diagram** A picture that uses circles to show relationships between sets. Elements that belong to more than one set are placed in the overlap between the circles.

**vertex** The point at which the rays of an angle, two sides of a polygon, or the edges of a polyhedron meet.

**vertical angles** Two intersecting lines form four adjacent angles. In the diagram, angles 2 and 4 are vertical angles. They have no sides in common. Their measures are equal. Similarly, angles 1 and 3 are vertical angles.

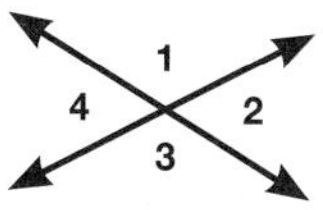


**volume** A measure of the amount of space occupied by a space figure.

# W

**whole number** Any of the numbers 0, 1, 2, 3, 4, and so on. Whole numbers are the numbers used for counting and zero.

# Scope and Sequence

| | PreK | K | 1 | 2 | 3 | 4 | 5 | 6 |
|---|---|---|---|---|---|---|---|---|
| **Addition (whole numbers)** | | | | | | | | |
| Meaning of addition | • | • | • | • | | | | |
| Basic facts | | | • | • | • | • | • | • |
| Missing addend problems | | | • | • | • | • | • | • |
| Three or more addends | | | • | • | • | • | • | • |
| Two-digit numbers | | | • | • | • | • | • | • |
| Three-digit numbers | | | | • | • | • | • | • |
| Greater numbers | | | | | • | • | • | • |
| Adding money | | | • | • | • | • | • | • |
| Estimating sums | | | • | • | • | • | • | • |
| **Algebra** | | | | | | | | |
| Properties of whole numbers | | | | • | • | • | • | • |
| Integers (negative numbers) | | | | | • | • | • | • |
| Operations with integers | | | | | | • | • | • |
| Missing-term problems | • | | | • | • | • | • | • |
| Making and solving number sentences and equations | | | | • | • | • | • | • |
| Variables | | | | | • | • | • | • |
| Parentheses and order of operations | | | | | | • | • | • |
| Inverse operations | | | • | • | • | • | • | • |
| Function machines / tables | | • | • | • | • | • | • | • |
| Function rules | | • | • | • | • | • | • | • |
| Inverse functions | | | • | • | • | • | • | • |
| Composite functions | | | | • | • | • | • | • |
| **Coordinate graphing** | | | | | | | | |
| One quadrant | | | | | • | • | • | • |
| Four quadrants | | | | | | • | • | • |
| Graphing linear functions | | | | | • | • | • | • |
| Graphing nonlinear functions | | | | | | | | • |
| Using formulas | | | | | | • | • | • |
| Square numbers | | | | | • | • | | • |
| Square roots | | | | | | • | | • |
| **Decimals and Money** | | | | | | | | |
| Place value | | | | • | • | • | • | • |
| Comparing and ordering | | | | • | • | • | • | • |
| Rounding | | | | | | • | • | • |
| Relating decimals and fractions | | | | • | • | • | • | • |
| Relating decimals and percents | | | | | | • | • | • |
| Adding | | | | • | • | • | • | • |
| Estimating sums | | | | • | | • | • | |
| Subtracting | | | | • | • | • | • | • |
| Estimating differences | | | | • | • | • | • | • |
| Multiplying by powers of 10 | | | | | • | • | • | • |
| Multiplying by a whole number | | | | | • | • | • | • |
| Multiplying by a decimal | | | | | | | • | • |
| Estimating products | | | | | | • | • | • |
| Dividing by powers of 10 | | | | | | • | • | • |
| Dividing by a whole number | | | | | • | • | • | • |
| Dividing by a decimal | | | | | | | | • |
| Estimating quotients | | | | | | | • | • |

| | PreK | K | 1 | 2 | 3 | 4 | 5 | 6 |
|---|---|---|---|---|---|---|---|---|
| Identifying and counting currency | | • | • | • | • | • | | |
| Exchanging money | | • | • | • | • | | | |
| Making change | | | • | • | • | | | |
| Computing with money | | • | • | • | • | • | • | • |
| **Division (whole numbers)** | | | | | | | | |
| Meaning of division | • | • | • | • | • | • | | |
| Basic facts | | | | • | • | • | • | • |
| Remainders | | | | | • | • | • | • |
| Missing-term problems | | | | • | • | • | • | • |
| One-digit divisors | | | | | • | • | • | • |
| Two-digit divisors | | | | | | • | • | • |
| Greater divisors | | | | | | | • | • |
| Dividing by multiples of 10 | | | | | | | • | • |
| Dividing money | | | | | • | • | • | • |
| Estimating quotients | | | | | • | • | • | • |
| **Fractions** | | | | | | | | |
| Fractions of a whole | | • | • | • | • | • | • | • |
| Fractions of a set | | | • | • | • | • | • | • |
| Fractions of a number | | | • | • | • | • | • | • |
| Comparing/ordering | | | • | • | • | • | • | • |
| Equivalent fractions | | | • | • | • | • | • | • |
| Reduced form | | | | | | • | • | • |
| Mixed numbers and improper fractions | | | | | • | • | • | • |
| Adding — like denominators | | | | | • | • | • | • |
| Adding — unlike denominators | | | | | | • | • | • |
| Adding mixed numbers | | | | | | • | • | • |
| Subtracting — like denominators | | | | | • | • | • | • |
| Subtracting — unlike denominators | | | | | | • | • | • |
| Subtracting mixed numbers | | | | | | • | • | • |
| Multiplying by a whole number | | | | | | • | • | • |
| Multiplying by a fraction or mixed number | | | | | | • | • | • |
| Reciprocals | | | | | | | • | • |
| Dividing a fraction by a whole number | | | | | | | • | • |
| Dividing by a fraction or mixed number | | | | | | | • | • |
| **Geometry** | | | | | | | | |
| Identifying/drawing figures | • | • | • | • | • | • | • | • |
| Classifying figures | • | • | • | • | • | • | • | • |
| Classifying triangles | | | • | • | • | • | • | • |
| Classifying quadrilaterals | | | • | • | • | • | • | • |
| Solid figures | | • | • | • | • | • | • | • |
| Congruence | • | • | • | • | • | • | • | • |
| Similarity | | | | | • | • | • | • |
| Line symmetry | | • | • | • | • | • | • | • |
| Rotational symmetry | | | | | | • | • | • |
| Translation/reflection/rotation | • | | | • | • | • | • | • |
| Measuring and classifying angles | | | | • | • | • | • | • |
| Parallel and perpendicular lines | | | | • | • | • | • | • |
| Relationships with parallel lines | | | | • | • | • | • | • |
| Perimeter | | | | • | • | • | • | • |

| | PreK | K | 1 | 2 | 3 | 4 | 5 | 6 |
|---|---|---|---|---|---|---|---|---|
| Radius and diameter | | | | | • | • | • | • |
| Circumference | | | | | • | | • | • |
| Areas of triangles | | | | | • | • | • | • |
| Areas of quadrilaterals | | | | • | • | • | • | • |
| Surface area | | | | | • | • | • | • |
| Volume | | | | • | • | • | • | • |
| Pythagorean Theorem | | | | | | • | | • |
| Points, lines, and planes (new category) | | | | | | • | • | • |
| Open and closed figures (new category) | | | • | | | | | |
| Spatial visualization | • | | | | | • | • | • |
| **Manipulatives** | | | | | | | | |
| Used in concept development | • | • | • | • | • | • | • | • |
| Used in reteaching and individualized instruction | • | • | • | • | • | • | • | • |
| **Measurement** | | | | | | | | |
| Converting within customary system | | | | • | • | • | • | • |
| Converting within metric system | | | | • | • | • | • | • |
| **Length** | | | | | | | | |
| Estimate | • | • | • | • | • | • | • | • |
| Compare | • | • | • | • | • | • | • | • |
| Use nonstandard units | • | • | • | • | • | • | • | |
| Use customary units | | | • | • | • | • | • | • |
| Use metric units | | | • | • | • | • | • | • |
| **Mass/Weight** | | | | | | | | |
| Estimate | • | • | • | • | • | | | |
| Compare | • | • | • | • | | | | |
| Use nonstandard units | | • | • | • | | | | |
| Use customary units | | | • | • | • | • | • | • |
| Use metric units | | | • | • | • | • | • | • |
| **Capacity** | | | | | | | | |
| Estimate | • | • | • | • | | | | |
| Compare | • | • | • | • | | | | |
| Use nonstandard units | | • | • | • | | | | |
| Use customary units | | | • | • | • | • | • | • |
| Use metric units | | | • | • | • | • | • | • |
| **Temperature** | | | | | | | | |
| Estimate | | • | | | | | | • |
| Use degrees Fahrenheit | | | • | • | • | • | • | • |
| Use degrees Celsius | | | • | • | • | • | • | • |
| **Telling time** | | | | | | | | |
| To the hour | | • | • | • | • | | | |
| To the half hour | | | • | • | • | | | |
| To the quarter hour | | | | • | • | | | |
| To the minute | | | | • | • | | | |
| Adding and subtracting time | | | | • | • | • | • | |
| A.M. and P.M. | | | | • | • | | | |
| Estimating time | | • | • | | | | | |
| Calculating elapsed time | | | • | • | • | • | • | |
| Reading a calendar | | • | • | • | • | | • | |
| Reading maps | | • | • | • | • | • | • | • |

| | PreK | K | 1 | 2 | 3 | 4 | 5 | 6 |
|---|---|---|---|---|---|---|---|---|
| **Mental Arithmetic** | | | | | | | | |
| **Basic fact strategies — addition and subtraction** | | | | | | | | |
| Use patterns | | | • | • | | | | |
| Count on | | | • | • | | | | |
| Count up or back | • | • | • | • | | | | |
| Use doubles | | | • | • | | | | |
| Use doubles plus 1 | | | • | • | | | | |
| Multiples of 10/Base-ten | | • | • | • | • | • | | |
| Use properties | | | • | • | • | | | |
| Use related facts | | | • | • | | | | |
| **Basic fact strategies — multiplication and division** | | | | | | | | |
| Use patterns | | | | • | • | • | | |
| Use skip-counting | | | | • | • | | | |
| Use properties | | | | | • | • | | |
| Use related facts | | | | | • | • | | |
| Chain calculations | | | | • | • | • | • | • |
| Multidigit addition and subtraction | | | | • | • | • | • | • |
| Multidigit multiplication and division | | | | | • | • | • | • |
| Multiples and powers of 10 | | | | • | • | • | • | • |
| Using computational patterns | | | | • | • | • | • | • |
| Approximation | | | | • | • | • | • | • |
| Find a fraction of a number | | | | | • | • | • | • |
| Find a percent of a number | | | | | | • | • | • |
| Use divisibility rules | | | | | | | • | • |
| Find equivalent fractions, decimals, and percents | | | | | | • | • | • |
| **Multiplication (whole numbers)** | | | | | | | | |
| Meaning of multiplication | | | • | • | • | • | • | • |
| Basic facts | | | | • | • | • | • | • |
| Missing-factor problems | | | | • | • | • | • | • |
| One-digit multipliers | | | | • | • | • | • | • |
| Two-digit multipliers | | | | | | • | • | • |
| Greater multipliers | | | | | | • | • | • |
| Multiplying by multiples of 10 | | | | | • | • | • | • |
| Multiplying money | | | | | • | • | • | • |
| Estimating products | | | | | • | • | • | • |
| **Number and Numeration** | | | | | | | | |
| Reading and writing numbers | • | • | • | • | • | • | • | • |
| Number lines | • | • | • | • | • | • | • | • |
| Counting | • | • | • | • | • | • | | |
| Skip-counting | | • | • | • | • | | | |
| Ordinal numbers | • | • | • | • | | | | |
| Place value | | | | • | • | • | • | • |
| Comparing and ordering numbers | • | • | • | • | • | • | • | • |
| Rounding | | | | • | • | • | • | • |
| Estimation / Approximation | | | • | • | • | • | • | • |
| Integers (negative numbers) | | | | | • | • | • | • |
| Even/odd numbers | | | • | • | • | • | | |
| Prime and composite numbers | | | | | | • | • | • |
| Factors and prime factorization | | | | | | • | • | • |

# Scope and Sequence

| | PreK | K | 1 | 2 | 3 | 4 | 5 | 6 |
|---|---|---|---|---|---|---|---|---|
| Common factors | | | | | | • | • | • |
| Common multiples | | | | | | • | • | • |
| Checking divisibility | | | | | | • | • | • |
| Exponents | | | | | | • | • | • |
| Exponential notation and scientific notation | | | | | | | • | • |
| Square roots | | | | | | • | | • |
| **Patterns, Relations, and Functions** | | | | | | | | |
| Classifying objects | • | • | • | • | | | | |
| Number patterns | • | • | • | • | • | • | • | • |
| Picture patterns | • | • | • | • | | | | |
| Geometric patterns | • | • | • | • | | • | | • |
| Ordered pairs | | | | | • | • | • | • |
| Graphing ordered pairs | | | | | • | • | • | • |
| Inequalities | | | • | • | • | • | • | • |
| Function machines / tables | | • | • | • | • | • | • | • |
| Function rules | | • | • | • | • | • | • | • |
| Graphing functions | | | | | • | • | • | • |
| **Probability** | | | | | | | | |
| Determining possible outcomes | | • | • | • | • | • | • | • |
| Predicting outcomes | | • | • | • | • | • | • | • |
| Conducting experiments | | • | • | • | • | • | • | • |
| Experimental probability | | • | • | • | • | • | • | • |
| Theoretical probability | | | | | | • | | • |
| Using probability to plan strategies | | | • | • | • | • | • | • |
| **Problem Solving** | | | | | | | | |
| Multistep problems | | | • | • | • | • | • | • |
| Multiple solutions | | | • | • | • | • | • | • |
| No solutions | | | • | • | • | • | • | • |
| Interpreting data | | • | • | • | • | • | • | • |
| Checking reasonableness | | • | • | • | • | • | • | • |
| Solving problems with too much information | | | • | • | • | • | • | • |
| Interpreting the quotient and remainder | | | | | • | • | • | • |
| Choosing the appropriate operation | | • | • | • | • | • | • | • |
| Using estimation | | • | • | • | • | • | • | • |
| Using guess, check, and adjust | | • | • | • | • | • | • | • |
| Solving a simpler problem | | | | • | • | • | • | • |
| Eliminating possibilities | | | | | • | • | • | • |
| Acting it out | • | • | • | • | • | • | • | • |
| Using/finding a pattern | | • | • | • | • | • | • | • |
| Using/making a table | | | • | • | • | • | • | • |
| Using/drawing a picture or diagram | • | • | • | • | • | • | • | • |
| Using manipulatives | • | • | • | • | • | • | • | • |
| **Ratio and Proportion** | | | | | | | | |
| Meaning / use of ratio and proportion | | | | | | • | • | • |
| Rates | | | | | | • | • | • |
| Similar figures | | | | | | • | • | • |
| Map scales | | | | | | | • | • |
| Meaning of percent | | | | | | • | • | • |
| Percent of a number | | | | | | • | • | • |

| | PreK | K | 1 | 2 | 3 | 4 | 5 | 6 |
|---|---|---|---|---|---|---|---|---|
| Percent discounts | | | | | | | • | • |
| Sales tax | | | | | | | • | • |
| Simple/compound interest | | | | | | | • | • |
| **Statistics and Graphing** | | | | | | | | |
| Surveying | | | • | • | • | • | • | • |
| Tallying | | | • | • | • | • | • | • |
| Making tables with data | | | • | • | • | • | • | • |
| Real and picture graphs | | • | • | • | • | • | | |
| Bar graphs | | • | • | • | • | • | • | • |
| Line graphs | | | | • | • | • | • | • |
| Circle graphs | | | | • | • | • | • | • |
| Analyzing graphs | | • | • | • | • | • | • | • |
| Finding the mean | | | | | • | • | • | • |
| Finding the median | | | | | • | • | • | • |
| Finding the mode | | | | | • | • | • | • |
| **Subtraction (whole numbers)** | | | | | | | | |
| Meaning of subtraction | • | • | • | • | | | | |
| Basic facts | | | • | • | • | • | • | • |
| Missing-term problems | | | • | • | • | • | • | • |
| Two-digit numbers | | | • | • | • | • | • | • |
| Three-digit numbers | | | | • | • | • | • | • |
| Greater numbers | | | | | • | • | • | • |
| Subtracting money | | | • | • | • | • | • | • |
| Estimating differences | | | | • | • | • | • | • |
| **Technology** | | | | | | | | |
| **Calculators** | | | | | | | | |
| Computation with whole numbers | | | | | | • | • | • |
| Computation with decimals | | | | | | • | • | • |
| Computation with fractions | | | | | | | • | • |
| Computation with integers (negative numbers) | | | | | | | • | • |
| Using function rules | | | | | | • | • | • |
| Order of operations | | | | | | | • | • |
| Function keys | | | | | | | • | • |
| **Computers** | | | | | | | | |
| Spreadsheets | | | | | • | • | • | • |
| Functions | | • | • | • | • | • | • | • |
| Graphs | | | • | • | • | • | • | • |
| Geometry | • | • | • | • | • | • | • | • |
| Charts and tables | | | | • | • | • | • | • |

# Game Directory

| Game | Principle Skills | Begin Using* | |
|---|---|---|---|
| | | Student Edition | Teacher's Edition |
| Add the Products Game | Multiplying two numbers from 0–5; column addition | 205 | 5.3 |
| Anything but 10 eGames | Mental addition; applying intuitive notions of probability | 341 | 8.6 |
| Baseball Game** eGames | Locating coordinates on a graph; using mathematical reasoning | | 4.15 |
| Checkbook Game | Adding and subtracting two-digit and three-digit numbers; maintaining a record of money transactions | | 9.11 |
| Cube 100 eGames | Adding; multiplying one- and two-digit numbers by one-digit numbers; using mathematical reasoning | 99 | 3.5 |
| Cubo Game | Using mental arithmetic (all four basic operations) | 125 | 3.14 |
| Customary Unit Game | Determining which customary units of weight and length make sense with given numbers to describe given objects | | 6.6 |
| Decimal Roll a Problem Game | Multiplication of one- and two-digit decimal numbers and whole numbers, place value, and mathematical reasoning | 427 | 9.12 |
| Don't Go Over 1000 eGames | Adding two three-digit numbers; place value; mathematical reasoning | 51 | 2.1 |
| Find the Distance 1 Game | Estimating straight distances to the nearest centimeter; comparing line lengths | | 9.8 |
| Find the Distance 2 Game | Estimating straight distances to the nearest centimeter; comparing line lengths | | 9.8 |
| Four Cube Division Game | Dividing by one-digit divisors; using place value | 513 | 11.3 |
| Four Cube Multiplication Game | Using multidigit multiplication; using place value; using mathematical reasoning | 253 | 6.3 |
| Fracto 1 Game eGames | Recognizing fractional areas of a circle; recognizing which fraction areas, when combined, are more than half the area of a circle | | 8.5 |
| Fracto 2 Game | Recognizing fractional areas of a rectangle; recognizing which fractional areas, when combined, are more than half the area of a rectangle | | 8.5 |
| Function Game | Using mental arithmetic; using mathematical reasoning | 157 | 4.6 |
| Get the Point eGames | Plotting points on a four-quadrant grid | 144 | 4.2 |
| Greater Number Card Game | Comparing and ordering fractions, decimals, and percentages | 311 | 7.6 |
| Harder Checkbook Game | Adding and subtracting multidigit numbers involving dollars and cents; maintaining a record of money transactions | | 9.11 |
| Harder Minutes Game | Telling time to the nearest minute | | 7.5 |
| Harder Multiplication Table Game | Using a multiplication table; multiplying with two factors of 10 or less | | 3.1 |

| Game | Principle Skills | Begin Using* Student Edition | Begin Using* Teacher's Edition |
|---|---|---|---|
| Harder Roll a Decimal | Using place value; subtracting decimals; using mathematical reasoning | 419 | 9.10 |
| Harder Shopping Game | Multiplying two-digit numbers by one-digit numbers; forming amounts of money; making change | | 5.8 |
| Harder Snake Game | Finding multiplication and division function rules | | 12.4 |
| Harder Store Game | Forming amounts of money; making change | | 9.9 |
| Inequality Game | Recognizing true and false inequality statements; adding two two-digit numbers; mathematical reasoning | 61 | 2.4 |
| Metric Unit Game | Determining which metric units of weight and length make sense with given numbers to describe given objects | | 9.15 |
| Minutes Game | Telling time to five-minute intervals | | 7.5 |
| More or Less Game e Games | Multiplying two-digit numbers; working with inequality relationships; using intuitive notions of probability | 277 | 6.9 |
| Multigo 1 Game e Games | Solving missing-factor problems related to the multiplication facts; using mathematical reasoning | | 3.10 |
| Multigo 2 Game e Games | Solving missing-factor problems related to the multiplication facts; using mathematical reasoning | | 3.10 |
| Multiple Crossing Game e Games | Practicing basic facts; using factors up to 10; using mathematical reasoning | | 6.1 |
| Multiplication Table Game e Games | Using a multiplication table; multiplying with two factors of 5 or less | | 3.1 |
| Order Game | Using place value; using intuitive notions of probability | 13 | 1.3 |
| Ordering Game | Comparing and ordering percentages and fractions of 1 | 301 | 7.3 |
| Roll a 15 e Games | Adding two, three, or four numbers (0–10); using intuitive notions of probability | 29 | 1.7 |
| Roll a Decimal Game | Using place value; comparing decimal numbers; using mathematical reasoning | 397 | 9.4 |
| Roll a Number Game | Using place value and intuitive notions of probability | 11 | 1.2 |
| Roll a Problem Game | Adding and subtracting multidigit numbers; place value; using intuitive notions of probability | 55 | 2.2 |
| Snake Game | Solving missing-term problems; using mental arithmetic | | 4.4 |
| Store Game | Forming amounts of money (multiples of $0.25); making change | | 9.9 |
| Transaction Game | Adding and subtracting money (dollars); maintaining a record of money transactions; using place value | | 9.11 |

*These games and their variations should be used many times throughout the year. Feel free to use them again any time after they are introduced.

** Games in red are from the Game Mat Kit.

e Games These games are available as ***eGames.***

**Math Focus:** Locating coordinates on a grid

**Object of the Game:** To score more runs

**Players:** Two

## MATERIALS

Four place markers per player (same color)

Two cubes

Two cubes

One ruler or straightedge (not in game package)

## SET UP

- Decide how many full innings will be played.
- Each player rolls the 0–5 ***Number Cube.*** The player who rolls the highest number goes first.

## HOW TO PLAY

1. When you bat, you make an ordered pair by rolling any cube to get the first number and another cube to get the second number. You must roll one cube at a time and use the numbers in order.
2. Place the straightedge through (0, 0) and through the point corresponding to the ordered pair that you rolled. For example, if you roll 9 and 5, the straightedge starts at (0, 0) and passes through (9, 5).
3. If the straightedge crosses OUT, it's an out.
4. If the straightedge crosses HIT, it's a hit. Move a marker to the appropriate base. On a hit, runners on base may also advance the same number of bases. For example, a runner on second can go to third during a single.
5. If you roll (0, 0), it is a bunt. You are out, but if there are runners on base, they may advance one base.
6. Write down the numbers you roll and all outs, hits, and runs.
7. Each player gets three outs per inning. The player with more runs at the end of the game wins.



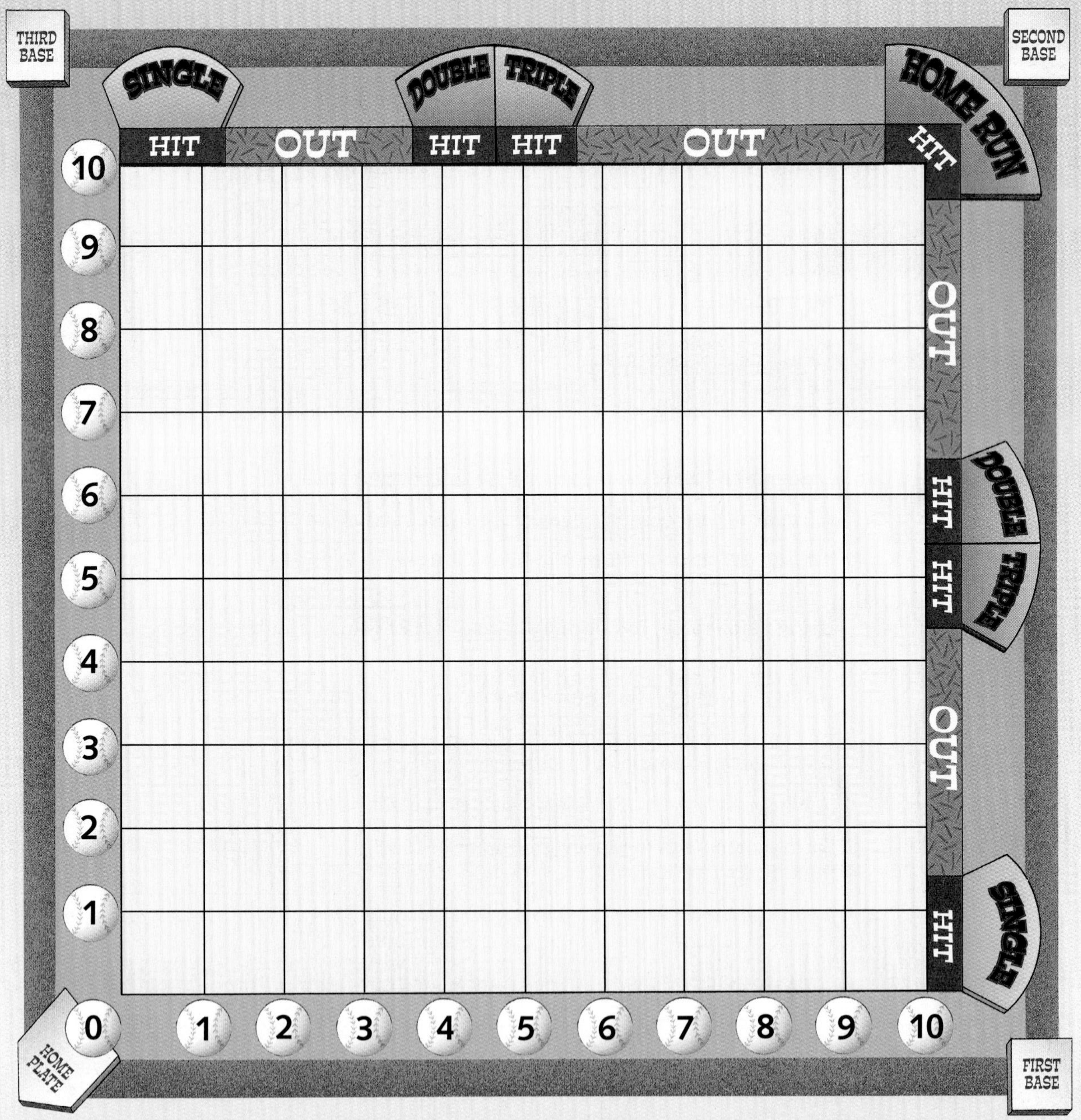

| Sunday | Monday | Tuesday | Wednesday | Thursday | Friday | Saturday |
|---|---|---|---|---|---|---|
| Start<br>Your Balance is $1000 | 1 Supermarket<br>Pay $35 | 2 Dentist Bill<br>Pay $50 | 3 Electric Bill<br>Pay $26 | 4 STOCK DIVIDEND<br>Earn $50 | 5 Insurance Bill<br>Pay $38 | 6 THEATER TICKETS<br>Pay $20 |
| 7 Eat in Restaurant<br>Pay $20 | 8 WORK OVERTIME<br>Earn $23 | 9 Supermarket<br>Pay $51 | 10 United Fund<br>Pay $100 | 11 Go Back 7 Spaces | 12 Income TAX<br>Pay $212 | 13 Go to Movies<br>Pay $5 |
| 14 Visit Museum<br>FREE | 15 RENT<br>Pay $150 | 16 Holiday!<br>No bills today | 17 Supermarket<br>Pay $47 | 18 BUY BOOKS<br>Pay $14 | 19 Telephone Bill<br>Pay $17 | 20 Receive Rebate Check<br>Earn $15 |
| 21 VISIT ZOO<br>FREE | 22 Supermarket<br>Pay $35 | 23 Go Back 7 Spaces | 24 Parking Ticket<br>Pay $5 | 25 Go Ahead 2 Spaces | 26 Automobile Repairs<br>Pay $285 | 27 WORK OVERTIME<br>Earn $48 |
| 28 Eat in Restaurant<br>Pay $22 | 29 NEW SHOES<br>Pay $15 | 30 Supermarket<br>Pay $51 | 31 Go Back 7 Spaces | Finish<br>Wait until all players finish | | |

# CHECKBOOK GAME

**Math Focus:**
- Adding and subtracting two-digit and three-digit numbers
- Maintaining a record of money transactions

**Object of the Game:** To have the largest balance at the end of the month

**Players:** Two or three

## MATERIALS

## SET UP

- Photocopies of the sample balance sheet can be handed out to students.
- Players prepare their balance sheets by writing "Start" on the first line under DATE and "$1000" on the first line under BALANCE.
- Players put their place markers on START.
- Players roll the 0–5 *Number Cube.* The person who rolls the highest number goes first.

## HOW TO PLAY

1. Players take turns rolling the cube and moving their markers the number of spaces indicated.
2. Players follow the directions on the spaces where they land, entering the date and all payments or earnings on their balance sheets and recalculating their balances.
3. Play continues until all the players have either reached FINISH or run out of money.
4. The player with the largest balance at the end of the game is declared the winner. The other players then check the addition and subtraction in the winner's balance sheet. If the balance does not check, the player with the highest correct balance becomes the winner.

## SAMPLE BALANCE SHEET

| Date | Earn | Pay | Balance |
|---|---|---|---|
| | | | |
| | | | |
| | | | |
| | | | |
| | | | |
| | | | |
| | | | |

| Sunday | Monday | Tuesday | Wednesday | Thursday | Friday | Saturday |
|---|---|---|---|---|---|---|
| **Start** Your Balance is $1000.00 | 1 Supermarket Pay $35.22 | 2 Dentist Bill Pay $50.00 | 3 Electric Bill Pay $26.14 | 4 STOCK DIVIDEND Earn $50.00 | 5 Insurance Bill Pay $38.17 | 6 THEATER TICKETS Pay $20.00 |
| 7 Eat in Restaurant Pay $20.82 | 8 WORK OVERTIME Earn $23.50 | 9 Supermarket Pay $51.62 | 10 United Fund Pay $100.00 | 11 Go Back 7 Spaces | 12 Income TAX Pay $212.00 | 13 Go to Movies Pay $5.00 |
| 14 Visit Museum FREE | 15 RENT Pay $150.00 | 16 Holiday! No bills today | 17 Supermarket Pay $47.94 | 18 BUY BOOKS Pay $14.50 | 19 Telephone Bill Pay $17.36 | 20 WORK OVERTIME Earn $43.71 |
| 21 VISIT ZOO FREE | 22 Supermarket Pay $35.61 | 23 Go Back 7 Spaces | 24 Parking Ticket Pay $5.00 | 25 Go Ahead 2 Spaces | 26 Automobile Repairs Pay $285.00 | 27 JOB BONUS Earn $250.00 |
| 28 Eat in Restaurant Pay $22.16 | 29 NEW SHOES Pay $15.45 | 30 Supermarket Pay $51.62 | 31 Go Back 7 Spaces | **Finish** Wait until all players finish | | |

# HARDER CHECKBOOK GAME

**Math Focus:**
- Adding and subtracting two-digit, three-digit, and four-digit numbers
- Maintaining a record of money transactions

**Object of the Game:** To have the largest balance at the end of the month

**Players:** Two or three

## MATERIALS

Place markers · Cube · One balance sheet per player

## SET UP

- Photocopies of the balance sheet for the **Harder Checkbook Game** can be handed out to students.
- Players prepare their balance sheets by writing "Start" on the first line under DATE and "$1000" on the first line under BALANCE.
- Players put their place markers on START.
- Players roll the 0–5 ***Number Cube.*** The person who rolls the highest number goes first.

## HOW TO PLAY

1. Players take turns rolling the cube and moving their markers the number of spaces indicated.
2. Players follow the directions on the spaces where they land, entering the date and all payments or earnings on their balance sheets and recalculating their balances.
3. Play continues until all the players have either reached FINISH or run out of money.
4. The player with the largest balance at the end of the game is declared the winner. The other players then check the addition and subtraction in the winner's balance sheet. If the balance does not check, the player with the highest correct balance becomes the winner.

## SAMPLE BALANCE SHEET

| Date | Earn | Pay | Balance |
|---|---|---|---|
| | | | |
| | | | |
| | | | |
| | | | |
| | | | |
| | | | |
| | | | |
| | | | |

HARDER CHECKBOOK GAME

# CUSTOMARY UNIT GAME

INCHES FEET YARDS OUNCES POUNDS TONS

**Math Focus:** Choosing appropriate customary units of weight and length for various objects

**Object of the Game:** To have the most counters at the end of the game

**Players:** Two, three, or four

## MATERIALS

Place markers | Cube | 24 counters or pennies

## SET UP

- Every circle on the mat must be covered with a counter.
- Players put their place markers on the space marked START.
- Players roll the 0–5 ***Number Cube.*** The person who rolls the greatest number goes first.
- Inform players that all lengths are given in inches, feet, or yards, and all weights are given in ounces, pounds, or tons.

## HOW TO PLAY

1. Players take turns rolling the cube and moving their place markers the number of spaces indicated.
2. After landing on a space, players must state *either* the appropriate customary unit of length *or* weight for the object pictured there.
3. Players check their answers by looking under the counter. If correct, the player keeps the counter; if incorrect, the player replaces it. A player can win only one counter per turn.
4. Once the counter on a circle has been won, the circle remains empty. Players who land on a space with two empty circles cannot win a counter and must wait until the next turn to roll again.
5. A player who rolls a 0 cannot win a counter.
6. Players who land on the space marked PENALTY must, if possible, place one of their own counters on any empty circle on the mat.
7. A player who lands on the space marked START collects one counter from every other player.
8. The player with the most counters at the end of the game wins.

START

BROOM: Length About 54 — inches; Weight About 36 — ounces

ROLL OF 50 PENNIES: Weight About 5 — ounces; Length About 4 — inches

BLUE WHALE: Weight About 220 — tons; Length About 100 — feet

LADDER: Weight About 30 — pounds; Length About 6 — feet

AIRPLANE: Length About 75 — yards; Weight About 400 — tons

NECKTIE: Weight About 2 — ounces; Length About 2 — feet

PENALTY
Cover a circle

TELESCOPE: Weight About 40 — pounds; Length About 100 — inches

HOT DOG: Length About 6 — inches; Weight About 2 — ounces

DICTIONARY: Weight About 3 — pounds; Length About 10 — inches

MOTORCYCLE: Weight About 600 — pounds; Length About 6 — feet

DOG: Weight About 40 — pounds; Length About 3 — feet

PIANO: Weight About 650 — pounds; Length About 2 — yards

INCHES FEET YARDS OUNCES POUNDS TONS

CUSTOMARY UNIT GAME

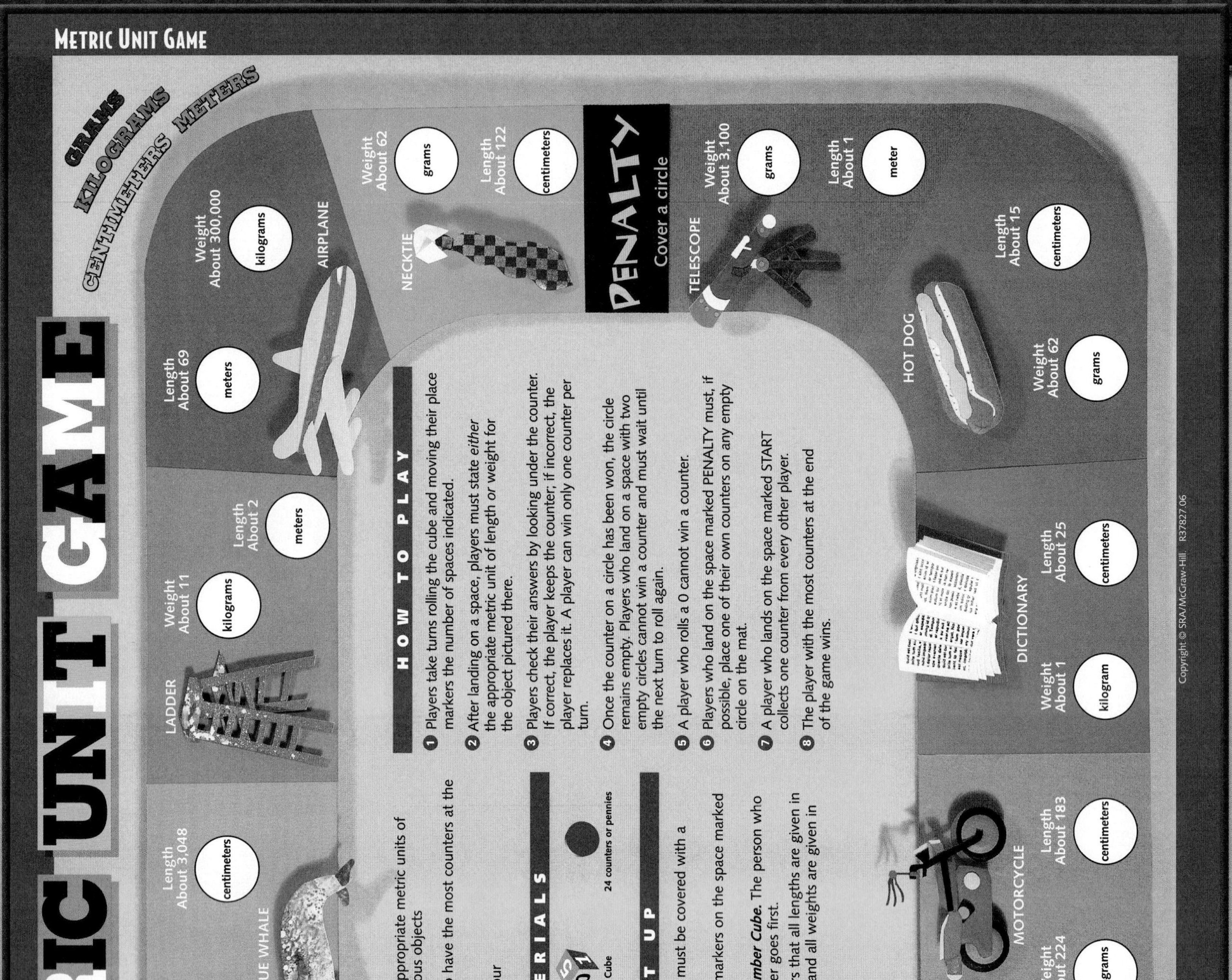
METRIC UNIT GAME
METRIC UNIT GAME
GRAMS KILOGRAMS CENTIMETERS METERS
Math Focus: Choosing appropriate metric units of weight and length for various objects
Object of the Game: To have the most counters at the end of the game
Players: Two, three, or four
MATERIALS
Place markers
0–5 Number Cube
24 counters or pennies
SET UP
▶ Every circle on the mat must be covered with a counter.
▶ Players put their place markers on the space marked START.
▶ Players roll the 0–5 Number Cube. The person who rolls the greatest number goes first.
▶ Optional: Inform players that all lengths are given in centimeters or meters, and all weights are given in grams or kilograms.
HOW TO PLAY
1 Players take turns rolling the cube and moving their place markers the number of spaces indicated.
2 After landing on a space, players must state either the appropriate metric unit of length or weight for the object pictured there.
3 Players check their answers by looking under the counter. If correct, the player keeps the counter; if incorrect, the player replaces it. A player can win only one counter per turn.
4 Once the counter on a circle has been won, the circle remains empty. Players who land on a space with two empty circles cannot win a counter and must wait until the next turn to roll again.
5 A player who rolls a 0 cannot win a counter.
6 Players who land on the space marked PENALTY must, if possible, place one of their own counters on any empty circle on the mat.
7 A player who lands on the space marked START collects one counter from every other player.
8 The player with the most counters at the end of the game wins.
START
PIANO
Weight About 242 kilograms
Length About 2 meters
BROOM
Weight About 1,120 grams
Length About 137 centimeters
ROLL OF 50 PENNIES
Weight About 124 grams
Length About 10 centimeters
BLUE WHALE
Weight About 164,000 kilograms
Length About 3,048 centimeters
LADDER
Weight About 11 kilograms
Length About 2 meters
AIRPLANE
Weight About 300,000 kilograms
Length About 69 meters
NECKTIE
Weight About 62 grams
Length About 122 centimeters
PENALTY
Cover a circle
TELESCOPE
Weight About 3,100 grams
Length About 1 meter
HOT DOG
Weight About 62 grams
Length About 15 centimeters
DICTIONARY
Weight About 1 kilogram
Length About 25 centimeters
MOTORCYCLE
Weight About 224 kilograms
Length About 183 centimeters
DOG
Weight About 15 kilograms
Length About 30 centimeters
Copyright © SRA/McGraw-Hill. R37827.06

# Find the Distance Game 1

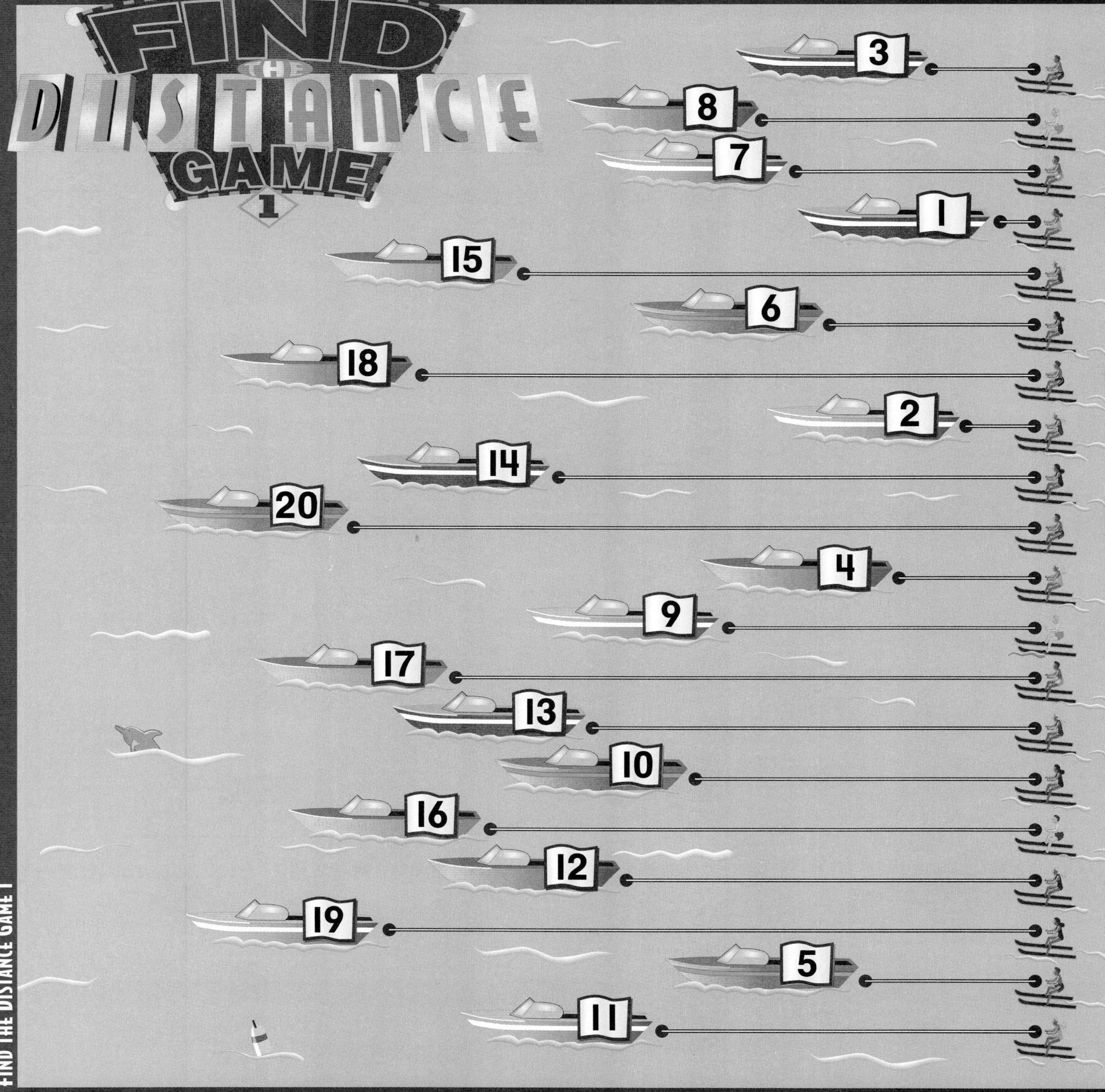


**Math Focus:** Estimating straight distances to the nearest centimeter; Comparing line lengths; Practicing basic addition facts

**Object of the Game:** To have the most counters at the end of the game

**Players:** Two or three

## MATERIALS

## SET UP

- Every number must be covered with a counter.
- Players roll the 0–5 ***Number Cube.*** The person who rolls the highest number goes first.

## HOW TO PLAY

1. Players take turns choosing two cubes to roll and finding their sum. The player then identifies the line on the mat which is that many centimeters long.
2. Players check their answers by looking under the counter. If correct, the player keeps the counter. If incorrect, the player replaces the counter and must wait until the next turn to roll again.
3. Players who roll a 0 or a sum that has already been won must wait until the next turn to roll again.
4. The player with the most counters at the end of the game wins.

**Measurement Key**

0 1 2 = **2** centimeters



FIND THE DISTANCE GAME 1

**Math Focus:** Estimating straight distances to the nearest centimeter; Comparing line lengths; Practicing basic addition facts

**Object of the Game:** To have the most counters at the end of the game

**Players:** Two or three

## MATERIALS

- Two cubes (0–5)
- Two cubes (5–10)
- Ten counters or pennies

## SET UP

- Every number must be covered with a counter.
- Players roll the 0–5 ***Number Cube.*** The person who rolls the highest number goes first.

## HOW TO PLAY

1. Players take turns choosing two cubes to roll and finding their sum. The player then identifies the line on the mat which is that many centimeters long.
2. Players check their answers by looking under the counter. If correct, the player keeps the counter. If incorrect, the player replaces the counter and must wait until the next turn to roll again.
3. Players who roll a 0 or a sum that has already been won must wait until the next turn to roll again.
4. The player with the most counters at the end of the game wins.

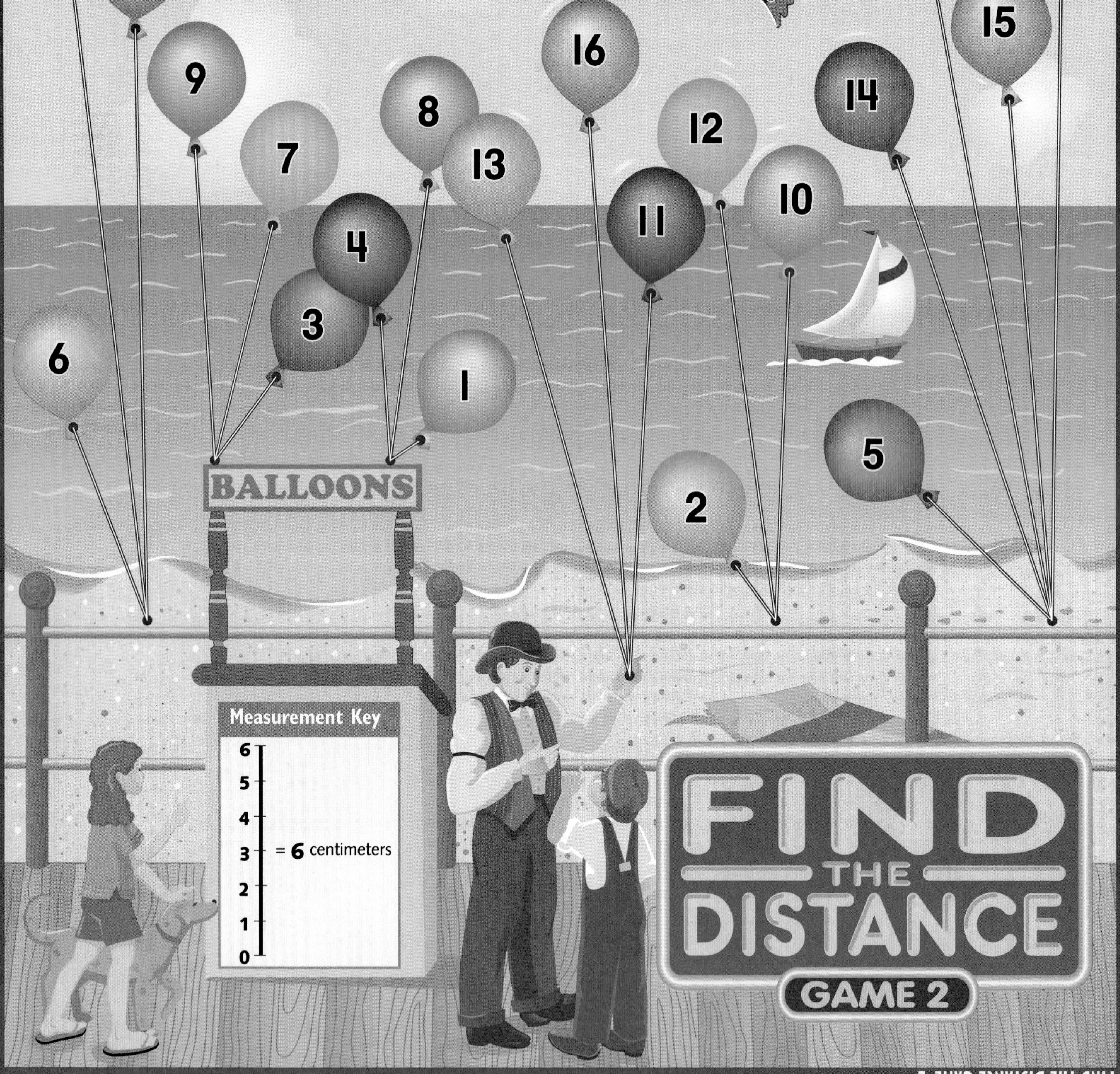


FIND THE DISTANCE GAME 2

**Math Focus:**

- Recognizing fractional areas of a circle from fifths to tenths
- Recognizing which common fractions equal more than 1/2 when added together

**Object of the Game:** To have more pies at the end of the game

**Players:** Two

## MATERIALS

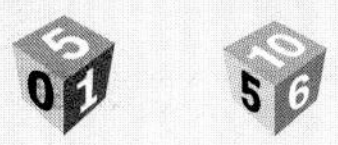


Cube   Cube

30 counters of the same color for each player, or 30 pennies and 30 dimes

## SET UP

- The first player chooses his or her counters and is followed by the second player.
- Players roll the 0–5 ***Number Cube.*** The person who rolls the highest number goes first.

## HOW TO PLAY

1. Take turns rolling the cubes to make proper fractions (equivalent to 1 or less). If you roll a 0 on either of the cubes, roll that cube again.
2. Cover an amount of pie equal to the fraction you rolled. For example, if you roll a 3 and a 7, cover 3/7 of a pie divided into sevenths. The sections you cover do not have to be in the same pie.
3. You can also cover sections of pies divided into different fractions, as long as the total amount you cover equals the fraction that you rolled. For example, if you roll a 3 and a 6, you could cover 4/8 of the pies divided into eighths, since 4/8 = 3/6. Or you could cover 3/9 of the ninths pies and 1/6 of the sixths pies, since 3/9 + 1/6 = 3/6.
4. If you cannot use the fraction you rolled, you must wait until your next turn to roll again.
5. You win a pie when you cover more than half of it. Place your counter in the center and return any of your opponent's counters.
6. If you cover half of a pie and your opponent covers the other half, neither of you can win that pie.
7. Keep playing until all the pies are either won or completely covered. The player who has more pies at the end of the game is the winner.



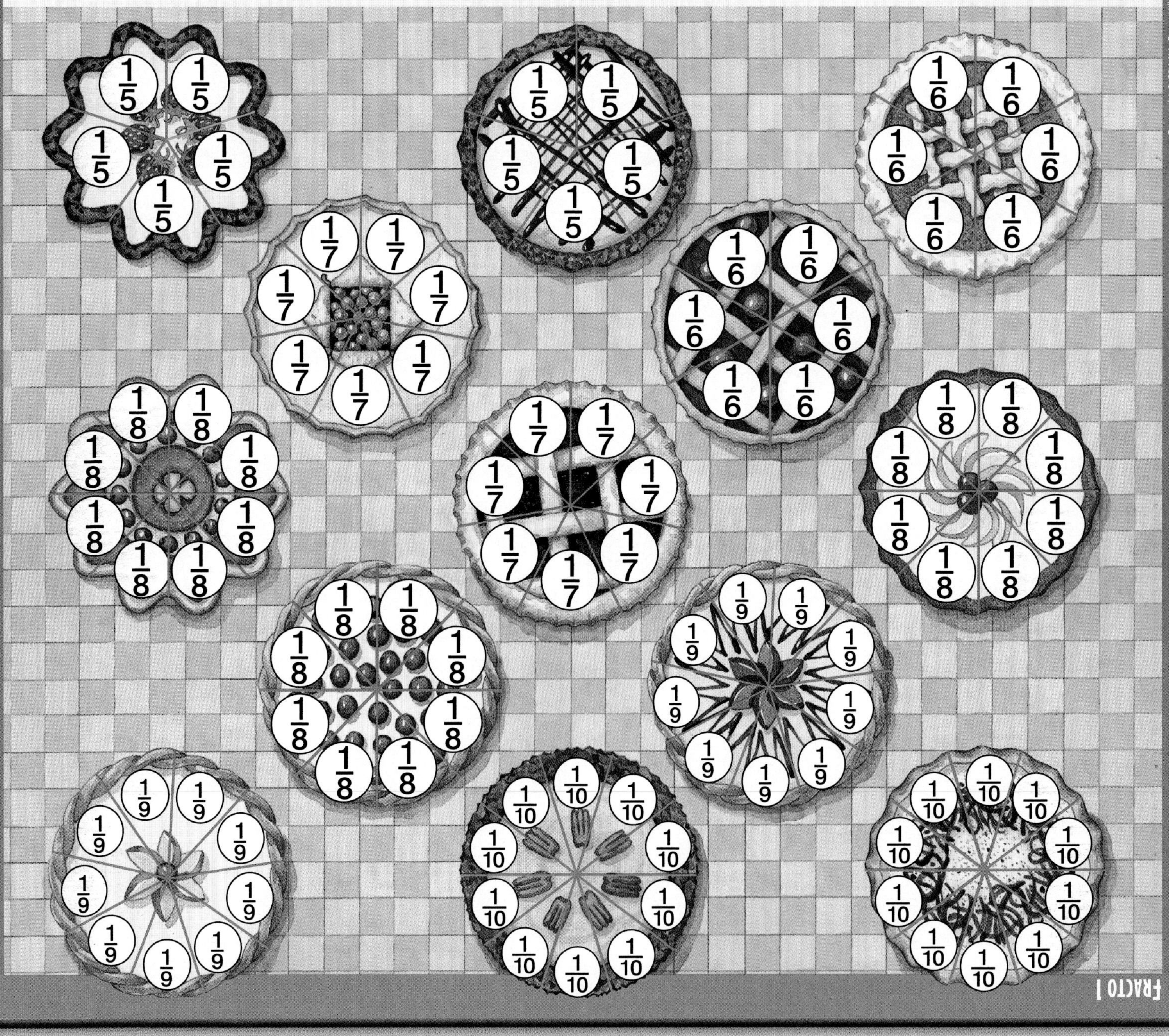


FRACTO 1

**Math Focus:**

- Recognizing fractional areas of a rectangle from fifths to tenths
- Recognizing which common fractions equal more than 1/2 when added together

**Object of the Game:** To have more loaves at the end of the game

**Players:** Two

## MATERIALS

30 counters of the same color for each player, or 30 pennies and 30 dimes

## SET UP

- The first player chooses his or her counters and is followed by the second player.
- Players roll the 0–5 ***Number Cube.*** The person who rolls the highest number goes first.

## HOW TO PLAY

1. Take turns rolling the cubes to make proper fractions (equivalent to 1 or less). If you roll a 0 on either of the cubes, roll that cube again.
2. Cover an amount of loaf equal to the fraction you rolled. For example, if you roll a 3 and a 7, cover 3/7 of a loaf divided into sevenths. The sections you cover do not have to be in the same loaf.
3. You may also cover sections of loaves divided into different fractions, as long as the total amount you cover equals the fraction that you rolled. For example, if you roll a 3 and a 6, you could cover 4/8 of the loaves divided into eighths, since 4/8 = 3/6. Or you could cover 3/9 of the ninths loaves and 1/6 of the sixths loaves, since 3/9 + 1/6 = 3/6.
4. If you cannot use the fraction you rolled, you must wait until your next turn to roll again.
5. You win a loaf when you cover more than half of it. Place your counter in the WINNER circle, and return any of your opponent's counters left on the loaf.
6. If you cover half of a loaf and your opponent covers the other half, neither of you can win that loaf.
7. Keep playing until all the loaves are either won or completely covered. The player who has more loaves at the end of the game is the winner.
8. In case of a tie, clear all the loaves and begin playing again. The first person to win a loaf is the winner

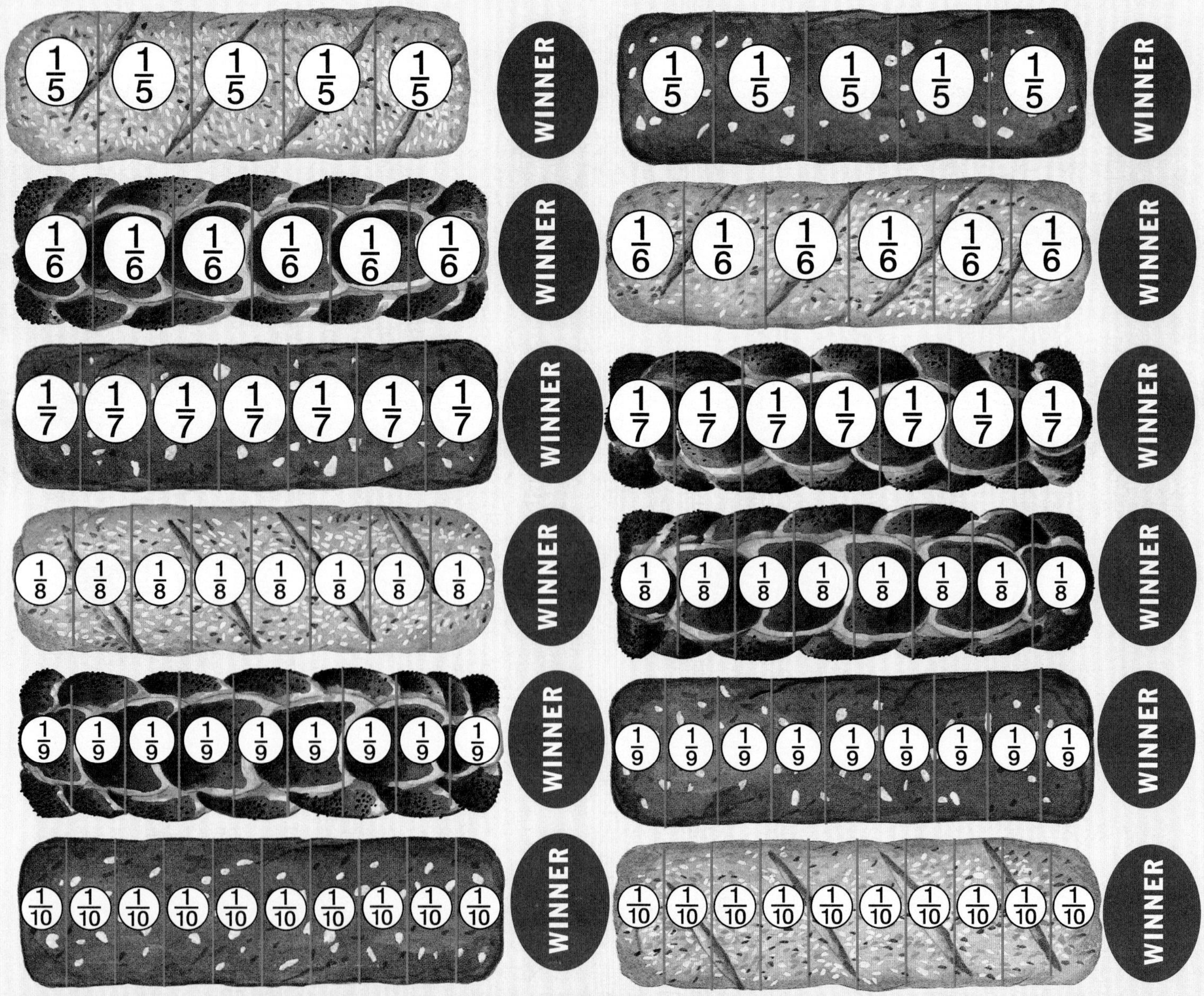


FRACTO 2

**Math Focus:** Telling time to five-minute intervals

**Object of the Game:** To have the most counters at the end of the game

**Players:** Two or three

## MATERIALS

Place markers · Cube · 16 counters or pennies

## SET UP

- The red answer circles in each space must be covered by a counter.
- Players put their place markers on the space marked GO.
- Players roll the 0–5 ***Number Cube.*** The person who rolls the highest number goes first.

## HOW TO PLAY

1. Players take turns rolling the cube and moving their place markers the number of spaces indicated. Players must correctly state the time indicated on the clock in each space where they land.
2. Players check their answers by looking under the counter. If correct, the player keeps the counter; if incorrect, the player replaces the counter.
3. A player who gives an incorrect answer and then rolls a 0 on the next turn may try again to win the counter.
4. Players who land on empty circles cannot win a counter and must wait until the next turn to roll again.
5. Players who land on the space marked PENALTY must, if possible, place one of their own counters on an empty circle.
6. The player with the most counters at the end of the game wins.

MINUTES

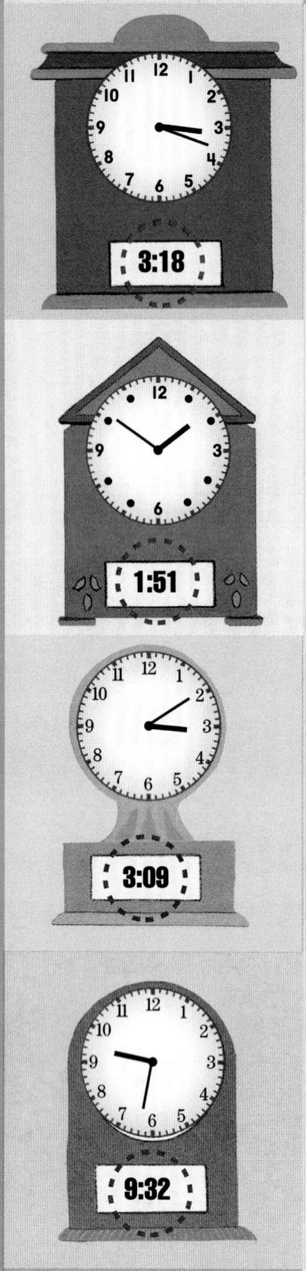

**Math Focus:** Telling time to the minute

**Object of the Game:** To have the most counters at the end of the game

**Players:** Two or three

## MATERIALS

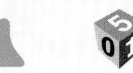

Place markers | Cube | 16 counters or pennies

## SET UP

- The red answer circles in each space must be covered by a counter.
- Players put their place markers on the space marked GO.
- Players roll the 0–5 ***Number Cube.*** The person who rolls the highest number goes first.

## HOW TO PLAY

1. Players take turns rolling the cube and moving their place markers the number of spaces indicated. Players must correctly state the time indicated on the clock in each space where they land.
2. Players check their answers by looking under the counter. If correct, the player keeps the counter; if incorrect, the player replaces the counter.
3. A player who gives an incorrect answer and then rolls a 0 on the next turn may try again to win the counter.
4. Players who land on empty circles cannot win a counter and must wait until the next turn to roll again.
5. Players who land on the space marked PENALTY must, if possible, place one of their own counters on an empty circle.
6. The player with the most counters at the end of the game wins.

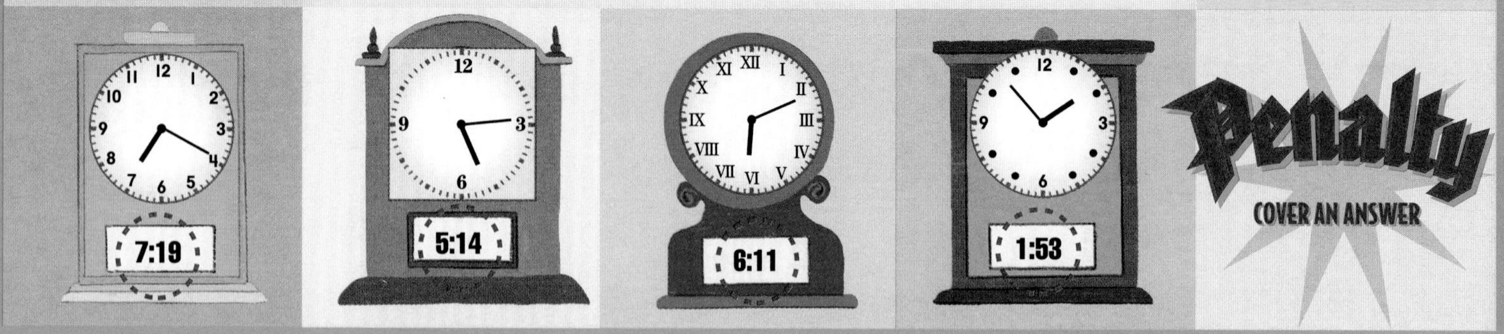


HARDER MINUTES

**Math Focus:** Solving missing-factor problems related to the multiplication facts

**Object of the Game:** To capture five squares in a straight line

**Players:** Two

### MATERIALS

- Cube (0–5)
- Cube (5–10)
- 15 counters or pennies per player

### SET UP

- Players roll the 0–5 ***Number Cube.*** The person who rolls the greater number goes first.
- The first player chooses either Card 1 or Card 2 on the game mat. The second player uses the other card.

### HOW TO PLAY

1. Players take turns rolling either cube and multiplying the number rolled by any other number between 0 and 10 to equal one of the products on their game card.
2. Players say the correct multiplication sentence. For example, a player who rolls a 7 and wants to capture the 42 square on his or her card would say "7 times 6 equals 42." If the sentence is correct, the player puts a counter on the appropriate square. If incorrect, the player cannot put down a counter.
3. The first player to capture five squares in a straight line (vertically, horizontally, or diagonally) is the winner.

1

| | | | | |
|---|---|---|---|---|
| 25 | 30 | 35 | 40 | 45 |
| 30 | 36 | 42 | 48 | 54 |
| 35 | 42 | 49 | 56 | 63 |
| 40 | 48 | 56 | 64 | 72 |
| 45 | 54 | 63 | 72 | 81 |

2

| | | | | |
|---|---|---|---|---|
| 15 | 18 | 21 | 24 | 27 |
| 20 | 24 | 28 | 32 | 36 |
| 25 | 30 | 35 | 40 | 45 |
| 30 | 36 | 42 | 48 | 54 |
| 35 | 42 | 49 | 56 | 63 |

MULTIGO 1

**Math Focus:** Solving missing-factor problems related to the multiplication facts

**Object of the Game:** To capture five squares in a straight line

**Players:** Two

## MATERIALS

- 0–5 Cube
- 5–10 Cube
- 15 counters or pennies per player

## SET UP

- Players roll the 0–5 ***Number Cube.*** The person who rolls the greater number goes first.
- The first player chooses Card 1, 2, or 3 on the game mat, and then the second player chooses a card.

## HOW TO PLAY

1. Players take turns rolling either cube and multiplying the number rolled by any other number between 0 and 10 to equal one of the products on their game card.
2. Players say the correct multiplication sentence. For example, a player who rolls a 7 and wants to capture the 42 square on his or her card would say "7 times 6 equals 42." If the sentence is correct, the player puts a counter on the appropriate square. If incorrect, the player cannot put down a counter.
3. The first player to capture five squares in a straight line (vertically, horizontally, or diagonally) is the winner.

**1**

| | | | | |
|---|---|---|---|---|
| 40 | 64 | 28 | 35 | 63 |
| 56 | 25 | 30 | 49 | 20 |
| 42 | 36 | 0 | 24 | 45 |
| 18 | 60 | 54 | 81 | 48 |
| 72 | 32 | 27 | 70 | 21 |

**2**

| | | | | |
|---|---|---|---|---|
| 81 | 10 | 63 | 40 | 90 |
| 28 | 35 | 15 | 49 | 72 |
| 12 | 42 | 0 | 56 | 32 |
| 54 | 64 | 36 | 16 | 48 |
| 70 | 27 | 45 | 30 | 24 |

**3**

| | | | | |
|---|---|---|---|---|
| 80 | 30 | 14 | 63 | 42 |
| 48 | 100 | 45 | 50 | 81 |
| 18 | 64 | 0 | 36 | 56 |
| 27 | 49 | 35 | 72 | 20 |
| 32 | 10 | 24 | 54 | 40 |

MULTIGO 2

# Multiple Crossing

| | 1 | 2 | 3 | 4 | 5 | 6 | 7 | 8 | 9 | 10 |
|---|---|---|---|---|---|---|---|---|---|---|
| 1 | 1 | 2 | 3 | 4 | 5 | 6 | 7 | 8 | 9 | 10 |
| 2 | 2 | 4 | 6 | 8 | 10 | 12 | 14 | 16 | 18 | 20 |
| 3 | 3 | 6 | 9 | 12 | 15 | 18 | 21 | 24 | 27 | 30 |
| 4 | 4 | 8 | 12 | 16 | 20 | 24 | 28 | 32 | 36 | 40 |
| 5 | 5 | 10 | 15 | 20 | 25 | 30 | 35 | 40 | 45 | 50 |
| 6 | 6 | 12 | 18 | 24 | 30 | 36 | 42 | 48 | 54 | 60 |
| 7 | 7 | 14 | 21 | 28 | 35 | 42 | 49 | 56 | 63 | 70 |
| 8 | 8 | 16 | 24 | 32 | 40 | 48 | 56 | 64 | 72 | 80 |
| 9 | 9 | 18 | 27 | 36 | 45 | 54 | 63 | 72 | 81 | 90 |
| 10 | 10 | 20 | 30 | 40 | 50 | 60 | 70 | 80 | 90 | 100 |

**Math Focus:** Practicing basic facts—using factors up to 10

**Object of the Game:** To be the first to complete a continuous path across the board

**Players:** Two

## MATERIALS

## SET UP

- Choose a direction. One of you will move horizontally (left to right), and the other will move vertically (up and down).
- Players roll the 0–5 ***Number Cube.*** The person who rolls the highest number chooses his or her counters and is followed by the second player.

## HOW TO PLAY

1. Take turns rolling any two cubes. Put a counter on any square that holds the product of the two numbers you rolled.
2. If you roll a 0, you cannot place a counter on a square.
3. The first player to make a continuous path from one side to the opposite side is the winner. Your path can go up, down, forward, backward, or diagonally, as long as all the squares are touching each other.

**Sample Game**

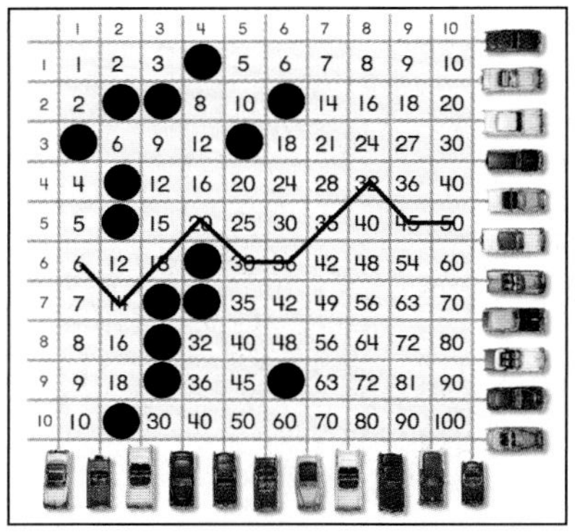

# Multiplication Table Game

**Math Focus:**
- Practicing basic facts–multiplying two factors of 5 or less
- Using a multiplication table

**Object of the Game:** To have more counters at the end of the game

**Players:** Two

## MATERIALS

Two cubes

36 counters or pennies

## SET UP

- Every circle on the mat must be covered with a counter.
- Players roll the 0–5 ***Number Cube.*** The person who rolls the higher number goes first.

## HOW TO PLAY

1. Players take turns rolling both cubes and making multiplication sentences out of the numbers. For example, if a 4 and a 2 are rolled, the player could say either "4 times 2 equals 8" or "2 times 4 equals 8."
2. After giving the multiplication sentence, players check their answers by looking under the appropriate counter. If correct, the player keeps the counter; if incorrect, the player replaces the counter.
3. Once the counter on a circle has been won, the circle remains empty. A player who cannot make a multiplication sentence that applies to a covered circle cannot win a counter that turn.
4. The player with more counters at the end of the game wins.

| × | 0 | 1 | 2 | 3 | 4 | 5 |
|---|---|---|---|---|---|---|
| 0 | 0 | 0 | 0 | 0 | 0 | 0 |
| 1 | 0 | 1 | 2 | 3 | 4 | 5 |
| 2 | 0 | 2 | 4 | 6 | 8 | 10 |
| 3 | 0 | 3 | 6 | 9 | 12 | 15 |
| 4 | 0 | 4 | 8 | 12 | 16 | 20 |
| 5 | 0 | 5 | 10 | 15 | 20 | 25 |

Multiplication Table Game

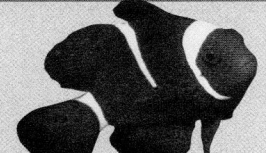

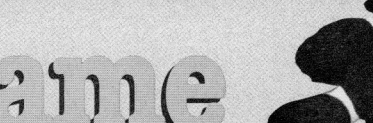

# HARDER Multiplication Table Game

Math Focus:
- Practicing basic facts–multiplying two factors of 10 or less
- Using a multiplication table

**Object of the Game:** To have more counters at the end of the game

**Players:** Two

## MATERIALS

Cube — Two cubes — 36 counters or pennies

## SET UP

- Every circle on the mat must be covered with a counter.
- Players roll the 0–5 ***Number Cube.*** The person who rolls the higher number goes first.

## HOW TO PLAY

1. There are actually two harder versions of this game. One game is played rolling one 0–5 and one 5–10 ***Number Cube.*** The second game is played with two 5–10 ***Number Cubes.*** Players take turns rolling both cubes and making multiplication sentences out of the numbers. For example, if a 4 and a 9 are rolled, the player could say either "4 times 9 equals 36" or "9 times 4 equals 36."
2. After giving the multiplication sentence, players check their answers by looking under the appropriate counter. If correct, the player keeps the counter; if incorrect, the player replaces the counter.
3. Once the counter on a circle has been won, the circle remains empty. A player who cannot make a multiplication sentence that applies to a covered circle cannot win a counter that turn.
4. The player with more counters at the end of the game wins.

| × | 5 | 6 | 7 | 8 | 9 | 10 |
|---|---|---|---|---|---|---|
| 0 | 0 | 0 | 0 | 0 | 0 | 0 |
| 1 | 5 | 6 | 7 | 8 | 9 | 10 |
| 2 | 10 | 12 | 14 | 16 | 18 | 20 |
| 3 | 15 | 18 | 21 | 24 | 27 | 30 |
| 4 | 20 | 24 | 28 | 32 | 36 | 40 |
| 5 | 25 | 30 | 35 | 40 | 45 | 50 |

| × | 5 | 6 | 7 | 8 | 9 | 10 |
|---|---|---|---|---|---|---|
| 5 | 25 | 30 | 35 | 40 | 45 | 50 |
| 6 | 30 | 36 | 42 | 48 | 54 | 60 |
| 7 | 35 | 42 | 49 | 56 | 63 | 70 |
| 8 | 40 | 48 | 56 | 64 | 72 | 80 |
| 9 | 45 | 54 | 63 | 72 | 81 | 90 |
| 10 | 50 | 60 | 70 | 80 | 90 | 100 |

HARDER MULTIPLICATION TABLE GAME

# Shopping Game

**Math Focus:**
- Practicing basic facts—multiplying with factors up to 9
- Forming amounts of money and making change

**Object of the Game:** To be the first to have $250

**Players:** Two, three, or four

## MATERIALS

Place markers

Cube

Per player:
one $50 bill
two $20 bills
three $10 bills
five $5 bills
five $1 bills

## SET UP

- Players select stores to own. If two are playing, each player chooses two stores; if three are playing, one store will not be owned by anyone.
- Players put their place markers on the space marked START.
- Players roll the 0–5 ***Number Cube.*** The person who rolls the highest number goes first.

## HOW TO PLAY

1. Players take turns rolling the cube and moving their place markers the number of spaces indicated.
2. After landing on a space, players roll the cube to see how many of the items pictured they must buy, and then they pay the store owner. For example, a player who lands on an item that costs $8 and then rolls a 3 must pay the owner $24 for three of the items.
3. Even if a player has already bought an item, the player must buy it again if he or she lands on that space again.
4. Players who roll a 0, land in their own stores, or land on stores that nobody owns buy nothing.
5. A player who lands on the space marked START collects $5 from every player.
6. The first player to have $250 wins.

# HARDER Shopping Game

**Math Focus:**
- Practicing basic facts—multiplying with factors up to 9
- Forming amounts of money and making change

**Object of the Game:** To be the first to have $450

**Players:** Two, three, or four

## MATERIALS

Place markers

Cube

Per player:
one $100 bill
two $50 bills
five $20 bills
three $10 bills
five $5 bills
five $1 bills

## SET UP

- Players select stores to own. If two are playing, each player chooses two stores; if three are playing, one store will not be owned by anyone.
- Players put their place markers on the space marked START.
- Players roll the 0–5 ***Number Cube.*** The person who rolls the highest number goes first.

## HOW TO PLAY

1. Players take turns rolling the cube and moving their place markers the number of spaces indicated.
2. After landing on a space, players roll the cube to see how many of the items pictured they must buy, and then they pay the store owner. For example, a player who lands on an item that costs $29 and then rolls a 4 must pay the owner $116 for four of the items.
3. Even if a player has already bought an item, the player must buy it again if he or she lands on that space again.
4. Players who roll a 0, land in their own stores, or land on stores that nobody owns buy nothing.
5. A player who lands on the space marked START collects $5 from every player.
6. The first player to have $450 wins.

HARDER SHOPPING GAME

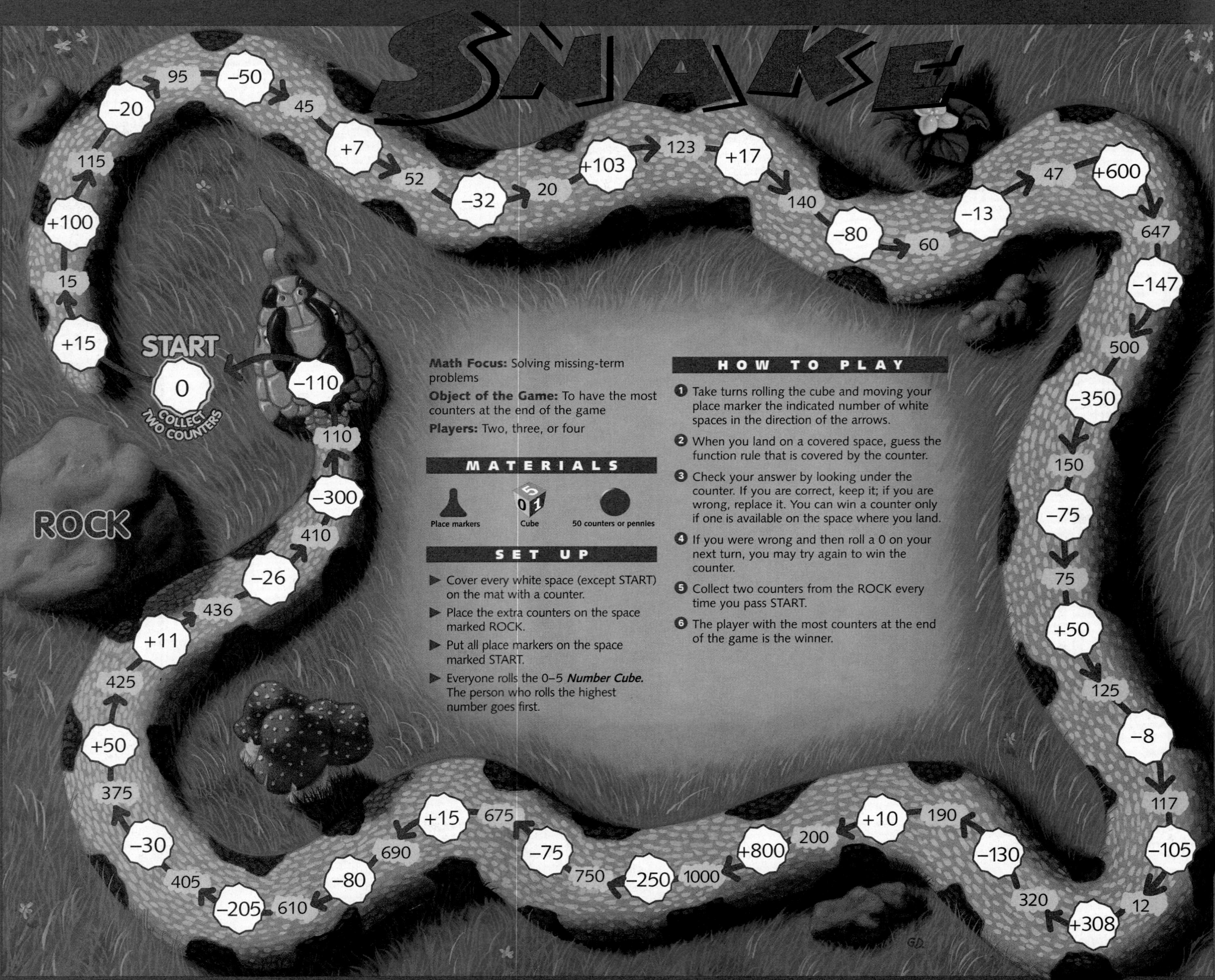


**Math Focus:** Solving missing-term problems

**Object of the Game:** To have the most counters at the end of the game

**Players:** Two, three, or four

## MATERIALS

Place markers — Cube — 50 counters or pennies

## SET UP

- Cover every white space (except START) on the mat with a counter.
- Place the extra counters on the space marked ROCK.
- Put all place markers on the space marked START.
- Everyone rolls the 0–5 ***Number Cube.*** The person who rolls the highest number goes first.

## HOW TO PLAY

1. Take turns rolling the cube and moving your place marker the indicated number of white spaces in the direction of the arrows.
2. When you land on a covered space, guess the function rule that is covered by the counter.
3. Check your answer by looking under the counter. If you are correct, keep it; if you are wrong, replace it. You can win a counter only if one is available on the space where you land.
4. If you were wrong and then roll a 0 on your next turn, you may try again to win the counter.
5. Collect two counters from the ROCK every time you pass START.
6. The player with the most counters at the end of the game is the winner.



SNAKE

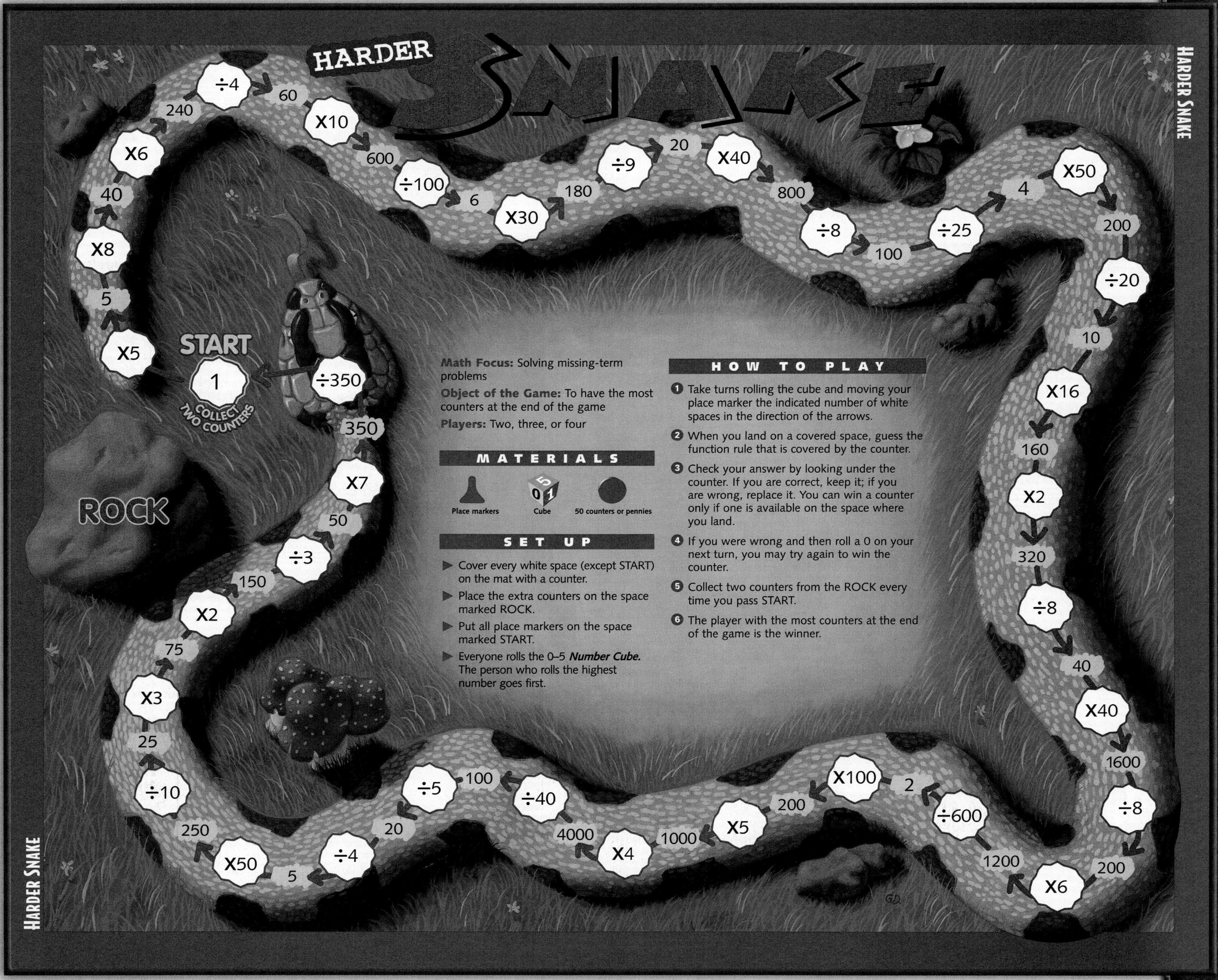


Math Focus: Solving missing-term problems

**Object of the Game:** To have the most counters at the end of the game

**Players:** Two, three, or four

## MATERIALS

Place markers | Cube | 50 counters or pennies

## SET UP

- Cover every white space (except START) on the mat with a counter.
- Place the extra counters on the space marked ROCK.
- Put all place markers on the space marked START.
- Everyone rolls the 0–5 ***Number Cube.*** The person who rolls the highest number goes first.

## HOW TO PLAY

1. Take turns rolling the cube and moving your place marker the indicated number of white spaces in the direction of the arrows.
2. When you land on a covered space, guess the function rule that is covered by the counter.
3. Check your answer by looking under the counter. If you are correct, keep it; if you are wrong, replace it. You can win a counter only if one is available on the space where you land.
4. If you were wrong and then roll a 0 on your next turn, you may try again to win the counter.
5. Collect two counters from the ROCK every time you pass START.
6. The player with the most counters at the end of the game is the winner.

HARDER SNAKE

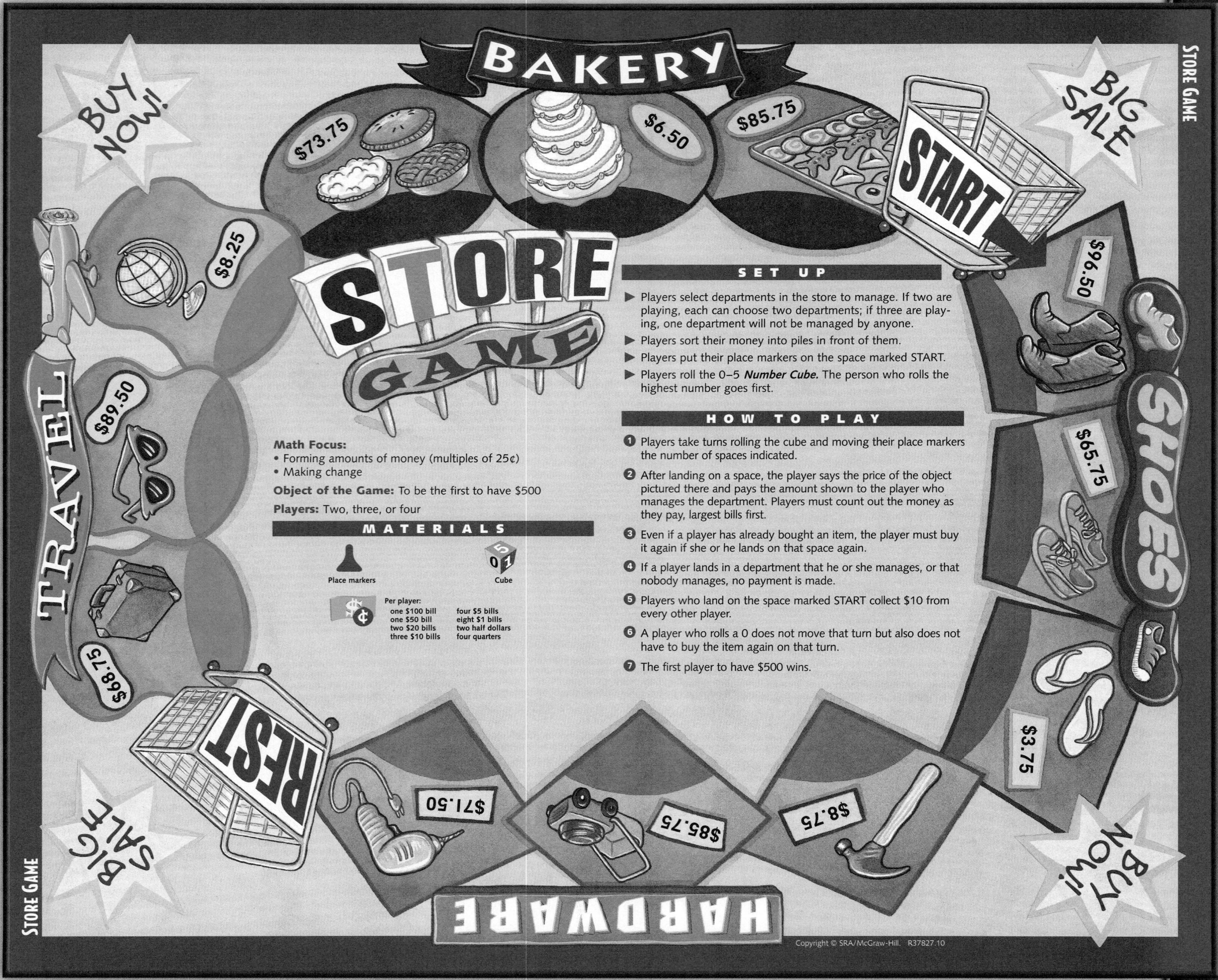


**Math Focus:**
- Forming amounts of money (multiples of 25¢)
- Making change

**Object of the Game:** To be the first to have $500

**Players:** Two, three, or four

## MATERIALS

Place markers

Cube

Per player:
one $100 bill
one $50 bill
two $20 bills
three $10 bills
four $5 bills
eight $1 bills
two half dollars
four quarters

## SET UP

- Players select departments in the store to manage. If two are playing, each can choose two departments; if three are playing, one department will not be managed by anyone.
- Players sort their money into piles in front of them.
- Players put their place markers on the space marked START.
- Players roll the 0–5 ***Number Cube.*** The person who rolls the highest number goes first.

## HOW TO PLAY

1. Players take turns rolling the cube and moving their place markers the number of spaces indicated.
2. After landing on a space, the player says the price of the object pictured there and pays the amount shown to the player who manages the department. Players must count out the money as they pay, largest bills first.
3. Even if a player has already bought an item, the player must buy it again if she or he lands on that space again.
4. If a player lands in a department that he or she manages, or that nobody manages, no payment is made.
5. Players who land on the space marked START collect $10 from every other player.
6. A player who rolls a 0 does not move that turn but also does not have to buy the item again on that turn.
7. The first player to have $500 wins.

# HARDER STORE GAME

**Math Focus:**

- Forming amounts of money
- Making change

**Object of the Game:** To be the first to have $20

**Players:** Two, three, or four

## MATERIALS

Place markers

Cube

Per player:
one $5 bill
seven $1 bills
two half dollars
four quarters
six dimes
six nickels
ten pennies

## SET UP

- Players select departments in the store to manage. If two are playing, each can choose two departments; if three are playing, one department will not be managed by anyone.
- Players sort their money into piles in front of them.
- Players put their place markers on the space marked START.
- Players roll the 0–5 ***Number Cube.*** The person who rolls the highest number goes first.

## HOW TO PLAY

1. Players take turns rolling the cube and moving their place markers the number of spaces indicated.
2. After landing on a space, the player says the price of the object pictured there and pays the amount shown to the player who manages the department. Players must count out the money as they pay, largest bills or coins first.
3. Even if a player has already bought an item, the player must buy it again if she or he lands on that space again.
4. If a player lands in a department that he or she manages, or that nobody manages, no payment is made.
5. Players who land on the space marked START collect $1 from every other player.
6. A player who rolls a 0 does not move that turn but also does not have to buy the item again on that turn.
7. The first player to have $20 wins.

**Math Focus:**

- Adding and subtracting amounts of money (dollars)
- Maintaining a record of money transactions

**Object of the Game:** To have the greatest balance at the end of the game

**Players:** Two or three

## MATERIALS

- Place markers
- Two cubes (0–5)
- Two cubes (5–10)
- One score sheet per player

## SET UP

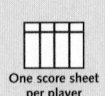

- The blank balance sheet for "Harder Transaction" can be photocopied for students to use.
- Put your place markers on the space marked START.
- On your score sheet write "Start" under DATE and "$1000" under BALANCE.
- Everyone rolls one 0–5 ***Number Cube.*** The person who rolls the highest number goes first.

| DATE | EARN | PAY | BALANCE |
|---|---|---|---|
| Start | | | $1000 |
| 3 | | –$24 | $ 976 |
| 8 | +$861 | | $1837 |
| 11 | | | |
| 4 | +76 | | $1913 |
| 6 | | –$45 | $1868 |
| | | | |

## HOW TO PLAY

1. Take turns rolling one 0-5 cube and moving your place marker the correct number of spaces.
2. When you land on a space that says "Earn" or "Pay," roll one cube for each blank line in the amount. Arrange the digits in the best order. Try to earn the most and pay the least. For example, if you roll a 7, 0, and 2 and have to pay, make the amount $207. If you are earning, make the amount $720.
3. Zero cannot be used as the first digit of an amount. Also, 10 cannot be used. If you roll a 10, roll that cube again.
4. On every turn write down what you earn or pay under the correct column, then add what you earned or subtract what you paid in the BALANCE column. Also, write down the date of each transaction.
5. Keep playing until everyone reaches FINISH or runs out of money.
6. The player with the greatest correct balance wins. Players must check the winner's addition and subtraction. Add to find each total in the winner's PAY column and EARN column. Then add the EARN total to $1000 and subtract the PAY total. This balance should match the winner's final balance. If there is a mistake in the balance, the player with the greatest correct balance wins instead.

**Reminder:** If you land on a space that says "Pay $_ _," roll two 0-5 cubes and choose the lesser amount to pay. If you land on a space that says "Earn $_ _," roll two 5-10 cubes and choose the greater combination of digits.



TRANSACTION

**Math Focus:**

- Adding and subtracting amounts of money (dollars and cents)
- Maintaining a record of money transactions

**Object of the Game:** To have the greatest balance at the end of the game

**Players:** Two or three

## MATERIALS

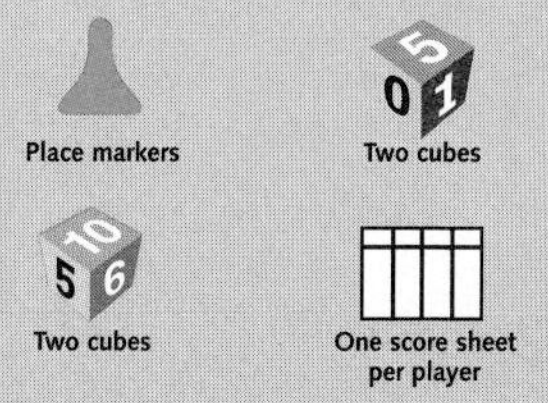


## SET UP

- The blank balance sheet below can be photocopied for students to use.
- Put your place markers on the space marked START.
- On your score sheet write "Start" under DATE and "$1000" under BALANCE.
- Everyone rolls one 0–5 ***Number Cube.*** The person who rolls the highest number goes first.

| DATE | EARN | PAY | BALANCE |
|---|---|---|---|
| | | | |
| | | | |
| | | | |
| | | | |
| | | | |
| | | | |
| | | | |

## HOW TO PLAY

1. Take turns rolling one 0-5 cube and moving your place marker the correct number of spaces.
2. When you land on a space that says "Earn" or "Pay," roll one cube for each blank line in the amount. Arrange the digits in the best order. Try to earn the most and pay the least. For example, if you roll a 7, 1, and 2 and have to pay, make the amount $1.27. If you are earning, make the amount $7.21.
3. Zero cannot be used as the first digit of an amount. Also, 10 cannot be used. If you roll a 10, roll that cube again.
4. On every turn write down what you earn or pay under the correct column, then add what you earned or subtract what you paid in the BALANCE column. Also write down the date of each transaction.
5. Keep playing until everyone reaches FINISH or runs out of money.
6. The player with the greatest correct balance wins. Players must check the winner's addition and subtraction. Add to find each total in the winner's PAY column and the EARN column. Then add the EARN total to $1000 and subtract the PAY total. This balance should match the winner's final balance. If there is a mistake in the balance, the player with the greatest correct balance wins instead.

**Reminder:** If you land on a space that says "Pay $_ _," roll two 0-5 cubes and choose the lesser amount to pay. If you land on a space that says "Earn $_ _._ _," roll four 5-10 cubes and choose the greatest combination of digits.

HARDER TRANSACTION

# Index

# B



# C

# Index



## D

# E



# F

# Index

## H



## I

# Index



## J



## K



## L



## M

# Index



## N



## O

## P

# Index

## S



## T